PROBLEM-SOLVING STRATEGIES

Extended Edition includes Chapters 1–44. Standard Edition includes Chapters 1–37.
Three-volume edition: Volume 1 includes Chapters 1–20, Volume 2 includes Chapters 21–37,
and Volume 3 includes Chapters 37–44.

ACTIVPHYSICS ONLINE™ ACTIVITIES

Activ ONLINE **Physics**   www.mastering physics.com

YOUNG & FREEDMAN

UNIVERSITY PHYSICS
Volume 2

Second Edition

Prepared Exclusively for the Physics Department, University of California, Davis

Taken from:

University Physics: With Modern Physics, Twelfth Edition
by Hugh D. Young and Roger A. Freedman

Cover Art: Zurich by Angela Sciaraffa

Taken from:

University Physics: with Modern Physics, Twelfth Edition
by Hugh D. Young and Roger A. Freedman
Copyright © 2008 by Pearson Education, Inc.
Published by Addison Wesley
Boston, Massachusetts 02116

This special edition published in cooperation with Pearson Custom Publishing.

Printed in the United States of America

10 9 8 7 6 5 4 3

ISBN 0-536-45172-9

2007460017

LG

Please visit our web site at *www.pearsoncustom.com*

PEARSON CUSTOM PUBLISHING
501 Boylston Street, Suite 900, Boston, MA 02116
A Pearson Education Company

PREFACE

This book is the product of more than half a century of leadership and innovation in physics education. When the first edition of University Physics by Francis W. Sears and Mark W. Zemansky was published in 1949, it was revolutionary among calculus-based physics textbooks in its emphasis on the fundamental principles of physics and how to apply them. The success of University Physics with generations of (several million) students and educators around the world is a testament to the merits of this approach, and to the many innovations it has introduced subsequently.

In preparing this new Twelfth Edition, we have further enhanced and developed *University Physics* to assimilate the best ideas from education research with enhanced problem-solving instruction, pioneering visual and conceptual pedagogy, the first systematically enhanced problems, and the most pedagogically proven and widely used online homework and tutorial system in the world.

New to This Edition

- **Problem solving.** The acclaimed, research-based **four-step problem-solving framework** (Identify, Set Up, Execute, and Evaluate) is now used throughout every Worked Example, chapter-specific Problem-Solving Strategy, and every Solution in the Instructor and Student Solutions Manuals. Worked Examples now incorporate black-and-white Pencil Sketches to focus students on this critical step—one that research shows students otherwise tend to skip when illustrated with highly rendered figures.

- **Instruction followed by practice.** A streamlined and systematic learning path of instruction followed by practice includes **Learning Goals** at the start of each chapter and **Visual Chapter Summaries** that consolidate each concept in words, math, and figures. Popular **Test Your Understanding** conceptual questions at the end of each section now use **multiple-choice and ranking formats** to allow students to instantly check their knowledge.

- **Instructional power of figures.** The instructional power of figures is enhanced using the research-proven technique of **"annotation"** (chalkboard-style commentary integrated into the figure to guide the student in interpreting the figure) and by **streamlined use of color and detail** (in mechanics, for example, color is used to focus the student on the object of interest while the rest of the image is in grayscale and without distracting detail).

- **Enhanced end-of-chapter problems.** Renowned for providing the most wide-ranging and best-tested problems available, the Twelfth Edition goes still further: It provides **the first library of physics problems systematically enhanced** based on student performance nationally. Using this analysis, more than 800 new problems make up the entire library of 3700.

- **MasteringPhysics™** (www.masteringphysics.com). Launched with the Eleventh Edition, MasteringPhysics is now the most widely adopted, educationally proven, and technically advanced online homework and tutorial system in the world. For the Twelfth Edition, MasteringPhysics provides a wealth of new content and technological enhancements. In addition to a library of more than 1200 tutorials and all the end-of-chapter problems, MasteringPhysics

Standard, Extended, and Three-Volume Editions

With MasteringPhysics™:
- **Standard Edition:** Chapters 1–37
  (ISBN-13: 978-0-321-50161-5)
  (ISBN-10: 0-321-50161-6)
- **Extended Edition:** Chapters 1–44
  (ISBN-13: 978-0-8053-2187-6)
  (ISBN-10: 0-8053-2187-X)
- **Volume 1:** Chapters 1–20
  (ISBN-13: 978-0-321-50056-4)
  (ISBN-10: 0-321-50056-3)
- **Volume 2:** Chapters 21–37
  (ISBN-13: 978-0-321-50039-7)
  (ISBN-10: 0-321-50039-3)
- **Volume 3:** Chapters 37–44
  (ISBN-13: 978-0-321-50040-3)
  (ISBN-10: 0-321-50040-7)

Without MasteringPhysics™:
- **Standard Edition:** Chapters 1–37
  (ISBN-13: 978-0-321-50147-9)
  (ISBN-10: 0-321-50147-0)
- **Extended Edition:** Chapters 1–44
  (ISBN-13: 978-0-321-50121-9)
  (ISBN-10: 0-321-50121-7)
- **Volume 1:** Chapters 1–20
  (ISBN-13: 978-0-321-50062-5)
  (ISBN-10: 0-321-50062-8)
- **Volume 2:** Chapters 21–37
  (ISBN-13: 978-0-321-50076-2)
  (ISBN-10: 0-321-50076-8)
- **Volume 3:** Chapters 37–44
  (ISBN-13: 978-0-321-50077-9)
  (ISBN-10: 0-321-50077-6)

now also provides specific tutorials for every Problem-Solving Strategy and key Test Your Understanding questions from each chapter. Answer types include algebraic, numerical, and multiple-choice answers, as well as ranking, sorting, graph drawing, vector drawing, and ray tracing.

Key Features of *University Physics*

A Guide for the Student Many physics students experience difficulty simply because they don't know how to use their textbook. The section entitled "How to Succeed in Physics by Really Trying," which precedes this preface, is a "user's manual" to all the features of this book. This section, written by Professor Mark Hollabaugh (Normandale Community College), also gives a number of helpful study hints. *Every* student should read this section!

Chapter Organization The first section of each chapter is an *Introduction* that gives specific examples of the chapter's content and connects it with what has come before. There are also a *Chapter Opening Question* and a list of *Learning Goals* to make the reader think about the subject matter of the chapter ahead. (To find the answer to the question, look for the **?** icon.) Most sections end with a *Test Your Understanding Question,* which can be conceptual or quantitative in nature. At the end of the last section of the chapter is a *Visual Chapter Summary* of the most important principles in the chapter, as well as a list of *Key Terms* with reference to the page number where each term is introduced. The answers to the Chapter Opening Question and Test Your Understanding Questions follow the Key Terms.

Questions and Problems At the end of each chapter is a collection of *Discussion Questions* that probe and extend the student's conceptual understanding. Following these are *Exercises,* which are single-concept problems keyed to specific sections of the text; *Problems,* usually requiring one or two nontrivial steps; and *Challenge Problems,* intended to challenge the strongest students. The problems include applications to such diverse fields as astrophysics, biology, and aerodynamics. Many problems have a conceptual part in which students must discuss and explain their results. The new questions, exercises, and problems for this edition were created and organized by Wayne Anderson (Sacramento City College), Laird Kramer (Florida International University), and Charlie Hibbard.

Problem-Solving Strategies and Worked Examples Throughout the book, *Problem-Solving Strategy* boxes provide students with specific tactics for solving particular types of problems. They address the needs of any students who have ever felt that they "understand the concepts but can't do the problems."

All Problem-Solving Strategy boxes follow the ISEE approach (Identify, Set Up, Execute, and Evaluate) to solving problems. This approach helps students see how to begin with a seemingly complex situation, identify the relevant physical concepts, decide what tools are needed to solve the problem, carry out the solution, and then evaluate whether the result makes sense.

Each Problem-Solving Strategy box is followed by one or more worked-out *Examples* that illustrate the strategy. Many other worked-out Examples are found in each chapter. Like the Problem-Solving Strategy boxes, all of the quantitative Examples use the ISEE approach. Several of the examples are purely qualitative and are labeled as *Conceptual Examples;* see, for instance, Conceptual Examples 6.5 (Comparing kinetic energies, p. 191), 8.1 (Momentum versus kinetic energy, p. 251) and 20.7 (A reversible adiabatic process, p. 693).

"Caution" paragraphs Two decades of physics education research have revealed a number of conceptual pitfalls that commonly plague beginning physics students. These include the ideas that force is required for motion, that electric current is "used up" as it goes around a circuit, and that the product of an object's mass and its acceleration is itself a force. The "Caution" paragraphs alert students to these and other pitfalls, and explain why the wrong way to think about a certain situation (which may have occurred to the student first) is indeed wrong. (See, for example, pp. 118, 159, and 559.)

Notation and units Students often have a hard time keeping track of which quantities are vectors and which are not. We use boldface italic symbols with an arrow on top for vector quantities, such as $\vec{v}$, $\vec{a}$, and $\vec{F}$; unit vectors such as $\hat{\imath}$, have a caret on top. Boldface $+$, $-$, $\times$, and $=$ signs are used in vector equations to emphasize the distinction between vector and scalar mathematical operations.

SI units are used exclusively (English unit conversions are included where appropriate). The joule is used as the standard unit of energy of all forms, including heat.

Flexibility The book is adaptable to a wide variety of course outlines. There is plenty of material for a three-semester or a five-quarter course. Most instructors will find that there is too much material for a one-year course, but it is easy to tailor the book to a variety of one-year course plans by omitting certain chapters or sections. For example, any or all of the chapters on fluid mechanics, sound and hearing, electromagnetic waves, or relativity can be omitted without loss of continuity. In any case, no instructor should feel constrained to work straight through the entire book.

Instructor Supplements

The **Instructor Solutions Manuals,** prepared by A. Lewis Ford (Texas A&M University), contain complete and detailed solutions to all end-of-chapter problems. All solutions follow consistently the same Identify/Set Up/Execute/Evaluate problem-solving framework used in the textbook. The *Instructor Solutions Manual for Volume 1* (ISBN 0-321-49968-9) covers Chapters 1–20, and the *Instructor Solutions Manual for Volumes 2 and 3* (ISBN 0-321-49210-2) covers Chapters 21–44.

The cross-platform **Media Manager CD-ROM** (ISBN 0-321-49916-6) provides a comprehensive library of more than 220 applets from ActivPhysics OnLine™ as well as all line figures from the textbook in JPEG format. In addition, all the key equations, Problem-Solving Strategies, tables, and chapter summaries are provided in editable Word format. In-class weekly multiple-choice questions for use with various Classroom Response Systems (CRS) are also provided, based on the Test Your Understanding questions in the text. The CD-ROM also provides the Instructor Solutions Manual in convenient editable Word format and as PDFs.

MasteringPhysics™ (www.masteringphysics.com) is the most advanced, educationally effective, and widely used physics homework and tutorial system in the world. It provides instructors with a library of extensively pretested end-of-chapter problems and rich, Socratic tutorials that incorporate a wide variety of answer types, wrong-answer feedback, and adaptive help (comprising hints or simpler sub-problems upon request). MasteringPhysics™ allows instructors to quickly build wide-ranging homework assignments of just the right difficulty and duration and provides them with efficient tools to analyze class trends—or the work of any student—in unprecedented detail and to compare the results either with the national average or with the performance of previous classes.

Five Easy Lessons: Strategies for Successful Physics Teaching (ISBN 0-8053-8702-1) by Randall D. Knight (California Polytechnic State University, San Luis Obispo) is packed with creative ideas on how to enhance any physics course. It is an invaluable companion for both novice and veteran physics instructors.

The **Transparency Acetates** (ISBN 0-321-50034-2) contain more than 200 key figures from *University Physics,* Twelfth Edition, in full color.

The **Printed Test Bank** (ISBN 0-321-50035-0) provides more than 2000 multiple-choice questions.

The **Computerized Test Bank** (ISBN 0-321-50126-8) includes all of the questions from the Printed Test Bank on a cross-platform CD-ROM. More than half the questions have numerical values that can be randomly assigned for each student.

Student Supplements

The **Study Guide,** by James R. Gaines, William F. Palmer, and Laird Kramer, reinforces the text's emphasis on problem-solving strategies and student misconceptions. The *Study Guide for Volume 1* (ISBN 0-321-50033-4) covers Chapters 1–20, and the *Study Guide for Volumes 2 and 3* (ISBN 0-321-50037-7) covers Chapters 21–44.

The **Student Solutions Manual,** by A. Lewis Ford (Texas A&M University), contains detailed, step-by-step solutions to more than half of the odd-numbered end-of-chapter problems from the textbook. All solutions follow consistently the same Identify/Set Up/Execute/Evaluate problem-solving framework used in the textbook. The *Student Solutions Manual for Volume 1* (ISBN 0-321-50063-6) covers Chapters 1–20, and the *Student Solutions Manual for Volumes 2 and 3* (ISBN 0-321-50038-5) covers Chapters 21–44.

 MasteringPhysics™ (www.masteringphysics.com) is the most advanced, widely used, and educationally proven physics tutorial system in the world. It is the result of eight years of detailed studies of how real students work physics problems, and of precisely where they need help. Studies show that students who use MasteringPhysics™ significantly improve their scores on final exams and conceptual tests such as the Force Concept Inventory. MasteringPhysics™ achieves this by providing students with instantaneous feedback specific to their wrong answers, simpler sub-problems upon request when they get stuck, and partial credit for their method. This individualized, 24/7 tutor system is recommended by nine out of ten students to their peers as the most effective and time-efficient way to study.

 ActivPhysics OnLine™ (www.masteringphysics.com), now included in the self-study area of MasteringPhysics, provides the most comprehensive library of applets and applet-based tutorials available. ActivPhysics OnLine was created by the educational pioneer Alan Van Heuvelen of Rutgers. Throughout *University Physics,* Twelfth Edition, in-margin icons direct the student to specific applets in ActivPhysics OnLine in for additional interactive help.

ActivPhysics OnLine™ **Workbooks, Volume 1** (0-8053-9060-X) and **Volume 2** (0-8053-9061-8) by Alan Van Heuvelen, Rutgers, and Paul d'Alessandris, Monroe Community College, provide a range of tutorials that use the critically acclaimed ActivPhysics OnLine applets to help students develop understanding and confidence. In particular, they focus on developing intuition, making predictions, testing assumptions experimentally, drawing effective diagrams, understanding key equations both qualitatively and quantitatively, and interpreting graphical information. These workbooks can be used for labs, homework, or self-study.

The **Addison-Wesley Tutor Center** (www.aw.com/tutorcenter) provides one-on-one tutoring via telephone, fax, e-mail, or interactive website. Qualified instructors answer questions and provide instruction with examples, problems, and other content from *University Physics,* Twelfth Edition, as well as help with MasteringPhysics™.

Acknowledgments

We would like to thank the hundreds of reviewers and colleagues who have offered valuable comments and suggestions over the life of this textbook. The continuing success of *University Physics* is due in large measure to their contributions.

Edward Adelson (Ohio State University), Ralph Alexander (University of Missouri at Rolla), J. G. Anderson, R. S. Anderson, Wayne Anderson (Sacramento City College), Alex Azima (Lansing Community College), Dilip Balamore (Nassau Community College), Harold Bale (University of North Dakota), Arun Bansil (Northeastern University), John Barach (Vanderbilt University), J. D. Barnett, H. H. Barschall, Albert Bartlett (University of Colorado), Paul Baum (CUNY, Queens College), Frederick Becchetti (University of Michigan), B. Bederson, David Bennum (University of Nevada, Reno), Lev I. Berger (San Diego State University), Robert Boeke (William Rainey Harper College), S. Borowitz, A. C. Braden, James Brooks (Boston University), Nicholas E. Brown (California Polytechnic State University, San Luis Obispo), Tony Buffa (California Polytechnic State University, San Luis Obispo), A. Capecelatro, Michael Cardamone (Pennsylvania State University), Duane Carmony (Purdue University), Troy Carter (UCLA), P. Catranides, John Cerne (SUNY at Buffalo), Roger Clapp (University of South Florida), William M. Cloud (Eastern Illinois University), Leonard Cohen (Drexel University), W. R. Coker (University of Texas, Austin), Malcolm D. Cole (University of Missouri at Rolla), H. Conrad, David Cook (Lawrence University), Gayl Cook (University of Colorado), Hans Courant (University of Minnesota), Bruce A. Craver (University of Dayton), Larry Curtis (University of Toledo), Jai Dahiya (Southeast Missouri State University), Steve Detweiler (University of Florida), George Dixon (Oklahoma State University), Donald S. Duncan, Boyd Edwards (West Virginia University), Robert Eisenstein (Carnegie Mellon University), Amy Emerson Missouri (Virginia Institute of Technology), William Faissler (Northeastern University), William Fasnacht (U.S. Naval Academy), Paul Feldker (St. Louis Community College), Carlos Figueroa (Cabrillo College), L. H. Fisher, Neil Fletcher (Florida State University), Robert Folk, Peter Fong (Emory University), A. Lewis Ford (Texas A&M University), D. Frantszog, James R. Gaines (Ohio State University), Solomon Gartenhaus (Purdue University), Ron Gautreau (New Jersey Institute of Technology), J. David Gavenda (University of Texas, Austin), Dennis Gay (University of North Florida), James Gerhart (University of Washington), N. S. Gingrich, J. L. Glathart, S. Goodwin, Rich Gottfried (Frederick Community College), Walter S. Gray (University of Michigan), Paul Gresser (University of Maryland), Benjamin Grinstein (UC San Diego), Howard Grotch (Pennsylvania State University), John Gruber (San Jose State University), Graham D. Gutsche (U.S. Naval Academy), Michael J. Harrison (Michigan State University), Harold Hart (Western Illinois University), Howard Hayden (University of Connecticut), Carl Helrich (Goshen College), Laurent Hodges (Iowa State University), C. D. Hodgman, Michael Hones (Villanova University), Keith Honey (West Virginia Institute of Technology), Gregory Hood (Tidewater Community College), John Hubisz (North Carolina State University), M. Iona, John Jaszczak (Michigan Technical University), Alvin Jenkins (North Carolina State University), Robert P. Johnson (UC Santa Cruz), Lorella Jones (University of Illinois), John Karchek (GMI Engineering & Management Institute), Thomas Keil (Worcester Polytechnic Institute), Robert Kraemer (Carnegie Mellon University), Jean P. Krisch (University of Michigan), Robert A. Kromhout, Andrew Kunz (Marquette University), Charles Lane (Berry College), Thomas N. Lawrence (Texas State University), Robert J. Lee, Alfred Leitner (Rensselaer Polytechnic University), Gerald P. Lietz (De Paul University), Gordon Lind (Utah State University), S. Livingston, Elihu Lubkin (University of Wisconsin, Milwaukee), Robert Luke (Boise State University), David Lynch (Iowa State University), Michael Lysak (San Bernardino Valley College), Jeffrey Mallow (Loyola University), Robert Mania (Kentucky State University), Robert Marchina (University of Memphis), David Markowitz (University of Connecticut), R. J. Maurer, Oren Maxwell (Florida International University), Joseph L. McCauley (University of Houston), T. K. McCubbin, Jr. (Pennsylvania State University), Charles McFarland (University of Missouri at Rolla), James Mcguire (Tulane University), Lawrence McIntyre (University of Arizona), Fredric Messing (Carnegie-Mellon University), Thomas Meyer (Texas A&M University), Andre Mirabelli (St. Peter's College, New Jersey), Herbert Muether (S.U.N.Y., Stony Brook), Jack Munsee (California State University, Long Beach), Lorenzo Narducci (Drexel University), Van E. Neie (Purdue University), David A. Nordling (U. S. Naval Academy), Benedict Oh (Pennsylvania State University), L. O. Olsen, Jim Pannell (DeVry Institute of Technology), W. F. Parks (University of Missouri), Robert Paulson (California State University, Chico), Jerry Peacher (University of Missouri at Rolla), Arnold Perlmutter (University of Miami), Lennart Peterson (University of Florida), R. J. Peterson (University of Colorado, Boulder), R. Pinkston, Ronald Poling (University of Minnesota), J. G. Potter, C. W. Price (Millersville University), Francis Prosser (University of Kansas), Shelden H. Radin, Michael Rapport (Anne Arundel Community College), R. Resnick, James A. Richards, Jr., John S. Risley (North Carolina State University), Francesc Roig (University of California, Santa Barbara), T. L. Rokoske, Richard Roth (Eastern Michigan University), Carl Rotter (University of West Virginia), S. Clark Rowland (Andrews University), Rajarshi Roy (Georgia Institute of Technology), Russell A. Roy (Santa Fe Community College), Dhiraj Sardar (University of Texas, San Antonio), Bruce Schumm (UC Santa Cruz), Melvin Schwartz (St. John's University), F. A. Scott, L. W. Seagondollar, Paul Shand (University of Northern Iowa), Stan Shepherd (Pennsylvania State University), Douglas Sherman (San Jose State), Bruce Sherwood (Carnegie Mellon University), Hugh Siefkin (Greenville College), Tomasz Skwarnicki (Syracuse University), C. P. Slichter, Charles W. Smith (University of Maine, Orono), Malcolm Smith (University of Lowell), Ross Spencer (Brigham Young University), Julien Sprott (University of Wisconsin), Victor Stanionis (Iona College), James Stith (American Institute of Physics), Chuck Stone (North Carolina A&T State University), Edward Strother (Florida Institute of Technology), Conley Stutz (Bradley University), Albert Stwertka (U.S. Merchant Marine Academy),

Martin Tiersten (CUNY, City College), David Toot (Alfred University), Somdev Tyagi (Drexel University), F. Verbrugge, Helmut Vogel (Carnegie Mellon University), Robert Webb (Texas A & M), Thomas Weber (Iowa State University), M. Russell Wehr, (Pennsylvania State University), Robert Weidman (Michigan Technical University), Dan Whalen (UC San Diego), Lester V. Whitney, Thomas Wiggins (Pennsylvania State University), David Willey (University of Pittsburgh, Johnstown), George Williams (University of Utah), John Williams (Auburn University), Stanley Williams (Iowa State University), Jack Willis, Suzanne Willis (Northern Illinois University), Robert Wilson (San Bernardino Valley College), L. Wolfenstein, James Wood (Palm Beach Junior College), Lowell Wood (University of Houston), R. E. Worley, D. H. Ziebell (Manatee Community College), George O. Zimmerman (Boston University)

In addition, we both have individual acknowledgments we would like to make.

I want to extend my heartfelt thanks to my colleagues at Carnegie Mellon, especially Professors Robert Kraemer, Bruce Sherwood, Ruth Chabay, Helmut Vogel, and Brian Quinn, for many stimulating discussions about physics pedagogy and for their support and encouragement during the writing of several successive editions of this book. I am equally indebted to the many generations of Carnegie Mellon students who have helped me learn what good teaching and good writing are, by showing me what works and what doesn't. It is always a joy and a privilege to express my gratitude to my wife Alice and our children Gretchen and Rebecca for their love, support, and emotional sustenance during the writing of several successive editions of this book. May all men and women be blessed with love such as theirs. — H. D. Y.

I would like to thank my past and present colleagues at UCSB, including Rob Geller, Carl Gwinn, Al Nash, Elisabeth Nicol, and Francesc Roig, for their wholehearted support and for many helpful discussions. I owe a special debt of gratitude to my early teachers Willa Ramsay, Peter Zimmerman, William Little, Alan Schwettman, and Dirk Walecka for showing me what clear and engaging physics teaching is all about, and to Stuart Johnson for inviting me to become a co-author of *University Physics* beginning with the 9th edition. I want to express special thanks to the editorial staff at Addison Wesley and their partners: to Adam Black for his editorial vision; to Margot Otway for her superb graphic sense and careful development of this edition; to Peter Murphy and Carol Reitz for their careful reading of the manuscript; to Wayne Anderson, Charlie Hibbard, Laird Kramer, and Larry Stookey for their work on the end-of-chapter problems; and to Laura Kenney, Chandrika Madhavan, Nancy Tabor, and Pat McCutcheon for keeping the editorial and production pipeline flowing. I want to thank my father for his continued love and support and for keeping a space open on his bookshelf for this book. Most of all, I want to express my gratitude and love to my wife Caroline, to whom I dedicate my contribution to this book. Hey, Caroline, the new edition's done at last — let's go flying! — R. A. F.

Please Tell Us What You Think!

We welcome communications from students and professors, especially concerning errors or deficiencies that you find in this edition. We have devoted a lot of time and effort to writing the best book we know how to write, and we hope it will help you to teach and learn physics. In turn, you can help us by letting us know what still needs to be improved! Please feel free to contact us either electronically or by ordinary mail. Your comments will be greatly appreciated.

October 2006

Hugh D. Young
Department of Physics
Carnegie Mellon University
Pittsburgh, PA 15213
hdy@andrew.cmu.edu

Roger A. Freedman
Department of Physics
University of California, Santa Barbara
Santa Barbara, CA 93106-9530
airboy@physics.ucsb.edu
http://www.physics.ucsb.edu/~airboy/

DETAILED CONTENTS

ELECTRIC CHARGE AND ELECTRIC FIELD

21

? Water makes life possible: The cells of your body could not function without water in which to dissolve essential biological molecules. What electrical properties of water make it such a good solvent?

Back in Chapter 5, we briefly mentioned the four kinds of fundamental forces. To this point the only one of these forces that we have examined in any detail is gravity. Now we are ready to examine the force of *electromagnetism,* which encompasses both electricity and magnetism. Our exploration of electromagnetic phenomena will occupy our attention for most of the remainder of this book.

Electromagnetic interactions involve particles that have a property called *electric charge,* an attribute that is as fundamental as mass. Just as objects with mass are accelerated by gravitational forces, so electrically charged objects are accelerated by electric forces. The annoying electric spark you feel when you scuff your shoes across a carpet and then reach for a metal doorknob is due to charged particles leaping between your finger and the doorknob. Electric currents, such as those in a flashlight or a television, are simply streams of charged particles flowing within wires in response to electric forces. Even the forces that hold atoms together to form solid matter, and that keep the atoms of solid objects from passing through each other, are fundamentally due to electric interactions between the charged particles within atoms.

We begin our study of electromagnetism in this chapter by examining the nature of electric charge. We'll find that electric charge is quantized and that it obeys a conservation principle. We then turn to a discussion of the interactions of electric charges that are at rest in our frame of reference, called *electrostatic* interactions. Such interactions are of tremendous importance in chemistry and biology and have many technological applications. Electrostatic interactions are governed by a simple relationship known as *Coulomb's law* and are most conveniently described by using the concept of *electric field.* In later chapters we'll expand our discussion to include electric charges in motion. This will lead us to an understanding of magnetism and, remarkably, of the nature of light.

While the key ideas of electromagnetism are conceptually simple, applying them to practical problems will make use of many of your mathematical skills, especially your knowledge of geometry and integral calculus. For this reason you may find this chapter and those that follow to be more mathematically demanding than earlier chapters. The reward for your extra effort will be a deeper understanding of principles that are at the heart of modern physics and technology.

21.1 **Electric Charge**

The ancient Greeks discovered as early as 600 B.C. that after they rubbed amber with wool, the amber could attract other objects. Today we say that the amber has acquired a net **electric charge,** or has become *charged*. The word "electric" is derived from the Greek word *elektron*, meaning amber. When you scuff your shoes across a nylon carpet, you become electrically charged, and you can charge a comb by passing it through dry hair.

Plastic rods and fur (real or fake) are particularly good for demonstrating **electrostatics,** the interactions between electric charges that are at rest (or nearly so). Figure 21.1a shows two plastic rods and a piece of fur. After we charge each rod by rubbing it with the piece of fur, we find that the rods repel each other.

When we rub glass rods with silk, the glass rods also become charged and repel each other (Fig. 21.1b). But a charged plastic rod *attracts* a charged glass rod; furthermore, the plastic rod and the fur attract each other, and the glass rod and the silk attract each other (Fig. 21.1c).

These experiments and many others like them have shown that there are exactly two kinds of electric charge: the kind on the plastic rod rubbed with fur and the kind on the glass rod rubbed with silk. Benjamin Franklin (1706–1790) suggested calling these two kinds of charge *negative* and *positive*, respectively, and these names are still used. The plastic rod and the silk have negative charge; the glass rod and the fur have positive charge.

Two positive charges or two negative charges repel each other. A positive charge and a negative charge attract each other.

21.1 Experiments in electrostatics. (a) Negatively charged objects repel each other. (b) Positively charged objects repel each other. (c) Positively charged objects and negatively charged objects attract each other.

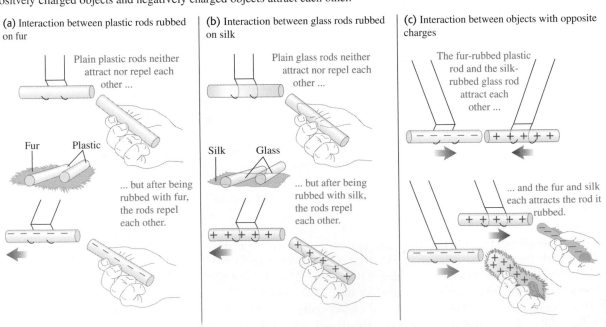

(a) Interaction between plastic rods rubbed on fur

Plain plastic rods neither attract nor repel each other ...

Fur   Plastic

... but after being rubbed with fur, the rods repel each other.

(b) Interaction between glass rods rubbed on silk

Plain glass rods neither attract nor repel each other ...

Silk   Glass

... but after being rubbed with silk, the rods repel each other.

(c) Interaction between objects with opposite charges

The fur-rubbed plastic rod and the silk-rubbed glass rod attract each other ...

... and the fur and silk each attracts the rod it rubbed.

21.2 Schematic diagram of the operation of a laser printer.

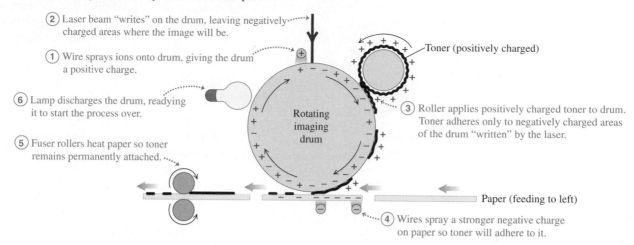

(2) Laser beam "writes" on the drum, leaving negatively charged areas where the image will be.

(1) Wire sprays ions onto drum, giving the drum a positive charge.

(6) Lamp discharges the drum, readying it to start the process over.

(5) Fuser rollers heat paper so toner remains permanently attached.

Toner (positively charged)

Rotating imaging drum

(3) Roller applies positively charged toner to drum. Toner adheres only to negatively charged areas of the drum "written" by the laser.

Paper (feeding to left)

(4) Wires spray a stronger negative charge on paper so toner will adhere to it.

> **CAUTION** **Electric attraction and repulsion** The attraction and repulsion of two charged objects are sometimes summarized as "Like charges repel, and opposite charges attract." But keep in mind that the phrase "like charges" does *not* mean that the two charges are exactly identical, only that both charges have the same algebraic *sign* (both positive or both negative). "Opposite charges" means that both objects have an electric charge, and those charges have different signs (one positive and the other negative). ▮

One technological application of forces between charged bodies is in a laser printer (Fig. 21.2). Initially the printer's light-sensitive imaging drum is given a positive charge. As the drum rotates, a laser beam shines on selected areas of the drum, leaving those areas with a *negative* charge. Positively charged particles of toner adhere only to the areas of the drum "written" by the laser. When a piece of paper is placed in contact with the drum, the toner particles stick to the paper and form an image.

Electric Charge and the Structure of Matter

When you charge a rod by rubbing it with fur or silk as in Fig. 21.1, there is no visible change in the appearance of the rod. What, then, actually happens to the rod when you charge it? To answer this question, we must look more closely at the structure and electric properties of atoms, the building blocks of ordinary matter of all kinds.

The structure of atoms can be described in terms of three particles: the negatively charged **electron**, the positively charged **proton,** and the uncharged **neutron** (Fig. 21.3). The proton and neutron are combinations of other entities called *quarks,* which have charges of $\pm\frac{1}{3}$ and $\pm\frac{2}{3}$ times the electron charge. Isolated quarks have not been observed, and there are theoretical reasons to believe that it is impossible in principle to observe a quark in isolation.

The protons and neutrons in an atom make up a small, very dense core called the **nucleus,** with dimensions of the order of 10^{-15} m. Surrounding the nucleus are the electrons, extending out to distances of the order of 10^{-10} m from the nucleus. If an atom were a few kilometers across, its nucleus would be the size of a tennis ball. The negatively charged electrons are held within the atom by the attractive electric forces exerted on them by the positively charged nucleus. (The protons and neutrons are held within the stable atomic nuclei by an attractive interaction, called the *strong nuclear force,* that overcomes the electric repulsion of the protons. The strong nuclear force has a short range, and its effects do not extend far beyond the nucleus.)

21.3 The structure of an atom. The particular atom depicted here is lithium (see Fig. 21.4a).

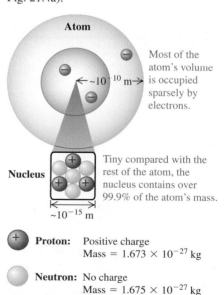

Atom

Most of the atom's volume is occupied sparsely by electrons.

$\leftarrow\sim10^{-10}$ m$\rightarrow$

Nucleus

Tiny compared with the rest of the atom, the nucleus contains over 99.9% of the atom's mass.

$\sim10^{-15}$ m

⊕ **Proton:** Positive charge
Mass $= 1.673 \times 10^{-27}$ kg

○ **Neutron:** No charge
Mass $= 1.675 \times 10^{-27}$ kg

⊖ **Electron:** Negative charge
Mass $= 9.109 \times 10^{-31}$ kg

The charges of the electron and proton are equal in magnitude.

21.4 (a) A neutral atom has as many electrons as it does protons. (b) A positive ion has a deficit of electrons. (c) A negative ion has an excess of electrons. (The electron "shells" are a schematic representation of the actual electron distribution, a diffuse cloud many times larger than the nucleus.)

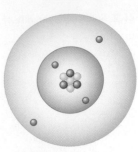
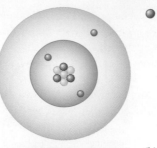
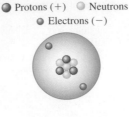

Protons (+)   Neutrons
Electrons (−)

(a) **Neutral lithium atom (Li):**

3 protons (3+)

4 neutrons

3 electrons (3−)

Electrons equal protons:
Zero net charge

(b) **Positive lithium ion (Li⁺):**

3 protons (3+)

4 neutrons

2 electrons (2−)

Fewer electrons than protons:
Positive net charge

(c) **Negative lithium ion (Li⁻):**

3 protons (3+)

4 neutrons

4 electrons (4−)

More electrons than protons:
Negative net charge

The masses of the individual particles, to the precision that they are presently known, are

$$\text{Mass of electron} = m_e = 9.1093826(16) \times 10^{-31}\,\text{kg}$$

$$\text{Mass of proton} = m_p = 1.67262171(29) \times 10^{-27}\,\text{kg}$$

$$\text{Mass of neutron} = m_n = 1.67492728(29) \times 10^{-27}\,\text{kg}$$

The numbers in parentheses are the uncertainties in the last two digits. Note that the masses of the proton and neutron are nearly equal and are roughly 2000 times the mass of the electron. Over 99.9% of the mass of any atom is concentrated in its nucleus.

The negative charge of the electron has (within experimental error) *exactly* the same magnitude as the positive charge of the proton. In a neutral atom the number of electrons equals the number of protons in the nucleus, and the net electric charge (the algebraic sum of all the charges) is exactly zero (Fig. 21.4a). The number of protons or electrons in a neutral atom of an element is called the **atomic number** of the element. If one or more electrons are removed, the remaining positively charged structure is called a **positive ion** (Fig. 21.4b). A **negative ion** is an atom that has *gained* one or more electrons (Fig. 21.4c). This gaining or losing of electrons is called **ionization.**

When the total number of protons in a macroscopic body equals the total number of electrons, the total charge is zero and the body as a whole is electrically neutral. To give a body an excess negative charge, we may either *add negative* charges to a neutral body or *remove positive* charges from that body. Similarly, we can create an excess positive charge by either *adding positive* charge or *removing negative* charge. In most cases, negatively charged (and highly mobile) electrons are added or removed, and a "positively charged body" is one that has lost some of its normal complement of electrons. When we speak of the charge of a body, we always mean its *net* charge. The net charge is always a very small fraction (typically no more than 10^{-12}) of the total positive charge or negative charge in the body.

Electric Charge Is Conserved

Implicit in the foregoing discussion are two very important principles. First is the **principle of conservation of charge:**

The algebraic sum of all the electric charges in any closed system is constant.

If we rub together a plastic rod and a piece of fur, both initially uncharged, the rod acquires a negative charge (since it takes electrons from the fur) and the fur acquires a positive charge of the *same* magnitude (since it has lost as many electrons as the rod has gained). Hence the total electric charge on the two bodies together does not change. In any charging process, charge is not created or destroyed; it is merely *transferred* from one body to another.

Conservation of charge is thought to be a *universal* conservation law. No experimental evidence for any violation of this principle has ever been observed. Even in high-energy interactions in which particles are created and destroyed, such as the creation of electron–positron pairs, the total charge of any closed system is exactly constant.

The second important principle is:

The magnitude of charge of the electron or proton is a natural unit of charge.

Every observable amount of electric charge is always an integer multiple of this basic unit. We say that charge is *quantized.* A familiar example of quantization is money. When you pay cash for an item in a store, you have to do it in one-cent increments. Cash can't be divided into amounts smaller than one cent, and electric charge can't be divided into amounts smaller than the charge of one electron or proton. (The quark charges, $\pm\frac{1}{3}$ and $\pm\frac{2}{3}$ of the electron charge, are probably not observable as isolated charges.) Thus the charge on any macroscopic body is always either zero or an integer multiple (negative or positive) of the electron charge.

Understanding the electric nature of matter gives us insight into many aspects of the physical world (Fig. 21.5). The chemical bonds that hold atoms together to form molecules are due to electric interactions between the atoms. They include the strong ionic bonds that hold sodium and chlorine atoms together to make table salt and the relatively weak bonds between the strands of DNA that record your body's genetic code. The normal force exerted on you by the chair in which you're sitting arises from electric forces between charged particles in the atoms of your seat and in the atoms of your chair. The tension force in a stretched string and the adhesive force of glue are likewise due to the electric interactions of atoms.

21.5 Most of the forces on this water skier are electric. Electric interactions between adjacent molecules give rise to the force of the water on the ski, the tension in the tow rope, and the resistance of the air on the skier's body. Electric interactions also hold the atoms of the skier's body together. Only one wholly nonelectric force acts on the skier: the force of gravity.

Test Your Understanding of Section 21.1   (a) Strictly speaking, does the plastic rod in Fig. 21.1 weigh more, less, or the same after rubbing it with fur? (b) What about the glass rod after rubbing it with silk? What about (c) the fur and (d) the silk? ∎

21.2 Conductors, Insulators, and Induced Charges

Some materials permit electric charge to move easily from one region of the material to another, while others do not. For example, Fig. 21.6a shows a copper wire supported by a nylon thread. Suppose you touch one end of the wire to a charged plastic rod and attach the other end to a metal ball that is initially uncharged; you then remove the charged rod and the wire. When you bring another charged body up close to the ball (Figs. 21.6b and 21.6c), the ball is attracted or repelled, showing that the ball has become electrically charged. Electric charge has been transferred through the copper wire between the ball and the surface of the plastic rod.

The copper wire is called a **conductor** of electricity. If you repeat the experiment using a rubber band or nylon thread in place of the wire, you find that *no* charge is transferred to the ball. These materials are called **insulators.** Conductors permit the easy movement of charge through them, while insulators do not. (The supporting nylon threads shown in Fig. 21.6 are insulators, which prevents charge from leaving the metal ball and copper wire.)

As an example, carpet fibers on a dry day are good insulators. As you walk across a carpet, the rubbing of your shoes against the fibers causes charge to build

21.6 Copper is a good conductor of electricity; nylon is a good insulator. (a) The copper wire conducts charge between the metal ball and the charged plastic rod to charge the ball negatively. Afterward, the metal ball is (b) repelled by a negatively charged plastic rod and (c) attracted to a positively charged glass rod.

(a)

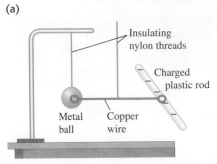

The wire conducts charge from the negatively charged plastic rod to the metal ball.

(b)

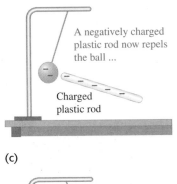

(c)

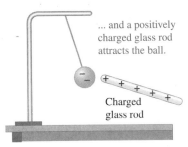

up on you, and this charge remains on you because it can't flow through the insulating fibers. If you then touch a conducting object such as a doorknob, a rapid charge transfer takes place between your finger and the doorknob, and you feel a shock. One way to prevent this is to wind some of the carpet fibers around conducting cores so that any charge that builds up on you can be transferred harmlessly to the carpet. Another solution is to coat the carpet fibers with an antistatic layer that does not easily transfer electrons to or from your shoes; this prevents any charge from building up on you in the first place.

Most metals are good conductors, while most nonmetals are insulators. Within a solid metal such as copper, one or more outer electrons in each atom become detached and can move freely throughout the material, just as the molecules of a gas can move through the spaces between the grains in a bucket of sand. The motion of these negatively charged electrons carries charge through the metal. The other electrons remain bound to the positively charged nuclei, which themselves are bound in nearly fixed positions within the material. In an insulator there are no, or very few, free electrons, and electric charge cannot move freely through the material. Some materials called *semiconductors* are intermediate in their properties between good conductors and good insulators.

Charging by Induction

We can charge a metal ball using a copper wire and an electrically charged plastic rod, as in Fig. 21.6a. In this process, some of the excess electrons on the rod are transferred from it to the ball, leaving the rod with a smaller negative charge. There is a different technique in which the plastic rod can give another body a charge of *opposite* sign without losing any of its own charge. This process is called charging by **induction.**

Figure 21.7 shows an example of charging by induction. An uncharged metal ball is supported on an insulating stand (Fig. 21.7a). When you bring a negatively charged rod near it, without actually touching it (Fig. 21.7b), the free electrons in the metal ball are repelled by the excess electrons on the rod, and they shift toward the right, away from the rod. They cannot escape from the ball because the supporting stand and the surrounding air are insulators. So we get excess negative charge at the right surface of the ball and a deficiency of negative charge (that is, a net positive charge) at the left surface. These excess charges are called **induced charges.**

Not all of the free electrons move to the right surface of the ball. As soon as any induced charge develops, it exerts forces toward the *left* on the other free electrons. These electrons are repelled by the negative induced charge on the right and attracted toward the positive induced charge on the left. The system reaches an equilibrium state in which the force toward the right on an electron, due to the charged rod, is just balanced by the force toward the left due to the induced charge. If we remove the charged rod, the free electrons shift back to the left, and the original neutral condition is restored.

21.7 Charging a metal ball by induction.

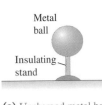

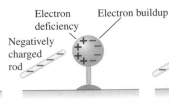

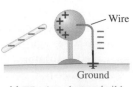

(a) Uncharged metal ball

(b) Negative charge on rod repels electrons, creating zones of negative and positive **induced charge**.

(c) Wire lets electron buildup (induced negative charge) flow into ground.

(d) Wire removed; ball now has only an electron-deficient region of positive charge.

(e) Rod removed; electrons rearrange themselves, ball has overall electron deficiency (net positive charge).

21.8 The charges within the molecules of an insulating material can shift slightly. As a result, a comb with either sign of charge attracts a neutral insulator. By Newton's third law the neutral insulator exerts an equal-magnitude attractive force on the comb.

(a) A charged comb picking up uncharged pieces of plastic

(b) How a negatively charged comb attracts an insulator

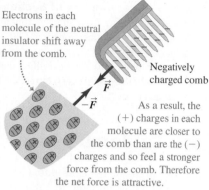

Electrons in each molecule of the neutral insulator shift away from the comb.

Negatively charged comb

$\vec{F}$
$-\vec{F}$

As a result, the (+) charges in each molecule are closer to the comb than are the (−) charges and so feel a stronger force from the comb. Therefore the net force is attractive.

(c) How a positively charged comb attracts an insulator

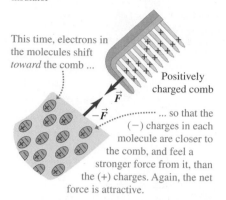

This time, electrons in the molecules shift *toward* the comb ...

Positively charged comb

$\vec{F}$
$-\vec{F}$

... so that the (−) charges in each molecule are closer to the comb, and feel a stronger force from it, than the (+) charges. Again, the net force is attractive.

What happens if, while the plastic rod is nearby, you touch one end of a conducting wire to the right surface of the ball and the other end to the earth (Fig. 21.7c)? The earth is a conductor, and it is so large that it can act as a practically infinite source of extra electrons or sink of unwanted electrons. Some of the negative charge flows through the wire to the earth. Now suppose you disconnect the wire (Fig. 21.7d) and then remove the rod (Fig. 21.7e); a net positive charge is left on the ball. The charge on the negatively charged rod has not changed during this process. The earth acquires a negative charge that is equal in magnitude to the induced positive charge remaining on the ball.

Charging by induction would work just as well if the mobile charges in the ball were positive charges instead of negatively charged electrons, or even if both positive and negative mobile charges were present. In a metallic conductor the mobile charges are always negative electrons, but it is often convenient to describe a process *as though* the moving charges were positive. In ionic solutions and ionized gases, both positive and negative charges are mobile.

Electric Forces on Uncharged Objects

Finally, we note that a charged body can exert forces even on objects that are *not* charged themselves. If you rub a balloon on the rug and then hold the balloon against the ceiling, it sticks, even though the ceiling has no net electric charge. After you electrify a comb by running it through your hair, you can pick up uncharged bits of paper or plastic with the comb (Fig. 21.8a). How is this possible?

This interaction is an induced-charge effect. Even in an insulator, electric charges can shift back and forth a little when there is charge nearby. This is shown in Fig. 21.8b; the negatively charged plastic comb causes a slight shifting of charge within the molecules of the neutral insulator, an effect called *polarization*. The positive and negative charges in the material are present in equal amounts, but the positive charges are closer to the plastic comb and so feel an attraction that is stronger than the repulsion felt by the negative charges, giving a net attractive force. (In Section 21.3 we will study how electric forces depend on distance.) Note that a neutral insulator is also attracted to a *positively* charged comb (Fig. 21.8c). Now the charges in the insulator shift in the opposite direction; the negative charges in the insulator are closer to the comb and feel an attractive force that is stronger than the repulsion felt by the positive charges in the insulator. Hence a charged object of *either* sign exerts an attractive force on an uncharged insulator.

The attraction between a charged object and an uncharged one has many important practical applications, including the electrostatic painting process used in the automobile industry (Fig. 21.9). A metal object to be painted is connected to the earth ("ground" in Fig. 21.9), and the paint droplets are given an electric charge as they exit the sprayer nozzle. Induced charges of the opposite sign

21.9 The electrostatic painting process (compare Figs. 21.7b and 21.7c).

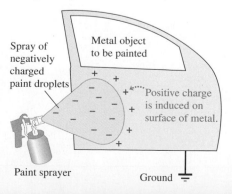

Spray of negatively charged paint droplets

Metal object to be painted

Positive charge is induced on surface of metal.

Paint sprayer

Ground

appear in the object as the droplets approach, just as in Fig. 21.7b, and they attract the droplets to the surface. This process minimizes overspray from clouds of stray paint particles and gives a particularly smooth finish.

Test Your Understanding of Section 21.2 You have two lightweight metal spheres, each hanging from an insulating nylon thread. One of the spheres has a net negative charge, while the other sphere has no net charge. (a) If the spheres are close together but do not touch, will they (i) attract each other, (ii) repel each other, or (iii) exert no force on each other? (b) You now allow the two spheres to touch. Once they have touched, will the two spheres (i) attract each other, (ii) repel each other, or (iii) exert no force on each other?

21.3 Coulomb's Law

Charles Augustin de Coulomb (1736–1806) studied the interaction forces of charged particles in detail in 1784. He used a torsion balance (Fig. 21.10a) similar to the one used 13 years later by Cavendish to study the much weaker gravitational interaction, as we discussed in Section 12.1. For **point charges,** charged bodies that are very small in comparison with the distance r between them, Coulomb found that the electric force is proportional to $1/r^2$. That is, when the distance r doubles, the force decreases to $\frac{1}{4}$ of its initial value; when the distance is halved, the force increases to four times its initial value.

The electric force between two point charges also depends on the quantity of charge on each body, which we will denote by q or Q. To explore this dependence, Coulomb divided a charge into two equal parts by placing a small charged spherical conductor into contact with an identical but uncharged sphere; by symmetry, the charge is shared equally between the two spheres. (Note the essential role of the principle of conservation of charge in this procedure.) Thus he could obtain one-half, one-quarter, and so on, of any initial charge. He found that the forces that two point charges q_1 and q_2 exert on each other are proportional to each charge and therefore are proportional to the *product q_1q_2* of the two charges.

Thus Coulomb established what we now call **Coulomb's law:**

The magnitude of the electric force between two point charges is directly proportional to the product of the charges and inversely proportional to the square of the distance between them.

21.10 **(a)** Measuring the electric force between point charges. **(b)** The electric forces between point charges obey Newton's third law: $\vec{F}_{1\ on\ 2} = -\vec{F}_{2\ on\ 1}$.

(a) A torsion balance of the type used by Coulomb to measure the electric force

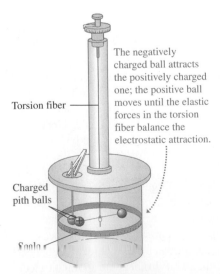

Torsion fiber

The negatively charged ball attracts the positively charged one; the positive ball moves until the elastic forces in the torsion fiber balance the electrostatic attraction.

Charged pith balls

Scale

(b) Interactions between point charges

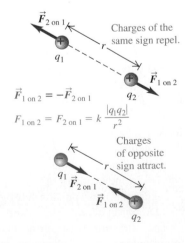

$\vec{F}_{2\ on\ 1}$

q_1

Charges of the same sign repel.

r

$\vec{F}_{1\ on\ 2}$

q_2

$\vec{F}_{1\ on\ 2} = -\vec{F}_{2\ on\ 1}$

$F_{1\ on\ 2} = F_{2\ on\ 1} = k\dfrac{|q_1q_2|}{r^2}$

q_1

Charges of opposite sign attract.

r

$\vec{F}_{2\ on\ 1}$

$\vec{F}_{1\ on\ 2}$

q_2

In mathematical terms, the magnitude F of the force that each of two point charges q_1 and q_2 a distance r apart exerts on the other can be expressed as

$$F = k\frac{|q_1 q_2|}{r^2} \tag{21.1}$$

where k is a proportionality constant whose numerical value depends on the system of units used. The absolute value bars are used in Eq. (21.1) because the charges q_1 and q_2 can be either positive or negative, while the force magnitude F is always positive.

The directions of the forces the two charges exert on each other are always along the line joining them. When the charges q_1 and q_2 have the same sign, either both positive or both negative, the forces are repulsive; when the charges have opposite signs, the forces are attractive (Fig. 21.10b). The two forces obey Newton's third law; they are always equal in magnitude and opposite in direction, even when the charges are not equal in magnitude.

The proportionality of the electric force to $1/r^2$ has been verified with great precision. There is no reason to suspect that the exponent is different from precisely 2. Thus the form of Eq. (21.1) is the same as that of the law of gravitation. But electric and gravitational interactions are two distinct classes of phenomena. Electric interactions depend on electric charges and can be either attractive or repulsive, while gravitational interactions depend on mass and are always attractive (because there is no such thing as negative mass).

Fundamental Electric Constants

The value of the proportionality constant k in Coulomb's law depends on the system of units used. In our study of electricity and magnetism we will use SI units exclusively. The SI electric units include most of the familiar units such as the volt, the ampere, the ohm, and the watt. (There is *no* British system of electric units.) The SI unit of electric charge is called one **coulomb** (1 C). In SI units the constant k in Eq. (21.1) is

$$k = 8.987551787 \times 10^9 \text{ N} \cdot \text{m}^2/\text{C}^2 \cong 8.988 \times 10^9 \text{ N} \cdot \text{m}^2/\text{C}^2$$

The value of k is known to such a large number of significant figures because this value is closely related to the speed of light in vacuum. (We will show this in Chapter 32 when we study electromagnetic radiation.) As we discussed in Section 1.3, this speed is *defined* to be exactly $c = 2.99792458 \times 10^8$ m/s. The numerical value of k is defined in terms of c to be precisely

$$k = (10^{-7} \text{ N} \cdot \text{s}^2/\text{C}^2)c^2$$

You should check this expression to confirm that k has the right units.

In principle we can measure the electric force F between two equal charges q at a measured distance r and use Coulomb's law to determine the charge. Thus we could regard the value of k as an operational definition of the coulomb. For reasons of experimental precision it is better to define the coulomb instead in terms of a unit of electric *current* (charge per unit time), the *ampere,* equal to 1 coulomb per second. We will return to this definition in Chapter 28.

In SI units we usually write the constant k in Eq. (21.1) as $1/4\pi\epsilon_0$, where ϵ_0 ("epsilon-nought" or "epsilon-zero") is another constant. This appears to complicate matters, but it actually simplifies many formulas that we will encounter in later chapters. From now on, we will usually write Coulomb's law as

$$F = \frac{1}{4\pi\epsilon_0}\frac{|q_1 q_2|}{r^2} \qquad \text{(Coulomb's law: force between two point charges)} \tag{21.2}$$

The constants in Eq. (21.2) are approximately

$$\epsilon_0 = 8.854 \times 10^{-12}\, \text{C}^2/\text{N} \cdot \text{m}^2 \quad \text{and} \quad \frac{1}{4\pi\epsilon_0} = k = 8.988 \times 10^9\, \text{N} \cdot \text{m}^2/\text{C}^2$$

In examples and problems we will often use the approximate value

$$\frac{1}{4\pi\epsilon_0} = 9.0 \times 10^9\, \text{N} \cdot \text{m}^2/\text{C}^2$$

which is within about 0.1% of the correct value.

As we mentioned in Section 21.1, the most fundamental unit of charge is the magnitude of the charge of an electron or a proton, which is denoted by e. The most precise value available as of the writing of this book is

$$e = 1.60217653(14) \times 10^{-19}\, \text{C}$$

One coulomb represents the negative of the total charge of about 6×10^{18} electrons. For comparison, a copper cube 1 cm on a side contains about 2.4×10^{24} electrons. About 10^{19} electrons pass through the glowing filament of a flashlight bulb every second.

In electrostatics problems (that is, problems that involve charges at rest), it's very unusual to encounter charges as large as 1 coulomb. Two 1-C charges separated by 1 m would exert forces on each other of magnitude 9×10^9 N (about 1 million tons)! The total charge of all the electrons in a copper one-cent coin is even greater, about 1.4×10^5 C, which shows that we can't disturb electric neutrality very much without using enormous forces. More typical values of charge range from about 10^{-9} to about 10^{-6} C. The microcoulomb $(1\, \mu\text{C} = 10^{-6}\, \text{C})$ and the nanocoulomb $(1\, \text{nC} = 10^{-9}\, \text{C})$ are often used as practical units of charge.

Example 21.1   Electric force versus gravitational force

An α particle ("alpha") is the nucleus of a helium atom. It has mass $m = 6.64 \times 10^{-27}$ kg and charge $q = +2e = 3.2 \times 10^{-19}$ C. Compare the force of the electric repulsion between two α particles with the force of gravitational attraction between them.

SOLUTION

IDENTIFY: This problem involves Newton's law for the gravitational force F_g between particles (see Section 12.1) and Coulomb's law for the electric force F_e between point charges. We are asked to compare these forces, so our target variable is the *ratio* of these two forces, F_e/F_g.

SET UP: Figure 21.11 shows our sketch. The magnitude of the repulsive electric force is given by Eq. (21.2):

$$F_e = \frac{1}{4\pi\epsilon_0} \frac{q^2}{r^2}$$

The magnitude F_g of the attractive gravitational force is given by Eq. (12.1):

$$F_g = G\frac{m^2}{r^2}$$

EXECUTE: The ratio of the electric force to the gravitational force is

$$\frac{F_e}{F_g} = \frac{1}{4\pi\epsilon_0 G}\frac{q^2}{m^2} = \frac{9.0 \times 10^9\, \text{N} \cdot \text{m}^2/\text{C}^2}{6.67 \times 10^{-11}\, \text{N} \cdot \text{m}^2/\text{kg}^2}\frac{(3.2 \times 10^{-19}\, \text{C})^2}{(6.64 \times 10^{-27}\, \text{kg})^2}$$

$$= 3.1 \times 10^{35}$$

EVALUATE: This astonishingly large number shows that the gravitational force in this situation is completely negligible in comparison to the electric force. This is always true for interactions of atomic and subatomic particles. (Notice that this result doesn't depend on the distance r between the two α particles.) But within objects the size of a person or a planet, the positive and negative charges are nearly equal in magnitude, and the net electric force is usually much *smaller* than the gravitational force.

21.11 Our sketch for this problem.

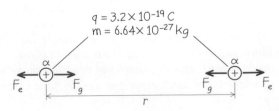

Superposition of Forces

Coulomb's law as we have stated it describes only the interaction of two *point* charges. Experiments show that when two charges exert forces simultaneously on a third charge, the total force acting on that charge is the *vector sum* of the forces that the two charges would exert individually. This important property, called the **principle of superposition of forces,** holds for any number of charges. By using this principle, we can apply Coulomb's law to *any* collection of charges. Several of the examples at the end of this section show applications of the superposition principle.

Strictly speaking, Coulomb's law as we have stated it should be used only for point charges *in a vacuum.* If matter is present in the space between the charges, the net force acting on each charge is altered because charges are induced in the molecules of the intervening material. We will describe this effect later. As a practical matter, though, we can use Coulomb's law unaltered for point charges in air. At normal atmospheric pressure, the presence of air changes the electric force from its vacuum value by only about one part in 2000.

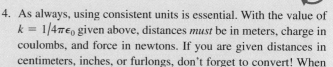

Problem-Solving Strategy 21.1. Coulomb's Law

IDENTIFY *the relevant concepts:* Coulomb's law comes into play whenever you need to know the electric force acting between charged particles.

SET UP *the problem* using the following steps:

1. Make a drawing showing the locations of the charged particles, and label each particle with its charge. This step is particularly important if more than two charged particles are present.
2. If three or more charges are present and they do not all lie on the same line, set up an xy-coordinate system.
3. Often you will need to find the electric force on just one particle. If so, identify that particle.

EXECUTE *the solution* as follows:

1. For each particle that exerts a force on the particle of interest, calculate the magnitude of that force using Eq.(21.2).
2. Sketch the electric force vectors acting on the particle(s) of interest due to each of the other particles (that is, make a free-body diagram). Remember that the force exerted by particle 1 on particle 2 points from particle 2 toward particle 1 if the two charges have opposite signs, but points from particle 2 directly away from particle 1 if the charges have the same sign.
3. Calculate the total electric force on the particle(s) of interest. Remember that the electric force, like any force, is a *vector.* When the forces acting on a charge are caused by two or more other charges, the total force on the charge is the *vector sum* of the individual forces. You may want to go back and review the vector algebra in Sections 1.7 through 1.9. It's often helpful to use components in an xy-coordinate system. Be sure to use correct vector notation; if a symbol represents a vector quantity, put an arrow over it. If you get sloppy with your notation, you will also get sloppy with your thinking.

4. As always, using consistent units is essential. With the value of $k = 1/4\pi\epsilon_0$ given above, distances *must* be in meters, charge in coulombs, and force in newtons. If you are given distances in centimeters, inches, or furlongs, don't forget to convert! When a charge is given in microcoulombs (μC) or nanocoulombs (nC), remember that $1\ \mu$C $= 10^{-6}$ C and 1 nC $= 10^{-9}$ C.
5. Some examples and problems in this and later chapters involve a continuous distribution of charge along a line or over a surface. In these cases the vector sum described in step 3 becomes a vector integral, usually carried out by use of components. We divide the total charge distribution into infinitesimal pieces, use Coulomb's law for each piece, and then integrate to find the vector sum. Sometimes this process can be done without explicit use of integration.
6. In many situations the charge distribution will be *symmetrical.* For example, you might be asked to find the force on a charge Q in the presence of two other identical charges q, one above and to the left of Q and the other below and to the left of Q. If the distances from Q to each of the other charges are the same, the force on Q from each charge has the same magnitude; if each force vector makes the same angle with the horizontal axis, adding these vectors to find the net force is particularly easy. Whenever possible, exploit any symmetries to simplify the problem-solving process.

EVALUATE *your answer:* Check whether your numerical results are reasonable, and confirm that the direction of the net electric force agrees with the principle that like charges repel and opposite charges attract.

Example 21.2 Force between two point charges

Two point charges, $q_1 = +25$ nC and $q_2 = -75$ nC, are separated by a distance of 3.0 cm (Fig. 21.12a). Find the magnitude and direction of (a) the electric force that q_1 exerts on q_2; and (b) the electric force that q_2 exerts on q_1.

SOLUTION

IDENTIFY: This problem asks for the electric forces that two charges exert on each other, so we will need to use Coulomb's law.

SET UP: We use Eq. (21.2) to calculate the magnitude of the force that each particle exerts on the other. We use Newton's third law to relate the forces that the two particles exert on each other.

EXECUTE: (a) After we convert charge to coulombs and distance to meters, the magnitude of the force that q_1 exerts on q_2 is

$$F_{1 \text{ on } 2} = \frac{1}{4\pi\epsilon_0}\frac{|q_1 q_2|}{r^2}$$

$$= (9.0 \times 10^9 \, \text{N} \cdot \text{m}^2/\text{C}^2)\frac{|(+25 \times 10^{-9} \, \text{C})(-75 \times 10^{-9} \, \text{C})|}{(0.030 \, \text{m})^2}$$

$$= 0.019 \, \text{N}$$

Since the two charges have opposite signs, the force is attractive; that is, the force that acts on q_2 is directed toward q_1 along the line joining the two charges, as shown in Fig. 21.12b.

21.12 What force does q_1 exert on q_2, and what force does q_2 exert on q_1? Gravitational forces are negligible.

(a) The two charges

(b) Free-body diagram for charge q_2

(c) Free-body diagram for charge q_1

(b) Newton's third law applies to the electric force. Even though the charges have different magnitudes, the magnitude of the force that q_2 exerts on q_1 is the *same* as the magnitude of the force that q_1 exerts on q_2:

$$F_{2 \text{ on } 1} = 0.019 \, \text{N}$$

Newton's third law also states that the direction of the force that q_2 exerts on q_1 is exactly opposite the direction of the force that q_1 exerts on q_2; this is shown in Fig. 21.12c.

EVALUATE: Note that the force on q_1 is directed toward q_2, as it must be, since charges of opposite sign attract each other.

Example 21.3 Vector addition of electric forces on a line

Two point charges are located on the positive x-axis of a coordinate system. Charge $q_1 = 1.0$ nC is 2.0 cm from the origin, and charge $q_2 = -3.0$ nC is 4.0 cm from the origin. What is the total force exerted by these two charges on a charge $q_3 = 5.0$ nC located at the origin? Gravitational forces are negligible.

SOLUTION

IDENTIFY: Here there are *two* electric forces acting on the charge q_3, and we must add these forces to find the total force.

SET UP: Figure 21.13a shows the coordinate system. Our target variable is the net electric force exerted *on* charge q_3 by the other two charges. This is the vector sum of the forces due to q_1 and q_2 individually.

EXECUTE: Figure 21.13b is a free-body diagram for charge q_3. Note that q_3 is repelled by q_1 (which has the same sign) and attracted to q_2 (which has the opposite sign). Converting charge to coulombs and distance to meters, we use Eq. (21.2) to find the magnitude $F_{1 \text{ on } 3}$ of the force of q_1 on q_3:

$$F_{1 \text{ on } 3} = \frac{1}{4\pi\epsilon_0}\frac{|q_1 q_3|}{r^2}$$

$$= (9.0 \times 10^9 \, \text{N} \cdot \text{m}^2/\text{C}^2)\frac{(1.0 \times 10^{-9} \, \text{C})(5.0 \times 10^{-9} \, \text{C})}{(0.020 \, \text{m})^2}$$

$$= 1.12 \times 10^{-4} \, \text{N} = 112 \, \mu\text{N}$$

This force has a negative x-component because q_1 is repelled (that is, pushed in the negative x-direction) by q_1.

The magnitude $F_{2 \text{ on } 3}$ of the force of q_2 on q_3 is

$$F_{2 \text{ on } 3} = \frac{1}{4\pi\epsilon_0}\frac{|q_2 q_3|}{r^2}$$

$$= (9.0 \times 10^9 \, \text{N} \cdot \text{m}^2/\text{C}^2)\frac{(3.0 \times 10^{-9} \, \text{C})(5.0 \times 10^{-9} \, \text{C})}{(0.040 \, \text{m})^2}$$

$$= 8.4 \times 10^{-5} \, \text{N} = 84 \, \mu\text{N}$$

This force has a positive x-component because q_3 is attracted (that is, pulled in the positive x-direction) by q_2. The sum of the x-components is

$$F_x = -112 \, \mu\text{N} + 84 \, \mu\text{N} = -28 \, \mu\text{N}$$

There are no y- or z-components. Thus the total force on q_3 is directed to the left, with magnitude 28 μN = 2.8×10^{-5} N.

EVALUATE: To check the magnitudes of the individual forces, note that q_2 has three times as much charge (in magnitude) as q_1 but is twice as far from q_3. From Eq. (21.2) this means that $F_{2 \text{ on } 3}$ must be $3/2^2 = \frac{3}{4}$ as large as $F_{1 \text{ on } 3}$. Indeed, our results show that this ratio is $(84 \, \mu\text{N})/(112 \, \mu\text{N}) = 0.75$. The direction of the net force also makes sense: $\vec{F}_{1 \text{ on } 3}$ is opposite to and has a larger magnitude than $\vec{F}_{2 \text{ on } 3}$, so the net force is in the direction of $\vec{F}_{1 \text{ on } 3}$.

21.13 Our sketches for this problem.

(a) Our diagram of the situation

(b) Free-body diagram for q_3

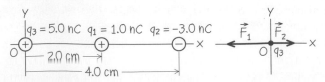

Example 21.4 | **Vector addition of electric forces in a plane**

Two equal positive point charges $q_1 = q_2 = 2.0 \ \mu\text{C}$ are located at $x = 0$, $y = 0.30$ m and $x = 0$, $y = -0.30$ m, respectively. What are the magnitude and direction of the total (net) electric force that these charges exert on a third point charge $Q = 4.0 \ \mu\text{C}$ at $x = 0.40$ m, $y = 0$?

SOLUTION

IDENTIFY: As in Example 21.3, we have to compute the force that each charge exerts on Q and then find the vector sum of the forces.

SET UP: Figure 21.14 shows the situation. Since the three charges do not all lie on a line, the best way to calculate the forces that q_1 and q_2 exert on Q is to use components.

21.14 Our sketch for this problem.

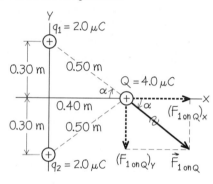

EXECUTE: Figure 21.14 shows the force on Q due to the upper charge q_1. From Coulomb's law the magnitude F of this force is

$$F_{1 \text{ on } Q} = (9.0 \times 10^9 \text{ N} \cdot \text{m}^2/\text{C}^2)\frac{(4.0 \times 10^{-6}\text{ C})(2.0 \times 10^{-6}\text{ C})}{(0.50 \text{ m})^2}$$

$$= 0.29 \text{ N}$$

The angle α is below the x-axis, so the components of this force are given by

$$(F_{1 \text{ on } Q})_x = (F_{1 \text{ on } Q})\cos\alpha = (0.29 \text{ N})\frac{0.40 \text{ m}}{0.50 \text{ m}} = 0.23 \text{ N}$$

$$(F_{1 \text{ on } Q})_y = -(F_{1 \text{ on } Q})\sin\alpha = -(0.29 \text{ N})\frac{0.30 \text{ m}}{0.50 \text{ m}} = -0.17 \text{ N}$$

The lower charge q_2 exerts a force with the same magnitude but at an angle α *above* the x-axis. From symmetry we see that its x-component is the same as that due to the upper charge, but its y-component has the opposite sign. So the components of the total force $\vec{F}$ on Q are

$$F_x = 0.23 \text{ N} + 0.23 \text{ N} = 0.46 \text{ N}$$
$$F_y = -0.17 \text{ N} + 0.17 \text{ N} = 0$$

The total force on Q is in the $+x$-direction, with magnitude 0.46 N.

EVALUATE: The total force on Q is in a direction that points neither directly away from q_1 nor directly away from q_2. Rather, this direction is a compromise that points away from the *system* of charges q_1 and q_2. Can you see that the total force would *not* be in the $+x$-direction if q_1 and q_2 were not equal or if the geometrical arrangement of the changes were not so symmetrical?

Test Your Understanding of Section 21.3 Suppose that charge q_2 in Example 21.4 were $-2.0 \ \mu\text{C}$. In this case, the total electric force on Q would be (i) in the positive x-direction; (ii) in the negative x-direction; (iii) in the positive y-direction; (iv) in the negative y-direction; (v) zero; (vi) none of these.

21.4 Electric Field and Electric Forces

When two electrically charged particles in empty space interact, how does each one know the other is there? What goes on in the space between them to communicate the effect of each one to the other? We can begin to answer these questions, and at the same time reformulate Coulomb's law in a very useful way, by using the concept of *electric field*.

Electric Field

To introduce this concept, let's look at the mutual repulsion of two positively charged bodies A and B (Fig. 21.15a). Suppose B has charge q_0, and let $\vec{F}_0$ be the electric force of A on B. One way to think about this force is as an "action-at-a-distance" force—that is, as a force that acts across empty space without needing any matter (such as a push rod or a rope) to transmit it through the intervening space. (Gravity can also be thought of as an "action-at-a-distance" force.) But a more fruitful way to visualize the repulsion between A and B is as a two-stage process. We first envision that body A, as a result of the charge that it carries, somehow *modifies the properties of the space around it*. Then body B, as

21.15 A charged body creates an electric field in the space around it.

(a) A and B exert electric forces on each other.

(b) Remove body B ...

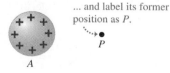

... and label its former position as P.

(c) Body A sets up an electric field $\vec{E}$ at point P.

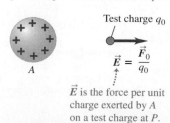

$\vec{E}$ is the force per unit charge exerted by A on a test charge at P.

a result of the charge that *it* carries, senses how space has been modified at its position. The response of body *B* is to experience the force $\vec{F}_0$.

To elaborate how this two-stage process occurs, we first consider body *A* by itself: We remove body *B* and label its former position as point *P* (Fig. 21.15b). We say that the charged body *A* produces or causes an **electric field** at point *P* (and at all other points in the neighborhood). This electric field is present at *P* even if there is no charge at *P*; it is a consequence of the charge on body *A* only. If a point charge q_0 is then placed at point *P*, it experiences the force $\vec{F}_0$. We take the point of view that this force is exerted on q_0 *by the field* at *P* (Fig. 21.15c). Thus the electric field is the intermediary through which *A* communicates its presence to q_0. Because the point charge q_0 would experience a force at *any* point in the neighborhood of *A*, the electric field that *A* produces exists at all points in the region around *A*.

We can likewise say that the point charge q_0 produces an electric field in the space around it and that this electric field exerts the force $-\vec{F}_0$ on body *A*. For each force (the force of *A* on q_0 and the force of q_0 on *A*), one charge sets up an electric field that exerts a force on the second charge. We emphasize that this is an *interaction* between *two* charged bodies. A single charge produces an electric field in the surrounding space, but this electric field cannot exert a net force on the charge that created it; this is an example of the general principle that a body cannot exert a net force on itself, as discussed in Section 4.3. (If this principle wasn't valid, you would be able to lift yourself to the ceiling by pulling up on your belt!)

The electric force on a charged body is exerted by the electric field created by *other* charged bodies.

To find out experimentally whether there is an electric field at a particular point, we place a small charged body, which we call a **test charge,** at the point (Fig. 21.15c). If the test charge experiences an electric force, then there is an electric field at that point. This field is produced by charges other than q_0.

Force is a vector quantity, so electric field is also a vector quantity. (Note the use of vector signs as well as boldface letters and plus, minus, and equals signs in the following discussion.) We define the *electric field* $\vec{E}$ at a point as the electric force $\vec{F}_0$ experienced by a test charge q_0 at the point, divided by the charge q_0. That is, the electric field at a certain point is equal to the *electric force per unit charge* experienced by a charge at that point:

$$\vec{E} = \frac{\vec{F}_0}{q_0} \qquad \text{(definition of electric field as electric force per unit charge)} \tag{21.3}$$

In SI units, in which the unit of force is 1 N and the unit of charge is 1 C, the unit of electric field magnitude is 1 newton per coulomb $(1 \text{ N}/\text{C})$.

If the field $\vec{E}$ at a certain point is known, rearranging Eq. (21.3) gives the force $\vec{F}_0$ experienced by a point charge q_0 placed at that point. This force is just equal to the electric field $\vec{E}$ produced at that point by charges other than q_0, multiplied by the charge q_0:

$$\vec{F}_0 = q_0\vec{E} \qquad \text{(force exerted on a point charge } q_0 \text{ by an electric field } \vec{E}) \tag{21.4}$$

The charge q_0 can be either positive or negative. If q_0 is *positive,* the force $\vec{F}_0$ experienced by the charge is the same direction as $\vec{E}$; if q_0 is *negative,* $\vec{F}_0$ and $\vec{E}$ are in opposite directions (Fig. 21.16).

While the electric field concept may be new to you, the basic idea—that one body sets up a field in the space around it and a second body responds to that

21.16 The force $\vec{F}_0 = q_0\vec{E}$ exerted on a point charge q_0 placed in an electric field $\vec{E}$.

The force on a positive test charge q_0 points in the direction of the electric field.

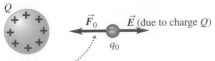

The force on a negative test charge q_0 points opposite to the electric field.

field—is one that you've actually used before. Compare Eq. (21.4) to the familiar expression for the gravitational force $\vec{F}_g$ that the earth exerts on a mass m_0:

$$\vec{F}_g = m_0\vec{g} \qquad (21.5)$$

In this expression, $\vec{g}$ is the acceleration due to gravity. If we divide both sides of Eq. (21.5) by the mass m_0, we obtain

$$\vec{g} = \frac{\vec{F}_g}{m_0}$$

Thus $\vec{g}$ can be regarded as the gravitational force per unit mass. By analogy to Eq. (21.3), we can interpret $\vec{g}$ as the *gravitational field*. Thus we treat the gravitational interaction between the earth and the mass m_0 as a two-stage process: The earth sets up a gravitational field $\vec{g}$ in the space around it, and this gravitational field exerts a force given by Eq. (21.5) on the mass m_0 (which we can regard as a *test mass*). In this sense, you've made use of the field concept every time you've used Eq. (21.5) for the force of gravity. The gravitational field $\vec{g}$, or gravitational force per unit mass, is a useful concept because it does not depend on the mass of the body on which the gravitational force is exerted; likewise, the electric field $\vec{E}$, or electric force per unit charge, is useful because it does not depend on the charge of the body on which the electric force is exerted.

CAUTION $\vec{F}_0 = q_0\vec{E}_0$ **is for *point* test charges only** The electric force experienced by a test charge q_0 can vary from point to point, so the electric field can also be different at different points. For this reason, Eq. (21.4) can be used only to find the electric force on a *point* charge. If a charged body is large enough in size, the electric field $\vec{E}$ may be noticeably different in magnitude and direction at different points on the body, and calculating the net electric force on the body can become rather complicated. ∎

We have so far ignored a subtle but important difficulty with our definition of electric field: In Fig. 21.15 the force exerted by the test charge q_0 on the charge distribution on body A may cause this distribution to shift around. This is especially true if body A is a conductor, on which charge is free to move. So the electric field around A when q_0 is present may not be the same as when q_0 is absent. But if q_0 is very small, the redistribution of charge on body A is also very small. So to make a completely correct definition of electric field, we take the *limit* of Eq. (21.3) as the test charge q_0 approaches zero and as the disturbing effect of q_0 on the charge distribution becomes negligible:

$$\vec{E} = \lim_{q_0 \to 0} \frac{\vec{F}_0}{q_0}$$

In practical calculations of the electric field $\vec{E}$ produced by a charge distribution, we will consider the charge distribution to be fixed, and so we will not need this limiting process.

Electric Field of a Point Charge

If the source distribution is a point charge q, it is easy to find the electric field that it produces. We call the location of the charge the **source point,** and we call the point P where we are determining the field the **field point.** It is also useful to introduce a *unit vector* $\hat{r}$ that points along the line from source point to field point (Fig. 21.17a). This unit vector is equal to the displacement vector $\vec{r}$ from the source point to the field point, divided by the distance $\hat{r} = |\vec{r}|$ between these two points; that is, $\hat{r} = \vec{r}/r$. If we place a small test charge q_0 at the field point P, at a distance r from the source point, the magnitude F_0 of the force is given by Coulomb's law, Eq. (21.2):

$$F_0 = \frac{1}{4\pi\epsilon_0}\frac{|qq_0|}{r^2}$$

21.17 The electric field $\vec{E}$ produced at point P by an isolated point charge q at S. Note that in both **(b)** and **(c)**, $\vec{E}$ is *produced* by q [see Eq. (21.7)] but *acts* on the charge q_0 at point P [see Eq. (21.4)].

(a)

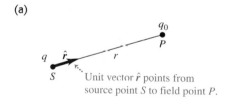

Unit vector $\hat{r}$ points from source point S to field point P.

(b)

At each point P, the electric field set up by an isolated *positive* point charge q points directly *away* from the charge in the *same* direction as $\hat{r}$.

(c)

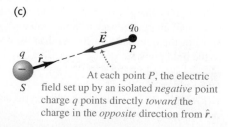

At each point P, the electric field set up by an isolated *negative* point charge q points directly *toward* the charge in the *opposite* direction from $\hat{r}$.

21.18 A point charge q produces an electric field $\vec{E}$ at *all* points in space. The field strength decreases with increasing distance.

(a) The field produced by a positive point charge points *away from* the charge.

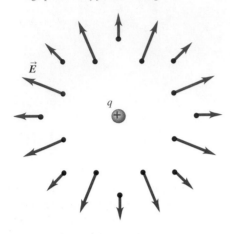

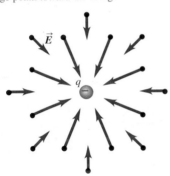

(b) The field produced by a negative point charge points *toward* the charge.

From Eq. (21.3) the magnitude E of the electric field at P is

$$E = \frac{1}{4\pi\epsilon_0}\frac{|q|}{r^2} \qquad \text{(magnitude of electric field of a point charge)} \quad (21.6)$$

Using the unit vector $\hat{r}$, we can write a *vector* equation that gives both the magnitude and direction of the electric field $\vec{E}$:

$$\vec{E} = \frac{1}{4\pi\epsilon_0}\frac{q}{r^2}\hat{r} \qquad \text{(electric field of a point charge)} \quad (21.7)$$

By definition, the electric field of a point charge always points *away from* a positive charge (that is, in the same direction as $\hat{r}$; see Fig. 21.17b) but *toward* a negative charge (that is, in the direction opposite $\hat{r}$; see Fig. 21.17c).

We have emphasized calculating the electric field $\vec{E}$ at a certain point. But since $\vec{E}$ can vary from point to point, it is not a single vector quantity but rather an *infinite* set of vector quantities, one associated with each point in space. This is an example of a **vector field.** Figure 21.18 shows a number of the field vectors produced by a positive or negative point charge. If we use a rectangular (x, y, z) coordinate system, each component of $\vec{E}$ at any point is in general a function of the coordinates (x, y, z) of the point. We can represent the functions as $E_x(x, y, z)$, $E_y(x, y, z)$, and $E_z(x, y, z)$. Vector fields are an important part of the language of physics, not just in electricity and magnetism. One everyday example of a vector field is the velocity $\vec{v}$ of wind currents; the magnitude and direction of $\vec{v}$, and hence its vector components, vary from point to point in the atmosphere.

In some situations the magnitude and direction of the field (and hence its vector components) have the same values everywhere throughout a certain region; we then say that the field is *uniform* in this region. An important example of this is the electric field inside a *conductor*. If there is an electric field within a conductor, the field exerts a force on every charge in the conductor, giving the free charges a net motion. By definition an electrostatic situation is one in which the charges have *no* net motion. We conclude that *in electrostatics the electric field at every point within the material of a conductor must be zero.* (Note that we are not saying that the field is necessarily zero in a *hole* inside a conductor.)

With the concept of electric field, our description of electric interactions has two parts. First, a given charge distribution acts as a source of electric field. Second, the electric field exerts a force on any charge that is present in the field. Our analysis often has two corresponding steps: first, calculating the field caused by a source charge distribution; second, looking at the effect of the field in terms of force and motion. The second step often involves Newton's laws as well as the principles of electric interactions. In the next section we show how to calculate fields caused by various source distributions, but first here are some examples of calculating the field due to a point charge and of finding the force on a charge due to a given field $\vec{E}$.

Example 21.5 **Electric-field magnitude for a point charge**

What is the magnitude of the electric field at a field point 2.0 m from a point charge $q = 4.0$ nC? (The point charge could represent any small charged object with this value of q, provided the dimensions of the object are much less than the distance from the object to the field point.)

SOLUTION

IDENTIFY: This problem uses the expression for the electric field due to a point charge.

SET UP: We are given the magnitude of the charge and the distance from the object to the field point, so we use Eq. (21.6) to calculate the field magnitude E.

EXECUTE: From Eq. (21.6),

$$E = \frac{1}{4\pi\epsilon_0}\frac{|q|}{r^2} = (9.0 \times 10^9 \text{ N} \cdot \text{m}^2/\text{C}^2)\frac{4.0 \times 10^{-9}\text{ C}}{(2.0 \text{ m})^2}$$

$$= 9.0 \text{ N/C}$$

EVALUATE: To check our result, we use the definition of electric field as the electric force per unit charge. We can first use Coulomb's law, Eq. (21.2), to find the magnitude F_0 of the force on a test charge q_0 placed 2.0 m from q:

$$F_0 = \frac{1}{4\pi\epsilon_0} \frac{|qq_0|}{r^2} = (9.0 \times 10^9 \text{ N} \cdot \text{m}^2/\text{C}^2) \frac{4.0 \times 10^{-9} \text{ C} |q_0|}{(2.0 \text{ m})^2}$$

$$= (9.0 \text{ N/C}) |q_0|$$

Then, from Eq. (21.3), the magnitude of $\vec{E}$ is

$$E = \frac{F_0}{|q_0|} = 9.0 \text{ N/C}$$

Because q is positive, the *direction* of $\vec{E}$ at this point is along the line from q toward q_0, as shown in Fig. 21.17b. However, the magnitude and direction of $\vec{E}$ do not depend on the sign of q_0. Do you see why not?

Example 21.6 Electric-field vector for a point charge

A point charge $q = -8.0$ nC is located at the origin. Find the electric-field vector at the field point $x = 1.2$ m, $y = -1.6$ m.

SOLUTION

IDENTIFY: In this problem we are asked to find the electric-field vector $\vec{E}$ due to a point charge. Hence we need to find either the components of $\vec{E}$ or its magnitude and direction.

SET UP: Figure 21.19 shows the situation. The electric field is given in vector form by Eq. (21.7). To use this equation, we first find the distance r from the source point S (the position of the charge q) to the field point P, as well as the unit vector $\hat{r}$ that points in the direction from S to P.

21.19 Our sketch for this problem.

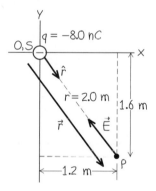

EXECUTE: The distance from the charge at the source point S (which in this example is at the origin O) to the field point P is

$$r = \sqrt{x^2 + y^2} = \sqrt{(1.2 \text{ m})^2 + (-1.6 \text{ m})^2} = 2.0 \text{ m}$$

The unit vector $\hat{r}$ is directed from the source point to the field point. This is equal to the displacement vector $\vec{r}$ from the source point to the field point (shown shifted to one side in Fig. 21.19 so as not to obscure the other vectors), divided by its magnitude r:

$$\hat{r} = \frac{\vec{r}}{r} = \frac{x\hat{i} + y\hat{j}}{r}$$

$$= \frac{(1.2 \text{ m})\hat{i} + (-1.6 \text{ m})\hat{i}}{2.0 \text{ m}} = 0.60\hat{i} - 0.80\hat{j}$$

Hence the electric-field vector is

$$\vec{E} = \frac{1}{4\pi\epsilon_0} \frac{q}{r^2} \hat{r}$$

$$= (9.0 \times 10^9 \text{ N} \cdot \text{m}^2/\text{C}^2) \frac{(-8.0 \times 10^{-9} \text{ C})}{(2.0 \text{ m})^2} (0.60\hat{i} - 0.80\hat{j})$$

$$= (-11 \text{ N/C})\hat{i} + (14 \text{ N/C})\hat{j}$$

EVALUATE: Since q is negative, $\vec{E}$ points from the field point to the charge (the source point), in the direction opposite to $\hat{r}$ (compare Fig. 21.17c). We leave the calculation of the magnitude and direction of $\vec{E}$ to you (see Exercise 21.36).

Example 21.7 Electron in a uniform field

When the terminals of a battery are connected to two large parallel conducting plates, the resulting charges on the plates cause an electric field $\vec{E}$ in the region between the plates that is very nearly uniform. (We will see the reason for this uniformity in the next section. Charged plates of this kind are used in common electrical devices called *capacitors*, to be discussed in Chapter 24.) If the plates are horizontal and separated by 1.0 cm and the plates are connected to a 100-volt battery, the magnitude of the field is $E = 1.00 \times 10^4$ N/C. Suppose the direction of $\vec{E}$ is vertically upward, as shown by the vectors in Fig. 21.20. (a) If an electron is released from rest at the upper plate, what is its acceleration? (b) What speed and kinetic energy does the electron acquire while traveling 1.0 cm to the lower plate? (c) How much time is

21.20 A uniform electric field between two parallel conducting plates connected to a 100-volt battery. (The separation of the plates is exaggerated in this figure relative to the dimensions of the plates.)

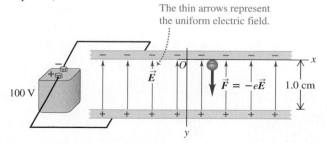

The thin arrows represent the uniform electric field.

Continued

required for it to travel this distance? An electron has charge $-e = -1.60 \times 10^{-19}$ C and mass $m = 9.11 \times 10^{-31}$ kg.

SOLUTION

IDENTIFY: This example involves several concepts: the relationship between electric field and electric force, the relationship between force and acceleration, the definition of kinetic energy, and the kinematic relationships among acceleration, distance, velocity, and time.

SET UP: Figure 21.20 shows our coordinate system. We are given the electric field, so we use Eq. (21.4) to find the force on the electron and Newton's second law to find its acceleration. Because the field is uniform between the plates, the force and acceleration are constant and we can use the constant-acceleration formulas from Chapter 3 to find the electron's velocity and travel time. We find the kinetic energy using the definition $K = \frac{1}{2}mv^2$.

EXECUTE: (a) Note that $\vec{E}$ is upward (in the $+y$-direction) but $\vec{F}$ is downward because the charge of the electron is negative. Thus F_y is negative. Because F_y is constant, the electron moves with constant acceleration a_y given by

$$a_y = \frac{F_y}{m} = \frac{-eE}{m} = \frac{(-1.60 \times 10^{-19} \text{ C})(1.00 \times 10^4 \text{ N/C})}{9.11 \times 10^{-31} \text{ kg}}$$

$$= -1.76 \times 10^{15} \text{ m/s}^2$$

This is an enormous acceleration! To give a 1000-kg car this acceleration, we would need a force of about 2×10^{18} N (about 2×10^{14} tons). The gravitational force on the electron is completely negligible compared to the electric force.

(b) The electron starts from rest, so its motion is in the y-direction only (the direction of the acceleration). We can find the electron's speed at any position using the constant-acceleration formula $v_y^2 = v_{0y}^2 + 2a_y(y - y_0)$. We have $v_{0y} = 0$ and $y_0 = 0$, so the speed $|v_y|$ when $y = -1.0$ cm $= -1.0 \times 10^{-2}$ m is

$$|v_y| = \sqrt{2a_y y} = \sqrt{2(-1.76 \times 10^{15} \text{ m/s}^2)(-1.0 \times 10^{-2} \text{ m})}$$

$$= 5.9 \times 10^6 \text{ m/s}$$

The velocity is downward, so its y-component is $v_y = -5.9 \times 10^6$ m/s. The electron's kinetic energy is

$$K = \frac{1}{2}mv^2 = \frac{1}{2}(9.11 \times 10^{-31} \text{ kg})(5.9 \times 10^6 \text{ m/s})^2$$

$$= 1.6 \times 10^{-17} \text{ J}$$

(c) From the constant-acceleration formula $v_y = v_{0y} + a_y t$, we find that the time required is very brief:

$$t = \frac{v_y - v_{0y}}{a_y} = \frac{(-5.9 \times 10^6 \text{ m/s}) - (0 \text{ m/s})}{-1.76 \times 10^{15} \text{ m/s}^2}$$

$$= 3.4 \times 10^{-9} \text{ s}$$

(We could also have found the time by solving the equation $y = y_0 + v_{0y}t + \frac{1}{2}a_y t^2$ for t.)

EVALUATE: This example shows that in problems about subatomic particles such as electrons, many quantities—including acceleration, speed, kinetic energy, and time—will have *very* different values from what we have seen for ordinary objects such as baseballs and automobiles.

Example 21.8 **An electron trajectory**

If we launch an electron into the electric field of Example 21.7 with an initial horizontal velocity v_0 (Fig. 21.21), what is the equation of its trajectory?

SOLUTION

IDENTIFY: We found the electron's acceleration in Example 21.7. Our goal is to find the trajectory that corresponds to that acceleration.

SET UP: The acceleration is constant and in the negative y-direction (there is no acceleration in the x-direction). Hence we can use the kinematic equations from Chapter 3 for two-dimensional motion with constant acceleration.

EXECUTE: We have $a_x = 0$ and $a_y = (-e)E/m$. At $t = 0$, $x_0 = y_0 = 0$, $v_{0x} = v_0$, and $v_{0y} = 0$; hence at time t,

$$x = v_0 t \quad \text{and} \quad y = \frac{1}{2}a_y t^2 = -\frac{1}{2}\frac{eE}{m}t^2$$

Eliminating t between these equations, we get

$$y = -\frac{1}{2}\frac{eE}{mv_0^2}x^2$$

EVALUATE: This is the equation of a parabola, just like the trajectory of a projectile launched horizontally in the earth's gravitational field (discussed in Section 3.3). For a given initial velocity of the electron, the curvature of the trajectory depends on the field magnitude E. If we reverse the signs of the charges on the two plates in Fig. 21.21, the direction of $\vec{E}$ reverses, and the electron trajectory will curve up, not down. Hence we can "steer" the electron by varying the charges on the plates. The electric field between charged conducting plates can be used in this way to control the trajectory of electron beams in oscilloscopes.

21.21 The parabolic trajectory of an electron in a uniform electric field.

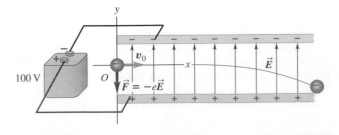

Test Your Understanding of Section 21.4   (a) A negative point charge moves along a straight-line path directly toward a stationary positive point charge. Which aspect(s) of the electric force on the negative point charge will remain constant as it moves? (i) magnitude; (ii) direction; (iii) both magnitude and direction; (iv) neither magnitude nor direction. (b) A negative point charge moves along a circular orbit around a positive point charge. Which aspect(s) of the electric force on the negative point charge will remain constant as it moves? (i) magnitude; (ii) direction; (iii) both magnitude and direction; (iv) neither magnitude nor direction.

21.5 Electric-Field Calculations

Activ Physics
ONLINE

11.5 Electric Field Due to a Dipole
11.6 Electric Field: Problems

Equation (21.7) gives the electric field caused by a single point charge. But in most realistic situations that involve electric fields and forces, we encounter charge that is *distributed* over space. The charged plastic and glass rods in Fig. 21.1 have electric charge distributed over their surfaces, as does the imaging drum of a laser printer (Fig. 21.2). In this section we'll learn to calculate electric fields caused by various distributions of electric charge. Calculations of this kind are of tremendous importance for technological applications of electric forces. To determine the trajectories of electrons in a TV tube, of atomic nuclei in an accelerator for cancer radiotherapy, or of charged particles in a semiconductor electronic device, you have to know the detailed nature of the electric field acting on the charges.

The Superposition of Electric Fields

To find the field caused by a charge distribution, we imagine the distribution to be made up of many point charges $q_1, q_2, q_3, \ldots$. (This is actually quite a realistic description, since we have seen that charge is carried by electrons and protons that are so small as to be almost pointlike.) At any given point P, each point charge produces its own electric field $\vec{E}_1, \vec{E}_2, \vec{E}_3, \ldots$, so a test charge q_0 placed at P experiences a force $\vec{F}_1 = q_0\vec{E}_1$ from charge q_1, a force $\vec{F}_2 = q_0\vec{E}_2$ from charge q_2, and so on. From the principle of superposition of forces discussed in Section 21.3, the *total* force $\vec{F}_0$ that the charge distribution exerts on q_0 is the vector sum of these individual forces:

$$\vec{F}_0 = \vec{F}_1 + \vec{F}_2 + \vec{F}_3 + \cdots = q_0\vec{E}_1 + q_0\vec{E}_2 + q_0\vec{E}_3 + \cdots$$

The combined effect of all the charges in the distribution is described by the *total* electric field $\vec{E}$ at point P. From the definition of electric field, Eq. (21.3), this is

$$\vec{E} = \frac{\vec{F}_0}{q_0} = \vec{E}_1 + \vec{E}_2 + \vec{E}_3 + \cdots$$

The total electric field at P is the vector sum of the fields at P due to each point charge in the charge distribution (Fig. 21.22). This is the **principle of superposition of electric fields.**

When charge is distributed along a line, over a surface, or through a volume, a few additional terms are useful. For a line charge distribution (such as a long, thin, charged plastic rod), we use λ (the Greek letter lambda) to represent the **linear charge density** (charge per unit length, measured in C/m). When charge is distributed over a surface (such as the surface of the imaging drum of a laser printer), we use σ (sigma) to represent the **surface charge density** (charge per unit area, measured in C/m^2). And when charge is distributed through a volume, we use ρ (rho) to represent the **volume charge density** (charge per unit volume, C/m^3).

Some of the calculations in the following examples may look fairly intricate; in electric-field calculations a certain amount of mathematical complexity is in the nature of things. After you've worked through the examples one step at a time, the process will seem less formidable. We will use many of the calculational techniques in these examples in Chapter 28 to calculate the *magnetic* fields caused by charges in motion.

21.22 Illustrating the principle of superposition of electric fields.

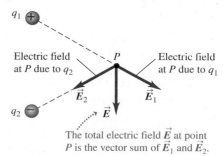

Electric field at P due to q_2

Electric field at P due to q_1

The total electric field $\vec{E}$ at point P is the vector sum of $\vec{E}_1$ and $\vec{E}_2$.

Problem-Solving Strategy 21.2 Electric-Field Calculations

IDENTIFY *the relevant concepts:* Use the principle of superposition whenever you need to calculate the electric field due to a charge distribution (two or more point charges, a distribution over a line, surface, or volume, or a combination of these).

SET UP *the problem* using the following steps:
1. Make a drawing that clearly shows the locations of the charges and your choice of coordinate axes.
2. On your drawing, indicate the position of the *field point* (the point at which you want to calculate the electric field $\vec{E}$). Sometimes the field point will be at some arbitrary position along a line. For example, you may be asked to find $\vec{E}$ at any point on the *x*-axis.

EXECUTE *the solution* as follows:
1. Be sure to use a consistent set of units. Distances must be in meters and charge must be in coulombs. If you are given centimeters or nanocoulombs, don't forget to convert.
2. When adding up the electric fields caused by different parts of the charge distribution, remember that electric field is a vector, so you *must* use vector addition. Don't simply add together the magnitudes of the individual fields; the directions are important, too.
3. Take advantage of any symmetries in the charge distribution. For example, if a positive charge and a negative charge of equal magnitude are placed symmetrically with respect to the field point, they produce electric fields of the same magnitude but with mirror-image directions. Exploiting these symmetries will simplify your calculations.

4. Most often you will use components to compute vector sums. Use the methods you learned in Chapter 1; review them if necessary. Use proper vector notation; distinguish carefully between scalars, vectors, and components of vectors. Be certain the components are consistent with your choice of coordinate axes.
5. In working out the directions of $\vec{E}$ vectors, be careful to distinguish between the *source point* and the *field point*. The field produced by a point charge always points from source point to field point if the charge is positive; it points in the opposite direction if the charge is negative.
6. In some situations you will have a continuous distribution of charge along a line, over a surface, or through a volume. Then you must define a small element of charge that can be considered as a point, find its electric field at point *P*, and find a way to add the fields of all the charge elements. Usually it is easiest to do this for each component of $\vec{E}$ separately, and often you will need to evaluate one or more integrals. Make certain the limits on your integrals are correct; especially when the situation has symmetry, make sure you don't count the charge twice.

EVALUATE *your answer:* Check that the direction of $\vec{E}$ is reasonable. If your result for the electric-field magnitude E is a function of position (say, the coordinate *x*), check your result in any limits for which you know what the magnitude should be. When possible, check your answer by calculating it in a different way.

Example 21.9 Field of an electric dipole

Point charges q_1 and q_2 of $+12$ nC and -12 nC, respectively, are placed 0.10 m apart (Fig. 21.23). This combination of two charges with equal magnitude and opposite sign is called an *electric dipole*. (Such combinations occur frequently in nature. For example, in Figs. 21.8b and 21.8c, each molecule in the neutral insulator is an electric dipole. We'll study dipoles in more detail in Section 21.7.) Compute the electric field caused by q_1, the field caused by q_2, and the total field (a) at point *a*; (b) at point *b*; and (c) at point *c*.

SOLUTION

IDENTIFY: We need to find the total electric field at three different points due to two point charges. We will use the principle of superposition: $\vec{E} = \vec{E}_1 + \vec{E}_2$.

SET UP: Figure 21.23 shows the coordinate system and the locations of the three field points *a*, *b*, and *c*.

21.23 Electric field at three points, *a*, *b*, and *c*, set up by charges q_1 and q_2, which form an electric dipole.

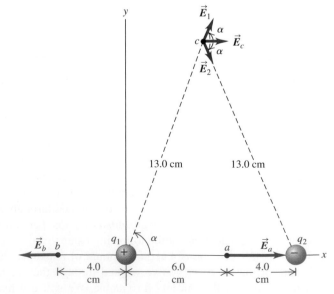

EXECUTE: (a) At point a the field $\vec{E}_1$ caused by the positive charge q_1 and the field $\vec{E}_2$ caused by the negative charge q_2 are both directed toward the right. The magnitudes of $\vec{E}_1$ and $\vec{E}_2$ are

$$E_1 = \frac{1}{4\pi\epsilon_0}\frac{|q_1|}{r^2} = (9.0 \times 10^9 \text{ N}\cdot\text{m}^2/\text{C}^2)\frac{12 \times 10^{-9}\text{ C}}{(0.060\text{ m})^2}$$
$$= 3.0 \times 10^4 \text{ N/C}$$

$$E_2 = \frac{1}{4\pi\epsilon_0}\frac{|q_2|}{r^2} = (9.0 \times 10^9 \text{ N}\cdot\text{m}^2/\text{C}^2)\frac{12 \times 10^{-9}\text{ C}}{(0.040\text{ m})^2}$$
$$= 6.8 \times 10^4 \text{ N/C}$$

The components of $\vec{E}_1$ and $\vec{E}_2$ are

$$E_{1x} = 3.0 \times 10^4 \text{ N/C} \qquad E_{1y} = 0$$
$$E_{2x} = 6.8 \times 10^4 \text{ N/C} \qquad E_{2y} = 0$$

Hence at point a the total electric field $\vec{E}_a = \vec{E}_1 + \vec{E}_2$ has components

$$(E_a)_x = E_{1x} + E_{2x} = (3.0 + 6.8) \times 10^4 \text{ N/C}$$
$$(E_a)_y = E_{1y} + E_{2y} = 0$$

At point a the total field has magnitude 9.8×10^4 N/C and is directed toward the right, so

$$\vec{E}_a = (9.8 \times 10^4 \text{ N/C})\hat{\imath}$$

(b) At point b the field $\vec{E}_1$ due to q_1 is directed toward the left, while the field $\vec{E}_2$ due to q_2 is directed toward the right. The magnitudes of $\vec{E}_1$ and $\vec{E}_2$ are

$$E_1 = \frac{1}{4\pi\epsilon_0}\frac{|q_1|}{r^2} = (9.0 \times 10^9 \text{ N}\cdot\text{m}^2/\text{C}^2)\frac{12 \times 10^{-9}\text{ C}}{(0.040\text{ m})^2}$$
$$= 6.8 \times 10^4 \text{ N/C}$$

$$E_2 = \frac{1}{4\pi\epsilon_0}\frac{|q_2|}{r^2} = (9.0 \times 10^9 \text{ N}\cdot\text{m}^2/\text{C}^2)\frac{12 \times 10^{-9}\text{ C}}{(0.140\text{ m})^2}$$
$$= 0.55 \times 10^4 \text{ N/C}$$

The components of $\vec{E}_1$, $\vec{E}_2$, and the total field $\vec{E}_b$ at point b are

$$E_{1x} = -6.8 \times 10^4 \text{ N/C} \qquad E_{1y} = 0$$
$$E_{2x} = 0.55 \times 10^4 \text{ N/C} \qquad E_{2y} = 0$$
$$(E_b)_x = E_{1x} + E_{2x} = (-6.8 + 0.55) \times 10^4 \text{ N/C}$$
$$(E_b)_y = E_{1y} + E_{2y} = 0$$

That is, the electric field at b has magnitude 6.2×10^4 N/C and is directed toward the left, so

$$\vec{E}_b = (-6.2 \times 10^4 \text{ N/C})\hat{\imath}$$

(c) At point c, both $\vec{E}_1$ and $\vec{E}_2$ have the same magnitude, since this point is equidistant from both charges and the charge magnitudes are the same:

$$E_1 = E_2 = \frac{1}{4\pi\epsilon_0}\frac{|q|}{r^2} = (9.0 \times 10^9 \text{ N}\cdot\text{m}^2/\text{C}^2)\frac{12 \times 10^{-9}\text{ C}}{(0.130\text{ m})^2}$$
$$= 6.39 \times 10^3 \text{ N/C}$$

The directions of $\vec{E}_1$ and $\vec{E}_2$ are shown in Fig 21.23. The x-components of both vectors are the same:

$$E_{1x} = E_{2x} = E_1\cos\alpha = (6.39 \times 10^3 \text{ N/C})\left(\frac{5}{13}\right)$$
$$= 2.46 \times 10^3 \text{ N/C}$$

From symmetry the y-components E_{1y} and E_{2y} are equal and opposite and so add to zero. Hence the components of the total field $\vec{E}_c$ are

$$(E_c)_x = E_{1x} + E_{2x} = 2(2.46 \times 10^3 \text{ N/C}) = 4.9 \times 10^3 \text{ N/C}$$
$$(E_c)_y = E_{1y} + E_{2y} = 0$$

So at point c the total electric field has magnitude 4.9×10^3 N/C and is directed toward the right, so

$$\vec{E}_c = (4.9 \times 10^3 \text{ N/C})\hat{\imath}$$

Does it surprise you that the field at point c is parallel to the line between the two charges?

EVALUATE: An alternative way to find the electric field at c is to use the vector expression for the field of a point charge, Eq. (21.7). The displacement vector $\vec{r}_1$ from q_1 to point c, a distance $r = 13.0$ cm away, is

$$\vec{r}_1 = r\cos\alpha\,\hat{\imath} + r\sin\alpha\,\hat{\jmath}$$

Hence the unit vector that points from q_1 to c is

$$\hat{r}_1 = \frac{\vec{r}_1}{r} = \cos\alpha\,\hat{\imath} + \sin\alpha\,\hat{\jmath}$$

and the field due to q_1 at point c is

$$\vec{E}_1 = \frac{1}{4\pi\epsilon_0}\frac{q_1}{r^2}\hat{r}_1 = \frac{1}{4\pi\epsilon_0}\frac{q_1}{r^2}(\cos\alpha\,\hat{\imath} + \sin\alpha\,\hat{\jmath})$$

By symmetry the unit vector $\hat{r}_2$ that points from q_2 to point c has the opposite x-component but the same y-component, so the field at c due to q_2 is

$$\vec{E}_2 = \frac{1}{4\pi\epsilon_0}\frac{q_2}{r^2}\hat{r}_2 = \frac{1}{4\pi\epsilon_0}\frac{q_2}{r^2}(-\cos\alpha\,\hat{\imath} + \sin\alpha\,\hat{\jmath})$$

Since $q_2 = -q_1$, the total field at c is

$$\vec{E}_c = \vec{E}_1 + \vec{E}_2$$
$$= \frac{1}{4\pi\epsilon_0}\frac{q_1}{r^2}(\cos\alpha\,\hat{\imath} + in\alpha\,\hat{\jmath}) + \frac{1}{4\pi\epsilon_0}\frac{(-q_1)}{r^2}(-\cos\alpha\,\hat{\imath} + \sin\alpha\,\hat{\jmath})$$
$$= \frac{1}{4\pi\epsilon_0}\frac{q_1}{r^2}(2\cos\alpha\,\hat{\imath})$$
$$= (9.0 \times 10^9 \text{ N}\cdot\text{m}^2/\text{C}^2)\frac{12 \times 10^{-9}\text{ C}}{(0.13\text{ m})^2}\left[2\left(\frac{5}{13}\right)\right]\hat{\imath}$$
$$= (4.9 \times 10^3 \text{ N/C})\hat{\imath}$$

as before.

Example 21.10 Field of a ring of charge

A ring-shaped conductor with radius a carries a total charge Q uniformly distributed around it (Fig. 21.24). Find the electric field at a point P that lies on the axis of the ring at a distance x from its center.

SOLUTION

IDENTIFY: This is a problem in the superposition of electric fields. The new wrinkle is that the charge is distributed continuously around the ring rather than in a number of point charges.

SET UP: The field point is an arbitrary point on the x-axis in Fig. 21.24. Our target variable is the electric field at such a point as a function of the coordinate x.

EXECUTE: As shown in Fig. 21.24, we imagine the ring divided into infinitesimal segments of length ds. Each segment has charge dQ and acts as a point-charge source of electric field. Let $d\vec{E}$ be the electric field from one such segment; the net electric field at P is then the sum of all contributions $d\vec{E}$ from all the segments that make up the ring. (This same technique works for any situation in which charge is distributed along a line or a curve.)

The calculation of $\vec{E}$ is greatly simplified because the field point P is on the symmetry axis of the ring. Consider two segments at the top and bottom of the ring: The contributions $d\vec{E}$ to the field at P from these segments have the same x-component but opposite y-components. Hence the total y-component of field due to this pair of segments is zero. When we add up the contributions from all such pairs of segments, the total field $\vec{E}$ will have only a component along the ring's symmetry axis (the x-axis), with no component perpendicular to that axis (that is, no y-component or z-component). So the field at P is described completely by its x-component E_x.

To calculate E_x, note that the square of the distance r from a ring segment to the point P is $r^2 = x^2 + a^2$. Hence the magnitude of this segment's contribution $d\vec{E}$ to the electric field at P is

$$dE = \frac{1}{4\pi\epsilon_0}\frac{dQ}{x^2 + a^2}$$

Using $\cos\alpha = x/r = x/(x^2 + a^2)^{1/2}$, the x-component dE_x of this field is

$$dE_x = dE\cos\alpha = \frac{1}{4\pi\epsilon_0}\frac{dQ}{x^2 + a^2}\frac{x}{\sqrt{x^2 + a^2}}$$
$$= \frac{1}{4\pi\epsilon_0}\frac{x\,dQ}{(x^2 + a^2)^{3/2}}$$

To find the *total* x-component E_x of the field at P, we integrate this expression over all segments of the ring:

$$E_x = \int\frac{1}{4\pi\epsilon_0}\frac{x\,dQ}{(x^2 + a^2)^{3/2}}$$

Since x does not vary as we move from point to point around the ring, all the factors on the right side except dQ are constant and can be taken outside the integral. The integral of dQ is just the total charge Q, and we finally get

$$\vec{E} = E_x\hat{\imath} = \frac{1}{4\pi\epsilon_0}\frac{Qx}{(x^2 + a^2)^{3/2}}\hat{\imath} \qquad (21.8)$$

EVALUATE: Our result for $\vec{E}$ shows that at the center of the ring $(x = 0)$ the field is zero. We should expect this; charges on opposite sides of the ring would push in opposite directions on a test charge at the center, and the forces would add to zero. When the field point P is much farther from the ring than its size (that is, $x \gg a$), the denominator in Eq. (21.8) becomes approximately equal to x^3, and the expression becomes approximately

$$\vec{E} = \frac{1}{4\pi\epsilon_0}\frac{Q}{x^2}\hat{\imath}$$

In other words, when we are so far from the ring that its size a is negligible in comparison to the distance x, its field is the same as that of a point charge. To an observer far from the ring, the ring would appear like a point, and the electric field reflects this.

In this example we used a *symmetry argument* to conclude that $\vec{E}$ had only an x-component at a point on the ring's axis of symmetry. We'll use symmetry arguments many times in this and subsequent chapters. Keep in mind, however, that such arguments can be used only in special cases. At a point in the xy-plane that is not on the x-axis in Fig. 21.24, the symmetry argument doesn't apply, and the field has in general both x- and y-components.

21.24 Calculating the electric field on the axis of a ring of charge. In this figure, the charge is assumed to be positive.

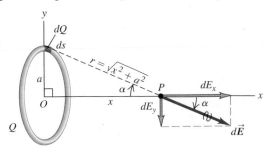

Example 21.11   Field of a line of charge

Positive electric charge Q is distributed uniformly along a line with length $2a$, lying along the y-axis between $y = -a$ and $y = +a$. (This might represent one of the charged rods in Fig. 21.1.) Find the electric field at point P on the x-axis at a distance x from the origin.

SOLUTION

IDENTIFY: As in Example 21.10, our target variable is the electric field due to a continuous distribution of charge.

SET UP: Figure 21.25 shows the situation. We need to find the electric field at P as a function of the coordinate x. The x-axis is the perpendicular bisector of the charged line, so as in Example 21.10 we will be able to make use of a symmetry argument.

EXECUTE: We divide the line charge into infinitesimal segments, each of which acts as a point charge; let the length of a typical segment at height y be dy. If the charge is distributed uniformly, the linear charge density λ at any point on the line is equal to $Q/2a$ (the total charge divided by the total length). Hence the charge dQ in a segment of length dy is

$$dQ = \lambda dy = \frac{Q dy}{2a}$$

The distance r from this segment to P is $(x^2 + y^2)^{1/2}$, so the magnitude of field dE at P due to this segment is

$$dE = \frac{1}{4\pi\epsilon_0} \frac{dQ}{r^2} = \frac{Q}{4\pi\epsilon_0} \frac{dy}{2a(x^2 + y^2)}$$

We represent this field in terms of its x- and y-components:

$$dE_x = dE \cos\alpha \qquad dE_y = -dE \sin\alpha$$

We note that $\sin\alpha = y/(x^2 + y^2)^{1/2}$ and $\cos\alpha = x/(x^2 + y^2)^{1/2}$; combining these with the expression for dE, we find

$$dE_x = \frac{Q}{4\pi\epsilon_0} \frac{x\,dy}{2a(x^2 + y^2)^{3/2}}$$

$$dE_y = -\frac{Q}{4\pi\epsilon_0} \frac{y\,dy}{2a(x^2 + y^2)^{3/2}}$$

To find the total field components E_x and E_y, we integrate these expressions, noting that to include all of Q, we must integrate from $y = -a$ to $y = +a$. We invite you to work out the details of the integration; an integral table is helpful. The final results are

$$E_x = \frac{1}{4\pi\epsilon_0} \frac{Qx}{2a} \int_{-a}^{a} \frac{dy}{(x^2 + y^2)^{3/2}} = \frac{Q}{4\pi\epsilon_0} \frac{1}{x\sqrt{x^2 + a^2}}$$

$$E_y = -\frac{1}{4\pi\epsilon_0} \frac{Q}{2a} \int_{-a}^{a} \frac{y\,dy}{(x^2 + y^2)^{3/2}} = 0$$

or, in vector form,

$$\vec{E} = \frac{1}{4\pi\epsilon_0} \frac{Q}{x\sqrt{x^2 + a^2}} \hat{\imath} \qquad (21.9)$$

EVALUATE: Using a symmetry argument as in Example 21.10, we could have guessed that E_y would be zero; if we place a positive test charge at P, the upper half of the line of charge pushes downward on it, and the lower half pushes up with equal magnitude.

21.25 Our sketch for this problem.

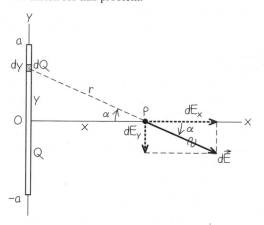

To explore our result, let's first see what happens in the limit that x is much larger than a. Then we can neglect a in the denominator of Eq. (21.9), and our result becomes

$$\vec{E} = \frac{1}{4\pi\epsilon_0} \frac{Q}{x^2} \hat{\imath}$$

This means that if point P is very far from the line charge in comparison to the length of the line, the field at P is the same as that of a point charge. We found a similar result for the charged ring in Example 21.10.

To further explore our exact result for $\vec{E}$, Eq. (21.9), let's express it in terms of the linear charge density $\lambda = Q/2a$. Substituting $Q = 2a\lambda$ into Eq. (21.9) and simplifying, we get

$$\vec{E} = \frac{1}{2\pi\epsilon_0} \frac{\lambda}{x\sqrt{(x^2/a^2) + 1}} \hat{\imath} \qquad (21.10)$$

Now we can answer the question: What is $\vec{E}$ at a distance x from a *very* long line of charge? To find the answer we take the *limit* of Eq. (21.10) as a becomes very large. In this limit, the term x^2/a^2 in the denominator becomes much smaller than unity and can be thrown away. We are left with

$$\vec{E} = \frac{\lambda}{2\pi\epsilon_0 x} \hat{\imath}$$

The field magnitude depends only on the distance of point P from the line of charge. So at any point P at a perpendicular distance r from the line in any direction, $\vec{E}$ has magnitude

$$E = \frac{\lambda}{2\pi\epsilon_0 r} \qquad \text{(infinite line of charge)}$$

Thus the electric field due to an infinitely long line of charge is proportional to $1/r$ rather than to $1/r^2$ as for a point charge. The direction of $\vec{E}$ is radially outward from the line if λ is positive and radially inward if λ is negative.

There's really no such thing in nature as an infinite line of charge. But when the field point is close enough to the line, there's very little difference between the result for an infinite line and the real-life finite case. For example, if the distance r of the field point from the center of the line is 1% of the length of the line, the value of E differs from the infinite-length value by less than 0.02%.

Example 21.12   Field of a uniformly charged disk

Find the electric field caused by a disk of radius R with a uniform positive surface charge density (charge per unit area) σ, at a point along the axis of the disk a distance x from its center. Assume that x is positive.

SOLUTION

IDENTIFY: This example is similar to Examples 21.10 and 21.11 in that our target variable is the electric field along a symmetry axis of a continuous charge distribution.

SET UP: Figure 21.26 shows the situation. We can represent the charge distribution as a collection of concentric rings of charge dQ, as shown in Fig. 21.26. From Example 21.10 we know the field of a single ring on its axis of symmetry, so all we have to do is add the contributions of the rings.

EXECUTE: A typical ring has charge dQ, inner radius r, and outer radius $r + dr$ (Fig. 21.26). Its area dA is approximately equal to its width dr times its circumference $2\pi r$, or $dA = 2\pi r\,dr$. The charge per unit area is $\sigma = dQ/dA$, so the charge of the ring is $dQ = \sigma\,dA = \sigma\,(2\pi r\,dr)$, or

$$dQ = 2\pi\sigma r\,dr$$

We use this in place of Q in the expression for the field due to a ring found in Example 21.10, Eq. (21.8), and also replace the ring radius a with r. The field component dE_x at point P due to charge dQ is

$$dE_x = \frac{1}{4\pi\epsilon_0}\frac{dQ}{r^2} = \frac{1}{4\pi\epsilon_0}\frac{(2\pi\sigma r\,dr)x}{(x^2 + r^2)^{3/2}}$$

21.26 Our sketch for this problem.

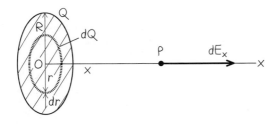

To find the total field due to all the rings, we integrate dE_x over r from $r = 0$ to $r = R$ (*not* from $-R$ to R):

$$E_x = \int_0^R \frac{1}{4\pi\epsilon_0}\frac{(2\pi\sigma r\,dr)x}{(x^2 + r^2)^{3/2}} = \frac{\sigma x}{2\epsilon_0}\int_0^R \frac{r\,dr}{(x^2 + r^2)^{3/2}}$$

Remember that x is a constant during the integration and that the integration variable is r. The integral can be evaluated by use of the substitution $z = x^2 + r^2$. We'll let you work out the details; the result is

$$\begin{aligned} E_x &= \frac{\sigma x}{2\epsilon_0}\left[-\frac{1}{\sqrt{x^2 + R^2}} + \frac{1}{x}\right] \\ &= \frac{\sigma}{2\epsilon_0}\left[1 - \frac{1}{\sqrt{(R^2/x^2) + 1}}\right] \end{aligned} \qquad (21.11)$$

The electric field due to the ring has no components perpendicular to the axis. Hence at point P in Fig. 21.26, $dE_y = dE_z = 0$ for each ring, and the total field has $E_y = E_z = 0$.

EVALUATE Suppose we keep increasing the radius R of the disk, simultaneously adding charge so that the surface charge density σ (charge per unit area) is constant. In the limit that R is much larger than the distance x of the field point from the disk, the term $1/\sqrt{(R^2/x^2) + 1}$ in Eq. (21.11) becomes negligibly small, and we get

$$E = \frac{\sigma}{2\epsilon_0} \qquad (21.12)$$

Our final result does not contain the distance x from the plane. Hence the electric field produced by an *infinite* plane sheet of charge is *independent of the distance from the sheet*. The field direction is everywhere perpendicular to the sheet, away from it. There is no such thing as an infinite sheet of charge, but if the dimensions of the sheet are much larger than the distance x of the field point P from the sheet, the field is very nearly given by Eq. (21.11).

If P is to the *left* of the plane $(x < 0)$, the result is the same except that the direction of $\vec{E}$ is to the left instead of the right. If the surface charge density is negative, the directions of the fields on both sides of the plane are toward it rather than away from it.

Example 21.13   Field of two oppositely charged infinite sheets

Two infinite plane sheets are placed parallel to each other, separated by a distance d (Fig. 21.27). The lower sheet has a uniform positive surface charge density σ, and the upper sheet has a uniform negative surface charge density $-\sigma$ with the same magnitude. Find the electric field between the two sheets, above the upper sheet, and below the lower sheet.

SOLUTION

IDENTIFY: From Example 21.12 we know the electric field due to a single infinite plane sheet of charge. Our goal is to find the electric field due to *two* such sheets.

SET UP: We use the principle of superposition to combine the electric fields produced by the two sheets, as shown in Fig. 21.27.

21.27 Finding the electric field due to two oppositely charged infinite sheets. The sheets are seen edge-on; only a portion of the infinite sheets can be shown!

EXECUTE: Let sheet 1 be the lower sheet of positive charge, and let sheet 2 be the upper sheet of negative charge; the fields due to each sheet are $\vec{E}_1$ and $\vec{E}_2$, respectively. From Eq. (21.12) of Example 21.12, both $\vec{E}_1$ and $\vec{E}_2$ have the same magnitude at all points, no matter how far from either sheet:

$$E_1 = E_2 = \frac{\sigma}{2\epsilon_0}$$

At all points, the direction of $\vec{E}_1$ is away from the positive charge of sheet 1, and the direction of $\vec{E}_2$ is toward the negative charge of sheet 2. These fields and the x- and y-axes are shown in Fig. 21.27.

> **CAUTION** **Electric fields are not "flows"** You may be surprised that $\vec{E}_1$ is unaffected by the presence of sheet 2 and that $\vec{E}_2$ is unaffected by the presence of sheet 1. Indeed, you may have thought that the field of one sheet would be unable to "penetrate" the other sheet. You might conclude this if you think of the electric field as some kind of physical substance that "flows" into or out of charges. But in fact there is no such substance, and the electric fields $\vec{E}_1$ and $\vec{E}_2$ depend only on the individual charge distributions that create them. The *total* field is just the vector sum of $\vec{E}_1$ and $\vec{E}_2$. ∎

At points between the sheets, $\vec{E}_1$ and $\vec{E}_2$ reinforce each other; at points above the upper sheet or below the lower sheet, $\vec{E}_1$ and $\vec{E}_2$ cancel each other. Thus the total field is

$$\vec{E} = \vec{E}_1 + \vec{E}_2 = \begin{cases} \mathbf{0} & \text{above the upper sheet} \\ \dfrac{\sigma}{\epsilon_0}\hat{\jmath} & \text{between the sheets} \\ \mathbf{0} & \text{below the lower sheet} \end{cases}$$

Because we considered the sheets to be infinite, our result does not depend on the separation d.

EVALUATE: Note that the field between the oppositely charged sheets is uniform. We used this in Examples 21.7 and 21.8, in which two large parallel conducting plates were connected to the terminals of a battery. The battery causes the two plates to become oppositely charged, giving a field between the plates that is essentially uniform if the plate separation is much smaller than the dimensions of the plates. In Chapter 23 we will examine how a battery can produce such separation of positive and negative charge. An arrangement of two oppositely charged conducting plates is called a *capacitor;* these devices prove to be of tremendous practical utility and are the principal subject of Chapter 24.

Test Your Understanding of Section 21.5 Suppose that the line of charge in Fig. 21.25 (Example 11.11) had charge $+Q$ distributed uniformly between $y = 0$ and $y = +a$ and had charge $-Q$ distributed uniformly between $y = 0$ and $y = -a$. In this situation, the electric field at P would be (i) in the positive x-direction; (ii) in the negative x-direction; (iii) in the positive y-direction; (iv) in the negative y-direction; (v) zero; (vi) none of these.

21.6 Electric Field Lines

The concept of an electric field can be a little elusive because you can't see an electric field directly. Electric field *lines* can be a big help for visualizing electric fields and making them seem more real. An **electric field line** is an imaginary line or curve drawn through a region of space so that its tangent at any point is in the direction of the electric-field vector at that point. Figure 21.28 shows the basic idea. (We used a similar concept in our discussion of fluid flow in Section 14.5. A *streamline* is a line or curve whose tangent at any point is in the direction of the velocity of the fluid at that point. However, the similarity between electric field lines and fluid streamlines is a mathematical one only; there is nothing "flowing" in an electric field.) The English scientist Michael Faraday (1791–1867) first introduced the concept of field lines. He called them "lines of force," but the term "field lines" is preferable.

Electric field lines show the direction of $\vec{E}$ at each point, and their spacing gives a general idea of the *magnitude* of $\vec{E}$ at each point. Where $\vec{E}$ is strong, we draw lines bunched closely together; where $\vec{E}$ is weaker, they are farther apart. At any particular point, the electric field has a unique direction, so only one field line can pass through each point of the field. In other words, *field lines never intersect*.

Figure 21.29 shows some of the electric field lines in a plane containing (a) a single positive charge; (b) two equal-magnitude charges, one positive and one negative (a dipole); and (c) two equal positive charges. Diagrams such as these are sometimes called *field maps;* they are cross sections of the actual three-dimensional patterns. The direction of the total electric field at every point in each diagram is along the tangent to the electric field line passing through the point. Arrowheads indicate the direction of the $\vec{E}$-field vector along each field

21.28 The direction of the electric field at any point is tangent to the field line through that point.

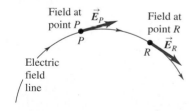

21.29 Electric field lines for three different charge distributions. In general, the magnitude of $\vec{E}$ is different at different points along a given field line.

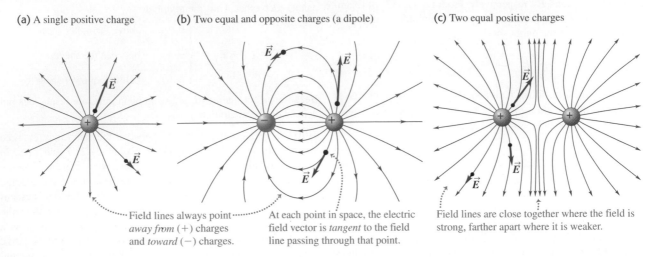

(a) A single positive charge

(b) Two equal and opposite charges (a dipole)

(c) Two equal positive charges

Field lines always point *away from* (+) charges and *toward* (−) charges.

At each point in space, the electric field vector is *tangent* to the field line passing through that point.

Field lines are close together where the field is strong, farther apart where it is weaker.

21.30 (a) Electric field lines produced by two equal point charges. The pattern is formed by grass seeds floating on a liquid above two charged wires. Compare this pattern with Fig. 21.29c. (b) The electric field causes polarization of the grass seeds, which in turn causes the seeds to align with the field.

(a)

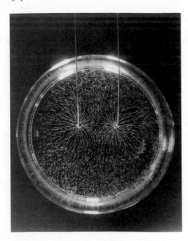

(b)

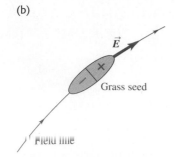

$\vec{E}$

Grass seed

Field line

line. The actual field vectors have been drawn at several points in each pattern. Notice that in general, the magnitude of the electric field is different at different points on a given field line; a field line is *not* a curve of constant electric-field magnitude!

Figure 21.29 shows that field lines are directed *away* from positive charges (since close to a positive point charge, $\vec{E}$ points away from the charge) and *toward* negative charges (since close to a negative point charge, $\vec{E}$ points toward the charge). In regions where the field magnitude is large, such as between the positive and negative charges in Fig. 21.29b, the field lines are drawn close together. In regions where the field magnitude is small, such as between the two positive charges in Fig. 21.29c, the lines are widely separated. In a *uniform* field, the field lines are straight, parallel, and uniformly spaced, as in Fig. 21.20.

Figure 21.30 is a view from above of a demonstration setup for visualizing electric field lines. In the arrangement shown here, the tips of two positively charged wires are inserted in a container of insulating liquid, and some grass seeds are floated on the liquid. The grass seeds are electrically neutral insulators, but the electric field of the two charged wires causes *polarization* of the grass seeds; there is a slight shifting of the positive and negative charges within the molecules of each seed, like that shown in Fig. 21.8. The positively charged end of each grass seed is pulled in the direction of $\vec{E}$ and the negatively charged end is pulled opposite $\vec{E}$. Hence the long axis of each grass seed tends to orient parallel to the electric field, in the direction of the field line that passes through the position of the seed (Fig. 21.30b).

CAUTION **Electric field lines are not the same as trajectories** It's a common misconception that if a charged particle of charge q is in motion where there is an electric field, the particle must move along an electric field line. Because $\vec{E}$ at any point is tangent to the field line that passes through that point, it is indeed true that the *force* $\vec{F} = q\vec{E}$ on the particle, and hence the particle's acceleration, are tangent to the field line. But we learned in Chapter 3 that when a particle moves on a curved path, its acceleration *cannot* be tangent to the path. So in general, the trajectory of a charged particle is *not* the same as a field line. ▮

Test Your Understanding of Section 21.6 Suppose the electric field lines in a region of space are straight lines. If a charged particle is released from rest in that region, will the trajectory of the particle be along a field line?

21.7 Electric Dipoles

An **electric dipole** is a pair of point charges with equal magnitude and opposite sign (a positive charge q and a negative charge $-q$) separated by a distance d. We introduced electric dipoles in Example 21.9 (Section 21.5); the concept is worth exploring further because many physical systems, from molecules to TV antennas, can be described as electric dipoles. We will also use this concept extensively in our discussion of dielectrics in Chapter 24.

Figure 21.31 a shows a molecule of water (H_2O), which in many ways behaves like an electric dipole. The water molecule as a whole is electrically neutral, but the chemical bonds within the molecule cause a displacement of charge; the result is a net negative charge on the oxygen end of the molecule and a net positive charge on the hydrogen end, forming an electric dipole. The effect is equivalent to shifting one electron only about 4×10^{-11} m (about the radius of a hydrogen atom), but the consequences of this shift are profound. Water is an excellent solvent for ionic substances such as table salt (sodium chloride, NaCl) precisely because the water molecule is an electric dipole (Fig. 21.31b). When dissolved in water, salt dissociates into a positive sodium ion (Na^+) and a negative chlorine ion (Cl^-), which tend to be attracted to the negative and positive ends, respectively, of water molecules; this holds the ions in solution. If water molecules were not electric dipoles, water would be a poor solvent, and almost all of the chemistry that occurs in aqueous solutions would be impossible. This includes all of the biochemical reactions that occur in all of the life on earth. In a very real sense, your existence as a living being depends on electric dipoles!

We examine two questions about electric dipoles. First, what forces and torques does an electric dipole experience when placed in an external electric field (that is, a field set up by charges outside the dipole)? Second, what electric field does an electric dipole itself produce?

Force and Torque on an Electric Dipole

To start with the first question, let's place an electric dipole in a *uniform* external electric field $\vec{E}$, as shown in Fig. 21.32. The forces $\vec{F}_+$ and $\vec{F}_-$ on the two charges both have magnitude qE, but their directions are opposite, and they add to zero. *The net force on an electric dipole in a uniform external electric field is zero.*

However, the two forces don't act along the same line, so their *torques* don't add to zero. We calculate torques with respect to the center of the dipole. Let the angle between the electric field $\vec{E}$ and the dipole axis be ϕ; then the lever arm for both $\vec{F}_+$ and $\vec{F}_-$ is $(d/2)\sin\phi$. The torque of $\vec{F}_+$ and the torque of $\vec{F}_-$ both have the same magnitude of $(qE)(d/2)\sin\phi$, and both torques tend to rotate the dipole clockwise (that is, $\vec{\tau}$ is directed into the page in Fig. 21.32). Hence the magnitude of the net torque is twice the magnitude of either individual torque:

$$\tau = (qE)(d\sin\phi) \tag{21.13}$$

where $d \sin \phi$ is the perpendicular distance between the lines of action of the two forces.

The product of the charge q and the separation d is the magnitude of a quantity called the **electric dipole moment,** denoted by p:

$$p = qd \quad \text{(magnitude of electric dipole moment)} \tag{21.14}$$

The units of p are charge times distance $(C \cdot m)$. For example, the magnitude of the electric dipole moment of a water molecule is $p = 6.13 \times 10^{-30}$ C $\cdot$ m.

CAUTION **The symbol p has multiple meanings** Be careful not to confuse dipole moment with momentum or pressure. There aren't as many letters in the alphabet as there are physical quantities, so some letters are used several times. The context usually makes it clear what we mean, but be careful. ∎

21.31 (a) A water molecule is an example of an electric dipole. (b) Each test tube contains a solution of a different substance in water. The large electric dipole moment of water makes it an excellent solvent.

(a) A water molecule, showing positive charge as red and negative charge as blue

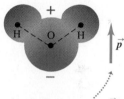

The electric dipole moment $\vec{p}$ is directed from the negative end to the positive end of the molecule.

(b) Various substances dissolved in water

21.32 The net force on this electric dipole is zero, but there is a torque directed into the page that tends to rotate the dipole clockwise.

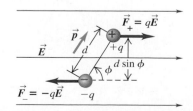

We further define the electric dipole moment to be a *vector* quantity $\vec{p}$. The magnitude of $\vec{p}$ is given by Eq. (21.14), and its direction is along the dipole axis from the negative charge to the positive charge as shown in Fig. 21.32.

In terms of p, Eq. (21.13) for the magnitude τ of the torque exerted by the field becomes

$$\tau = pE \sin\phi \qquad \text{(magnitude of the torque on an electric dipole)} \quad (21.15)$$

Since the angle ϕ in Fig. 21.32 is the angle between the directions of the vectors $\vec{p}$ and $\vec{E}$, this is reminiscent of the expression for the magnitude of the *vector product* discussed in Section 1.10. (You may want to review that discussion.) Hence we can write the torque on the dipole in vector form as

$$\vec{\tau} = \vec{p} \times \vec{E} \qquad \text{(torque on an electric dipole, in vector form)} \quad (21.16)$$

You can use the right-hand rule for the vector product to verify that in the situation shown in Fig. 21.32, $\vec{\tau}$ is directed into the page. The torque is greatest when $\vec{p}$ and $\vec{E}$ are perpendicular and is zero when they are parallel or antiparallel. The torque always tends to turn $\vec{p}$ to line it up with $\vec{E}$. The position $\phi = 0$, with $\vec{p}$ parallel to $\vec{E}$, is a position of stable equilibrium, and the position $\phi = \pi$, with $\vec{p}$ and $\vec{E}$ anti-parallel, is a position of unstable equilibrium. The polarization of a grass seed in the apparatus of Fig. 21.30b gives it an electric dipole moment; the torque exerted by $\vec{E}$ then causes the seed to align with $\vec{E}$ and hence with the field lines.

Potential Energy of an Electric Dipole

When a dipole changes direction in an electric field, the electric-field torque does *work* on it, with a corresponding change in potential energy. The work dW done by a torque τ during an infinitesimal displacement $d\phi$ is given by Eq. (10.19): $dW = \tau \, d\phi$. Because the torque is in the direction of decreasing ϕ, we must write the torque as $\tau = -pE \sin\phi$, and

$$dW = \tau \, d\phi = -pE \sin\phi \, d\phi$$

In a finite displacement from ϕ_1 to ϕ_2 the total work done on the dipole is

$$W = \int_{\phi_1}^{\phi_2} (-pE \sin\phi) \, d\phi$$
$$= pE \cos\phi_2 - pE \cos\phi_1$$

The work is the negative of the change of potential energy, just as in Chapter 7: $W = U_1 - U_2$. So we see that a suitable definition of potential energy U for this system is

$$U(\phi) = -pE \cos\phi \qquad (21.17)$$

In this expression we recognize the *scalar product* $\vec{p} \cdot \vec{E} = pE\cos\phi$, so we can also write

$$U = -\vec{p} \cdot \vec{E} \qquad \text{(potential energy for a dipole in an electric field)} \quad (21.18)$$

The potential energy has its minimum value $U = -pE$ (i.e., its most negative value) at the stable equilibrium position, where $\phi = 0$ and $\vec{p}$ is parallel to $\vec{E}$. The potential energy is maximum when $\phi = \pi$ and $\vec{p}$ is antiparallel to $\vec{E}$; then $U = +pE$. At $\phi = \pi/2$, where $\vec{p}$ is perpendicular to $\vec{E}$, U is zero. We could of course define U differently so that it is zero at some other orientation of $\vec{p}$, but our definition is simplest.

Equation (21.18) gives us another way to look at the effect shown in Fig. 21.30. The electric field $\vec{E}$ gives each grass seed an electric dipole moment, and the grass seed then aligns itself with $\vec{E}$ to minimize the potential energy.

Example 21.14   Force and torque on an electric dipole

Figure 21.33a shows an electric dipole in a uniform electric field with magnitude 5.0×10^5 N/C directed parallel to the plane of the figure. The charges are $\pm 1.6 \times 10^{-19}$ C; both lie in the plane and are separated by 0.125 nm $= 0.125 \times 10^{-9}$ m. (Both the charge magnitude and the distance are typical of molecular quantities.) Find (a) the net force exerted by the field on the dipole; (b) the magnitude and direction of the electric dipole moment; (c) the magnitude and direction of the torque; (d) the potential energy of the system in the position shown.

SOLUTION

IDENTIFY: This problem uses the ideas of this section about an electric dipole placed in an electric field.

SET UP: We use the relationship $\vec{F} = q\vec{E}$ for each point charge to find the force on the dipole as a whole. Equation (21.14) tells us

21.33 (a) An electric dipole. (b) Directions of the electric dipole moment, electric field, and torque.

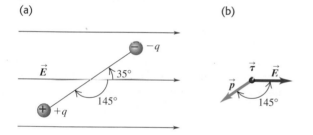

the dipole moment, Eq. (21.16) tells us the torque on the dipole, and Eq. (21.18) tells us the potential energy of the system.

EXECUTE: (a) Since the field is uniform, the forces on the two charges are equal and opposite, and the total force is zero.

(b) The magnitude p of the electric dipole moment $\vec{p}$ is

$$p = qd = (1.6 \times 10^{-19}\,\text{C})(0.125 \times 10^{-9}\,\text{m})$$
$$= 2.0 \times 10^{-29}\,\text{C} \cdot \text{m}$$

The direction of $\vec{p}$ is from the negative to the positive charge, 145° clockwise from the electric-field direction (Fig. 21.33b).

(c) The magnitude of the torque is

$$\tau = pE \sin \phi = (2.0 \times 10^{-29}\,\text{C})(5.0 \times 10^5\,\text{N/C})(\sin 145°)$$
$$= 5.7 \times 10^{-24}\,\text{N} \cdot \text{m}$$

From the right-hand rule for vector products (see Section 1.10), the direction of the torque $\vec{\tau} = \vec{p} \times \vec{E}$ is out of the page. This corresponds to a counterclockwise torque that tends to align $\vec{p}$ with $\vec{E}$.

(d) The potential energy is

$$U = -pE \cos\phi$$
$$= -(2.0 \times 10^{-29}\,\text{C} \cdot \text{m})(5.0 \times 10^5\,\text{N/C})(\cos 145°)$$
$$= 8.2 \times 10^{-24}\,\text{J}$$

EVALUATE: The dipole moment, torque, and potential energy are all exceedingly small. Don't be surprised by this result: Remember that we are looking at a single molecule, which is a very small object indeed!

In this discussion we have assumed that $\vec{E}$ is uniform, so there is no net force on the dipole. If $\vec{E}$ is not uniform, the forces at the ends may not cancel completely, and the net force may not be zero. Thus a body with zero net charge but an electric dipole moment can experience a net force in a nonuniform electric field. As we mentioned in Section 21.1, an uncharged body can be polarized by an electric field, giving rise to a separation of charge and an electric dipole moment. This is how uncharged bodies can experience electrostatic forces (see Fig. 21.8).

Field of an Electric Dipole

Now let's think of an electric dipole as a *source* of electric field. What does the field look like? The general shape of things is shown by the field map of Fig. 21.29b. At each point in the pattern the total $\vec{E}$ field is the vector sum of the fields from the two individual charges, as in Example 21.9 (Section 21.5). Try drawing diagrams showing this vector sum for several points.

To get quantitative information about the field of an electric dipole, we have to do some calculating, as illustrated in the next example. Notice the use of the principle of superposition of electric fields to add up the contributions to the field of the individual charges. Also notice that we need to use approximation techniques even for the relatively simple case of a field due to two charges. Field calculations often become very complicated, and computer analysis is typically used to determine the field due to an arbitrary charge distribution.

Example 21.15 **Field of an electric dipole, revisited**

In Fig. 21.34 an electric dipole is centered at the origin, with $\vec{p}$ in the direction of the $+y$-axis. Derive an approximate expression for the electric field at a point on the y-axis for which y is much larger than d. Use the binomial expansion of $(1 + x)^n$—that is, $(1 + x)^n \cong 1 + nx + n(n - 1)x^2/2 + \cdots$ —for the case $|x| < 1$. (This problem illustrates a useful calculational technique.)

SOLUTION

IDENTIFY: We use the principle of superposition: The total electric field is the vector sum of the field produced by the positive charge and the field produced by the negative charge.

SET UP: At the field point shown in Fig. 21.34, the field of the positive charge has a positive (upward) y-component and the field of the negative charge has a negative (downward) y-component. We add these components to find the total field and then apply the approximation that y is much greater than d.

21.34 Finding the electric field of an electric dipole at a point on its axis.

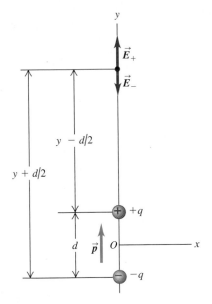

EXECUTE: The total y-component E_y of electric field from the two charges is

$$E_y = \frac{q}{4\pi\epsilon_0}\left[\frac{1}{(y - d/2)^2} - \frac{1}{(y + d/2)^2}\right]$$
$$= \frac{q}{4\pi\epsilon_0 y^2}\left[\left(1 - \frac{d}{2y}\right)^{-2} - \left(1 + \frac{d}{2y}\right)^{-2}\right]$$

We used this same approach in Example 21.9 (Section 21.5). Now comes the approximation. When y is much greater than d—that is, when we are far away from the dipole compared to its size—the quantity $d/2y$ is much smaller than 1. With $n = -2$ and $d/2y$ playing the role of x in the binomial expansion, we keep only the first two terms. The terms we discard are much smaller than those we keep, and we have

$$\left(1 - \frac{d}{2y}\right)^{-2} \cong 1 + \frac{d}{y} \quad \text{and} \quad \left(1 + \frac{d}{2y}\right)^{-2} \cong 1 - \frac{d}{y}$$

Hence E_y is given approximately by

$$E \cong \frac{q}{4\pi\epsilon_0 y^2}\left[1 + \frac{d}{y} - \left(1 - \frac{d}{y}\right)\right]$$
$$= \frac{qd}{2\pi\epsilon_0 y^3}$$
$$= \frac{p}{2\pi\epsilon_0 y^3}$$

EVALUATE: An alternative route to this expression is to put the fractions in the E_y expression over a common denominator and combine, then approximate the denominator $(y - d/2)^2(y + d/2)^2$ as y^4. We leave the details to you (see Exercise 21.65).

For points P off the coordinate axes, the expressions are more complicated, but at *all* points far away from the dipole (in any direction) the field drops off as $1/r^3$. We can compare this with the $1/r^2$ behavior of a point charge, the $1/r$ behavior of a long line charge, and the independence of r for a large sheet of charge. There are charge distributions for which the field drops off even more quickly. An *electric quadrupole* consists of two equal dipoles with opposite orientation, separated by a small distance. The field of a quadrupole at large distances drops off as $1/r^4$.

Test Your Understanding of Section 21.7 An electric dipole is placed in a region of uniform electric field $\vec{E}$, with the electric dipole moment $\vec{p}$, pointing in the direction opposite to $\vec{E}$. Is the dipole (i) in stable equilibrium, (ii) in unstable equilibrium, or (iii) neither? (*Hint:* You many want to review Section 7.5.)

Electric charge, conductors, and insulators: The fundamental quantity in electrostatics is electric charge. There are two kinds of charge, positive and negative. Charges of the same sign repel each other; charges of opposite sign attract. Charge is conserved; the total charge in an isolated system is constant.

All ordinary matter is made of protons, neutrons, and electrons. The positive protons and electrically neutral neutrons in the nucleus of an atom are bound together by the nuclear force; the negative electrons surround the nucleus at distances much greater than the nuclear size. Electric interactions are chiefly responsible for the structure of atoms, molecules, and solids.

Conductors are materials that permit electric charge to move easily within them. Insulators permit charge to move much less readily. Most metals are good conductors; most nonmetals are insulators.

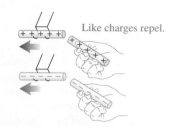
Like charges repel.

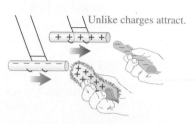
Unlike charges attract.

Coulomb's law: Coulomb's law is the basic law of interaction for point electric charges. For charges q_1 and q_2 separated by a distance r, the magnitude of the force on either charge is proportional to the product $q_1 q_2$ and inversely proportional to r^2. The force on each charge is along the line joining the two charges—repulsive if q_1 and q_2 have the same sign, attractive if they have opposite signs. The forces form an action–reaction pair and obey Newton's third law. In SI units the unit of electric charge is the coulomb, abbreviated C. (See Examples 21.1 and 21.2.)

The principle of superposition of forces states that when two or more charges each exert a force on a charge, the total force on that charge is the vector sum of the forces exerted by the individual charges. (See Examples 21.3 and 21.4.)

$$F = \frac{1}{4\pi\epsilon_0} \frac{|q_1 q_2|}{r^2} \quad (21.2)$$

$$\frac{1}{4\pi\epsilon_0} = 8.988 \times 10^9 \ \text{N} \cdot \text{m}^2/\text{C}^2$$

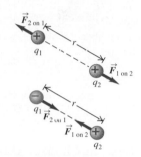

Electric field: Electric field $\vec{E}$, a vector quantity, is the force per unit charge exerted on a test charge at any point, provided the test charge is small enough that it does not disturb the charges that cause the field. The electric field produced by a point charge is directed radially away from or toward the charge. (See Examples 21.5–21.8.)

$$\vec{E} = \frac{\vec{F}_0}{q_0} \quad (21.3)$$

$$\vec{E} = \frac{1}{4\pi\epsilon_0} \frac{q}{r^2} \hat{r} \quad (21.7)$$

Superposition of electric fields: The principle of superposition of electric fields states that the electric field $\vec{E}$ of any combination of charges is the vector sum of the fields caused by the individual charges. To calculate the electric field caused by a continuous distribution of charge, divide the distribution into small elements, calculate the field caused by each element, and then carry out the vector sum or each component sum, usually by integrating. Charge distributions are described by linear charge density λ, surface charge density σ, and volume charge density ρ. (See Examples 21.9–21.13.)

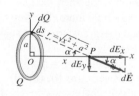

Electric field lines: Field lines provide a graphical representation of electric fields. At any point on a field line, the tangent to the line is in the direction of $\vec{E}$ at that point. The number of lines per unit area (perpendicular to their direction) is proportional to the magnitude of $\vec{E}$ at the point.

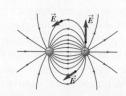

Electric dipoles: An electric dipole is a pair of electric charges of equal magnitude q but opposite sign, separated by a distance d. The electric dipole moment $\vec{p}$ is defined to have magnitude $p = qd$. The direction of $\vec{p}$ is from negative toward positive charge. An electric dipole in an electric field $\vec{E}$ experiences a torque $\vec{\tau}$ equal to the vector product of $\vec{p}$ and $\vec{E}$. The magnitude of the torque depends on the angle ϕ between $\vec{p}$ and $\vec{E}$. The potential energy U for an electric dipole in an electric field also depends on the relative orientation of $\vec{p}$ and $\vec{E}$. (See Examples 21.14 and 21.15.)

$$\tau = pE \sin \phi \tag{21.15}$$
$$\vec{\tau} = \vec{p} \times \vec{E} \tag{21.16}$$
$$U = -\vec{p} \cdot \vec{E} \tag{21.18}$$

Key Terms

electric charge, *710*
electrostatics, *710*
electron, *711*
proton, *711*
neutron, *711*
nucleus, *711*
atomic number, *712*
positive ion, *712*
negative ion, *712*
ionization, *712*
principle of conservation of charge, *712*

conductor, *713*
insulator, *713*
induction, *714*
induced charge, *714*
point charge, *716*
Coulomb's law, *716*
coulomb, *717*
principle of superposition of forces, *719*
electric field, *722*
test charge, *722*
source point, *723*

field point, *723*
vector field, *724*
principle of superposition of electric fields, *727*
linear charge density, *727*
surface charge density, *727*
volume charge density, *727*
electric field line, *733*
electric dipole, *735*
electric dipole moment, *735*

Answer to Chapter Opening Question ?

Water molecules have a permanent electric dipole moment: One end of the molecule has a positive charge and the other end has a negative charge. These ends attract negative and positive ions, respectively, holding the ions apart in solution. Water is less effective as a solvent for materials whose molecules do not ionize (called *nonionic* substances), such as oils.

Answers to Test Your Understanding Questions

21.1 Answers: (a) the plastic rod weighs more, (b) the glass rod weighs less, (c) the fur weighs a little less, (d) the silk weighs a little less   The plastic rod gets a negative charge by taking electrons from the fur, so the rod weighs a little more and the fur weighs a little less after the rubbing. By contrast, the glass rod gets a positive charge by giving electrons to the silk. Hence, after they are rubbed together, the glass rod weighs a little less and the silk weighs a little more. The weight change is *very* small: The number of electrons transferred is a small fraction of a mole, and a mole of electrons has a mass of only $(6.02 \times 10^{23}$ electrons$)(9.11 \times 10^{-31}$ kg/electron$) = 5.48 \times 10^{-7}$ kg $= 0.548$ milligram!

21.2 Answers: (a) (i), (b) (ii)   Before the two spheres touch, the negatively charged sphere exerts a repulsive force on the electrons in the other sphere, causing zones of positive and negative induced charge (see Fig. 21.7b). The positive zone is closer to the negatively charged sphere than the negative zone, so there is a net force of attraction that pulls the spheres together, like the comb and insulator in Fig. 21.8b. Once the two metal spheres touch, some of the excess electrons on the negatively charged sphere will flow onto the other sphere (because metals are conductors). Then both spheres will have a net negative charge and will repel each other.

21.3 Answer: (iv)   The force exerted by q_1 on Q is still as in Example 21.4. The magnitude of the force exerted by q_2 on Q is still equal to $F_{1 \text{ on } Q}$, but the direction of the force is now *toward* q_2 at an angle α below the x-axis. Hence the x-components of the two forces cancel while the (negative) y-components add together, and the total electric force is in the negative y-direction.

21.4 Answers: (a) (ii), (b) (i)   The electric field $\vec{E}$ produced by a positive point charge points directly away from the charge (see Fig. 21.18a) and has a magnitude that depends on the distance r from the charge to the field point. Hence a second, negative point charge $q < 0$ will feel a force $\vec{F} = q\vec{E}$ that points directly toward the positive charge and has a magnitude that depends on the distance r between the two charges. If the negative charge moves directly toward the positive charge, the direction of the force remains the same (along the line of the negative charge's motion) but the force magnitude increases as the distance r decreases. If the negative charge moves in a circle around the positive charge, the force magnitude stays the same (because the distance r is constant) but the force direction changes (when the negative charge is on the right side of the positive charge, the force is to the left; when the negative charge is on the left side of the positive charge, the force is to the right).

21.5 Answer: (iv)   Think of a pair of segments of length dy, one at coordinate $y > 0$ and the other at coordinate $-y < 0$. The upper segment has a positive charge and produces an electric field $d\vec{E}$ at P that points away from the segment, so this $d\vec{E}$ has a positive x-component and a negative y-component, like the vector $d\vec{E}$ in Fig. 21.25. The lower segment has the same amount of negative charge. It produces a $d\vec{E}$ that has the same magnitude but points *toward* the lower segment, so it has a negative x-component and a negative y-component. By symmetry, the two x-components are equal but opposite, so they cancel. Thus the total electric field has only a negative y-component.

21.6 Answer: yes If the field lines are straight, $\vec{E}$ must point in the same direction throughout the region. Hence the force $\vec{F} = q\vec{E}$ on a particle of charge q is always in the same direction. A particle released from rest accelerates in a straight line the direction of $\vec{F}$, and so its trajectory is a straight line that will be along a field line.

21.7 Answer: (ii) Equations (21.17) and (21.18) tell is that the potential energy for a dipole in an electric field is $U = -\vec{p} \cdot \vec{E} = -pE\cos\phi$, where ϕ is the angle between the directions of $\vec{p}$ and $\vec{E}$. If $\vec{p}$ and $\vec{E}$ point in opposite directions, so that $\phi = 180°$, we have $\cos\phi = -1$ and $U = +pE$. This is the maximum value that U can have. From our discussion of energy diagrams in Section 7.5, it follows that this is a situation of unstable equilibrium.

Another way to see this is from Eq. (21.15), which tells us that the magnitude of the torque on an electric dipole is $\tau = pE\sin\phi$.

This is zero if $\phi = 180°$, so there is no torque, and if left undisturbed the dipole will not rotate. However, if the dipole is disturbed slightly so that ϕ is a little less than $180°$, there will be a nonzero torque that tries to rotate the dipole toward $\phi = 0$ so that $\vec{p}$ and $\vec{E}$ point in the same direction. Hence if the dipole is disturbed from the equilibrium orientation at $\phi = 180°$, it moves farther away from that orientation—which is the hallmark of unstable equilbrium.

You can show that the situation in which $\vec{p}$ and $\vec{E}$ point in the same direction ($\phi = 0$) is a case of *stable* equilibrium: The potential energy is minimum, and if the dipole is displaced slightly there is a torque that tries to return it to the original orientation (a *restoring* torque).

PROBLEMS

For instructor-assigned homework, go to **www.masteringphysics.com**

Discussion Questions

Q21.1. If you peel two strips of transparent tape off the same roll and immediately let them hang near each other, they will repel each other. If you then stick the sticky side of one to the shiny side of the other and rip them apart, they will attract each other. Give a plausible explanation, involving transfer of electrons between the strips of tape, for this sequence of events.

Q21.2. Two metal spheres are hanging from nylon threads. When you bring the spheres close to each other, they tend to attract. Based on this information alone, discuss all the possible ways that the spheres could be charged. Is it possible that after the spheres touch, they will cling together? Explain.

Q21.3. The electric force between two charged particles becomes weaker with increasing distance. Suppose instead that the electric force were *independent* of distance. In this case, would a charged comb still cause a neutral insulator to become polarized as in Fig. 21.8? Why or why not? Would the neutral insulator still be attracted to the comb? Again, why or why not?

Q21.4. Your clothing tends to cling together after going through the dryer. Why? Would you expect more or less clinging if all your clothing were made of the same material (say, cotton) than if you dried different kinds of clothing together? Again, why? (You may want to experiment with your next load of laundry.)

Q21.5. An uncharged metal sphere hangs from a nylon thread. When a positively charged glass rod is brought close to the metal sphere, the sphere is drawn toward the rod. But if the sphere touches the rod, it suddenly flies away from the rod. Explain why the sphere is first attracted and then repelled.

Q21.6. The free electrons in a metal are gravitationally attracted toward the earth. Why, then, don't they all settle to the bottom of the conductor, like sediment settling to the bottom of a river?

Q21.7. Some of the free electrons in a good conductor (such as a piece of copper) move at speeds of 10^6 m/s or faster. Why don't these electrons fly out of the conductor completely?

Q21.8. Good electrical conductors, such as metals, are typically good conductors of heat; electrical insulators, such as wood, are typically poor conductors of heat. Explain why there should be a relationship between electrical conduction and heat conduction in these materials.

Q21.9. Defend this statement: "If there were only one electrically charged particle in the entire universe, the concept of electric charge would be meaningless."

Q21.10. Two identical metal objects are mounted on insulating stands. Describe how you could place charges of opposite sign but exactly equal magnitude on the two objects.

Q21.11. You can use plastic food wrap to cover a container by stretching the material across the top and pressing the overhanging material against the sides. What makes it stick? (*Hint:* The answer involves the electric force.) Does the food wrap stick to itself with equal tenacity? Why or why not? Does it work with metallic containers? Again, why or why not?

Q21.12. If you walk across a nylon rug and then touch a large metal object such as a doorknob, you may get a spark and a shock. Why does this tend to happen more on dry days than on humid days? (*Hint:* See Fig. 21.31.) Why are you less likely to get a shock if you touch a *small* metal object, such as a paper clip?

Q21.13. You have a negatively charged object. How can you use it to place a net negative charge on an insulated metal sphere? To place a net positive charge on the sphere?

Q21.14. When two point charges of equal mass and charge are released on a frictionless table, each has an initial acceleration a_0. If instead you keep one fixed and release the other one, what will be its initial acceleration: a_0, $2a_0$, or $a_0/2$? Explain.

Q21.15. A point charge of mass m and charge Q and another point charge of mass m but charge $2Q$ are released on a frictionless table. If the charge Q has an initial acceleration a_0, what will be the acceleration of $2Q$: a_0, $2a_0$, $4a_0$, $a_0/2$, or $a_0/4$? Explain.

Q21.16. A proton is placed in a uniform electric field and then released. Then an electron is placed at this same point and released. Do these two particles experience the same force? The same acceleration? Do they move in the same direction when released?

Q21.17. In Example 21.1 (Section 21.3) we saw that the electric force between two α particles is of the order of 10^{35} times as strong as the gravitational force. So why do we readily feel the gravity of the earth but no electrical force from it?

Q21.18. What similarities do electrical forces have with gravitational forces? What are the most significant differences?

Q21.19. At a distance R from a point charge its electric field is E_0. At what distance (in terms of R) from the point charge would the electric field be $\frac{1}{3}E_0$

Q21.20. Atomic nuclei are made of protons and neutrons. This shows that there must be another kind of interaction in addition to gravitational and electric forces. Explain.

Q21.21. Sufficiently strong electric fields can cause atoms to become positively ionized—that is, to lose one or more electrons. Explain how this can happen. What determines how strong the field must be to make this happen?

Q21.22. The electric fields at point P due to the positive charges q_1 and q_2 are shown in Fig. 21.35. Does the fact that they cross each other violate the statement in Section 21.6 that electric field lines never cross? Explain.

Figure 21.35
Question Q21.22.

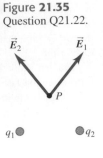

Q21.23. The air temperature and the velocity of the air have different values at different places in the earth's atmosphere. Is the air velocity a vector field? Why or why not? Is the air temperature a vector field? Again, why or why not?

Exercises

Section 21.3 Coulomb's Law

21.1. Excess electrons are placed on a small lead sphere with mass 8.00 g so that its net charge is -3.20×10^{-9} C. (a) Find the number of excess electrons on the sphere. (b) How many excess electrons are there per lead atom? The atomic number of lead is 82, and its atomic mass is 207 g/mol.

21.2. Lightning occurs when there is a flow of electric charge (principally electrons) between the ground and a thundercloud. The maximum rate of charge flow in a lightning bolt is about 20,000 C/s; this lasts for 100 μs or less. How much charge flows between the ground and the cloud in this time? How many electrons flow during this time?

21.3. Estimate how many electrons there are in your body. Make any assumptions you feel are necessary, but clearly state what they are. (*Hint:* Most of the atoms in your body have equal numbers of electrons, protons, and neutrons.) What is the combined charge of all these electrons?

21.4. Particles in a Gold Ring. You have a pure (24-karat) gold ring with mass 17.7 g. Gold has an atomic mass of 197 g/mol and an atomic number of 79. (a) How many protons are in the ring, and what is their total positive charge? (b) If the ring carries no net charge, how many electrons are in it?

21.5. An average human weighs about 650 N. If two such generic humans each carried 1.0 coulomb of excess charge, one positive and one negative, how far apart would they have to be for the electric attraction between them to equal their 650-N weight?

21.6. Two small spheres spaced 20.0 cm apart have equal charge. How many excess electrons must be present on each sphere if the magnitude of the force of repulsion between them is 4.57×10^{-21} N?

21.7. Two small plastic spheres are given positive electrical charges. When they are 15.0 cm apart, the repulsive force between them has magnitude 0.220 N. What is the charge on each sphere (a) if the two charges are equal and (b) if one sphere has four times the charge of the other?

21.8. Two small aluminum spheres, each having mass 0.0250 kg, are separated by 80.0 cm. (a) How many electrons does each sphere contain? (The atomic mass of aluminum is 26.982 g/mol, and its atomic number is 13.) (b) How many electrons would have to be removed from one sphere and added to the other to cause an attractive force between the spheres of magnitude 1.00×10^4 N (roughly 1 ton)? Assume that the spheres may be treated as point charges. (c) What fraction of all the electrons in each sphere does this represent?

21.9. Two very small 8.55-g spheres, 15.0 cm apart from center to center, are charged by adding equal numbers of electrons to each of them. Disregarding all other forces, how many electrons would you have to add to each sphere so that the two spheres will accelerate at 25.0g when released? Which way will they accelerate?

21.10. (a) Assuming that only gravity is acting on it, how far does an electron have to be from a proton so that its acceleration is the same as that of a freely falling object at the earth's surface? (b) Suppose the earth were made only of protons but had the same size and mass it presently has. What would be the acceleration of an electron released at the surface? Is it necessary to consider the gravitational attraction as well as the electrical force? Why or why not?

21.11. In an experiment in space, one proton is held fixed and another proton is released from rest a distance of 2.50 mm away. (a) What is the initial acceleration of the proton after it is released? (b) Sketch qualitative (no numbers!) acceleration–time and velocity–time graphs of the released proton's motion.

21.12. A negative charge -0.550 μC exerts an upward 0.200-N force on an unknown charge 0.300 m directly below it. (a) What is the unknown charge (magnitude and sign)? (b) What are the magnitude and direction of the force that the unknown charge exerts on the -0.550-μC charge?

21.13. Three point charges are arranged on a line. Charge $q_3 = +5.00$ nC and is at the origin. Charge $q_2 = -3.00$ nC and is at $x = +4.00$ cm. Charge q_1 is at $x = +2.00$ cm. What is q_1 (magnitude and sign) if the net force on q_3 is zero?

21.14. In Example 21.4, suppose the point charge on the y-axis at $y = -0.30$ m has negative charge -2.0 μC, and the other charges remain the same. Find the magnitude and direction of the net force on Q. How does your answer differ from that in Example 21.3? Explain the differences.

21.15. In Example 21.3, calculate the net force on charge q_1.

21.16. In Example 21.4, what is the net force (magnitude and direction) on charge q_1 exerted by the other two charges?

21.17. Three point charges are arranged along the x-axis. Charge $q_1 = +3.00$ μC is at the origin, and charge $q_2 = -5.00$ μC is at $x = 0.200$ m. Charge $q_3 = -8.00$ μC. Where is q_3 located if the net force on q_1 is 7.00 N in the $-x$-direction?

21.18. Repeat Exercise 21.17, for $q_3 = +8.00$ μC.

21.19. Two point charges are located on the y-axis as follows: charge $q_1 = -1.50$ nC at $y = -0.600$ m, and charge $q_2 = +3.20$ nC at the origin $(y = 0)$. What is the total force (magnitude and direction) exerted by these two charges on a third charge $q_3 = +5.00$ nC located at $y = -0.400$ m?

21.20. Two point charges are placed on the x-axis as follows: Charge $q_1 = +4.00$ nC is located at $x = 0.200$ m, and charge $q_2 = +5.00$ nC is at $x = -0.300$ m. What are the magnitude and direction of the total force exerted by these two charges on a negative point charge $q_3 = -6.00$ nC that is placed at the origin?

21.21. A positive point charge q is placed on the $+y$-axis at $y = a$, and a negative point charge $-q$ is placed on the $-y$-axis at $y = -a$. A negative point charge $-Q$ is located at some point on the $+x$-axis. (a) In a free-body diagram, show the forces that act on the charge $-Q$. (b) Find the x- and y-components of the net force that the two charges q and $-q$ exert on $-Q$. (Your answer should involve only k, q, Q, a and the coordinate x of the third charge.) (c) What is the net force on the charge $-Q$ when it is at the origin $(x = 0)$? (d) Graph the y-component of the net force on the charge $-Q$ as a function of x for values of x between $-4a$ and $+4a$.

21.22. Two positive point charges q are placed on the y-axis at $y = a$ and $y = -a$. A negative point charge $-Q$ is located at some point on the $+x$-axis. (a) In a free-body diagram, show the forces that act on the charge $-Q$. (b) Find the x- and y-components of the net force that the two positive charges exert on $-Q$. (Your answer should involve only k, q, Q, a and the coordinate x of the third charge.) (c) What is the net force on the charge $-Q$ when it is at the origin $(x = 0)$? (d) Graph the x-component of the net force on the charge $-Q$ as a function of x for values of x between $-4a$ and $+4a$.

21.23. Four identical charges Q are placed at the corners of a square of side L. (a) In a free-body diagram, show all of the forces that act on one of the charges. (b) Find the magnitude and direction of the total force exerted on one charge by the other three charges.

21.24. Two charges, one of $2.50 \ \mu C$ and the other of $-3.50 \ \mu C$, are placed on the x-axis, one at the origin and the other at $x = 0.600$ m, as shown in Fig. 21.36. Find the position on the x-axis where the net force on a small charge $+q$ would be zero.

Figure 21.36 Exercise 21.24.

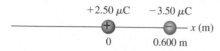

Section 21.4 Electric Field and Electric Forces

21.25. A proton is placed in a uniform electric field of 2.75×10^3 N/C. Calculate: (a) the magnitude of the electric force felt by the proton; (b) the proton's acceleration; (c) the proton's speed after $1.00 \ \mu s$ in the field, assuming it starts from rest.

21.26. A particle has charge -3.00 nC. (a) Find the magnitude and direction of the electric field due to this particle at a point 0.250 m directly above it. (b) At what distance from this particle does its electric field have a magnitude of 12.0 N/C?

21.27. A proton is traveling horizontally to the right at 4.50×10^6 m/s. (a) Find the magnitude and direction of the weakest electric field that can bring the proton uniformly to rest over a distance of 3.20 cm. (b) How much time does it take the proton to stop after entering the field? (c) What minimum field (magnitude and direction) would be needed to stop an electron under the conditions of part (a)?

21.28. An electron is released from rest in a uniform electric field. The electron accelerates vertically upward, traveling 4.50 m in the first $3.00 \ \mu s$ after it is released. (a) What are the magnitude and direction of the electric field? (b) Are we justified in ignoring the effects of gravity? Justify your answer quantitatively.

21.29. (a) What must the charge (sign and magnitude) of a 1.45-g particle be for it to remain stationary when placed in a downward-directed electric field of magnitude 650 N/C? (b) What is the magnitude of an electric field in which the electric force on a proton is equal in magnitude to its weight?

21.30. (a) What is the electric field of an iron nucleus at a distance of 6.00×10^{-10} m from the nucleus? The atomic number of iron is 26. Assume that the nucleus may be treated as a point charge. (b) What is the electric field of a proton at a distance of 5.29×10^{-11} m from the proton? (This is the radius of the electron orbit in the Bohr model for the ground state of the hydrogen atom.)

21.31. Two point charges are separated by 25.0 cm (Fig. 21.37). Find the net electric field these charges produce at (a) point A and

Figure 21.37 Exercise 21.31.

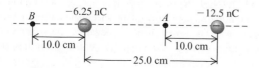

(b) point B. (c) What would be the magnitude and direction of the electric force this combination of charges would produce on a proton at A?

21.32. Electric Field of the Earth. The earth has a net electric charge that causes a field at points near its surface equal to 150 N/C and directed in toward the center of the earth. (a) What magnitude and sign of charge would a 60-kg human have to acquire to overcome his or her weight by the force exerted by the earth's electric field? (b) What would be the force of repulsion between two people each with the charge calculated in part (a) and separated by a distance of 100 m? Is use of the earth's electric field a feasible means of flight? Why or why not?

21.33. An electron is projected with an initial speed $v_0 = 1.60 \times 10^6$ m/s into the uniform field between the parallel plates in Fig. 21.38. Assume that the field between the plates is uniform and directed vertically downward, and that the field outside the plates is zero. The electron enters the field at a point midway between the plates. (a) If the electron just misses the upper plate as it emerges from the field, find the magnitude of the electric field. (b) Suppose that in Fig. 21.38 the electron is replaced by a proton with the same initial speed v_0. Would the proton hit one of the plates? If the proton would not hit one of the plates, what would be the magnitude and direction of its vertical displacement as it exits the region between the plates? (c) Compare the paths traveled by the electron and the proton and explain the differences. (d) Discuss whether it is reasonable to ignore the effects of gravity for each particle.

Figure 21.38
Exercise 21.33.

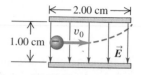

21.34. Point charge $q_1 = -5.00$ nC is at the origin and point charge $q_2 = +3.00$ nC is on the x-axis at $x = 3.00$ cm. Point P is on the y-axis at $y = 4.00$ cm. (a) Calculate the electric fields $\vec{E}_1$ and $\vec{E}_2$ at point P due to the charges q_1 and q_2. Express your results in terms of unit vectors (see Example 21.6). (b) Use the results of part (a) to obtain the resultant field at P, expressed in unit vector form.

21.35. In Exercise 21.33, what is the speed of the electron as it emerges from the field?

21.36. (a) Calculate the magnitude and direction (relative to the $+x$-axis) of the electric field in Example 21.6. (b) A -2.5-nC point charge is placed at the point P in Fig. 21.19. Find the magnitude and direction of (i) the force that the -8.0-nC charge at the origin exerts on this charge and (ii) the force that this charge exerts on the -8.0-nC charge at the origin.

21.37. (a) For the electron in Examples 21.7 and 21.8, compare the weight of the electron to the magnitude of the electric force on the electron. Is it appropriate to ignore the gravitational force on the electron in these examples? Explain. (b) A particle with charge $+e$ is placed at rest between the charged plates in Fig. 21.20. What must the mass of this object be if it is to remain at rest? Give your answer in kilograms and in multiples of the electron mass. (c) Does the answer to part (b) depend on where between the plates the object is placed? Why or why not?

21.38. A uniform electric field exists in the region between two oppositely charged plane parallel plates. A proton is released from rest at the surface of the positively charged plate and strikes the surface of the opposite plate, 1.60 cm distant from the first, in a time interval of 1.50×10^{-6} s. (a) Find the magnitude of the electric field. (b) Find the speed of the proton when it strikes the negatively charged plate.

21.39. A point charge is at the origin. With this point charge as the source point, what is the unit vector $\hat{r}$ in the direction of (a) the field point at $x = 0$, $y = -1.35$ m; (b) the field point at $x = 12.0$ cm, $y = 12.0$ cm; (c) the field point at $x = -1.10$ m, $y = 2.60$ m? Express your results in terms of the unit vectors $\hat{\imath}$ and $\hat{\jmath}$.

21.40. A $+8.75$-μC point charge is glued down on a horizontal frictionless table. It is tied to a -6.50-μC point charge by a light, nonconducting 2.50-cm wire. A uniform electric field of magnitude 1.85×10^8 N/C is directed parallel to the wire, as shown in Fig. 21.39. (a) Find the tension in the wire. (b) What would the tension be if both charges were negative?

Figure 21.39 Exercise 21.40.

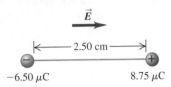

$\vec{E}$

$\leftarrow$ 2.50 cm $\rightarrow$

$-6.50\ \mu$C $8.75\ \mu$C

21.41. (a) An electron is moving east in a uniform electric field of 1.50 N/C directed to the west. At point A, the velocity of the electron is 4.50×10^5 m/s toward the east. What is the speed of the electron when it reaches point B, 0.375 m east of point A? (b) A proton is moving in the uniform electric field of part (a). At point A, the velocity of the proton is 1.90×10^4 m/s, east. What is the speed of the proton at point B?

21.42. Electric Field in the Nucleus. Protons in the nucleus are of the order of 10^{-15} m (1 fm) apart. (a) What is the magnitude of the electric field produced by a proton at a distance of 1.50 fm from it? (b) How does this field compare in magnitude to the field in Example 21.7?

Section 21.5 Electric-Field Calculations

21.43. Two positive point charges q are placed on the x-axis, one at $x = a$ and one at $x = -a$. (a) Find the magnitude and direction of the electric field at $x = 0$. (b) Derive an expression for the electric field at points on the x-axis. Use your result to graph the x-component of the electric field as a function of x, for values of x between $-4a$ and $+4a$.

21.44. Two particles having charges $q_1 = 0.500$ nC and $q_2 = 8.00$ nC are separated by a distance of 1.20 m. At what point along the line connecting the two charges is the total electric field due to the two charges equal to zero?

21.45. A $+2.00$-nC point charge is at the origin, and a second -5.00-nC point charge is on the x-axis at $x = 0.800$ m. (a) Find the electric field (magnitude and direction) at each of the following points on the x-axis: (i) $x = 0.200$ m; (ii) $x = 1.20$ m; (iii) $x = -0.200$ m. (b) Find the net electric force that the two charges would exert on an electron placed at each point in part (a).

21.46. Repeat Exercise 21.44, but now let $q_1 = -4.00$ nC.

21.47. Three negative point charges lie along a line as shown in Fig. 21.40. Find the magnitude and direction of the electric field this combination of charges produces at point P, which lies 6.00 cm. from the -2.00-μC charge measured perpendiular to the line connecting the three charges.

21.48. A positive point charge q is placed at $x = a$, and a negative point charge $-q$ is placed at $x = -a$. (a) Find the magnitude and direction of the electric field at $y = 0$.

Figure 21.40
Exercise 21.47.

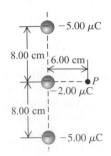

$-5.00\ \mu$C

8.00 cm | 6.00 cm

$\bullet P$
$-2.00\ \mu$C

8.00 cm

$-5.00\ \mu$C

(b) Derive an expression for the electric field at points on the x-axis. Use your result to graph the x-component of the electric field as a function of x, for values of x between $-4a$ and $+4a$.

21.49. In a rectangular coordinate system a positive point charge $q = 6.00 \times 10^{-9}$ C is placed at the point $x = +0.150$ m, $y = 0$, and an identical point charge is placed at $x = -0.150$ m, $y = 0$. Find the x- and y-components, the magnitude, and the direction of the electric field at the following points: (a) the origin; (b) $x = 0.300$ m, $y = 0$; (c) $x = 0.150$ m, $y = -0.400$ m; (d) $x = 0$, $y = 0.200$ m.

21.50. A point charge $q_1 = -4.00$ nC is at the point $x = 0.600$ m, $y = 0.800$ m, and a second point charge $q_2 = +6.00$ nC is at the point $x = 0.600$ m, $y = 0$. Calculate the magnitude and direction of the net electric field at the origin due to these two point charges.

21.51. Repeat Exercise 21.49 for the case where the point charge at $x = +0.150$ m, $y = 0$ is positive and the other is negative, each with magnitude 6.00×10^{-9} C.

21.52. A very long, straight wire has charge per unit length 1.50×10^{-10} C/m. At what distance from the wire is the electric-field magnitude equal to 2.50 N/C?

21.53. Positive electric charge is distributed along the y-axis with charge per unit length λ. (a) Consider the case where charge is distributed only between the points $y = a$ and $y = -a$. For points on the $+x$-axis, graph the x-component of the electric field as a function of x for values of x between $x = a/2$ and $x = 4a$. (b) Consider instead the case where charge is distributed along the entire y-axis with the same charge per unit length λ. Using the same graph as in part (a), plot the x-component of the electric field as a function of x for values of x between $x = a/2$ and $x = 4a$. Label which graph refers to which situation.

21.54. A straight, nonconducting plastic wire 8.50 cm long carries a charge density of $+175$ nC/m distributed uniformly along its length. It is lying on a horizontal tabletop. (a) Find the magnitude and direction of the electric field this wire produces at a point 6.00 cm directly above its midpoint. (b) If the wire is now bent into a circle lying flat on the table, find the magnitude and direction of the electric field it produces at a point 6.00 cm directly above its center.

21.55. A ring-shaped conductor with radius $a = 2.50$ cm has a total positive charge $Q = +0.125$ nC uniformly distributed around it, as shown in Fig. 21.24. The center of the ring is at the origin of coordinates O. (a) What is the electric field (magnitude and direction) at point P, which is on the x-axis at $x = 40.0$ cm? (b) A point charge $q = -2.50$ μC is placed at the point P described in part (a). What are the magnitude and direction of the force exerted by the charge q on the ring?

21.56. A charge of -6.50 nC is spread uniformly over the surface of one face of a nonconducting disk of radius 1.25 cm. (a) Find the magnitude and direction of the electric field this disk produces at a point P on the axis of the disk a distance of 2.00 cm from its center. (b) Suppose that the charge were all pushed away from the center and distributed uniformly on the outer rim of the disk. Find the magnitude and direction of the electric field at point P. (c) If the charge is all brought to the center of the disk, find the magnitude and direction of the electric field at point P. (d) Why is the field in part (a) stronger than the field in part (b)? Why is the field in part (c) the strongest of the three fields?

21.57. Two horizontal, infinite, plane sheets of charge are separated by a distance d. The lower sheet has negative charge with uniform surface charge density $\sigma < 0$. The upper sheet has positive charge with uniform surface charge density $\sigma > 0$. What is the electric field (magnitude, and direction if the field is nonzero) (a) above the upper sheet, (b) below the lower sheet, (c) between the sheets?

Section 21.6 Electric Field Lines

21.58. Infinite sheet A carries a positive uniform charge density σ, and sheet B, which is to the right of A and parallel to it, carries a uniform negative charge density -2σ. (a) Sketch the electric field lines for this pair of sheets. Include the region between the sheets as well as the regions to the left of A and to the right of B. (b) Repeat part (a) for the case in which sheet B carries a charge density of $+2\sigma$.

21.59. Suppose the charge shown in Fig. 21.29a is fixed in position. A small, positively charged particle is then placed at some point in the figure and released. Will the trajectory of the particle follow an electric field line? Why or why not? Suppose instead that the particle is placed at some point in Fig. 21.29b and released (the positive and negative charges shown in the figure are fixed in position). Will its trajectory follow an electric field line? Again, why or why not? Explain any differences between your answers for the two different situations.

21.60. Sketch the electric field lines for a disk of radius R with a positive uniform surface charge density σ. Use what you know about the electric field very close to the disk and very far from the disk to make your sketch.

21.61. (a) Sketch the electric field lines for an infinite line of charge. You may find it helpful to show the field lines in a plane containing the line of charge in one sketch and the field lines in a plane perpendicular to the line of charge in a second sketch. (b) Explain how your sketches show (i) that the magnitude E of the electric field depends only on the distance r from the line of charge and (ii) that E decreases like $1/r$.

21.62. Figure 21.41 shows some of the electric field lines due to three point charges arranged along the vertical axis. All three charges have the same magnitude. (a) What are the signs of the three charges? Explain your reasoning. (b) At what point(s) is the magnitude of the electric field the smallest? Explain your reasoning. Explain how the fields produced by each individual point charge combine to give a small net field at this point or points.

Figure 21.41
Exercise 21.62.

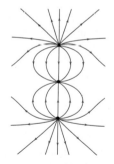

Section 21.7 Electric Dipoles

21.63. Point charges $q_1 = -4.5$ nC and $q_2 = +4.5$ nC are separated by 3.1 mm, forming an electric dipole. (a) Find the electric dipole moment (magnitude and direction). (b) The charges are in a uniform electric field whose direction makes an angle of $36.9°$ with the line connecting the charges. What is the magnitude of this field if the torque exerted on the dipole has magnitude 7.2×10^{-9} N·m?

21.64. The ammonia molecule (NH_3) has a dipole moment of 5.0×10^{-30} C·m. Ammonia molecules in the gas phase are placed in a uniform electric field $\vec{E}$ with magnitude 1.6×10^6 N/C. (a) What is the change in electric potential energy when the dipole moment of a molecule changes its orientation with respect to $\vec{E}$ from parallel to perpendicular? (b) At what absolute temperature T

is the average translational kinetic energy $\frac{3}{2}kT$ of a molecule equal to the change in potential energy calculated in part (a)? (*Note:* Above this temperature, thermal agitation prevents the dipoles from aligning with the electric field.)

21.65. In Example 21.15, the approximate result $E \cong p/2\pi\epsilon_0 y^3$ was derived for the electric field of a dipole at points on the dipole axis. (a) Rederive this result by putting the fractions in the expression for E_y over a common denominator, as described in Example 21.15. (b) Explain why the approximate result also gives the correct approximate expression for E_y for $y < 0$.

21.66. The dipole moment of the water molecule (H_2O) is 6.17×10^{-30} C·m. Consider a water molecule located at the origin whose dipole moment $\vec{p}$ points in the $+x$-direction. A chlorine ion (Cl^-), of charge -1.60×10^{-19} C, is located at $x = 3.00 \times 10^{-9}$ m. Find the magnitude and direction of the electric force that the water molecule exerts on the chlorine ion. Is this force attractive or repulsive? Assume that x is much larger than the separation d between the charges in the dipole, so that the approximate expression for the electric field along the dipole axis derived in Example 21.15 can be used.

21.67. Surface Tension. The surface of a polar liquid, such as water, can be viewed as a series of dipoles strung together in the stable arrangement in which the dipole moment vectors are parallel to the surface and all point in the same direction. Suppose now that something presses inward on the surface, distorting the dipoles as shown in Fig. 21.42. (a) Show that the two slanted dipoles exert a net upward force on the dipole between them, and hence oppose the downward external force. (b) Show that the dipoles attract each other and hence resist being separated. The force between dipoles opposes penetration of the liquid's surface and is a simple model for surface tension (see Section 14.3 and Fig. 14.15).

Figure 21.42 Exercise 21.67.

21.68. Consider the electric dipole of Example 21.15. (a) Derive an expression for the magnitude of the electric field produced by the dipole at a point on the x-axis in Fig. 21.34. What is the direction of this electric field? (b) How does the electric field at points on the x-axis depend on x when x is very large?

21.69. Torque on a Dipole. An electric dipole with dipole moment $\vec{p}$ is in a uniform electric field $\vec{E}$. (a) Find the orientations of the dipole for which the torque on the dipole is zero. (b) Which of the orientations in part (a) is stable, and which is unstable? (*Hint:* Consider a small displacement away from the equilibrium position and see what happens.) (c) Show that for the stable orientation in part (b), the dipole's own electric field tends to oppose the external field.

21.70. A dipole consisting of charges $\pm e$, 220 nm apart, is placed between two very large (essentially infinite) sheets carrying equal but opposite charge densities of $125 \mu C/m^2$. (a) What is the maximum potential energy this dipole can have due to the sheets, and how should it be oriented relative to the sheets to attain this value? (b) What is the maximum torque the sheets can exert on the dipole, and how should it be oriented relative to the sheets to attain this value? (c) What net force do the two sheets exert on the dipole?

21.71. Three charges are at the corners of an isosceles triangle as shown in Fig. 21.43. The ± 5.00-μC charges form a dipole. (a) Find the force (magnitude and direction) the -10.00-μC charge exerts on the dipole. (b) For an axis perpendicular to the line connecting the ± 5.00-μC charges at the midpoint of this line, find the torque (magnitude and direction) exerted on the dipole by the -10.00-μC charge.

Figure 21.43 Exercise 21.71.

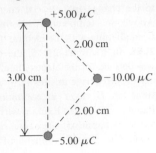

+5.00 μC
2.00 cm
3.00 cm
$-10.00 \mu C$
2.00 cm
$-5.00 \mu C$

Problems

21.72. A charge $q_1 = +5.00$ nC is placed at the origin of an xy-coordinate system, and a charge $q_2 = -2.00$ nC is placed on the positive x-axis at $x = 4.00$ cm. (a) If a third charge $q_3 = +6.00$ nC is now placed at the point $x = 4.00$ cm, $y = 3.00$ cm, find the x- and y-components of the total force exerted on this charge by the other two. (b) Find the magnitude and direction of this force.

21.73. Two positive point charges Q are held fixed on the x-axis at $x = a$ and $x = -a$. A third positive point charge q, with mass m, is placed on the x-axis away from the origin at a coordinate x such that $|x| \ll a$. The charge q, which is free to move along the x-axis, is then released. (a) Find the frequency of oscillation of the charge q. (*Hint:* Review the definition of simple harmonic motion in Section 13.2. Use the binomial expansion $(1 + z)^n = 1 + nz + n(n - 1)z^2/2 + \cdots$, valid for the case $|z| < 1$.) (b) Suppose instead that the charge q were placed on the y-axis at a coordinate y such that $|y| \ll a$, and then released. If this charge is free to move anywhere in the xy-plane, what will happen to it? Explain your answer.

21.74. Two identical spheres with mass m are hung from silk threads of length L, as shown in Fig. 21.44. Each sphere has the same charge, so $q_1 = q_2 = q$. The radius of each sphere is very small compared to the distance between the spheres, so they may be treated as point charges. Show that if the angle θ is small, the equilibrium separation d between the spheres is $d = (q^2L/2\pi\epsilon_0mg)^{1/3}$. (*Hint:* If θ is small, then $\tan\theta \cong \sin\theta$.)

21.75. Two small spheres with mass $m = 15.0$ g are hung by silk threads of length $L = 1.20$ m from a common point (Fig. 21.44). When the spheres are given equal quantities of negative charge, so that $q_1 = q_2 = q$, each thread hangs at $\theta = 25.0°$ from the vertical. (a) Draw a diagram showing the forces on each sphere. Treat the spheres as point charges. (b) Find the magnitude of q. (c) Both threads are now shortened to length $L = 0.600$ m, while the charges q_1 and q_2 remain unchanged. What new angle will each thread make with the vertical? (*Hint:* This part of the problem can be solved numerically by using trial values for θ and adjusting the values of θ until a self-consistent answer is obtained.)

21.76. Two identical spheres are each attached to silk threads of length $L = 0.500$ m and hung from a common point (Fig. 21.44). Each sphere has mass $m = 8.00$ g. The radius of each sphere is

Figure 21.44 Problems 21.74, 21.75, and 21.76.

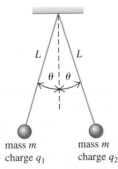

L L
θ θ
mass m charge q_1
mass m charge q_2

very small compared to the distance between the spheres, so they may be treated as point charges. One sphere is given positive charge q_1, and the other a different positive charge q_2; this causes the spheres to separate so that when the spheres are in equilibrium, each thread makes an angle $\theta = 20.0°$ with the vertical. (a) Draw a free-body diagram for each sphere when in equilibrium, and label all the forces that act on each sphere. (b) Determine the magnitude of the electrostatic force that acts on each sphere, and determine the tension in each thread. (c) Based on the information you have been given, what can you say about the magnitudes of q_1 and q_2? Explain your answers. (d) A small wire is now connected between the spheres, allowing charge to be transferred from one sphere to the other until the two spheres have equal charges; the wire is then removed. Each thread now makes an angle of $30.0°$ with the vertical. Determine the original charges. (*Hint:* The total charge on the pair of spheres is conserved.)

21.77. Sodium chloride (NaCl, ordinary table salt) is made up of positive sodium ions (Na^+) and negative chloride ions (Cl^-). (a) If a point charge with the same charge and mass as all the Na^+ ions in 0.100 mol of NaCl is 2.00 cm from a point charge with the same charge and mass as all the Cl^- ions, what is the magnitude of the attractive force between these two point charges? (b) If the positive point charge in part (a) is held in place and the negative point charge is released from rest, what is its initial acceleration? (See Appendix D for atomic masses.) (c) Does it seem reasonable that the ions in NaCl could be separated in this way? Why or why not? (In fact, when sodium chloride dissolves in water, it breaks up into Na^+ and Cl^- ions. However, in this situation there are additional electric forces exerted by the water molecules on the ions.)

21.78. Two point charges q_1 and q_2 are held in place 4.50 cm apart. Another point charge $Q = -1.75$ μC of mass 5.00 g is initially located 3.00 cm from each of these charges (Fig. 21.45) and released from rest. You observe that the initial acceleration of Q is 324 m/s² upward, parallel to the line connecting the two point charges. Find q_1 and q_2.

21.79. Three identical point charges q are placed at each of three corners of a square of side L. Find the magnitude and direction of the net force on a point charge $-3q$ placed (a) at the center of the square and (b) at the vacant corner of the square. In each case, draw a free-body diagram showing the forces exerted on the $-3q$ charge by each of the other three charges.

21.80. Three point charges are placed on the y-axis: a charge q at $y = a$, a charge $-2q$ at the origin, and a charge q at $y = -a$. Such an arrangement is called an electric quadrupole. (a) Find the magnitude and direction of the electric field at points on the positive x-axis. (b) Use the binomial expansion to find an approximate expression for the electric field valid for $x \gg a$. Contrast this behavior to that of the electric field of a point charge and that of the electric field of a dipole.

21.81. Strength of the Electric Force. Imagine two 1.0-g bags of protons, one at the earth's north pole and the other at the south pole. (a) How many protons are in each bag? (b) Calculate the gravitational attraction and the electrical repulsion that each bag exerts on the other. (c) Are the forces in part (b) large enough for you to feel if you were holding one of the bags?

Figure 21.45 Problem 21.78.

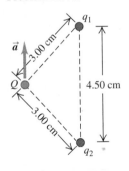

q_1
$\vec{a}$
3.00 cm
Q
4.50 cm
3.00 cm
q_2

21.82. Electric Force Within the Nucleus. Typical dimensions of atomic nuclei are of the order of 10^{-15} m (1 fm). (a) If two protons in a nucleus are 2.0 fm apart, find the magnitude of the electric force each one exerts on the other. Express the answer in newtons and in pounds. Would this force be large enough for a person to feel? (b) Since the protons repel each other so strongly, why don't they shoot out of the nucleus?

21.83. If Atoms Were Not Neutral . . . Because the charges on the electron and proton have the same absolute value, atoms are electrically neutral. Suppose this were not precisely true, and the absolute value of the charge of the electron were less than the charge of the proton by 0.00100%. (a) Estimate what the net charge of this textbook would be under these circumstances. Make any assumptions you feel are justified, but state clearly what they are. (*Hint:* Most of the atoms in this textbook have equal numbers of electrons, protons, and neutrons.) (b) What would be the magnitude of the electric force between two textbooks placed 5.0 m apart? Would this force be attractive or repulsive? Estimate what the acceleration of each book would be if the books were 5.0 m apart and there were no nonelectrical forces on them. (c) Discuss how the fact that ordinary matter is stable shows that the absolute values of the charges on the electron and proton must be identical to a *very* high level of accuracy.

21.84. Two tiny balls of mass m carry equal but opposite charges of magnitude q. They are tied to the same ceiling hook by light strings of length L. When a horizontal uniform electric field E is turned on, the balls hang with an angle θ between the strings (Fig. 21.46). (a) Which ball (the right or the left) is positive, and which is negative?

Figure **21.46** Problem 21.84.

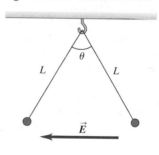

(b) Find the angle θ between the strings in terms of E, q, m, and g. (c) As the electric field is gradually increased in strength, what does your result from part (b) give for the largest possible angle θ?

21.85. Two small, copper spheres each have radius 1.00 mm. (a) How many atoms does each sphere contain? (b) Assume that each copper atom contains 29 protons and 29 electrons. We know that electrons and protons have charges of exactly the same magnitude, but let's explore the effect of small differences (see also Problem 21.83). If the charge of a proton is $+e$ and the magnitude of the charge of an electron is 0.100% smaller, what is the net charge of each sphere and what force would one sphere exert on the other if they were separated by 1.00 m?

21.86. Operation of an Inkjet Printer. In an inkjet printer, letters are built up by squirting drops of ink at the paper from a rapidly moving nozzle. The ink drops, which have a mass of 1.4×10^{-8} g each, leave the nozzle and travel toward the paper at 20 m/s, passing through a charging unit that gives each drop a positive charge q by removing some electrons from it. The drops then pass between parallel deflecting plates 2.0 cm long where there is a uniform vertical electric field with magnitude 8.0×10^4 N/C. If a drop is to be deflected 0.30 mm by the time it reaches the end of the deflection plates, what magnitude of charge must be given to the drop?

21.87. A proton is projected into a uniform electric field that points vertically upward and has magnitude E. The initial velocity of the proton has a magnitude v_0 and is directed at an angle α below the horizontal. (a) Find the maximum distance h_{max} that the proton descends vertically below its initial elevation. You can ignore

gravitational forces. (b) After what horizontal distance d does the proton return to its original elevation? (c) Sketch the trajectory of the proton. (d) Find the numerical values of h_{max} and d if $E = 500$ N/C, $v_0 = 4.00 \times 10^5$ m/s, and $\alpha = 30.0°$.

21.88. A negative point charge $q_1 = -4.00$ nC is on the x-axis at $x = 0.60$ m. A second point charge q_2 is on the x-axis at $x = -1.20$ m. What must the sign and magnitude of q_2 be for the net electric field at the origin to be (a) 50.0 N/C in the $+x$-direction and (b) 50.0 N/C in the $-x$-direction?

21.89. Positive charge Q is distributed uniformly along the x-axis from $x = 0$ to $x = a$. A positive point charge q is located on the positive x-axis at $x = a + r$, a distance r to the right of the end of Q (Fig. 21.47). (a) Calculate the

Figure **21.47** Problem 21.89.

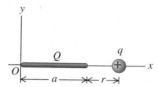

x- and y-components of the electric field produced by the charge distribution Q at points on the positive x-axis where $x > a$. (b) Calculate the force (magnitude and direction) that the charge distribution Q exerts on q. (c) Show that if $r \gg a$, the magnitude of the force in part (b) is approximately $Qq/4\pi\epsilon_0 r^2$. Explain why this result is obtained.

21.90. Positive charge Q is distributed uniformly along the positive y-axis between $y = 0$ and $y = a$. A negative point charge $-q$ lies on the positive x-axis, a distance x from the origin (Fig. 21.48). (a) Calculate the x- and y-components of the electric field produced by the charge distribution Q at points on the positive x-axis. (b) Calculate the x- and y-components of the force that

Figure **21.48** Problem 21.90.

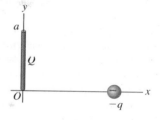

the charge distribution Q exerts on q. (c) Show that if $x \gg a$, $F_x \cong -Qq/4\pi\epsilon_0 x^2$ and $F_y \cong +Qqa/8\pi\epsilon_0 x^3$. Explain why this result is obtained.

21.91. A charged line like that shown in Fig. 21.25 extends from $y = 2.50$ cm to $y = -2.50$ cm. The total charge distributed uniformly along the line is -9.00 nC. (a) Find the electric field (magnitude and direction) on the x-axis at $x = 10.0$ cm. (b) Is the magnitude of the electric field you calculated in part (a) larger or smaller than the electric field 10.0 cm from a point charge that has the same total charge as this finite line of charge? In terms of the approximation used to derive $E = Q/4\pi\epsilon_0 x^2$ for a point charge from Eq. (21.9), explain why this is so. (c) At what distance x does the result for the finite line of charge differ by 1.0% from that for the point charge?

21.92. A Parallel Universe. Imagine a parallel universe in which the electric force has the same properties as in our universe but there is no gravity. In this parallel universe, the sun carries charge Q, the earth carries charge $-Q$, and the electric attraction between them keeps the earth in orbit. The earth in the parallel universe has the same mass, the same orbital radius, and the same orbital period as in our universe. Calculate the value of Q. (Consult Appendix F as needed.)

21.93. A uniformly charged disk like the disk in Fig. 21.26 has radius 2.50 cm and carries a total charge of 4.0×10^{-12} C. (a) Find the electric field (magnitude and direction) on the x-axis at $x = 20.0$ cm. (b) Show that for $x \gg R$, Eq. (21.11) becomes $E = Q/4\pi\epsilon_0 x^2$, where Q is the total charge on the disk. (c) Is the magnitude of the electric field you calculated in part (a) larger or smaller than the electric field 20.0 cm from a point charge that has the same total charge as this disk? In terms of the approximation used in part (b) to derive $E = Q/4\pi\epsilon_0 x^2$ for a point charge from Eq. (21.11), explain why this is so. (d) What is the percent difference between the electric fields produced by the finite disk and by a point charge with the same charge at $x = 20.0$ cm and at $x = 10.0$ cm?

21.94. (a) Let $f(x)$ be an even function of x so that $f(x) = f(-x)$. Show that $\int_{-a}^{a} f(x)\,dx = 2\int_{0}^{a} f(x)\,dx$. (*Hint:* Write the integral from $-a$ to a as the sum of the integral from $-a$ to 0 and the integral from 0 to a. In the first integral, make the change of variable $x' = -x$.) (b) Let $g(x)$ be an odd function of x so that $g(x) = -g(-x)$. Use the method given in the hint for part (a) to show that $\int_{-a}^{a} g(x)\,dx = 0$. (c) Use the result of part (b) to show why E_y in Example 21.11 (Section 21.5) is zero.

21.95. Positive charge $+Q$ is distributed uniformly along the $+x$-axis from $x = 0$ to $x = a$. Negative charge $-Q$ is distributed uniformly along the $-x$-axis from $x = 0$ to $x = -a$. (a) A positive point charge q lies on the positive y-axis, a distance y from the origin. Find the force (magnitude and direction) that the positive and negative charge distributions together exert on q. Show that this force is proportional to y^{-3} for $y \gg a$. (b) Suppose instead that the positive point charge q lies on the positive x-axis, a distance $x > a$ from the origin. Find the force (magnitude and direction) that the charge distribution exerts on q. Show that this force is proportional to x^{-3} for $x \gg a$.

21.96. Positive charge Q is uniformly distributed around a semicircle of radius a (Fig. 21.49). Find the electric field (magnitude and direction) at the center of curvature P.

Figure 21.49 Problem 21.96.

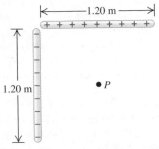

21.97. Negative charge $-Q$ is distributed uniformly around a quarter-circle of radius a that lies in the first quadrant, with the center of curvature at the origin. Find the x- and y-components of the net electric field at the origin.

21.98. A small sphere with mass m carries a positive charge q and is attached to one end of a silk fiber of length L. The other end of the fiber is attached to a large vertical insulating sheet that has a positive surface charge density σ. Show that when the sphere is in equilibrium, the fiber makes an angle equal to $\arctan(q\sigma/2mg\epsilon_0)$ with the vertical sheet.

21.99. Two 1.20-m nonconducting wires meet at a right angle. One segment carries $+2.50\ \mu\text{C}$ of charge distributed uniformly along its length, and the other carries $-2.50\ \mu\text{C}$ distributed uniformly along it, as shown in Fig. 21.50. (a) Find the magnitude and direction of the electric field these wires produce at point P, which is 60.0 cm from each wire. (b) If an electron is released at P, what are the magnitude and direction of the net force that these wires exert on it?

Figure 21.50 Problem 21.99.

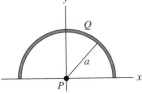

21.100. Two very large parallel sheets are 5.00 cm apart. Sheet A carries a uniform surface charge density of $-9.50\mu\text{C/m}^2$, and sheet B, which is to the right of A, carries a uniform charge of

$-11.6\ \mu\text{C/m}^2$. Assume the sheets are large enough to be treated as infinite. Find the magnitude and direction of the net electric field these sheets produce at a point (a) 4.00 cm to the right of sheet A; (b) 4.00 cm to the left of sheet A; (c) 4.00 cm to the right of sheet B.

21.101. Repeat Problem 21.100 for the case where sheet B is positive.

21.102. Two very large horizontal sheets are 4.25 cm apart and carry equal but opposite uniform surface charge densities of magnitude σ. You want to use these sheets to hold stationary in the region between them an oil droplet of mass 324 μg that carries an excess of five electrons. Assuming that the drop is in vacuum, (a) which way should the electric field between the plates point, and (b) what should σ be?

21.103. An infinite sheet with positive charge per unit area σ lies in the xy-plane. A second infinite sheet with negative charge per unit area $-\sigma$ lies in the yz-plane. Find the net electric field at all points that do not lie in either of these planes. Express your answer in terms of the unit vectors $\hat{\imath}$, $\hat{\jmath}$, and $\hat{k}$.

21.104. A thin disk with a circular hole at its center, called an *annulus*, has inner radius R_1 and outer radius R_2 (Fig. 21.51). The disk has a uniform positive surface charge density σ on its surface. (a) Determine the total electric charge on the annulus. (b) The annulus lies in the yz-plane, with its center at the origin. For an arbitrary point on the x-axis (the axis of the annulus), find the magnitude and direction of the electric field $\vec{E}$. Consider points both above and below the annulus in Fig. 21.51. (c) Show that at points on the x-axis that are sufficiently close to the origin, the magnitude of the electric field is approximately proportional to the distance between the center of the annulus and the point. How close is "sufficiently close"? (d) A point particle with mass m and negative charge $-q$ is free to move along the x-axis (but cannot move off the axis). The particle is originally placed at rest at $x = 0.01R_1$ and released. Find the frequency of oscillation of the particle. (*Hint:* Review Section 13.2. The annulus is held stationary.)

Figure 21.51
Problem 21.104.

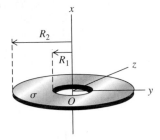

Challenge Problems

21.105. Three charges are placed as shown in Fig. 21.52. The magnitude of q_1 is 2.00 μC, but its sign and the value of the charge q_2 are not known. Charge q_3 is $+4.00\ \mu$C, and the net force $\vec{F}$ on q_3 is entirely in the negative x-direction. (a) Considering the different possible signs of q_1 and q_2 there are four possible force diagrams representing the forces $\vec{F}_1$ and $\vec{F}_2$ that q_1 and q_2 exert on q_3. Sketch these four possible force configurations. (b) Using the sketches from part (a) and the direction of $\vec{F}$, deduce the signs of the charges q_1 and q_2. (c) Calculate the magnitude of q_2. (d) Determine F, the magnitude of the net force on q_3.

Figure 21.52 Challenge Problem 21.105.

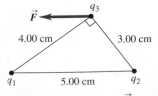

21.106. Two charges are placed as shown in Fig. 21.53. The magnitude of q_1 is 3.00 μC, but its sign and the value of the charge q_2 are not known. The direction of the net electric field $\vec{E}$ at point P is

entirely in the negative y-direction. (a) Considering the different possible signs of q_1 and q_2, there are four possible diagrams that could represent the electric fields $\vec{E}_1$ and $\vec{E}_2$ produced by q_1 and q_2. Sketch the four possible electric field configurations. (b) Using the sketches from part (a) and the direction of $\vec{E}$, deduce the signs of q_1 and q_2. (c) Determine the magnitude of $\vec{E}$.

Figure 21.53 Challenge Problem 21.106.

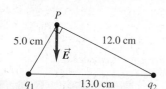

21.107. Two thin rods of length L lie along the x-axis, one between $x = a/2$ and $x = a/2 + L$ and the other between $x = -a/2$ and $x = -a/2 - L$. Each rod has positive charge Q distributed uniformly along its length. (a) Calculate the electric field produced by the second rod at points along the positive x-axis. (b) Show that the magnitude of the force that one rod exerts on the other is

$$F = \frac{Q^2}{4\pi\epsilon_0 L^2} \ln\left[\frac{(a+L)^2}{a(a+2L)}\right]$$

(c) Show that if $a \gg L$, the magnitude of this force reduces to $F = Q^2/4\pi\epsilon_0 a^2$. (*Hint:* Use the expansion $\ln(1+z) = z - z^2/2 + z^3/3 - \cdots$, valid for $|z| \ll 1$. Carry *all* expansions to at least order L^2/a^2.) Interpret this result.

22 GAUSS'S LAW

LEARNING GOALS

By studying this chapter, you will learn:

- How you can determine the amount of charge within a closed surface by examining the electric field on the surface.

- What is meant by electric flux, and how to calculate it.

- How Gauss's law relates the electric flux through a closed surface to the charge enclosed by the surface.

- How to use Gauss's law to calculate the electric field due to a symmetrical charge distribution.

- Where the charge is located on a charged conductor.

? This child acquires an electric charge by touching the charged metal sphere. The charged hairs on the child's head repel and stand out. If the child stands *inside* a large, charged metal sphere, will her hair stand on end?

O ften, there are both an easy way and a hard way to do a job; the easy way may involve nothing more than using the right tools. In physics, an important tool for simplifying problems is the *symmetry properties* of systems. Many physical systems have symmetry; for example, a cylindrical body doesn't look any different after you've rotated it around its axis, and a charged metal sphere looks just the same after you've turned it about any axis through its center.

Gauss's law is part of the key to using symmetry considerations to simplify electric-field calculations. For example, the field of a straight-line or plane-sheet charge distribution, which we derived in Section 21.5 using some fairly strenuous integrations, can be obtained in a few lines with the help of Gauss's law. But Gauss's law is more than just a way to make certain calculations easier. Indeed, it is a fundamental statement about the relationship between electric charges and electric fields. Among other things, Gauss's law can help us understand how electric charge distributes itself over conducting bodies.

Here's what Gauss's law is all about. Given any general distribution of charge, we surround it with an imaginary surface that encloses the charge. Then we look at the electric field at various points on this imaginary surface. Gauss's law is a relationship between the field at *all* the points on the surface and the total charge enclosed within the surface. This may sound like a rather indirect way of expressing things, but it turns out to be a tremendously useful relationship. Above and beyond its use as a calculational tool, Gauss's law can help us gain deeper insights into electric fields. We will make use of these insights repeatedly in the next several chapters as we pursue our study of electromagnetism.

22.1 Charge and Electric Flux

In Chapter 21 we asked the question, "Given a charge distribution, what is the electric field produced by that distribution at a point P?" We saw that the answer could be found by representing the distribution as an assembly of point charges,

The discussion of Gauss's law in this section is based on and inspired by the innovative ideas of Ruth W. Chabay and Bruce A. Sherwood in *Electric and Magnetic Interactions* (John Wiley & Sons, 1994).

each of which produces an electric field $\vec{E}$ given by Eq. (21.7). The total field at P is then the vector sum of the fields due to all the point charges.

But there is an alternative relationship between charge distributions and electric fields. To discover this relationship, let's stand the question of Chapter 21 on its head and ask, "If the electric field pattern is known in a given region, what can we determine about the charge distribution in that region?"

Here's an example. Consider the box shown in Fig. 22.1a, which may or may not contain electric charge. We'll imagine that the box is made of a material that has no effect on any electric fields; it's of the same breed as the massless rope and the frictionless incline. Better still, let the box represent an *imaginary* surface that may or may not enclose some charge. We'll refer to the box as a **closed surface** because it completely encloses a volume. How can you determine how much (if any) electric charge lies within the box?

Knowing that a charge distribution produces an electric field and that an electric field exerts a force on a test charge, you move a test charge q_0 around the vicinity of the box. By measuring the force $\vec{F}$ experienced by the test charge at different positions, you make a three-dimensional map of the electric field $\vec{E} = \vec{F}/q_0$ outside the box. In the case shown in Fig. 22.1b, the map turns out to be the same as that of the electric field produced by a positive point charge (Fig. 21.29a). From the details of the map, you can find the exact value of the point charge inside the box.

To determine the contents of the box, we actually need to measure $\vec{E}$ only on the *surface* of the box. In Fig. 22.2a there is a single positive point charge inside the box, and in Fig. 22.2b there are two such charges. The field patterns on the surfaces of the boxes are different in detail, but in both cases the electric field points out of the box. Figures 22.2c and 22.2d show cases with one and two negative point charges, respectively, inside the box. Again, the details of $\vec{E}$ on the surface of the box are different, but in both cases the field points into the box.

Activ
ONLINE
Physics

11.7   Electric Flux

22.1 How can you measure the charge inside a box without opening it?

(a) A box containing an unknown amount of charge

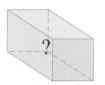

(b) Using a test charge outside the box to probe the amount of charge inside the box

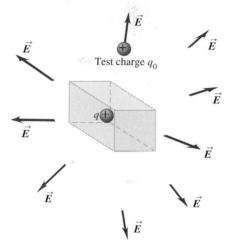

22.2 The electric field on the surface of boxes containing (a) a single positive point charge, (b) two positive point charges, (c) a single negative point charge, or (d) two negative point charges.

(a) Positive charge inside box, outward flux

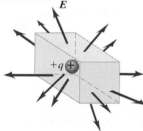

(b) Positive charges inside box, outward flux

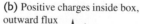

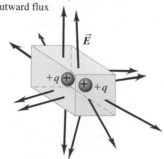

(c) Negative charge inside box, inward flux

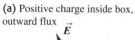

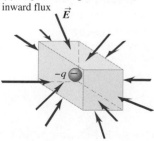

(d) Negative charges inside box, inward flux

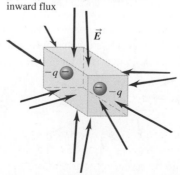

Electric Flux and Enclosed Charge

In Section 21.4 we mentioned the analogy between electric-field vectors and the velocity vectors of a fluid in motion. This analogy can be helpful, even though an electric field does not actually "flow." Using this analogy, in Figs. 22.2a and 22.2b, in which the electric field vectors point out of the surface, we say that there is an outward **electric flux.** (The word "flux" comes from a Latin word meaning "flow.") In Figs. 22.2c and 22.2d the $\vec{E}$ vectors point into the surface, and the electric flux is *inward*.

Figure 22.2 suggests a simple relationship: Positive charge inside the box goes with an outward electric flux through the box's surface, and negative charge inside goes with an inward electric flux. What happens if there is *zero* charge inside the box? In Fig. 22.3a the box is empty and $\vec{E} = \mathbf{0}$ everywhere, so there is no electric flux into or out of the box. In Fig. 22.3b, one positive and one negative point charge of equal magnitude are enclosed within the box, so the *net* charge inside the box is zero. There is an electric field, but it "flows into" the box on half of its surface and "flows out of" the box on the other half. Hence there is no *net* electric flux into or out of the box.

The box is again empty in Fig. 22.3c. However, there is charge present *outside* the box; the box has been placed with one end parallel to a uniformly charged infinite sheet, which produces a uniform electric field perpendicular to the sheet (as we learned in Example 21.12 of Section 21.5). On one end of the box, $\vec{E}$ points into the box; on the opposite end, $\vec{E}$ points out of the box; and on the sides, $\vec{E}$ is parallel to the surface and so points neither into nor out of the box. As in Fig. 22.3b, the inward electric flux on one part of the box exactly compensates for the outward electric flux on the other part. So in all of the cases shown in Fig. 22.3, there is no *net* electric flux through the surface of the box, and no *net* charge is enclosed in the box.

Figures 22.2 and 22.3 demonstrate a connection between the *sign* (positive, negative, or zero) of the *net* charge enclosed by a closed surface and the sense (outward, inward, or none) of the net electric flux through the surface. There is also a connection between the *magnitude* of the net charge inside the closed surface and the *strength* of the net "flow" of $\vec{E}$ over the surface. In both Figs. 22.4a and 22.4b there is a single point charge inside the box, but in Fig. 22.4b the magnitude of the charge is twice as great, and so $\vec{E}$ is everywhere twice as great in magnitude as in Fig. 22.4a. If we keep in mind the fluid-flow analogy, this means that the net outward electric flux is also twice as great in Fig. 22.4b as in Fig. 22.4a. This suggests that the net electric flux through the surface of the box is *directly proportional* to the magnitude of the net charge enclosed by the box.

22.3 Three cases in which there is zero *net* charge inside a box and no net electric flux through the surface of the box. **(a)** An empty box with $\vec{E} = \mathbf{0}$. **(b)** A box containing one positive and one equal-magnitude negative point charge. **(c)** An empty box immersed in a uniform electric field.

(a) No charge inside box, zero flux

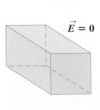

$\vec{E} = 0$

(b) Zero *net* charge inside box, inward flux cancels outward flux.

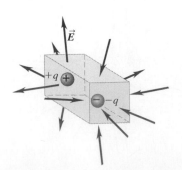

$\vec{E}$

$+q$

$-q$

(c) No charge inside box, inward flux cancels outward flux.

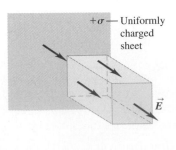

$+\sigma$ — Uniformly charged sheet

$\vec{E}$

This conclusion is independent of the size of the box. In Fig. 22.4c the point charge $+q$ is enclosed by a box with twice the linear dimensions of the box in Fig.22.4a. The magnitude of the electric field of a point charge decreases with distance according to $1/r^2$, so the average magnitude of $\vec{E}$ on each face of the large box in Fig. 22.4c is just $\frac{1}{4}$ of the average magnitude on the corresponding face in Fig. 22.4a. But each face of the large box has exactly four times the area of the corresponding face of the small box. Hence the outward electric flux is the *same* for the two boxes if we *define* electric flux as follows: For each face of the box, take the product of the average perpendicular component of $\vec{E}$ and the area of that face; then add up the results from all faces of the box. With this definition the net electric flux due to a single point charge inside the box is independent of the size of the box and depends only on the net charge inside the box.

We have seen that there is a relationship between the net amount of charge inside a closed surface and the electric flux through that surface. For the special cases of a closed surface in the shape of a rectangular box and charge distributions made up of point charges or infinite charged sheets, we have found:

1. Whether there is a net outward or inward electric flux through a closed surface depends on the sign of the enclosed charge.
2. Charges *outside* the surface do not give a net electric flux through the surface.
3. The net electric flux is directly proportional to the net amount of charge enclosed within the surface but is otherwise independent of the size of the closed surface.

These observations are a qualitative statement of *Gauss's law*.

Do these observations hold true for other kinds of charge distributions and for closed surfaces of arbitrary shape? The answer to these questions will prove to be yes. But to explain why this is so, we need a precise mathematical statement of what we mean by electric flux. This is developed in the next section.

Test Your Understanding of Section 22.1 If all of the dimensions of the box in Fig. 22.2a are increased by a factor of 3, what effect will this change have on the electric flux through the box? (i) The flux will be $3^2 = 9$ times greater; (ii) the flux will be 3 times greater; (iii) the flux will be unchanged; (iv) the flux will be $\left(\frac{1}{3}\right)$ as great; (v) the flux will be $\left(\frac{1}{3}\right)^2 = \frac{1}{9}$ as great; (vi) not enough information is given to decide.

22.2 Calculating Electric Flux

In the preceding section we introduced the concept of *electric flux*. Qualitatively, the electric flux through a surface is a description of whether the electric field $\vec{E}$ points into or out of the surface. We used this to give a rough qualitative statement of Gauss's law: The net electric flux through a closed surface is directly proportional to the net charge inside that surface. To be able to make full use of this law, we need to know how to *calculate* electric flux. To do this, let's again make use of the analogy between an electric field $\vec{E}$ and the field of velocity vectors $\vec{v}$ in a flowing fluid. (Again, keep in mind that this is only an analogy; an electric field is *not* a flow.)

Flux: Fluid-Flow Analogy

Figure 22.5 shows a fluid flowing steadily from left to right. Let's examine the volume flow rate dV/dt (in, say, cubic meters per second) through the wire rectangle with area A. When the area is perpendicular to the flow velocity $\vec{v}$ (Fig. 22.5a) and the flow velocity is the same at all points in the fluid, the volume flow rate dV/dt is the area A multiplied by the flow speed v:

$$\frac{dV}{dt} = vA$$

22.4 (a) A box enclosing a positive point charge $+q$. (b) Doubling the charge causes the magnitude of $\vec{E}$ to double, and it doubles the electric flux through the surface. (c) If the charge stays the same but the dimensions of the box are doubled, the flux stays the same. The magnitude of $\vec{E}$ on the surface decreases by a factor of $\frac{1}{4}$, but the area through which $\vec{E}$ "flows" increases by a factor of 4.

(a) A box containing a charge
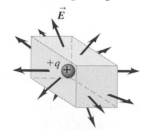

(b) Doubling the enclosed charge doubles the flux.
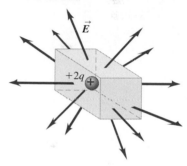

(c) Doubling the box dimensions *does not change* the flux.
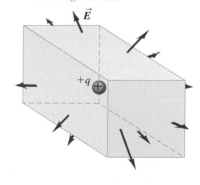

22.5 The volume flow rate of fluid through the wire rectangle (a) is vA when the area of the rectangle is perpendicular to $\vec{v}$ and (b) is $vA\cos\phi$ when the rectangle is tilted at an angle ϕ.

(a) A wire rectangle in a fluid

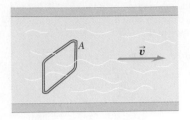

(b) The wire rectangle tilted by an angle ϕ

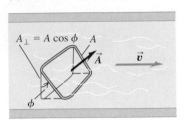

When the rectangle is tilted at an angle ϕ (Fig. 22.5b) so that its face is not perpendicular to $\vec{v}$, the area that counts is the silhouette area that we see when we look in the direction of $\vec{v}$. This area, which is outlined in red and labeled $A_\perp$ in Fig. 22.5b, is the *projection* of the area A onto a surface perpendicular to $\vec{v}$. Two sides of the projected rectangle have the same length as the original one, but the other two are foreshortened by a factor of $\cos\phi$, so the projected area $A_\perp$ is equal to $A\cos\phi$. Then the volume flow rate through A is

$$\frac{dV}{dt} = vA\cos\phi$$

If $\phi = 90°$, $dV/dt = 0$; the wire rectangle is edge-on to the flow, and no fluid passes through the rectangle.

Also, $v\cos\phi$ is the component of the vector $\vec{v}$ perpendicular to the plane of the area A. Calling this component $v_\perp$, we can rewrite the volume flow rate as

$$\frac{dV}{dt} = v_\perp A$$

We can express the volume flow rate more compactly by using the concept of *vector area* $\vec{A}$, a vector quantity with magnitude A and a direction perpendicular to the plane of the area we are describing. The vector area $\vec{A}$ describes both the size of an area and its orientation in space. In terms of $\vec{A}$, we can write the volume flow rate of fluid through the rectangle in Fig. 22.5b as a scalar (dot) product:

$$\frac{dV}{dt} = \vec{v} \cdot \vec{A}$$

Flux of a Uniform Electric Field

Using the analogy between electric field and fluid flow, we now define electric flux in the same way as we have just defined the volume flow rate of a fluid; we simply replace the fluid velocity $\vec{v}$ by the electric field $\vec{E}$. The symbol that we use for electric flux is Φ_E (the capital Greek letter phi; the subscript E is a reminder that this is *electric* flux). Consider first a flat area A perpendicular to a uniform electric field $\vec{E}$ (Fig. 22.6a). We define the electric flux through this area to be the product of the field magnitude E and the area A:

$$\Phi_E = EA$$

Roughly speaking, we can picture Φ_E in terms of the field lines passing through A. Increasing the area means that more lines of $\vec{E}$ pass through the area, increasing the flux; stronger field means more closely spaced lines of $\vec{E}$ and therefore more lines per unit area, so again the flux increases.

If the area A is flat but not perpendicular to the field $\vec{E}$, then fewer field lines pass through it. In this case the area that counts is the silhouette area that we see when looking in the direction of $\vec{E}$. This is the area $A_\perp$ in Fig. 22.6b and is equal to $A\cos\phi$ (compare to Fig. 22.5b). We generalize our definition of electric flux for a uniform electric field to

$$\Phi_E = EA\cos\phi \qquad \text{(electric flux for uniform } \vec{E}\text{, flat surface)} \qquad (22.1)$$

Since $E\cos\phi$ is the component of $\vec{E}$ perpendicular to the area, we can rewrite Eq. (22.1) as

$$\Phi_E = E_\perp A \qquad \text{(electric flux for uniform } \vec{E}\text{, flat surface)} \qquad (22.2)$$

In terms of the vector area $\vec{A}$ perpendicular to the area, we can write the electric flux as the scalar product of $\vec{E}$ and $\vec{A}$:

$$\Phi_E = \vec{E} \cdot \vec{A} \qquad \text{(electric flux for uniform } \vec{E}\text{, flat surface)} \qquad (22.3)$$

22.6 A flat surface in a uniform electric field. The electric flux Φ_E through the surface equals the scalar product of the electric field $\vec{E}$ and the area vector $\vec{A}$.

(a) Surface is face-on to electric field:
• $\vec{E}$ and $\vec{A}$ are parallel (the angle between $\vec{E}$ and $\vec{A}$ is $\phi = 0$).
• The flux $\Phi_E = \vec{E} \cdot \vec{A} = EA$.

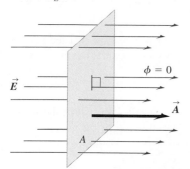

(b) Surface is tilted from a face-on orientation by an angle ϕ:
• The angle between $\vec{E}$ and $\vec{A}$ is ϕ.
• The flux $\Phi_E = \vec{E} \cdot \vec{A} = EA \cos \phi$.

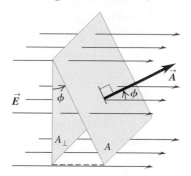

(c) Surface is edge-on to electric field:
• $\vec{E}$ and $\vec{A}$ are perpendicular (the angle between $\vec{E}$ and $\vec{A}$ is $\phi = 90°$).
• The flux $\Phi_E = \vec{E} \cdot \vec{A} = EA \cos 90° = 0$.

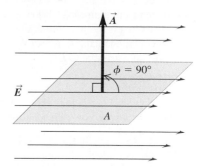

Equations (22.1), (22.2), and (22.3) express the electric flux for a *flat* surface and a *uniform* electric field in different but equivalent ways. The SI unit for electric flux is $1 \ \text{N} \cdot \text{m}^2/\text{C}$. Note that if the area is edge-on to the field, $\vec{E}$ and $\vec{A}$ are perpendicular and the flux is zero (Fig. 22.6c).

We can represent the direction of a vector area $\vec{A}$ by using a *unit vector* $\hat{n}$ perpendicular to the area; $\hat{n}$ stands for "normal." Then

$$\vec{A} = A\hat{n} \qquad (22.4)$$

A surface has two sides, so there are two possible directions for $\hat{n}$ and $\vec{A}$. We must always specify which direction we choose. In Section 22.1 we related the charge inside a *closed* surface to the electric flux through the surface. With a closed surface we will always choose the direction of $\hat{n}$ to be *outward*, and we will speak of the flux *out of* a closed surface. Thus what we called "outward electric flux" in Section 22.1 corresponds to a *positive* value of Φ_E, and what we called "inward electric flux" corresponds to a *negative* value of Φ_E.

Flux of a Nonuniform Electric Field

What happens if the electric field $\vec{E}$ isn't uniform but varies from point to point over the area A? Or what if A is part of a curved surface? Then we divide A into many small elements dA, each of which has a unit vector $\hat{n}$ perpendicular to it and a vector area $d\vec{A} = \hat{n} \, dA$. We calculate the electric flux through each element and integrate the results to obtain the total flux:

$$\Phi_E = \int E \cos \phi \, dA = \int E_\perp \, dA = \int \vec{E} \cdot d\vec{A} \qquad \begin{array}{l} \text{(general definition} \\ \text{of electric flux)} \end{array} \qquad (22.5)$$

We call this integral the **surface integral** of the component $E_\perp$ over the area, or the surface integral of $\vec{E} \cdot d\vec{A}$. The various forms of the integral all express the same thing in different terms. In specific problems, one form is sometimes more convenient than another. Example 22.3 at the end of this section illustrates the use of Eq. (22.5).

In Eq. (22.5) the electric flux $\int E_\perp \, dA$ is equal to the *average* value of the perpendicular component of the electric field, multiplied by the area of the surface. This is the same definition of electric flux that we were led to in Section 22.1, now expressed more mathematically. In the next section we will see the connection between the total electric flux through *any* closed surface, no matter what its shape, and the amount of charge enclosed within that surface.

Example 22.1   Electric flux through a disk

A disk with radius 0.10 m is oriented with its normal unit vector $\hat{n}$ at an angle of 30° to a uniform electric field $\vec{E}$ with magnitude 2.0×10^3 N/C (Fig. 22.7). (Since this isn't a closed surface, it has no "inside" or "outside." That's why we have to specify the direction of $\hat{n}$ in the figure.) (a) What is the electric flux through the disk? (b) What is the flux through the disk if it is turned so that its normal is perpendicular to $\vec{E}$? (c) What is the flux through the disk if its normal is parallel to $\vec{E}$?

SOLUTION

IDENTIFY: This problem is about a flat surface in a uniform electric field, so we can apply the ideas of this section.

SET UP: The orientation of the disk is like that of the rectangle in Fig. 22.6b. We calculate the electric flux using Eq. (22.1).

EXECUTE: (a) The area is $A = \pi (0.10 \text{ m})^2 = 0.0314 \text{ m}^2$ and the angle between $\vec{E}$ and $\vec{A} = A\hat{n}$ is $\phi = 30°$, so

$$\Phi_E = EA\cos\phi = (2.0 \times 10^3 \text{ N/C})(0.0314 \text{ m}^2)(\cos 30°)$$
$$= 54 \text{ N} \cdot \text{m}^2/\text{C}$$

(b) The normal to the disk is now perpendicular to $\vec{E}$, so $\phi = 90°$, $\cos\phi = 0$, and $\Phi_E = 0$. There is no flux through the disk.

(c) The normal to the disk is parallel to $\vec{E}$, so $\phi = 0$, $\cos\phi = 1$, and the flux has its maximum possible value. From Eq. (22.1),

$$\Phi_E = EA\cos\phi = (2.0 \times 10^3 \text{ N/C})(0.0314 \text{ m}^2)(1)$$
$$= 63 \text{ N} \cdot \text{m}^2/\text{C}$$

EVALUATE: As a check on our results, note that the answer to part (a) is smaller than the answer to part (c). Is this as it should be?

22.7 The electric flux Φ_E through a disk depends on the angle between its normal $\hat{n}$ and the electric field $\vec{E}$.

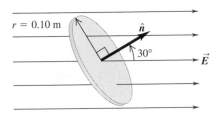

Example 22.2   Electric flux through a cube

A cube of side L is placed in a region of uniform electric field $\vec{E}$. Find the electric flux through each face of the cube and the total flux through the cube when (a) it is oriented with two of its faces perpendicular to the field $\vec{E}$, as in Fig. 22.8a; and (b) when the cube is turned by an angle θ, as in Fig. 22.8b.

SOLUTION

IDENTIFY: In this problem we are to find the electric flux through each face of the cube as well as the total flux (the sum of the fluxes through the six faces).

SET UP: Since $\vec{E}$ is uniform and each of the six faces of the cube is a flat surface, we find the flux through each face using Eqs. (22.3) and (22.4). We then calculate the total flux through the cube by adding the six individual fluxes.

EXECUTE: (a) The unit vectors for each face ($\hat{n}_1$ through $\hat{n}_6$) are shown in the figure; the direction of each unit vector is *outward* from the closed surface of the cube. The angle between $\vec{E}$ and $\hat{n}_1$ is 180°; the angle between $\vec{E}$ and $\hat{n}_2$ is 0°; and the angle between $\vec{E}$ and each of the other four unit vectors is 90°. Each face of the cube has area L^2, so the fluxes through each of the faces are

$$\Phi_{E1} = \vec{E} \cdot \hat{n}_1 A = EL^2 \cos 180° = -EL^2$$
$$\Phi_{E2} = \vec{E} \cdot \hat{n}_2 A = EL^2 \cos 0° = +EL^2$$
$$\Phi_{E3} = \Phi_{E4} = \Phi_{E5} = \Phi_{E6} = EL^2 \cos 90° = 0$$

The flux is negative on face 1, where $\vec{E}$ is directed into the cube, and positive on face 2, where $\vec{E}$ is directed out of the cube. The *total* flux through the cube is the sum of the fluxes through the six faces:

$$\Phi_E = \Phi_{E1} + \Phi_{E2} + \Phi_{E3} + \Phi_{E4} + \Phi_{E5} + \Phi_{E6}$$
$$= -EL^2 + EL^2 + 0 + 0 + 0 + 0 = 0$$

22.8 Electric flux of a uniform field $\vec{E}$ through a cubical box of side L in two orientations.

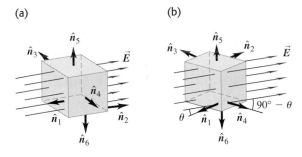

(b) The fluxes through faces 1 and 3 are negative, since $\vec{E}$ is directed into those faces; the field is directed out of faces 2 and 4, so the fluxes through those faces are positive. We find

$$\Phi_{E1} = \vec{E} \cdot \hat{n}_1 A = EL^2 \cos(180° - \theta) = -EL^2 \cos\theta$$
$$\Phi_{E2} = \vec{E} \cdot \hat{n}_2 A = +EL^2 \cos\theta$$
$$\Phi_{E3} = \vec{E} \cdot \hat{n}_3 A = EL^2 \cos(90° + \theta) = -EL^2 \sin\theta$$
$$\Phi_{E4} = \vec{E} \cdot \hat{n}_4 A = EL^2 \cos(90° - \theta) = +EL^2 \sin\theta$$
$$\Phi_{E5} = \Phi_{E6} = EL^2 \cos 90° = 0$$

The total flux $\Phi_E = \Phi_{E1} + \Phi_{E2} + \Phi_{E3} + \Phi_{E4} + \Phi_{E5} + \Phi_{E6}$ through the surface of the cube is again zero.

EVALUATE: It's no surprise that the total flux is zero for both orientations. We came to this same conclusion in our discussion of Fig. 22.3c in Section 22.1. There we observed that there was zero net flux of a uniform electric field through a closed surface that contains no electric charge.

Electric flux through a sphere

A positive point charge $q = 3.0 \ \mu C$ is surrounded by a sphere with radius 0.20 m centered on the charge (Fig. 22.9). Find the electric flux through the sphere due to this charge.

SOLUTION

IDENTIFY: Here the surface is not flat and the electric field is not uniform, so we must use the general definition of electric flux.

SET UP: We use Eq. (22.5) to calculate the electric flux (our target variable). Because the sphere is centered on the point charge, at any point on the spherical surface, $\vec{E}$ is directed out of the sphere perpendicular to the surface. The positive direction for both $\hat{n}$ and $E_\perp$ is outward, so $E_\perp = E$ and the flux through a surface element dA is $\vec{E} \cdot d\vec{A} = E \, dA$. This greatly simplifies the integral in Eq. (22.5).

EXECUTE: At any point on the sphere the magnitude of $\vec{E}$ is

$$E = \frac{q}{4\pi\epsilon_0 r^2} = (9.0 \times 10^9 \ \text{N} \cdot \text{m}^2/\text{C}^2) \frac{3.0 \times 10^{-6} \ \text{C}}{(0.20 \ \text{m})^2}$$

$$= 6.75 \times 10^5 \ \text{N/C}$$

Because E is the same at every point, it can be taken outside the integral $\Phi_E = \int E \, dA$ in Eq. (22.5). What remains is the integral $\int dA$, which is just the total area $A = 4\pi r^2$ of the spherical surface. Thus the total flux out of the sphere is

$$\Phi_E = EA = (6.75 \times 10^5 \ \text{N/C})(4\pi)(0.20 \ \text{m})^2$$

$$= 3.4 \times 10^5 \ \text{N} \cdot \text{m}^2/\text{C}$$

22.9 Electric flux through a sphere centered on a point charge.

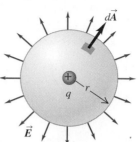

EVALUATE: Notice that we divided by $r^2 = (0.20 \ \text{m})^2$ to find E, then multiplied by $r^2 = (0.20 \ \text{m})^2$ to find Φ_E; hence the radius r of the sphere cancels out of the result for Φ_E. We would have obtained the same flux with a sphere of radius 2.0 m or 200 m. We came to essentially the same conclusion in our discussion of Fig. 22.4 in Section 22.1, where we considered rectangular closed surfaces of two different sizes enclosing a point charge. There we found that the flux of $\vec{E}$ was independent of the size of the surface; the same result holds true for a spherical surface. Indeed, the flux through *any* surface enclosing a single point charge is independent of the shape or size of the surface, as we'll soon see.

Test Your Understanding of Section 22.2 Rank the following surfaces in order from most positive to most negative electric flux. (i) a flat rectangular surface with vector area $\vec{A} = (6.0 \ \text{m}^2)\hat{i}$ in a uniform electric field $\vec{E} = (4.0 \ \text{N/C})\hat{j}$; (ii) a flat circular surface with vector area $\vec{A} = (3.0 \ \text{m}^2)\hat{j}$ in a uniform electric field $\vec{E} = (4.0 \ \text{N/C})\hat{i} + (2.0 \ \text{N/C})\hat{j}$; (iii) a flat square surface with vector area $\vec{A} = (3.0 \ \text{m}^2)\hat{i} + (7.0 \ \text{m}^2)\hat{j}$ in a uniform electric field $\vec{E} = (4.0 \ \text{N/C})\hat{i} - (2.0 \ \text{N/C})\hat{j}$; (iv) a flat oval surface with vector area $\vec{A} = (3.0 \ \text{m}^2)\hat{i} - (7.0 \ \text{m}^2)\hat{j}$ in a uniform electric field $\vec{E} = (4.0 \ \text{N/C})\hat{i} - (2.0 \ \text{N/C})\hat{j}$.

22.3 Gauss's Law

Gauss's law is an alternative to Coulomb's law. While completely equivalent to Coulomb's law, Gauss's law provides a different way to express the relationship between electric charge and electric field. It was formulated by Carl Friedrich Gauss (1777–1855), one of the greatest mathematicians of all time. Many areas of mathematics bear the mark of his influence, and he made equally significant contributions to theoretical physics (Fig. 22.10).

Point Charge Inside a Spherical Surface

Gauss's law states that the total electric flux through any closed surface (a surface enclosing a definite volume) is proportional to the total (net) electric charge inside the surface. In Section 22.1 we observed this relationship qualitatively for certain special cases; now we'll develop it more rigorously. We'll start with the field of a single positive point charge q. The field lines radiate out equally in all directions. We place this charge at the center of an imaginary spherical surface with radius R. The magnitude E of the electric field at every point on the surface is given by

$$E = \frac{1}{4\pi\epsilon_0} \frac{q}{R^2}$$

22.10 Carl Friedrich Gauss helped develop several branches of mathematics, including differential geometry, real analysis, and number theory. The "bell curve" of statistics is one of his inventions. Gauss also made state-of-the-art investigations of the earth's magnetism and calculated the orbit of the first asteroid to be discovered.

22.11 Projection of an element of area dA of a sphere of radius R onto a concentric sphere of radius $2R$. The projection multiplies each linear dimension by 2, so the area element on the larger sphere is 4 dA.

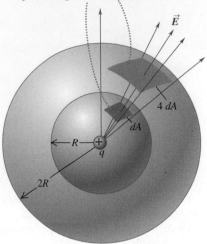

The same number of field lines and the same flux pass through both of these area elements.

At each point on the surface, $\vec{E}$ is perpendicular to the surface, and its magnitude is the same at every point, just as in Example 22.3 (Section 22.2). The total electric flux is the product of the field magnitude E and the total area $A = 4\pi R^2$ of the sphere:

$$\Phi_E = EA = \frac{1}{4\pi\epsilon_0}\frac{q}{R^2}(4\pi R^2) = \frac{q}{\epsilon_0} \tag{22.6}$$

The flux is independent of the radius R of the sphere. It depends only on the charge q enclosed by the sphere.

We can also interpret this result in terms of field lines. Figure 22.11 shows two spheres with radii R and $2R$ centered on the point charge q. Every field line that passes through the smaller sphere also passes through the larger sphere, so the total flux through each sphere is the same.

What is true of the entire sphere is also true of any portion of its surface. In Fig.22.11 an area dA is outlined on the sphere of radius R and then projected onto the sphere of radius $2R$ by drawing lines from the center through points on the boundary of dA. The area projected on the larger sphere is clearly 4 dA. But since the electric field due to a point charge is inversely proportional to r^2, the field magnitude is $\frac{1}{4}$ as great on the sphere of radius $2R$ as on the sphere of radius R. Hence the electric flux is the same for both areas and is independent of the radius of the sphere.

Point Charge Inside a Nonspherical Surface

This projection technique shows us how to extend this discussion to nonspherical surfaces. Instead of a second sphere, let us surround the sphere of radius R by a surface of irregular shape, as in Fig. 22.12a. Consider a small element of area dA on the irregular surface; we note that this area is *larger* than the corresponding element on a spherical surface at the same distance from q. If a normal to dA makes an angle ϕ with a radial line from q, two sides of the area projected onto the spherical surface are foreshortened by a factor $\cos\phi$ (Fig. 22.12b). The other two sides are unchanged. Thus the electric flux through the spherical surface element is equal to the flux $E\,dA\cos\phi$ through the corresponding irregular surface element.

We can divide the entire irregular surface into elements dA, compute the electric flux $E\,dA\cos\phi$ for each, and sum the results by integrating, as in Eq. (22.5). Each of the area elements projects onto a corresponding spherical surface element. Thus the *total* electric flux through the irregular surface, given by any of the forms of Eq. (22.5), must be the same as the total flux through a sphere, which Eq.(22.6) shows is equal to q/ϵ_0. Thus, for the irregular surface,

$$\Phi_E = \oint \vec{E} \cdot d\vec{A} = \frac{q}{\epsilon_0} \tag{22.7}$$

22.12 Calculating the electric flux through a nonspherical surface.

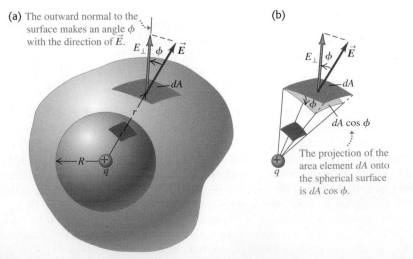

(a) The outward normal to the surface makes an angle ϕ with the direction of $\vec{E}$.

$E_\perp$ ϕ $\vec{E}$

dA

r

R q

(b)

$E_\perp$ ϕ $\vec{E}$

dA

ϕ

$dA\cos\phi$

q

The projection of the area element dA onto the spherical surface is $dA\cos\phi$.

Equation (22.7) holds for a surface of *any* shape or size, provided only that it is a *closed* surface enclosing the charge q. The circle on the integral sign reminds us that the integral is always taken over a *closed* surface.

The area elements $d\vec{A}$ and the corresponding unit vectors $\hat{n}$ always point *out of* the volume enclosed by the surface. The electric flux is then positive in areas where the electric field points out of the surface and negative where it points inward. Also, $E_\perp$ is positive at points where $\vec{E}$ points out of the surface and negative at points where $\vec{E}$ points into the surface.

If the point charge in Fig. 22.12 is negative, the $\vec{E}$ field is directed radially *inward;* the angle ϕ is then greater than 90°, its cosine is negative, and the integral in Eq. (22.7) is negative. But since q is also negative, Eq. (22.7) still holds.

For a closed surface enclosing *no* charge,

$$\Phi_E = \oint \vec{E} \cdot d\vec{A} = 0$$

This is the mathematical statement that when a region contains no charge, any field lines caused by charges *outside* the region that enter on one side must leave again on the other side. (In Section 22.1 we came to the same conclusion by considering the special case of a rectangular box in a uniform field.) Figure 22.13 illustrates this point. *Electric field lines can begin or end inside a region of space only when there is charge in that region.*

General Form of Gauss's Law

Now comes the final step in obtaining the general form of Gauss's law. Suppose the surface encloses not just one point charge q but several charges q_1, q_2, q_3, ... The total (resultant) electric field $\vec{E}$ at any point is the vector sum of the $\vec{E}$ fields of the individual charges. Let Q_{encl} be the *total* charge enclosed by the surface: $Q_{encl} = q_1 + q_2 + q_3 + \cdots$. Also let $\vec{E}$ be the *total* field at the position of the surface area element $d\vec{A}$, and let $E_\perp$ be its component perpendicular to the plane of that element (that is, parallel to $d\vec{A}$). Then we can write an equation like Eq. (22.7) for each charge and its corresponding field and add the results. When we do, we obtain the general statement of Gauss's law:

$$\Phi_E = \oint \vec{E} \cdot d\vec{A} = \frac{Q_{encl}}{\epsilon_0} \qquad \text{(Gauss's law)} \qquad (22.8)$$

The total electric flux through a closed surface is equal to the total (net) electric charge inside the surface, divided by ϵ_0.

CAUTION **Gaussian surfaces are imaginary** Remember that the closed surface in Gauss's law is *imaginary;* there need not be any material object at the position of the surface. We often refer to a closed surface used in Gauss's law as a **Gaussian surface.**

Using the definition of Q_{encl} and the various ways to express electric flux given in Eq. (22.5), we can express Gauss's law in the following equivalent forms:

$$\Phi_E = \oint E\cos\phi \, dA = \oint E_\perp \, dA = \oint \vec{E} \cdot d\vec{A} = \frac{Q_{encl}}{\epsilon_0} \qquad \begin{array}{l}\text{(various forms} \\ \text{of Gauss's law)}\end{array} \qquad (22.9)$$

As in Eq. (22.5), the various forms of the integral all express the same thing, the total electric flux through the Gaussian surface, in different terms. One form is sometimes more convenient than another.

As an example, Fig. 22.14a shows a spherical Gaussian surface of radius r around a positive point charge $+q$. The electric field points out of the Gaussian surface, so at every point on the surface $\vec{E}$ is in the same direction as $d\vec{A}$, $\phi = 0$, and

22.13 A point charge *outside* a closed surface that encloses no charge. If an electric field line from the external charge enters the surface at one point, it must leave at another.

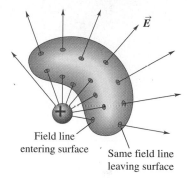

Field line entering surface Same field line leaving surface

22.14 Spherical Gaussian surfaces around (a) a positive point charge and (b) a negative point charge.

(a) Gaussian surface around positive charge: positive (outward) flux

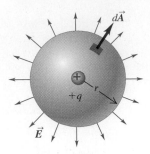

(b) Gaussian surface around negative charge: negative (inward) flux

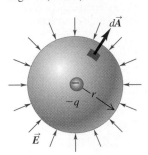

$E_\perp$ is equal to the field magnitude $E = q/4\pi\epsilon_0 r^2$. Since E is the same at all points on the surface, we can take it outside the integral in Eq. (22.9). Then the remaining integral is $\int dA = A = 4\pi r^2$, the area of the sphere. Hence Eq. (22.9) becomes

$$\Phi_E = \oint E_\perp \, dA = \oint \frac{q}{4\pi\epsilon_0 r^2} \, dA = \frac{q}{4\pi\epsilon_0 r^2} \oint dA = \frac{q}{4\pi\epsilon_0 r^2} 4\pi r^2 = \frac{q}{\epsilon_0}$$

The enclosed charge Q_{encl} is just the charge $+q$, so this agrees with Gauss's law. If the Gaussian surface encloses a *negative* point charge as in Fig. 22.14b, then $\vec{E}$ points *into* the surface at each point in the direction opposite $d\vec{A}$. Then $\phi = 180°$ and $E_\perp$ is equal to the negative of the field magnitude: $E_\perp = -E = -|-q|/4\pi\epsilon_0 r^2 = -q/4\pi\epsilon_0 r^2$. Equation (22.9) then becomes

$$\Phi_E = \oint E_\perp \, dA = \oint \left(\frac{-q}{4\pi\epsilon_0 r^2} \right) dA = \frac{-q}{4\pi\epsilon_0 r^2} \oint dA = \frac{-q}{4\pi\epsilon_0 r^2} 4\pi r^2 = \frac{-q}{\epsilon_0}$$

This again agrees with Gauss's law because the enclosed charge in Fig. 22.14b is $Q_{\text{encl}} = -q$.

In Eqs. (22.8) and (22.9), Q_{encl} is always the algebraic sum of all the positive and negative charges enclosed by the Gaussian surface, and $\vec{E}$ is the *total* field at each point on the surface. Also note that in general, this field is caused partly by charges inside the surface and partly by charges outside. But as Fig. 22.13 shows, the outside charges do *not* contribute to the total (net) flux through the surface. So Eqs. (22.8) and (22.9) are correct even when there are charges outside the surface that contribute to the electric field at the surface. When $Q_{\text{encl}} = 0$, the total flux through the Gaussian surface must be zero, even though some areas may have positive flux and others may have negative flux (see Fig. 22.3b).

Gauss's law is the definitive answer to the question we posed at the beginning of Section 22.1: "If the electric field pattern is known in a given region, what can we determine about the charge distribution in that region?" It provides a relationship between the electric field on a closed surface and the charge distribution within that surface. But in some cases we can use Gauss's law to answer the reverse question: "If the charge distribution is known, what can we determine about the electric field that the charge distribution produces?" Gauss's law may seem like an unappealing way to address this question, since it may look as though evaluating the integral in Eq. (22.8) is a hopeless task. Sometimes it is, but other times it is surprisingly easy. Here's an example in which *no* integration is involved at all; we'll work out several more examples in the next section.

Conceptual Example 22.4 | **Electric flux and enclosed charge**

Figure 22.15 shows the field produced by two point charges $+q$ and $-q$ of equal magnitude but opposite sign (an electric dipole). Find the electric flux through each of the closed surfaces A, B, C, and D.

SOLUTION

The definition of electric flux given in Eq. (22.5) involves a surface integral, and so it might seem that integration is called for. But Gauss's law says that the total electric flux through a closed surface is equal to the total enclosed charge divided by ϵ_0. By inspection of Fig. 22.15, surface A (shown in red) encloses the positive charge, so $Q_{\text{encl}} = +q$; surface B (shown in blue) encloses the negative charge, so $Q_{\text{encl}} = -q$; surface C (shown in yellow), which encloses *both* charges, has $Q_{\text{encl}} = +q + (-q) = 0$; and surface D (shown in purple), which has no charges enclosed within it, also has $Q_{\text{encl}} = 0$. Hence, without having to do any integration, we can

22.15 The net number of field lines leaving a closed surface is proportional to the total charge enclosed by that surface.

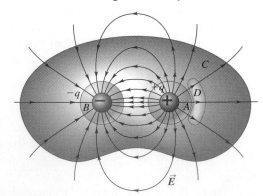

conclude that the total fluxes for the various surfaces are $\Phi_E = +q/\epsilon_0$ for surface A, $\Phi_E = -q/\epsilon_0$ for surface B, and $\Phi_E = 0$ for both surface C and surface D.

These results depend only on the charges enclosed within each Gaussian surface, not on the precise shapes of the surfaces. For example, compare surface C to the rectangular surface shown in Fig. 22.3b, which also encloses both charges of an electric dipole. In that case as well, we concluded that the net flux of $\vec{E}$ was zero; the inward flux on one part of the surface exactly compensates for the outward flux on the remainder of the surface.

We can draw similar conclusions by examining the electric field lines. Surface A encloses only the positive charge; in Fig. 22.15, 18 lines are depicted crossing A in an outward direction. Surface B encloses only the negative charge; it is crossed by these same 18 lines, but in an inward direction. Surface C encloses *both* charges. It is intersected by lines at 16 points; at 8 intersections the lines are outward, and at 8 they are inward. The *net* number of lines crossing in an outward direction is zero, and the net charge inside the surface is also zero. Surface D is intersected at 6 points; at 3 points the lines are outward, and at the other 3 they are inward. The net number of lines crossing in an outward direction and the total charge enclosed are both zero. There are points on the surfaces where $\vec{E}$ is not perpendicular to the surface, but this doesn't affect the counting of the field lines.

Test Your Understanding of Section 22.3 Figure 22.16 shows six point charges that all lie in the same plane. Five Gaussian surfaces—S_1, S_2, S_3, S_4, and S_5—each enclose part of this plane, and Fig. 22.16 shows the intersection of each surface with the plane. Rank these five surfaces in order of the electric flux through them, from most positive to most negative.

22.16 Five Gaussian surfaces and six point charges.

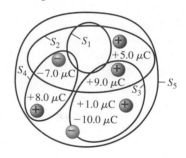

22.4 Applications of Gauss's Law

Gauss's law is valid for *any* distribution of charges and for *any* closed surface. Gauss's law can be used in two ways. If we know the charge distribution, and if it has enough symmetry to let us evaluate the integral in Gauss's law, we can find the field. Or if we know the field, we can use Gauss's law to find the charge distribution, such as charges on conducting surfaces.

In this section we present examples of both kinds of applications. As you study them, watch for the role played by the symmetry properties of each system. We will use Gauss's law to calculate the electric fields caused by several simple charge distributions; the results are collected in a table in the chapter summary.

In practical problems we often encounter situations in which we want to know the electric field caused by a charge distribution on a conductor. These calculations are aided by the following remarkable fact: *When excess charge is placed on a solid conductor and is at rest, it resides entirely on the surface, not in the interior of the material.* (By *excess* we mean charges other than the ions and free electrons that make up the neutral conductor.) Here's the proof. We know from Section 21.4 that in an electrostatic situation (with all charges at rest) the electric field $\vec{E}$ at every point in the interior of a conducting material is zero. If $\vec{E}$ were *not* zero, the excess charges would move. Suppose we construct a Gaussian surface inside the conductor, such as surface A in Fig. 22.17. Because $\vec{E} = \mathbf{0}$ everywhere on this surface, Gauss's law requires that the net charge inside the surface is zero. Now imagine shrinking the surface like a collapsing balloon until it encloses a region so small that we may consider it as a point P; then the charge at that point must be zero. We can do this anywhere inside the conductor, so *there can be no excess charge at any point within a solid conductor; any excess charge must reside on the conductor's surface.* (This result is for a *solid* conductor. In the next section we'll discuss what can happen if the conductor has cavities in its interior.) We will make use of this fact frequently in the examples that follow.

22.17 Under electrostatic conditions (charges not in motion), any excess charge on a solid conductor resides entirely on the conductor's surface.

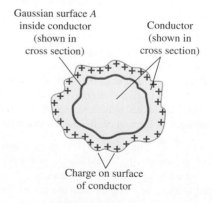

Gaussian surface A inside conductor (shown in cross section)

Conductor (shown in cross section)

Charge on surface of conductor

Problem-Solving Strategy 22.1   Gauss's Law

IDENTIFY *the relevant concepts:* Gauss's law is most useful in situations where the charge distribution has spherical or cylindrical symmetry or is distributed uniformly over a plane. In these situations we determine the direction of $\vec{E}$ from the symmetry of the charge distribution. If we are given the charge distribution, we can use Gauss's law to find the magnitude of $\vec{E}$. Alternatively, if we are given the field, we can use Gauss's law to determine the details of the charge distribution. In either case, begin your analysis by asking the question: What is the symmetry?

SET UP *the problem* using the following steps:
1. Select the surface that you will use with Gauss's law. We often call it a *Gaussian surface*. If you are trying to find the field at a particular point, then that point must lie on your Gaussian surface.
2. The Gaussian surface does not have to be a real physical surface, such as a surface of a solid body. Often the appropriate surface is an imaginary geometric surface; it may be in empty space, embedded in a solid body, or both.
3. Usually you can evaluate the integral in Gauss's law (without using a computer) only if the Gaussian surface and the charge distribution have some symmetry property. If the charge distribution has cylindrical or spherical symmetry, choose the Gaussian surface to be a coaxial cylinder or a concentric sphere, respectively.

EXECUTE *the solution* as follows:
1. Carry out the integral in Eq. (22.9). This may look like a daunting task, but the symmetry of the charge distribution and your careful choice of a Gaussian surface make it straightforward.

2. Often you can think of the closed Gaussian surface as being made up of several separate surfaces, such as the sides and ends of a cylinder. The integral $\oint E_\perp \, dA$ over the entire closed surface is always equal to the sum of the integrals over all the separate surfaces. Some of these integrals may be zero, as in points 4 and 5 below.
3. If $\vec{E}$ is *perpendicular* (normal) at every point to a surface with area A, if it points *outward* from the interior of the surface, and if it also has the same *magnitude* at every point on the surface, then $E_\perp = E = $ constant, and $\int E_\perp \, dA$ over that surface is equal to EA. If instead $\vec{E}$ is perpendicular and *inward*, then $E_\perp = -E$ and $\int E_\perp \, dA = -EA$.
4. If $\vec{E}$ is *tangent* to a surface at every point, then $E_\perp = 0$ and the integral over that surface is zero.
5. If $\vec{E} = \mathbf{0}$ at every point on a surface, the integral is zero.
6. In the integral $\oint E_\perp \, dA$, $E_\perp$ is always the perpendicular component of the *total* electric field at each point on the closed Gaussian surface. In general, this field may be caused partly by charges within the surface and partly by charges outside it. Even when there is *no* charge within the surface, the field at points on the Gaussian surface is not necessarily zero. In that case, however, the *integral* over the Gaussian surface—that is, the total electric flux through the Gaussian surface—is always zero.
7. Once you have evaluated the integral, use Eq. (22.9) to solve for your target variable.

EVALUATE *your answer:* Often your result will be a *function* that describes how the magnitude of the electric field varies with position. Examine this function with a critical eye to see whether it makes sense.

Example 22.5   Field of a charged conducting sphere

We place positive charge q on a solid conducting sphere with radius R (Fig. 22.18). Find $\vec{E}$ at any point inside or outside the sphere.

SOLUTION

IDENTIFY: As we discussed earlier in this section, all the charge must be on the surface of the sphere. The system has spherical symmetry.

SET UP: To take advantage of the symmetry, we take as our Gaussian surface an imaginary sphere of radius r centered on the conductor. To calculate the field outside the conductor, we take r to be greater than the conductor's radius R; to calculate the field inside, we take r to be less than R. In either case, the point where we want to calculate $\vec{E}$ lies on the Gaussian surface.

EXECUTE: The role of symmetry deserves careful discussion before we do any calculations. When we say that the system is spherically symmetric, we mean that if we rotate it through any angle about any axis through the center, the system after rotation is indistinguishable from the original unrotated system. The charge is free to move on the conductor, and there is nothing about the con-

22.18 Calculating the electric field of a conducting sphere with positive charge q. Outside the sphere, the field is the same as if all of the charge were concentrated at the center of the sphere.

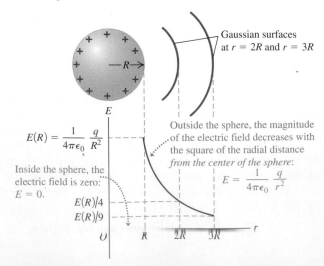

Gaussian surfaces at $r = 2R$ and $r = 3R$

$$E(R) = \frac{1}{4\pi\epsilon_0} \frac{q}{R^2}$$

Inside the sphere, the electric field is zero: $E = 0$.

$E(R)/4$

$E(R)/9$

Outside the sphere, the magnitude of the electric field decreases with the square of the radial distance *from the center of the sphere:*

$$E = \frac{1}{4\pi\epsilon_0} \frac{q}{r^2}$$

ductor that would make it tend to concentrate more in some regions than others. So we conclude that the charge is distributed *uniformly* over the surface.

Symmetry also shows that the direction of the electric field must be *radial,* as shown in Fig. 22.18. If we again rotate the system, the field pattern of the rotated system must be identical to that of the original system. If the field had a component at some point that was perpendicular to the radial direction, that component would have to be different after at least some rotations. Thus there can't be such a component, and the field must be radial. For the same reason the magnitude E of the field can depend only on the distance r from the center and must have the same value at all points on a spherical surface concentric with the conductor.

Our choice of a sphere as a Gaussian surface takes advantage of these symmetry properties. We first consider the field outside the conductor, so we choose $r > R$. The entire conductor is within the Gaussian surface, so the enclosed charge is q. The area of the Gaussian surface is $4\pi r^2$; $\vec{E}$ is uniform over the surface and perpendicular to it at each point. The flux integral $\oint E_\perp \, dA$ in Gauss's law is therefore just $E(4\pi r^2)$, and Eq. (22.8) gives

$$E(4\pi r^2) = \frac{q}{\epsilon_0} \quad \text{and}$$

$$E = \frac{1}{4\pi\epsilon_0} \frac{q}{r^2} \quad \text{(outside a charged conducting sphere)}$$

This expression for the field at any point *outside* the sphere $(r > R)$ is the same as for a point charge; the field due to the charged sphere is the same as though the entire charge were concentrated at its center. Just outside the surface of the sphere, where $r = R$,

$$E = \frac{1}{4\pi\epsilon_0} \frac{q}{R^2}$$

(at the surface of a charged conducting sphere)

CAUTION **Flux can be positive or negative** Remember that we have chosen the charge q to be *positive.* If the charge is negative, the electric field is radially *inward* instead of radially outward, and the electric flux through the Gaussian surface is negative. The electric field magnitudes outside and at the surface of the sphere are given by the same expressions as above, except that q denotes the *magnitude* (absolute value) of the charge. ∎

To find $\vec{E}$ inside the conductor, we use a spherical Gaussian surface with radius $r < R$. The spherical symmetry again tells us that $E(4\pi r^2) = Q_{encl}/\epsilon_0$. But because all of the charge is on the surface of the conductor, our Gaussian surface (which lies entirely within the conductor) encloses *no* charge. So $Q_{encl} = 0$ and, therefore, the electric field inside the conductor is zero.

EVALUATE: We already knew that $\vec{E} = 0$ inside the conductor, as it must be inside any solid conductor when the charges are at rest. Figure 22.18 shows E as a function of the distance r from the center of the sphere. Note that in the limit as $R \rightarrow 0$, the sphere becomes a point charge; there is then only an "outside," and the field is everywhere given by $E = q/4\pi\epsilon_0 r^2$. Thus we have deduced Coulomb's law from Gauss's law. (In Section 22.3 we deduced Gauss's law from Coulomb's law, so this completes the demonstration of their logical equivalence.)

We can also use this method for a conducting spherical *shell* (a spherical conductor with a concentric spherical hole in the center) if there is no charge inside the hole. We use a spherical Gaussian surface with radius r less than the radius of the hole. If there *were* a field inside the hole, it would have to be radial and spherically symmetric as before, so $E = Q_{encl}/4\pi\epsilon_0 r^2$. But now there is no enclosed charge, so $Q_{encl} = 0$ and $E = 0$ inside the hole.

Can you use this same technique to find the electric field in the interspace between a charged sphere and a concentric hollow conducting sphere that surrounds it?

Example 22.6 **Field of a line charge**

Electric charge is distributed uniformly along an infinitely long, thin wire. The charge per unit length is λ (assumed positive). Find the electric field. (This is an approximate representation of the field of a uniformly charged *finite* wire, provided that the distance from the field point to the wire is much less than the length of the wire.)

SOLUTION

IDENTIFY: The system has *cylindrical* symmetry. The field must point away from the positive charges. To determine the direction of $\vec{E}$ more precisely, as well as how its magnitude can depend on position, we use symmetry as in Example 22.5.

SET UP: Cylindrical symmetry means that we can rotate the system through any angle about its axis, and we can shift it by any amount along the axis; in each case the resulting system is indistinguishable from the original. Hence $\vec{E}$ at each point can't change when either of these operations is carried out. The field can't have any component parallel to the wire; if it did, we would have to explain why the field lines that begin on the wire pointed in one direction parallel to the wire and not the other. Also, the field can't have any component tangent to a circle in a plane perpendicular to the wire with its center on the wire. If it did, we would have to explain why the component pointed in one direction around the

wire rather than the other. All that's left is a component radially outward from the wire at each point. So the field lines outside a uniformly charged, infinite wire are *radial* and lie in planes perpendicular to the wire. The field *magnitude* can depend only on the radial distance from the wire.

These symmetry properties suggest that we use as a Gaussian surface a *cylinder* with arbitrary radius r and arbitrary length l, with its ends perpendicular to the wire (Fig. 22.19).

22.19 A coaxial cylindrical Gaussian surface is used to find the electric field outside an infinitely long, charged wire.

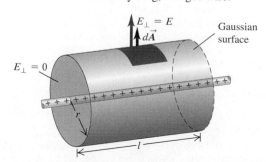

Continued

EXECUTE: We break the surface integral for the flux Φ_E into an integral over each flat end and one over the curved side walls. There is no flux through the ends because $\vec{E}$ lies in the plane of the surface and $E_\perp = 0$. To find the flux through the side walls, note that $\vec{E}$ is perpendicular to the surface at each point, so $E = E_\perp$; by symmetry, E has the same value everywhere on the walls. The area of the side walls is $2\pi r l$. (To make a paper cylinder with radius r and height l, you need a paper rectangle with width $2\pi r$, height l, and area $2\pi r l$.) Hence the total flux Φ_E through the entire cylinder is the sum of the flux through the side walls, which is $(E)(2\pi r l)$, and the zero flux through the two ends. Finally, we need the total enclosed charge, which is the charge per unit length multiplied by the length of wire inside the Gaussian surface, or $Q_{encl} = \lambda l$. From Gauss's law, Eq. (22.8),

$$\Phi_E = (E)(2\pi r l) = \frac{\lambda l}{\epsilon_0} \quad \text{and}$$

$$E = \frac{1}{2\pi\epsilon_0}\frac{\lambda}{r} \quad \text{(field of an infinite line of charge)}$$

This is the same result that we found in Example 21.11 (Section 21.5) by much more laborious means.

We have assumed that λ is *positive*. If it is *negative*, $\vec{E}$ is directed radially inward toward the line of charge, and in the above expression for the field magnitude E we must interpret λ as the *magnitude* (absolute value) of the charge per unit length.

EVALUATE: Note that although the *entire* charge on the wire contributes to the field, only the part of the total charge that is within the Gaussian surface is considered when we apply Gauss's law. This may seem strange; it looks as though we have somehow obtained the right answer by ignoring part of the charge and the field of a *short* wire of length l would be the same as that of a very long wire. But we *do* include the entire charge on the wire when we make use of the *symmetry* of the problem. If the wire is short, the symmetry with respect to shifts along the axis is not present, and the field is not uniform in magnitude over our Gaussian surface. Gauss's law is then no longer useful and *cannot* be used to find the field; the problem is best handled by the integration technique used in Example 21.11.

We can use a Gaussian surface like that in Fig. 22.19 to show that the field at points outside a long, uniformly charged cylinder is the same as though all the charge were concentrated on a line along its axis. We can also calculate the electric field in the space between a charged cylinder and a coaxial hollow conducting cylinder surrounding it. We leave these calculations to you (see Problems 22.37 and 22.40).

Example 22.7   Field of an infinite plane sheet of charge

Find the electric field caused by a thin, flat, infinite sheet on which there is a uniform positive charge per unit area σ.

SOLUTION

IDENTIFY: The field must point away from the positively charged sheet. As in Examples 22.5 and 22.6, before doing calculations we use the symmetry (in this case, *planar* symmetry) to learn more about the direction and position dependence of $\vec{E}$.

SET UP: Planar symmetry means that the charge distribution doesn't change if we slide it in any direction parallel to the sheet. From this we conclude that at each point, $\vec{E}$ is perpendicular to the sheet. The symmetry also tells us that the field must have the same magnitude E at any given distance on either side of the sheet. To take advantage of these symmetry properties, we use as our Gaussian surface a cylinder with its axis perpendicular to the sheet of charge, with ends of area A (Fig. 22.20).

EXECUTE: The charged sheet passes through the middle of the cylinder's length, so the cylinder ends are equidistant from the sheet. At each end of the cylinder, $\vec{E}$ is perpendicular to the surface and $E_\perp$ is equal to E; hence the flux through each end is $+EA$.

Because $\vec{E}$ is perpendicular to the charged sheet, it is parallel to the curved *side* walls of the cylinder, so $E_\perp$ at these walls is zero and there is no flux through these walls. The total flux integral in Gauss's law is then $2EA$ (EA from each end and zero from the side walls). The net charge within the Gaussian surface is the charge per unit area multiplied by the sheet area enclosed by the surface, or $Q_{encl} = \sigma A$. Hence Gauss's law, Eq. (22.8), gives

$$2EA = \frac{\sigma A}{\epsilon_0} \quad \text{and}$$

$$E = \frac{\sigma}{2\epsilon_0} \quad \text{(field of an infinite sheet of charge)}$$

This is the same result that we found in Example 21.12 (Section 21.5) using a much more complex calculation. The field is uniform and directed perpendicular to the plane of the sheet. Its magnitude is *independent* of the distance from the sheet. The field lines are therefore straight, parallel to each other, and perpendicular to the sheet.

If the charge density is negative, $\vec{E}$ is directed *toward* the sheet, the flux through the Gaussian surface in Fig. 22.20 is negative, and σ in the expression $E = \sigma/2\epsilon_0$ denotes the magnitude (absolute value) of the charge density.

22.20 A cylindrical Gaussian surface is used to find the field of an infinite plane sheet of charge.

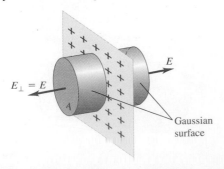

$E_\perp = E$

E

Gaussian surface

EVALUATE: The assumption that the sheet is infinitely large is an idealization; nothing in nature is really infinitely large. But the result $E = \sigma/2\epsilon_0$ is a good approximation for points that are close to the sheet (compared to the sheet's dimensions) and not too near its edges. At such points, the field is very nearly uniform and perpendicular to the plane.

Example 22.8 Field between oppositely charged parallel conducting plates

Two large plane parallel conducting plates are given charges of equal magnitude and opposite sign; the charge per unit area is $+\sigma$ for one and $-\sigma$ for the other. Find the electric field in the region between the plates.

SOLUTION

IDENTIFY: The field between and around the plates is approximately as shown in Fig. 22.21a. Because opposite charges attract, most of the charge accumulates at the opposing faces of the plates. A small amount of charge resides on the *outer* surfaces of the plates, and there is some spreading or "fringing" of the field at the edges. But if the plates are very large in comparison to the distance between them, the amount of charge on the outer surfaces is negligibly small, and the fringing can be neglected except near the edges. In this case we can assume that the field is uniform in the interior region between plates, as in Fig. 22.21b, and that the charges are distributed uniformly over the opposing surfaces.

SET UP: To exploit this symmetry, we can use the shaded Gaussian surfaces S_1, S_2, S_3, and S_4. These surfaces are cylinders with ends of area A like the one shown in perspective in Fig. 22.20; they are shown in a side view in Fig. 22.21b. One end of each surface lies within one of the conducting plates.

EXECUTE: For the surface labeled S_1, the left-hand end is within plate 1 (the positive plate). Since the field is zero within the volume of any solid conductor under electrostatic conditions, there is no electric flux through this end. The electric field between the plates is perpendicular to the right-hand end, so on that end, $E_\perp$ is

equal to E and the flux is EA; this is positive, since $\vec{E}$ is directed out of the Gaussian surface. There is no flux through the side walls of the cylinder, since these walls are parallel to $\vec{E}$. So the total flux integral in Gauss's law is EA. The net charge enclosed by the cylinder is σA, so Eq. (22.8) yields

$$ EA = \frac{\sigma A}{\epsilon_0} \quad \text{and} \quad E = \frac{\sigma}{\epsilon_0} \quad \begin{array}{l}\text{(field between oppositely}\\\text{charged conducting plates)}\end{array} $$

The field is uniform and perpendicular to the plates, and its magnitude is independent of the distance from either plate. This same result can be obtained by using the Gaussian surface S_4; furthermore, the surfaces S_2 and S_3 can be used to show that $E = 0$ to the left of plate 1 and to the right of plate 2. We leave these calculations to you (see Exercise 22.27).

EVALUATE: We obtained the same results in Example 21.13 (Section 21.5) by using the principle of superposition of electric fields. The fields due to the two sheets of charge (one on each plate) are $\vec{E}_1$ and $\vec{E}_2$; from Example 22.7, both of these have magnitude $\sigma/2\epsilon_0$. The total (resultant) electric field at any point is the vector sum $\vec{E} = \vec{E}_1 + \vec{E}_2$. At points a and c in Fig. 22.21b, $\vec{E}_1$ and $\vec{E}_2$ have opposite directions, and their resultant is zero. This is also true at every point within the material of each plate, consistent with the requirement that with charges at rest there can be no field within a solid conductor. At any point b between the plates, $\vec{E}_1$ and $\vec{E}_2$ have the same direction; their resultant has magnitude $E = \sigma/\epsilon_0$, just as we found above using Gauss's law.

22.21 Electric field between oppositely charged parallel plates.

(a) Realistic drawing

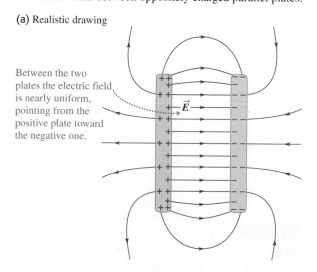

Between the two plates the electric field is nearly uniform, pointing from the positive plate toward the negative one.

(b) Idealized model

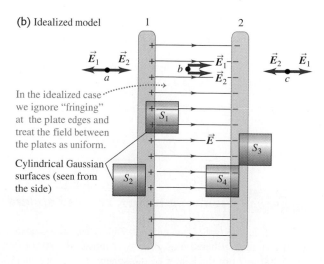

In the idealized case we ignore "fringing" at the plate edges and treat the field between the plates as uniform.

Cylindrical Gaussian surfaces (seen from the side)

Example 22.9   Field of a uniformly charged sphere

Positive electric charge Q is distributed uniformly *throughout the volume* of an *insulating* sphere with radius R. Find the magnitude of the electric field at a point P a distance r from the center of the sphere.

SOLUTION

IDENTIFY: As in Example 22.5, the system is spherically symmetric. Hence we can use the conclusions of that example about the direction and magnitude of $\vec{E}$.

SET UP: To make use of the symmetry, we choose as our Gaussian surface a sphere with radius r, concentric with the charge distribution.

EXECUTE: From symmetry the magnitude E of the electric field has the same value at every point on the Gaussian surface, and the direction of $\vec{E}$ is radial at every point on the surface, so $E_\perp = E$. Hence the total electric flux through the Gaussian surface is the product of E and the total area of the surface $A = 4\pi r^2$, that is, $\Phi_E = 4\pi r^2 E$.

The amount of charge enclosed within the Gaussian surface depends on the radius r. Let's first find the field magnitude *inside* the charged sphere of radius R; the magnitude E is evaluated at the radius of the Gaussian surface, so we choose $r < R$. The volume charge density ρ is the charge Q divided by the volume of the entire charged sphere of radius R:

$$\rho = \frac{Q}{4\pi R^3/3}$$

22.22 The magnitude of the electric field of a uniformly charged insulating sphere. Compare this with the field for a conducting sphere (Fig. 22.18).

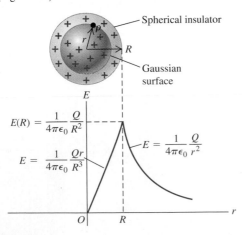

The volume V_{encl} enclosed by the Gaussian surface is $\frac{4}{3}\pi r^3$, so the total charge Q_{encl} enclosed by that surface is

$$Q_{encl} = \rho V_{encl} = \left(\frac{Q}{4\pi R^3/3}\right)\left(\frac{4}{3}\pi r^3\right) = Q\frac{r^3}{R^3}$$

Then Gauss's law, Eq. (22.8), becomes

$$4\pi r^2 E = \frac{Q}{\epsilon_0}\frac{r^3}{R^3} \quad \text{or}$$

$$E = \frac{1}{4\pi\epsilon_0}\frac{Qr}{R^3} \quad \text{(field inside a uniformly charged sphere)}$$

The field magnitude is proportional to the distance r of the field point from the center of the sphere. At the center $(r = 0)$, $E = 0$.

To find the field magnitude *outside* the charged sphere, we use a spherical Gaussian surface of radius $r > R$. This surface encloses the entire charged sphere, so $Q_{encl} = Q$, and Gauss's law gives

$$4\pi r^2 E = \frac{Q}{\epsilon_0} \quad \text{or}$$

$$E = \frac{1}{4\pi\epsilon_0}\frac{Q}{r^2} \quad \text{(field outside a uniformly charged sphere)}$$

For *any* spherically symmetric charged body the electric field outside the body is the same as though the entire charge were concentrated at the center. (We made this same observation in Example 22.5.)

Figure 22.22 shows a graph of E as a function of r for this problem. For $r < R$, E is directly proportional to r, and for $r > R$, E varies as $1/r^2$. If the charge is negative instead of positive, $\vec{E}$ is radially *inward* and Q in the expressions for E is interpreted as the magnitude (absolute value) of the charge.

EVALUATE: Notice that if we set $r = R$ in either of the two expressions for E (inside or outside the sphere), we get the same result $E = Q/4\pi\epsilon_0 R^2$ for the magnitude of the field at the surface of the sphere. This is because the magnitude E is a *continuous* function of r. By contrast, for the charged conducting sphere of Example 22.5 the electric-field magnitude is *discontinuous* at $r = R$ (it jumps from $E = 0$ just inside the sphere to $E = Q/4\pi\epsilon_0 R^2$ just outside the sphere). In general, the electric field $\vec{E}$ is discontinuous in magnitude, direction, or both wherever there is a *sheet* of charge, such as at the surface of a charged conducting sphere (Example 22.5), at the surface of an infinite charged sheet (Example 22.7), or at the surface of a charged conducting plate (Example 22.8).

The general technique used in this example can be applied to *any* spherically symmetric distribution of charge, whether it is uniform or not. Such charge distributions occur within many atoms and atomic nuclei, which is why Gauss's law is a useful tool in atomic and nuclear physics.

Example 22.10   Field of a hollow charged sphere

A thin-walled, hollow sphere of radius 0.250 m has an unknown amount of charge distributed uniformly over its surface. At a distance of 0.300 m from the center of the sphere, the electric field points directly toward the center of the sphere and has magnitude $1.80 \times 10^2\ \text{N/C}$. How much charge is on the sphere?

SOLUTION

IDENTIFY: The charge distribution is spherically symmetric. As in Examples 22.5 and 22.9, it follows that the electric field is radial everywhere and its magnitude is a function only of the radial distance r from the center of the sphere.

SET UP: We again use a spherical Gaussian surface that is concentric with the charge distribution and that passes through the point of interest at $r = 0.300$ m.

EXECUTE: The charge distribution is the same as if the charge were on the surface of a 0.250-m-radius conducting sphere. Hence we can borrow the results of Example 22.5. A key difference from that example is that because the electric field here is directed toward the sphere, the charge must be *negative*. Furthermore, because the electric field is directed into the Gaussian surface, $E_\perp = -E$ and the flux is $\oint E_\perp \, dA = -E(4\pi r^2)$.

By Gauss's law, the flux is equal to the charge q on the sphere (all of which is enclosed by the Gaussian surface) divided by ϵ_0. Solving for q, we find

$$q = -E(4\pi\epsilon_0 r^2) = -(1.80 \times 10^2 \text{ N/C})(4\pi)$$
$$\times (8.854 \times 10^{-12} \text{ C}^2/\text{N} \cdot \text{m}^2)(0.300 \text{ m})^2$$
$$= -8.01 \times 10^{-10} \text{ C} = -0.801 \text{ nC}$$

EVALUATE: To determine the charge, we had to know the electric field at *all* points on the Gaussian surface so that we could calculate the flux integral. This was possible here because the charge distribution is highly symmetric. If the charge distribution is irregular or lacks symmetry, however, Gauss's law is not very useful for calculating the charge distribution from the field, or vice versa.

Test Your Understanding of Section 22.4   You place a known amount of charge Q on the irregularly shaped conductor shown in Fig. 22.17. If you know the size and shape of the conductor, can you use Gauss's law to calculate the electric field at an arbitrary position outside the conductor?

22.5 **Charges on Conductors**

We have learned that in an electrostatic situation (in which there is no net motion of charge) the electric field at every point within a conductor is zero and that any excess charge on a solid conductor is located entirely on its surface (Fig. 22.23a). But what if there is a *cavity* inside the conductor (Fig. 22.23b)? If there is no charge within the cavity, we can use a Gaussian surface such as A (which lies completely within the material of the conductor) to show that the *net* charge on the *surface of the cavity* must be zero, because $\vec{E} = 0$ everywhere on the Gaussian surface. In fact, we can prove in this situation that there can't be any charge *anywhere* on the cavity surface. We will postpone detailed proof of this statement until Chapter 23.

Suppose we place a small body with a charge q inside a cavity within a conductor (Fig. 22.23c). The conductor is uncharged and is insulated from the charge q. Again $\vec{E} = 0$ everywhere on surface A, so according to Gauss's law the *total* charge inside this surface must be zero. Therefore there must be a charge $-q$ distributed on the surface of the cavity, drawn there by the charge q inside the cavity. The *total* charge on the conductor must remain zero, so a charge $+q$ must appear either on its outer surface or inside the material. But we showed in Section 22.4 that in an electrostatic situation there can't be any excess charge within the material of a conductor. So we conclude that the charge $+q$ must appear on the outer surface. By the same reasoning, if the conductor originally had a charge q_C, then the total charge on the outer surface must be $q_C + q$ after the charge q is inserted into the cavity.

22.23 Finding the electric field within a charged conductor.

(a) Solid conductor with charge q_C

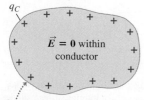

The charge q_C resides entirely on the surface of the conductor. The situation is electrostatic, so $\vec{E} = 0$ within the conductor.

(b) The same conductor with an internal cavity

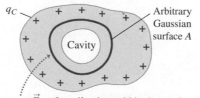

Because $\vec{E} = 0$ at all points within the conductor, the electric field at all points on the Gaussian surface must be zero.

(c) An isolated charge q placed in the cavity

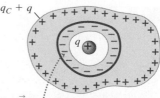

For $\vec{E}$ to be zero at all points on the Gaussian surface, the surface of the cavity must have a total charge $-q$.

Conceptual Example 22.11   **A conductor with a cavity**

A solid conductor with a cavity carries a total charge of $+7$ nC. Within the cavity, insulated from the conductor, is a point charge of -5 nC. How much charge is on each surface (inner and outer) of the conductor?

SOLUTION

Figure 22.24 shows the situation. If the charge in the cavity is $q = -5$ nC, the charge on the inner cavity surface must be $-q = -(-5$ nC$) = +5$ nC. The conductor carries a *total* charge of $+7$ nC, none of which is in the interior of the material. If $+5$ nC is on the inner surface of the cavity, then there must be $(+7$ nC$) - (+5$ nC$) = +2$ nC on the outer surface of the conductor.

22.24 Our sketch for this problem. There is zero electric field inside the bulk conductor and hence zero flux through the Gaussian surface shown, so the charge on the cavity wall must be the opposite of the point charge.

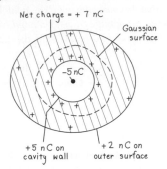

Testing Gauss's Law Experimentally

We can now consider a historic experiment, shown in Fig. 22.25. We mount a conducting container, such as a metal pail with a lid, on an insulating stand. The container is initially uncharged. Then we hang a charged metal ball from an insulating thread (Fig. 22.25a), lower it into the pail, and put the lid on (Fig. 22.25b). Charges are induced on the walls of the container, as shown. But now we let the ball *touch* the inner wall (Fig. 22.25c). The surface of the ball becomes, in effect, part of the cavity surface. The situation is now the same as Fig. 22.23b; if Gauss's law is correct, the net charge on the cavity surface must be zero. Thus the ball must lose all its charge. Finally, we pull the ball out; we find that it has indeed lost all its charge.

This experiment was performed in the 19th century by the English scientist Michael Faraday, using a metal icepail with a lid, and it is called **Faraday's ice-pail experiment.** (Similar experiments were carried out in the 18th century by Benjamin Franklin in America and Joseph Priestley in England, although with much less precision.) The result confirms the validity of Gauss's law and therefore of Coulomb's law. Faraday's result was significant because Coulomb's experimental method, using a torsion balance and dividing of charges, was not very precise; it is very difficult to confirm the $1/r^2$ dependence of the electrostatic force with great precision by direct force measurements. By contrast, experiments like Faraday's test the validity of Gauss's law, and therefore of Coulomb's law, with much greater precision.

22.25 (a) A charged conducting ball suspended by an insulating thread outside a conducting container on an insulating stand. (b) The ball is lowered into the container, and the lid is put on. (c) The ball is touched to the inner surface of the container.

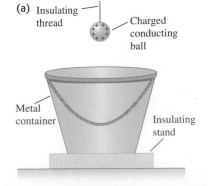

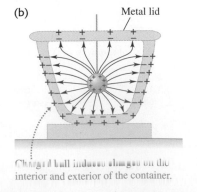

Charged ball induces charges on the interior and exterior of the container.

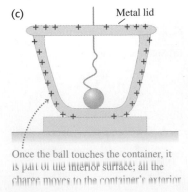

Once the ball touches the container, it is part of the interior surface; all the charge moves to the container's exterior.

A modern version of Faraday's experiment is shown in Fig. 22.26. The details of the box labeled "Power supply" aren't important; its job is to place charge on the outer sphere and remove it, on demand. The inner box with a dial is a sensitive *electrometer,* an instrument that can detect motion of extremely small amounts of charge between the outer and inner spheres. If Gauss's law is correct, there can never be any charge on the inner surface of the outer sphere. If so, there should be no flow of charge between spheres while the outer sphere is being charged and discharged. The fact that no flow is actually observed is a very sensitive confirmation of Gauss's law and therefore of Coulomb's law. The precision of the experiment is limited mainly by the electrometer, which can be astonishingly sensitive. Experiments have shown that the exponent 2 in the $1/r^2$ of Coulomb's law does not differ from precisely 2 by more than 10^{-16}. So there is no reason to suspect that it is anything other than exactly 2.

The same principle behind Faraday's icepail experiment is used in a *Van de Graaff electrostatic generator* (Fig. 22.27). The charged conducting sphere of Fig. 22.26 is replaced by a charged belt that continuously carries charge to the inside of a conducting shell, only to have it carried away to the outside surface of the shell. As a result, the charge on the shell and the electric field around it can become very large very rapidly. The Van de Graaff generator is used as an accelerator of charged particles and for physics demonstrations.

This principle also forms the basis for *electrostatic shielding.* Suppose we have a very sensitive electronic instrument that we want to protect from stray electric fields that might cause erroneous measurements. We surround the instrument with a conducting box, or we line the walls, floor, and ceiling of the room with a conducting material such as sheet copper. The external electric field redistributes the free electrons in the conductor, leaving a net positive charge on the outer

22.26 The outer spherical shell can be alternately charged and discharged by the power supply. If there were any flow of charge between the inner and outer shells, it would be detected by the electrometer inside the inner shell.

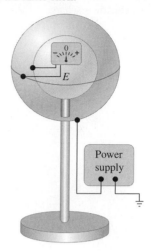

22.27 Cutaway view of the essential parts of a Van de Graaff electrostatic generator. The electron sink at the bottom draws electrons from the belt, giving it a positive charge; at the top the belt attracts electrons away from the conducting shell, giving the shell a positive charge.

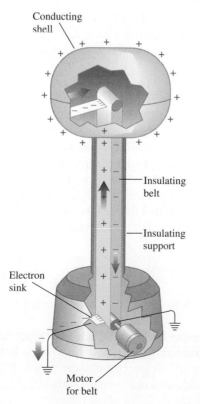

22.28 (a) A conducting box (a Faraday cage) immersed in a uniform electric field. The field of the induced charges on the box combines with the uniform field to give zero total field inside the box. (b) Electrostatic shielding can protect you from a dangerous electric discharge.

(a)

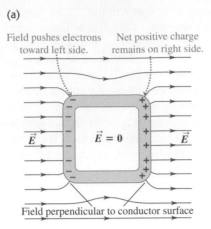

Field pushes electrons toward left side.   Net positive charge remains on right side.

$\vec{E}$ $\vec{E} = 0$ $\vec{E}$

Field perpendicular to conductor surface

(b)

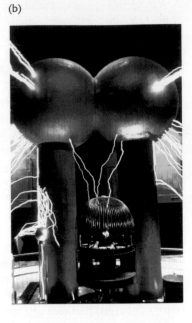

surface in some regions and a net negative charge in others (Fig. 22.28). This charge distribution causes an additional electric field such that the *total* field at every point inside the box is zero, as Gauss's law says it must be. The charge distribution on the box also alters the shapes of the field lines near the box, as the figure shows. Such a setup is often called a *Faraday cage*. The same physics tells you that one of the safest places to be in a lightning storm is inside an automobile; if the car is struck by lightning, the charge tends to remain on the metal skin of the vehicle, and little or no electric field is produced inside the passenger compartment.

Field at the Surface of a Conductor

Finally, we note that there is a direct relationship between the $\vec{E}$ field at a point just outside any conductor and the surface charge density σ at that point. In general, σ varies from point to point on the surface. We will show in Chapter 23 that at any such point, the direction of $\vec{E}$ is always *perpendicular* to the surface (see Fig. 22.28a).

To find a relationship between σ at any point on the surface and the perpendicular component of the electric field at that point, we construct a Gaussian surface in the form of a small cylinder (Fig. 22.29). One end face, with area A, lies within the conductor and the other lies just outside. The electric field is zero at all points within the conductor. Outside the conductor the component of $\vec{E}$ perpendicular to the side walls of the cylinder is zero, and over the end face the perpendicular component is equal to $E_\perp$. (If σ is positive, the electric field points out of the conductor and $E_\perp$ is positive; if σ is negative, the field points inward and $E_\perp$ is negative.) Hence the total flux through the surface is $E_\perp A$. The charge enclosed within the Gaussian surface is σA, so from Gauss's law,

22.29 The field just outside a charged conductor is perpendicular to the surface, and its perpendicular component $E_\perp$ is equal to σ/ϵ_0.

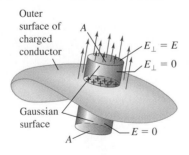

Outer surface of charged conductor

A

$E_\perp = E$

$E_\perp = 0$

Gaussian surface

$E = 0$

A

$$E_\perp A = \frac{\sigma A}{\epsilon_0} \quad \text{and} \quad E_\perp = \frac{\sigma}{\epsilon_0} \qquad \text{(field at the surface of a conductor)} \qquad (22.10)$$

We can check this with the results we have obtained for spherical, cylindrical, and plane surfaces.

We showed in Example 22.8 that the field magnitude between two infinite flat oppositely charged conducting plates also equals σ/ϵ_0. In this case the field magnitude is the same at *all* distances from the plates, but in all other cases it decreases with increasing distance from the surface.

Field at the surface of a conducting sphere

Verify Eq. (22.10) for a conducting sphere with radius R and total charge q.

SOLUTION

In Example 22.5 (Section 22.4) we showed that the electric field just outside the surface is

$$E = \frac{1}{4\pi\epsilon_0}\frac{q}{R^2}$$

The surface charge density is uniform and equal to q divided by the surface area of the sphere:

$$\sigma = \frac{q}{4\pi R^2}$$

Comparing these two expressions, we see that $E = \sigma/\epsilon_0$, as Eq. (22.10) states.

Electric field of the earth

The earth (a conductor) has a net electric charge. The resulting electric field near the surface can be measured with sensitive electronic instruments; its average value is about 150 N/C, directed toward the center of the earth. (a) What is the corresponding surface charge density? (b) What is the *total* surface charge of the earth?

SOLUTION

IDENTIFY: We are given the electric field magnitude at the surface of the conducting earth, and we are asked to calculate the surface charge density and the total charge on the entire surface of the earth.

SET UP: Given the perpendicular electric field, we determine the surface charge density σ using Eq. (22.10). The total surface charge on the earth is then the product of σ and the earth's surface area.

EXECUTE: (a) We know from the direction of the field that σ is negative (corresponding to $\vec{E}$ being directed *into* the surface, so $E_\perp$ is negative). From Eq. (22.10),

$$\sigma = \epsilon_0 E_\perp = (8.85 \times 10^{-12}\ \mathrm{C^2/N \cdot m^2})(-150\ \mathrm{N/C})$$
$$= -1.33 \times 10^{-9}\ \mathrm{C/m^2} = -1.33\ \mathrm{nC/m^2}$$

(b) The earth's surface area is $4\pi R_E^2$, where $R_E = 6.38 \times 10^6$ m is the radius of the earth (see Appendix F). The total charge Q is the product $4\pi R_E^2 \sigma$, or

$$Q = 4\pi(6.38 \times 10^6\ \mathrm{m})^2(-1.33 \times 10^{-9}\ \mathrm{C/m^2})$$
$$= -6.8 \times 10^5\ \mathrm{C} = -680\ \mathrm{kC}$$

EVALUATE: You can check our result in part (b) using the result of Example 22.5. Solving for Q, we find

$$Q = 4\pi\epsilon_0 R^2 E_\perp$$
$$= \frac{1}{9.0 \times 10^9\ \mathrm{N \cdot m^2/C^2}}(6.38 \times 10^6\ \mathrm{m})^2(-150\ \mathrm{N/C})$$
$$= -6.8 \times 10^5\ \mathrm{C}$$

One electron has a charge of -1.60×10^{-19} C. Hence this much excess negative electric charge corresponds to there being $(-6.8 \times 10^5\ \mathrm{C})/(-1.60 \times 10^{-19}\ \mathrm{C}) = 4.2 \times 10^{24}$ excess electrons on the earth, or about 7 moles of excess electrons. This is compensated by an equal *deficiency* of electrons in the earth's upper atmosphere, so the combination of the earth and its atmosphere is electrically neutral.

Test Your Understanding of Section 22.5   A hollow conducting sphere has no net charge. There is a positive point charge q at the center of the spherical cavity within the sphere. You connect a conducting wire from the outside of the sphere to ground. Will you measure an electric field outside the sphere?

CHAPTER 22 SUMMARY

Electric flux: Electric flux is a measure of the "flow" of electric field through a surface. It is equal to the product of an area element and the perpendicular component of $\vec{E}$, integrated over a surface. (See Examples 22.1–22.3.)

$$\Phi_E = \int E\cos\phi\, dA$$

$$= \int E_\perp \, dA = \int \vec{E} \cdot d\vec{A} \qquad (22.5)$$

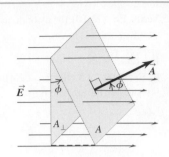

Gauss's law: Gauss's law states that the total electric flux through a closed surface, which can be written as the surface integral of the component of $\vec{E}$ normal to the surface, equals a constant times the total charge Q_{encl} enclosed by the surface. Gauss's law is logically equivalent to Coulomb's law, but its use greatly simplifies problems with a high degree of symmetry. (See Examples 22.4–22.10.)

When excess charge is placed on a conductor and is at rest, it resides entirely on the surface, and $\vec{E} = \mathbf{0}$ everywhere in the material of the conductor. (See Examples 22.11–22.13.)

$$\Phi_E = \oint E\cos\phi\, dA$$

$$= \oint E_\perp \, dA = \oint \vec{E} \cdot d\vec{A}$$

$$= \frac{Q_{encl}}{\epsilon_0} \qquad (22.8),\ (22.9)$$

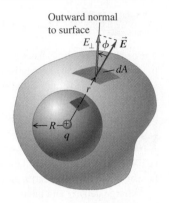

Electric field of various symmetric charge distributions: The following table lists electric fields caused by several symmetric charge distributions. In the table, q, Q, λ, and σ refer to the *magnitudes* of the quantities.

Charge Distribution	Point in Electric Field	Electric Field Magnitude
Single point charge q	Distance r from q	$E = \dfrac{1}{4\pi\epsilon_0}\dfrac{q}{r^2}$
Charge q on surface of conducting sphere with radius R	Outside sphere, $r > R$	$E = \dfrac{1}{4\pi\epsilon_0}\dfrac{q}{r^2}$
	Inside sphere, $r < R$	$E = 0$
Infinite wire, charge per unit length λ	Distance r from wire	$E = \dfrac{1}{2\pi\epsilon_0}\dfrac{\lambda}{r}$
Infinite conducting cylinder with radius R, charge per unit length λ	Outside cylinder, $r > R$	$E = \dfrac{1}{2\pi\epsilon_0}\dfrac{\lambda}{r}$
	Inside cylinder, $r < R$	$E = 0$
Solid insulating sphere with radius R, charge Q distributed uniformly throughout volume	Outside sphere, $r > R$	$E = \dfrac{1}{4\pi\epsilon_0}\dfrac{Q}{r^2}$
	Inside sphere, $r < R$	$E = \dfrac{1}{4\pi\epsilon_0}\dfrac{Qr}{R^3}$
Infinite sheet of charge with uniform charge per unit area σ	Any point	$E = \dfrac{\sigma}{2\epsilon_0}$
Two oppositely charged conducting plates with surface charge densities $+\sigma$ and $-\sigma$	Any point between plates	$E = \dfrac{\sigma}{\epsilon_0}$

Key Terms

Answer to Chapter Opening Question ?

No. The electric field inside a cavity within a conductor is zero, so there is no electric effect on the child. (See Section 22.5.)

Answers to Test Your Understanding Questions

22.1 Answer: (iii) Each part of the surface of the box will be three times farther from the charge $+q$, so the electric field will be $\left(\frac{1}{3}\right)^2 = \frac{1}{9}$ as strong. But the area of the box will increase by a factor of $3^2 = 9$. Hence the electric flux will be multiplied by a factor of $\left(\frac{1}{9}\right)(9) = 1$. In other words, the flux will be unchanged.

22.2 Answer: (iv), (ii), (i), (iii) In each case the electric field in uniform, so the flux is $\Phi_E = \vec{E} \cdot \vec{A}$. We use the relationships for the scalar products of unit vectors: $\hat{\imath} \cdot \hat{\imath} = \hat{\jmath} \cdot \hat{\jmath} = 1, \hat{\imath} \cdot \hat{\jmath} = 0$. In case (i) we have $\Phi_E = (4.0\,\text{N/C})(6.0\,\text{m}^2)\hat{\imath} \cdot \hat{\jmath} = 0$ (the electric field and vector area are perpendicular, so there is zero flux). In case (ii) we have $\Phi_E [(4.0\,\text{N/C})\hat{\imath} + (2.0\,\text{N/C})\hat{\jmath}] \cdot (3.0\,\text{m}^2)\hat{\jmath} = (2.0\,\text{N/C}) \cdot (3.0\,\text{m}^2) = 6.0\,\text{N} \cdot \text{m}^2/\text{C}$. Similarly, in case (iii) we have $\Phi_E = [(4.0\,\text{N/C})\hat{\imath} - (2.0\,\text{N/C})\hat{\jmath}] \cdot [(3.0\,\text{m}^2)\hat{\imath} + (7.0\,\text{m}^2)\hat{\jmath}] = (4.0\,\text{N/C})(3.0\,\text{m}^2) - (2.0\,\text{N/C})(7.0\,\text{m}^2) = -2\,\text{N} \cdot \text{m}^2/\text{C}$, and in case (iv) we have $\Phi_E = [(4.0\,\text{N/C})\hat{\imath} - (2.0\,\text{N/C})\hat{\jmath}] \cdot [(3.0\,\text{m}^2)\hat{\imath} - (7.0\,\text{m}^2)\hat{\jmath}] = (4.0\,\text{N/C})(3.0\,\text{m}^2) + (2.0\,\text{N/C})(7.0\,\text{m}^2) = 26\,\text{N} \cdot \text{m}^2/\text{C}$.

22.3 Answer: S_2, S_5, S_4, S_1 and S_3 (tie) Gauss's law tells us that the flux through a closed surface is proportional to the amount of charge enclosed within that surface. So an ordering of these surfaces by their fluxes is the same as an ordering by the amount of enclosed charge. Surface S_1 encloses no charge, surface S_2 encloses $9.0\,\mu\text{C} + 5.0\,\mu\text{C} + (-7.0\,\mu\text{C}) = 7.0\,\mu\text{C}$, surface S_3 encloses $9.0\,\mu\text{C} + 1.0\,\mu\text{C} + (-10.0\,\mu\text{C}) = 0$, surface S_4 encloses $8.0\,\mu\text{C} + (-7.0\,\mu\text{C}) = 1.0\,\mu\text{C}$, and surface S_5 encloses $8.0\,\mu\text{C} + (-7.0\,\mu\text{C}) + (-10.0\,\mu\text{C}) + (1.0\,\mu\text{C}) + (9.0\,\mu\text{C}) + (5.0\,\mu\text{C}) = 6.0\,\mu\text{C}$.

22.4 Answer: no You might be tempted to draw a Gaussian surface that is an enlarged version of the conductor, with the same shape and placed so that it completely encloses the conductor. While you know the flux through this Gaussian surface (by Gauss's law, it's $\Phi_E = Q/\epsilon_0$), the direction of the electric field need not be perpendicular to the surface and the magnitude of the field need not be the same at all points on the surface. It's not possible to do the flux integral $\oint E_\perp\, dA$, and we can't calculate the electric field. Gauss's law is useful for calculating the electric field only when the charge distribution is *highly* symmetric.

22.5 Answer: no Before you connect the wire to the sphere, the presence of the point charge will induce a charge $-q$ on the inner surface of the hollow sphere and a charge q on the outer surface (the net charge on the sphere is zero). There will be an electric field outside the sphere due to the charge on the outer surface. Once you touch the conducting wire to the sphere, however, electrons will flow from ground to the outer surface of the sphere to neutralize the charge there (see Fig. 21.7c). As a result the sphere will have no charge on its outer surface and no electric field outside.

PROBLEMS

For instructor-assigned homework, go to **www.masteringphysics.com**

Discussion Questions

Q22.1. A rubber balloon has a single point charge in its interior. Does the electric flux through the balloon depend on whether or not it is fully inflated? Explain your reasoning.

Q22.2. Suppose that in Fig. 22.15 both charges were positive. What would be the fluxes through each of the four surfaces in the example?

Q22.3. In Fig. 22.15, suppose a third point charge were placed outside the purple Gaussian surface C. Would this affect the electric flux through any of the surfaces A, B, C, or D in the figure? Why or why not?

Q22.4. A certain region of space bounded by an imaginary closed surface contains no charge. Is the electric field always zero everywhere on the surface? If not, under what circumstances is it zero on the surface?

Q22.5. A spherical Gaussian surface encloses a point charge q. If the point charge is moved from the center of the sphere to a point away from the center, does the electric field at a point on the surface change? Does the total flux through the Gaussian surface change? Explain.

Q22.6. You find a sealed box on your doorstep. You suspect that the box contains several charged metal spheres packed in insulating material. How can you determine the total net charge inside the box without opening the box? Or isn't this possible?

Q22.7. During the flow of electric current in a conducting wire, one or more electrons from each atom are free to move along the wire, somewhat like water flowing through a pipe. Would you expect to find an electric field outside a wire carrying such a steady flow of electrons? Explain.

Q22.8. If the electric field of a point charge were proportional to $1/r^3$ instead of $1/r^2$, would Gauss's law still be valid? Explain your reasoning. (*Hint:* Consider a spherical Gaussian surface centered on a single point charge.)

Q22.9. Suppose the disk in Example 22.1 (Section 22.2), instead of having its normal vector oriented at just two or three particular angles to the electric field, began to rotate continuously, so that its normal vector was first parallel to the field, then perpendicular to it, then opposite to it, and so on. Sketch a graph of the resulting electric flux versus time, for an entire rotation of 360°.

Q22.10. In a conductor, one or more electrons from each atom are free to roam throughout the volume of the conductor. Does this contradict the statement that any excess charge on a solid conductor must reside on its surface? Why or why not?

Q22.11. You charge up the van de Graaff generator shown in Fig. 22.27, and then bring an identical but uncharged hollow conducting sphere near it, without letting the two spheres touch. Sketch the distribution of charges on the second sphere. What is the net flux through the second sphere? What is the electric field inside the second sphere?

Q22.12. The magnitude of $\vec{E}$ at the surface of an irregularly shaped solid conductor must be greatest in regions where the surface curves most sharply, such as point A in Fig. 22.30, and must be least in flat regions such as point B in Fig. 22.30. Explain why this must be so by considering how electric field lines must be arranged near a conducting surface. How does the surface charge density compare at points A and B ? Explain.

Figure **22.30**
Question Q22.12.

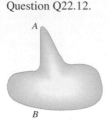

Q22.13. A lightning rod is a rounded copper rod mounted on top of a building and welded to a heavy copper cable running down into the ground. Lightning rods are used to protect houses and barns from lightning; the lightning current runs through the copper rather than through the building. Why? Why should the end of the rod be rounded? (*Hint:* The answer to Discussion Question Q22.12 may be helpful.)

Q22.14. A solid conductor has a cavity in its interior. Would the presence of a point charge inside the cavity affect the electric field outside the conductor? Why or why not? Would the presence of a point charge outside the conductor affect the electric field inside the cavity? Again, why or why not?

Q22.15. Explain this statement: "In a static situation, the electric field at the surface of a conductor can have no component parallel to the surface because this would violate the condition that the charges on the surface are at rest." Would this same statement be valid for the electric field at the surface of an *insulator?* Explain your answer and the reason for any differences between the cases of a conductor and an insulator.

Q22.16. A solid copper sphere has a net positive charge. The charge is distributed uniformly over the surface of the sphere, and the electric field inside the sphere is zero. Then a negative point charge outside the sphere is brought close to the surface of the sphere. Is all the net charge on the sphere still on its surface? If so, is this charge still distributed uniformly over the surface? If it is not uniform, how is it distributed? Is the electric field inside the sphere still zero? In each case justify your answers.

Q22.17. Some modern aircraft are made primarily of composite materials that do not conduct electricity. The U.S. Federal Aviation Administration requires that such aircraft have conducting wires embedded in their surfaces to provide protection when flying near thunderstorms. Explain the physics behind this requirement.

Exercises

Section 22.2 Calculating Electric Flux

22.1. A flat sheet of paper of area 0.250 m² is oriented so that the normal to the sheet is at an angle of 60° to a uniform electric field of magnitude 14 N/C. (a) Find the magnitude of the electric flux through the sheet. (b) Does the answer to part (a) depend on the shape of the sheet? Why or why not? (c) For what angle ϕ between the normal to the sheet and the electric field is the magnitude of the flux through the sheet (i) largest and (ii) smallest? Explain your answers.

22.2. A flat sheet is in the shape of a rectangle with sides of lengths 0.400 m and 0.600 m. The sheet is immersed in a uniform electric field of magnitude 75.0 N/C that is directed at 20° from the plane of the sheet (Fig. 22.31). Find the magnitude of the electric flux through the sheet.

Figure **22.31** Exercise 22.2.

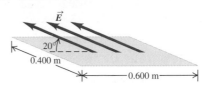

22.3. You measure an electric field of 1.25×10^6 N/C at a distance of 0.150 m from a point charge. (a) What is the electric flux through a sphere at that distance from the charge? (b) What is the magnitude of the charge?

22.4. A cube has sides of length $L = 0.300$ m. It is placed with one corner at the origin as shown in Fig. 22.32. The electric field is not uniform but is given by $\vec{E} = (-5.00 \text{ N/C} \cdot \text{m}) x \hat{\imath} + (3.00 \text{ N/C} \cdot \text{m}) z \hat{k}$. (a) Find the electric flux through each of the six cube faces S_1, S_2, S_3, S_4, S_5, and S_6. (b) Find the total electric charge inside the cube.

Figure **22.32** Exercises 22.4 and 22.6; Problem 22.32.

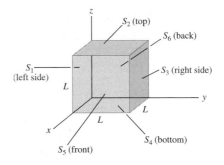

22.5. A hemispherical surface with radius r in a region of uniform electric field $\vec{E}$ has its axis aligned parallel to the direction of the field. Calculate the flux through the surface.

22.6. The cube in Fig. 22.32 has sides of length $L = 10.0$ cm. The electric field is uniform, has magnitude $E = 4.00 \times 10^3$ N/C, and is parallel to the xy -plane at an angle of 36.9° measured from the $+x$-axis toward the $+y$-axis. (a) What is the electric flux through each of the six cube faces S_1, S_2, S_3, S_4, S_5, and S_6? (b) What is the total electric flux through all faces of the cube?

22.7. It was shown in Example 21.11 (Section 21.5) that the electric field due to an infinite line of charge is perpendicular to the line and has magnitude $E = \lambda/2\pi\epsilon_0 r$. Consider an imaginary cylinder with radius $r = 0.250$ m and length $l = 0.400$ m that has an infinite line of positive charge running along its axis. The charge per unit length on the line is $\lambda = 6.00 \ \mu\text{C/m}$. (a) What is the electric flux through the cylinder due to this infinite line of charge? (b) What is the flux through the cylinder if its radius is increased to $r = 0.500$ m? (c) What is the flux through the cylinder if its length is increased to $l = 0.800$ m?

Section 22.3 Gauss's Law

22.8. The three small spheres shown in Fig. 22.33 carry charges $q_1 = 4.00$ nC, $q_2 = -7.80$ nC, and $q_3 = 2.40$ nC. Find the net electric flux through each of the following closed surfaces shown in cross section in the figure: (a) S_1; (b) S_2; (c) S_3; (d) S_4; (e) S_5. (f) Do your answers to parts (a)–(e) depend on how the charge is distributed over each small sphere? Why or why not?

Figure 22.33 Exercise 22.8.

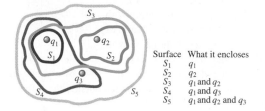

Surface	What it encloses
S_1	q_1
S_2	q_2
S_3	q_1 and q_2
S_4	q_1 and q_3
S_5	q_1 and q_2 and q_3

22.9. A charged paint is spread in a very thin uniform layer over the surface of a plastic sphere of diameter 12.0 cm, giving it a charge of -15.0 μC. Find the electric field (a) just inside the paint layer; (b) just outside the paint layer; (c) 5.00 cm outside the surface of the paint layer.

22.10. A point charge $q_1 = 4.00$ nC is located on the x-axis at $x = 2.00$ m, and a second point charge $q_2 = -6.00$ nC is on the y-axis at $y = 1.00$ m. What is the total electric flux due to these two point charges through a spherical surface centered at the origin and with radius (a) 0.500 m, (b) 1.50 m, (c) 2.50 m?

22.11. In a certain region of space, the electric field $\vec{E}$ is uniform. (a) Use Gauss's law to prove that this region of space must be electrically neutral; that is, the volume charge density ρ must be zero. (b) Is the converse true? That is, in a region of space where there is no charge, must $\vec{E}$ be uniform? Explain.

22.12. (a) In a certain region of space, the volume charge density ρ has a uniform positive value. Can $\vec{E}$ be uniform in this region? Explain. (b) Suppose that in this region of uniform positive ρ there is a "bubble" within which $\rho = 0$. Can $\vec{E}$ be uniform within this bubble? Explain.

22.13. A 9.60-μC point charge is at the center of a cube with sides of length 0.500 m. (a) What is the electric flux through one of the six faces of the cube? (b) How would your answer to part (a) change if the sides were 0.250 m long? Explain.

22.14. Electric Fields in an Atom. The nuclei of large atoms, such as uranium, with 92 protons, can be modeled as spherically symmetric spheres of charge. The radius of the uranium nucleus is approximately 7.4×10^{-15} m. (a) What is the electric field this nucleus produces just outside its surface? (b) What magnitude of electric field does it produce at the distance of the electrons, which is about 1.0×10^{-10} m? (c) The electrons can be modeled as forming a uniform shell of negative charge. What net electric field do they produce at the location of the nucleus?

22.15. A point charge of $+5.00$ μC is located on the x-axis at $x = 4.00$ m, next to a spherical surface of radius 3.00 m centered at the origin. (a) Calculate the magnitude of the electric field at $x = 3.00$ m. (b) Calculate the magnitude of the electric field at $x = -3.00$ m. (c) According to Gauss's law, the net flux through the sphere is zero because it contains no charge. Yet the field due to the external charge is much stronger on the near side of the sphere (i.e., at $x = 3.00$ m) than on the far side (at $x = -3.00$ m). How, then, can the flux into the sphere (on the near side) equal the flux out of it (on the far side)? Explain. A sketch will help.

Section 22.4 Applications of Gauss's Law and Section 22.5 Charges on Conductors

22.16. A solid metal sphere with radius 0.450 m carries a net charge of 0.250 nC. Find the magnitude of the electric field (a) at a point 0.100 m outside the surface of the sphere and (b) at a point inside the sphere, 0.100 m below the surface.

22.17. On a humid day, an electric field of 2.00×10^4 N/C is enough to produce sparks about an inch long. Suppose that in your physics class, a van de Graaff generator (see Fig. 22.27) with a sphere radius of 15.0 cm is producing sparks 6 inches long. (a) Use Gauss's law to calculate the amount of charge stored on the surface of the sphere before you bravely discharge it with your hand. (b) Assume all the charge is concentrated at the center of the sphere, and use Coulomb's law to calculate the electric field at the surface of the sphere.

22.18. Some planetary scientists have suggested that the planet Mars has an electric field somewhat similar to that of the earth, producing a net electric flux of 3.63×10^{16} N $\cdot$ m^2/C at the planet's surface. Calculate: (a) the total electric charge on the planet; (b) the electric field at the planet's surface (refer to the astronomical data inside the back cover); (c) the charge density on Mars, assuming all the charge is uniformly distributed over the planet's surface.

22.19. How many excess electrons must be added to an isolated spherical conductor 32.0 cm in diameter to produce an electric field of 1150 N/C just outside the surface?

22.20. The electric field 0.400 m from a very long uniform line of charge is 840 N/C. How much charge is contained in a 2.00-cm section of the line?

22.21. A very long uniform line of charge has charge per unit length 4.80 μC/m and lies along the x-axis. A second long uniform line of charge has charge per unit length -2.40 μC/m and is parallel to the x-axis at $y = 0.400$ m. What is the net electric field (magnitude and direction) at the following points on the y-axis: (a) $y = 0.200$ m and (b) $y = 0.600$ m?

22.22. (a) At a distance of 0.200 cm from the center of a charged conducting sphere with radius 0.100 cm, the electric field is 480 N/C. What is the electric field 0.600 cm from the center of the sphere? (b) At a distance of 0.200 cm from the axis of a very long charged conducting cylinder with radius 0.100 cm, the electric field is 480 N/C. What is the electric field 0.600 cm from the axis of the cylinder? (c) At a distance of 0.200 cm from a large uniform sheet of charge, the electric field is 480 N/C. What is the electric field 1.20 cm from the sheet?

22.23. A hollow, conducting sphere with an outer radius of 0.250 m and an inner radius of 0.200 m has a uniform surface charge density of $+6.37 \times 10^{-6}$ C/m^2. A charge of -0.500 μC is now introduced into the cavity inside the sphere. (a) What is the new charge density on the outside of the sphere? (b) Calculate the strength of the electric field just outside the sphere. (c) What is the electric flux through a spherical surface just inside the inner surface of the sphere?

22.24. A point charge of -2.00 μC is located in the center of a spherical cavity of radius 6.50 cm inside an insulating charged solid. The charge density in the solid is $\rho = 7.35 \times 10^{-4}$ C/m^3. Calculate the electric field inside the solid at a distance of 9.50 cm from the center of the cavity.

22.25. The electric field at a distance of 0.145 m from the surface of a solid insulating sphere with radius 0.355 m is 1750 N/C. (a) Assuming the sphere's charge is uniformly distributed, what is the charge density inside it? (b) Calculate the electric field inside the sphere at a distance of 0.200 m from the center.

22.26. A conductor with an inner cavity, like that shown in Fig. 22.23c, carries a total charge of +5.00 nC. The charge within the cavity, insulated from the conductor, is −6.00 nC. How much charge is on (a) the inner surface of the conductor and (b) the outer surface of the conductor?

22.27. Apply Gauss's law to the Gaussian surfaces S_2, S_3, and S_4 in Fig. 22.21b to calculate the electric field between and outside the plates.

22.28. A square insulating sheet 80.0 cm on a side is held horizontally. The sheet has 7.50 nC of charge spread uniformly over its area. (a) Calculate the electric field at a point 0.100 mm above the center of the sheet. (b) Estimate the electric field at a point 100 m above the center of the sheet. (c) Would the answers to parts (a) and (b) be different if the sheet were made of a conducting material? Why or why not?

22.29. An infinitely long cylindrical conductor has radius R and uniform surface charge density σ. (a) In terms of σ and R, what is the charge per unit length λ for the cylinder? (b) In terms of σ, what is the magnitude of the electric field produced by the charged cylinder at a distance $r > R$ from its axis? (c) Express the result of part (b) in terms of λ and show that the electric field outside the cylinder is the same as if all the charge were on the axis. Compare your result to the result for a line of charge in Example 22.6 (Section 22.4).

22.30. Two very large, nonconducting plastic sheets, each 10.0 cm thick, carry uniform charge densities σ_1, σ_2, σ_3, and σ_4 on their surfaces, as shown in Fig. 22.34. These surface charge densities have the values $\sigma_1 = -6.00\ \mu C/m^2$, $\sigma_2 = +5.00\ \mu C/m^2$, $\sigma_3 = +2.00\ \mu C/m^2$, and $\sigma_4 = +4.00\ \mu C/m^2$. Use Gauss's law to find the magnitude and direction of the electric field at the following points, far from the edges of these sheets: (a) point A, 5.00 cm from the left face of the left-hand sheet; (b) point B, 1.25 cm from the inner surface of the right-hand sheet; (c) point C, in the middle of the right-hand sheet.

Figure **22.34**
Exercise 22.30.

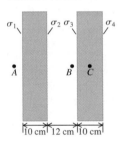

22.31. A negative charge $-Q$ is placed inside the cavity of a hollow metal solid. The outside of the solid is grounded by connecting a conducting wire between it and the earth. (a) Is there any excess charge induced on the inner surface of the piece of metal? If so, find its sign and magnitude. (b) Is there any excess charge on the outside of the piece of metal? Why or why not? (c) Is there an electric field in the cavity? Explain. (d) Is there an electric field within the metal? Why or why not? Is there an electric field outside the piece of metal? Explain why or why not. (e) Would someone outside the solid measure an electric field due to the charge $-Q$? Is it reasonable to say that the grounded conductor has *shielded* the region from the effects of the charge $-Q$? In principle, could the same thing be done for gravity? Why or why not?

Problems

22.32. A cube has sides of length L. It is placed with one corner at the origin as shown in Fig. 22.32. The electric field is uniform and given by $\vec{E} = -B\hat{\imath} + C\hat{\jmath} - D\hat{k}$, where B, C, and D are positive constants. (a) Find the electric flux through each of the six cube faces S_1, S_2, S_3, S_4, S_5, and S_6. (b) Find the electric flux through the entire cube.

22.33. The electric field $\vec{E}$ in Fig. 22.35 is everywhere parallel to the x-axis, so the components E_y and E_z are zero. The x-component of the field E_x depends on x but not on y and z. At points in the yz-plane (where $x = 0$), $E_x = 125\ N/C$. (a) What is the electric flux through surface I in Fig. 22.35? (b) What is the electric flux through surface II? (c) The volume shown in the figure is a small section of a very large insulating slab 1.0 m thick. If there is a total charge of -24.0 nC within the volume shown, what are the magnitude and direction of $\vec{E}$ at the face opposite surface I? (d) Is the electric field produced only by charges within the slab, or is the field also due to charges outside the slab? How can you tell?

Figure **22.35**
Problem 22.33.

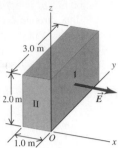

22.34. A flat, square surface with sides of length L is described by the equations

$$x = L \qquad (0 \le y \le L, 0 \le z \le L)$$

(a) Draw this square and show the x-, y-, and z-axes. (b) Find the electric flux through the square due to a positive point charge q located at the origin $(x = 0, y = 0, z = 0)$. (*Hint:* Think of the square as part of a cube centered on the origin.)

22.35. The electric field $\vec{E}_1$ at one face of a parallelepiped is uniform over the entire face and is directed out of the face. At the opposite face, the electric field $\vec{E}_2$ is also uniform over the entire face and is directed into that face (Fig. 22.36). The two faces in question are inclined at 30.0° from the horizontal, while $\vec{E}_1$ and $\vec{E}_2$ are both horizontal; $\vec{E}_1$ has a magnitude of 2.50×10^4 N/C, and $\vec{E}_2$ has a magnitude of 7.00×10^4 N/C. (a) Assuming that no other electric field lines cross the surfaces of the parallelepiped, determine the net charge contained within. (b) Is the electric field produced only by the charges within the parallelepiped, or is the field also due to charges outside the parallelepiped? How can you tell?

Figure **22.36**
Problem 22.35.

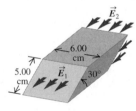

22.36. A long line carrying a uniform linear charge density $+50.0\ \mu C/m$ runs parallel to and 10.0 cm from the surface of a large, flat plastic sheet that has a uniform surface charge density of $-100\ \mu C/m^2$ on one side. Find the location of all points where an α particle would feel no force due to this arrangement of charged objects.

22.37. The Coaxial Cable. A long coaxial cable consists of an inner cylindrical conductor with radius a and an outer coaxial cylinder with inner radius b and outer radius c. The outer cylinder is mounted on insulating supports and has no net charge. The inner cylinder has a uniform positive charge per unit length λ. Calculate the electric field (a) at any point between the cylinders a distance r from the axis and (b) at any point outside the outer cylinder. (c) Graph the magnitude of the electric field as a function of the distance r from the axis of the cable, from $r = 0$ to $r = 2c$. (d) Find the charge per unit length on the inner surface and on the outer surface of the outer cylinder.

22.38. A very long conducting tube (hollow cylinder) has inner radius a and outer radius b. It carries charge per unit length $+\alpha$, where α is a positive constant with units of C/m. A line of charge lies along the axis of the tube. The line of charge has charge per unit length $+\alpha$. (a) Calculate the electric field in terms of α and the distance r from the axis of the tube for (i) $r < a$; (ii) $a < r < b$; (iii) $r > b$. Show your results in a graph of E as a function of r. (b) What is the charge per unit length on (i) the inner surface of the tube and (ii) the outer surface of the tube?

22.39. Repeat Problem 22.38, but now let the conducting tube have charge per unit length $-\alpha$. As in Problem 22.38, the line of charge has charge per unit length $+\alpha$.

22.40. A very long, solid cylinder with radius R has positive charge uniformly distributed throughout it, with charge per unit volume ρ. (a) Derive the expression for the electric field inside the volume at a distance r from the axis of the cylinder in terms of the charge density ρ. (b) What is the electric field at a point outside the volume in terms of the charge per unit length λ in the cylinder? (c) Compare the answers to parts (a) and (b) for $r = R$. (d) Graph the electric-field magnitude as a function of r from $r = 0$ to $r = 3R$.

22.41. A small sphere with a mass of 0.002 g and carrying a charge of 5.00×10^{-8} C hangs from a thread near a very large, charged conducting sheet, as shown in Fig. 22.37. The charge density on the sheet is 2.50×10^{-9} C/m². Find the angle of the thread.

Figure 22.37
Problem 22.41.

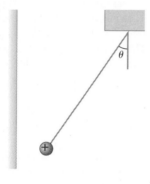

22.42. A Sphere in a Sphere. A solid conducting sphere carrying charge q has radius a. It is inside a concentric hollow conducting sphere with inner radius b and outer radius c. The hollow sphere has no net charge. (a) Derive expressions for the electric-field magnitude in terms of the distance r from the center for the regions $r < a$, $a < r < b$, $b < r < c$, and $r > c$. (b) Graph the magnitude of the electric field as a function of r from $r = 0$ to $r = 2c$. (c) What is the charge on the inner surface of the hollow sphere? (d) On the outer surface? (e) Represent the charge of the small sphere by four plus signs. Sketch the field lines of the system within a spherical volume of radius $2c$.

22.43. A solid conducting sphere with radius R that carries positive charge Q is concentric with a very thin insulating shell of radius $2R$ that also carries charge Q. The charge Q is distributed uniformly over the insulating shell. (a) Find the electric field (magnitude and direction) in each of the regions $0 < r < R$, $R < r < 2R$, and $r > 2R$. (b) Graph the electric-field magnitude as a function of r.

22.44. A conducting spherical shell with inner radius a and outer radius b has a positive point charge Q located at its center. The total charge on the shell is $-3Q$, and it is insulated from its surroundings (Fig. 22.38). (a) Derive expressions for the electric-field magnitude in terms of the distance r from the center for the regions $r < a$, $a < r < b$, and $r > b$. (b) What is the surface charge density on the inner surface of the conducting shell? (c) What is the surface charge density on the outer surface of the conducting shell? (d) Sketch the electric field lines and the location of all charges. (e) Graph the electric-field magnitude as a function of r.

Figure 22.38
Problem 22.44.

22.45. Concentric Spherical Shells. A small conducting spherical shell with inner radius a and outer radius b is concentric with a larger conducting spherical shell with inner radius c and outer radius d (Fig. 22.39). The inner shell has total charge $+2q$, and the outer shell has charge $+4q$. (a) Calculate the electric field (magnitude and direction) in terms of q and the distance r from the common center of the two shells for (i) $r < a$; (ii) $a < r < b$; (iii) $b < r < c$; (iv) $c < r < d$; (v) $r > d$. Show your results in a graph of the radial component of $\vec{E}$ as a function of r. (b) What is the total charge on the (i) inner surface of the small shell; (ii) outer surface of the small shell; (iii) inner surface of the large shell; (iv) outer surface of the large shell?

Figure 22.39
Problem 22.45.

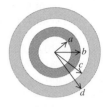

22.46. Repeat Problem 22.45, but now let the outer shell have charge $-2q$. As in Problem 22.45, the inner shell has charge $+2q$.

22.47. Repeat Problem 22.45, but now let the outer shell have charge $-4q$. As in Problem 22.45, the inner shell has charge $+2q$.

22.48. A solid conducting sphere with radius R carries a positive total charge Q. The sphere is surrounded by an insulating shell with inner radius R and outer radius $2R$. The insulating shell has a uniform charge density ρ. (a) Find the value of ρ so that the net charge of the entire system is zero. (b) If ρ has the value found in part (a), find the electric field (magnitude and direction) in each of the regions $0 < r < R$, $R < r < 2R$, and $r > 2R$. Show your results in a graph of the radial component of $\vec{E}$ as a function of r. (c) As a general rule, the electric field is discontinuous only at locations where there is a thin sheet of charge. Explain how your results in part (b) agree with this rule.

22.49. Negative charge $-Q$ is distributed uniformly over the surface of a thin spherical insulating shell with radius R. Calculate the force (magnitude and direction) that the shell exerts on a positive point charge q located (a) a distance $r > R$ from the center of the shell (outside the shell) and (b) a distance $r < R$ from the center of the shell (inside the shell).

22.50. (a) How many excess electrons must be distributed uniformly within the volume of an isolated plastic sphere 30.0 cm in diameter to produce an electric field of 1150 N/C just outside the surface of the sphere? (b) What is the electric field at a point 10.0 cm outside the surface of the sphere?

22.51. A single isolated, large conducting plate (Fig. 22.40) has a charge per unit area σ on its surface. Because the plate is a conductor, the electric field at its surface is perpendicular to the surface and has magnitude $E = \sigma/\epsilon_0$. (a) In Example 22.7 (Section 22.4) it was shown that the field caused by a large, uniformly charged sheet with charge per unit area σ has magnitude $E = \sigma/2\epsilon_0$, exactly *half* as much as for a charged conducting plate. Why is there a difference? (b) Regarding the charge distribution on the conducting plate as being two sheets of charge (one on each surface), each with charge per unit area σ, use the result of Example 22.7 and the principle of superposition to show that $E = 0$ inside the plate and $E = \sigma/\epsilon_0$ outside the plate.

Figure 22.40 Problem 22.51.

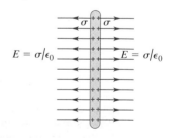

22.52. Thomson's Model of the Atom. In the early years of the 20th century, a leading model of the structure of the atom was that of the English physicist J. J. Thomson (the discoverer of the electron). In Thomson's model, an atom consisted of a sphere of positively charged material in which were embedded negatively charged electrons, like chocolate chips in a ball of cookie dough. Consider such an atom consisting of one electron with mass m and charge $-e$, which may be regarded as a point charge, and a uniformly charged sphere of charge $+e$ and radius R. (a) Explain why the equilibrium position of the electron is at the center of the nucleus. (b) In Thomson's model, it was assumed that the positive material provided little or no resistance to the motion of the electron. If the electron is displaced from equilibrium by a distance less than R, show that the resulting motion of the electron will be simple harmonic, and calculate the frequency of oscillation. (*Hint:* Review the definition of simple harmonic motion in Section 13.2. If it can be shown that the net force on the electron is of this form, then it follows that the motion is simple harmonic. Conversely, if the net force on the electron does not follow this form, the motion is not simple harmonic.) (c) By Thomson's time, it was known that excited atoms emit light waves of only certain frequencies. In his model, the frequency of emitted light is the same as the oscillation frequency of the electron or electrons in the atom. What would the radius of a Thomson-model atom have to be for it to produce red light of frequency 4.57×10^{14} Hz? Compare your answer to the radii of real atoms, which are of the order of 10^{-10} m (see Appendix F for data about the electron). (d) If the electron were displaced from equilibrium by a distance greater than R, would the electron oscillate? Would its motion be simple harmonic? Explain your reasoning. (*Historical note:* In 1910, the atomic nucleus was discovered, proving the Thomson model to be incorrect. An atom's positive charge is not spread over its volume as Thomson supposed, but is concentrated in the tiny nucleus of radius 10^{-14} to 10^{-15} m.)

22.53. Thomson's Model of the Atom, Continued. Using Thomson's (outdated) model of the atom described in Problem 22.52, consider an atom consisting of two electrons, each of charge $-e$, embedded in a sphere of charge $+2e$ and radius R. In equilibrium, each electron is a distance d from the center of the atom (Fig. 22.41). Find the distance d in terms of the other properties of the atom.

Figure 22.41
Problem 22.53.

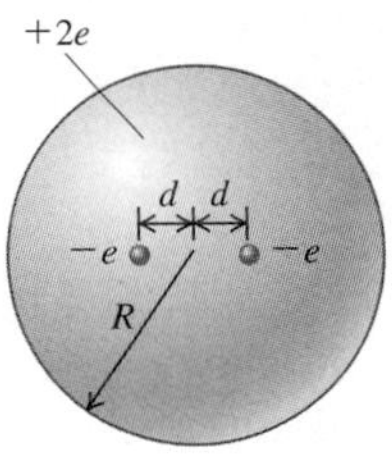

22.54. A Uniformly Charged Slab. A slab of insulating material has thickness $2d$ and is oriented so that its faces are parallel to the yz-plane and given by the planes $x = d$ and $x = -d$. The y- and z-dimensions of the slab are very large compared to d and may be treated as essentially infinite. The slab has a uniform positive charge density ρ. (a) Explain why the electric field due to the slab is zero at the center of the slab $(x = 0)$. (b) Using Gauss's law, find the electric field due to the slab (magnitude and direction) at all points in space.

22.55. A Nonuniformly Charged Slab. Repeat Problem 22.54, but now let the charge density of the slab be given by $\rho(x) = \rho_0 (x/d)^2$, where ρ_0 is a positive constant.

22.56. Can Electric Forces Alone Give Stable Equilibrium? In Chapter 21, several examples were given of calculating the force exerted on a point charge by other point charges in its surroundings. (a) Consider a positive point charge $+q$. Give an example of how you would place two other point charges of your choosing so that the net force on charge $+q$ will be zero. (b) If the net force on charge $+q$ is zero, then that charge is in equilibrium. The equilibrium will be *stable* if, when the charge $+q$ is displaced slightly in *any* direction from its position of equilibrium, the net force on the charge pushes it back toward the equilibrium position. For this to be the case, what must the direction of the electric field $\vec{E}$ be due to the other charges at points surrounding the equilibrium position of $+q$? (c) Imagine that the charge $+q$ is moved very far away, and imagine a small Gaussian surface centered on the position where $+q$ was in equilibrium. By applying Gauss's law to this surface, show that it is *impossible* to satisfy the condition for stability described in part (b). In other words, a charge $+q$ cannot be held in stable equilibrium by electrostatic forces alone. This result is known as *Earnshaw's theorem.* (d) Parts (a)–(c) referred to the equilibrium of a positive point charge $+q$. Prove that Earnshaw's theorem also applies to a negative point charge $-q$.

22.57. A nonuniform, but spherically symmetric, distribution of charge has a charge density $\rho(r)$ given as follows:

$$\rho(r) = \rho_0 \left(1 - r/R\right) \quad \text{for } r \leq R$$
$$\rho(r) = 0 \quad\quad\quad\quad\quad \text{for } r \geq R$$

where $\rho_0 = 3Q/\pi R^3$ is a positive constant. (a) Show that the total charge contained in the charge distribution is Q. (b) Show that the electric field in the region $r \geq R$ is identical to that produced by a point charge Q at $r = 0$. (c) Obtain an expression for the electric field in the region $r \leq R$. (d) Graph the electric-field magnitude E as a function of r. (e) Find the value of r at which the electric field is maximum, and find the value of that maximum field.

22.58. A nonuniform, but spherically symmetric, distribution of charge has a charge density $\rho(r)$ given as follows:

$$\rho(r) = \rho_0 \left(1 - 4r/3R\right) \quad \text{for } r \leq R$$
$$\rho(r) = 0 \quad\quad\quad\quad\quad\quad \text{for } r \geq R$$

where ρ_0 is a positive constant. (a) Find the total charge contained in the charge distribution. (b) Obtain an expression for the electric field in the region $r \geq R$. (c) Obtain an expression for the electric field in the region $r \leq R$. (d) Graph the electric-field magnitude E as a function of r. (e) Find the value of r at which the electric field is maximum, and find the value of that maximum field.

22.59. Gauss's Law for Gravitation. The gravitational force between two point masses separated by a distance r is proportional to $1/r^2$, just like the electric force between two point charges. Because of this similarity between gravitational and electric interactions, there is also a Gauss's law for gravitation. (a) Let $\vec{g}$ be the acceleration due to gravity caused by a point mass m at the origin, so that $\vec{g} = -(Gm/r^2)\hat{r}$. Consider a spherical Gaussian surface with radius r centered on this point mass, and show that the flux of $\vec{g}$ through this surface is given by

$$\oint \vec{g} \cdot d\vec{A} = -4\pi Gm$$

(b) By following the same logical steps used in Section 22.3 to obtain Gauss's law for the electric field, show that the flux of $\vec{g}$ through *any* closed surface is given by

$$\oint \vec{g} \cdot d\vec{A} = -4\pi G M_{\text{encl}}$$

where M_{encl} is the total mass enclosed within the closed surface.

22.60. Applying Gauss's Law for Gravitation. Using Gauss's law for gravitation (derived in part (b) of Problem 22.59), show that the following statements are true: (a) For any spherically symmetric mass distribution with total mass M, the acceleration due to gravity outside the distribution is the same as though all the mass were concentrated at the center. (*Hint:* See Example 22.5 in Section 22.4.) (b) At any point inside a spherically symmetric shell of mass, the acceleration due to gravity is zero. (*Hint:* See Example 22.5.) (c) If we could drill a hole through a spherically sym metric planet to its center, and if the density were uniform, we would find that the magnitude of $\vec{g}$ is directly proportional to the distance r from the center. (*Hint:* See Example 22.9 in Section 22.4.) We proved these results in Section 12.6 using some fairly strenuous analysis; the proofs using Gauss's law for gravitation are *much* easier.

22.61. (a) An insulating sphere with radius a has a uniform charge density ρ. The sphere is not centered at the origin but at $\vec{r} = \vec{b}$. Show that the electric field inside the sphere is given by $\vec{E} = \rho(\vec{r} - \vec{b})/3\epsilon_0$. (b) An insulating sphere of radius R has a spherical hole of radius a located within its volume and centered a distance b from the center of the sphere, where $a < b < R$ (a cross section of the sphere is shown in Fig. 22.42). The solid part of the sphere has a uniform volume charge density ρ. Find the magnitude and direction of the electric field $\vec{E}$ inside the hole, and show that $\vec{E}$ is uniform over the entire hole. [*Hint:* Use the principle of superposition and the result of part (a).]

Figure 22.42 Problem 22.61.

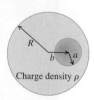

Charge density ρ

22.62. A very long, solid insulating cylinder with radius R has a cylindrical hole with radius a bored along its entire length. The axis of the hole is a distance b from the axis of the cylinder, where $a < b < R$ (Fig. 22.43). The solid material of the cylinder has a uniform volume charge density ρ. Find the magnitude and direction of the electric field $\vec{E}$ inside the hole, and show that $\vec{E}$ is uniform over the entire hole. (*Hint:* See Problem 22.61.)

Figure 22.43 Problem 22.62.

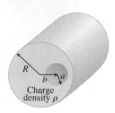

Charge density ρ

22.63. Positive charge Q is distributed uniformly over each of two spherical volumes with radius R. One sphere of charge is centered at the origin and the other at $x = 2R$ (Fig. 22.44). Find the magnitude and direction of the net electric field due to these two distributions of charge at the following points on the x-axis: (a) $x = 0$; (b) $x = R/2$; (c) $x = R$; (d) $x = 3R$.

Figure 22.44 Problem 22.63.

22.64. Repeat Problem 22.63, but now let the left-hand sphere have positive charge Q and let the right-hand sphere have negative charge $-Q$.

22.65. Electric Field Inside a Hydrogen Atom. A hydrogen atom is made up of a proton of charge $+Q = 1.60 \times 10^{-19}$ C and an electron of charge $-Q = -1.60 \times 10^{-19}$ C. The proton may be regarded as a point charge at $r = 0$, the center of the atom. The motion of the electron causes its charge to be "smeared out" into a spherical distribution around the proton, so that the electron is equivalent to a charge per unit volume of

$$\rho(r) = -\frac{Q}{\pi a_0^3} e^{-2r/a_0}$$

where $a_0 = 5.29 \times 10^{-11}$ m is called the *Bohr radius*. (a) Find the total amount of the hydrogen atom's charge that is enclosed within a sphere with radius r centered on the proton. Show that as $r \rightarrow \infty$, the enclosed charge goes to zero. Explain this result. (b) Find the electric field (magnitude and direction) caused by the charge of the hydrogen atom as a function of r. (c) Graph the electric-field magnitude E as a function of r.

Challenge Problems

22.66. A region in space contains a total positive charge Q that is distributed spherically such that the volume charge density $\rho(r)$ is given by

$$
\begin{aligned}
\rho(r) &= \alpha & &\text{for } r \leq R/2 \\
\rho(r) &= 2\alpha(1 - r/R) & &\text{for } R/2 \leq r \leq R \\
\rho(r) &= 0 & &\text{for } r \geq R
\end{aligned}
$$

Here α is a positive constant having units of C/m^3. (a) Determine α in terms of Q and R. (b) Using Gauss's law, derive an expression for the magnitude of $\vec{E}$ as a function of r. Do this separately for all three regions. Express your answers in terms of the total charge Q. Be sure to check that your results agree on the boundaries of the regions. (c) What fraction of the total charge is contained within the region $r \leq R/2$? (d) If an electron with charge $q' = -e$ is oscillating back and forth about $r = 0$ (the center of the distribution) with an amplitude less than $R/2$, show that the motion is simple harmonic. (*Hint:* Review the discussion of simple harmonic motion in Section 13.2. If, and only if, the net force on the electron is proportional to its displacement from equilibrium, then the motion is simple harmonic.) (e) What is the period of the motion in part (d)? (f) If the amplitude of the motion described in part (e) is greater than $R/2$, is the motion still simple harmonic? Why or why not?

22.67. A region in space contains a total positive charge Q that is distributed spherically such that the volume charge density $\rho(r)$ is given by

$$
\begin{aligned}
\rho(r) &= 3\alpha r/(2R) & &\text{for } r \leq R/2 \\
\rho(r) &= \alpha[1 - (r/R)^2] & &\text{for } R/2 \leq r \leq R \\
\rho(r) &= 0 & &\text{for } r \geq R
\end{aligned}
$$

Here α is a positive constant having units of C/m^3. (a) Determine α in terms of Q and R. (b) Using Gauss's law, derive an expression for the magnitude of the electric field as a function of r. Do this separately for all three regions. Express your answers in terms of the total charge Q. (c) What fraction of the total charge is contained within the region $R/2 \leq r \leq R$? (d) What is the magnitude of $\vec{E}$ at $r = R/2$? (e) If an electron with charge $q' = -e$ is released from rest at any point in any of the three regions, the resulting motion will be oscillatory but not simple harmonic. Why? (See Challenge Problem 22.66.)

ELECTRIC POTENTIAL

LEARNING GOALS

By studying this chapter, you will learn:

- How to calculate the electric potential energy of a collection of charges.

- The meaning and significance of electric potential.

- How to calculate the electric potential that a collection of charges produces at a point in space.

- How to use equipotential surfaces to visualize how the electric potential varies in space.

- How to use electric potential to calculate the electric field.

? In one type of welding, electric charge flows between the welding tool and the metal pieces that are to be joined together. This produces a glowing arc whose high temperature fuses the pieces together. Why must the tool be held close to the pieces being welded?

This chapter is about energy associated with electrical interactions. Every time you turn on a light, a CD player, or an electric appliance, you are making use of electrical energy, an indispensable ingredient of our technological society. In Chapters 6 and 7 we introduced the concepts of *work* and *energy* in the context of mechanics; now we'll combine these concepts with what we've learned about electric charge, electric forces, and electric fields. Just as the energy concept made it possible to solve some kinds of mechanics problems very simply, using energy ideas makes it easier to solve a variety of problems in electricity.

When a charged particle moves in an electric field, the field exerts a force that can do *work* on the particle. This work can always be expressed in terms of electric potential energy. Just as gravitational potential energy depends on the height of a mass above the earth's surface, electric potential energy depends on the position of the charged particle in the electric field. We'll describe electric potential energy using a new concept called *electric potential,* or simply *potential.* In circuits, a difference in potential from one point to another is often called *voltage.* The concepts of potential and voltage are crucial to understanding how electric circuits work and have equally important applications to electron beams used in cancer radiotherapy, high-energy particle accelerators, and many other devices.

23.1 Electric Potential Energy

The concepts of work, potential energy, and conservation of energy proved to be extremely useful in our study of mechanics. In this section we'll show that these concepts are just as useful for understanding and analyzing electrical interactions.

Let's begin by reviewing three essential points from Chapters 6 and 7. First, when a force $\vec{F}$ acts on a particle that moves from point a to point b, the work $W_{a \to b}$ done by the force is given by a *line integral:*

$$W_{a \to b} = \int_a^b \vec{F} \cdot d\vec{l} = \int_a^b F \cos \phi \, dl \quad \text{(work done by a force)} \quad (23.1)$$

where $d\vec{l}$ is an infinitesimal displacement along the particle's path and ϕ is the angle between $\vec{F}$ and $d\vec{l}$ at each point along the path.

Second, if the force $\vec{F}$ is *conservative,* as we defined the term in Section 7.3, the work done by $\vec{F}$ can always be expressed in terms of a **potential energy** U. When the particle moves from a point where the potential energy is U_a to a point where it is U_b, the change in potential energy is $\Delta U = U_b - U_a$ and the work $W_{a\to b}$ done by the force is

$$W_{a\to b} = U_a - U_b = -(U_b - U_a) = -\Delta U \quad \begin{array}{c}\text{(work done by a}\\\text{conservative force)}\end{array} \quad (23.2)$$

When $W_{a\to b}$ is positive, U_a is greater than U_b, ΔU is negative, and the potential energy *decreases.* That's what happens when a baseball falls from a high point (a) to a lower point (b) under the influence of the earth's gravity; the force of gravity does positive work, and the gravitational potential energy decreases (Fig. 23.1). When a tossed ball is moving upward, the gravitational force does negative work during the ascent, and the potential energy increases.

Third, the work–energy theorem says that the change in kinetic energy $\Delta K = K_b - K_a$ during any displacement is equal to the *total* work done on the particle. If the only work done on the particle is done by conservative forces, then Eq. (23.2) gives the total work, and $K_b - K_a = -(U_b - U_a)$. We usually write this as

$$K_a + U_a = K_b + U_b \qquad (23.3)$$

That is, the total mechanical energy (kinetic plus potential) is *conserved* under these circumstances.

Electric Potential Energy in a Uniform Field

Let's look at an electrical example of these basic concepts. In Fig. 23.2 a pair of charged parallel metal plates sets up a uniform, downward electric field with magnitude E. The field exerts a downward force with magnitude $F = q_0E$ on a positive test charge q_0. As the charge moves downward a distance d from point a to point b, the force on the test charge is constant and independent of its location. So the work done by the electric field is the product of the force magnitude and the component of displacement in the (downward) direction of the force:

$$W_{a\to b} = Fd = q_0Ed \qquad (23.4)$$

This work is positive, since the force is in the same direction as the net displacement of the test charge.

The y-component of the electric force, $F_y = -q_0E$, is constant, and there is no x- or z-component. This is exactly analogous to the gravitational force on a mass m near the earth's surface; for this force, there is a constant y-component $F_y = -mg$ and the x- and z-components are zero. Because of this analogy, we can conclude that the force exerted on q_0 by the uniform electric field in Fig. 23.2 is *conservative,* just as is the gravitational force. This means that the work $W_{a\to b}$ done by the field is independent of the path the particle takes from a to b. We can represent this work with a *potential-energy* function U, just as we did for gravitational potential energy in Section 7.1. The potential energy for the gravitational force $F_y = -mg$ was $U = mgy$; hence the potential energy for the electric force $F_y = -q_0E$ is

$$U = q_0Ey \qquad (23.5)$$

When the test charge moves from height y_a to height y_b, the work done on the charge by the field is given by

$$W_{a\to b} = -\Delta U = -(U_b - U_a) = -(q_0Ey_b - q_0Ey_a) = q_0E(y_a - y_b) \quad (23.6)$$

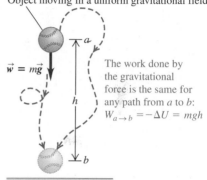

23.1 The work done on a baseball moving in a uniform gravitational field.

Object moving in a uniform gravitational field

The work done by the gravitational force is the same for any path from a to b: $W_{a\to b} = -\Delta U = mgh$

$\vec{w} = m\vec{g}$

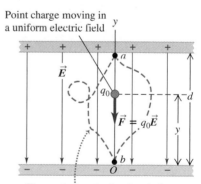

23.2 The work done on a point charge moving in a uniform electric field. Compare with Fig. 23.1.

Point charge moving in a uniform electric field

$\vec{E}$

q_0

$\vec{F} = q_0\vec{E}$

The work done by the electric force is the same for any path from a to b: $W_{a\to b} = -\Delta U = q_0Ed$

23.3 A positive charge moving (a) in the direction of the electric field $\vec{E}$ and (b) in the direction opposite $\vec{E}$.

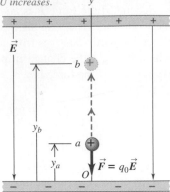

(a) Positive charge moves in the direction of $\vec{E}$:
• Field does *positive* work on charge.
• *U decreases.*

(b) Positive charge moves opposite $\vec{E}$:
• Field does *negative* work on charge.
• *U increases.*

When y_a is greater than y_b (Fig. 23.3a), the positive test charge q_0 moves downward, in the same direction as $\vec{E}$; the displacement is in the same direction as the force $\vec{F} = q_0\vec{E}$, so the field does positive work and U decreases. [In particular, if $y_a - y_b = d$ as in Fig. 23.2, Eq. (23.6) gives $W_{a\to b} = q_0Ed$, in agreement with Eq. (23.4).] When y_a is less than y_b (Fig. 23.3b), the positive test charge q_0 moves upward, in the opposite direction to $\vec{E}$; the displacement is opposite the force, the field does negative work, and U increases.

If the test charge q_0 is *negative,* the potential energy increases when it moves with the field and decreases when it moves against the field (Fig. 23.4).

Whether the test charge is positive or negative, the following general rules apply: *U increases* if the test charge q_0 moves in the direction *opposite* the electric force $\vec{F} = q_0\vec{E}$ (Figs. 23.3b and 23.4a); *U decreases* if q_0 moves in the *same* direction as $\vec{F} = q_0\vec{E}$ (Figs. 23.3a and 23.4b). This is the same behavior as for gravitational potential energy, which increases if a mass m moves upward (opposite the direction of the gravitational force) and decreases if m moves downward (in the same direction as the gravitational force).

CAUTION **Electric potential energy** The relationship between electric potential energy change and motion in an electric field is an important one that we'll use often. It's also a relationship that takes a little effort to truly understand. Take the time to review the preceding paragraph thoroughly and to study Figs. 23.3 and 23.4 carefully. Doing so now will help you tremendously later! ∎

Electric Potential Energy of Two Point Charges

The idea of electric potential energy isn't restricted to the special case of a uniform electric field. Indeed, we can apply this concept to a point charge in *any* electric field caused by a static charge distribution. Recall from Chapter 21 that

23.4 A negative charge moving (a) in the direction of the electric field $\vec{E}$ and (b) in the direction opposite $\vec{E}$. Compare with Fig. 23.3.

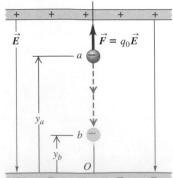

(a) Negative charge moves in the direction of $\vec{E}$:
• Field does *negative* work on charge.
• *U increases.*

(b) Negative charge moves opposite $\vec{E}$:
• Field does *positive* work on charge.
• *U decreases.*

we can represent any charge distribution as a collection of point charges. Therefore it's useful to calculate the work done on a test charge q_0 moving in the electric field caused by a single, stationary point charge q.

We'll consider first a displacement along the *radial* line in Fig. 23.5, from point a to point b. The force on q_0 is given by Coulomb's law, and its radial component is

$$F_r = \frac{1}{4\pi\epsilon_0}\frac{qq_0}{r^2} \tag{23.7}$$

If q and q_0 have the same sign ($+$ or $-$) the force is repulsive and F_r is positive; if the two charges have opposite signs, the force is attractive and F_r is negative. The force is *not* constant during the displacement, and we have to integrate to calculate the work $W_{a\to b}$ done on q_0 by this force as q_0 moves from a to b. We find

$$W_{a\to b} = \int_{r_a}^{r_b} F_r\,dr = \int_{r_a}^{r_b}\frac{1}{4\pi\epsilon_0}\frac{qq_0}{r^2}\,dr = \frac{qq_0}{4\pi\epsilon_0}\left(\frac{1}{r_a}-\frac{1}{r_b}\right) \tag{23.8}$$

The work done by the electric force for this particular path depends only on the endpoints.

In fact, the work is the same for *all possible* paths from a to b. To prove this, we consider a more general displacement (Fig. 23.6) in which a and b do not lie on the same radial line. From Eq. (23.1) the work done on q_0 during this displacement is given by

$$W_{a\to b} = \int_{r_a}^{r_b} F\cos\phi\,dl = \int_{r_a}^{r_b}\frac{1}{4\pi\epsilon_0}\frac{qq_0}{r^2}\cos\phi\,dl$$

But the figure shows that $\cos\phi\,dl = dr$. That is, the work done during a small displacement $d\vec{l}$ depends only on the change dr in the distance r between the charges, which is the *radial component* of the displacement. Thus Eq. (23.8) is valid even for this more general displacement; the work done on q_0 by the electric field $\vec{E}$ produced by q depends only on r_a and r_b, not on the details of the path. Also, if q_0 returns to its starting point a by a different path, the total work done in the round-trip displacement is zero (the integral in Eq. (23.8) is from r_a back to r_a). These are the needed characteristics for a conservative force, as we defined it in Section 7.3. Thus the force on q_0 is a *conservative* force.

We see that Eqs. (23.2) and (23.8) are consistent if we define $qq_0/4\pi\epsilon_0 r_a$ to be the potential energy U_a when q_0 is at point a, a distance r_a from q, and we define $qq_0/4\pi\epsilon_0 r_b$ to be the potential energy U_b when q_0 is at point b, a distance r_b from

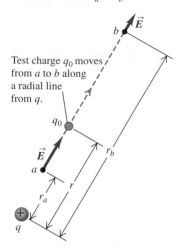

23.5 Test charge q_0 moves along a straight line extending radially from charge q. As it moves from a to b, the distance varies from r_a to r_b.

Test charge q_0 moves from a to b along a radial line from q.

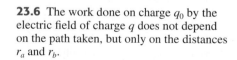

23.6 The work done on charge q_0 by the electric field of charge q does not depend on the path taken, but only on the distances r_a and r_b.

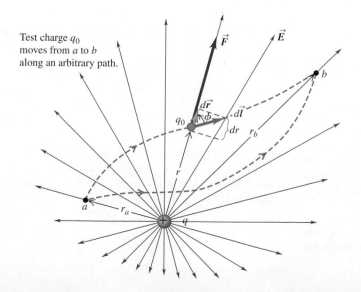

Test charge q_0 moves from a to b along an arbitrary path.

23.7 Graphs of the potential energy U of two point charges q and q_0 versus their separation r.

(a) q and q_0 have the same sign.

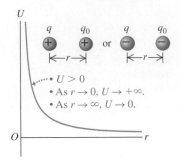

- $U > 0$
- As $r \rightarrow 0$, $U \rightarrow +\infty$.
- As $r \rightarrow \infty$, $U \rightarrow 0$.

(b) q and q_0 have opposite signs.

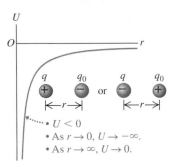

- $U < 0$
- As $r \rightarrow 0$, $U \rightarrow -\infty$.
- As $r \rightarrow \infty$, $U \rightarrow 0$.

q. Thus the potential energy U when the test charge q_0 is at *any* distance r from charge q is

$$U = \frac{1}{4\pi\epsilon_0} \frac{qq_0}{r} \qquad \text{(electric potential energy of two point charges } q \text{ and } q_0\text{)} \qquad (23.9)$$

Note that we have *not* assumed anything about the signs of q and q_0; Eq. (23.9) is valid for any combination of signs. The potential energy is positive if the charges q and q_0 have the same sign (Fig. 23.7a) and negative if they have opposite signs (Fig. 23.7b).

CAUTION **Electric potential energy vs. electric force** Be careful not to confuse Eq. (23.9) for the potential energy of two point charges with the similar expression in Eq. (23.7) for the radial component of the electric force that one charge exerts on the other. The potential energy U is proportional to $1/r$, while the force component F_r is proportional to $1/r^2$. ▮

Potential energy is always defined relative to some reference point where $U = 0$. In Eq. (23.9), U is zero when q and q_0 are infinitely far apart and $r = \infty$. Therefore U represents the work that would be done on the test charge q_0 by the field of q if q_0 moved from an initial distance r to infinity. If q and q_0 have the same sign, the interaction is repulsive, this work is positive, and U is positive at any finite separation (Fig. 23.7a). If the charges have opposite signs, the interaction is attractive, the work done is negative, and U is negative (Fig. 23.7b).

We emphasize that the potential energy U given by Eq. (23.9) is a *shared* property of the two charges q and q_0; it is a consequence of the *interaction* between these two bodies. If the distance between the two charges is changed from r_a to r_b, the change in potential energy is the same whether q is held fixed and q_0 is moved or q_0 is held fixed and q is moved. For this reason, we never use the phrase "the electric potential energy *of* a point charge." (Likewise, if a mass m is at a height h above the earth's surface, the gravitational potential energy is a shared property of the mass m and the earth. We emphasized this in Sections 7.1 and 12.3.)

Gauss's law tells us that the electric field outside any spherically symmetric charge distribution is the same as though all the charge were concentrated at the center. Therefore Eq. (23.9) also holds if the test charge q_0 is outside any spherically symmetric charge distribution with total charge q at a distance r from the center.

Example 23.1 **Conservation of energy with electric forces**

A positron (the antiparticle of the electron) has a mass of 9.11×10^{-31} kg and a charge $+e = +1.60 \times 10^{-19}$ C. Suppose a positron moves in the vicinity of an alpha particle, which has a charge $+2e = 3.20 \times 10^{-19}$ C. The alpha particle is more than 7000 times as massive as the positron, so we assume that it is at rest in some inertial frame of reference. When the positron is 1.00×10^{-10} m from the alpha particle, it is moving directly away from the alpha particle at a speed of 3.00×10^6 m/s. (a) What is the positron's speed when the two particles are 2.00×10^{-10} m apart? (b) What is the positron's speed when it is very far away from the alpha particle? (c) How would the situation change if the moving particle were an electron (same mass as the positron but opposite charge)?

SOLUTION

IDENTIFY: The electric force between the positron and the alpha particle is conservative, so mechanical energy (kinetic plus potential) is conserved.

SET UP: The kinetic and potential energies at any two points a and b are related by Eq. (23.3), $K_a + U_a = K_b + U_b$, and the potential energy at any distance r is given by Eq. (23.9). We are given complete information about the system at a point a where the two charges are 1.00×10^{-10} m apart. We use Eqs. (23.3) and (23.9) to find the speed at two different values of r in parts (a) and (b), and for the case where the charge $+e$ is replaced by $-e$ in part (c).

EXECUTE: (a) In this part, $r_b = 2.00 \times 10^{-10}$ m and we want to find the final speed v_b of the positron. This appears in the expression for the final kinetic energy, $K_b = \frac{1}{2}mv_b^2$; solving the energy-conservation equation for K_b, we have

$$K_b = K_a + U_a - U_b$$

The values of the energies on the right-hand side of this expression are

$$K_a = \frac{1}{2}mv_a^2 = \frac{1}{2}(9.11 \times 10^{-31}\ \text{kg})(3.00 \times 10^6\ \text{m/s})^2$$

$$= 4.10 \times 10^{-18}\ \text{J}$$

$$U_a = \frac{1}{4\pi\epsilon_0}\frac{qq_0}{r_a}$$

$$= (9.0 \times 10^9\ \text{N}\cdot\text{m}^2/\text{C}^2)\frac{(3.20 \times 10^{-19}\ \text{C})(1.60 \times 10^{-19}\ \text{C})}{1.00 \times 10^{-10}\ \text{m}}$$

$$= 4.61 \times 10^{-18}\ \text{J}$$

$$U_b = (9.0 \times 10^9\ \text{N}\cdot\text{m}^2/\text{C}^2)\frac{(3.20 \times 10^{-19}\ \text{C})(1.60 \times 10^{-19}\ \text{C})}{2.00 \times 10^{-10}\ \text{m}}$$

$$= 2.30 \times 10^{-18}\ \text{J}$$

Hence the final kinetic energy is

$$K_b = \frac{1}{2}mv_b^2 = K_a + U_a - U_b$$

$$= 4.10 \times 10^{-18}\ \text{J} + 4.61 \times 10^{-18}\ \text{J} - 2.30 \times 10^{-18}\ \text{J}$$

$$= 6.41 \times 10^{-18}\ \text{J}$$

and the final speed of the positron is

$$v_b = \sqrt{\frac{2K_b}{m}} = \sqrt{\frac{2(6.41 \times 10^{-18}\ \text{J})}{9.11 \times 10^{-31}\ \text{kg}}} = 3.8 \times 10^6\ \text{m/s}$$

The force is repulsive, so the positron speeds up as it moves away from the stationary alpha particle.

(b) When the final positions of the positron and alpha particle are very far apart, the separation r_b approaches infinity and the final potential energy U_b approaches zero. Then the final kinetic energy of the positron is

$$K_b = K_a + U_a - U_b = 4.10 \times 10^{-18}\ \text{J} + 4.61 \times 10^{-18}\ \text{J} - 0$$

$$= 8.71 \times 10^{-18}\ \text{J}$$

and its final speed is

$$v_b = \sqrt{\frac{2K_b}{m}} = \sqrt{\frac{2(8.71 \times 10^{-18}\ \text{J})}{9.11 \times 10^{-31}\ \text{kg}}} = 4.4 \times 10^6\ \text{m/s}$$

Comparing to part (a), we see that as the positron moves from $r = 2.00 \times 10^{-10}$ m to infinity, the additional work done on it by the electric field of the alpha particle increases the speed by only about 16%. This is because the electric force decreases rapidly with distance.

(c) If the moving charge is negative, the force on it is attractive rather than repulsive, and we expect it to slow down rather than speed up. The only difference in the above calculations is that both potential-energy quantities are negative. From part (a), at a distance $r_b = 2.00 \times 10^{-10}$ m we have

$$K_b = K_a + U_a - U_b$$

$$= 4.10 \times 10^{-18}\ \text{J} + (-4.61 \times 10^{-18}\ \text{J}) - (-2.30 \times 10^{-18}\ \text{J})$$

$$= 1.79 \times 10^{-18}\ \text{J}$$

$$v_b = \sqrt{\frac{2K_b}{m}} = 2.0 \times 10^6\ \text{m/s}$$

From part (b), at $r_b = \infty$ the kinetic energy of the electron would seem to be

$$K_b = K_a + U_a - U_b$$

$$= 4.10 \times 10^{-18}\ \text{J} + (-4.61 \times 10^{-18}\ \text{J}) - 0$$

$$= -5.1 \times 10^{-19}\ \text{J}$$

But kinetic energies can *never* be negative! This result means that the electron can never reach $r_b = \infty$; the attractive force brings the electron to a halt at a finite distance from the alpha particle. The electron will then begin to move back toward the alpha particle. You can solve for the distance r_b at which the electron comes momentarily to rest by setting K_b equal to zero in the equation for conservation of mechanical energy.

EVALUATE: It's useful to compare our calculations with Fig. 23.7. In parts (a) and (b), the charges have the same sign; since $r_b > r_a$, the potential energy U_b is less than U_a. In part (c), the charges have opposite signs; since $r_b > r_a$, the potential energy U_b is greater (that is, less negative) than U_a.

Electric Potential Energy with Several Point Charges

Suppose the electric field $\vec{E}$ in which charge q_0 moves is caused by *several* point charges $q_1, q_2, q_3, \ldots$ at distances $r_1, r_2, r_3, \ldots$ from q_0, as in Fig. 23.8. For example, q_0 could be a positive ion moving in the presence of other ions (Fig. 23.9). The total electric field at each point is the *vector sum* of the fields due to the individual charges, and the total work done on q_0 during any displacement is the sum of the contributions from the individual charges. From Eq. (23.9) we conclude that the potential energy associated with the test charge q_0 at point a in Fig. 23.8 is the *algebraic* sum (*not* a vector sum):

$$U = \frac{q_0}{4\pi\epsilon_0}\left(\frac{q_1}{r_1} + \frac{q_2}{r_2} + \frac{q_3}{r_3} + \cdots\right) = \frac{q_0}{4\pi\epsilon_0}\sum_i \frac{q_i}{r_i} \qquad \begin{array}{l}\text{(point charge } q_0 \\ \text{and collection} \\ \text{of charges } q_i)\end{array} \quad (23.10)$$

23.8 The potential energy associated with a charge q_0 at point a depends on the other charges q_1, q_2, and q_3 and on their distances r_1, r_2, and r_3 from point a.

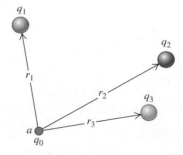

When q_0 is at a different point b, the potential energy is given by the same expression, but $r_1, r_2, \ldots$ are the distances from $q_1, q_2, \ldots$ to point b. The work

23.9 This ion engine for spacecraft uses electric forces to eject a stream of positive xenon ions (Xe^+) at speeds in excess of 30 km/s. The thrust produced is very low (about 0.09 newton) but can be maintained continuously for days, in contrast to chemical rockets, which produce a large thrust for a short time (see Fig. 8.33). Such ion engines have been used for maneuvering interplanetary spacecraft.

done on charge q_0 when it moves from a to b along any path is equal to the difference $U_a - U_b$ between the potential energies when q_0 is at a and at b.

We can represent *any* charge distribution as a collection of point charges, so Eq. (23.10) shows that we can always find a potential-energy function for *any* static electric field. It follows that **for every electric field due to a static charge distribution, the force exerted by that field is conservative.**

Equations (23.9) and (23.10) define U to be zero when all the distances $r_1, r_2, \ldots$ are infinite—that is, when the test charge q_0 is very far away from all the charges that produce the field. As with any potential-energy function, the point where $U = 0$ is arbitrary; we can always add a constant to make U equal zero at any point we choose. In electrostatics problems it's usually simplest to choose this point to be at infinity. When we analyze electric circuits in Chapters 25 and 26, other choices will be more convenient.

Equation (23.10) gives the potential energy associated with the presence of the test charge q_0 in the $\vec{E}$ field produced by $q_1, q_2, q_3, \ldots$. But there is also potential energy involved in assembling these charges. If we start with charges $q_1, q_2, q_3, \ldots$ all separated from each other by infinite distances and then bring them together so that the distance between q_i and q_j is r_{ij}, the *total* potential energy U is the sum of the potential energies of interaction for each pair of charges. We can write this as

$$U = \frac{1}{4\pi\epsilon_0} \sum_{i<j} \frac{q_i q_j}{r_{ij}} \tag{23.11}$$

This sum extends over all *pairs* of charges; we don't let $i = j$ (because that would be an interaction of a charge with itself), and we include only terms with $i < j$ to make sure that we count each pair only once. Thus, to account for the interaction between q_3 and q_4, we include a term with $i = 3$ and $j = 4$ but not a term with $i = 4$ and $j = 3$.

Interpreting Electric Potential Energy

As a final comment, here are two viewpoints on electric potential energy. We have defined it in terms of the work done *by the electric field* on a charged particle moving in the field, just as in Chapter 7 we defined potential energy in terms of the work done by gravity or by a spring. When a particle moves from point a to point b, the work done on it by the electric field is $W_{a \to b} = U_a - U_b$. Thus the potential-energy difference $U_a - U_b$ equals *the work that is done by the electric force when the particle moves from a to b*. When U_a is greater than U_b, the field does positive work on the particle as it "falls" from a point of higher potential energy (a) to a point of lower potential energy (b).

An alternative but equivalent viewpoint is to consider how much work we would have to do to "raise" a particle from a point b where the potential energy is U_b to a point a where it has a greater value U_a (pushing two positive charges closer together, for example). To move the particle slowly (so as not to give it any kinetic energy), we need to exert an additional external force $\vec{F}_{\text{ext}}$ that is equal and opposite to the electric-field force and does positive work. The potential-energy difference $U_a - U_b$ is then defined as *the work that must be done by an external force to move the particle slowly from b to a against the electric force.* Because $\vec{F}_{\text{ext}}$ is the negative of the electric-field force and the displacement is in the opposite direction, this definition of the potential difference $U_a - U_b$ is equivalent to that given above. This alternative viewpoint also works if U_a is less than U_b, corresponding to "lowering" the particle; an example is moving two positive charges away from each other. In this case, $U_a - U_b$ is again equal to the work done by the external force, but now this work is negative.

We will use both of these viewpoints in the next section to interpret what is meant by electric *potential*, or potential energy per unit charge.

Example 23.2   A system of point charges

Two point charges are located on the x-axis, $q_1 = -e$ at $x = 0$ and $q_2 = +e$ at $x = a$. (a) Find the work that must be done by an external force to bring a third point charge $q_3 = +e$ from infinity to $x = 2a$. (b) Find the total potential energy of the system of three charges.

SOLUTION

IDENTIFY: This problem involves the relationship between the work done to move a point charge and the change in potential energy. It also involves the expression for the potential energy of a collection of point charges.

SET UP: Figure 23.10 shows the final arrangement of the three charges. To find the work required to bring q_3 in from infinity, we use Eq. (23.10) to find the potential energy associated with q_3 in the presence of q_1 and q_2. We then use Eq. (23.11) to find the total potential energy of the system.

23.10 Our sketch of the situation after the third charge has been brought in from infinity.

$$q_1 = -e \qquad q_2 = +e \qquad q_3 = +e$$

$$\underset{x=0}{\ominus} \qquad \underset{x=a}{\oplus} \qquad \underset{x=2a}{\oplus} \longrightarrow x$$

EXECUTE: (a) The work that must be done on q_3 by an external force $\vec{F}_{ext}$ is equal to the difference between two quantities: the potential energy U associated with q_3 when it is at $x = 2a$ and the potential energy when it is infinitely far away. The second of these is zero, so the work that must be done is equal to U. The distances between the charges are $r_{13} = 2a$ and $r_{23} = a$, so from Eq. (23.10),

$$W = U = \frac{q_3}{4\pi\epsilon_0}\left(\frac{q_1}{r_{13}} + \frac{q_2}{r_{23}}\right) = \frac{+e}{4\pi\epsilon_0}\left(\frac{-e}{2a} + \frac{+e}{a}\right) = \frac{+e^2}{8\pi\epsilon_0 a}$$

If q_3 is brought in from infinity along the $+x$-axis, it is attracted by q_1 but is repelled more strongly by q_2; hence positive work must be done to push q_3 to the position at $x = 2a$.

(b) The total potential energy of the assemblage of three charges is given by Eq. (23.11):

$$U = \frac{1}{4\pi\epsilon_0}\sum_{i<j}\frac{q_i q_j}{r_{ij}} = \frac{1}{4\pi\epsilon_0}\left(\frac{q_1 q_2}{r_{12}} + \frac{q_1 q_3}{r_{13}} + \frac{q_2 q_3}{r_{23}}\right)$$

$$= \frac{1}{4\pi\epsilon_0}\left(\frac{(-e)(e)}{a} + \frac{(-e)(e)}{2a} + \frac{(e)(e)}{a}\right) = \frac{-e^2}{8\pi\epsilon_0 a}$$

EVALUATE: Since our result in part (b) is negative, the system has lower potential energy than it would if the three charges were infinitely far apart. An external force would have to do *negative* work to bring the three charges from infinity to assemble this entire arrangement and would have to do *positive* work to move the three charges back to infinity.

Test Your Understanding of Section 23.1   Consider the system of three point charges in Example 21.4 (Section 21.3) and shown in Fig. 21.14. (a) What is the sign of the total potential energy of this system? (i) positive; (ii) negative; (iii) zero. (b) What is the sign of the total amount of work you would have to do to move these charges infinitely far from each other? (i) positive; (ii) negative; (iii) zero.

23.2 Electric Potential

In Section 23.1 we looked at the potential energy U associated with a test charge q_0 in an electric field. Now we want to describe this potential energy on a "per unit charge" basis, just as electric field describes the force per unit charge on a charged particle in the field. This leads us to the concept of *electric potential,* often called simply *potential.* This concept is very useful in calculations involving energies of charged particles. It also facilitates many electric-field calculations because electric potential is closely related to the electric field $\vec{E}$. When we need to determine an electric field, it is often easier to determine the potential first and then find the field from it.

Potential is *potential energy per unit charge.* We define the potential V at any point in an electric field as the potential energy U *per unit charge* associated with a test charge q_0 at that point:

$$V = \frac{U}{q_0} \quad \text{or} \quad U = q_0 V \tag{23.12}$$

Potential energy and charge are both scalars, so potential is a scalar quantity. From Eq. (23.12) its units are found by dividing the units of energy by those of charge. The SI unit of potential, called one **volt** (1 V) in honor of the Italian

Activ
ONLINE
Physics

11.13 Electrical Potential Energy and Potential

scientist and electrical experimenter Alessandro Volta (1745–1827), equals 1 joule per coulomb:

$$1 \text{ V} = 1 \text{ volt} = 1 \text{ J/C} = 1 \text{ joule/coulomb}$$

Let's put Eq. (23.2), which equates the work done by the electric force during a displacement from a to b to the quantity $-\Delta U = -(U_b - U_a)$, on a "work per unit charge" basis. We divide this equation by q_0, obtaining

$$\frac{W_{a \to b}}{q_0} = -\frac{\Delta U}{q_0} = -\left(\frac{U_b}{q_0} - \frac{U_a}{q_0}\right) = -(V_b - V_a) = V_a - V_b \quad (23.13)$$

where $V_a = U_a/q_0$ is the potential energy per unit charge at point a and similarly for V_b. We call V_a and V_b the *potential at point a* and *potential at point b*, respectively. Thus the work done per unit charge by the electric force when a charged body moves from a to b is equal to the potential at a minus the potential at b.

The difference $V_a - V_b$ is called the *potential of a with respect to b*; we sometimes abbreviate this difference as $V_{ab} = V_a - V_b$ (note the order of the subscripts). This is often called the potential difference between a and b, but that's ambiguous unless we specify which is the reference point. In electric circuits, which we will analyze in later chapters, the potential difference between two points is often called **voltage** (Fig. 23.11). Equation (23.13) then states: $\mathbf{V_{ab}}$, **the potential of** $\boldsymbol{a}$ **with respect to** $\boldsymbol{b}$, **equals the work done by the electric force when a UNIT charge moves from** $\boldsymbol{a}$ **to** $\boldsymbol{b}$.

Another way to interpret the potential difference V_{ab} in Eq. (23.13) is to use the alternative viewpoint mentioned at the end of Section 23.1. In that viewpoint, $U_a - U_b$ is the amount of work that must be done by an *external* force to move a particle of charge q_0 slowly from b to a against the electric force. The work that must be done *per unit charge* by the external force is then $(U_a - U_b)/q_0 = V_a - V_b = V_{ab}$. In other words: $\mathbf{V_{ab}}$, **the potential of** $\boldsymbol{a}$ **with respect to** $\boldsymbol{b}$, **equals the work that must be done to move a UNIT charge slowly from** $\boldsymbol{b}$ **to** $\boldsymbol{a}$ **against the electric force.**

An instrument that measures the difference of potential between two points is called a *voltmeter*. In Chapter 26 we will discuss the principle of the common type of moving-coil voltmeter. There are also much more sensitive potential-measuring devices that use electronic amplification. Instruments that can measure a potential difference of 1 μV are common, and sensitivities down to 10^{-12} V can be attained.

23.11 The voltage of this battery equals the difference in potential $V_{ab} = V_a - V_b$ between its positive terminal (point a) and its negative terminal (point b).

Point a

ENERGY PLUS

ALKALINE

LONGER LASTING POWER

Point b

$V_{ab} = 1.5$ volts

Calculating Electric Potential

To find the potential V due to a single point charge q, we divide Eq. (23.9) by q_0:

$$V = \frac{U}{q_0} = \frac{1}{4\pi\epsilon_0}\frac{q}{r} \quad \text{(potential due to a point charge)} \quad (23.14)$$

where r is the distance from the point charge q to the point at which the potential is evaluated. If q is positive, the potential that it produces is positive at all points; if q is negative, it produces a potential that is negative everywhere. In either case, V is equal to zero at $r = \infty$, an infinite distance from the point charge. Note that potential, like electric field, is independent of the test charge q_0 that we use to define it.

Similarly, we divide Eq. (23.10) by q_0 to find the potential due to a collection of point charges:

$$V = \frac{U}{q_0} = \frac{1}{4\pi\epsilon_0}\sum_i \frac{q_i}{r_i} \quad \text{(potential due to a collection of point charges)} \quad (23.15)$$

In this expression, r_i is the distance from the ith charge, q_i, to the point at which V is evaluated. Just as the electric field due to a collection of point charges is the *vector* sum of the fields produced by each charge, the electric potential due to a collection of point charges is the *scalar* sum of the potentials due to each charge. When we have a continuous distribution of charge along a line, over a surface, or through a volume, we divide the charge into elements dq, and the sum in Eq. (23.15) becomes an integral:

$$V = \frac{1}{4\pi\epsilon_0} \int \frac{dq}{r} \qquad \text{(potential due to a continuous distribution of charge)} \qquad (23.16)$$

where r is the distance from the charge element dq to the field point where we are finding V. We'll work out several examples of such cases. The potential defined by Eqs. (23.15) and (23.16) is zero at points that are infinitely far away from *all* the charges. Later we'll encounter cases in which the charge distribution itself extends to infinity. We'll find that in such cases we cannot set $V = 0$ at infinity, and we'll need to exercise care in using and interpreting Eqs. (23.15) and (23.16).

CAUTION **What is electric potential?** Before getting too involved in the details of how to calculate electric potential, you should stop and remind yourself what potential is. The electric *potential* at a certain point is the potential energy that would be associated with a *unit* charge placed at that point. That's why potential is measured in joules per coulomb, or volts. Keep in mind, too, that there doesn't have to be a charge at a given point for a potential V to exist at that point. (In the same way, an electric field can exist at a given point even if there's no charge there to respond to it.) ▮

Finding Electric Potential from Electric Field

When we are given a collection of point charges, Eq. (23.15) is usually the easiest way to calculate the potential V. But in some problems in which the electric field is known or can be found easily, it is easier to determine V from $\vec{E}$. The force $\vec{F}$ on a test charge q_0 can be written as $\vec{F} = q_0\vec{E}$, so from Eq. (23.1) the work done by the electric force as the test charge moves from a to b is given by

$$W_{a \to b} = \int_a^b \vec{F} \cdot d\vec{l} = \int_a^b q_0\vec{E} \cdot d\vec{l}$$

If we divide this by q_0 and compare the result with Eq. (23.13), we find

$$V_a - V_b = \int_a^b \vec{E} \cdot d\vec{l} = \int_a^b E\cos\phi \, dl \qquad \text{(potential difference as an integral of } \vec{E}) \qquad (23.17)$$

The value of $V_a - V_b$ is independent of the path taken from a to b, just as the value of $W_{a \to b}$ is independent of the path. To interpret Eq. (23.17), remember that $\vec{E}$ is the electric force per unit charge on a test charge. If the line integral $\int_a^b \vec{E} \cdot d\vec{l}$ is positive, the electric field does positive work on a positive test charge as it moves from a to b. In this case the electric potential energy decreases as the test charge moves, so the potential energy per unit charge decreases as well; hence V_b is less than V_a and $V_a - V_b$ is positive.

As an illustration, consider a positive point charge (Fig. 23.12a). The electric field is directed away from the charge, and $V = q/4\pi\epsilon_0 r$ is positive at any finite distance from the charge. If you move away from the charge, in the direction of $\vec{E}$, you move toward lower values of V; if you move toward the charge, in the direction opposite $\vec{E}$, you move toward greater values of V. For the negative point charge in Fig. 23.12b, $\vec{E}$ is directed toward the charge and $V = q/4\pi\epsilon_0 r$ is negative at any finite distance from the charge. In this case, if you move toward the charge, you are moving in the direction of $\vec{E}$ and in the direction of decreasing (more negative) V. Moving away from the charge, in the direction opposite $\vec{E}$,

23.12 If you move in the direction of $\vec{E}$, electric potential V decreases; if you move in the direction opposite $\vec{E}$, V increases.

(a) A positive point charge

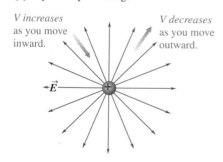

V increases as you move inward.   *V decreases* as you move outward.

$\vec{E}$

(b) A negative point charge

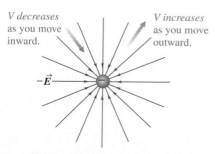

V decreases as you move inward.   *V increases* as you move outward.

$-\vec{E}$

moves you toward increasing (less negative) values of V. The general rule, valid for *any* electric field, is: Moving *with* the direction of $\vec{E}$ means moving in the direction of *decreasing* V, and moving *against* the direction of $\vec{E}$ means moving in the direction of *increasing* V.

Also, a positive test charge q_0 experiences an electric force in the direction of $\vec{E}$, toward lower values of V; a negative test charge experiences a force opposite $\vec{E}$, toward higher values of V. Thus a positive charge tends to "fall" from a high-potential region to a lower-potential region. The opposite is true for a negative charge.

Notice that Eq. (23.17) can be rewritten as

$$V_a - V_b = -\int_b^a \vec{E} \cdot d\vec{l} \tag{23.18}$$

This has a negative sign compared to the integral in Eq. (23.17), and the limits are reversed; hence Eqs. (23.17) and (23.18) are equivalent. But Eq. (23.18) has a slightly different interpretation. To move a unit charge slowly against the electric force, we must apply an *external* force per unit charge equal to $-\vec{E}$, equal and opposite to the electric force per unit charge $\vec{E}$. Equation (23.18) says that $V_a - V_b = V_{ab}$, the potential of a with respect to b, equals the work done per unit charge by this external force to move a unit charge from b to a. This is the same alternative interpretation we discussed under Eq. (23.13).

Equations (23.17) and (23.18) show that the unit of potential difference $(1\ \text{V})$ is equal to the unit of electric field $(1\ \text{N/C})$ multiplied by the unit of distance $(1\ \text{m})$. Hence the unit of electric field can be expressed as 1 *volt per meter* $(1\ \text{V/m})$, as well as $1\ \text{N/C}$:

$$1\ \text{V/m} = 1\ \text{volt/meter} = 1\ \text{N/C} = 1\ \text{newton/coulomb}$$

In practice, the volt per meter is the usual unit of electric-field magnitude.

Electron Volts

The magnitude e of the electron charge can be used to define a unit of energy that is useful in many calculations with atomic and nuclear systems. When a particle with charge q moves from a point where the potential is V_b to a point where it is V_a, the change in the potential energy U is

$$U_a - U_b = q(V_a - V_b) = qV_{ab}$$

If the charge q equals the magnitude e of the electron charge, 1.602×10^{-19} C, and the potential difference is $V_{ab} = 1$ V, the change in energy is

$$U_a - U_b = (1.602 \times 10^{-19}\ \text{C})(1\ \text{V}) = 1.602 \times 10^{-19}\ \text{J}$$

This quantity of energy is defined to be 1 **electron volt** $(1\ \text{eV})$:

$$1\ \text{eV} = 1.602 \times 10^{-19}\ \text{J}$$

The multiples meV, keV, MeV, GeV, and TeV are often used.

CAUTION **Electron volts vs. volts** Remember that the electron volt is a unit of energy, *not* a unit of potential or potential difference! ∎

When a particle with charge e moves through a potential difference of 1 volt, the change in potential *energy* is 1 eV. If the charge is some multiple of e—say Ne—the change in potential energy in electron volts is N times the potential difference in volts. For example, when an alpha particle, which has charge $2e$, moves between two points with a potential difference of 1000 V, the change in potential energy is $2(1000\ \text{eV}) = 2000\ \text{eV}$. To confirm this, we write

$$U_a - U_b = qV_{ab} = (2e)(1000\ \text{V}) = (2)(1.602 \times 10^{-19}\ \text{C})(1000\ \text{V})$$
$$= 3.204 \times 10^{-16}\ \text{J} = 2000\ \text{eV}$$

Although we have defined the electron volt in terms of *potential* energy, we can use it for *any* form of energy, such as the kinetic energy of a moving particle. When we speak of a "one-million-electron-volt proton," we mean a proton with a kinetic energy of one million electron volts (1 MeV), equal to $(10^6)(1.602 \times 10^{-19} \text{ J}) = 1.602 \times 10^{-13} \text{ J}$ (Fig. 23.13).

23.13 This accelerator at the Fermi National Accelerator Laboratory in Illinois gives protons a kinetic energy of 400 MeV $(4 \times 10^8 \text{ eV})$. Additional acceleration stages increase their kinetic energy to 980 GeV, or 0.98 TeV $(9.8 \times 10^{11} \text{ eV})$.

Example 23.3   Electric force and electric potential

A proton (charge $+e = 1.602 \times 10^{-19}$ C) moves in a straight line from point a to point b inside a linear accelerator, a total distance $d = 0.50$ m. The electric field is uniform along this line, with magnitude $E = 1.5 \times 10^7$ V/m $= 1.5 \times 10^7$ N/C in the direction from a to b. Determine (a) the force on the proton; (b) the work done on it by the field; (c) the potential difference $V_a - V_b$.

SOLUTION

IDENTIFY: This problem uses the relationship between electric field (which we are given) and electric force (which is one of our target variables). It also uses the relationship among force, work, and potential energy difference.

SET UP: We are given the electric field, so it is straightforward to find the electric force on the proton. Calculating the work done on the proton by this force is also straightforward because $\vec{E}$ is uniform, which means that the force is constant. Once the work is known, we find the potential difference using Eq. (23.13).

EXECUTE: (a) The force on the proton is in the same direction as the electric field, and its magnitude is

$$F = qE = (1.602 \times 10^{-19} \text{ C})(1.5 \times 10^7 \text{ N/C})$$
$$= 2.4 \times 10^{-12} \text{ N}$$

(b) The force is constant and in the same direction as the displacement, so the work done on the proton is

$$W_{a \to b} = Fd = (2.4 \times 10^{-12} \text{ N})(0.50 \text{ m}) = 1.2 \times 10^{-12} \text{ J}$$

$$= (1.2 \times 10^{-12} \text{ J}) \frac{1 \text{ eV}}{1.602 \times 10^{-19} \text{ J}}$$

$$= 7.5 \times 10^6 \text{ eV} = 7.5 \text{ MeV}$$

(c) From Eq. (23.13) the potential difference is the work per unit charge, which is

$$V_a - V_b = \frac{W_{a \to b}}{q} = \frac{1.2 \times 10^{-12} \text{ J}}{1.602 \times 10^{-19} \text{ C}} = 7.5 \times 10^6 \text{ J/C}$$
$$= 7.5 \times 10^6 \text{ V} = 7.5 \text{ MV}$$

We can get this same result even more easily by remembering that 1 electron volt equals 1 volt multiplied by the charge e. Since the work done is 7.5×10^6 eV and the charge is e, the potential difference is $(7.5 \times 10^6 \text{ eV})/e = 7.5 \times 10^6$ V.

EVALUATE: We can check our result in part (c) by using Eq. (23.17) or (23.18) to calculate an integral of the electric field. The angle ϕ between the constant field $\vec{E}$ and the displacement is zero, so Eq. (23.17) becomes

$$V_a - V_b = \int_a^b E \cos\phi \, dl = \int_a^b E \, dl = E \int_a^b dl$$

The integral of dl from a to b is just the distance d, so we again find

$$V_a - V_b = Ed = (1.5 \times 10^7 \text{ V/m})(0.50 \text{ m}) = 7.5 \times 10^6 \text{ V}$$

Example 23.4 | **Potential due to two point charges**

An electric dipole consists of two point charges, $q_1 = +12$ nC and $q_2 = -12$ nC, placed 10 cm apart (Fig. 23.14). Compute the potentials at points a, b, and c by adding the potentials due to either charge, as in Eq. (23.15).

SOLUTION

IDENTIFY: This is the same arrangement of charges as in Example 21.9 (Section 21.5). In that example we calculated electric *field* at each point by doing a *vector* sum. Our target variable in this problem is the electric *potential* V at three points.

SET UP: To find V at each point, we do the *algebraic* sum in Eq. (23.15):

$$V = \frac{1}{4\pi\epsilon_0} \sum_i \frac{q_i}{r_i}$$

EXECUTE: At point a the potential due to the positive charge q_1 is

$$\frac{1}{4\pi\epsilon_0} \frac{q_1}{r_1} = (9.0 \times 10^9 \text{ N} \cdot \text{m}^2/\text{C}^2) \frac{12 \times 10^{-9} \text{ C}}{0.060 \text{ m}}$$

$$= 1800 \text{ N} \cdot \text{m/C}$$

$$= 1800 \text{ J/C} = 1800 \text{ V}$$

and the potential due to the negative charge q_2 is

$$\frac{1}{4\pi\epsilon_0} \frac{q_2}{r_2} = (9.0 \times 10^9 \text{ N} \cdot \text{m}^2/\text{C}^2) \frac{(-12 \times 10^{-9} \text{ C})}{0.040 \text{ m}}$$

$$= -2700 \text{ N} \cdot \text{m/C}$$

$$= -2700 \text{ J/C} = -2700 \text{ V}$$

The potential V_a at point a is the sum of these:

$$V_a = 1800 \text{ V} + (-2700 \text{ V}) = -900 \text{ V}$$

By similar calculations you can show that at point b the potential due to the positive charge is $+2700$ V, the potential due to the negative charge is -770 V, and

$$V_b = 2700 \text{ V} + (-770 \text{ V}) = 1930 \text{ V}$$

23.14 What are the potentials at points a, b, and c due to this electric dipole?

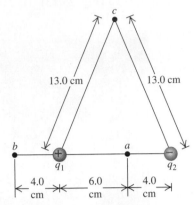

At point c the potential due to the positive charge is

$$\frac{1}{4\pi\epsilon_0} \frac{q_1}{r_1} = (9.0 \times 10^9 \text{ N} \cdot \text{m}^2/\text{C}^2) \frac{12 \times 10^{-9} \text{ C}}{0.13 \text{ m}} = 830 \text{ V}$$

The potential due to the negative charge is -830 V, and the total potential is zero:

$$V_c = 830 \text{ V} + (-830 \text{ V}) = 0$$

The potential is also equal to zero at infinity (infinitely far from both charges).

EVALUATE: Comparing this example with Example 21.9 shows that it's much easier to calculate electric potential (a scalar) than electric field (a vector). We'll take advantage of this simplification whenever possible.

Example 23.5 | **Potential and potential energy**

Compute the potential energy associated with a point charge of $+4.0$ nC if it is placed at points a, b, and c in Fig. 23.14.

SOLUTION

IDENTIFY: We know the value of the electric potential at each of these points, and we need to find the potential energy for a point charge placed at each point.

SET UP: For any point charge q, the associated potential energy is $U = qV$. We use the values of V from Example 23.4.

EXECUTE: At point a,

$$U_a = qV_a = (4.0 \times 10^{-9} \text{ C})(-900 \text{ J/C}) = -3.6 \times 10^{-6} \text{ J}$$

At point b,

$$U_b = qV_b = (4.0 \times 10^{-9} \text{ C})(1930 \text{ J/C}) = 7.7 \times 10^{-6} \text{ J}$$

At point c,

$$U_c = qV_c = 0$$

All of these values correspond to U and V being zero at infinity.

EVALUATE: Note that *no* net work is done on the 4.0-nC charge if it moves from point c to infinity *by any path*. In particular, let the path be along the perpendicular bisector of the line joining the other two charges q_1 and q_2 in Fig. 23.14. As shown in Example 21.9 (Section 21.5), at points on the bisector the direction of $\vec{E}$ is perpendicular to the bisector. Hence the force on the 4.0-nC charge is perpendicular to the path, and no work is done in any displacement along it.

Example 23.6   Finding potential by integration

By integrating the electric field as in Eq. (23.17), find the potential at a distance r from a point charge q.

SOLUTION

IDENTIFY: This problem asks us to find the electric potential from the electric field.

SET UP: To find the potential V at a distance r from the point charge, we let point a in Eq. (23.17) be at distance r and let point b be at infinity (Fig. 23.15). As usual, we choose the potential to be zero at an infinite distance from the charge.

EXECUTE: To carry out the integral, we can choose any path we like between points a and b. The most convenient path is a straight radial line as shown in Fig. 23.15, so that $d\vec{l}$ is in the radial direction and has magnitude dr. If q is positive, $\vec{E}$ and $d\vec{l}$ are always parallel, so $\phi = 0$ and Eq. (23.17) becomes

$$V - 0 = \int_r^\infty E\,dr = \int_r^\infty \frac{q}{4\pi\epsilon_0 r^2}\,dr$$

$$= -\frac{q}{4\pi\epsilon_0 r}\bigg|_r^\infty = 0 - \left(-\frac{q}{4\pi\epsilon_0 r}\right)$$

$$V = \frac{q}{4\pi\epsilon_0 r}$$

This agrees with Eq. (23.14). If q is negative, $\vec{E}$ is radially inward while $d\vec{l}$ is still radially outward, so $\phi - 180°$. Since $\cos 180° = -1$, this adds a minus sign to the above result. However, the field magnitude E is always positive, and since q is negative, we must write $E = |q|/4\pi\epsilon_0 r - q/4\pi\epsilon_0 r$, giving another minus sign. The two minus signs cancel, and the above result for V is valid for point charges of either sign.

23.15 Calculating the potential by integrating $\vec{E}$ for a single point charge.

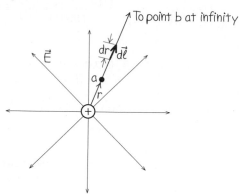

EVALUATE: We can get the same result by using Eq. (21.7) for the electric field, which is valid for either sign of q, and writing $d\vec{l} = \hat{r}\,dr$:

$$V - 0 = V = \int_r^\infty \vec{E} \cdot d\vec{l}$$

$$= \int_r^\infty \frac{1}{4\pi\epsilon_0}\frac{q}{r^2}\hat{r}\cdot\hat{r}\,dr = \int_r^\infty \frac{q}{4\pi\epsilon_0 r^2}\,dr$$

$$V = \frac{q}{4\pi\epsilon_0 r}$$

Example 23.7   Moving through a potential difference

In Fig. 23.16 a dust particle with mass $m = 5.0 \times 10^{-9}\,\text{kg} = 5.0\,\mu\text{g}$ and charge $q_0 = 2.0\,\text{nC}$ starts from rest at point a and moves in a straight line to point b. What is its speed v at point b?

SOLUTION

IDENTIFY: This problem involves the change in speed and hence kinetic energy of the particle, so we can use an energy approach. This problem would be difficult to solve without using energy techniques, since the force that acts on the particle varies in magnitude as the particle moves from a to b.

SET UP: Only the conservative electric force acts on the particle, so mechanical energy is conserved:

$$K_a + U_a = K_b + U_b$$

EXECUTE: For this situation, $K_a = 0$ and $K_b = \frac{1}{2}mv^2$. We get the potential energies (U) from the potentials (V) using Eq. (23.12):

23.16 The particle moves from point a to point b; its acceleration is not constant.

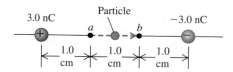

$U_a = q_0 V_a$ and $U_b = q_0 V_b$. Substituting these into the energy-conservation equation and solving for v, we find

$$0 + q_0 V_a = \frac{1}{2}mv^2 + q_0 V_b$$

$$v = \sqrt{\frac{2q_0(V_a - V_b)}{m}}$$

Continued

We calculate the potentials using Eq. (23.15), just as we did in Example 23.4:

$$V_a = (9.0 \times 10^9 \text{ N} \cdot \text{m}^2/\text{C}^2)$$

$$\times \left(\frac{3.0 \times 10^{-9} \text{ C}}{0.010 \text{ m}} + \frac{(-3.0 \times 10^{-9} \text{ C})}{0.020 \text{ m}} \right) = 1350 \text{ V}$$

$$V_b = (9.0 \times 10^9 \text{ N} \cdot \text{m}^2/\text{C}^2)$$

$$\times \left(\frac{3.0 \times 10^{-9} \text{ C}}{0.020 \text{ m}} + \frac{(-3.0 \times 10^{-9} \text{ C})}{0.010 \text{ m}} \right) = -1350 \text{ V}$$

$$V_a - V_b = (1350 \text{ V}) - (-1350 \text{ V}) = 2700 \text{ V}$$

Finally,

$$v = \sqrt{\frac{2(2.0 \times 10^{-9} \text{ C})(2700 \text{ V})}{5.0 \times 10^{-9} \text{ kg}}} = 46 \text{ m/s}$$

EVALUATE: Our result makes sense: The positive test charge gains speed as it moves away from the positive charge and toward the negative charge. To check unit consistency in the final line of the calculation, note that 1 V = 1 J/C, so the numerator under the radical has units of J or kg · m²/s².

We can use exactly this same method to find the speed of an electron accelerated across a potential difference of 500 V in an oscilloscope tube or 20 kV in a TV picture tube. The end-of-chapter problems include several examples of such calculations.

Test Your Understanding of Section 23.2   If the electric *potential* at a certain point is zero, does the electric *field* at that point have to be zero? (*Hint:* Consider point *c* in Example 23.4 and Example 21.9.)

23.3 Calculating Electric Potential

When calculating the potential due to a charge distribution, we usually follow one of two routes. If we know the charge distribution, we can use Eq. (23.15) or (23.16). Or if we know how the electric field depends on position, we can use Eq. (23.17), defining the potential to be zero at some convenient place. Some problems require a combination of these approaches.

As you read through these examples, compare them with the related examples of calculating electric *field* in Section 21.5. You'll see how much easier it is to calculate scalar electric potentials than vector electric fields. The moral is clear: Whenever possible, solve problems using an energy approach (using electric potential and electric potential energy) rather than a dynamics approach (using electric fields and electric forces).

Problem-Solving Strategy 23.1 | Calculating Electric Potential

IDENTIFY *the relevant concepts:* Remember that potential is *potential energy per unit charge.* Understanding this statement can get you a long way.

SET UP *the problem* using the following steps:
1. Make a drawing that clearly shows the locations of the charges (which may be point charges or a continuous distribution of charge) and your choice of coordinate axes.
2. Indicate on your drawing the position of the point at which you want to calculate the electric potential V. Sometimes this position will be an arbitrary one (say, a point a distance r from the center of a charged sphere).

EXECUTE *the solution* as follows:
1. To find the potential due to a collection of point charges, use Eq. (23.15). If you are given a continuous charge distribution, devise a way to divide it into infinitesimal elements and then use Eq. (23.16). Carry out the integration, using appropriate limits to include the entire charge distribution. In the integral, be careful about which geometric quantities vary and which are held constant.
2. If you are given the electric field, or if you can find it using any of the methods presented in Chapter 21 or 22, it may be easier to use Eq. (23.17) or (23.18) to calculate the potential difference between points *a* and *b*. When appropriate, make use of your freedom to define V to be zero at some convenient place, and choose this place to be point *b*. (For point charges, this will usually be at infinity. For other distributions of charge—especially those that themselves extend to infinity—it may be convenient or necessary to define V_b to be zero at some finite distance from the charge distribution. This is just like defining U to be zero at ground level in gravitational problems.) Then the potential at any other point, say *a*, can be found from Eq. (23.17) or (23.18) with $V_b = 0$.
3. Remember that potential is a *scalar* quantity, not a *vector*. It doesn't have components! However, you may have to use components of the vectors $\vec{E}$ and $d\vec{l}$ when you use Eq. (23.17) or (23.18).

EVALUATE *your answer:* Check whether your answer agrees with your intuition. If your result gives V as a function of position, make a graph of this function to see whether it makes sense. If you know the electric field, you can make a rough check of your result for V by verifying that V decreases if you move in the direction of $\vec{E}$.

Example 23.8 **A charged conducting sphere**

A solid conducting sphere of radius R has a total charge q. Find the potential everywhere, both outside and inside the sphere.

SOLUTION

IDENTIFY: We used Gauss's law in Example 22.5 (Section 22.4) to find the electric field at all points for this charge distribution. We can use that result to determine the potential at all points.

SET UP: We choose the origin at the center of the sphere. Since we know E at all values of the distance r from the center of the sphere, we can determine V as a function of r.

EXECUTE: From Example 22.5, at all points *outside* the sphere the field is the same as if the sphere were removed and replaced by a point charge q. We take $V = 0$ at infinity, as we did for a point charge. Then the potential at a point outside the sphere at a distance r from its center is the same as the potential due to a point charge q at the center:

$$V = \frac{1}{4\pi\epsilon_0}\frac{q}{r}$$

The potential at the surface of the sphere is $V_{surface} = q/4\pi\epsilon_0 R$.

Inside the sphere, $\vec{E}$ is zero everywhere; otherwise, charge would move within the sphere. Hence if a test charge moves from any point to any other point inside the sphere, no work is done on that charge. This means that the potential is the same at every point inside the sphere and is equal to its value $q/4\pi\epsilon_0 R$ at the surface.

EVALUATE: Figure 23.17 shows the field and potential as a function of r for a positive charge q. In this case the electric field points radially away from the sphere. As you move away from the sphere, in the direction of $\vec{E}$, V decreases (as it should). The electric field at the surface has magnitude $E_{surface} = |q|/4\pi\epsilon_0 R^2$.

23.17 Electric field magnitude E and potential V at points inside and outside a positively charged spherical conductor.

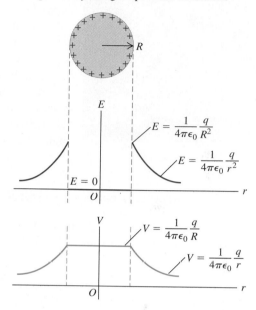

Ionization and Corona Discharge

The results of Example 23.8 have numerous practical consequences. One consequence relates to the maximum potential to which a conductor in air can be raised. This potential is limited because air molecules become *ionized*, and air becomes a conductor, at an electric-field magnitude of about 3×10^6 V/m. Assume for the moment that q is positive. When we compare the expressions in Example 23.8 for the potential $V_{surface}$ and field magnitude $E_{surface}$ at the surface of a charged conducting sphere, we note that $V_{surface} = E_{surface}R$. Thus, if E_m represents the electric-field magnitude at which air becomes conductive (known as the *dielectric strength* of air), then the maximum potential V_m to which a spherical conductor can be raised is

$$V_m = RE_m$$

For a conducting sphere 1 cm in radius in air, $V_m = (10^{-2}\,\text{m})(3 \times 10^6\,\text{V/m}) = $ 30,000 V. No amount of "charging" could raise the potential of a conducting sphere of this size in air higher than about 30,000 V; attempting to raise the potential further by adding extra charge would cause the surrounding air to become ionized and conductive, and the extra added charge would leak into the air.

To attain even higher potentials, high-voltage machines such as Van de Graaff generators use spherical terminals with very large radii (see Fig. 22.27 and the photograph that opens Chapter 22). For example, a terminal of radius $R = 2$ m has a maximum potential $V_m = (2\,\text{m})(3 \times 10^6\,\text{V/m}) = 6 \times 10^6\,\text{V} = 6$ MV. Such machines are sometimes placed in pressurized tanks filled with a gas such as sulfur hexafluoride (SF_6) that has a larger value of E_m than does air and, therefore, can withstand even larger fields without becoming conductive.

23.18 The metal mast at the top of the Empire State Building acts as a lightning rod. It is struck by lightning as many as 500 times each year.

Our result in Example 23.8 also explains what happens with a charged conductor with a very *small* radius of curvature, such as a sharp point or thin wire. Because the maximum potential is proportional to the radius, even relatively small potentials applied to sharp points in air produce sufficiently high fields just outside the point to ionize the surrounding air, making it become a conductor. The resulting current and its associated glow (visible in a dark room) are called *corona*. Laser printers and photocopying machines use corona from fine wires to spray charge on the imaging drum (see Fig. 21.2).

A large-radius conductor is used in situations where it's important to *prevent* corona. An example is the metal ball at the end of a car radio antenna, which prevents the static that would be caused by corona. Another example is the blunt end of a metal lightning rod (Fig. 23.18). If there is an excess charge in the atmosphere, as happens during thunderstorms, a substantial charge of the opposite sign can build up on this blunt end. As a result, when the atmospheric charge is discharged through a lightning bolt, it tends to be attracted to the charged lightning rod rather than to other nearby structures that could be damaged. (A conducting wire connecting the lightning rod to the ground then allows the acquired charge to dissipate harmlessly.) A lightning rod with a sharp end would allow less charge buildup and hence would be less effective.

Example 23.9 **Oppositely charged parallel plates**

Find the potential at any height y between the two oppositely charged parallel plates discussed in Section 23.1 (Fig. 23.19).

SOLUTION

IDENTIFY: From Section 23.1 we know the electric *potential energy* U for a test charge q_0 as a function of y. Our goal here is to find the electric *potential* V due to the charges on the plates as a function of y.

SET UP: From Eq. (23.5), $U = q_0 E y$ at a point a distance y above the bottom plate. We use this expression to determine the potential V at such a point.

EXECUTE: The potential $V(y)$ at coordinate y is the potential energy per unit charge:

$$V(y) = \frac{U(y)}{q_0} = \frac{q_0 E y}{q_0} = Ey$$

We have chosen $U(y)$, and therefore $V(y)$, to be zero at point b, where $y = 0$. Even if we choose the potential to be different from zero at b, it is still true that

$$V(y) - V_b = Ey$$

The potential decreases as we move in the direction of $\vec{E}$ from the upper to the lower plate. At point a, where $y = d$ and $V(y) = V_a$,

$$V_a - V_b = Ed \quad \text{and} \quad E = \frac{V_a - V_b}{d} = \frac{V_{ab}}{d}$$

where V_{ab} is the potential of the positive plate with respect to the negative plate. That is, the electric field equals the potential difference between the plates divided by the distance between them. For a given potential difference V_{ab}, the smaller the distance d between the two plates, the greater the magnitude E of the electric field. (This relationship between E and V_{ab} holds *only* for the planar geometry we have described. It does *not* work for situations such as concentric cylinders or spheres in which the electric field is not uniform.)

23.19 The charged parallel plates from Fig. 23.2

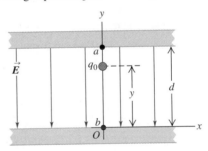

EVALUATE: Our result tells us how to measure the charge density on the charges on the two plates in Fig. 23.19. In Example 22.8 (Section 22.4), we derived the expression $E = \sigma/\epsilon_0$ for the electric field E between two conducting plates having surface charge densities $+\sigma$ and $-\sigma$. Setting this expression equal to $E = V_{ab}/d$ gives

$$\sigma = \frac{\epsilon_0 V_{ab}}{d}$$

The surface charge density on the positive plate is directly proportional to the potential difference between the plates, and its value σ can be determined by measuring V_{ab}. This technique is useful because no instruments are available that read surface charge density directly. On the negative plate the surface charge density is $-\sigma$.

CAUTION **"Zero potential" is arbitrary** You might think that if a conducting body has zero potential, it must necessarily also have zero net charge. But that just isn't so! As an example, the plate at $y = 0$ in Fig. 23.19 has zero potential ($V = 0$) but has a nonzero charge per unit area $-\sigma$. Remember that there's nothing particularly special about the place where potential is zero; we can *define* this place to be wherever we want it to be.

Example 23.10   An infinite line charge or charged conducting cylinder

Find the potential at a distance r from a very long line of charge with linear charge density (charge per unit length) λ.

SOLUTION

IDENTIFY: One approach to this problem is to divide the line of charge into infinitesimal elements, as we did in Example 21.11 (Section 21.5) to find the electric field produced by such a line. We could then integrate as in Eq. (23.16) to find the net potential V. In this case, however, our task is greatly simplified because we already know the electric field.

SET UP: In both Example 21.11 and Example 22.6 (Section 22.4), we found that the electric field at a distance r from a long straight-line charge (Fig. 23.20a) has only a radial component, given by

$$E_r = \frac{1}{2\pi\epsilon_0}\frac{\lambda}{r}.$$

We use this expression to find the potential by integrating $\vec{E}$ as in Eq. (23.17).

EXECUTE: Since the field has only a radial component, the scalar product $\vec{E}\cdot d\vec{l}$ is equal to $E_r dr$. Hence the potential of any point a with respect to any other point b, at radial distances r_a and r_b from the line of charge, is

$$V_a - V_b = \int_a^b \vec{E}\cdot d\vec{l} = \int_a^b E_r dr = \frac{\lambda}{2\pi\epsilon_0}\int_{r_a}^{r_b}\frac{dr}{r} = \frac{\lambda}{2\pi\epsilon_0}\ln\frac{r_b}{r_a}$$

If we take point b at infinity and set $V_b = 0$, we find that V_a is *infinite*:

$$V_a = \frac{\lambda}{2\pi\epsilon_0}\ln\frac{\infty}{r_a} = \infty$$

This shows that if we try to define V to be zero at infinity, then V must be infinite at *any* finite distance from the line charge. This is *not* a useful way to define V for this problem! The difficulty is that the charge distribution itself extends to infinity.

To get around this difficulty, remember that we can define V to be zero at any point we like. We set $V_b = 0$ at point b at an arbi-

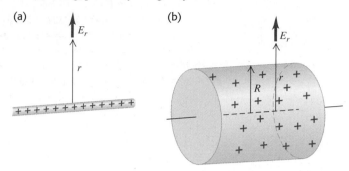

23.20 Electric field outside (a) a long positively charged wire and (b) a long, positively charged cylinder.

trary radial distance r_0. Then the potential $V = V_a$ at point a at a radial distance r is given by $V - 0 = (\lambda/2\pi\epsilon_0)\ln(r_0/r)$, or

$$V = \frac{\lambda}{2\pi\epsilon_0}\ln\frac{r_0}{r}$$

EVALUATE: According to our result, if λ is positive, then V decreases as r increases. This is as it should be: V decreases as we move in the direction of $\vec{E}$.

From Example 22.6, the expression for E_r with which we started also applies outside a long charged conducting cylinder with charge per unit length λ (Fig. 23.20b). Hence our result also gives the potential for such a cylinder, but only for values of r (the distance from the cylinder axis) equal to or greater than the radius R of the cylinder. If we choose r_0 to be the cylinder radius R, so that $V = 0$ when $r = R$, then at any point for which $r > R$,

$$V = \frac{\lambda}{2\pi\epsilon_0}\ln\frac{R}{r}$$

Inside the cylinder, $\vec{E} = \mathbf{0}$, and V has the same value (zero) as on the cylinder's surface.

Example 23.11   A ring of charge

Electric charge is distributed uniformly around a thin ring of radius a, with total charge Q (Fig. 23.21). Find the potential at a point P on the ring axis at a distance x from the center of the ring.

SOLUTION

IDENTIFY: We already know the electric field at all points along the x-axis from Example 21.10 (Section 21.5), so we could solve the problem by integrating $\vec{E}$ as in Eq. (23.17) to find V along this axis. Alternatively, we could divide the ring up into infinitesimal segments and use Eq. (23.16) to find V.

SET UP: Figure 23.21 shows that it's far easier to find V on the axis by using the infinitesimal-segment approach. That's because

23.21 All the charge in a ring of charge Q is the same distance r from a point P on the ring axis.

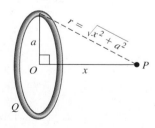

Continued

all parts of the ring (that is, all elements of the charge distribution) are the same distance r from point P.

EXECUTE: Figure 23.21 shows that the distance from each charge element dq on the ring to the point P is $r = \sqrt{x^2 + a^2}$. Hence we can take the factor $1/r$ outside the integral in Eq. (23.16), and

$$V = \frac{1}{4\pi\epsilon_0} \int \frac{dq}{r} = \frac{1}{4\pi\epsilon_0} \frac{1}{\sqrt{x^2 + a^2}} \int dq = \frac{1}{4\pi\epsilon_0} \frac{Q}{\sqrt{x^2 + a^2}}$$

Potential is a *scalar* quantity; there is no need to consider components of vectors in this calculation, as we had to do when we found

the electric field at P. So the potential calculation is a lot simpler than the field calculation.

EVALUATE: When x is much larger than a, the above expression for V becomes approximately equal to $V = Q/4\pi\epsilon_0 x$. This corresponds to the potential of a point charge Q at distance x. So when we are very far away from a charged ring, it looks like a point charge. (We drew a similar conclusion about the electric field of a ring in Example 21.10.)

These results for V can also be found by integrating the expression for E_x found in Example 21.10 (see Problem 23.69).

Example 23.12   A line of charge

Electric charge Q is distributed uniformly along a line or thin rod of length $2a$. Find the potential at a point P along the perpendicular bisector of the rod at a distance x from its center.

SOLUTION

IDENTIFY: This is the same situation as in Example 21.11 (Section 21.5), where we found an expression for the electric field $\vec{E}$ at an arbitrary point on the x-axis. We could integrate $\vec{E}$ using Eq. (23.17) to find V. Instead, we'll integrate over the charge distribution using Eq. (23.16) to get a bit more experience with this approach.

SET UP: Figure 23.22 shows the situation. Unlike the situation in Example 23.11, each charge element dQ is a different distance from point P.

EXECUTE: As in Example 21.11, the element of charge dQ corresponding to an element of length dy on the rod is given by $dQ = (Q/2a)dy$. The distance from dQ to P is $\sqrt{x^2 + y^2}$, and the contribution dV that it makes to the potential at P is

$$dV = \frac{1}{4\pi\epsilon_0} \frac{Q}{2a} \frac{dy}{\sqrt{x^2 + y^2}}$$

To get the potential at P due to the entire rod, we integrate dV over the length of the rod from $y = -a$ to $y = a$:

$$V = \frac{1}{4\pi\epsilon_0} \frac{Q}{2a} \int_{-a}^{a} \frac{dy}{\sqrt{x^2 + y^2}}$$

23.22 Our sketch for this problem.

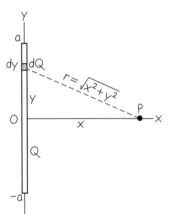

You can look up the integral in a table. The final result is

$$V = \frac{1}{4\pi\epsilon_0} \frac{Q}{2a} \ln\left(\frac{\sqrt{a^2 + x^2} + a}{\sqrt{a^2 + x^2} - a} \right)$$

EVALUATE: We can check our result by letting x approach infinity. In this limit the point P is infinitely far from all of the charge, so we expect V to approach zero; we invite you to verify that it does so.

As in Example 23.11, this problem is simpler than finding $\vec{E}$ at point P because potential is a scalar quantity and no vector calculations are involved.

Test Your Understanding of Section 23.3   If the electric *field* at a certain point is zero, does the electric *potential* at that point have to be zero? (*Hint:* Consider the center of the ring in Example 23.11 and Example 21.10.)

23.4 Equipotential Surfaces

Field lines (see Section 21.6) help us visualize electric fields. In a similar way, the potential at various points in an electric field can be represented graphically by *equipotential surfaces*. These use the same fundamental idea as topographic maps like those used by hikers and mountain climbers (Fig. 23.23). On a topographic map, contour lines are drawn through points that are all at the same elevation. Any number of these could be drawn, but typically only a few contour lines are shown at equal spacings of elevation. If a mass m is moved over the terrain along such a contour line, the gravitational potential energy mgy does not change because the elevation y is constant. Thus contour lines on a topographic map are really curves of constant gravitational potential energy. Contour lines are close together in regions where the terrain is steep and there are large changes in elevation over a small horizontal distance; the contour lines are farther apart where the terrain is gently sloping. A ball allowed to roll downhill will experience the greatest downhill gravitational force where contour lines are closest together.

By analogy to contour lines on a topographic map, an **equipotential surface** is a three-dimensional surface on which the *electric potential V* is the same at every point. If a test charge q_0 is moved from point to point on such a surface, the *electric* potential energy q_0V remains constant. In a region where an electric field is present, we can construct an equipotential surface through any point. In diagrams we usually show only a few representative equipotentials, often with equal potential differences between adjacent surfaces. No point can be at two different potentials, so equipotential surfaces for different potentials can never touch or intersect.

23.23 Contour lines on a topographic map are curves of constant elevation and hence of constant gravitational potential energy.

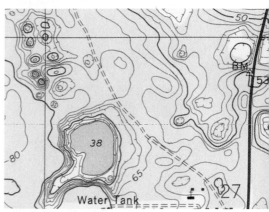

Equipotential Surfaces and Field Lines

Because potential energy does not change as a test charge moves over an equipotential surface, the electric field can do no work on such a charge. It follows that $\vec{E}$ must be perpendicular to the surface at every point so that the electric force $q_0\vec{E}$ is always perpendicular to the displacement of a charge moving on the surface. **Field lines and equipotential surfaces are always mutually perpendicular.** In general, field lines are curves, and equipotentials are curved surfaces. For the special case of a *uniform* field, in which the field lines are straight, parallel, and equally spaced, the equipotentials are parallel *planes* perpendicular to the field lines.

Figure 23.24 shows three arrangements of charges. The field lines in the plane of the charges are represented by red lines, and the intersections of the equipotential surfaces with this plane (that is, cross sections of these surfaces) are shown as blue lines. The actual equipotential surfaces are three-dimensional. At each crossing of an equipotential and a field line, the two are perpendicular.

In Fig. 23.24 we have drawn equipotentials so that there are equal potential differences between adjacent surfaces. In regions where the magnitude of $\vec{E}$ is large, the equipotential surfaces are close together because the field does a rela-

23.24 Cross sections of equipotential surfaces (blue lines) and electric field lines (red lines) for assemblies of point charges. There are equal potential differences between adjacent surfaces. Compare these diagrams to those in Fig. 21.29, which showed only the electric field lines.

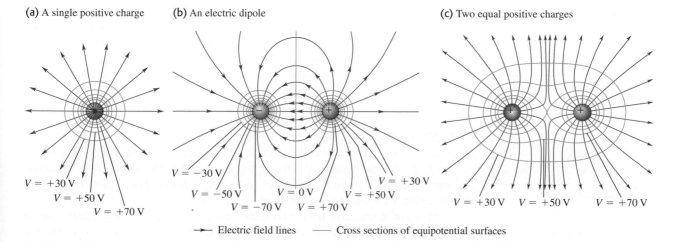

23.25 When charges are at rest, a conducting surface is always an equipotential surface. Field lines are perpendicular to a conducting surface.

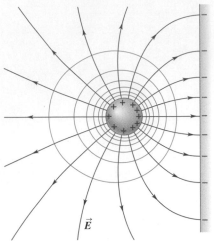

$\vec{E}$

—— Cross sections of equipotential surfaces

23.26 At all points on the surface of a conductor, the electric field must be perpendicular to the surface. If $\vec{E}$ had a tangential component, a net amount of work would be done on a test charge by moving it around a loop as shown here—which is impossible because the electric force is conservative.

An impossible electric field
If the electric field just outside a conductor had a tangential component $E_\parallel$, a charge could move in a loop with net work done.

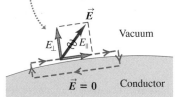

$\vec{E}$

Vacuum

$E_\perp$ $E_\parallel$

$\vec{E} = 0$ Conductor

23.27 A cavity in a conductor. If the cavity contains no charge, every point in the cavity is at the same potential, the electric field is zero everywhere in the cavity, and there is no charge anywhere on the surface of the cavity.

Cross section of equipotential surface through P

Gaussian surface (in cross section)

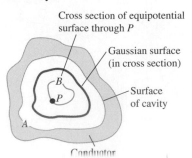

B
P

Surface of cavity

A

Conductor

tively large amount of work on a test charge in a relatively small displacement. This is the case near the point charge in Fig. 23.24a or between the two point charges in Fig. 23.24b; note that in these regions the field lines are also closer together. This is directly analogous to the downhill force of gravity being greatest in regions on a topographic map where contour lines are close together. Conversely, in regions where the field is weaker, the equipotential surfaces are farther apart; this happens at larger radii in Fig. 23.24a, to the left of the negative charge or the right of the positive charge in Fig. 23.24b, and at greater distances from both charges in Fig.23.24c. (It may appear that two equipotential surfaces intersect at the center of Fig.23.24c, in violation of the rule that this can never happen. In fact this is a single figure-8–shaped equipotential surface.)

CAUTION *E* **need not be constant over an equipotential surface** On a given equipotential surface, the potential *V* has the same value at every point. In general, however, the electric-field magnitude *E* is *not* the same at all points on an equipotential surface. For instance, on the equipotential surface labeled "*V* = −30 V" in Fig. 23.24b, the magnitude *E* is less to the left of the negative charge than it is between the two charges. On the figure-8–shaped equipotential surface in Fig. 23.24c, *E* = 0 at the middle point halfway between the two charges; at any other point on this surface, *E* is nonzero.

Equipotentials and Conductors

Here's an important statement about equipotential surfaces: **When all charges are at rest, the surface of a conductor is always an equipotential surface.** Since the electric field $\vec{E}$ is always perpendicular to an equipotential surface, we can prove this statement by proving that **when all charges are at rest, the electric field just outside a conductor must be perpendicular to the surface at every point** (Fig. 23.25). We know that $\vec{E} = \mathbf{0}$ everywhere inside the conductor; otherwise, charges would move. In particular, at any point just inside the surface the component of $\vec{E}$ tangent to the surface is zero. It follows that the tangential component of $\vec{E}$ is also zero just *outside* the surface. If it were not, a charge could move around a rectangular path partly inside and partly outside (Fig. 23.26) and return to its starting point with a net amount of work having been done on it. This would violate the conservative nature of electrostatic fields, so the tangential component of $\vec{E}$ just outside the surface must be zero at every point on the surface. Thus $\vec{E}$ is perpendicular to the surface at each point, proving our statement.

Finally, we can now prove a theorem that we quoted without proof in Section 22.5. The theorem is as follows: In an electrostatic situation, if a conductor contains a cavity and if no charge is present inside the cavity, then there can be no net charge *anywhere* on the surface of the cavity. This means that if you're inside a charged conducting box, you can safely touch any point on the inside walls of the box without being shocked. To prove this theorem, we first prove that *every point in the cavity is at the same potential.* In Fig. 23.27 the conducting surface *A* of the cavity is an equipotential surface, as we have just proved. Suppose point *P* in the cavity is at a different potential; then we can construct a different equipotential surface *B* including point *P*.

Now consider a Gaussian surface, shown in Fig. 23.27, between the two equipotential surfaces. Because of the relationship between $\vec{E}$ and the equipotentials, we know that the field at every point between the equipotentials is from *A* toward *B*, or else at every point it is from *B* toward *A*, depending on which equipotential surface is at higher potential. In either case the flux through this Gaussian surface is certainly not zero. But then Gauss's law says that the charge enclosed by the Gaussian surface cannot be zero. This contradicts our initial assumption that there is *no* charge in the cavity. So the potential at *P* cannot be different from that at the cavity wall.

The entire region of the cavity must therefore be at the same potential. But for this to be true, *the electric field inside the cavity must be zero everywhere,*

Finally, Gauss's law shows that the electric field at any point on the surface of a conductor is proportional to the surface charge density σ at that point. We conclude that *the surface charge density on the wall of the cavity is zero at every point*. This chain of reasoning may seem tortuous, but it is worth careful study.

CAUTION   **Equipotential surfaces vs. Gaussian surfaces**   Don't confuse equipotential surfaces with the Gaussian surfaces we encountered in Chapter 22. Gaussian surfaces have relevance only when we are using Gauss's law, and we can choose *any* Gaussian surface that's convenient. We are *not* free to choose the shape of equipotential surfaces; the shape is determined by the charge distribution. ▮

Test Your Understanding of Section 23.4   Would the shapes of the equipotential surfaces in Fig. 23.24 change if the sign of each charge were reversed?
▮

23.5 Potential Gradient

Electric field and potential are closely related. Equation (23.17), restated here, expresses one aspect of that relationship:

$$V_a - V_b = \int_a^b \vec{E} \cdot d\vec{l}$$

Act|v
ONLINE
Phys|cs

11.12.3   Electric Potential, Field, and Force

If we know $\vec{E}$ at various points, we can use this equation to calculate potential differences. In this section we show how to turn this around; if we know the potential V at various points, we can use it to determine $\vec{E}$. Regarding V as a function of the coordinates (x, y, z) of a point in space, we will show that the components of $\vec{E}$ are directly related to the *partial derivatives* of V with respect to x, y, and z.

In Eq. (23.17), $V_a - V_b$ is the potential of a with respect to b—that is, the change of potential encountered on a trip from b to a. We can write this as

$$V_a - V_b = \int_b^a dV = -\int_a^b dV$$

where dV is the infinitesimal change of potential accompanying an infinitesimal element $d\vec{l}$ of the path from b to a. Comparing to Eq. (23.17), we have

$$-\int_a^b dV = \int_a^b \vec{E} \cdot d\vec{l}$$

These two integrals must be equal for *any* pair of limits a and b, and for this to be true the *integrands* must be equal. Thus, for *any* infinitesimal displacement $d\vec{l}$,

$$-dV = \vec{E} \cdot d\vec{l}$$

To interpret this expression, we write $\vec{E}$ and $d\vec{l}$ in terms of their components: $\vec{E} = \hat{\imath} E_x + \hat{\jmath} E_y + \hat{k} E_z$ and $d\vec{l} = \hat{\imath} dx + \hat{\jmath} dy + \hat{k} dz$. Then we have

$$-dV = E_x dx + E_y dy + E_z dz$$

Suppose the displacement is parallel to the x-axis, so $dy = dz = 0$. Then $-dV = E_x dx$ or $E_x = -(dV/dx)_{y, z\,\text{constant}}$, where the subscript reminds us that only x varies in the derivative; recall that V is in general a function of x, y, and z. But this is just what is meant by the partial derivative $\partial V/\partial x$. The y- and z-components of $\vec{E}$ are related to the corresponding derivatives of V in the same way, so we have

$$E_x = -\frac{\partial V}{\partial x} \qquad E_y = -\frac{\partial V}{\partial y} \qquad E_z = -\frac{\partial V}{\partial z} \qquad \begin{array}{l}(\text{components of } \vec{E} \\ \text{in terms of } V)\end{array} \qquad (23.19)$$

This is consistent with the units of electric field being V/m. In terms of unit vectors we can write $\vec{E}$ as

$$\vec{E} = -\left(\hat{\imath}\frac{\partial V}{\partial x} + \hat{\jmath}\frac{\partial V}{\partial y} + \hat{k}\frac{\partial V}{\partial z}\right) \qquad (\vec{E} \text{ in terms of } V) \qquad (23.20)$$

In vector notation the following operation is called the **gradient** of the function f:

$$\vec{\nabla}f = \left(\hat{\imath}\frac{\partial}{\partial x} + \hat{\jmath}\frac{\partial}{\partial y} + \hat{k}\frac{\partial}{\partial z}\right)f \qquad (23.21)$$

The operator denoted by the symbol $\vec{\nabla}$ is called "grad" or "del." Thus in vector notation,

$$\vec{E} = -\vec{\nabla}V \qquad (23.22)$$

This is read "$\vec{E}$ is the negative of the gradient of V" or "$\vec{E}$ equals negative grad V." The quantity $\vec{\nabla}V$ is called the *potential gradient*.

At each point, the potential gradient points in the direction in which V *increases* most rapidly with a change in position. Hence at each point the direction of $\vec{E}$ is the direction in which V *decreases* most rapidly and is always perpendicular to the equipotential surface through the point. This agrees with our observation in Section 23.2 that moving in the direction of the electric field means moving in the direction of decreasing potential.

Equation (23.22) doesn't depend on the particular choice of the zero point for V. If we were to change the zero point, the effect would be to change V at every point by the same amount; the derivatives of V would be the same.

If $\vec{E}$ is radial with respect to a point or an axis and r is the distance from the point or the axis, the relationship corresponding to Eqs. (23.19) is

$$E_r = -\frac{\partial V}{\partial r} \qquad \text{(radial electric field)} \qquad (23.23)$$

Often we can compute the electric field caused by a charge distribution in either of two ways: directly, by adding the $\vec{E}$ fields of point charges, or by first calculating the potential and then taking its gradient to find the field. The second method is often easier because potential is a *scalar* quantity, requiring at worst the integration of a scalar function. Electric field is a *vector* quantity, requiring computation of components for each element of charge and a separate integration for each component. Thus, quite apart from its fundamental significance, potential offers a very useful computational technique in field calculations. Below, we present two examples in which a knowledge of V is used to find the electric field.

We stress once more that if we know $\vec{E}$ as a function of position, we can calculate V using Eq. (23.17) or (23.18), and if we know V as a function of position, we can calculate $\vec{E}$ using Eq. (23.19), (23.20), or (23.23). Deriving V from $\vec{E}$ requires integration, and deriving $\vec{E}$ from V requires differentiation.

Example 23.13 Potential and field of a point charge

From Eq. (23.14) the potential at a radial distance r from a point charge q is $V = q/4\pi\epsilon_0 r$. Find the vector electric field from this expression for V.

SOLUTION

IDENTIFY: This problem uses the relationship between the electric potential as a function of position and the electric field vector.

SET UP: By symmetry, the electric field has only a radial component E_r. We use Eq. (23.23) to find this component.

EXECUTE: From Eq. (23.23),

$$E_r = -\frac{\partial V}{\partial r} = -\frac{\partial}{\partial r}\left(\frac{1}{4\pi\epsilon_0}\frac{q}{r}\right) = \frac{1}{4\pi\epsilon_0}\frac{q}{r^2}$$

so the vector electric field is

$$\vec{E} = \hat{r}E_r = \frac{1}{4\pi\epsilon_0}\frac{q}{r^2}\hat{r}$$

EVALUATE: Our result agrees with Eq. (21.7), as it must.

An alternative approach is to ignore the radial symmetry, write the radial distance as $r = \sqrt{x^2 + y^2 + z^2}$, and take the derivatives of V with respect to x, y, and z as in Eq. (23.20). We find

$$\frac{\partial V}{\partial x} = \frac{\partial}{\partial x}\left(\frac{1}{4\pi\epsilon_0}\frac{q}{\sqrt{x^2 + y^2 + z^2}}\right) = -\frac{1}{4\pi\epsilon_0}\frac{qx}{(x^2 + y^2 + z^2)^{3/2}}$$

$$= -\frac{qx}{4\pi\epsilon_0 r^3}$$

and similarly

$$\frac{\partial V}{\partial y} = -\frac{qy}{4\pi\epsilon_0 r^3} \qquad \frac{\partial V}{\partial z} = -\frac{qz}{4\pi\epsilon_0 r^3}$$

From Eq. (23.20), the electric field is

$$\vec{E} = -\left[\hat{i}\left(-\frac{qx}{4\pi\epsilon_0 r^3}\right) + \hat{j}\left(-\frac{qy}{4\pi\epsilon_0 r^3}\right) + \hat{k}\left(-\frac{qz}{4\pi\epsilon_0 r^3}\right)\right]$$

$$= \frac{1}{4\pi\epsilon_0}\frac{q}{r^2}\left(\frac{x\hat{i} + y\hat{j} + z\hat{k}}{r}\right) = \frac{1}{4\pi\epsilon_0}\frac{q}{r^2}\hat{r}$$

This approach gives us the same answer, but with a bit more effort. Clearly it's best to exploit the symmetry of the charge distribution whenever possible.

Example 23.14   Potential and field of a ring of charge

In Example 23.11 (Section 23.3) we found that for a ring of charge with radius a and total charge Q, the potential at a point P on the ring axis a distance x from the center is

$$V = \frac{1}{4\pi\epsilon_0}\frac{Q}{\sqrt{x^2 + a^2}}$$

Find the electric field at P.

SOLUTION

IDENTIFY: We are given V as a function of x along the x-axis, and we wish to find the electric field at a point on this axis.

SET UP: From the symmetry of the charge distribution shown in Fig. 23.21, the electric field along the symmetry axis of the ring can have only an x-component. We find it using the first of Eqs. (23.19).

EXECUTE: The x-component of the electric field is

$$E_x = -\frac{\partial V}{\partial x} = \frac{1}{4\pi\epsilon_0}\frac{Qx}{(x^2 + a^2)^{3/2}}$$

EVALUATE: This agrees with the result that we obtained in Example 21.10 (Section 21.5).

CAUTION **Don't use expressions where they don't apply** In this example, V does not appear to be a function of y or z, but it would *not* be correct to conclude that $\partial V/\partial y = \partial V/\partial z = 0$ and $E_y = E_z = 0$ everywhere. The reason is that our expression for V is valid *only for points on the x-axis*, where $y = z = 0$. Hence our expression for E_x is likewise valid on the x-axis only. If we had the complete expression for V valid at *all* points in space, then we could use it to find the components of $\vec{E}$ at any point using Eq. (23.19).

Test Your Understanding of Section 23.5   In a certain region of space the potential is given by $V = A + Bx + Cy^3 + Dxy$, where A, B, C, and D are positive constants. Which of these statements about the electric field $\vec{E}$ in this region of space is correct? (There may be more than one correct answer.) (i) Increasing the value of A will increase the value of $\vec{E}$ at all points; (ii) increasing the value of A will decrease the value of $\vec{E}$ at all points; (iii) $\vec{E}$ has no z-component; (iv) the electric field is zero at the origin $(x = 0, y = 0, z = 0)$.

Electric potential energy: The electric force caused by any collection of charges at rest is a conservative force. The work W done by the electric force on a charged particle moving in an electric field can be represented by the change in a potential-energy function U.

The electric potential energy for two point charges q and q_0 depends on their separation r. The electric potential energy for a charge q_0 in the presence of a collection of charges q_1, q_2, q_3 depends on the distance from q_0 to each of these other charges. (See Examples 23.1 and 23.2.)

$$W_{a \to b} = U_a - U_b \qquad (23.2)$$

$$U = \frac{1}{4\pi\epsilon_0}\frac{qq_0}{r} \qquad (23.9)$$
(two point charges)

$$U = \frac{q_0}{4\pi\epsilon_0}\left(\frac{q_1}{r_1} + \frac{q_2}{r_2} + \frac{q_3}{r_3} + \cdots\right)$$
$$= \frac{q_0}{4\pi\epsilon_0}\sum_i \frac{q_i}{r_i} \qquad (23.10)$$
(q_0 in presence of other point charges)

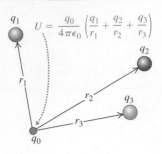

$$U = \frac{q_0}{4\pi\epsilon_0}\left(\frac{q_1}{r_1} + \frac{q_2}{r_2} + \frac{q_3}{r_3}\right)$$

Electric potential: Potential, denoted by V, is potential energy per unit charge. The potential difference between two points equals the amount of work that would be required to move a unit positive test charge between those points. The potential V due to a quantity of charge can be calculated by summing (if the charge is a collection of point charges) or by integrating (if the charge is a distribution). (See Examples 23.3, 23.4, 23.5, 23.7, 23.11, and 23.12.)

The potential difference between two points a and b, also called the potential of a with respect to b, is given by the line integral of $\vec{E}$. The potential at a given point can be found by first finding $\vec{E}$ and then carrying out this integral. (See Examples 23.6, 23.8, 23.9, and 23.10.)

$$V = \frac{U}{q_0} = \frac{1}{4\pi\epsilon_0}\frac{q}{r} \qquad (23.14)$$
(due to a point charge)

$$V = \frac{U}{q_0} = \frac{1}{4\pi\epsilon_0}\sum_i \frac{q_i}{r_i} \qquad (23.15)$$
(due to a collection of point charges)

$$V = \frac{1}{4\pi\epsilon_0}\int \frac{dq}{r} \qquad (23.16)$$
(due to a charge distribution)

$$V_a - V_b = \int_a^b \vec{E} \cdot d\vec{l} = \int_a^b E\cos\phi\, dl \qquad (23.17)$$

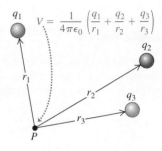

$$V = \frac{1}{4\pi\epsilon_0}\left(\frac{q_1}{r_1} + \frac{q_2}{r_2} + \frac{q_3}{r_3}\right)$$

Equipotential surfaces: An equipotential surface is a surface on which the potential has the same value at every point. At a point where a field line crosses an equipotential surface, the two are perpendicular. When all charges are at rest, the surface of a conductor is always an equipotential surface and all points in the interior of a conductor are at the same potential. When a cavity within a conductor contains no charge, the entire cavity is an equipotential region and there is no surface charge anywhere on the surface of the cavity.

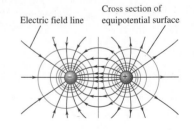

Electric field line   Cross section of equipotential surface

Finding electric field from electric potential: If the potential V is known as a function of the coordinates x, y, and z, the components of electric field $\vec{E}$ at any point are given by partial derivatives of V. (See Examples 23.13 and 23.14.)

$$E_x = -\frac{\partial V}{\partial x} \quad E_y = -\frac{\partial V}{\partial y} \quad E_z = -\frac{\partial V}{\partial z} \qquad (23.19)$$

$$\vec{E} = -\left(\hat{\imath}\frac{\partial V}{\partial x} + \hat{\jmath}\frac{\partial V}{\partial y} + \hat{k}\frac{\partial V}{\partial z}\right) \qquad (23.20)$$
(vector form)

Key Terms

(electric) potential energy, *781*

(electric) potential, *787*

volt, *787*

voltage, *788*

electron volt, *790*

equipotential surface, *799*

gradient, *802*

Answer to Chapter Opening Question ?

A large, constant potential difference V_{ab} is maintained between the welding tool (a) and the metal pieces to be welded (b). From Example 23.9 (Section 23.3) the electric field between two conductors separated by a distance d has magnitude $E = V_{ab}/d$. Hence d must be small in order for the field magnitude E to be large enough to ionize the gas between the conductors a and b (see Section 23.3) and produce an arc through this gas.

Answers to Test Your Understanding Questions

23.1 Answers: (a) (i), (b) (ii)   The three charges q_1, q_2, and q_3 are all positive, so all three of the terms in the sum in Eq. (23.11)— $q_1 q_2/r_{12}$, $q_1 q_3/r_{13}$, and $q_2 q_3/r_{23}$—are positive. Hence the total electric potential energy U is positive. This means that it would take positive work to bring the three charges from infinity to the positions shown in Fig. 21.14, and hence *negative* work to move the three charges from these positions back to infinity.

23.2 Answer: no   If $V = 0$ at a certain point, $\vec{E}$ does *not* have to be zero at that point. An example is point c in Figs. 21.23 and 23.14, for which there is an electric field in the $+x$-direction (see Example 21.9 in Section 21.5) even though $V = 0$ (see Example 23.4). This isn't a surprising result because V and $\vec{E}$ are quite different quantities: V is the net amount of work required to bring a unit charge from infinity to the point in question, whereas $\vec{E}$ is the electric force that acts on a unit charge when it arrives at that point.

23.3 Answer: no   If $\vec{E} = 0$ at a certain point, V does *not* have to be zero at that point. An example is point O at the center of the charged ring in Figs. 21.24 and 23.21. From Example 21.10 (Section 21.5), the electric field is zero at O because the electric-field contributions from different parts of the ring completely cancel. From Example 23.11, however, the potential at O is *not* zero: This point corresponds to $x = 0$, so $V = (1/4\pi\epsilon_0)(Q/a)$. This value of V corresponds to the work that would have to be done to move a unit positive test charge along a path from infinity to point O; it is nonzero because the charged ring repels the test charge, so positive work must be done to move the test charge toward the ring.

23.4 Answer: no   If the positive charges in Fig. 23.24 were replaced by negative charges, and vice versa, the equipotential surfaces would be the same but the sign of the potential would be reversed. For example, the surfaces in Fig. 23.24b with potential $V = +30$ V and $V = -50$ V would have potential $V = -30$ V and $V = +50$ V, respectively.

23.5 Answer: (iii)   From Eqs. (23.19), the components of the electric field are $E_x = -\partial V/\partial x = B + Dy$, $E_y = -\partial V/\partial y = 3Cy^2 + Dx$, and $E_z = -\partial V/\partial z = 0$. The value of A has no effect, which means that we can add a constant to the electric potential at all points without changing $\vec{E}$ or the potential difference between two points. The potential does not depend on z, so the z-component of $\vec{E}$ is zero. Note that at the origin the electric field is not zero because it has a nonzero x-component: $E_x = B$, $E_y = 0$, $E_z = 0$.

PROBLEMS

For instructor-assigned homework, go to **www.masteringphysics.com**

Discussion Questions

Q23.1. A student asked, "Since electrical potential is always proportional to potential energy, why bother with the concept of potential at all?" How would you respond?

Q23.2. The potential (relative to a point at infinity) midway between two charges of equal magnitude and opposite sign is zero. Is it possible to bring a test charge from infinity to this midpoint in such a way that no work is done in any part of the displacement? If so, describe how it can be done. If it is not possible, explain why.

Q23.3. Is it possible to have an arrangement of two point charges separated by a finite distance such that the electric potential energy of the arrangement is the same as if the two charges were infinitely far apart? Why or why not? What if there are three charges? Explain your reasoning.

Q23.4. Since potential can have any value you want depending on the choice of the reference level of zero potential, how does a voltmeter know what to read when you connect it between two points?

Q23.5. If $\vec{E}$ is zero everywhere along a certain path that leads from point A to point B, what is the potential difference between those two points? Does this mean that $\vec{E}$ is zero everywhere along *any* path from A to B? Explain.

Q23.6. If $\vec{E}$ is zero throughout a certain region of space, is the potential necessarily also zero in this region? Why or why not? If not, what *can* be said about the potential?

Q23.7. If you carry out the integral of the electric field $\int \vec{E} \cdot d\vec{l}$ for a *closed* path like that shown in Fig. 23.28, the integral will *always* be equal to zero, independent of the shape of the path and independent of where charges may be located relative to the path. Explain why.

Figure **23.28** Question Q23.7.

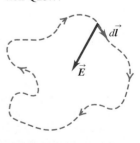

Q23.8. The potential difference between the two terminals of an AA battery (used in flashlights and portable stereos) is 1.5 V. If two AA batteries are placed end to end with the positive terminal of one battery touching the negative terminal of the other, what is the potential difference between the terminals at the exposed ends of the combination? What if the two positive terminals are touching each other? Explain your reasoning.

Q23.9. It is easy to produce a potential difference of several thousand volts between your body and the floor by scuffing your shoes across a nylon carpet. When you touch a metal doorknob, you get a mild shock. Yet contact with a power line of comparable voltage would probably be fatal. Why is there a difference?

Q23.10. If the electric potential at a single point is known, can $\vec{E}$ at that point be determined? If so, how? If not, why not?

Q23.11. Because electric field lines and equipotential surfaces are always perpendicular, two equipotential surfaces can never cross; if they did, the direction of $\vec{E}$ would be ambiguous at the crossing points. Yet two equipotential surfaces appear to cross at the center of Fig. 23.24c. Explain why there is no ambiguity about the direction of $\vec{E}$ in this particular case.

Q23.12. The electric field due to a very large sheet of charge is independent of the distance from the sheet, yet the fields due to the individual point charges on the sheet all obey an inverse-square law. Why doesn't the field of the sheet get weaker at greater distances?

Q23.13. We often say that if point A is at a higher potential than point B, A is at positive potential and B is at negative potential. Does it necessarily follow that a point at positive potential is positively charged, or that a point at negative potential is negatively charged? Illustrate your answers with clear, simple examples.

Q23.14. A conducting sphere is to be charged by bringing in positive charge a little at a time until the total charge is Q. The total work required for this process is alleged to be proportional to Q^2. Is this correct? Why or why not?

Q23.15. Three pairs of parallel metal plates $(A, B, \text{and } C)$ are connected as shown in Fig. 23.29, and a battery maintains a potential of 1.5 V across ab. What can you say about the potential difference across each pair of plates? Why?

Figure 23.29 Question Q23.15.

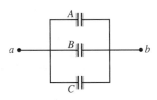

Q23.16. A conducting sphere is placed between two charged parallel plates such as those shown in Fig. 23.2. Does the electric field inside the sphere depend on precisely where between the plates the sphere is placed? What about the electric potential inside the sphere? Do the answers to these questions depend on whether or not there is a net charge on the sphere? Explain your reasoning.

Q23.17. A conductor that carries a net charge Q has a hollow, empty cavity in its interior. Does the potential vary from point to point within the material of the conductor? What about within the cavity? How does the potential inside the cavity compare to the potential within the material of the conductor?

Q23.18. A high-voltage dc power line falls on a car, so the entire metal body of the car is at a potential of 10,000 V with respect to the ground. What happens to the occupants (a) when they are sitting in the car and (b) when they step out of the car? Explain your reasoning.

Q23.19. When a thunderstorm is approaching, sailors at sea sometimes observe a phenomenon called "St. Elmo's fire," a bluish flickering light at the tips of masts. What causes this? Why does it occur at the tips of masts? Why is the effect most pronounced when the masts are wet? (*Hint:* Seawater is a good conductor of electricity.)

Q23.20. A positive point charge is placed near a very large conducting plane. A professor of physics asserted that the field caused by this configuration is the same as would be obtained by removing the plane and placing a negative point charge of equal magnitude in the mirror-image position behind the initial position of the plane. Is this correct? Why or why not? (*Hint:* Inspect Fig. 23.24b.)

Q23.21. In electronics it is customary to define the potential of ground (thinking of the earth as a large conductor) as zero. Is this consistent with the fact that the earth has a net electric charge that is not zero? (Refer to Exercise 21.32.)

Exercises

Section 23.1 Electric Potential Energy

23.1. A point charge $q_1 = +2.40 \ \mu\text{C}$ is held stationary at the origin. A second point charge $q_2 = -4.30 \ \mu\text{C}$ moves from the point $x = 0.150$ m, $y = 0$ to the point $x = 0.250$ m, $y = 0.250$ m. How much work is done by the electric force on q_2?

23.2. A point charge q_1 is held stationary at the origin. A second charge q_2 is placed at point a, and the electric potential energy of the pair of charges is $+5.4 \times 10^{-8}$ J. When the second charge is moved to point b, the electric force on the charge does -1.9×10^{-8} J of work. What is the electric potential energy of the pair of charges when the second charge is at point b?

23.3. Energy of the Nucleus. How much work is needed to assemble an atomic nucleus containing three protons (such as Be) if we model it as an equilateral triangle of side 2.00×10^{-15} m with a proton at each vertex? Assume the protons started from very far away.

23.4. (a) How much work would it take to push two protons very slowly from a separation of 2.00×10^{-10} m (a typical atomic distance) to 3.00×10^{-15} m (a typical nuclear distance)? (b) If the protons are both released from rest at the closer distance in part (a), how fast are they moving when they reach their original separation?

23.5. A small metal sphere, carrying a net charge of $q_1 = -2.80 \ \mu\text{C}$, is held in a stationary position by insulating supports. A second small metal sphere, with a net charge of $q_2 = -7.80 \ \mu\text{C}$ and mass 1.50 g, is projected toward q_1. When the two spheres are 0.800 m apart, q_2 is moving toward q_1 with speed 22.0 m/s (Fig. 23.30). Assume that the two spheres can be treated as point charges. You can ignore the force of gravity. (a) What is the speed of q_2 when the spheres are 0.400 m apart? (b) How close does q_2 get to q_1?

Figure 23.30 Exercise 23.5.

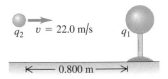

23.6. How far from a -7.20-μC point charge must a $+2.30$-μC point charge be placed for the electric potential energy U of the pair of charges to be -0.400 J? (Take U to be zero when the charges have infinite separation.)

23.7. A point charge $Q = +4.60 \ \mu\text{C}$ is held fixed at the origin. A second point charge $q = +1.20 \ \mu\text{C}$ with mass of 2.80×10^{-4} kg is placed on the x-axis, 0.250 m from the origin. (a) What is the electric potential energy U of the pair of charges? (Take U to be zero when the charges have infinite separation.) (b) The second point charge is released from rest. What is its speed when its distance from the origin is (i) 0.500 m; (ii) 5.00 m; (iii) 50.0 m?

23.8. Three equal 1.20-μC point charges are placed at the corners of an equilateral triangle whose sides are 0.500 m long. What is the potential energy of the system? (Take as zero the potential energy of the three charges when they are infinitely far apart.)

23.9. A point charge $q_1 = 4.00$ nC is placed at the origin, and a second point charge $q_2 = -3.00$ nC is placed on the x-axis at $x = +20.0$ cm. A third point charge $q_3 = 2.00$ nC is to be placed on the x-axis between q_1 and q_2. (Take as zero the potential energy of the three charges when they are infinitely far apart.) (a) What is the potential energy of the system of the three charges if q_3 is placed at $x = +10.0$ cm? (b) Where should q_3 be placed to make the potential energy of the system equal to zero?

23.10. Four electrons are located at the corners of a square 10.0 nm on a side, with an alpha particle at its midpoint. How much work is needed to move the alpha particle to the midpoint of one of the sides of the square?

23.11. Three point charges, which initially are infinitely far apart, are placed at the corners of an equilateral triangle with sides d. Two of the point charges are identical and have charge q. If zero net work is required to place the three charges at the corners of the triangle, what must the value of the third charge be?

23.12. Two protons are aimed directly toward each other by a cyclotron accelerator with speeds of 1000 km/s, measured relative to the earth. Find the maximum electrical force that these protons will exert on each other.

Section 23.2 Electric Potential

23.13. A uniform electric field is directed due east. Point B is 2.00 m west of point A, point C is 2.00 m east of point A, and point D is 2.00 m south of A. For each point, B, C, and D, is the potential at that point larger, smaller, or the same as at point A? Give the reasoning behind your answers.

23.14. Identical point charges $q = +5.00 \ \mu$C are placed at opposite corners of a square. The length of each side of the square is 0.200 m. A point charge $q_0 = -2.00 \ \mu$C is placed at one of the empty corners. How much work is done on q_0 by the electric force when q_0 is moved to the other empty corner?

23.15. A small particle has charge $-5.00 \ \mu$C and mass 2.00×10^{-4} kg. It moves from point A, where the electric potential is $V_A = +200$ V, to point B, where the electric potential is $V_B = +800$ V. The electric force is the only force acting on the particle. The particle has speed 5.00 m/s at point A. What is its speed at point B? Is it moving faster or slower at B than at A? Explain.

23.16. A particle with a charge of $+4.20$ nC is in a uniform electric field $\vec{E}$ directed to the left. It is released from rest and moves to the left; after it has moved 6.00 cm, its kinetic energy is found to be $+1.50 \times 10^{-6}$ J. (a) What work was done by the electric force? (b) What is the potential of the starting point with respect to the end point? (c) What is the magnitude of $\vec{E}$?

23.17. A charge of 28.0 nC is placed in a uniform electric field that is directed vertically upward and has a magnitude of 4.00×10^4 V/m. What work is done by the electric force when the charge moves (a) 0.450 m to the right; (b) 0.670 m upward; (c) 2.60 m at an angle of $45.0°$ downward from the horizontal?

23.18. Two stationary point charges $+3.00$ nC and $+2.00$ nC are separated by a distance of 50.0 cm. An electron is released from rest at a point midway between the two charges and moves along the line connecting the two charges. What is the speed of the electron when it is 10.0 cm from the $+3.00$-nC charge?

23.19. A point charge has a charge of 2.50×10^{-11} C. At what distance from the point charge is the electric potential (a) 90.0 V and (b) 30.0 V? Take the potential to be zero at an infinite distance from the charge.

23.20. Two charges of equal magnitude Q are held a distance d apart. Consider only points on the line passing through both charges. (a) If the two charges have the same sign, find the location of all points (if there are any) at which (i) the potential (relative to infinity) is zero (is the electric field zero at these points?), and (ii) the electric field is zero (is the potential zero at these points?). (b) Repeat part (a) for two charges having opposite signs.

23.21. Two point charges $q_1 = +2.40$ nC and $q_2 = -6.50$ nC are 0.100 m apart. Point A is midway between them; point B is 0.080 m from q_1 and 0.060 m from q_2 (Fig. 23.31). Take the electric potential to be zero at infinity. Find (a) the potential at point A; (b) the potential at point B; (c) the work done by the electric field on a charge of 2.50 nC that travels from point B to point A.

Figure 23.31 Exercise 23.21.

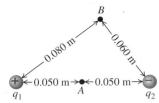

23.22. Two positive point charges, each of magnitude q, are fixed on the y-axis at the points $y = +a$ and $y = -a$. Take the potential to be zero at an infinite distance from the charges. (a) Show the positions of the charges in a diagram. (b) What is the potential V_0 at the origin? (c) Show that the potential at any point on the x-axis is

$$V = \frac{1}{4\pi\epsilon_0}\frac{2q}{\sqrt{a^2 + x^2}}$$

(d) Graph the potential on the x-axis as a function of x over the range from $x = -4a$ to $x = +4a$. (e) What is the potential when $x \gg a$? Explain why this result is obtained.

23.23. A positive charge $+q$ is located at the point $x = 0$, $y = -a$, and a negative charge $-q$ is located at the point $x = 0$, $y = +a$. (a) Show the positions of the charges in a diagram. (b) Derive an expression for the potential V at points on the x-axis as a function of the coordinate x. Take V to be zero at an infinite distance from the charges. (c) Graph V at points on the x-axis as a function of x over the range from $x = -4a$ to $x = +4a$. (d) What is the answer to part (b) if the two charges are interchanged so that $+q$ is at $y = +a$ and $-q$ is at $y = -a$?

23.24. Consider the arrangement of charges described in Exercise 23.23. (a) Derive an expression for the potential V at points on the y-axis as a function of the coordinate y. Take V to be zero at an infinite distance from the charges. (b) Graph V at points on the y-axis as a function of y over the range from $y = -4a$ to $y = +4a$. (c) Show that for $y \gg a$, the potential at a point on the positive y-axis is given by $V = (1/4\pi\epsilon_0)2qa/y^2$. (d) What are the answers to parts (a) and (c) if the two charges are interchanged so that $+q$ is at $y = +a$ and $-q$ is at $y = -a$?

23.25. A positive charge q is fixed at the point $x = 0$, $y = 0$, and a negative charge $-2q$ is fixed at the point $x = a$, $y = 0$. (a) Show the positions of the charges in a diagram. (b) Derive an expression for the potential V at points on the x-axis as a function of the coordinate x. Take V to be zero at an infinite distance from the charges. (c) At which positions on the x-axis is $V = 0$? (d) Graph V at points on the x-axis as a function of x in the range from $x = -2a$ to $x = +2a$. (e) What does the answer to part (b) become when $x \gg a$? Explain why this result is obtained.

23.26. Consider the arrangement of point charges described in Exercise 23.25. (a) Derive an expression for the potential V at points on the y-axis as a function of the coordinate y. Take V to be zero at an infinite distance from the charges. (b) At which positions on the y-axis is $V = 0$? (c) Graph V at points on the y-axis as a function of y in the range from $y = -2a$ to $y = +2a$. (d) What does the answer to part (a) become when $y \gg a$? Explain why this result is obtained.

23.27. Before the advent of solid-state electronics, vacuum tubes were widely used in radios and other devices. A simple type of vacuum tube known as a *diode* consists essentially of two electrodes within a highly evacuated enclosure. One electrode, the *cathode,* is maintained at a high temperature and emits electrons from its surface. A potential difference of a few hundred volts is maintained between the cathode and the other electrode, known as the *anode,* with the anode at the higher potential. Suppose that in a particular vacuum tube the potential of the anode is 295 V higher than that of the cathode. An electron leaves the surface of the cathode with zero initial speed. Find its speed when it strikes the anode.

23.28. At a certain distance from a point charge, the potential and electric-field magnitude due to that charge are 4.98 V and 12.0 V/m, respectively. (Take the potential to be zero at infinity.) (a) What is the distance to the point charge? (b) What is the magnitude of the charge? (c) Is the electric field directed toward or away from the point charge?

23.29. A uniform electric field has magnitude E and is directed in the negative x-direction. The potential difference between point a (at $x = 0.60$ m) and point b (at $x = 0.90$ m) is 240 V. (a) Which point, a or b, is at the higher potential? (b) Calculate the value of E. (c) A negative point charge $q = -0.200$ μC is moved from b to a. Calculate the work done on the point charge by the electric field.

23.30. For each of the following arrangements of two point charges, find all the points along the line passing through both charges for which the electric potential V is zero (take $V = 0$ infinitely far from the charges) and for which the electric field E is zero: (a) charges $+Q$ and $+2Q$ separated by a distance d, and (b) charges $-Q$ and $+2Q$ separated by a distance d. (c) Are both V and E zero at the same places? Explain.

23.31. (a) An electron is to be accelerated from 3.00×10^6 m/s to 8.00×10^6 m/s. Through what potential difference must the electron pass to accomplish this? (b) Through what potential difference must the electron pass if it is to be slowed from 8.00×10^6 m/s to a halt?

Section 23.3 Calculating Electric Potential

23.32. A total electric charge of 3.50 nC is distributed uniformly over the surface of a metal sphere with a radius of 24.0 cm. If the potential is zero at a point at infinity, find the value of the potential at the following distances from the center of the sphere: (a) 48.0 cm; (b) 24.0 cm; (c) 12.0 cm.

23.33. A uniformly charged thin ring has radius 15.0 cm and total charge +24.0 nC. An electron is placed on the ring's axis a distance 30.0 cm from the center of the ring and is constrained to stay on the axis of the ring. The electron is then released from rest. (a) Describe the subsequent motion of the electron. (b) Find the speed of the electron when it reaches the center of the ring.

23.34. An infinitely long line of charge has linear charge density 5.00×10^{-12} C/m. A proton (mass 1.67×10^{-27} kg, charge $+1.60 \times 10^{-19}$ C) is 18.0 cm from the line and moving directly toward the line at 1.50×10^3 m/s. (a) Calculate the proton's initial kinetic energy. (b) How close does the proton get to the line of charge? (*Hint:* See Example 23.10.)

23.35. A very long wire carries a uniform linear charge density λ. Using a voltmeter to measure potential difference, you find that when one probe of the meter is placed 2.50 cm from the wire and the other probe is 1.00 cm farther from the wire, the meter reads 575 V. (a) What is λ? (b) If you now place one probe at 3.50 cm from the wire and the other probe 1.00 cm farther away, will the voltmeter read 575 V? If not, will it read more or less than 575 V? Why? (c) If you place both probes 3.50 cm from the wire but 17.0 cm from each other, what will the voltmeter read?

23.36. A very long insulating cylinder of charge of radius 2.50 cm carries a uniform linear density of 15.0 nC/m. If you put one probe

of a voltmeter at the surface, how far from the surface must the other probe be placed so that the voltmeter reads 175 V?

23.37. A very long insulating cylindrical shell of radius 6.00 cm carries charge of linear density 8.50 μC/m spread uniformly over its outer surface. What would a voltmeter read if it were connected between (a) the surface of the cylinder and a point 4.00 cm above the surface, and (b) the surface and a point 1.00 cm from the central axis of the cylinder?

23.38. A ring of diameter 8.00 cm is fixed in place and carries a charge of $+5.00$ μC uniformly spread over its circumference. (a) How much work does it take to move a tiny $+3.00$-μC charged ball of mass 1.50 g from very far away to the center of the ring? (b) Is it necessary to take a path along the axis of the ring? Why? (c) If the ball is slightly displaced from the center of the ring, what will it do and what is the maximum speed it will reach?

23.39. Two very large, parallel metal plates carry charge densities of the same magnitude but opposite signs (Fig. 23.32). Assume they are close enough together to be treated as ideal infinite plates. Taking the potential to be zero at the left surface of the negative plate, sketch a graph of the potential as a function of x. Include *all* regions from the left of the plates to the right of the plates.

Figure 23.32 Exercise 23.39.

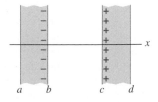

23.40. Two large, parallel conducting plates carrying opposite charges of equal magnitude are separated by 2.20 cm. (a) If the surface charge density for each plate has magnitude 47.0 nC/m², what is the magnitude of $\vec{E}$ in the region between the plates? (b) What is the potential difference between the two plates? (c) If the separation between the plates is doubled while the surface charge density is kept constant at the value in part (a), what happens to the magnitude of the electric field and to the potential difference?

23.41. Two large, parallel, metal plates carry opposite charges of equal magnitude. They are separated by 45.0 mm, and the potential difference between them is 360 V. (a) What is the magnitude of the electric field (assumed to be uniform) in the region between the plates? (b) What is the magnitude of the force this field exerts on a particle with charge $+2.40$ nC? (c) Use the results of part (b) to compute the work done by the field on the particle as it moves from the higher-potential plate to the lower. (d) Compare the result of part (c) to the change of potential energy of the same charge, computed from the electric potential.

23.42. (a) How much excess charge must be placed on a copper sphere 25.0 cm in diameter so that the potential of its center, relative to infinity, is 1.50 kV? (b) What is the potential of the sphere's surface relative to infinity?

23.43. (a) Show that V for a spherical shell of radius R, that has charge q distributed uniformly over its surface, is the same as V for a solid conductor with radius R and charge q. (b) You rub an inflated balloon on the carpet and it acquires a potential that is 1560 V lower than its potential before it became charged. If the charge is uniformly distributed over the surface of the balloon and if the radius of the balloon is 15 cm, what is the net charge on the balloon? (c) In light of its 1200-V potential difference relative to you, do you think this balloon is dangerous? Explain.

23.44. The electric field at the surface of a charged, solid, copper sphere with radius 0.200 m is 3800 N/C, directed toward the center of the sphere. What is the potential at the center of the sphere, if we take the potential to be zero infinitely far from the sphere?

Section 23.4 Equipotential Surfaces and Section 23.5 Potential Gradient

23.45. A potential difference of 480 V is established between large, parallel, metal plates. Let the potential of one plate be 480 V and the other be 0 V. The plates are separated by $d = 1.70$ cm. (a) Sketch the equipotential surfaces that correspond to 0, 120, 240, 360, and 480 V. (b) In your sketch, show the electric field lines. Does your sketch confirm that the field lines and equipotential surfaces are mutually perpendicular?

23.46. A very large plastic sheet carries a uniform charge density of -6.00 nC/m^2 on one face. (a) As you move away from the sheet along a line perpendicular to it, does the potential increase or decrease? How do you know, without doing any calculations? Does your answer depend on where you choose the reference point for potential? (b) Find the spacing between equipotential surfaces that differ from each other by 1.00 V. What type of surfaces are these?

23.47. In a certain region of space, the electric potential is $V(x, y, z) = Axy - Bx^2 + Cy$, where $A, B,$ and C are positive constants. (a) Calculate the x-, y-, and z-components of the electric field. (b) At which points is the electric field equal to zero?

23.48. The potential due to a point charge Q at the origin may be written as

$$V = \frac{Q}{4\pi\epsilon_0 r} = \frac{Q}{4\pi\epsilon_0 \sqrt{x^2 + y^2 + z^2}}$$

(a) Calculate $E_x, E_y,$ and E_z using Eqs. (23.19). (b) Show that the results of part (a) agrees with Eq. (21.7) for the electric field of a point charge.

23.49. A metal sphere with radius r_a is supported on an insulating stand at the center of a hollow, metal, spherical shell with radius r_b. There is charge $+q$ on the inner sphere and charge $-q$ on the outer spherical shell. (a) Calculate the potential $V(r)$ for (i) $r < r_a$; (ii) $r_a < r < r_b$; (iii) $r > r_b$. (*Hint:* The net potential is the sum of the potentials due to the individual spheres.) Take V to be zero when r is infinite. (b) Show that the potential of the inner sphere with respect to the outer is

$$V_{ab} = \frac{q}{4\pi\epsilon_0}\left(\frac{1}{r_a} - \frac{1}{r_b}\right)$$

(c) Use Eq. (23.23) and the result from part (a) to show that the electric field at any point between the spheres has magnitude

$$E(r) = \frac{V_{ab}}{(1/r_a - 1/r_b)}\frac{1}{r^2}$$

(d) Use Eq. (23.23) and the result from part (a) to find the electric field at a point outside the larger sphere at a distance r from the center, where $r > r_b$. (e) Suppose the charge on the outer sphere is not $-q$ but a negative charge of different magnitude, say $-Q$. Show that the answers for parts (b) and (c) are the same as before but the answer for part (d) is different.

23.50. A metal sphere with radius $r_a = 1.20$ cm is supported on an insulating stand at the center of a hollow, metal, spherical shell with radius $r_b = 9.60$ cm. Charge $+q$ is put on the inner sphere and charge $-q$ on the outer spherical shell. The magnitude of q is chosen to make the potential difference between the spheres 500 V, with the inner sphere at higher potential. (a) Use the result of Exercise 23.49(b) to calculate q. (b) With the help of the result of Exercise 23.49(a), sketch the equipotential surfaces that correspond to 500, 400, 300, 200, 100, and 0 V. (c) In your sketch, show the electric field lines. Are the electric field lines and equipo-

tential surfaces mutually perpendicular? Are the equipotential surfaces closer together when the magnitude of $\vec{E}$ is largest?

23.51. A very long cylinder of radius 2.00 cm carries a uniform charge density of 1.50 nC/m. (a) Describe the shape of the equipotential surfaces for this cylinder. (b) Taking the reference level for the zero of potential to be the surface of the cylinder, find the radius of equipotential surfaces having potentials of 10.0 V, 20.0 V, and 30.0 V. (c) Are the equipotential surfaces equally spaced? If not, do they get closer together or farther apart as r increases?

Problems

23.52. Figure 23.33 shows the potential of a charge distribution as a function of x. Sketch a graph of the electric field E_x over the region shown.

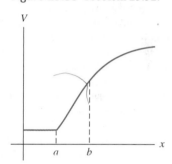

Figure **23.33** Problem 23.52.

23.53. A particle with charge $+7.60$ nC is in a uniform electric field directed to the left. Another force, in addition to the electric force, acts on the particle so that when it is released from rest, it moves to the right. After it has moved 8.00 cm, the additional force has done 6.50×10^{-5} J of work and the particle has 4.35×10^{-5} J of kinetic energy. (a) What work was done by the electric force? (b) What is the potential of the starting point with respect to the end point? (c) What is the magnitude of the electric field?

23.54. In the *Bohr model* of the hydrogen atom, a single electron revolves around a single proton in a circle of radius r. Assume that the proton remains at rest. (a) By equating the electric force to the electron mass times its acceleration, derive an expression for the electron's speed. (b) Obtain an expression for the electron's kinetic energy, and show that its magnitude is just half that of the electric potential energy. (c) Obtain an expression for the total energy, and evaluate it using $r = 5.29 \times 10^{-11}$ m. Give your numerical result in joules and in electron volts.

23.55. A vacuum tube diode (see Exercise 23.27) consists of concentric cylindrical electrodes, the negative cathode and the positive anode. Because of the accumulation of charge near the cathode, the electric potential between the electrodes is not a linear function of the position, even with planar geometry, but is given by

$$V(x) = Cx^{4/3}$$

where x is the distance from the cathode and C is a constant, characteristic of a particular diode and operating conditions. Assume that the distance between the cathode and anode is 13.0 mm and the potential difference between electrodes is 240 V. (a) Determine the value of C. (b) Obtain a formula for the electric field between the electrodes as a function of x. (c) Determine the force on an electron when the electron is halfway between the electrodes.

23.56. Two oppositely charged identical insulating spheres, each 50.0 cm in diameter and carrying a uniform charge of magnitude 175 μC, are placed

Figure 23.34 Problem 23.56.

1.00 m apart center to center (Fig. 23.34). (a) If a voltmeter is connected between the nearest points (*a* and *b*) on their surfaces, what will it read? (b) Which point, *a* or *b*, is at the higher potential? How can you know this without any calculations?

23.57. An Ionic Crystal. Figure 23.35 shows eight point charges arranged at the corners of a cube with sides of length *d*. The values of the charges are $+q$ and $-q$, as shown. This is a model of one cell of a cubic ionic crystal. In sodium chloride (NaCl), for instance, the positive ions are Na^+ and the negative ions are Cl^-. (a) Calculate the potential energy *U* of this arrangement. (Take as zero the

Figure 23.35 Problem 23.57.

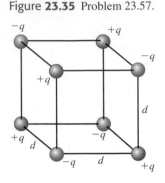

potential energy of the eight charges when they are infinitely far apart.) (b) In part (a), you should have found that $U < 0$. Explain the relationship between this result and the observation that such ionic crystals exist in nature.

23.58. (a) Calculate the potential energy of a system of two small spheres, one carrying a charge of 2.00 μC and the other a charge of $-3.50\ \mu C$, with their centers separated by a distance of 0.250 m. Assume zero potential energy when the charges are infinitely separated. (b) Suppose that one of the spheres is held in place and the other sphere, which has a mass of 1.50 g, is shot away from it. What minimum initial speed would the moving sphere need in order to escape completely from the attraction of the fixed sphere? (To escape, the moving sphere would have to reach a velocity of zero when it was infinitely distant from the fixed sphere.)

23.59. The H_2^+ Ion. The H_2^+ ion is composed of two protons, each of charge $+e = 1.60 \times 10^{-19}$ C, and an electron of charge $-e$ and mass 9.11×10^{-31} kg. The separation between the protons is 1.07×10^{-10} m. The protons and the electron may be treated as point charges. (a) Suppose the electron is located at the point midway between the two protons. What is the potential energy of the interaction between the electron and the two protons? (Do not include the potential energy due to the interaction between the two protons.) (b) Suppose the electron in part (a) has a velocity of magnitude 1.50×10^6 m/s in a direction along the perpendicular bisector of the line connecting the two protons. How far from the point midway between the two protons can the electron move? Because the masses of the protons are much greater than the electron mass, the motions of the protons are very slow and can be ignored. (*Note:* A realistic description of the electron motion requires the use of quantum mechanics, not Newtonian mechanics.)

23.60. A small sphere with mass 1.50 g hangs by a thread between two parallel vertical plates 5.00 cm apart (Fig. 23.36). The plates are insulating and have uniform surface charge densities $+\sigma$ and $-\sigma$. The charge on the sphere is $q = 8.90 \times 10^{-6}$ C. What potential difference between the plates will cause the thread to assume an angle of 30.0° with the vertical?

Figure 23.36 Problem 23.60.

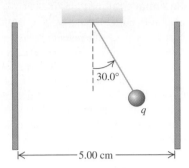

23.61. Coaxial Cylinders. A long metal cylinder with radius *a* is supported on an insulating stand on the axis of a long, hollow, metal tube with radius *b*. The positive charge per unit length on the inner cylinder is λ, and there is an equal negative charge per unit length on the outer cylinder. (a) Calculate the potential $V(r)$ for (i) $r < a$; (ii) $a < r < b$; (iii) $r > b$. (*Hint:* The net potential is the sum of the potentials due to the individual conductors.) Take $V = 0$ at $r = b$. (b) Show that the potential of the inner cylinder with respect to the outer is

$$V_{ab} = \frac{\lambda}{2\pi\epsilon_0}\ln\frac{b}{a}$$

(c) Use Eq. (23.23) and the result from part (a) to show that the electric field at any point between the cylinders has magnitude

$$E(r) = \frac{V_{ab}}{\ln(b/a)}\frac{1}{r}$$

(d) What is the potential difference between the two cylinders if the outer cylinder has no net charge?

23.62. A *Geiger counter* detects radiation such as alpha particles by using the fact that the radiation ionizes the air along its path. A thin wire lies on the axis of a hollow metal cylinder and is insulated from it (Fig. 23.37). A large potential difference is established between the wire and the outer cylinder, with the wire at higher potential; this sets up a strong electric field directed radially outward. When ionizing radiation enters the device, it ionizes a few air molecules. The free electrons produced are accelerated by the electric field toward the wire and, on the way there, ionize many more air molecules. Thus a current pulse is produced that can be detected by appropriate electronic circuitry and converted to an audible "click." Suppose the radius of the central wire is 145 μm and the radius of the hollow cylinder is 1.80 cm. What potential difference between the wire and the cylinder produces an

Figure 23.37 Problem 23.62.

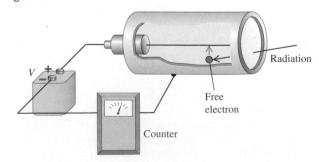

electric field of 2.00×10^4 V/m at a distance of 1.20 cm from the axis of the wire? (The wire and cylinder are both very long in comparison to their radii, so the results of Problem 23.61 apply.)

23.63. Deflection in a CRT. Cathode-ray tubes (CRTs) are often found in oscilloscopes and computer monitors. In Fig. 23.38 an electron with an initial speed of 6.50×10^6 m/s is projected along the axis midway between the deflection plates of a cathode-ray tube. The uniform electric field between the plates has a magnitude of 1.10×10^3 V/m and is upward. (a) What is the force (magnitude and direction) on the electron when it is between the plates? (b) What is the acceleration of the electron (magnitude and direction) when acted on by the force in part (a)? (c) How far below the axis has the electron moved when it reaches the end of the plates? (d) At what angle with the axis is it moving as it leaves the plates? (e) How far below the axis will it strike the fluorescent screen S?

Figure 23.38 Problem 23.63.

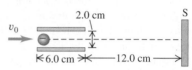

23.64. Deflecting Plates of an Oscilloscope. The vertical deflecting plates of a typical classroom oscilloscope are a pair of parallel square metal plates carrying equal but opposite charges. Typical dimensions are about 3.0 cm on a side, with a separation of about 5.0 mm. The plates are close enough that we can ignore fringing at the ends. Under these conditions: (a) how much charge is on each plate, and (b) how strong is the electric field between the plates? (c) If an electron is ejected at rest from the negative plates, how fast is it moving when it reaches the positive plate?

23.65. *Electrostatic precipitators* use electric forces to remove pollutant particles from smoke, in particular in the smokestacks of coal-burning power plants. One form of precipitator consists of a vertical, hollow, metal cylinder with a thin wire, insulated from the cylinder, running along its axis (Fig. 23.39). A large potential difference is established between the wire and the outer cylinder, with the wire at lower potential. This sets up a strong radial electric field directed inward. The field produces a region of ionized air near the wire. Smoke enters the precipitator at the bottom, ash and dust in it pick up electrons, and the charged pollutants are accelerated

Figure 23.39 Problem 23.65.

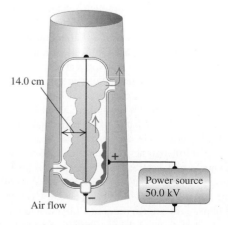

toward the outer cylinder wall by the electric field. Suppose the radius of the central wire is 90.0 μm, the radius of the cylinder is 14.0 cm, and a potential difference of 50.0 kV is established between the wire and the cylinder. Also assume that the wire and cylinder are both very long in comparison to the cylinder radius, so the results of Problem 23.61 apply. (a) What is the magnitude of the electric field midway between the wire and the cylinder wall? (b) What magnitude of charge must a 30.0-μg ash particle have if the electric field computed in part (a) is to exert a force ten times the weight of the particle?

23.66. A disk with radius R has uniform surface charge density σ. (a) By regarding the disk as a series of thin concentric rings, calculate the electric potential V at a point on the disk's axis a distance x from the center of the disk. Assume that the potential is zero at infinity. (*Hint:* Use the result of Example 23.11 in Section 23.3.) (b) Calculate $-\partial V/\partial x$. Show that the result agrees with the expression for E_x calculated in Example 21.12 (Section 21.5).

23.67. (a) From the expression for E obtained in Problem 22.40, find the expressions for the electric potential V as a function of r, both inside and outside the cylinder. Let $V = 0$ at the surface of the cylinder. In each case, express your result in terms of the charge per unit length λ of the charge distribution. (b) Graph V and E as functions of r from $r = 0$ to $r = 3R$.

23.68. Alpha particles ($mass = 6.7 \times 10^{-27}$ kg, charge $= +2e$) are shot directly at a gold foil target. We can model the gold nucleus as a uniform sphere of charge and assume that the gold does not move. (a) If the radius of the gold nucleus is 5.6×10^{-15} m, what minimum speed do the alpha particles need when they are far away to reach the surface of the gold nucleus? (Ignore relativistic effects.) (b) Give good physical reasons why we can ignore the effects of the orbital electrons when the alpha particle is (i) outside the electron orbits and (ii) inside the electron orbits.

23.69. For the ring of charge described in Example 23.11 (Section 23.3), integrate the expression for E_x found in Example 21.10 (Section 21.5) to find the potential at point P on the ring's axis. Assume that $V = 0$ at infinity. Compare your result to that obtained in Example 23.11 using Eq. (23.16).

23.70. A thin insulating rod is bent into a semicircular arc of radius a, and a total electric charge Q is distributed uniformly along the rod. Calculate the potential at the center of curvature of the arc if the potential is assumed to be zero at infinity.

23.71. Self-Energy of a Sphere of Charge. A solid sphere of radius R contains a total charge Q distributed uniformly throughout its volume. Find the energy needed to assemble this charge by bringing infinitesimal charges from far away. This energy is called the "self-energy" of the charge distribution. (*Hint:* After you have assembled a charge q in a sphere of radius r, how much energy would it take to add a spherical shell of thickness dr having charge dq? Then integrate to get the total energy.)

23.72. (a) From the expression for E obtained in Example 22.9 (Section 22.4), find the expression for the electric potential V as a function of r both inside and outside the uniformly charged sphere. Assume that $V = 0$ at infinity. (b) Graph V and E as functions of r from $r = 0$ to $r = 3R$.

23.73. A solid insulating sphere with radius R has charge Q uniformly distributed throughout its volume. (a) Use the results of Problem 23.72 to find the magnitude of the potential difference between the surface of the sphere and its center. (b) Which is at higher potential, the surface or the center, if (i) Q is positive and (ii) Q is negative?

23.74. An insulating spherical shell with inner radius 25.0 cm and outer radius 60.0 cm carries a charge of $+150.0\ \mu C$ uniformly distributed over its outer surface (see Exercise 23.43). Point a is at the center of the shell, point b is on the inner surface, and point c is on the outer surface. (a) What will a voltmeter read if it is connected between the following points: (i) a and b; (ii) b and c; (iii) c and infinity; (iv) a and c? (b) Which is at higher potential: (i) a or b; (ii) b or c; (iii) a or c? (c) Which, if any, of the answers would change sign if the charges were $-150\ \mu C$?

23.75. Exercise 23.43 shows that, outside a spherical shell with uniform surface charge, the potential is the same as if all the charge were concentrated into a point charge at the center of the sphere. (a) Use this result to show that for two uniformly charged insulating shells, the force they exert on each other and their mutual electrical energy are the same as if all the charge were concentrated at their centers. (*Hint:* See Section 12.6.) (b) Does this same result hold for solid insulating spheres, with charge distributed uniformly throughout their volume? (c) Does this same result hold for the force between two charged conducting shells? Between two charged solid conductors? Explain.

23.76. Two plastic spheres, each carrying charge uniformly distributed throughout its interior, are initially placed in contact and then released. One sphere is 60.0 cm in diameter, has mass 50.0 g and contains $-10.0\ \mu C$ of charge. The other sphere is 40.0 cm in diameter, has mass 150.0 g, and contains $-30.0\ \mu C$ of charge. Find the maximum acceleration and the maximum speed achieved by each sphere (relative to the fixed point of their initial location in space), assuming that no other forces are acting on them. (*Hint:* The uniformly distributed charges behave as though they were concentrated at the centers of the two spheres.)

23.77. Use the electric field calculated in Problem 22.43 to calculate the potential difference between the solid conducting sphere and the thin insulating shell.

23.78. Consider a solid conducting sphere inside a hollow conducting sphere, with radii and charges specified in Problem 22.42. Take $V = 0$ as $r \to \infty$. Use the electric field calculated in Problem 22.42 to calculate the potential V at the following values of r: (a) $r = c$ (at the outer surface of the hollow sphere); (b) $r = b$ (at the inner surface of the hollow sphere); (c) $r = a$ (at the surface of the solid sphere); (d) $r = 0$ (at the center of the solid sphere).

23.79. Electric charge is distributed uniformly along a thin rod of length a, with total charge Q. Take the potential to be zero at infinity. Find the potential at the following points (Fig. 23.40): (a) point P, a distance x to the right of the rod, and (b) point R, a distance y above the right-hand end of the rod. (c) In parts (a) and (b), what does your result reduce to as x or y becomes much larger than a?

Figure 23.40 Problem 23.79.

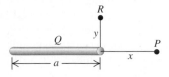

23.80. (a) If a spherical raindrop of radius 0.650 mm carries a charge of -1.20 pC uniformly distributed over its volume, what is the potential at its surface? (Take the potential to be zero at an infinite distance from the raindrop.) (b) Two identical raindrops, each with radius and charge specified in part (a), collide and merge into one larger raindrop. What is the radius of this larger drop, and what is the potential at its surface, if its charge is uniformly distributed over its volume?

23.81. Two metal spheres of different sizes are charged such that the electric potential is the same at the surface of each. Sphere A has a radius three times that of sphere B. Let Q_A and Q_B be the charges on the two spheres, and let E_A and E_B be the electric-field magnitudes at the surfaces of the two spheres. What are (a) the ratio Q_B/Q_A and (b) the ratio E_B/E_A?

23.82. An alpha particle with kinetic energy 11.0 MeV makes a head-on collision with a lead nucleus at rest. What is the distance of closest approach of the two particles? (Assume that the lead nucleus remains stationary and that it may be treated as a point charge. The atomic number of lead is 82. The alpha particle is a helium nucleus, with atomic number 2.)

23.83. A metal sphere with radius R_1 has a charge Q_1. Take the electric potential to be zero at an infinite distance from the sphere. (a) What are the electric field and electric potential at the surface of the sphere? This sphere is now connected by a long, thin conducting wire to another sphere of radius R_2 that is several meters from the first sphere. Before the connection is made, this second sphere is uncharged. After electrostatic equilibrium has been reached, what are (b) the total charge on each sphere; (c) the electric potential at the surface of each sphere (d) the electric field at the surface of each sphere? Assume that the amount of charge on the wire is much less than the charge on each sphere.

23.84. Use the charge distribution and electric field calculated in Problem 22.57. (a) Show that for $r \geq R$ the potential is identical to that produced by a point charge Q. (Take the potential to be zero at infinity.) (b) Obtain an expression for the electric potential valid in the region $r \leq R$.

23.85. Nuclear Fusion in the Sun. The source of the sun's energy is a sequence of nuclear reactions that occur in its core. The first of these reactions involves the collision of two protons, which fuse together to form a heavier nucleus and release energy. For this process, called *nuclear fusion,* to occur, the two protons must first approach until their surfaces are essentially in contact. (a) Assume both protons are moving with the same speed and they collide head-on. If the radius of the proton is 1.2×10^{-15} m, what is the minimum speed that will allow fusion to occur? The charge distribution within a proton is spherically symmetric, so the electric field and potential outside a proton are the same as if it were a point charge. The mass of the proton is 1.67×10^{-27} kg. (b) Another nuclear fusion reaction that occurs in the sun's core involves a collision between two helium nuclei, each of which has 2.99 times the mass of the proton, charge $+2e$, and radius 1.7×10^{-15} m. Assuming the same collision geometry as in part (a), what minimum speed is required for this fusion reaction to take place if the nuclei must approach a center-to-center distance of about 3.5×10^{-15} m? As for the proton, the charge of the helium nucleus is uniformly distributed throughout its volume. (c) In Section 18.3 it was shown that the average translational kinetic energy of a particle with mass m in a gas at absolute temperature T is $\frac{3}{2}kT$, where k is the Boltzmann constant (given in Appendix F). For two protons with kinetic energy equal to this average value to be able to undergo the process described in part (a), what absolute temperature is required? What absolute temperature is required for two average helium nuclei to be able to undergo the process described in part (b)? (At these temperatures, atoms are completely ionized, so nuclei and electrons move separately.) (d) The temperature in the sun's core is about 1.5×10^7 K. How does this compare to the temperatures calculated in parts (c)? How can the reactions described in parts (a) and (b) occur at all in the interior of the sun? (*Hint:* See the discussion of the distribution of molecular speeds in Section 18.5.)

23.86. The electric potential V in a region of space is given by

$$V(x, y, z) = A(x^2 - 3y^2 + z^2)$$

where A is a constant. (a) Derive an expression for the electric field $\vec{E}$ at any point in this region. (b) The work done by the field when a 1.50-μC test charge moves from the point $(x, y, z) = (0, 0, 0.250 \text{ m})$ to the origin is measured to be 6.00×10^{-5} J. Determine A. (c) Determine the electric field at the point $(0, 0, 0.250$ m). (d) Show that in every plane parallel to the xz-plane the equipotential contours are circles. (e) What is the radius of the equipotential contour corresponding to $V = 1280$ V and $y = 2.00$ m?

23.87. Nuclear Fission. The unstable nucleus of uranium-236 can be regarded as a uniformly charged sphere of charge $Q = +92e$ and radius $R = 7.4 \times 10^{-15}$ m. In nuclear fission, this can divide into two smaller nuclei, each with half the charge and half the volume of the original uranium-236 nucleus. This is one of the reactions that occurred in the nuclear weapon that exploded over Hiroshima, Japan, in August 1945. (a) Find the radii of the two "daughter" nuclei of charge $+46e$. (b) In a simple model for the fission process, immediately after the uranium-236 nucleus has undergone fission, the "daughter" nuclei are at rest and just touching, as shown in Fig. 23.41. Calculate the kinetic energy that each of the "daughter" nuclei will have when they are very far apart. (c) In this model the sum of the kinetic energies of the two "daughter" nuclei, calculated in part (b), is the energy released by the fission of one uranium-236 nucleus. Calculate the energy released by the fission of 10.0 kg of uranium-236. The atomic mass of uranium-236 is 236 u, where 1 u = 1 atomic mass unit = 1.66×10^{-24} kg. Express your answer both in joules and in kilotons of TNT (1 kiloton of TNT releases 4.18×10^{12} J when it explodes). (d) In terms of this model, discuss why an atomic bomb could just as well be called an "electric bomb."

Figure 23.41 Problem 23.87.

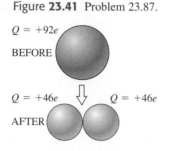

BEFORE $Q = +92e$

$Q = +46e$ $\Downarrow$ $Q = +46e$

AFTER

Challenge Problems

23.88. In a certain region, a charge distribution exists that is spherically symmetric but nonuniform. That is, the volume charge density $\rho(r)$ depends on the distance r from the center of the distribution but not on the spherical polar angles θ and ϕ. The electric potential $V(r)$ due to this charge distribution is

$$V(r) = \begin{cases} \dfrac{\rho_0 a^2}{18\epsilon_0} \left[1 - 3\left(\dfrac{r}{a}\right)^2 + 2\left(\dfrac{r}{a}\right)^3 \right] & \text{for } r \le a \\ 0 & \text{for } r \ge a \end{cases}$$

where ρ_0 is a constant having units of C/m^3 and a is a constant having units of meters. (a) Derive expressions for $\vec{E}$ for the regions $r \le a$ and $r \ge a$. [Hint: Use Eq. (23.23).] Explain why $\vec{E}$ has only a radial component. (b) Derive an expression for $\rho(r)$ in each of the two regions $r \le a$ and $r \ge a$. [Hint: Use Gauss's law for two spherical shells, one of radius r and the other of radius $r + dr$. The charge contained in the infinitesimal spherical shell of radius dr is $dq = 4\pi r^2 \rho(r) dr$.] (c) Show that the net charge contained in the volume of a sphere of radius greater than or equal to a is zero. [Hint: Integrate the expressions derived in part (b) for $\rho(r)$ over a spherical volume of radius greater than or equal to a.] Is this result consistent with the electric field for $r > a$ that you calculated in part (a)?

23.89. In experiments in which atomic nuclei collide, head-on collisions like that described in Problem 23.82 do happen, but "near misses" are more common. Suppose the alpha particle in Problem 23.82 was not "aimed" at the center of the lead nucleus, but had an initial nonzero angular momentum (with respect to the stationary lead nucleus) of magnitude $L = p_0 b$, where p_0 is the magnitude of the initial momentum of the alpha particle and $b = 1.00 \times 10^{-12}$ m. What is the distance of closest approach? Repeat for $b = 1.00 \times 10^{-13}$ m and $b = 1.00 \times 10^{-14}$ m.

23.90. A hollow, thin-walled insulating cylinder of radius R and length L (like the cardboard tube in a roll of toilet paper) has charge Q uniformly distributed over its surface. (a) Calculate the electric potential at all points along the axis of the tube. Take the origin to be at the center of the tube, and take the potential to be zero at infinity. (b) Show that if $L \ll R$, the result of part (a) reduces to the potential on the axis of a ring of charge of radius R (See Example 23.11 in Section 23.3). (c) Use the result of part (a) to find the electric field at all points along the axis of the tube.

23.91. The Millikan Oil-Drop Experiment. The charge of an electron was first measured by the American physicist Robert Millikan during 1909–1913. In his experiment, oil is sprayed in very fine drops (around 10^{-4} mm in diameter) into the space between two parallel horizontal plates separated by a distance d. A potential difference V_{AB} is maintained between the parallel plates, causing a downward electric field between them. Some of the oil drops acquire a negative charge because of frictional effects or because of ionization of the surrounding air by x rays or radioactivity. The drops are observed through a microscope. (a) Show that an oil drop of radius r at rest between the plates will remain at rest if the magnitude of its charge is

$$q = \frac{4\pi}{3} \frac{\rho r^3 g d}{V_{AB}}$$

where ρ is the density of the oil. (Ignore the buoyant force of the air.) By adjusting V_{AB} to keep a given drop at rest, the charge on that drop can be determined, provided its radius is known. (b) Millikan's oil drops were much too small to measure their radii directly. Instead, Millikan determined r by cutting off the electric field and measuring the *terminal speed* v_t of the drop as it fell. (We discussed the concept of terminal speed in Section 5.3.) The viscous force F on a sphere of radius r moving with speed v through a fluid with viscosity η is given by Stokes's law: $F = 6\pi\eta r v$. When the drop is falling at v_t, the viscous force just balances the weight $w = mg$ of the drop. Show that the magnitude of the charge on the drop is

$$q = 18\pi \frac{d}{V_{AB}} \sqrt{\frac{\eta^3 v_t^3}{2\rho g}}$$

Within the limits of their experimental error, every one of the thousands of drops that Millikan and his coworkers measured had a charge equal to some small integer multiple of a basic charge e. That is, they found drops with charges of $\pm 2e$, $\pm 5e$, and so on, but none with values such as $0.76e$ or $2.49e$. A drop with charge $-e$ has acquired one extra electron; if its charge is $-2e$, it has acquired two extra electrons, and so on. (c) A charged oil drop in a Millikan oil-drop apparatus is observed to fall 1.00 mm at constant speed in 39.3 s if $V_{AB} = 0$. The same drop can be held at rest between two plates separated by 1.00 mm if $V_{AB} = 9.16$ V. How many excess electrons has the drop acquired, and what is the radius of the drop? The viscosity of air is 1.81×10^{-5} N $\cdot$ s/m^2, and the density of the oil is 824 kg/m^3.

23.92. Two point charges are moving to the right along the x-axis. Point charge 1 has charge $q_1 = 2.00\ \mu\text{C}$, mass $m_1 = 6.00 \times 10^{-5}$ kg, and speed v_1. Point charge 2 is to the right of q_1 and has charge $q_2 = -5.00\ \mu\text{C}$, mass $m_2 = 3.00 \times 10^{-5}$ kg, and speed v_2. At a particular instant, the charges are separated by a distance of 9.00 mm and have speeds $v_1 = 400$ m/s and $v_2 = 1300$ m/s. The only forces on the particles are the forces they exert on each other. (a) Determine the speed v_{cm} of the center of mass of the system. (b) The *relative energy* E_{rel} of the system is defined as the total energy minus the kinetic energy contributed by the motion of the center of mass:

$$E_{rel} = E - \frac{1}{2}(m_1 + m_2)v_{cm}^2$$

where $E = \frac{1}{2}m_1v_1^2 + \frac{1}{2}m_2v_2^2 + q_1q_2/4\pi\epsilon_0 r$ is the total energy of the system and r is the distance between the charges. Show that $E_{rel} = \frac{1}{2}\mu v^2 + q_1q_2/4\pi\epsilon_0 r$, where $\mu = m_1m_2/(m_1 + m_2)$ is called the *reduced mass* of the system and $v = v_2 - v_1$ is the relative speed of the moving particles. (c) For the numerical values given above, calculate the numerical value of E_{rel}. (d) Based on the result of part (c), for the conditions given above, will the particles escape from one another? Explain. (e) If the particles do escape, what will be their final relative speed when $r \rightarrow \infty$? If the particles do not escape, what will be their distance of maximum separation? That is, what will be the value of r when $v = 0$? (f) Repeat parts (c)–(e) for $v_1 = 400$ m/s and $v_2 = 1800$ m/s when the separation is 9.00 mm.

CAPACITANCE AND DIELECTRICS

24

?The energy used in a camera's flash unit is stored in a capacitor, which consists of two closely spaced conductors that carry opposite charges. If the amount of charge on the conductors is doubled, by what factor does the stored energy increase?

LEARNING GOALS

By studying this chapter, you will learn:

- The nature of capacitors, and how to calculate a quantity that measures their ability to store charge.

- How to analyze capacitors connected in a network.

- How to calculate the amount of energy stored in a capacitor.

- What dielectrics are, and how they make capacitors more effective.

W hen you set an old-fashioned spring mousetrap or pull back the string of an archer's bow, you are storing mechanical energy as elastic potential energy. A capacitor is a device that stores *electric* potential energy and electric charge. To make a capacitor, just insulate two conductors from each other. To store energy in this device, transfer charge from one conductor to the other so that one has a negative charge and the other has an equal amount of positive charge. Work must be done to move the charges through the resulting potential difference between the conductors, and the work done is stored as electric potential energy.

Capacitors have a tremendous number of practical applications in devices such as electronic flash units for photography, pulsed lasers, air bag sensors for cars, and radio and television receivers. We'll encounter many of these applications in later chapters (particularly Chapter 31, in which we'll see the crucial role played by capacitors in the alternating-current circuits that pervade our technological society). In this chapter, however, our emphasis is on the fundamental properties of capacitors. For a particular capacitor, the ratio of the charge on each conductor to the potential difference between the conductors is a constant, called the *capacitance*. The capacitance depends on the sizes and shapes of the conductors and on the insulating material (if any) between them. Compared to the case in which there is only vacuum between the conductors, the capacitance increases when an insulating material (a *dielectric*) is present. This happens because a redistribution of charge, called *polarization,* takes place within the insulating material. Studying polarization will give us added insight into the electrical properties of matter.

Capacitors also give us a new way to think about electric potential energy. The energy stored in a charged capacitor is related to the electric field in the space between the conductors. We will see that electric potential energy can be regarded as being stored *in the field itself*. The idea that the electric field is itself a storehouse of energy is at the heart of the theory of electromagnetic waves and our modern understanding of the nature of light, to be discussed in Chapter 32.

24.1 Any two conductors a and b insulated from each another form a capacitor.

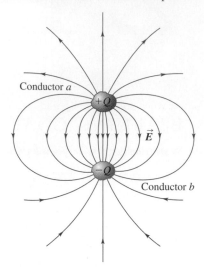

Conductor a

$+Q$

$\vec{E}$

$-Q$

Conductor b

11.11.6 Electric Potential: Qualitative Introduction

11.12.1 and 11.12.3 Electric Potential, Field and, Force

24.1 Capacitors and Capacitance

Any two conductors separated by an insulator (or a vacuum) form a **capacitor** (Fig. 24.1). In most practical applications, each conductor initially has zero net charge and electrons are transferred from one conductor to the other; this is called *charging* the capacitor. Then the two conductors have charges with equal magnitude and opposite sign, and the *net* charge on the capacitor as a whole remains zero. We will assume throughout this chapter that this is the case. When we say that a capacitor has charge Q, or that a charge Q is *stored* on the capacitor, we mean that the conductor at higher potential has charge $+Q$ and the conductor at lower potential has charge $-Q$ (assuming that Q is positive). Keep this in mind in the following discussion and examples.

In circuit diagrams a capacitor is represented by either of these symbols:

$$\dashv\vdash \qquad \dashv\mathord{\in}$$

In either symbol the vertical lines (straight or curved) represent the conductors and the horizontal lines represent wires connected to either conductor. One common way to charge a capacitor is to connect these two wires to opposite terminals of a battery. Once the charges Q and $-Q$ are established on the conductors, the battery is disconnected. This gives a fixed *potential difference* V_{ab} between the conductors (that is, the potential of the positively charged conductor a with respect to the negatively charged conductor b) that is just equal to the voltage of the battery.

The electric field at any point in the region between the conductors is proportional to the magnitude Q of charge on each conductor. It follows that the potential difference V_{ab} between the conductors is also proportional to Q. If we double the magnitude of charge on each conductor, the charge density at each point doubles, the electric field at each point doubles, and the potential difference between conductors doubles; however, the *ratio* of charge to potential difference does not change. This ratio is called the **capacitance** C of the capacitor:

$$C = \frac{Q}{V_{ab}} \qquad \text{(definition of capacitance)} \qquad (24.1)$$

The SI unit of capacitance is called one **farad** (1 F), in honor of the 19th-century English physicist Michael Faraday. From Eq. (24.1), one farad is equal to one *coulomb per volt* $\left(1\ \mathrm{C/V}\right)$:

$$1\ \mathrm{F} = 1\ \text{farad} = 1\ \mathrm{C/V} = 1\ \text{coulomb/volt}$$

CAUTION **Capacitance vs. coulombs** Don't confuse the symbol C for capacitance (which is always in italics) with the abbreviation C for coulombs (which is never italicized). ▮

The greater the capacitance C of a capacitor, the greater the magnitude Q of charge on either conductor for a given potential difference V_{ab} and hence the greater the amount of stored energy. (Remember that potential is potential energy per unit charge.) Thus *capacitance is a measure of the ability of a capacitor to store energy*. We will see that the value of the capacitance depends only on the shapes and sizes of the conductors and on the nature of the insulating material between them. (The above remarks about capacitance being independent of Q and V_{ab} do not apply to certain special types of insulating materials. We won't discuss these materials in this book, however.)

Calculating Capacitance: Capacitors in Vacuum

We can calculate the capacitance C of a given capacitor by finding the potential difference V_{ab} between the conductors for a given magnitude of charge Q and then using Eq. (24.1). For now we'll consider only *capacitors in vacuum;* that is, we'll assume that the conductors that make up the capacitor are separated by empty space.

The simplest form of capacitor consists of two parallel conducting plates, each with area A, separated by a distance d that is small in comparison with their dimensions (Fig. 24.2a). When the plates are charged, the electric field is almost completely localized in the region between the plates (Fig. 24.2b). As we discussed in Example 22.8 (Section 22.4), the field between such plates is essentially *uniform*, and the charges on the plates are uniformly distributed over their opposing surfaces. We call this arrangement a **parallel-plate capacitor.**

We worked out the electric-field magnitude E for this arrangement in Example 21.13 (Section 21.5) using the principle of superposition of electric fields and again in Example 22.8 (Section 22.4) using Gauss's law. It would be a good idea to review those examples. We found that $E = \sigma/\epsilon_0$, where σ is the magnitude (absolute value) of the surface charge density on each plate. This is equal to the magnitude of the total charge Q on each plate divided by the area A of the plate, or $\sigma = Q/A$, so the field magnitude E can be expressed as

$$E = \frac{\sigma}{\epsilon_0} = \frac{Q}{\epsilon_0 A}$$

The field is uniform and the distance between the plates is d, so the potential difference (voltage) between the two plates is

$$V_{ab} = Ed = \frac{1}{\epsilon_0}\frac{Qd}{A}$$

From this we see that the capacitance C of a parallel-plate capacitor in vacuum is

$$C = \frac{Q}{V_{ab}} = \epsilon_0\frac{A}{d} \qquad \text{(capacitance of a parallel-plate capacitor in vacuum)} \qquad (24.2)$$

The capacitance depends only on the geometry of the capacitor; it is directly proportional to the area A of each plate and inversely proportional to their separation d. The quantities A and d are constants for a given capacitor, and ϵ_0 is a universal constant. Thus in vacuum the capacitance C is a constant independent of the charge on the capacitor or the potential difference between the plates. If one of the capacitor plates is flexible, the capacitance C changes as the plate separation d changes. This is the operating principle of a condenser microphone (Fig. 24.3).

When matter is present between the plates, its properties affect the capacitance. We will return to this topic in Section 24.4. Meanwhile, we remark that if the space contains air at atmospheric pressure instead of vacuum, the capacitance differs from the prediction of Eq. (24.2) by less than 0.06%.

In Eq. (24.2), if A is in square meters and d in meters, C is in farads. The units of ϵ_0 are $C^2/N \cdot m^2$, so we see that

$$1\ F = 1\ C^2/N \cdot m = 1\ C^2/J$$

Because $1\ V = 1\ J/C$ (energy per unit charge), this is consistent with our definition $1\ F = 1\ C/V$. Finally, the units of ϵ_0 can be expressed as $1\ C^2/N \cdot m^2 = 1\ F/m$, so

$$\epsilon_0 = 8.85 \times 10^{-12}\ F/m$$

24.2 A charged parallel-plate capacitor.

(a) Arrangement of the capacitor plates

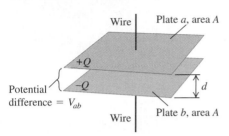

(b) Side view of the electric field $\vec{E}$

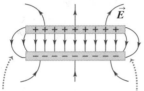

When the separation of the plates is small compared to their size, the fringing of the field is slight.

24.3 Inside a condenser microphone is a capacitor with one rigid plate and one flexible plate. The two plates are kept at a constant potential difference V_{ab}. Sound waves cause the flexible plate to move back and forth, varying the capacitance C and causing charge to flow to and from the capacitor in accordance with the relationship $C = Q/V_{ab}$. Thus a sound wave is converted to a charge flow that can be amplified and recorded digitally.

24.4 A commercial capacitor is labeled with the value of its capacitance. For these capacitors, $C = 2200\ \mu\text{F}$, $1000\ \mu\text{F}$, and $470\ \mu\text{F}$.

This relationship is useful in capacitance calculations, and it also helps us to verify that Eq. (24.2) is dimensionally consistent.

One farad is a very large capacitance, as the following example shows. In many applications the most convenient units of capacitance are the *microfarad* $(1\ \mu\text{F} = 10^{-6}\ \text{F})$ and the *picofarad* $(1\ \text{pF} = 10^{-12}\ \text{F})$. For example, the flash unit in a point-and-shoot camera uses a capacitor of a few hundred microfarads (Fig. 24.4), while capacitances in a radio tuning circuit are typically from 10 to 100 picofarads.

For *any* capacitor in vacuum, the capacitance C depends only on the shapes, dimensions, and separation of the conductors that make up the capacitor. If the conductor shapes are more complex than those of the parallel-plate capacitor, the expression for capacitance is more complicated than in Eq. (24.2). In the following examples we show how to calculate C for two other conductor geometries.

Example 24.1 Size of a 1-F capacitor

A parallel-plate capacitor has a capacitance of 1.0 F. If the plates are 1.0 mm apart, what is the area of the plates?

SOLUTION

IDENTIFY: This problem uses the relationship among the capacitance, plate separation, and plate area (our target variable) for a parallel-plate capacitor.

SET UP: We are given the values of C and d for a parallel-plate capacitor, so we use Eq. (24.2) and solve for the target variable A.

EXECUTE: From Eq. (24.2), the area A is

$$A = \frac{Cd}{\epsilon_0} = \frac{(1.0\ \text{F})(1.0 \times 10^{-3}\ \text{m})}{8.85 \times 10^{-12}\ \text{F/m}}$$
$$= 1.1 \times 10^8\ \text{m}^2$$

EVALUATE: This corresponds to a square about 10 km (about 6 miles) on a side! This area is about a third larger than Manhattan Island. Clearly this is not a very practical design for a capacitor.

In fact, it's now possible to make 1-F capacitors a few centimeters on a side. The trick is to have an appropriate substance between the plates rather than a vacuum. We'll explore this further in Section 24.4.

Example 24.2 Properties of a parallel-plate capacitor

The plates of a parallel-plate capacitor in vacuum are 5.00 mm apart and 2.00 m^2 in area. A potential difference of 10,000 V $(10.0\ \text{kV})$ is applied across the capacitor. Compute (a) the capacitance; (b) the charge on each plate; and (c) the magnitude of the electric field in the space between them.

SOLUTION

IDENTIFY: We are given the plate area A, the plate spacing d, and the potential difference V_{ab} for this parallel-plate capacitor. Our target variables are the capacitance C, charge Q, and electric-field magnitude E.

SET UP: We use Eq. (24.2) to calculate C and then find the charge Q on each plate using the given potential difference V_{ab} and Eq. (24.1). Once we have Q, we find the electric field between the plates using the relationship $E = Q/\epsilon_0 A$.

EXECUTE: (a) From Eq. (24.2),

$$C = \epsilon_0 \frac{A}{d} = \frac{(8.85 \times 10^{-12}\ \text{F/m})(2.00\ \text{m}^2)}{5.00 \times 10^{-3}\ \text{m}}$$
$$= 3.54 \times 10^{-9}\ \text{F} = 0.00354\ \mu\text{F}$$

(b) The charge on the capacitor is

$$Q = CV_{ab} = (3.54 \times 10^{-9}\ \text{C/V})(1.00 \times 10^4\ \text{V})$$
$$= 3.54 \times 10^{-5}\ \text{C} = 35.4\ \mu\text{C}$$

The plate at higher potential has charge $+35.4\ \mu\text{C}$ and the other plate has charge $-35.4\ \mu\text{C}$.

(c) The electric-field magnitude is

$$E = \frac{\sigma}{\epsilon_0} = \frac{Q}{\epsilon_0 A} = \frac{3.54 \times 10^{-5}\ \text{C}}{(8.85 \times 10^{-12}\ \text{C}^2/\text{N} \cdot \text{m}^2)(2.00\ \text{m}^2)}$$
$$= 2.00 \times 10^6\ \text{N/C}$$

EVALUATE: An alternative way to get the result in part (c) is to recall that the electric field is equal in magnitude to the potential gradient [Eq. (23.22)]. Since the field between the plates is uniform,

$$E = \frac{V_{ab}}{d} = \frac{1.00 \times 10^4\ \text{V}}{5.00 \times 10^{-3}\ \text{m}} = 2.00 \times 10^6\ \text{V/m}$$

(Remember that the newton per coulomb and the volt per meter are equivalent units.)

Example 24.3   A spherical capacitor

Two concentric spherical conducting shells are separated by vacuum. The inner shell has total charge $+Q$ and outer radius r_a, and the outer shell has charge $-Q$ and inner radius r_b (Fig. 24.5). (The inner shell is attached to the outer shell by thin insulating rods that have negligible effect on the capacitance.) Find the capacitance of this spherical capacitor.

SOLUTION

IDENTIFY: This isn't a parallel-plate capacitor, so we can't use the relationships developed for that particular geometry. Instead, we'll go back to the fundamental definition of capacitance: the magnitude of the charge on either conductor divided by the potential difference between the conductors.

SET UP: We use Gauss's law to find the electric field between the spherical conductors. From this value we determine the potential difference V_{ab} between the two conductors; we then use Eq. (24.1) to find the capacitance $C = Q/V_{ab}$.

EXECUTE: Using the same procedure as in Example 22.5 (Section 22.4), we take as our Gaussian surface a sphere with radius r between the two spheres and concentric with them. Gauss's law, Eq. (22.8), states that the electric flux through this surface is equal to the total charge enclosed within the surface, divided by ϵ_0:

$$\oint \vec{E} \cdot d\vec{A} = \frac{Q_{encl}}{\epsilon_0}$$

By symmetry, $\vec{E}$ is constant in magnitude and parallel to $d\vec{A}$ at every point on this surface, so the integral in Gauss's law is equal

24.5 A spherical capacitor.

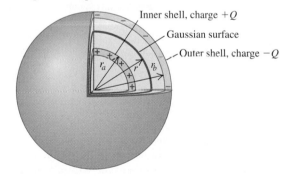

- Inner shell, charge $+Q$
- Gaussian surface
- Outer shell, charge $-Q$

to $(E)(4\pi r^2)$. The total charge enclosed is $Q_{encl} = Q$, so we have

$$(E)(4\pi r^2) = \frac{Q}{\epsilon_0}$$

$$E = \frac{Q}{4\pi\epsilon_0 r^2}$$

The electric field between the spheres is just that due to the charge on the inner sphere; the outer sphere has no effect. We found in Example 22.5 that the charge on a conducting sphere produces zero field *inside* the sphere, which also tells us that the outer conductor makes no contribution to the field between the conductors.

The above expression for E is the same as that for a point charge Q, so the expression for the potential can also be taken to be the same as for a point charge, $V = Q/4\pi\epsilon_0 r$. Hence the potential of the inner (positive) conductor at $r = r_a$ with respect to that of the outer (negative) conductor at $r = r_b$ is

$$V_{ab} = V_a - V_b = \frac{Q}{4\pi\epsilon_0 r_a} - \frac{Q}{4\pi\epsilon_0 r_b}$$

$$= \frac{Q}{4\pi\epsilon_0}\left(\frac{1}{r_a} - \frac{1}{r_b}\right) = \frac{Q}{4\pi\epsilon_0}\frac{r_b - r_a}{r_a r_b}$$

Finally, the capacitance is

$$C = \frac{Q}{V_{ab}} = 4\pi\epsilon_0 \frac{r_a r_b}{r_b - r_a}$$

As an example, if $r_a = 9.5$ cm and $r_b = 10.5$ cm,

$$C = 4\pi(8.85 \times 10^{-12}\,\text{F/m})\frac{(0.095\,\text{m})(0.105\,\text{m})}{0.010\,\text{m}}$$

$$= 1.1 \times 10^{-10}\,\text{F} = 110\,\text{pF}$$

EVALUATE: We can relate this result to the capacitance of a parallel-plate capacitor. The quantity $4\pi r_a r_b$ is intermediate between the areas $4\pi r_a^2$ and $4\pi r_b^2$ of the two spheres; in fact, it's the *geometric mean* of these two areas, which we can denote by A_{gm}. The distance between spheres is $d = r_b - r_a$, so we can rewrite the above result as $C = \epsilon_0 A_{gm}/d$. This is exactly the same form as for parallel plates: $C = \epsilon_0 A/d$. The point is that if the distance between spheres is very small in comparison to their radii, they behave like parallel plates with the same area and spacing.

Example 24.4   A cylindrical capacitor

A long cylindrical conductor has a radius r_a and a linear charge density $+\lambda$. It is surrounded by a coaxial cylindrical conducting shell with inner radius r_b and linear charge density $-\lambda$ (Fig. 24.6). Calculate the capacitance per unit length for this capacitor, assuming that there is vacuum in the space between cylinders.

SOLUTION

IDENTIFY: As in Example 24.3, we use the fundamental definition of capacitance.

SET UP: We first find expressions for the potential difference V_{ab} between the cylinders and the charge Q in a length L of the cylinders; we then find the capacitance of a length L using Eq. (24.1). Our target variable is this capacitance divided by L.

EXECUTE: To find the potential difference between the cylinders, we use a result that we worked out in Example 23.10 (Section 23.3). There we found that at a point outside a charged

Continued

24.6 A long cylindrical capacitor. The linear charge density λ is assumed to be positive in this figure. The magnitude of charge in a length L of either cylinder is λL.

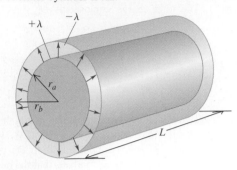

cylinder a distance r from the axis, the potential due to the cylinder is

$$V = \frac{\lambda}{2\pi\epsilon_0} \ln \frac{r_0}{r}$$

where r_0 is the (arbitrary) radius at which $V = 0$. We can use this same result for the potential *between* the cylinders in the present problem because, according to Gauss's law, the charge on the outer cylinder doesn't contribute to the field between cylinders (see Example 24.3). In our case, we take the radius r_0 to be r_b, the radius of the inner surface of the outer cylinder, so that the outer conducting cylinder is at $V = 0$. Then the potential at the outer surface of the inner cylinder (where $r = r_a$) is just equal to the

potential V_{ab} of the inner (positive) cylinder a with respect to the outer (negative) cylinder b, or

$$V_{ab} = \frac{\lambda}{2\pi\epsilon_0} \ln \frac{r_b}{r_a}$$

This potential difference is positive (assuming that λ is positive, as in Fig. 24.6) because the inner cylinder is at higher potential than the outer.

The total charge Q in a length L is $Q = \lambda L$, so from Eq. (24.1) the capacitance C of a length L is

$$C = \frac{Q}{V_{ab}} = \frac{\lambda L}{\dfrac{\lambda}{2\pi\epsilon_0} \ln \dfrac{r_b}{r_a}} = \frac{2\pi\epsilon_0 L}{\ln\left(r_b/r_a\right)}$$

The capacitance per unit length is

$$\frac{C}{L} = \frac{2\pi\epsilon_0}{\ln\left(r_b/r_a\right)}$$

Substituting $\epsilon_0 = 8.85 \times 10^{-12}$ F/m $= 8.85$ pF/m, we get

$$\frac{C}{L} = \frac{55.6 \text{ pF/m}}{\ln\left(r_b/r_a\right)}$$

EVALUATE: We see that the capacitance of the coaxial cylinders is determined entirely by the dimensions, just as for the parallel-plate case. Ordinary coaxial cables are made like this but with an insulating material instead of vacuum between the inner and outer conductors. A typical cable for TV antennas and VCR connections has a capacitance per unit length of 69 pF/m.

Test Your Understanding of Section 24.1 A capacitor has vacuum in the space between the conductors. If you double the amount of charge on each conductor, what happens to the capacitance? (i) It increases; (ii) it decreases; (iii) it remains the same; (iv) the answer depends on the size or shape of the conductors.

24.2 **Capacitors in Series and Parallel**

24.7 An assortment of commercially available capacitors.

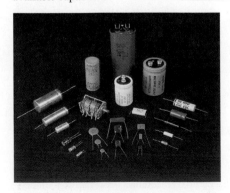

Capacitors are manufactured with certain standard capacitances and working voltages (Fig. 24.7). However, these standard values may not be the ones you actually need in a particular application. You can obtain the values you need by combining capacitors; many combinations are possible, but the simplest combinations are a series connection and a parallel connection.

Capacitors in Series

Figure 24.8a is a schematic diagram of a **series connection.** Two capacitors are connected in series (one after the other) by conducting wires between points a and b. Both capacitors are initially uncharged. When a constant positive potential difference V_{ab} is applied between points a and b, the capacitors become charged; the figure shows that the charge on *all* conducting plates has the same magnitude. To see why, note first that the top plate of C_1 acquires a positive charge Q. The electric field of this positive charge pulls negative charge up to the bottom plate of C_1 until all of the field lines that begin on the top plate end on the bottom plate. This requires that the bottom plate have charge $-Q$. These negative charges had to come from the top plate of C_2, which becomes positively charged with charge $+Q$. This positive charge then pulls negative charge $-Q$ from the connection at point b onto the bottom plate of C_2. The total charge on the lower plate of C_1 and the upper plate of C_2 together must always be zero because these plates aren't connected to anything except each other. Thus *in a series connection the magnitude of charge on all plates is the same.*

Referring to Fig. 24.8a, we can write the potential differences between points a and c, c and b, and a and b as

$$V_{ac} = V_1 = \frac{Q}{C_1} \qquad V_{cb} = V_2 = \frac{Q}{C_2}$$

$$V_{ab} = V = V_1 + V_2 = Q\left(\frac{1}{C_1} + \frac{1}{C_2}\right)$$

and so

$$\frac{V}{Q} = \frac{1}{C_1} + \frac{1}{C_2} \tag{24.3}$$

Following a common convention, we use the symbols V_1, V_2, and V to denote the potential *differences* V_{ac} (across the first capacitor), V_{cb} (across the second capacitor), and V_{ab} (across the entire combination of capacitors), respectively.

The **equivalent capacitance** C_{eq} of the series combination is defined as the capacitance of a *single* capacitor for which the charge Q is the same as for the combination, when the potential difference V is the same. In other words, the combination can be replaced by an *equivalent capacitor* of capacitance C_{eq}. For such a capacitor, shown in Fig. 24.8b,

$$C_{eq} = \frac{Q}{V} \quad \text{or} \quad \frac{1}{C_{eq}} = \frac{V}{Q} \tag{24.4}$$

Combining Eqs. (24.3) and (24.4), we find

$$\frac{1}{C_{eq}} = \frac{1}{C_1} + \frac{1}{C_2}$$

We can extend this analysis to any number of capacitors in series. We find the following result for the *reciprocal* of the equivalent capacitance:

$$\frac{1}{C_{eq}} = \frac{1}{C_1} + \frac{1}{C_2} + \frac{1}{C_3} + \cdots \quad \text{(capacitors in series)} \tag{24.5}$$

The reciprocal of the equivalent capacitance of a series combination equals the sum of the reciprocals of the individual capacitances. In a series connection the equivalent capacitance is always *less than* any individual capacitance.

> **CAUTION** **Capacitors in series** The magnitude of charge is the same on all plates of all the capacitors in a series combination; however, the potential differences of the individual capacitors are *not* the same unless their individual capacitances are the same. The potential differences of the individual capacitors add to give the total potential difference across the series combination: $V_{total} = V_1 + V_2 + V_3 + \cdots$. ∎

Capacitors in Parallel

The arrangement shown in Fig. 24.9a is called a **parallel connection.** Two capacitors are connected in parallel between points a and b. In this case the upper plates of the two capacitors are connected by conducting wires to form an equipotential surface, and the lower plates form another. Hence *in a parallel connection the potential difference for all individual capacitors is the same* and is equal to $V_{ab} = V$. The charges Q_1 and Q_2 are not necessarily equal, however,

24.8 A series connection of two capacitors.

(a) Two capacitors in series

Capacitors in series:
• The capacitors have the same charge Q.
• Their potential differences add:
$V_{ac} + V_{cb} = V_{ab}.$

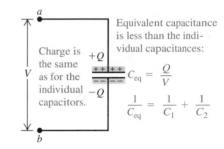

(b) The equivalent single capacitor

Charge is the same as for the individual capacitors.

Equivalent capacitance is less than the individual capacitances:

$$C_{eq} = \frac{Q}{V}$$

$$\frac{1}{C_{eq}} = \frac{1}{C_1} + \frac{1}{C_2}$$

24.9 A parallel connection of two capacitors.

(a) Two capacitors in parallel

Capacitors in parallel:
• The capacitors have the same potential V.
• The charge on each capacitor depends on its capacitance: $Q_1 = C_1 V$, $Q_2 = C_2 V$.

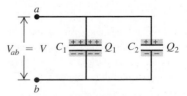

(b) The equivalent single capacitor

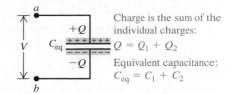

Charge is the sum of the individual charges:
$$Q = Q_1 + Q_2$$

Equivalent capacitance:
$$C_{eq} = C_1 + C_2$$

since charges can reach each capacitor independently from the source (such as a battery) of the voltage V_{ab}. The charges are

$$Q_1 = C_1V \quad \text{and} \quad Q_2 = C_2V$$

The *total* charge Q of the combination, and thus the total charge on the equivalent capacitor, is

$$Q = Q_1 + Q_2 = (C_1 + C_2)V$$

so

$$\frac{Q}{V} = C_1 + C_2 \qquad (24.6)$$

The parallel combination is equivalent to a single capacitor with the same total charge $Q = Q_1 + Q_2$ and potential difference V as the combination (Fig. 24.9b). The equivalent capacitance of the combination, C_{eq}, is the same as the capacitance Q/V of this single equivalent capacitor. So from Eq. (24.6),

$$C_{eq} = C_1 + C_2$$

In the same way we can show that for any number of capacitors in parallel,

$$C_{eq} = C_1 + C_2 + C_3 + \cdots \qquad \text{(capacitors in parallel)} \qquad (24.7)$$

The equivalent capacitance of a parallel combination equals the *sum* of the individual capacitances. In a parallel connection the equivalent capacitance is always *greater than* any individual capacitance.

> **CAUTION** **Capacitors in parallel** The potential differences are the same for all the capacitors in a parallel combination; however, the charges on individual capacitors are *not* the same unless their individual capacitances are the same. The charges on the individual capacitors add to give the total charge on the parallel combination: $Q_{total} = Q_1 + Q_2 + Q_3 + \cdots$. [Compare these statements to those in the "Caution" paragraph following Eq. (24.5).]

Problem-Solving Strategy 24.1   Equivalent Capacitance

IDENTIFY *the relevant concepts:* The concept of equivalent capacitance is useful whenever two or more capacitors are connected.

SET UP *the problem* using the following steps:
1. Make a drawing of the capacitor arrangement.
2. Identify whether the capacitors are connected in series or in parallel. With more complicated combinations, you can sometimes identify parts that are simple series or parallel connections.
3. Keep in mind that when we say a capacitor has charge Q, we always mean that the plate at higher potential has charge $+Q$ and the other plate has charge $-Q$.

EXECUTE *the solution* as follows:
1. When capacitors are connected in series, as in Fig. 24.8a, they always have the same charge, assuming that they were uncharged before they were connected. The potential differences are *not* equal unless the capacitances are equal. The total potential difference across the combination is the sum of the individual potential differences.

2. When capacitors are connected in parallel, as in Fig. 24.9a, the potential difference V is always the same for all of the individual capacitors. The charges on the individual capacitors are *not* equal unless the capacitances are equal. The total charge on the combination is the sum of the individual charges.

3. For more complicated combinations, find the parts that are simple series or parallel connections and replace them with their equivalent capacitances, in a step-by-step reduction. If you then need to find the charge or potential difference for an individual capacitor, you may have to retrace your path to the original capacitors.

EVALUATE *your answer:* Check whether your result makes sense. If the capacitors are connected in series, the equivalent capacitance C_{eq} must be *smaller* than any of the individual capacitances. By contrast, if the capacitors are connected in parallel, C_{eq} must be *greater* than any of the individual capacitances.

Example 24.5   Capacitors in series and in parallel

In Figs. 24.8 and 24.9, let $C_1 = 6.0 \,\mu\text{F}$, $C_2 = 3.0 \,\mu\text{F}$, and $V_{ab} = 18$ V. Find the equivalent capacitance, and find the charge and potential difference for each capacitor when the two capacitors are connected (a) in series and (b) in parallel.

SOLUTION

IDENTIFY: This problem uses the ideas discussed in this section about capacitor connections.

SET UP: In both parts, one of the target variables is the equivalent capacitance C_{eq}. For the series combination in part (a), it is given by Eq. (24.5); for the parallel combination in part (b), C_{eq} is given by Eq. (24.6). In each part we find the charge and potential difference using the definition of capacitance, Eq. (24.1), and the rules outlined in the Problem-Solving Strategy 24.1.

EXECUTE: (a) Using Eq. (24.5) for the equivalent capacitance of the series combination (Fig. 24.8a), we find

$$\frac{1}{C_{eq}} = \frac{1}{C_1} + \frac{1}{C_2} = \frac{1}{6.0 \,\mu\text{F}} + \frac{1}{3.0 \,\mu\text{F}} \qquad C_{eq} = 2.0 \,\mu\text{F}$$

The charge Q on each capacitor in series is the same as the charge on the equivalent capacitor:

$$Q = C_{eq}V = (2.0 \,\mu\text{F})(18 \text{ V}) = 36 \,\mu\text{C}$$

The potential difference across each capacitor is inversely proportional to its capacitance:

$$V_{ac} = V_1 = \frac{Q}{C_1} = \frac{36 \,\mu\text{C}}{6.0 \,\mu\text{F}} = 6.0 \text{ V}$$

$$V_{cb} = V_2 = \frac{Q}{C_2} = \frac{36 \,\mu\text{C}}{3.0 \,\mu\text{F}} = 12.0 \text{ V}$$

(b) To find the equivalent capacitance of the parallel combination (Fig. 24.9a), we use Eq. (24.6):

$$C_{eq} = C_1 + C_2 = 6.0 \,\mu\text{F} + 3.0 \,\mu\text{F} = 9.0 \,\mu\text{F}$$

The potential difference across each of the two capacitors in parallel is the same as that across the equivalent capacitor, 18 V. The charges Q_1 and Q_2 are directly proportional to the capacitances C_1 and C_2, respectively:

$$Q_1 = C_1V = (6.0 \,\mu\text{F})(18 \text{ V}) = 108 \,\mu\text{C}$$
$$Q_2 = C_2V = (3.0 \,\mu\text{F})(18 \text{ V}) = 54 \,\mu\text{C}$$

EVALUATE: Note that the equivalent capacitance C_{eq} for the series combination in part (a) is indeed less than either C_1 or C_2, while for the parallel combination in part (b) the equivalent capacitance is indeed greater than either C_1 or C_2.

It's instructive to compare the potential differences and charges in each part of the example. For two capacitors in series, as in part (a), the charge is the same on either capacitor and the *larger* potential difference appears across the capacitor with the *smaller* capacitance. Furthermore, $V_{ac} + V_{cb} = V_{ab} = 18$ V, as it must. By contrast, for two capacitors in parallel, as in part (b), each capacitor has the same potential difference and the *larger* charge appears on the capacitor with the *larger* capacitance. Can you show that the total charge $Q_1 + Q_2$ on the parallel combination is equal to the charge $Q = C_{eq}V$ on the equivalent capacitor?

Example 24.6   A capacitor network

Find the equivalent capacitance of the combination shown in Fig. 24.10a.

SOLUTION

IDENTIFY: The five capacitors in Fig. 24.10a are neither all in series nor all in parallel. We can, however, identify portions of the

arrangement that *are* either in series or parallel, which we combine to find the net equivalent capacitance.

SET UP: We use Eq. (24.5) to analyze portions of the network that are series connections and Eq. (24.7) to analyze portions that are parallel connections.

24.10 (a) A capacitor network between points a and b. (b) The 12-μF and 6-μF capacitors in series in (a) are replaced by an equivalent 4-μF capacitor. (c) The 3-μF, 11-μF, and 4-μF capacitors in parallel in (b) are replaced by an equivalent 18-μF capacitor. (d) Finally, the 18-μF and 9-μF capacitors in series in (c) are replaced by an equivalent 6-μF capacitor.

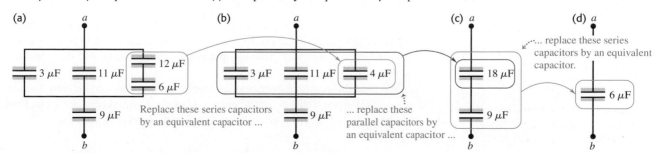

Continued

EXECUTE: We first replace the 12-μF and 6-μF series combination by its equivalent capacitance; calling that C', we use Eq. (24.5):

$$\frac{1}{C'} = \frac{1}{12 \ \mu\text{F}} + \frac{1}{6 \ \mu\text{F}} \qquad C' = 4 \ \mu\text{F}$$

This gives us the equivalent combination shown in Fig. 24.10b. Next we find the equivalent capacitance of the three capacitors in parallel, using Eq. (24.7). Calling their equivalent capacitance C'', we have

$$C'' = 3 \ \mu\text{F} + 11 \ \mu\text{F} + 4 \ \mu\text{F} = 18 \ \mu\text{F}$$

This gives us the simpler equivalent combination shown in Fig. 24.10c. Finally, we find the equivalent capacitance C_{eq} of these two capacitors in series (Fig. 24.10d):

$$\frac{1}{C_{eq}} = \frac{1}{18 \ \mu\text{F}} + \frac{1}{9 \ \mu\text{F}} \qquad C_{eq} = 6 \ \mu\text{F}$$

EVALUATE: The equivalent capacitance of the network is 6 μF; that is, if a potential difference V_{ab} is applied across the terminals of the network, the net charge on the network is 6 μF times V_{ab}. How is this net charge related to the charges on the individual capacitors in Fig. 24.10a?

Test Your Understanding of Section 24.2 You want to connect a 4-μF capacitor and an 8-μF capacitor. (a) With which type of connection will the 4-μF capacitor have a greater *potential difference* across it than the 8-μF capacitor? (i) series; (ii) parallel; (iii) either series or parallel; (iv) neither series nor parallel. (b) With which type of connection will the 4-μF capacitor have a greater *charge* than the 8-μF capacitor? (i) series; (ii) parallel; (iii) either series or parallel; (iv) neither series nor parallel.

24.3 Energy Storage in Capacitors and Electric-Field Energy

Many of the most important applications of capacitors depend on their ability to store energy. The electric potential energy stored in a charged capacitor is just equal to the amount of work required to charge it—that is, to separate opposite charges and place them on different conductors. When the capacitor is discharged, this stored energy is recovered as work done by electrical forces.

We can calculate the potential energy U of a charged capacitor by calculating the work W required to charge it. Suppose that when we are done charging the capacitor, the final charge is Q and the final potential difference is V. From Eq. (24.1) these quantities are related by

$$V = \frac{Q}{C}$$

Let q and v be the charge and potential difference, respectively, at an intermediate stage during the charging process; then $v = q/C$. At this stage the work dW required to transfer an additional element of charge dq is

$$dW = v \, dq = \frac{q \, dq}{C}$$

The total work W needed to increase the capacitor charge q from zero to a final value Q is

$$W = \int_0^W dW = \frac{1}{C} \int_0^Q q \, dq = \frac{Q^2}{2C} \qquad \text{(work to charge a capacitor)} \quad (24.8)$$

This is also equal to the total work done by the electric field on the charge when the capacitor discharges. Then q *decreases* from an initial value Q to zero as the elements of charge dq "fall" through potential differences v that vary from V down to zero.

If we define the potential energy of an *uncharged* capacitor to be zero, then W in Eq. (24.8) is equal to the potential energy U of the charged capacitor. The final stored charge is $Q = CV$, so we can express U (which is equal to W) as

$$U = \frac{Q^2}{2C} = \frac{1}{2}CV^2 = \frac{1}{2}QV \qquad \begin{array}{l}\text{(potential energy stored}\\ \text{in a capacitor)}\end{array} \quad (24.9)$$

When Q is in coulombs, C in farads (coulombs per volt), and V in volts (joules per coulomb), U is in joules.

The last form of Eq. (24.9), $U = \frac{1}{2}QV$, shows that the total work W required to charge the capacitor is equal to the total charge Q multiplied by the *average* potential difference $\frac{1}{2}V$ during the charging process.

The expression $U = \frac{1}{2}(Q^2/C)$ in Eq. (24.9) shows that a charged capacitor is the electrical analog of a stretched spring with elastic potential energy $U = \frac{1}{2}kx^2$. The charge Q is analogous to the elongation x, and the *reciprocal* of the capacitance, $1/C$, is analogous to the force constant k. The energy supplied to a capacitor in the charging process is analogous to the work we do on a spring when we stretch it.

Equations (24.8) and (24.9) tell us that capacitance measures the ability of a capacitor to store both energy and charge. If a capacitor is charged by connecting it to a battery or other source that provides a fixed potential difference V, then increasing the value of C gives a greater charge $Q = CV$ and a greater amount of stored energy $U = \frac{1}{2}CV^2$. If instead the goal is to transfer a given quantity of charge Q from one conductor to another, Eq. (24.8) shows that the work W required is inversely proportional to C; the greater the capacitance, the easier it is to give a capacitor a fixed amount of charge.

Applications of Capacitors: Energy Storage

Most practical applications of capacitors take advantage of their ability to store and release energy. In electronic flash units used by photographers, the energy stored in a capacitor (see Fig. 24.4) is released by depressing the camera's shutter button. This provides a conducting path from one capacitor plate to the other through the flash tube. Once this path is established, the stored energy is rapidly converted into a brief but intense flash of light. An extreme example of the same principle is the Z machine at Sandia National Laboratories in New Mexico, which is used in experiments in controlled nuclear fusion (Fig. 24.11). A bank of charged capacitors releases more than a million joules of energy in just a few billionths of a second. For that brief space of time, the power output of the Z machine is 2.9×10^{14} W, or about 80 times the electric output of all the electric power plants on earth combined!

In other applications, the energy is released more slowly. Springs in the suspension of an automobile, help smooth out the ride by absorbing the energy from sudden jolts and releasing that energy gradually; in an analogous way, a capacitor in an electronic circuit can smooth out unwanted variations in voltage due to power surges. And just as the presence of a spring gives a mechanical system a natural frequency at which it responds most strongly to an applied periodic force, so the presence of a capacitor gives an electric circuit a natural frequency for current oscillations. This idea is used in tuned circuits such as those in radio and television receivers, which respond to broadcast signals at one particular frequency and ignore signals at other frequencies. We'll discuss these circuits in detail in Chapter 31.

The energy-storage properties of capacitors also have some undesirable practical effects. Adjacent pins on the underside of a computer chip act like a capacitor, and the property that makes capacitors useful for smoothing out voltage variations acts to retard the rate at which the potentials of the chip's pins can be changed. This tendency limits how rapidly the chip can perform computations, an effect that becomes more important as computer chips become smaller and are pushed to operate at faster speeds.

Electric-Field Energy

We can charge a capacitor by moving electrons directly from one plate to another. This requires doing work against the electric field between the plates. Thus we can think of the energy as being stored *in the field* in the region between the

24.11 The Z machine uses a large number of capacitors in parallel to give a tremendous equivalent capacitance C (see Section 24.2). Hence a large amount of energy $U = \frac{1}{2}CV^2$ can be stored with even a modest potential difference V. The arcs shown here are produced when the capacitors discharge their energy into a target, which is no larger than a spool of thread. This heats the target to a temperature higher than 2×10^9 K.

plates. To develop this relationship, let's find the energy *per unit volume* in the space between the plates of a parallel-plate capacitor with plate area A and separation d. We call this the **energy density,** denoted by u. From Eq. (24.9) the total stored potential energy is $\frac{1}{2}CV^2$ and the volume between the plates is just Ad; hence the energy density is

$$u = \text{Energy density} = \frac{\frac{1}{2}CV^2}{Ad} \tag{24.10}$$

From Eq. (24.2) the capacitance C is given by $C = \epsilon_0 A/d$. The potential difference V is related to the electric field magnitude E by $V = Ed$. If we use these expressions in Eq. (24.10), the geometric factors A and d cancel, and we find

$$u = \frac{1}{2}\epsilon_0 E^2 \qquad \text{(electric energy density in a vacuum)} \tag{24.11}$$

Although we have derived this relationship only for a parallel-plate capacitor, it turns out to be valid for any capacitor in vacuum and indeed *for any electric field configuration in vacuum.* This result has an interesting implication. We think of vacuum as space with no matter in it, but vacuum can nevertheless have electric fields and therefore energy. Thus "empty" space need not be truly empty after all. We will use this idea and Eq. (24.11) in Chapter 32 in connection with the energy transported by electromagnetic waves.

CAUTION **Electrical-field energy is electric potential energy** It's a common misconception that electric-field energy is a new kind of energy, different from the electric potential energy described before. This is *not* the case; it is simply a different way of interpreting electric potential energy. We can regard the energy of a given system of charges as being a shared property of all the charges, or we can think of the energy as being a property of the electric field that the charges create. Either interpretation leads to the same value of the potential energy. ▌

Example 24.7   **Transferring charge and energy between capacitors**

In Fig. 24.12 we charge a capacitor of capacitance $C_1 = 8.0\ \mu\text{F}$ by connecting it to a source of potential difference $V_0 = 120\ \text{V}$ (not shown in the figure). The switch S is initially open. Once C_1 is charged, the source of potential difference is disconnected. (a) What is the charge Q_0 on C_1 if switch S is left open? (b) What is the energy stored in C_1 if switch S is left open? (c) The capacitor of capacitance $C_2 = 4.0\ \mu\text{F}$ is initially uncharged. After we close switch S, what is the potential difference across each capacitor, and what is the charge on each capacitor? (d) What is the total energy of the system after we close switch S?

24.12 When the switch S is closed, the charged capacitor C_1 is connected to an uncharged capacitor C_2. The center part of the switch is an insulating handle; charge can flow only between the two upper terminals and between the two lower terminals.

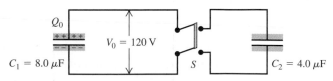

SOLUTION

IDENTIFY: Initially we have a single capacitor with a given potential difference between its plates. After the switch is closed, one wire connects the upper plates of the two capacitors and another wire connects the lower plates; in other words, the capacitors are connected in parallel.

SET UP: In parts (a) and (b) we find the charge and stored energy for capacitor C_1 using Eqs. (24.1) and (24.9), respectively. In part (c) we use the character of the parallel connection to determine how the charge Q_0 is shared between the two capacitors. In part (d) we again use Eq. (24.9) to find the energy stored in capacitors C_1 and C_2; the total energy is the sum of these values.

EXECUTE: (a) The charge Q_0 on C_1 is

$$Q_0 = C_1 V_0 = (8.0\ \mu\text{F})(120\ \text{V}) = 960\ \mu\text{C}$$

(b) The energy initially stored in the capacitor is

$$U_{\text{initial}} = \frac{1}{2}Q_0 V_0 = \frac{1}{2}(960 \times 10^{-6}\ \text{C})(120\ \text{V}) = 0.058\ \text{J}$$

(c) When the switch is closed, the positive charge Q_0 becomes distributed over the upper plates of both capacitors and the negative charge $-Q_0$ is distributed over the lower plates of both capacitors. Let Q_1 and Q_2 be the magnitudes of the final charges on the two capacitors. From conservation of charge,

$$Q_1 + Q_2 = Q_0$$

In the final state, when the charges are no longer moving, both upper plates are at the same potential; they are connected by a conducting wire and so form a single equipotential surface. Both lower plates are also at the same potential, different from that of the upper plates. The final potential difference V between the plates is therefore the same for both capacitors, as we would expect for a parallel connection. The capacitor charges are

$$Q_1 = C_1 V \qquad Q_2 = C_2 V$$

When we combine these with the preceding equation for conservation of charge, we find

$$V = \frac{Q_0}{C_1 + C_2} = \frac{960 \ \mu\text{C}}{8.0 \ \mu\text{F} + 4.0 \ \mu\text{F}} = 80 \text{ V}$$

$$Q_1 = 640 \ \mu\text{C} \qquad Q_2 = 320 \ \mu\text{C}$$

(d) The final energy of the system is the sum of the energies stored in each capacitor:

$$U_{\text{final}} = \frac{1}{2}Q_1 V + \frac{1}{2}Q_2 V = \frac{1}{2}Q_0 V$$

$$= \frac{1}{2}(960 \times 10^{-6} \text{ C})(80 \text{ V}) = 0.038 \text{ J}$$

EVALUATE: The final energy is less than the original energy $U_{\text{initial}} = 0.058$ J; the difference has been converted to energy of some other form. The conductors become a little warmer because of their resistance, and some energy is radiated as electromagnetic waves. We'll study the circuit behavior of capacitors in detail in Chapters 26 and 31.

Example 24.8   Electric-field energy

Suppose you want to store 1.00 J of electric potential energy in a volume of 1.00 m³ in vacuum. (a) What is the magnitude of the required electric field? (b) If the field magnitude is 10 times larger, how much energy is stored per cubic meter?

SOLUTION

IDENTIFY: We use the relationship between the electric-field magnitude E and the energy density u, which equals the electric-field energy divided by the volume occupied by the field.

SET UP: In part (a) we use the given information to find u, then we use Eq. (24.11) to find the required value of E. This same equation gives us the relationship between changes in E and the corresponding changes in u.

EXECUTE: (a) The desired energy density is $u = 1.00$ J/m³. We solve Eq. (24.11) for E:

$$E = \sqrt{\frac{2u}{\epsilon_0}} = \sqrt{\frac{2(1.00 \text{ J/m}^3)}{8.85 \times 10^{-12} \text{ C}^2/\text{N} \cdot \text{m}^2}}$$

$$= 4.75 \times 10^5 \text{ N/C} = 4.75 \times 10^5 \text{ V/m}$$

(b) Equation (24.11) shows that u is proportional to E^2. If E increases by a factor of 10, u increases by a factor of $10^2 = 100$, and the energy density is 100 J/m³.

EVALUATE: The value of E found in part (a) is sizable, corresponding to a potential difference of nearly a half million volts over a distance of 1 meter. We will see in Section 24.4 that the field magnitudes in practical insulators can be as great as this or even larger.

Example 24.9   Two ways to calculate energy stored in a capacitor

The spherical capacitor described in Example 24.3 (Section 24.1) has charges $+Q$ and $-Q$ on its inner and outer conductors. Find the electric potential energy stored in the capacitor (a) by using the capacitance C found in Example 24.3 and (b) by integrating the electric-field energy density.

SOLUTION

IDENTIFY: This problem asks us to think about the energy stored in a capacitor, U, in two different ways: in terms of the work done to put the charges on the two conductors, $U = Q^2/2C$, and in terms of the energy in the electric field between the two conductors. Both descriptions are equivalent, so both must give us the same answer for U.

SET UP: In Example 24.3 we found the capacitance C and the field magnitude E between the conductors. We find the stored energy U in part (a) using the expression for C in Eq. (24.9). In part (b) we use the expression for E in Eq. (24.11) to find the electric-field energy density u between the conductors. The field magnitude depends on the distance r from the center of the capacitor, so u also depends on r. Hence we cannot find U by simply multiplying u by the volume between the conductors; instead, we must integrate u over this volume.

EXECUTE: (a) From Example 24.3, the spherical capacitor has capacitance

$$C = 4\pi\epsilon_0 \frac{r_a r_b}{r_b - r_a}$$

where r_a and r_b are the radii of the inner and outer conducting spheres. From Eq. (24.9) the energy stored in this capacitor is

$$U = \frac{Q^2}{2C} = \frac{Q^2}{8\pi\epsilon_0} \frac{r_b - r_a}{r_a r_b}$$

(b) The electric field in the volume between the two conducting spheres has magnitude $E = Q/4\pi\epsilon_0 r^2$. The electric field is zero inside the inner sphere and is also zero outside the inner surface of the outer sphere, because a Gaussian surface with radius $r < r_a$ or $r > r_b$ encloses zero net charge. Hence the energy density is nonzero only in the space between the spheres $(r_a < r < r_b)$. In this region,

$$u = \frac{1}{2}\epsilon_0 E^2 = \frac{1}{2}\epsilon_0 \left(\frac{Q}{4\pi\epsilon_0 r^2}\right)^2 = \frac{Q^2}{32\pi^2\epsilon_0 r^4}$$

The energy density is *not* uniform; it decreases rapidly with increasing distance from the center of the capacitor. To find the

Continued

total electric-field energy, we integrate u (the energy per unit volume) over the volume between the inner and outer conducting spheres. Dividing this volume up into spherical shells of radius r, surface area $4\pi r^2$, thickness dr, and volume $dV = 4\pi r^2\, dr$, we have

$$U = \int u\, dV = \int_{r_a}^{r_b} \left(\frac{Q^2}{32\pi^2\epsilon_0 r^4}\right) 4\pi r^2\, dr$$

$$= \frac{Q^2}{8\pi\epsilon_0}\int_{r_a}^{r_b}\frac{dr}{r^2} = \frac{Q^2}{8\pi\epsilon_0}\left(-\frac{1}{r_b}+\frac{1}{r_a}\right)$$

$$= \frac{Q^2}{8\pi\epsilon_0}\frac{r_b - r_a}{r_a r_b}$$

EVALUATE: We obtain the same result for U with either approach, as we must. We emphasize that electric potential energy can be regarded as being associated with either the *charges,* as in part (a), or the *field,* as in part (b); regardless of which viewpoint you choose, the amount of stored energy is the same.

Test Your Understanding of Section 24.3   You want to connect a 4-μF capacitor and an 8-μF capacitor. With which type of connection will the 4-μF capacitor have a greater amount of *stored energy* than the 8-μF capacitor? (i) series; (ii) parallel; (iii) either series or parallel; (iv) neither series nor parallel.

24.4 Dielectrics

24.13 A common type of capacitor uses dielectric sheets to separate the conductors.

Conductor (metal foil)

Conductor (metal foil)

Dielectric (plastic sheet)

Most capacitors have a nonconducting material, or **dielectric,** between their conducting plates. A common type of capacitor uses long strips of metal foil for the plates, separated by strips of plastic sheet such as Mylar. A sandwich of these materials is rolled up, forming a unit that can provide a capacitance of several microfarads in a compact package (Fig. 24.13).

Placing a solid dielectric between the plates of a capacitor serves three functions. First, it solves the mechanical problem of maintaining two large metal sheets at a very small separation without actual contact.

Second, using a dielectric increases the maximum possible potential difference between the capacitor plates. As we described in Section 23.3, any insulating material, when subjected to a sufficiently large electric field, experiences a partial ionization that permits conduction through it. This is called **dielectric breakdown.** Many dielectric materials can tolerate stronger electric fields without breakdown than can air. Thus using a dielectric allows a capacitor to sustain a higher potential difference V and so store greater amounts of charge and energy.

Third, the capacitance of a capacitor of given dimensions is *greater* when there is a dielectric material between the plates than when there is vacuum. We can demonstrate this effect with the aid of a sensitive *electrometer,* a device that measures the potential difference between two conductors without letting any appreciable charge flow from one to the other. Figure 24.14a shows an electrometer connected across a charged capacitor, with magnitude of charge Q on each plate and potential difference V_0. When we insert an uncharged sheet of dielectric, such as glass, paraffin, or polystyrene, between the plates, experiment shows that the potential difference *decreases* to a smaller value V (Fig. 24.14b). When we remove the dielectric, the potential difference returns to its original value V_0, showing that the original charges on the plates have not changed.

The original capacitance C_0 is given by $C_0 = Q/V_0$, and the capacitance C with the dielectric present is $C = Q/V$. The charge Q is the same in both cases, and V is less than V_0, so we conclude that the capacitance C with the dielectric present is *greater* than C_0. When the space between plates is completely filled by the dielectric, the ratio of C to C_0 (equal to the ratio of V_0 to V) is called the **dielectric constant** of the material, K:

$$K = \frac{C}{C_0} \qquad \text{(definition of dielectric constant)} \qquad (24.12)$$

When the charge is constant, $Q = C_0V_0 = CV$ and $C/C_0 = V_0/V$. In this case, Eq. (24.12) can be rewritten as

$$V = \frac{V_0}{K} \qquad \text{(when } Q \text{ is constant)} \qquad (24.13)$$

With the dielectric present, the potential difference for a given charge Q is *reduced* by a factor K.

The dielectric constant K is a pure number. Because C is always greater than C_0, K is always greater than unity. Some representative values of K are given in Table 24.1. For vacuum, $K = 1$ by definition. For air at ordinary temperatures and pressures, K is about 1.0006; this is so nearly equal to 1 that for most purposes an air capacitor is equivalent to one in vacuum. Note that while water has a very large value of K, it is usually not a very practical dielectric for use in capacitors. The reason is that while pure water is a very poor conductor, it is also an excellent ionic solvent. Any ions that are dissolved in the water will cause charge to flow between the capacitor plates, so the capacitor discharges.

Table 24.1 Values of Dielectric Constant K at 20°C

Material	K	Material	K
Vacuum	1	Polyvinyl chloride	3.18
Air (1 atm)	1.00059	Plexiglas	3.40
Air (100 atm)	1.0548	Glass	5–10
Teflon	2.1	Neoprene	6.70
Polyethylene	2.25	Germanium	16
Benzene	2.28	Glycerin	42.5
Mica	3–6	Water	80.4
Mylar	3.1	Strontium titanate	310

No real dielectric is a perfect insulator. Hence there is always some *leakage current* between the charged plates of a capacitor with a dielectric. We tacitly ignored this effect in Section 24.2 when we derived expressions for the equivalent capacitances of capacitors in series, Eq. (24.5), and in parallel, Eq. (24.7). But if a leakage current flows for a long enough time to substantially change the charges from the values we used to derive Eqs. (24.5) and (24.7), those equations may no longer be accurate.

Induced Charge and Polarization

When a dielectric material is inserted between the plates while the charge is kept constant, the potential difference between the plates decreases by a factor K. Therefore the electric field between the plates must decrease by the same factor. If E_0 is the vacuum value and E is the value with the dielectric, then

$$E = \frac{E_0}{K} \qquad \text{(when } Q \text{ is constant)} \qquad (24.14)$$

Since the electric-field magnitude is smaller when the dielectric is present, the surface charge density (which causes the field) must be smaller as well. The surface charge on the conducting plates does not change, but an *induced* charge of the opposite sign appears on each surface of the dielectric (Fig. 24.15). The dielectric was originally electrically neutral and is still neutral; the induced surface charges arise as a result of *redistribution* of positive and negative charge within the dielectric material, a phenomenon called **polarization.** We first encountered polarization in Section 21.2, and we suggest that you reread the discussion of Fig. 21.8. We will assume that the induced surface charge is *directly proportional* to the electric-field magnitude E in the material; this is indeed the case for many common dielectrics. (This direct proportionality is analogous to

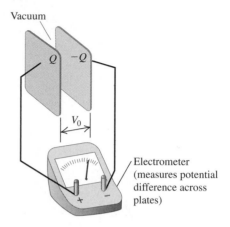

24.14 Effect of a dielectric between the plates of a parallel-plate capacitor. (a) With a given charge, the potential difference is V_0. (b) With the same charge but with a dielectric between the plates, the potential difference V is smaller than V_0.

(a)

Vacuum

Electrometer (measures potential difference across plates)

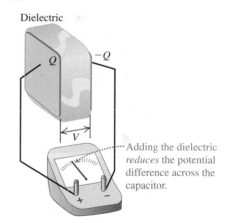

(b)

Dielectric

Adding the dielectric *reduces* the potential difference across the capacitor.

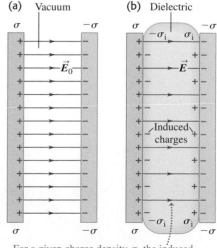

24.15 Electric field lines with (a) vacuum between the plates and (b) dielectric between the plates.

(a) Vacuum   (b) Dielectric

Induced charges

For a given charge density σ, the induced charges on the dielectric's surfaces reduce the electric field between the plates.

Hooke's law for a spring.) In that case, K is a constant for any particular material. When the electric field is very strong or if the dielectric is made of certain crystalline materials, the relationship between induced charge and the electric field can be more complex; we won't consider such cases here.

We can derive a relationship between this induced surface charge and the charge on the plates. Let's denote the magnitude of the charge per unit area induced on the surfaces of the dielectric (the induced surface charge density) by σ_i. The magnitude of the surface charge density on the capacitor plates is σ, as usual. Then the *net* surface charge on each side of the capacitor has magnitude $(\sigma - \sigma_i)$, as shown in Fig. 24.15b. As we found in Example 21.13 (Section 21.5) and in Example 22.8 (Section 22.4), the field between the plates is related to the net surface charge density by $E = \sigma_{net}/\epsilon_0$. Without and with the dielectric, respectively, we have

$$E_0 = \frac{\sigma}{\epsilon_0} \qquad E = \frac{\sigma - \sigma_i}{\epsilon_0} \tag{24.15}$$

Using these expressions in Eq. (24.14) and rearranging the result, we find

$$\sigma_i = \sigma \left(1 - \frac{1}{K} \right) \qquad \text{(induced surface charge density)} \tag{24.16}$$

This equation shows that when K is very large, σ_i is nearly as large as σ. In this case, σ_i nearly cancels σ, and the field and potential difference are much smaller than their values in vacuum.

The product $K\epsilon_0$ is called the **permittivity** of the dielectric, denoted by ϵ:

$$\epsilon = K\epsilon_0 \qquad \text{(definition of permittivity)} \tag{24.17}$$

In terms of ϵ we can express the electric field within the dielectric as

$$E = \frac{\sigma}{\epsilon} \tag{24.18}$$

The capacitance when the dielectric is present is given by

$$C = KC_0 = K\epsilon_0 \frac{A}{d} = \epsilon \frac{A}{d} \qquad \begin{array}{l} \text{(parallel-plate capacitor,} \\ \text{dielectric between plates)} \end{array} \tag{24.19}$$

We can repeat the derivation of Eq. (24.11) for the energy density u in an electric field for the case in which a dielectric is present. The result is

$$u = \frac{1}{2}K\epsilon_0 E^2 = \frac{1}{2}\epsilon E^2 \qquad \text{(electric energy density in a dielectric)} \tag{24.20}$$

In empty space, where $K = 1$, $\epsilon = \epsilon_0$ and Eqs. (24.19) and (24.20) reduce to Eqs. (24.2) and (24.11), respectively, for a parallel-plate capacitor in vacuum. For this reason, ϵ_0 is sometimes called the "permittivity of free space" or the "permittivity of vacuum." Because K is a pure number, ϵ and ϵ_0 have the same units, $C^2/N \cdot m^2$ or F/m.

Equation (24.19) shows that extremely high capacitances can be obtained with plates that have a large surface area A and are separated by a small distance d by a dielectric with a large value of K. In an *electrolytic double-layer capacitor*, tiny carbon granules adhere to each plate: The value of A is the combined surface area of the granules, which can be tremendous. The plates with granules attached are separated by a very thin dielectric sheet. A capacitor of this kind can have a capacitance of 5000 farads yet fit in the palm of your hand (compare Example 24.1 in Section 24.1).

Several practical devices make use of the way in which a capacitor responds to a change in dielectric constant. One example is an electric stud finder, used by home repair workers to locate metal studs hidden behind a wall's surface. It consists of a metal plate with associated circuitry. The plate acts as one half of a capacitor, with the wall acting as the other half. If the stud finder moves over a metal stud, the effective dielectric constant for the capacitor changes, changing the capacitance and triggering a signal.

Problem-Solving Strategy 24.2 **Dielectrics**

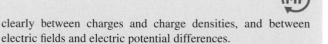

IDENTIFY *the relevant concepts:* The relationships in this section are useful whenever there is an electric field in a dielectric, such as a dielectric between charged capacitor plates. Typically you will be asked to relate the potential difference between the plates, the electric field in the capacitor, the charge density on the capacitor plates, and the induced charge density on the surfaces of the capacitor.

SET UP *the problem* using the following steps:
1. Make a drawing of the situation.
2. Identify the target variables, and choose which of the key equations of this section will help you find those variables.

EXECUTE *the solution* as follows:
1. In problems such as the next example, it is easy to get lost in a blizzard of formulas. Ask yourself at each step what kind of quantity each symbol represents. For example, distinguish

clearly between charges and charge densities, and between electric fields and electric potential differences.
2. As you calculate, continually check for consistency of units. This effort is a bit more complex with electrical quantities than it was in mechanics. Distances must always be in meters. Remember that a microfarad is 10^{-6} farad, and so on. Don't confuse the numerical value of ϵ_0 with the value of $1/4\pi\epsilon_0$. There are several alternative sets of units for electric-field magnitude, including N/C and V/m. The units of ϵ_0 are $C^2/N \cdot m^2$ or F/m.

EVALUATE *your answer:* When you check numerical values, remember that with a dielectric present, (a) the capacitance is always greater than without a dielectric; (b) for a given amount of charge on the capacitor, the electric field and potential difference are less than without a dielectric; and (c) the induced surface charge density σ_i on the dielectric is always less in magnitude than the charge density σ on the capacitor plates.

Example 24.10 **A capacitor with and without a dielectric**

Suppose the parallel plates in Fig. 24.15 each have an area of 2000 cm² (2.00×10^{-1} m²) and are 1.00 cm (1.00×10^{-2} m) apart. The capacitor is connected to a power supply and charged to a potential difference $V_0 = 3000$ V $= 3.00$ kV. It is then disconnected from the power supply, and a sheet of insulating plastic material is inserted between the plates, completely filling the space between them. We find that the potential difference decreases to 1000 V while the charge on each capacitor plate remains constant. Compute (a) the original capacitance C_0; (b) the magnitude of charge Q on each plate; (c) the capacitance C after the dielectric is inserted; (d) the dielectric constant K of the dielectric; (e) the permittivity ϵ of the dielectric; (f) the magnitude of the induced charge Q_i on each face of the dielectric; (g) the original electric field E_0 between the plates; and (h) the electric field E after the dielectric is inserted.

SOLUTION

IDENTIFY: This problem uses most of the relationships we have discussed for capacitors and dielectrics.

SET UP: Most of the target variables can be obtained in several different ways. The methods used below are a representative sample; we encourage you to think of others and compare your results.

EXECUTE: (a) With vacuum between the plates, we use Eq. (24.19) with $K = 1$:

$$C_0 = \epsilon_0 \frac{A}{d} = (8.85 \times 10^{-12} \text{ F/m})\frac{2.00 \times 10^{-1} \text{ m}^2}{1.00 \times 10^{-2} \text{ m}}$$

$$= 1.77 \times 10^{-10} \text{ F} = 177 \text{ pF}$$

(b) Using the definition of capacitance, Eq. (24.1),

$$Q = C_0 V_0 = (1.77 \times 10^{-10} \text{ F})(3.00 \times 10^3 \text{ V})$$

$$= 5.31 \times 10^{-7} \text{ C} = 0.531 \ \mu\text{C}$$

(c) When the dielectric is inserted, the charge remains the same but the potential decreases to $V = 1000$ V. Hence from Eq. (24.1), the new capacitance is

$$C = \frac{Q}{V} = \frac{5.31 \times 10^{-7} \text{ C}}{1.00 \times 10^3 \text{ V}} = 5.31 \times 10^{-10} \text{ F} = 531 \text{ pF}$$

(d) From Eq. (24.12), the dielectric constant is

$$K = \frac{C}{C_0} = \frac{5.31 \times 10^{-10} \text{ F}}{1.77 \times 10^{-10} \text{ F}} = \frac{531 \text{ pF}}{177 \text{ pF}} = 3.00$$

Alternatively, from Eq. (24.13),

$$K = \frac{V_0}{V} = \frac{3000 \text{ V}}{1000 \text{ V}} = 3.00$$

(e) Using K from part (d) in Eq. (24.17), the permittivity is

$$\epsilon = K\epsilon_0 = (3.00)(8.85 \times 10^{-12} \text{ C}^2/\text{N} \cdot \text{m}^2)$$

$$= 2.66 \times 10^{-11} \text{ C}^2/\text{N} \cdot \text{m}^2$$

(f) Multiplying Eq. (24.15) by the area of each plate gives the induced charge $Q_i = \sigma_i A$ in terms of the charge $Q = \sigma A$ on each plate:

$$Q_i = Q\left(1 - \frac{1}{K}\right) = (5.31 \times 10^{-7} \text{ C})\left(1 - \frac{1}{3.00}\right)$$

$$= 3.54 \times 10^{-7} \text{ C}$$

Continued

(g) Since the electric field between the plates is uniform, its magnitude is the potential difference divided by the plate separation:

$$E_0 = \frac{V_0}{d} = \frac{3000 \text{ V}}{1.00 \times 10^{-2} \text{ m}} = 3.00 \times 10^5 \text{ V/m}$$

(h) With the new potential difference after the dielectric is inserted,

$$E = \frac{V}{d} = \frac{1000 \text{ V}}{1.00 \times 10^{-2} \text{ m}} = 1.00 \times 10^5 \text{ V/m}$$

or, from Eq. (24.17),

$$E = \frac{\sigma}{\epsilon} = \frac{Q}{\epsilon A} = \frac{5.31 \times 10^{-7} \text{ C}}{(2.66 \times 10^{-11} \text{ C}^2/\text{N} \cdot \text{m}^2)(2.00 \times 10^{-1} \text{ m}^2)}$$
$$= 1.00 \times 10^5 \text{ V/m}$$

or, from Eq. (24.15),

$$E = \frac{\sigma - \sigma_i}{\epsilon_0} = \frac{Q - Q_i}{\epsilon_0 A}$$
$$= \frac{(5.31 - 3.54) \times 10^{-7} \text{ C}}{(8.85 \times 10^{-12} \text{ C}^2/\text{N} \cdot \text{m}^2)(2.00 \times 10^{-1} \text{ m}^2)}$$
$$= 1.00 \times 10^5 \text{ V/m}$$

or, from Eq. (24.14),

$$E = \frac{E_0}{K} = \frac{3.00 \times 10^5 \text{ V/m}}{3.00} = 1.00 \times 10^5 \text{ V/m}$$

EVALUATE: It's always useful to check the results by finding them in more than one way, as we did in parts (d) and (h). Our results show that inserting the dielectric increased the capacitance by a factor of $K = 3.00$ and reduced the electric field between the plates by a factor of $1/K = 1/3.00$. It did so by developing induced charges on the faces of the dielectric of magnitude $Q(1 - 1/K) = Q(1 - 1/3.00) = 0.667Q$.

Example 24.11   Energy storage with and without a dielectric

Find the total energy stored in the electric field of the capacitor in Example 24.10 and the energy density, both before and after the dielectric sheet is inserted.

SOLUTION

IDENTIFY: In this problem we have to extend the analysis of Example 24.10 to include the ideas of energy stored in a capacitor and electric-field energy.

SET UP: We use Eq. (24.9) to find the stored energy before and after the dielectric is inserted, and Eq. (24.20) to find the energy density.

EXECUTE: Let the original energy be U_0 and let the energy with the dielectric in place be U. From Eq. (24.9),

$$U_0 = \frac{1}{2}C_0V_0^2 = \frac{1}{2}(1.77 \times 10^{-10} \text{ F})(3000 \text{ V})^2 = 7.97 \times 10^{-4} \text{ J}$$

$$U = \frac{1}{2}CV^2 = \frac{1}{2}(5.31 \times 10^{-10} \text{ F})(1000 \text{ V})^2 = 2.66 \times 10^{-4} \text{ J}$$

The final energy is one-third of the original energy.

The energy density without the dielectric is given by Eq. (24.20) with $K = 1$:

$$u_0 = \frac{1}{2}\epsilon_0 E_0^2 = \frac{1}{2}(8.85 \times 10^{-12} \text{ C}^2/\text{N} \cdot \text{m}^2)(3.0 \times 10^5 \text{ N/C})^2$$
$$= 0.398 \text{ J/m}^3$$

With the dielectric in place,

$$u = \frac{1}{2}\epsilon E^2 = \frac{1}{2}(2.66 \times 10^{-11} \text{ C}^2/\text{N} \cdot \text{m}^2)(1.00 \times 10^5 \text{ N/C})^2$$
$$= 0.133 \text{ J/m}^3$$

The energy density with the dielectric is one-third of the original energy density.

EVALUATE: We can check our answer for u_0 by noting that the volume between the plates is $V = (0.200 \text{ m})^2(0.0100 \text{ m}) = 0.00200 \text{ m}^3$. Since the electric field is uniform between the plates, u_0 is uniform as well and the energy density is just the stored energy divided by the volume:

$$u_0 = \frac{U_0}{V} = \frac{7.97 \times 10^{-4} \text{ J}}{0.00200 \text{ m}^3} = 0.398 \text{ J/m}^3$$

which agrees with our earlier answer. You should use the same approach to check the value for U, the energy density with the dielectric.

We can generalize the results of this example. When a dielectric is inserted into a capacitor while the charge on each plate remains the same, the permittivity ϵ increases by a factor of K (the dielectric constant), the electric field decreases by a factor of $1/K$, and the energy density $u = \frac{1}{2}\epsilon E^2$ decreases by a factor of $1/K$. Where did the energy go? The answer lies in the fringing field at the edges of a real parallel-plate capacitor. As Fig. 24.16 shows, that field tends to pull the dielectric into the space between the plates, doing work on it as it does so. We could attach a spring to the left end of the dielectric in Fig. 24.16 and use this force to stretch the spring. Because work is done by the field, the field energy density decreases.

24.16 The fringing field at the edges of the capacitor exerts forces $\vec{F}_{-i}$ and $\vec{F}_{+i}$ on the negative and positive induced surface charges of a dielectric, pulling the dielectric into the capacitor.

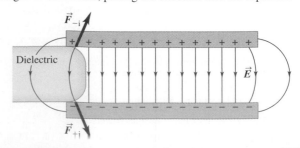

Dielectric Breakdown

We mentioned earlier that when any dielectric material is subjected to a sufficiently strong electric field, *dielectric breakdown* takes place and the dielectric becomes a conductor (Fig. 24.17). This occurs when the electric field is so strong that electrons are ripped loose from their molecules and crash into other molecules, liberating even more electrons. This avalanche of moving charge, forming a spark or arc discharge, often starts quite suddenly.

Because of dielectric breakdown, capacitors always have maximum voltage ratings. When a capacitor is subjected to excessive voltage, an arc may form through a layer of dielectric, burning or melting a hole in it. This arc creates a conducting path (a short circuit) between the conductors. If a conducting path remains after the arc is extinguished, the device is rendered permanently useless as a capacitor.

The maximum electric-field magnitude that a material can withstand without the occurrence of breakdown is called its **dielectric strength.** This quantity is affected significantly by temperature, trace impurities, small irregularities in the metal electrodes, and other factors that are difficult to control. For this reason we can give only approximate figures for dielectric strengths. The dielectric strength of dry air is about 3×10^6 V/m. Values of dielectric strength for a few common insulating materials are shown in Table 24.2. Note that the values are all substantially greater than the value for air. For example, a layer of polycarbonate 0.01 mm thick (about the smallest practical thickness) has 10 times the dielectric strength of air and can withstand a maximum voltage of about $(3 \times 10^7 \text{ V/m})(1 \times 10^{-5} \text{ m}) = 300$ V.

24.17 A very strong electric field caused dielectric breakdown in a block of Plexiglas. The resulting flow of charge etched this pattern into the block.

Table 24.2 Dielectric Constant and Dielectric Strength of Some Insulating Materials

Material	Dielectric Constant, K	Dielectric Strength, E_m (V/m)
Polycarbonate	2.8	3×10^7
Polyester	3.3	6×10^7
Polypropylene	2.2	7×10^7
Polystyrene	2.6	2×10^7
Pyrex glass	4.7	1×10^7

Test Your Understanding of Section 24.4   The space between the plates of an isolated parallel-plate capacitor is filled by a slab of dielectric with dielectric constant K. The two plates of the capacitor have charges Q and $-Q$. You pull out the dielectric slab. If the charges do not change, how does the energy in the capacitor change when you remove the slab? (i) It increases; (ii) it decreases; (iii) it remains the same.

*24.5 Molecular Model of Induced Charge

In Section 24.4 we discussed induced surface charges on a dielectric in an electric field. Now let's look at how these surface charges can arise. If the material were a *conductor,* the answer would be simple. Conductors contain charge that is free to move, and when an electric field is present, some of the charge redistributes itself on the surface so that there is no electric field inside the conductor. But an ideal dielectric has *no* charges that are free to move, so how can a surface charge occur?

To understand this, we have to look again at rearrangement of charge at the *molecular* level. Some molecules, such as H_2O and N_2O, have equal amounts of positive and negative charges but a lopsided distribution, with excess positive charge concentrated on one side of the molecule and negative charge on the other. As we described in Section 21.7, such an arrangement is called an *electric dipole,* and the molecule is called a *polar molecule.* When no electric field is present in a gas or liquid with polar molecules, the molecules are oriented randomly (Fig. 24.18a). When they are placed in an electric field, however, they tend

24.18 Polar molecules (a) without and (b) with an applied electric field $\vec{E}$.

(a)

In the absence of an electric field, polar molecules orient randomly.

(b)

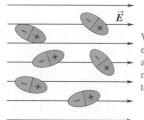

When an electric field is applied, the molecules tend to align with it.

24.19 Nonpolar molecules (a) without and (b) with an applied electric field $\vec{E}$.

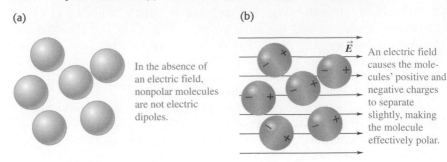

(a)

In the absence of an electric field, nonpolar molecules are not electric dipoles.

(b)

$\vec{E}$

An electric field causes the molecules' positive and negative charges to separate slightly, making the molecule effectively polar.

to orient themselves as in Fig. 24.18b, as a result of the electric-field torques described in Section 21.7. Because of thermal agitation, the alignment of the molecules with $\vec{E}$ is not perfect.

Even a molecule that is *not* ordinarily polar *becomes* a dipole when it is placed in an electric field because the field pushes the positive charges in the molecules in the direction of the field and pushes the negative charges in the opposite direction. This causes a redistribution of charge within the molecule (Fig. 24.19). Such dipoles are called *induced* dipoles.

With either polar or nonpolar molecules, the redistribution of charge caused by the field leads to the formation of a layer of charge on each surface of the dielectric material (Fig. 24.20). These layers are the surface charges described in Section 24.4; their surface charge density is denoted by σ_i. The charges are *not* free to move indefinitely, as they would be in a conductor, because each charge is bound to a molecule. They are in fact called **bound charges** to distinguish them from the **free charges** that are added to and removed from the conducting capacitor plates. In the interior of the material the net charge per unit volume remains zero. As we have seen, this redistribution of charge is called *polarization*, and we say that the material is *polarized*.

The four parts of Fig. 24.21 show the behavior of a slab of dielectric when it is inserted in the field between a pair of oppositely charged capacitor plates. Figure 24.21a shows the original field. Figure 24.21b is the situation after the dielectric has been inserted but before any rearrangement of charges has occurred.

24.20 Polarization of a dielectric in an electric field $\vec{E}$ gives rise to thin layers of bound charges on the surfaces, creating surface charge densities σ_i and $-\sigma_i$. The sizes of the molecules are greatly exaggerated for clarity.

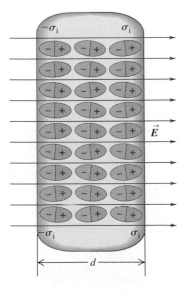

24.21 (a) Electric field of magnitude E_0 between two charged plates. (b) Introduction of a dielectric of dielectric constant K. (c) The induced surface charges and their field. (d) Resultant field of magnitude E_0/K.

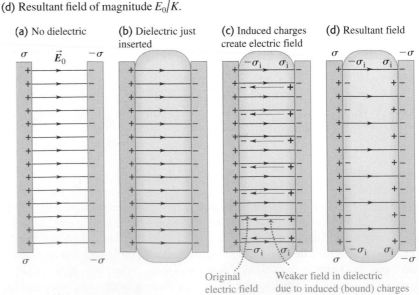

(a) No dielectric

(b) Dielectric just inserted

(c) Induced charges create electric field

(d) Resultant field

Original electric field

Weaker field in dielectric due to induced (bound) charges

Figure 24.21c shows by thinner arrows the additional field set up in the dielectric by its induced surface charges. This field is *opposite* to the original field, but it is not great enough to cancel the original field completely because the charges in the dielectric are not free to move indefinitely. The resultant field in the dielectric, shown in Fig. 24.21d, is therefore decreased in magnitude. In the field-line representation, some of the field lines leaving the positive plate go through the dielectric, while others terminate on the induced charges on the faces of the dielectric.

As we discussed in Section 21.2, polarization is also the reason a charged body, such as an electrified plastic rod, can exert a force on an *uncharged* body such as a bit of paper or a pith ball. Figure 24.22 shows an uncharged dielectric sphere B in the radial field of a positively charged body A. The induced positive charges on B experience a force toward the right, while the force on the induced negative charges is toward the left. The negative charges are closer to A, and thus are in a stronger field, than are the positive charges. The force toward the left is stronger than that toward the right, and B is attracted toward A, even though its net charge is zero. The attraction occurs whether the sign of A's charge is positive or negative (see Fig. 21.8). Furthermore, the effect is not limited to dielectrics; an uncharged conducting body would be attracted in the same way.

24.22 A neutral sphere B in the radial electric field of a positively charged sphere A is attracted to the charge because of polarization.

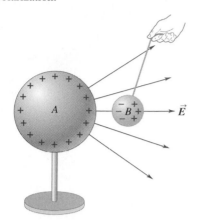

Test Your Understanding of Section 24.5   A parallel-plate capacitor has charges Q and $-Q$ on its two plates. A dielectric slab with $K = 3$ is then inserted into the space between the plates as shown in Fig. 24.21. Rank the following electric-field magnitudes in order from largest to smallest. (i) the field before the slab is inserted; (ii) the resultant field after the slab is inserted; (iii) the field due to the bound charges.

*24.6 Gauss's Law in Dielectrics

We can extend the analysis of Section 24.4 to reformulate Gauss's law in a form that is particularly useful for dielectrics. Figure 24.23 is a close-up view of the left capacitor plate and left surface of the dielectric in Fig. 24.15b. Let's apply Gauss's law to the rectangular box shown in cross section by the purple line; the surface area of the left and right sides is A. The left side is embedded in the conductor that forms the left capacitor plate, and so the electric field everywhere on that surface is zero. The right side is embedded in the dielectric, where the electric field has magnitude E, and $E_\perp = 0$ everywhere on the other four sides. The total charge enclosed, including both the charge on the capacitor plate and the induced charge on the dielectric surface, is $Q_{encl} = (\sigma - \sigma_i)A$, so Gauss's law gives

$$EA = \frac{(\sigma - \sigma_i)A}{\epsilon_0}$$ (24.21)

This equation is not very illuminating as it stands because it relates two unknown quantities: E inside the dielectric and the induced surface charge density σ_i. But now we can use Eq. (24.16), developed for this same situation, to simplify this equation by eliminating σ_i. Equation (24.16) is

$$\sigma_i = \sigma\left(1 - \frac{1}{K}\right) \quad \text{or} \quad \sigma - \sigma_i = \frac{\sigma}{K}$$

Combining this with Eq. (24.21), we get

$$EA = \frac{\sigma A}{K\epsilon_0} \quad \text{or} \quad KEA = \frac{\sigma A}{\epsilon_0}$$ (24.22)

Equation (24.22) says that the flux of $K\vec{E}$, not $\vec{E}$, through the Gaussian surface in Fig. 24.23 is equal to the enclosed *free* charge σA divided by ϵ_0. It turns out

24.23 Gauss's law with a dielectric. This figure shows a close-up of the left-hand capacitor plate in Fig. 24.15b. The Gaussian surface is a rectangular box that lies half in the conductor and half in the dielectric.

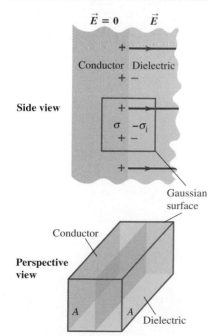

that for *any* Gaussian surface, whenever the induced charge is proportional to the electric field in the material, we can rewrite Gauss's law as

$$\oint K\vec{E} \cdot d\vec{A} = \frac{Q_{\text{encl-free}}}{\epsilon_0} \quad \text{(Gauss's law in a dielectric)} \qquad (24.23)$$

where $Q_{\text{encl-free}}$ is the total *free* charge (not bound charge) enclosed by the Gaussian surface. The significance of these results is that the right sides contain only the *free* charge on the conductor, not the bound (induced) charge. In fact, although we have not proved it, Eq. (24.23) remains valid even when different parts of the Gaussian surface are embedded in dielectrics having different values of K, provided that the value of K in each dielectric is independent of the electric field (usually the case for electric fields that are not too strong) and that we use the appropriate value of K for each point on the Gaussian surface.

Example 24.12 A spherical capacitor with dielectric

In the spherical capacitor of Example 24.3 (Section 24.1), the volume between the concentric spherical conducting shells is filled with an insulating oil with dielectric constant K. Use Gauss's law to find the capacitance.

SOLUTION

IDENTIFY: This is essentially the same problem as Example 24.3. The only difference is the presence of the dielectric.

SET UP: As we did in Example 24.3, we use a spherical Gaussian surface of radius r between the two spheres. Since a dielectric is present, we use Gauss's law in the form of Eq. (24.23).

EXECUTE: The spherical symmetry of the problem is not changed by the presence of the dielectric, so we have

$$\oint K\vec{E} \cdot d\vec{A} = \oint KE \, dA = KE \oint dA = (KE)(4\pi r^2) = \frac{Q}{\epsilon_0}$$

$$E = \frac{Q}{4\pi K\epsilon_0 r^2} = \frac{Q}{4\pi \epsilon r^2}$$

where $\epsilon = K\epsilon_0$ is the permittivity of the dielectric (introduced in Section 24.4). Compared to the case in which there is vacuum between the conducting shells, the electric field is reduced by a factor of $1/K$. The potential difference V_{ab} between the shells is likewise reduced by a factor of $1/K$, and so the capacitance $C = Q/V_{ab}$ is *increased* by a factor of K, just as for a parallel-plate capacitor when a dielectric is inserted. Using the result for the vacuum case in Example 24.3, we find that the capacitance with the dielectric is

$$C = \frac{4\pi K\epsilon_0 r_a r_b}{r_b - r_a} = \frac{4\pi \epsilon r_a r_b}{r_b - r_a}$$

EVALUATE: In this case the dielectric completely fills the volume between the two conductors, so the capacitance is just K times the value with no dielectric. The result is more complicated if the dielectric only partially fills this volume (see Challenge Problem 24.76).

Test Your Understanding of Section 24.6 A single point charge q is imbedded in a dielectric of dielectric constant K. At a point inside the dielectric a distance r from the point charge, what is the magnitude of the electric field? (i) $q/4\pi\epsilon_0 r^2$; (ii) $Kq/4\pi\epsilon_0 r^2$; (iii) $q/4\pi K\epsilon_0 r^2$; (iv) none of these.

Capacitors and capacitance: A capacitor is any pair of conductors separated by an insulating material. When the capacitor is charged, there are charges of equal magnitude Q and opposite sign on the two conductors, and the potential V_{ab} of the positively charged conductor with respect to the negatively charged conductor is proportional to Q. The capacitance C is defined as the ratio of Q to V_{ab}. The SI unit of capacitance is the farad (F): $1\text{ F} = 1\text{ C/V}$.

A parallel-plate capacitor consists of two parallel conducting plates, each with area A, separated by a distance d. If they are separated by vacuum, the capacitance depends only on A and d. For other geometries, the capacitance can be found by using the definition $C = Q/V_{ab}$. (See Examples 24.1–24.4.)

$$C = \frac{Q}{V_{ab}} \tag{24.1}$$

$$C = \frac{Q}{V_{ab}} = \epsilon_0 \frac{A}{d} \tag{24.2}$$

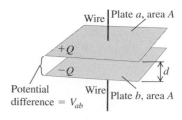

Capacitors in series and parallel: When capacitors with capacitances $C_1, C_2, C_3, \ldots$ are connected in series, the reciprocal of the equivalent capacitance C_{eq} equals the sum of the reciprocals of the individual capacitances. When capacitors are connected in parallel, the equivalent capacitance C_{eq} equals the sum of the individual capacitances. (See Examples 24.5 and 24.6.)

$$\frac{1}{C_{eq}} = \frac{1}{C_1} + \frac{1}{C_2} + \frac{1}{C_3} + \cdots \tag{24.5}$$
(capacitors in series)

$$C_{eq} = C_1 + C_2 + C_3 + \cdots \tag{24.7}$$
(capacitors in parallel)

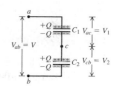

Energy in a capacitor: The energy U required to charge a capacitor C to a potential difference V and a charge Q is equal to the energy stored in the capacitor. This energy can be thought of as residing in the electric field between the conductors; the energy density u (energy per unit volume) is proportional to the square of the electric-field magnitude. (See Examples 24.7–24.9.)

$$U = \frac{Q^2}{2C} = \frac{1}{2}CV^2 = \frac{1}{2}QV \tag{24.9}$$

$$u = \frac{1}{2}\epsilon_0 E^2 \tag{24.11}$$

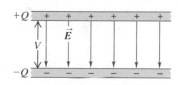

Dielectrics: When the space between the conductors is filled with a dielectric material, the capacitance increases by a factor K, called the dielectric constant of the material. The quantity $\epsilon = K\epsilon_0$ is called the permittivity of the dielectric. For a fixed amount of charge on the capacitor plates, induced charges on the surface of the dielectric decrease the electric field and potential difference between the plates by the same factor K. The surface charge results from polarization, a microscopic rearrangement of charge in the dielectric. (See Example 24.10.)

Under sufficiently strong fields, dielectrics become conductors, a situation called dielectric breakdown. The maximum field that a material can withstand without breakdown is called its dielectric strength.

In a dielectric, the expression for the energy density is the same as in vacuum but with ϵ_0 replaced by $\epsilon = K\epsilon$. (See Example 24.11.)

Gauss's law in a dielectric has almost the same form as in vacuum, with two key differences: $\vec{E}$ is replaced by $K\vec{E}$ and Q_{encl} is replaced by $Q_{encl\text{-}free}$, which includes only the free charge (not bound charge) enclosed by the Gaussian surface. (See Example 24.12.)

$$C = KC_0 = K\epsilon_0 \frac{A}{d} = \epsilon \frac{A}{d} \tag{24.19}$$
(parallel-plate capacitor filled with dielectric)

$$u = \frac{1}{2}K\epsilon_0 E^2 = \frac{1}{2}\epsilon E^2 \tag{24.20}$$

$$\oint K\vec{E} \cdot d\vec{A} = \frac{Q_{encl\text{-}free}}{\epsilon_0} \tag{24.23}$$

Dielectric between plates

Key Terms

Answer to Chapter Opening Question ?

Equation (24.9) shows that the energy stored in a capacitor with capacitance C and charge Q is $U = Q^2/2C$. If the charge Q is doubled, the stored energy increases by a factor of $2^2 = 4$. Note that if the value of Q is too great, the electric-field magnitude inside the capacitor will exceed the dielectric strength of the material between the plates and dielectric breakdown will occur (see Section 24.4). This puts a practical limit on the amount of energy that can be stored.

Answers to Test Your Understanding Questions

24.1 Answer: (iii) The capacitance does not depend on the value of the charge Q. Doubling the value of Q causes the potential difference V_{ab} to double, so the capacitance $C = Q/V_{ab}$ remains the same. These statements are true no matter what the geometry of the capacitor.

24.2 Answers: (a) (i), (b) (iv) In a series connection the two capacitors carry the same charge Q but have different potential differences $V_{ab} = Q/C$; the capacitor with the smaller capacitance C has the greater potential difference. In a parallel connection the two capacitors have the same potential difference V_{ab} but carry different charges $Q = CV_{ab}$; the capacitor with the larger capacitance C has the greater charge. Hence a 4-μF capacitor will have a greater potential difference than an 8-μF capacitor if the two are connected in series. The 4-μF capacitor cannot carry more charge than the 8-μF capacitor no matter how they are connected: In a series connection they will carry the same charge, and in a parallel connection the 8-μF capacitor will carry more charge.

24.3 Answer: (i) Capacitors connected in series carry the same charge Q. To compare the amount of energy stored, we use the expression $U = Q^2/2C$ from Eq. (24.9); it shows that the capacitor with the *smaller* capacitance ($C = 4\ \mu$F) has more stored energy in a series combination. By contrast, capacitors in parallel have the same potential difference V, so to compare them we use $U = \frac{1}{2}CV^2$ from Eq. (24.9). It shows that in a parallel combination, the capacitor with the *larger* capacitance ($C = 8\ \mu$F) has more stored energy. (If we had instead used $U = \frac{1}{2}CV^2$ to analyze the series combination, we would have to account for the different potential differences across the two capacitors. Likewise, using $U = Q^2/2C$ to study the parallel combination would require us to account for the different charges on the capacitors.)

24.4 Answers: (i) Here Q remains the same, so we use $U = Q^2/2C$ from Eq. (24.9) for the stored energy. Removing the dielectric lowers the capacitance by a factor of $1/K$; since U is inversely proportional to C, the stored energy *increases* by a factor of K. It takes work to pull the dielectric slab out of the capacitor because the fringing field tries to pull the slab back in (Fig. 24.16). The work that you do goes into the energy stored in the capacitor.

24.5 Answer: (i), (iii), (ii) Equation (24.14) says that if E_0 is the initial electric-field magnitude (before the dielectric slab is inserted), then the resultant field magnitude after the slab is inserted is $E_0/K = E_0/3$. The magnitude of the resultant field equals the difference between the initial field magnitude and the magnitude E_i of the field due to the bound charges (see Fig. 24.21). Hence $E_0 - E_i = E_0/3$ and $E_i = 2E_0/3$.

24.6 Answer: (iii) Equation (24.23) shows that this situation is the same as an isolated point charge in vacuum but with $\vec{E}$ replaced by $K\vec{E}$. Hence KE at the point of interest is equal to $q/4\pi\epsilon_0 r^2$, and so $E = q/4\pi K\epsilon_0 r^2$. As in Example 24.12, filling the space with a dielectric reduces the electric field by a factor of $1/K$.

PROBLEMS

For instructor-assigned homework, go to **www.masteringphysics.com**

Discussion Questions

Q24.1. Equation (24.2) shows that the capacitance of a parallel-plate capacitor becomes larger as the plate separation d decreases. However, there is a practical limit to how small d can be made, which places limits on how large C can be. Explain what sets the limit on d. (*Hint:* What happens to the magnitude of the electric field as $d \to 0$?)

Q24.2. Suppose several different parallel-plate capacitors are charged up by a constant-voltage source. Thinking of the actual movement and position of the charges on an atomic level, why does it make sense that the capacitances are proportional to the surface areas of the plates? Why does it make sense that the capacitances are inversely proportional to the distance between the plates?

Q24.3. Suppose the two plates of a capacitor have different areas. When the capacitor is charged by connecting it to a battery, do the charges on the two plates have equal magnitude, or may they be different? Explain your reasoning.

Q24.4. At the Fermi National Accelerator Laboratory (Fermilab) in Illinois, protons are accelerated around a ring 2 km in radius to speeds that approach that of light. The energy for this is stored in capacitors the size of a house. When these capacitors are being charged, they make a very loud creaking sound. What is the origin of this sound?

Q24.5. In the parallel-plate capacitor of Fig. 24.2, suppose the plates are pulled apart so that the separation d is much larger than the size of the plates. (a) Is it still accurate to say that the electric field between the plates is uniform? Why or why not? (b) In the situation shown in Fig. 24.2, the potential difference between the plates is $V_{ab} = Qd/\epsilon_0 A$. If the plates are pulled apart as described above, is V_{ab} more or less than this formula would indicate? Explain your reasoning. (c) With the plates pulled apart as described above, is the capacitance more than, less than, or the same as that given by Eq. (24.2)? Explain your reasoning.

Q24.6. A parallel-plate capacitor is charged by being connected to a battery and is kept connected to the battery. The separation between the plates is then doubled. How does the electric field change? The charge on the plates? The total energy? Explain your reasoning.

Q24.7. A parallel-plate capacitor is charged by being connected to a battery and is then disconnected from the battery. The separation between the plates is then doubled. How does the electric field change? The potential difference? The total energy? Explain your reasoning.

Q24.8. Two parallel-plate capacitors, identical except that one has twice the plate separation of the other, are charged by the same voltage source. Which capacitor has a stronger electric field between the plates? Which capacitor has a greater charge? Which has greater energy density? Explain your reasoning.

Q24.9. The charged plates of a capacitor attract each other, so to pull the plates farther apart requires work by some external force. What becomes of the energy added by this work? Explain your reasoning.

Q24.10. The two plates of a capacitor are given charges $\pm Q$. The capacitor is then disconnected from the charging device so that the charges on the plates can't change, and the capacitor is immersed in a tank of oil. Does the electric field between the plates increase, decrease, or stay the same? Explain your reasoning. How can this field be measured?

Q24.11. As shown in Table 24.1, water has a very large dielectric constant $K = 80.4$. Why do you think water is not commonly used as a dielectric in capacitors?

Q24.12. Is dielectric strength the same thing as dielectric constant? Explain any differences between the two quantities. Is there a simple relationship between dielectric strength and dielectric constant (see Table 24.2)?

Q24.13. A capacitor made of aluminum foil strips separated by Mylar film was subjected to excessive voltage, and the resulting dielectric breakdown melted holes in the Mylar. After this, the capacitance was found to be about the same as before, but the breakdown voltage was much less. Why?

Q24.14. Suppose you bring a slab of dielectric close to the gap between the plates of a charged capacitor, preparing to slide it between the plates. What force will you feel? What does this force tell you about the energy stored between the plates once the dielectric is in place, compared to before the dielectric is in place?

Q24.15. The freshness of fish can be measured by placing a fish between the plates of a capacitor and measuring the capacitance. How does this work? (*Hint:* As time passes, the fish dries out. See Table 24.1.)

Q24.16. *Electrolytic* capacitors use as their dielectric an extremely thin layer of nonconducting oxide between a metal plate and a conducting solution. Discuss the advantage of such a capacitor over one constructed using a solid dielectric between the metal plates.

Q24.17. In terms of the dielectric constant K, what happens to the electric flux through the Gaussian surface shown in Fig. 24.23 when the dielectric is inserted into the previously empty space between the plates? Explain.

Q24.18. A parallel-plate capacitor is connected to a power supply that maintains a fixed potential difference between the plates. (a) If a sheet of dielectric is then slid between the plates, what happens to (i) the electric field between the plates, (ii) the magnitude of charge on each plate, and (iii) the energy stored in the capacitor? (b) Now suppose that before the dielectric is inserted, the charged capacitor is disconnected from the power supply. In this case, what happens to (i) the electric field between the plates, (ii) the magnitude of charge on each plate, (iii) the energy stored in the capacitor? Explain any differences between the two situations.

Q24.19. Liquid dielectrics that have polar molecules (such as water) always have dielectric constants that decrease with increasing temperature. Why?

Q24.20. A conductor is an extreme case of a dielectric, since if an electric field is applied to a conductor, charges are free to move within the conductor to set up "induced charges." What is the dielectric constant of a perfect conductor? Is it $K = 0$, $K \to \infty$, or something in between? Explain your reasoning.

Exercises

Section 24.1 Capacitors and Capacitance

24.1. A capacitor has a capacitance of $7.28 \ \mu\text{F}$. What amount of charge must be placed on each of its plates to make the potential difference between its plates equal to 25.0 V?

24.2. The plates of a parallel-plate capacitor are 3.28 mm apart, and each has an area of $12.2 \ \text{cm}^2$. Each plate carries a charge of magnitude $4.35 \times 10^{-8} \ \text{C}$. The plates are in vacuum. (a) What is the capacitance? (b) What is the potential difference between the plates? (c) What is the magnitude of the electric field between the plates?

24.3. A parallel-plate air capacitor of capacitance 245 pF has a charge of magnitude $0.148 \ \mu\text{C}$ on each plate. The plates are 0.328 mm apart. (a) What is the potential difference between the plates? (b) What is the area of each plate? (c) What is the electric-field magnitude between the plates? (d) What is the surface charge density on each plate?

24.4. Capacitance of an Oscilloscope. Oscilloscopes have parallel metal plates inside them to deflect the electron beam. These plates are called the *deflecting plates*. Typically, they are squares 3.0 cm on a side and separated by 5.0 mm, with vacuum in between. What is the capacitance of these deflecting plates and hence of the oscilloscope? (*Note:* This capacitance can sometimes have an effect on the circuit you are trying to study and must be taken into consideration in your calculations.)

24.5. A $10.0 \text{-} \mu\text{F}$ parallel-plate capacitor with circular plates is connected to a 12.0-V battery. (a) What is the charge on each plate? (b) How much charge would be on the plates if their separation were doubled while the capacitor remained connected to the battery? (c) How much charge would be on the plates if the capacitor were connected to the 12.0-V battery after the radius of each plate was doubled without changing their separation?

24.6. A $10.0 \text{-} \mu\text{F}$ parallel-plate capacitor is connected to a 12.0-V battery. After the capacitor is fully charged, the battery is disconnected without loss of any of the charge on the plates. (a) A voltmeter is connected across the two plates without discharging them. What does it read? (b) What would the voltmeter read if (i) the plate separation were doubled; (ii) the radius of each plate were doubled and, but their separation was unchanged?

24.7. How far apart would parallel pennies have to be to make a 1.00-pF capacitor? Does your answer suggest that you are justified in treating these pennies as infinite sheets? Explain.

24.8. A 5.00-pF, parallel-plate, air-filled capacitor with circular plates is to be used in a circuit in which it will be subjected to potentials of up to 1.00×10^2 V. The electric field between the plates is to be no greater than 1.00×10^4 N/C. As a budding electrical engineer for Live-Wire Electronics, your tasks are to (a) design the capacitor by finding what its physical dimensions and separation must be; (b) find the maximum charge these plates can hold.

24.9. A capacitor is made from two hollow, coaxial, iron cylinders, one inside the other. The inner cylinder is negatively charged and the outer is positively charged; the magnitude of the charge on each is 10.0 pC. The inner cylinder has radius 0.50 mm, the outer one has radius 5.00 mm, and the length of each cylinder is 18.0 cm. (a) What is the capacitance? (b) What applied potential difference is necessary to produce these charges on the cylinders?

24.10. A cylindrical capacitor consists of a solid inner conducting core with radius 0.250 cm, surrounded by an outer hollow conducting tube. The two conductors are separated by air, and the length of the cylinder is 12.0 cm. The capacitance is 36.7 pF. (a) Calculate the inner radius of the hollow tube. (b) When the capacitor is charged to 125 V, what is the charge per unit length λ on the capacitor?

24.11. A cylindrical capacitor has an inner conductor of radius 1.5 mm and an outer conductor of radius 3.5 mm. The two conductors are separated by vacuum, and the entire capacitor is 2.8 m long. (a) What is the capacitance per unit length? (b) The potential of the inner conductor is 350 mV higher than that of the outer conductor. Find the charge (magnitude and sign) on both conductors.

24.12. A spherical capacitor is formed from two concentric, spherical, conducting shells separated by vacuum. The inner sphere has radius 15.0 cm and the capacitance is 116 pF. (a) What is the radius of the outer sphere? (b) If the potential difference between the two spheres is 220 V, what is the magnitude of charge on each sphere?

24.13. A spherical capacitor contains a charge of 3.30 nC when connected to a potential difference of 220 V. If its plates are separated by vacuum and the inner radius of the outer shell is 4.00 cm, calculate: (a) the capacitance; (b) the radius of the inner sphere; (c) the electric field just outside the surface of the inner sphere.

Section 24.2 Capacitors in Series and Parallel

24.14. For the system of capacitors shown in Fig. 24.24, find the equivalent capacitance (a) between b and c, and (b) between a and c.

Figure 24.24 Exercise 24.14.

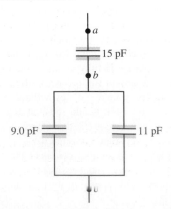

24.15. In Fig. 24.25, each capacitor has $C = 4.00\ \mu$F and $V_{ab} = +28.0$ V. Calculate (a) the charge on each capacitor; (b) the potential difference across each capacitor; (c) the potential difference between points a and d.

24.16. In Fig. 24.8a, let $C_1 = 3.00\ \mu$F, $C_2 = 5.00\ \mu$F, and $V_{ab} = +52.0$ V. Calculate (a) the charge on each capacitor and (b) the potential difference across each capacitor.

24.17. In Fig. 24.9a, let $C_1 = 3.00\ \mu$F, $C_2 = 5.00\ \mu$F, and $V_{ab} = +52.0$ V. Calculate (a) the charge on each capacitor and (b) the potential difference across each capacitor.

24.18. In Fig. 24.26, $C_1 = 6.00\ \mu$F, $C_2 = 3.00\ \mu$F, and $C_3 = 5.00\ \mu$F. The capacitor network is connected to an applied potential V_{ab}. After the charges on the capacitors have reached their final values, the charge on C_2 is 40.0 μC. (a) What are the charges on capacitors C_1 and C_3? (b) What is the applied voltage V_{ab}?

24.19. In Fig. 24.26, $C_1 = 3.00\ \mu$F and $V_{ab} = 120$ V. The charge on capacitor C_1 is 150 μC. Calculate the voltage across the other two capacitors.

24.20. Two parallel-plate vacuum capacitors have plate spacings d_1 and d_2 and equal plate areas A. Show that when the capacitors are connected in series, the equivalent capacitance is the same as for a single capacitor with plate area A and spacing $d_1 + d_2$.

24.21. Two parallel-plate vacuum capacitors have areas A_1 and A_2 and equal plate spacings d. Show that when the capacitors are connected in parallel, the equivalent capacitance is the same as for a single capacitor with plate area $A_1 + A_2$ and spacing d.

24.22. Figure 24.27 shows a system of four capacitors, where the potential difference across ab is 50.0 V. (a) Find the equivalent capacitance of this system between a and b. (b) How much charge is stored by this combination of capacitors? (c) How much charge is stored in each of the 10.0-μF and the 9.0-μF capacitors?

24.23. Suppose the 3-μF capacitor in Fig. 24.10a were removed and replaced by a different one, and that this changed the equivalent capacitance between points a and b to 8 μF. What would be the capacitance of the replacement capacitor?

Figure 24.25 Exercise 24.15.

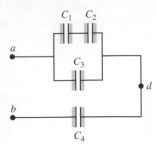

Figure 24.26 Exercises 24.18 and 24.19.

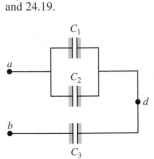

Figure 24.27 Exercise 24.22.

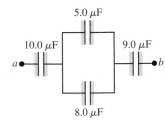

Section 24.3 Energy Storage in Capacitors and Electric-Field Energy

24.24. A parallel-plate air capacitor has a capacitance of 920 pF. The charge on each plate is 2.55 μC. (a) What is the potential difference between the plates? (b) If the charge is kept constant, what will be the potential difference between the plates if the separation is doubled? (c) How much work is required to double the separation?

24.25. A 5.80-μF, parallel-plate, air capacitor has a plate separation of 5.00 mm and is charged to a potential difference of 400 V. Calculate the energy density in the region between the plates, in units of J/m^3.

24.26. An air capacitor is made from two flat parallel plates 1.50 mm apart. The magnitude of charge on each plate is 0.0180 μC when the potential difference is 200 V. (a) What is the capacitance? (b) What is the area of each plate? (c) What maximum voltage can be applied without dielectric breakdown? (Dielectric breakdown for air occurs at an electric-field strength of 3.0×10^6 V/m.) (d) When the charge is 0.0180 μC, what total energy is stored?

24.27. A 450-μF capacitor is charged to 295 V. Then a wire is connected between the plates. How many joules of thermal energy are produced as the capacitor discharges if all of the energy that was stored goes into heating the wire?

24.28. A capacitor of capacitance C is charged to a potential difference V_0. The terminals of the charged capacitor are then connected to those of an uncharged capacitor of capacitance $C/2$. Compute (a) the original charge of the system; (b) the final potential difference across each capacitor; (c) the final energy of the system; (d) the decrease in energy when the capacitors are connected. (e) Where did the "lost" energy go?

24.29. A parallel-plate vacuum capacitor with plate area A and separation x has charges $+Q$ and $-Q$ on its plates. The capacitor is disconnected from the source of charge, so the charge on each plate remains fixed. (a) What is the total energy stored in the capacitor? (b) The plates are pulled apart an additional distance dx. What is the change in the stored energy? (c) If F is the force with which the plates attract each other, then the change in the stored energy must equal the work $dW = Fdx$ done in pulling the plates apart. Find an expression for F. (d) Explain why F is *not* equal to QE, where E is the electric field between the plates.

24.30. A parallel-plate vacuum capacitor has 8.38 J of energy stored in it. The separation between the plates is 2.30 mm. If the separation is decreased to 1.15 mm, what is the energy stored (a) if the capacitor is disconnected from the potential source so the charge on the plates remains constant, and (b) if the capacitor remains connected to the potential source so the potential difference between the plates remains constant?

24.31. (a) How much charge does a battery have to supply to a 5.0-μF capacitor to create a potential difference of 1.5 V across its plates? How much energy is stored in the capacitor in this case? (b) How much charge would the battery have to supply to store 1.0 J of energy in the capacitor? What would be the potential across the capacitor in that case?

24.32. For the capacitor network shown in Fig. 24.28, the potential difference across ab is 36 V. Find (a) the total charge stored in this network; (b) the charge on each capacitor; (c) the total energy stored in the network; (d) the energy stored in each capacitor; (e) the potential differences across each capacitor.

Figure 24.28 Exercise 24.32.

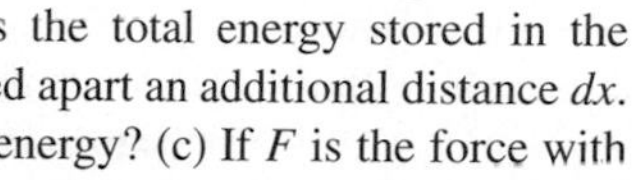

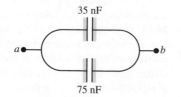

24.33. For the capacitor network shown in Fig. 24.29, the potential difference across ab is 220 V. Find (a) the total charge stored in this network; (b) the charge on each capacitor; (c) the total energy stored in the network; (d) the energy

Figure 24.29 Exercise 24.33

stored in each capacitor; (e) the potential difference across each capacitor.

24.34. A 0.350-m-long cylindrical capacitor consists of a solid conducting core with a radius of 1.20 mm and an outer hollow conducting tube with an inner radius of 2.00 mm. The two conductors are separated by air and charged to a potential difference of 6.00 V. Calculate (a) the charge per length for the capacitor; (b) the total charge on the capacitor; (c) the capacitance; (d) the energy stored in the capacitor when fully charged.

24.35. A cylindrical air capacitor of length 15.0 m stores 3.20×10^{-9} J of energy when the potential difference between the two conductors is 4.00 V. (a) Calculate the magnitude of the charge on each conductor. (b) Calculate the ratio of the radii of the inner and outer conductors.

24.36. A capacitor is formed from two concentric spherical conducting shells separated by vacuum. The inner sphere has radius 12.5 cm, and the outer sphere has radius 14.8 cm. A potential difference of 120 V is applied to the capacitor. (a) What is the energy density at $r = 12.6$ cm, just outside the inner sphere? (b) What is the energy density at $r = 14.7$ cm, just inside the outer sphere? (c) For a parallel-plate capacitor the energy density is uniform in the region between the plates, except near the edges of the plates. Is this also true for a spherical capacitor?

24.37. You have two identical capacitors and an external potential source. (a) Compare the total energy stored in the capacitors when they are connected to the applied potential in series and in parallel. (b) Compare the maximum amount of charge stored in each case. (c) Energy storage in a capacitor can be limited by the maximum electric field between the plates. What is the ratio of the electric field for the series and parallel combinations?

Section 24.4 Dielectrics

24.38. A parallel-plate capacitor has capacitance $C_0 = 5.00$ pF when there is air between the plates. The separation between the plates is 1.50 mm. (a) What is the maximum magnitude of charge Q that can be placed on each plate if the electric field in the region between the plates is not to exceed 3.00×10^4 V/m? (b) A dielectric with $K = 2.70$ is inserted between the plates of the capacitor, completely filling the volume between the plates. Now what is the maximum magnitude of charge on each plate if the electric field between the plates is not to exceed 3.00×10^4 V/m?

24.39. Two parallel plates have equal and opposite charges. When the space between the plates is evacuated, the electric field is $E = 3.20 \times 10^5$ V/m. When the space is filled with dielectric, the electric field is $E = 2.50 \times 10^5$ V/m. (a) What is the charge density on each surface of the dielectric? (b) What is the dielectric constant?

24.40. A budding electronics hobbyist wants to make a simple 1.0-nF capacitor for tuning her crystal radio, using two sheets of aluminum foil as plates, with a few sheets of paper between them as a dielectric. The paper has a dielectric constant of 3.0, and the thickness of one sheet of it is 0.20 mm. (a) If the sheets of paper measure 22 × 28 cm and she cuts the aluminum foil to the same dimensions, how many sheets of paper should she use between her plates to get the proper capacitance? (b) Suppose for convenience she wants to use a single sheet of posterboard, with the same dielectric constant but a thickness of 12.0 mm, instead of the paper. What area of aluminum foil will she need for her plates to get her 1.0 nF of capacitance? (c) Suppose she goes high-tech and finds a sheet of Teflon of the same thickness as the posterboard to use as a dielectric. Will she need a larger or smaller area of Teflon than of posterboard? Explain.

24.41. The dielectric to be used in a parallel-plate capacitor has a dielectric constant of 3.60 and a dielectric strength of 1.60×10^7 V/m. The capacitor is to have a capacitance of 1.25×10^{-9} F and must be able to withstand a maximum potential difference of 5500 V. What is the minimum area the plates of the capacitor may have?

24.42. Show that Eq. (24.20) holds for a parallel-plate capacitor with a dielectric material between the plates. Use a derivation analogous to that used for Eq. (24.11).

24.43. A capacitor has parallel plates of area 12 cm^2 separated by 2.0 mm. The space between the plates is filled with polystyrene (see Table 24.2). (a) Find the permittivity of polystyrene. (b) Find the maximum permissible voltage across the capacitor to avoid dielectric breakdown. (c) When the voltage equals the value found in part (b), find the surface charge density on each plate and the induced surface-charge density on the surface of the dielectric.

24.44. A constant potential difference of 12 V is maintained between the terminals of a 0.25-μF, parallel-plate, air capacitor. (a) A sheet of Mylar is inserted between the plates of the capacitor, completely filling the space between the plates. When this is done, how much additional charge flows onto the positive plate of the capacitor (see Table 24.1)? (b) What is the total induced charge on either face of the Mylar sheet? (c) What effect does the Mylar sheet have on the electric field between the plates? Explain how you can reconcile this with the increase in charge on the plates, which acts to *increase* the electric field.

24.45. When a 360-nF air capacitor $(1 \text{ nF} = 10^{-9} \text{ F})$ is connected to a power supply, the energy stored in the capacitor is 1.85×10^{-5} J. While the capacitor is kept connected to the power supply, a slab of dielectric is inserted that completely fills the space between the plates. This increases the stored energy by 2.32×10^{-5} J. (a) What is the potential difference between the capacitor plates? (b) What is the dielectric constant of the slab?

24.46. A parallel-plate capacitor has capacitance $C = 12.5$ pF when the volume between the plates is filled with air. The plates are circular, with radius 3.00 cm. The capacitor is connected to a battery and a charge of magnitude 25.0 pC goes onto each plate. With the capacitor still connected to the battery, a slab of dielectric is inserted between the plates, completely filling the space between the plates. After the dielectric has been inserted, the charge on each plate has magnitude 45.0 pC. (a) What is the dielectric constant K of the dielectric? (b) What is the potential difference between the plates before and after the dielectric has been inserted? (c) What is the electric field at a point midway between the plates before and after the dielectric has been inserted?

24.47. A 12.5-μF capacitor is connected to a power supply that keeps a constant potential difference of 24.0 V across the plates. A piece of material having a dielectric constant of 3.75 is placed between the plates, completely filling the space between them. (a) How much energy is stored in the capacitor before and after the dielectric is inserted? (b) By how much did the energy change during the insertion? Did it increase or decrease?

*Section 24.6 Gauss's Law in Dielectrics

***24.48.** A parallel-plate capacitor has plates with area 0.0225 m^2 separated by 1.00 mm of Teflon. (a) Calculate the charge on the plates when they are charged to a potential difference of 12.0 V. (b) Use Gauss's law (Eq. 24.23) to calculate the electric field inside the Teflon. (c) Use Gauss's law to calculate the electric field if the voltage source is disconnected and the Teflon is removed.

***24.49.** A parallel-plate capacitor has the volume between its plates filled with plastic with dielectric constant K. The magnitude of the charge on each plate is Q. Each plate has area A, and the distance between the plates is d. (a) Use Gauss's law as stated in Eq. (24.23) to calculate the magnitude of the electric field in the dielectric. (b) Use the electric field determined in part (a) to calculate the potential difference between the two plates. (c) Use the result of part (b) to determine the capacitance of the capacitor. Compare your result to Eq. (24.12).

Problems

24.50. A parallel-plate air capacitor is made by using two plates 16 cm square, spaced 4.7 mm apart. It is connected to a 12-V battery. (a) What is the capacitance? (b) What is the charge on each plate? (c) What is the electric field between the plates? (d) What is the energy stored in the capacitor? (e) If the battery is disconnected and then the plates are pulled apart to a separation of 9.4 mm, what are the answers to parts (a)–(d)?

24.51. Suppose the battery in Problem 24.50 remains connected while the plates are pulled apart. What are the answers then to parts (a)–(d) after the plates have been pulled apart?

24.52. Cell Membranes. Cell membranes (the walled enclosure around a cell) are typically about 7.5 nm thick. They are partially permeable to allow charged material to pass in and out, as needed. Equal but opposite charge densities build up on the inside and outside faces of such a membrane, and these charges prevent additional charges from passing through the cell wall. We can model a cell membrane as a parallel-plate capacitor, with the membrane itself containing proteins embedded in an organic material to give the membrane a dielectric constant of about 10. (See Fig. 24.30.) (a) What is the capacitance per square centimeter of such a cell wall? (b) In its normal resting state, a cell has a potential difference of 85 mV across its membrane. What is the electric field inside this membrane?

Figure 24.30
Problem 24.52.

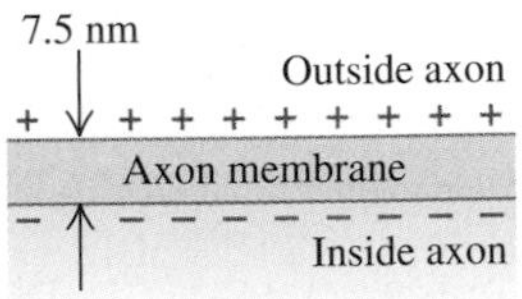

24.53. Electronic flash units for cameras contain a capacitor for storing the energy used to produce the flash. In one such unit, the flash lasts for $\frac{1}{675}$ s with an average light power output of 2.70×10^5 W. (a) If the conversion of electrical energy to light is 95% efficient (the rest of the energy goes to thermal energy), how much energy must be stored in the capacitor for one flash? (b) The capacitor has a potential difference between its plates of 125 V when the stored energy equals the value calculated in part (a). What is the capacitance?

24.54. In one type of computer keyboard, each key holds a small metal plate that serves as one plate of a parallel-plate, air-filled capacitor. When the key is depressed, the plate separation decreases and the capacitance increases. Electronic circuitry detects the change in capacitance and thus detects that the key has been pressed. In one particular keyboard, the area of each metal plate is 42.0 mm^2, and the separation between the plates is 0.700 mm before the key is depressed. (a) Calculate the capacitance before the key is depressed. (b) If the circuitry can detect a change in capacitance of 0.250 pF, how far must the key be depressed before the circuitry detects its depression?

24.55. Consider a cylindrical capacitor like that shown in Fig. 24.6. Let $d = r_b - r_a$ be the spacing between the inner and outer conductors. (a) Let the radii of the two conductors be only slightly different, so that $d \ll r_a$. Show that the result derived in Example 24.4 (Section 24.1) for the capacitance of a cylindrical capacitor then reduces to Eq. (24.2), the equation for the capacitance of a parallel-plate capacitor, with A being the surface area of each cylinder. Use the result that $\ln(1 + z) \cong z$ for $|z| \ll 1$. (b) Even though the earth is essentially spherical, its surface appears flat to us because its radius is so large. Use this idea to explain why the result of part (a) makes sense from a purely geometrical standpoint.

24.56. In Fig. 24.9a, let $C_1 = 9.0\,\mu\text{F}$, $C_2 = 4.0\,\mu\text{F}$, and $V_{ab} = 28$ V. Suppose the charged capacitors are disconnected from the source and from each other, and then reconnected to each other with plates of *opposite* sign together. By how much does the energy of the system decrease?

24.57. For the capacitor network shown in Fig. 24.31, the potential difference across ab is 12.0 V. Find (a) the total energy stored in this network and (b) the energy stored in the 4.80-μF capacitor.

Figure 24.31 Problem 24.57.

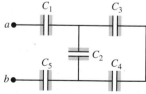

24.58. Several 0.25-μF capacitors are available. The voltage across each is not to exceed 600 V. You need to make a capacitor with capacitance 0.25 μF to be connected across a potential difference of 960 V. (a) Show in a diagram how an equivalent capacitor with the desired properties can be obtained. (b) No dielectric is a perfect insulator that would not permit the flow of any charge through its volume. Suppose that the dielectric in one of the capacitors in your diagram is a moderately good conductor. What will happen in this case when your combination of capacitors is connected across the 960-V potential difference?

24.59. In Fig. 24.32, $C_1 = C_5 = 8.4\,\mu\text{F}$ and $C_2 = C_3 = C_4 = 4.2\,\mu\text{F}$. The applied potential is $V_{ab} = 220$ V. (a) What is the equivalent capacitance of the network between points a and b? (b) Calculate the charge on each capacitor and the potential difference across each capacitor.

Figure 24.32 Problem 24.59.

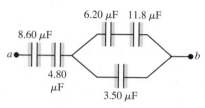

Figure 24.33 Problem 24.60.

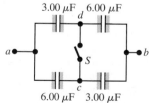

24.60. The capacitors in Fig. 24.33 are initially uncharged and are connected, as in the diagram, with switch S open. The applied potential difference is $V_{ab} = +210$ V. (a) What is the potential difference V_{cd}? (b) What is the potential difference across each capacitor after switch S is closed? (c) How much charge flowed through the switch when it was closed?

24.61. Three capacitors having capacitances of 8.4, 8.4, and 4.2 μF are connected in series across a 36-V potential difference. (a) What is the charge on the 4.2-μF capacitor? (b) What is the total energy stored in all three capacitors? (c) The capacitors are disconnected from the potential difference without allowing them to discharge.

They are then reconnected in parallel with each other, with the positively charged plates connected together. What is the voltage across each capacitor in the parallel combination? (d) What is the total energy now stored in the capacitors?

24.62. Capacitance of a Thundercloud. The charge center of a thundercloud, drifting 3.0 km above the earth's surface, contains 20 C of negative charge. Assuming the charge center has a radius of 1.0 km, and modeling the charge center and the earth's surface as parallel plates, calculate: (a) the capacitance of the system; (b) the potential difference between charge center and ground; (c) the average strength of the electric field between cloud and ground; (d) the electrical energy stored in the system.

24.63. In Fig. 24.34, each capacitance C_1 is 6.9 μF, and each capacitance C_2 is 4.6 μF. (a) Compute the equivalent capacitance of the network between points a and b. (b) Compute the charge on each of the three capacitors nearest a and b when $V_{ab} = 420$ V. (c) With 420 V across a and b, compute V_{cd}.

Figure 24.34 Problem 24.63.

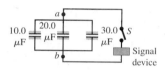

24.64. Each combination of capacitors between points a and b in Fig. 24.35 is first connected across a 120-V battery, charging the combination to 120 V. These combinations are then connected to make the circuits shown. When the switch S is thrown, a surge of charge for the discharging capacitors flows to trigger the signal device. How much charge flows through the signal device?

24.65. A parallel-plate capacitor with only air between the plates is charged by connecting it to a battery. The capacitor is then disconnected from the battery, without any of the charge leaving the plates. (a) A voltmeter reads 45.0 V when placed across the capacitor. When a dielectric is inserted between the plates, completely filling the space, the voltmeter reads 11.5 V. What is the dielectric constant of this material? (b) What will the voltmeter read if the dielectric is now pulled partway out so it fills only one-third of the space between the plates?

24.66. An air capacitor is made by using two flat plates, each with area A, separated by a distance d. Then a metal slab having thickness a (less than d) and the same shape and size as the plates is inserted between them, parallel to the plates and not touching either plate (Fig. 24.36). (a) What is the capacitance of this arrangement? (b) Express the capacitance as a multiple of the capacitance C_0 when the metal slab is not present. (c) Discuss what happens to the capacitance in the limits $a \to 0$ and $a \to d$.

Figure 24.35 Problem 24.64.

(a)

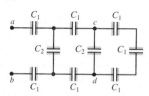

(b)

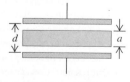

Figure 24.36 Problem 24.66.

24.67. Capacitance of the Earth. (a) Discuss how the concept of capacitance can also be applied to a *single* conductor. (*Hint:* In the relationship $C = Q/V_{ab}$, think of the second conductor as being located at infinity.) (b) Use Eq. (24.1) to show that $C = 4\pi\epsilon_0 R$ for a solid conducting sphere of radius R. (c) Use your result in part (b) to calculate the capacitance of the earth, which is a good conductor of radius 6380 km. Compare to typical capacitors used in electronic circuits that have capacitances ranging from 10 pF to 100 μF.

24.68. A solid conducting sphere of radius R carries a charge Q. Calculate the electric-field energy density at a point a distance r from the center of the sphere for (a) $r < R$ and (b) $r > R$. (c) Calculate the total electric-field energy associated with the charged sphere. (*Hint:* Consider a spherical shell of radius r and thickness dr that has volume $dV = 4\pi r^2\, dr$, and find the energy stored in this volume. Then integrate from $r = 0$ to $r \to \infty$.) (d) Explain why the result of part (c) can be interpreted as the amount of work required to assemble the charge Q on the sphere. (e) By using Eq. (24.9) and the result of part (c), show that the capacitance of the sphere is as given in Problem 24.67.

24.69. Earth-Ionosphere Capacitance. The earth can be considered as a single-conductor capacitor (see Problem 24.67). It can also be considered in combination with a charged layer of the atmosphere, the ionosphere, as a spherical capacitor with two plates, the surface of the earth being the negative plate. The ionosphere is at a level of about 70 km, and the potential difference between earth and ionosphere is about 350,000 V. Calculate: (a) the capacitance of this system; (b) the total charge on the capacitor; (c) the energy stored in the system.

24.70. The inner cylinder of a long, cylindrical capacitor has radius r_a and linear charge density $+\lambda$. It is surrounded by a coaxial cylindrical conducting shell with inner radius r_b and linear charge density $-\lambda$ (see Fig. 24.6). (a) What is the energy density in the region between the conductors at a distance r from the axis? (b) Integrate the energy density calculated in part (a) over the volume between the conductors in a length L of the capacitor to obtain the total electric-field energy per unit length. (c) Use Eq. (24.9) and the capacitance per unit length calculated in Example 24.4 (Section 24.1) to calculate U/L. Does your result agree with that obtained in part (b)?

24.71. A parallel-plate capacitor has the space between the plates filled with two slabs of dielectric, one with constant K_1 and one with constant K_2 (Fig. 24.37). Each slab has thickness $d/2$, where d is the plate separation. Show that the capacitance is

Figure 24.37 Problem 24.71.

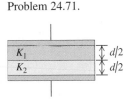

$$C = \frac{2\epsilon_0 A}{d}\left(\frac{K_1 K_2}{K_1 + K_2}\right)$$

24.72. A parallel-plate capacitor has the space between the plates filled with two slabs of dielectric, one with constant K_1 and one with constant K_2 (Fig. 24.38). The thickness of each slab is the same as the plate separation d, and each slab fills half of the volume between the plates. Show that the capacitance is

Figure 24.38 Problem 24.72.

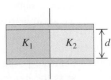

$$C = \frac{\epsilon_0 A (K_1 + K_2)}{2d}$$

Challenge Problems

24.73. Capacitors in networks cannot always be grouped into simple series or parallel combinations. As an example, Fig. 24.39a shows three capacitors C_x, C_y, and C_z in a *delta network,* so called because of its triangular shape. This network has *three* terminals a, b, and c and hence cannot be transformed into a single equivalent capacitor. It can be shown that as far as any effect on the external circuit is concerned, a delta network is equivalent to what is called a *Y network.* For example, the delta network of Fig. 24.39a can be replaced by the Y network of Fig. 24.39b. (The name "Y network" also refers to the shape of the network.) (a) Show that the transformation equations that give C_1, C_2, and C_3 in terms of C_x, and C_y, and C_z are

$$C_1 = (C_x C_y + C_y C_z + C_z C_x)/C_x$$
$$C_2 = (C_x C_y + C_y C_z + C_z C_x)/C_y$$
$$C_3 = (C_x C_y + C_y C_z + C_z C_x)/C_z$$

(*Hint:* The potential difference V_{ac} must be the same in both circuits, as V_{bc} must be. Also, the charge q_1 that flows from point a along the wire as indicated must be the same in both circuits, as must q_2. Obtain a relationship for V_{ac} as a function of q_1 and q_2 and the capacitances for each network, and obtain a separate relationship for V_{bc} as a function of the charges for each network. The coefficients of corresponding charges in corresponding equations must be the same for both networks.) (b) For the network shown in Fig. 24.39c, determine the equivalent capacitance between the terminals at the left end of the network. (*Hint:* Use the delta-Y transformation derived in part (a). Use points a, b, and c to form the delta, and transform the delta into a Y. The capacitors can then be combined using the relationships for series and parallel combinations of capacitors.) (c) Determine the charges of, and the potential differences across, each capacitor in Fig. 24.39c.

Figure 24.39 Challenge Problem 24.73.

(a)

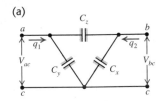

(b)

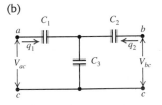

(c)

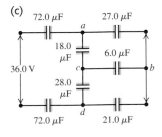

24.74. The parallel-plate air capacitor in Fig. 24.40 consists of two horizontal conducting plates of equal area A. The bottom plate rests on a fixed support, and the top plate is suspended by four

Figure 24.40 Challenge Problem 24.74.

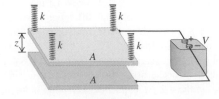

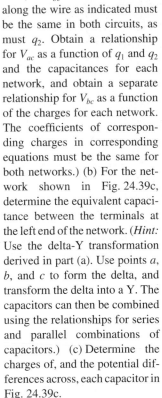

springs with spring constant k, positioned at each of the four corners of the top plate as shown in the figure. When uncharged, the plates are separated by a distance z_0. A battery is connected to the plates and produces a potential difference V between them. This causes the plate separation to decrease to z. Neglect any fringing effects. (a) Show that the electrostatic force between the charged plates has a magnitude $\epsilon_0 A V^2/2z^2$. (*Hint:* See Exercise 24.29.) (b) Obtain an expression that relates the plate separation z to the potential difference V. The resulting equation will be cubic in z. (c) Given the values $A = 0.300 \text{ m}^2$, $z_0 = 1.20$ mm, $k = 25.0 \text{ N/m}$, and $V = 120$ V, find the two values of z for which the top plate will be in equilibrium. (*Hint:* You can solve the cubic equation by plugging a trial value of z into the equation and then adjusting your guess until the equation is satisfied to three significant figures. Locating the roots of the cubic equation graphically can help you pick starting values of z for this trial-and-error procedure. One root of the cubic equation has a nonphysical negative value.) (d) For each of the two values of z found in part (c), is the equilibrium stable or unstable? For stable equilibrium a small displacement of the object will give rise to a net force tending to return the object to the equilibrium position. For unstable equilibrium a small displacement gives rise to a net force that takes the object farther away from equilibrium.

24.75. Two square conducting plates with sides of length L are separated by a distance D. A dielectric slab with constant K with dimensions $L \times L \times D$ is inserted a distance x into the space between the plates, as shown in Fig. 24.41. (a) Find the capacitance C of this system (see Problem 24.72). (b) Suppose that the capacitor is connected to a battery that maintains a constant potential difference V between the plates. If the dielectric slab is inserted an additional distance dx into the space between the plates, show that the change in stored energy is

Figure 24.41 Challenge Problem 24.75.

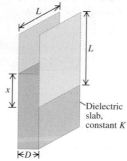

Dielectric slab, constant K

$$dU = +\frac{(K-1)\epsilon_0 V^2 L}{2D}dx$$

(c) Suppose that before the slab is moved by dx, the plates are disconnected from the battery, so that the charges on the plates remain constant. Determine the magnitude of the charge on each plate, and then show that when the slab is moved dx farther into the space between the plates, the stored energy changes by an amount that is the *negative* of the expression for dU given in part (b). (d) If F is the force exerted on the slab by the charges on the plates, then dU should equal the work done *against* this force to move the slab a distance dx. Thus $dU = -F\,dx$. Show that applying this expression to the result of part (b) suggests that the electric force on the slab pushes it *out* of the capacitor, while the result of part (c) suggests that the force pulls the slab *into* the capacitor. (e) Figure 24.16 shows that the force in fact pulls the slab into the capacitor. Explain why the result of part (b) gives an incorrect answer for the direction of this force, and calculate the magnitude

of the force. (This method does not require knowledge of the nature of the fringing field.)

24.76. An isolated spherical capacitor has charge $+Q$ on its inner conductor (radius r_a) and charge $-Q$ on its outer conductor (radius r_b). Half of the volume between the two conductors is then filled with a liquid dielectric of constant K, as shown in cross section in Fig. 24.42. (a) Find the capacitance of the half-filled capacitor. (b) Find the magnitude of $\vec{E}$ in the volume between the two conductors as a function of distance r from the center of the capacitor. Give answers for both the upper and lower halves of this volume. (c) Find the surface density of free charge on the upper and lower halves of the inner and outer conductors. (d) Find the surface density of bound charge on the inner $(r = r_a)$ and outer $(r = r_b)$ surfaces of the dielectric. (e) What is the surface density of bound charge on the flat surface of the dielectric? Explain.

Figure 24.42 Challenge Problem 24.76.

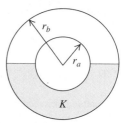

24.77. Three square metal plates A, B, and C, each 12.0 cm on a side and 1.50 mm thick, are arranged as in Fig. 24.43. The plates are separated by sheets of paper 0.45 mm thick and with dielectric constant 4.2. The outer plates are connected together and connected to point b. The inner plate is connected to point a. (a) Copy the diagram and show by plus and minus signs the charge distribution on the plates when point a is maintained at a positive potential relative to point b. (b) What is the capacitance between points a and b?

Figure 24.43 Challenge Problem 24.77.

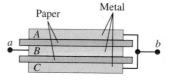

Paper   Metal

a A B C b

24.78. A fuel gauge uses a capacitor to determine the height of the fuel in a tank. The effective dielectric constant K_{eff} changes from a value of 1 when the tank is empty to a value of K, the dielectric constant of the fuel, when the tank is full. The appropriate electronic circuitry can determine the effective dielectric constant of the combined air and fuel between the capacitor plates. Each of the two rectangular plates has a width w and a length L (Fig. 24.44). The height of the fuel between the plates is h. You can ignore any fringing effects. (a) Derive an expression for K_{eff} as a function of h. (b) What is the effective dielectric constant for a tank $\frac{1}{4}$ full, $\frac{1}{2}$ full, and $\frac{3}{4}$ full if the fuel is gasoline $(K = 1.95)$? (c) Repeat part (b) for methanol $(K = 33.0)$. (d) For which fuel is this fuel gauge more practical?

Figure 24.44 Challenge Problem 24.78.

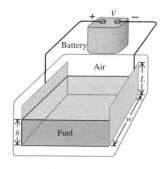

Battery   Air   Fuel

25 CURRENT, RESISTANCE, AND ELECTROMOTIVE FORCE

LEARNING GOALS

By studying this chapter, you will learn:

- The meaning of electric current, and how charges move in a conductor.

- What is meant by the resistivity and conductivity of a substance.

- How to calculate the resistance of a conductor from its dimensions and its resistivity.

- How an electromotive force (emf) makes it possible for current to flow in a circuit.

- How to do calculations involving energy and power in circuits.

? In a flashlight, is the amount of current that flows out of the bulb less than, greater than, or equal to the amount of current that flows into the bulb?

In the past four chapters we studied the interactions of electric charges *at rest;* now we're ready to study charges *in motion.* An *electric current* consists of charges in motion from one region to another. When this motion takes place within a conducting path that forms a closed loop, the path is called an *electric circuit.*

Fundamentally, electric circuits are a means for conveying *energy* from one place to another. As charged particles move within a circuit, electric potential energy is transferred from a source (such as a battery or generator) to a device in which that energy is either stored or converted to another form: into sound in a stereo system or into heat and light in a toaster or light bulb. From a technological standpoint, electric circuits are useful because they allow energy to be transported without any moving parts (other than the moving charged particles themselves). Electric circuits are at the heart of flashlights, CD players, computers, radio and television transmitters and receivers, and household and industrial power distribution systems. The nervous systems of animals and humans are specialized electric circuits that carry vital signals from one part of the body to another.

In Chapter 26 we will see how to analyze electric circuits and will examine some practical applications of circuits. Before we can do so, however, you must understand the basic properties of electric currents. These properties are the subject of this chapter. We'll begin by describing the nature of electric conductors and considering how they are affected by temperature. We'll learn why a short, fat, cold copper wire is a better conductor than a long, skinny, hot steel wire. We'll study the properties of batteries and see how they cause current and energy transfer in a circuit. In this analysis we will use the concepts of current, potential difference (or voltage), resistance, and electromotive force. Finally, we'll look at electric current in a material from a microscopic viewpoint.

25.1 Current

A **current** is any motion of charge from one region to another. In this section we'll discuss currents in conducting materials. The vast majority of technological applications of charges in motion involve currents of this kind.

In electrostatic situations (discussed in Chapters 21 through 24) the electric field is zero everywhere within the conductor, and there is *no* current. However, this does not mean that all charges within the conductor are at rest. In an ordinary metal such as copper or alumium, some of the electrons are free to move within the conducting material. These free electrons move randomly in all directions, somewhat like the molecules of a gas but with much greater speeds, of the order of 10^6 m/s. The electrons nonetheless do not escape from the conducting material, because they are attracted to the positive ions of the material. The motion of the electrons is random, so there is no *net* flow of charge in any direction and hence no current.

Now consider what happens if a constant, steady electric field $\vec{E}$ is established inside a conductor. (We'll see later how this can be done.) A charged particle (such as a free electron) inside the conducting material is then subjected to a steady force $\vec{F} = q\vec{E}$. If the charged particle were moving in *vacuum,* this steady force would cause a steady acceleration in the direction of $\vec{F}$, and after a time the charged particle would be moving in that direction at high speed. But a charged particle moving in a *conductor* undergoes frequent collisions with the massive, nearly stationary ions of the material. In each such collision the particle's direction of motion undergoes a random change. The net effect of the electric field $\vec{E}$ is that in addition to the random motion of the charged particles within the conductor, there is also a very slow net motion or *drift* of the moving charged particles as a group in the direction of the electric force $\vec{F} = q\vec{E}$ (Fig. 25.1). This motion is described in terms of the **drift velocity** $\vec{v}_d$ of the particles. As a result, there is a net current in the conductor.

While the random motion of the electrons has a very fast average speed of about 10^6 m/s, the drift speed is very slow, often on the order of 10^{-4} m/s. Given that the electrons move so slowly, you may wonder why the light comes on immediately when you turn on the switch of a flashlight. The reason is that the electric field is set up in the wire with a speed approaching the speed of light, and electrons start to move all along the wire at very nearly the same time. The time that it takes any individual electron to get from the switch to the light bulb isn't really relevant. A good analogy is a group of soldiers standing at attention when the sergeant orders them to start marching; the order reaches the soldiers' ears at the speed of sound, which is much faster than their marching speed, so all the soldiers start to march essentially in unison.

The Direction of Current Flow

The drift of moving charges through a conductor can be interpreted in terms of work and energy. The electric field $\vec{E}$ does work on the moving charges. The resulting kinetic energy is transferred to the material of the conductor by means of collisions with the ions, which vibrate about their equilibrium positions in the crystalline structure of the conductor. This energy transfer increases the average vibrational energy of the ions and therefore the temperature of the material. Thus much of the work done by the electric field goes into heating the conductor, *not* into making the moving charges move ever faster and faster. This heating is sometimes useful, as in an electric toaster, but in many situations is simply an unavoidable by-product of current flow.

In different current-carrying materials, the charges of the moving particles may be positive or negative. In metals the moving charges are always (negative) electrons, while in an ionized gas (plasma) or an ionic solution the moving

25.1 If there is no electric field inside a conductor, an electron moves randomly from point P_1 to point P_2 in a time Δt. If an electric field $\vec{E}$ is present, the electric force $\vec{F} = q\vec{E}$ imposes a small drift (greatly exaggerated here) that takes the electron to point P'_2, a distance $v_d \Delta t$ from P_2 in the direction of the force.

Conductor without internal $\vec{E}$ field

Path of electron without $\vec{E}$ field. Electron moves randomly.

Path of electron with $\vec{E}$ field. The motion is mostly random, but ...

P_1

P_2 P'_2

$v_d \Delta t$

...the $\vec{E}$ field results in a net displacement along the wire.

Conductor with internal $\vec{E}$ field

$\vec{E}$ $\vec{F} = q\vec{E}$ $\vec{E}$

An electron has a negative charge q, so the force on it due to the $\vec{E}$ field is in the direction opposite to $\vec{E}$.

25.2 The same current can be produced by (a) positive charges moving in the direction of the electric field $\vec{E}$ or (b) the same number of negative charges moving at the same speed in the direction opposite to $\vec{E}$.

(a)

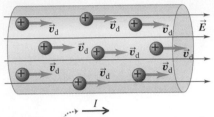

A **conventional current** is treated as a flow of positive charges, regardless of whether the free charges in the conductor are positive, negative, or both.

(b)

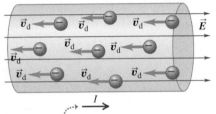

In a metallic conductor, the moving charges are electrons — but the *current* still points in the direction positive charges would flow.

25.3 The current I is the time rate of charge transfer through the cross-sectional area A. The random component of each moving charged particle's motion averages to zero, and the current is in the same direction as $\vec{E}$ whether the moving charges are positive (as shown here) or negative (see Fig. 25.2b).

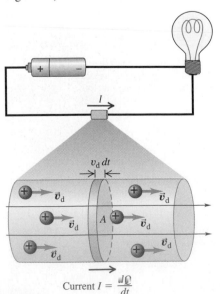

Current $I = \dfrac{dQ}{dt}$

charges may include both electrons and positively charged ions. In a semiconductor material such as germanium or silicon, conduction is partly by electrons and partly by motion of *vacancies*, also known as *holes;* these are sites of missing electrons and act like positive charges.

Fig. 25.2 shows segments of two different current-carrying materials. In Fig. 25.2a the moving charges are positive, the electric force is in the same direction as $\vec{E}$, and the drift velocity $\vec{v}_d$ is from left to right. In Fig. 25.2b the charges are negative, the electric force is opposite to $\vec{E}$, and the drift velocity $\vec{v}_d$ is from right to left. In both cases there is a net flow of positive charge from left to right, and positive charges end up to the right of negative ones. We *define* the current, denoted by I, to be in the direction in which there is a flow of *positive* charge. Thus we describe currents as though they consisted entirely of positive charge flow, even in cases in which we know that the actual current is due to electrons. Hence the current is to the right in both Figs. 25.2a and 25.2b. This choice or convention for the direction of current flow is called **conventional current.** While the direction of the conventional current is *not* necessarily the same as the direction in which charged particles are actually moving, we'll find that the sign of the moving charges is of little importance in analyzing electric circuits.

Fig. 25.3 shows a segment of a conductor in which a current is flowing. We consider the moving charges to be *positive,* so they are moving in the same direction as the current. We define the current through the cross-sectional area A to be *the net charge flowing through the area per unit time.* Thus, if a net charge dQ flows through an area in a time dt, the current I through the area is

$$I = \frac{dQ}{dt} \qquad \text{(definition of current)} \qquad (25.1)$$

CAUTION **Current is not a vector** Although we refer to the *direction* of a current, current as defined by Eq. (25.1) is *not* a vector quantity. In a current-carrying wire, the current is always along the length of the wire, regardless of whether the wire is straight or curved. No single vector could describe motion along a curved path, which is why current is not a vector. We'll usually describe the direction of current either in words (as in "the current flows clockwise around the circuit") or by choosing a current to be positive if it flows in one direction along a conductor and negative if it flows in the other direction. ∎

The SI unit of current is the **ampere;** one ampere is defined to be *one coulomb per second* ($1\ \text{A} = 1\ \text{C/s}$). This unit is named in honor of the French scientist André Marie Ampère (1775–1836). When an ordinary flashlight (D-cell size) is turned on, the current in the flashlight is about 0.5 to 1 A; the current in the wires of a car engine's starter motor is around 200 A. Currents in radio and television circuits are usually expressed in *milliamperes* ($1\ \text{mA} = 10^{-3}\ \text{A}$) or *microamperes* ($1\ \mu\text{A} = 10^{-6}\ \text{A}$), and currents in computer circuits are expressed in *nanoamperes* ($1\ \text{nA} = 10^{-9}\ \text{A}$) or *picoamperes* ($1\ \text{pA} = 10^{-12}\ \text{A}$).

Current, Drift Velocity, and Current Density

We can express current in terms of the drift velocity of the moving charges. Let's consider again the situation of Fig. 25.3, a conductor with cross-sectional area A and an electric field $\vec{E}$ directed from left to right. To begin with, we'll assume that the free charges in the conductor are positive; then the drift velocity is in the same direction as the field.

Suppose there are n moving charged particles per unit volume. We call n the **concentration** of particles; its SI unit is m^{-3}. Assume that all the particles move with the same drift velocity with magnitude v_d. In a time interval dt, each particle moves a distance $v_d\, dt$. The particles that flow out of the right end of the shaded cylinder with length $v_d\, dt$ during dt are the particles that were within this cylinder at the beginning of the interval dt. The volume of the cylinder is $A v_d\, dt$, and the number of particles within it is $nAv_d\,dt$. If each particle has a charge q, the charge dQ that flows out of the end of the cylinder during time dt is

$$dQ = q(nAv_d\,dt) = nqv_dA\,dt$$

and the current is

$$I = \frac{dQ}{dt} = nqv_dA$$

The current *per unit cross-sectional area* is called the **current density** J:

$$J = \frac{I}{A} = nqv_d$$

The units of current density are amperes per square meter (A/m^2).

If the moving charges are negative rather than positive, as in Fig. 25.2b, the drift velocity is opposite to $\vec{E}$. But the *current* is still in the same direction as $\vec{E}$ at each point in the conductor. Hence the current I and current density J don't depend on the sign of the charge, and so in the above expressions for I and J we replace the charge q by its absolute value $|q|$:

$$I = \frac{dQ}{dt} = n|q|v_dA \qquad \text{(general expression for current)} \qquad (25.2)$$

$$J = \frac{I}{A} = n|q|v_d \qquad \text{(general expression for current density)} \qquad (25.3)$$

The current in a conductor is the product of the concentration of moving charged particles, the magnitude of charge of each such particle, the magnitude of the drift velocity, and the cross-sectional area of the conductor.

We can also define a *vector* current density $\vec{J}$ that includes the direction of the drift velocity:

$$\vec{J} = nq\vec{v}_d \qquad \text{(vector current density)} \qquad (25.4)$$

There are *no* absolute value signs in Eq. (25.4). If q is positive, $\vec{v}_d$ is in the same direction as $\vec{E}$; if q is negative, $\vec{v}_d$ is opposite to $\vec{E}$. In cither case, $\vec{J}$ is in the same direction as $\vec{E}$. Equation (25.3) gives the *magnitude* J of the vector current density $\vec{J}$.

CAUTION **Current density vs. current** Note that current density $\vec{J}$ is a vector, but current I is not. The difference is that the current density $\vec{J}$ describes how charges flow at a certain point, and the vector's direction tells you about the direction of the flow at that point. By contrast, the current I describes how charges flow through an extended object such as a wire. For example, I has the same value at all points in the circuit of Fig. 25.3, but $\vec{J}$ does not: the current density is directed downward in the left-hand side of the loop and upward in the right-hand side. The magnitude of $\vec{J}$ can also vary around a circuit. In Fig. 25.3 the current density magnitude $J = I/A$ is less in the battery (which has a large cross-sectional area A) than in the wires (which have a small cross-sectional area). ▮

In general, a conductor may contain several different kinds of moving charged particles having charges $q_1, q_2, \ldots$, concentrations $n_1, n_2, \ldots$, and drift velocities with magnitudes $v_{d1}, v_{d2}, \ldots$. An example is current flow in an ionic solution (Fig. 25.4). In a sodium chloride solution, current can be carried by both positive sodium ions and negative chlorine ions; the total current I is found by adding up the currents due to each kind of charged particle, using Eq. (25.2). Likewise, the total vector current density $\vec{J}$ is found by using Eq. (25.4) for each kind of charged particle and adding the results.

We will see in Section 25.4 that it is possible to have a current that is *steady* (that is, one that is constant in time) only if the conducting material forms a

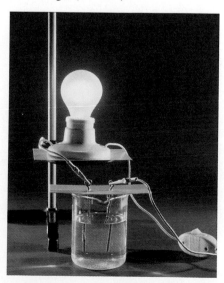

25.4 Part of the electric circuit that includes this light bulb passes through a beaker with a solution of sodium chloride. The current in the solution is carried by both positive charges (Na^+ ions) and negative charges (Cl^- ions).

closed loop, called a *complete circuit*. In such a steady situation, the total charge in every segment of the conductor is constant. Hence the rate of flow of charge *out* at one end of a segment at any instant equals the rate of flow of charge *in* at the other end of the segment, and *the current is the same at all cross sections of the circuit*. We'll make use of this observation when we analyze electric circuits later in this chapter.

In many simple circuits, such as flashlights or cordless electric drills, the direction of the current is always the same; this is called *direct current*. But home appliances such as toasters, refrigerators, and televisions use *alternating current*, in which the current continuously changes direction. In this chapter we'll consider direct current only. Alternating current has many special features worthy of detailed study, which we'll examine in Chapter 31.

Example 25.1 | Current density and drift velocity in a wire

An 18-gauge copper wire (the size usually used for lamp cords) has a nominal diameter of 1.02 mm. This wire carries a constant current of 1.67 A to a 200-watt lamp. The density of free electrons is 8.5×10^{28} electrons per cubic meter. Find the magnitudes of (a) the current density and (b) the drift velocity.

SOLUTION

IDENTIFY: This problem uses the relationships among current, current density, and drift velocity.

SET UP: We are given the current and the dimensions of the wire, so we use Eq. (25.3) to find the magnitude J of the current density. We then use Eq. (25.3) again to find the drift speed v_d from J and the concentration of electrons.

EXECUTE: (a) The cross-sectional area is

$$A = \frac{\pi d^2}{4} = \frac{\pi (1.02 \times 10^{-3} \text{ m})^2}{4} = 8.17 \times 10^{-7} \text{ m}^2$$

The magnitude of the current density is

$$J = \frac{I}{A} = \frac{1.67 \text{ A}}{8.17 \times 10^{-7} \text{ m}^2} = 2.04 \times 10^6 \text{ A/m}^2$$

(b) Solving Eq. (25.3) for the drift velocity magnitude v_d, we find

$$v_d = \frac{J}{n|q|} = \frac{2.04 \times 10^6 \text{ A/m}^2}{(8.5 \times 10^{28} \text{ m}^{-3})|-1.60 \times 10^{-19} \text{ C}|}$$
$$= 1.5 \times 10^{-4} \text{ m/s} = 0.15 \text{ mm/s}$$

EVALUATE: At this speed an electron would require 6700 s, or about 1 hr 50 min, to travel the length of a wire 1 m long. The speeds of random motion of the electrons are of the order of 10^6 m/s. So in this example the drift speed is around 10^{10} times slower than the speed of random motion. Picture the electrons as bouncing around frantically, with a very slow and sluggish drift!

Test Your Understanding of Section 25.1 Suppose we replaced the wire in Example 25.1 with 12-gauge copper wire, which has twice the diameter of 18-gauge wire. If the current remains the same, what effect would this have on the magnitude of the drift velocity v_d? (i) none—v_d would be unchanged; (ii) v_d would be twice as great; (iii) v_d would be four times greater; (iv) v_d would be half as great; (v) v_d would be one-fourth as great.

25.2 Resistivity

The current density $\vec{J}$ in a conductor depends on the electric field $\vec{E}$ and on the properties of the material. In general, this dependence can be quite complex. But for some materials, especially metals, at a given temperature, $\vec{J}$ is nearly *directly proportional* to $\vec{E}$, and the ratio of the magnitudes of E and J is constant. This relationship, called Ohm's law, was discovered in 1826 by the German physicist Georg Simon Ohm (1787–1854). The word "law" should actually be in quotation marks, since **Ohm's law,** like the ideal-gas equation and Hooke's law, is an *idealized model* that describes the behavior of some materials quite well but is not a general description of *all* matter. In the following discussion we'll assume that Ohm's law is valid, even though there are many situations in which it is not. The situation is comparable to our representation of the behavior of the static and kinetic friction forces; we treated these friction forces as being directly proportional to the normal force, even though we knew that this was at best an approximate description.

Table 25.1 Resistivities at Room Temperature (20 °C)

Substance		$\rho\,(\Omega\cdot m)$	Substance	$\rho\,(\Omega\cdot m)$
Conductors			**Semiconductors**	
Metals	Silver	1.47×10^{-8}	Pure carbon (graphite)	3.5×10^{-5}
	Copper	1.72×10^{-8}	Pure germanium	0.60
	Gold	2.44×10^{-8}	Pure silicon	2300
	Aluminum	2.75×10^{-8}	**Insulators**	
	Tungsten	5.25×10^{-8}	Amber	5×10^{14}
	Steel	20×10^{-8}	Glass	10^{10}–10^{14}
	Lead	22×10^{-8}	Lucite	$>10^{13}$
	Mercury	95×10^{-8}	Mica	10^{11}–10^{15}
Alloys	Manganin (Cu 84%, Mn 12%, Ni 4%)	44×10^{-8}	Quartz (fused)	75×10^{16}
	Constantan (Cu 60%, Ni 40%)	49×10^{-8}	Sulfur	10^{15}
	Nichrome	100×10^{-8}	Teflon	$>10^{13}$
			Wood	10^{8}–10^{11}

We define the **resistivity** ρ of a material as the ratio of the magnitudes of electric field and current density:

$$\rho = \frac{E}{J} \qquad \text{(definition of resistivity)} \qquad (25.5)$$

The greater the resistivity, the greater the field needed to cause a given current density, or the smaller the current density caused by a given field. From Eq. (25.5) the units of ρ are $(V/m)/(A/m^2) = V \cdot m/A$. As we will discuss in the next section, 1 V/A is called one *ohm* (1 Ω; we use the Greek letter Ω, or omega, which is alliterative with "ohm"). So the SI units for ρ are $\Omega \cdot m$ (ohm-meters). Table 25.1 lists some representative values of resistivity. A perfect conductor would have zero resistivity, and a perfect insulator would have an infinite resistivity. Metals and alloys have the smallest resistivities and are the best conductors. The resistivities of insulators are greater than those of the metals by an enormous factor, on the order of 10^{22}.

The reciprocal of resistivity is **conductivity.** Its units are $(\Omega \cdot m)^{-1}$. Good conductors of electricity have larger conductivity than insulators. Conductivity is the direct electrical analog of thermal conductivity. Comparing Table 25.1 with Table 17.5 (Thermal Conductivities), we note that good electrical conductors, such as metals, are usually also good conductors of heat. Poor electrical conductors, such as ceramic and plastic materials, are also poor thermal conductors. In a metal the free electrons that carry charge in electrical conduction also provide the principal mechanism for heat conduction, so we should expect a correlation between electrical and thermal conductivity. Because of the enormous difference in conductivity between electrical conductors and insulators, it is easy to confine electric currents to well-defined paths or circuits (Fig. 25.5). The variation in *thermal* conductivity is much less, only a factor of 10^3 or so, and it is usually impossible to confine heat currents to that extent.

Semiconductors have resistivities intermediate between those of metals and those of insulators. These materials are important because of the way their resistivities are affected by temperature and by small amounts of impurities.

A material that obeys Ohm's law reasonably well is called an *ohmic* conductor or a *linear* conductor. For such materials, at a given temperature, ρ is a *constant* that does not depend on the value of E. Many materials show substantial departures from Ohm's-law behavior; they are *nonohmic,* or *nonlinear.* In these materials, J depends on E in a more complicated manner.

Analogies with fluid flow can be a big help in developing intuition about electric current and circuits. For example, in the making of wine or maple syrup, the product is sometimes filtered to remove sediments. A pump forces the fluid through the filter under pressure; if the flow rate (analogous to J) is proportional to the pressure difference between the upstream and downstream sides (analogous to E), the behavior is analogous to Ohm's law.

25.5 The copper "wires," or traces, on this circuit board are printed directly onto the surface of the dark-colored insulating board. Even though the traces are very close to each other (only about a millimeter apart), the board has such a high resistivity (and low conductivity) compared to the copper that no current can flow between the traces.

Conducting paths (traces)

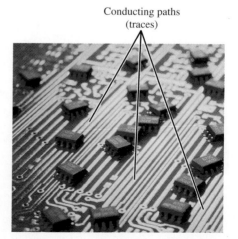

25.6 Variation of resistivity ρ with absolute temperature T for (a) a normal metal, (b) a semiconductor, and (c) a superconductor. In (a) the linear approximation to ρ as a function of T is shown as a green line; the approximation agrees exactly at $T = T_0$, where $\rho = \rho_0$.

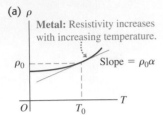

(a) ρ

Metal: Resistivity increases with increasing temperature.

Slope $= \rho_0 \alpha$

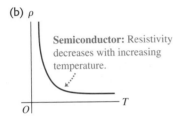

(b) ρ

Semiconductor: Resistivity decreases with increasing temperature.

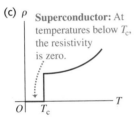

(c) ρ

Superconductor: At temperatures below T_c, the resistivity is zero.

Resistivity and Temperature

The resistivity of a *metallic* conductor nearly always increases with increasing temperature, as shown in Fig. 25.6a. As temperature increases, the ions of the conductor vibrate with greater amplitude, making it more likely that a moving electron will collide with an ion as in Fig. 25.1; this impedes the drift of electrons through the conductor and hence reduces the current. Over a small temperature range (up to 100 C° or so), the resistivity of a metal can be represented approximately by the equation

$$\rho(T) = \rho_0[1 + \alpha(T - T_0)]$$

(temperature dependence of resistivity) (25.6)

where ρ_0 is the resistivity at a reference temperature T_0 (often taken as 0°C or 20°C) and $\rho(T)$ is the resistivity at temperature T, which may be higher or lower than T_0. The factor α is called the **temperature coefficient of resistivity.** Some representative values are given in Table 25.2. The resistivity of the alloy manganin is practically independent of temperature.

Table 25.2 Temperature Coefficients of Resistivity (Approximate Values Near Room Temperature)

Material	$\alpha [(°C)^{-1}]$	Material	$\alpha [(°C)^{-1}]$
Aluminum	0.0039	Lead	0.0043
Brass	0.0020	Manganin	0.00000
Carbon (graphite)	−0.0005	Mercury	0.00088
Constantan	0.00001	Nichrome	0.0004
Copper	0.00393	Silver	0.0038
Iron	0.0050	Tungsten	0.0045

The resistivity of graphite (a nonmetal) *decreases* with increasing temperature, since at higher temperatures, more electrons are "shaken loose" from the atoms and become mobile; hence the temperature coefficient of resistivity of graphite is negative. This same behavior occurs for semiconductors (Fig. 25.6b). Measuring the resistivity of a small semiconductor crystal is therefore a sensitive measure of temperature; this is the principle of a type of thermometer called a *thermistor*.

Some materials, including several metallic alloys and oxides, show a phenomenon called *superconductivity*. As the temperature decreases, the resistivity at first decreases smoothly, like that of any metal. But then at a certain critical temperature T_c a phase transition occurs and the resistivity suddenly drops to zero, as shown in Fig. 25.6c. Once a current has been established in a superconducting ring, it continues indefinitely without the presence of any driving field.

Superconductivity was discovered in 1911 by the Dutch physicist Heike Kamerlingh Onnes (1853–1926). He discovered that at very low temperatures, below 4.2 K, the resistivity of mercury suddenly dropped to zero. For the next 75 years, the highest T_c attained was about 20 K. This meant that superconductivity occurred only when the material was cooled using expensive liquid helium, with a boiling-point temperature of 4.2 K, or explosive liquid hydrogen, with a boiling point of 20.3 K. But in 1986 Karl Müller and Johannes Bednorz discovered an oxide of barium, lanthanum, and copper with a T_c of nearly 40 K, and the race was on to develop "high-temperature" superconducting materials.

By 1987 a complex oxide of yttrium, copper, and barium had been found that has a value of T_c well above the 77 K boiling temperature of liquid nitrogen, a refrigerant that is both inexpensive and safe. The current (2006) record for T_c at atmospheric pressure is 138 K, and materials that are superconductors at room temperature may become a reality. The implications of these discoveries for power-distribution systems, computer design, and transportation are enormous. Meanwhile, superconducting electromagnets cooled by liquid helium are used in particle accelerators and some experimental magnetic-levitation railroads. Superconductors have other exotic properties that require an understanding of magnetism to explore; we will discuss these further in Chapter 29.

Test Your Understanding of Section 25.2 You maintain a constant electric field inside a piece of semiconductor while lowering the semiconductor's temperature. What happens to the current density in the semiconductor? (i) It increases; (ii) it decreases; (iii) it remains the same.

25.3 Resistance

For a conductor with resistivity ρ, the current density $\vec{J}$ at a point where the electric field is $\vec{E}$ is given by Eq. (25.5), which we can write as

$$\vec{E} = \rho\vec{J} \tag{25.7}$$

When Ohm's law is obeyed, ρ is constant and independent of the magnitude of the electric field, so $\vec{E}$ is directly proportional to $\vec{J}$. Often, however, we are more interested in the total current in a conductor than in $\vec{J}$ and more interested in the potential difference between the ends of the conductor than in $\vec{E}$. This is so largely because current and potential difference are much easier to measure than are $\vec{J}$ and $\vec{E}$.

Suppose our conductor is a wire with uniform cross-sectional area A and length L, as shown in Fig. 25.7. Let V be the potential difference between the higher-potential and lower-potential ends of the conductor, so that V is positive. The *direction* of the current is always from the higher-potential end to the lower-potential end. That's because current in a conductor flows in the direction of $\vec{E}$, no matter what the sign of the moving charges (Fig. 25.2), and because $\vec{E}$ points in the direction of *decreasing* electric potential (see Section 23.2). As the current flows through the potential difference, electric potential energy is lost; this energy is transferred to the ions of the conducting material during collisions.

We can also relate the *value* of the current I to the potential difference between the ends of the conductor. If the magnitudes of the current density $\vec{J}$ and the electric field $\vec{E}$ are uniform throughout the conductor, the total current I is given by $I = JA$, and the potential difference V between the ends is $V = EL$. When we solve these equations for J and E, respectively, and substitute the results in Eq. (25.7), we obtain

$$\frac{V}{L} = \frac{\rho I}{A} \quad \text{or} \quad V = \frac{\rho L}{A}I \tag{25.8}$$

This shows that when ρ is constant, the total current I is proportional to the potential difference V.

The ratio of V to I for a particular conductor is called its **resistance** R:

$$R = \frac{V}{I} \tag{25.9}$$

Comparing this definition of R to Eq. (25.8), we see that the resistance R of a particular conductor is related to the resistivity ρ of its material by

$$R = \frac{\rho L}{A} \quad \begin{array}{l}\text{(relationship between} \\ \text{resistance and resistivity)}\end{array} \tag{25.10}$$

If ρ is constant, as is the case for ohmic materials, then so is R.

The equation

$$V = IR \quad \begin{array}{l}\text{(relationship among voltage,} \\ \text{current, and resistance)}\end{array} \tag{25.11}$$

is often called Ohm's law, but it is important to understand that the real content of Ohm's law is the direct proportionality (for some materials) of V to I or of J to E. Equation (25.9) or (25.11) *defines* resistance R for *any* conductor, whether or not it obeys Ohm's law, but only when R is constant can we correctly call this relationship Ohm's law.

25.7 A conductor with uniform cross section. The current density is uniform over any cross section, and the electric field is constant along the length.

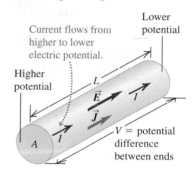

25.8 A long fire hose offers substantial resistance to water flow. To make water pass through the hose rapidly, the upstream end of the hose must be at much higher pressure than the end where the water emerges. In an analogous way, there must be a large potential difference between the ends of a long wire in order to cause a substantial electric current through the wire.

Interpreting Resistance

Equation (25.10) shows that the resistance of a wire or other conductor of uniform cross section is directly proportional to its length and inversely proportional to its cross-sectional area. It is also proportional to the resistivity of the material of which the conductor is made.

The flowing-fluid analogy is again useful. In analogy to Eq. (25.10), a narrow water hose offers more resistance to flow than a fat one, and a long hose has more resistance than a short one (Fig. 25.8). We can increase the resistance to flow by stuffing the hose with cotton or sand; this corresponds to increasing the resistivity. The flow rate is approximately proportional to the pressure difference between the ends. Flow rate is analogous to current, and pressure difference is analogous to potential difference ("voltage"). Let's not stretch this analogy too far, though; the water flow rate in a pipe is usually *not* proportional to its cross-sectional area (see Section 14.6).

The SI unit of resistance is the **ohm,** equal to one volt per ampere $(1\ \Omega = 1\ \text{V}/\text{A})$. The *kilohm* $(1\ \text{k}\Omega = 10^3\ \Omega)$ and the *megohm* $(1\ \text{M}\Omega = 10^6\ \Omega)$ are also in common use. A 100-m length of 12-gauge copper wire, the size usually used in household wiring, has a resistance at room temperature of about 0.5 Ω. A 100-W, 120-V light bulb has a resistance (at operating temperature) of 140 Ω. If the same current I flows in both the copper wire and the light bulb, the potential difference $V = IR$ is much greater across the light bulb, and much more potential energy is lost per charge in the light bulb. This lost energy is converted by the light bulb filament into light and heat. You don't want your household wiring to glow white-hot, so its resistance is kept low by using wire of low resistivity and large cross-sectional area.

Because the resistivity of a material varies with temperature, the resistance of a specific conductor also varies with temperature. For temperature ranges that are not too great, this variation is approximately a linear relationship, analogous to Eq. (25.6):

$$R(T) = R_0[1 + \alpha(T - T_0)] \qquad (25.12)$$

Table 25.3 Color Codes for Resistors

Color	Value as Digit	Value as Multiplier
Black	0	1
Brown	1	10
Red	2	10^2
Orange	3	10^3
Yellow	4	10^4
Green	5	10^5
Blue	6	10^6
Violet	7	10^7
Gray	8	10^8
White	9	10^9

In this equation, $R(T)$ is the resistance at temperature T and R_0 is the resistance at temperature T_0, often taken to be 0°C or 20°C. The *temperature coefficient of resistance* α is the same constant that appears in Eq. (25.6) if the dimensions L and A in Eq. (25.10) do not change appreciably with temperature; this is indeed the case for most conducting materials (see Problem 25.67). Within the limits of validity of Eq. (25.12), the *change* in resistance resulting from a temperature change $T - T_0$ is given by $R_0\alpha(T - T_0)$.

A circuit device made to have a specific value of resistance between its ends is called a **resistor.** Resistors in the range 0.01 to 10^7 Ω can be bought off the shelf. Individual resistors used in electronic circuitry are often cylindrical, a few millimeters in diameter and length, with wires coming out of the ends. The resistance may be marked with a standard code using three or four color bands near one end (Fig. 25.9), according to the scheme shown in Table 25.3. The first two bands (starting with the band nearest an end) are digits, and the third is a power-of-10 multiplier, as shown in Fig. 25.9. For example, green–violet–red means $57 \times 10^2 \Omega$, or 5.7 kΩ. The fourth band, if present, indicates the precision (tolerance) of the value; no band means ±20%, a silver band ±10%, and a gold band ±5%. Another important characteristic of a resistor is the maximum *power* it can dissipate without damage. We'll return to this point in Section 25.5.

For a resistor that obeys Ohm's law, a graph of current as a function of potential difference (voltage) is a straight line (Fig. 25.10a). The slope of the line is $1/R$. If the sign of the potential difference changes, so does the sign of the current produced; in Fig. 25.7 this corresponds to interchanging the higher- and lower-potential ends of the conductor, so the electric field, current density, and current

25.9 This resistor has a resistance of 5.7 kΩ with a precision (tolerance) of ±10%.

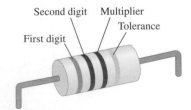

Second digit   Multiplier

Tolerance

First digit

25.10 Current–voltage relationships for two devices. Only for a resistor that obeys Ohm's law as in (a) is current I proportional to voltage V.

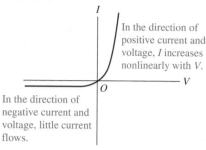

(a)

Ohmic resistor (e.g., typical metal wire): At a given temperature, current is proportional to voltage.

Slope $= \dfrac{1}{R}$

(b)

Semiconductor diode: a nonohmic resistor

In the direction of positive current and voltage, I increases nonlinearly with V.

In the direction of negative current and voltage, little current flows.

all reverse direction. In devices that do not obey Ohm's law, the relationship of voltage to current may not be a direct proportion, and it may be different for the two directions of current. Figure 25.10b shows the behavior of a semiconductor *diode*, a device used to convert alternating current to direct current and to perform a wide variety of logic functions in computer circuitry. For positive potentials V of the anode (one of two terminals of the diode) with respect to the cathode (the other terminal), I increases exponentially with increasing V; for negative potentials the current is extremely small. Thus a positive potential difference V causes a current to flow in the positive direction, but a potential difference of the other sign causes little or no current. Hence a diode acts like a one-way valve in a circuit.

Example 25.2   Electric field, potential difference, and resistance in a wire

The 18-gauge copper wire in Example 25.1 (Section 25.1) has a diameter of 1.02 mm and a cross-sectional area of 8.20×10^{-7} m². It carries a current of 1.67 A. Find (a) the electric-field magnitude in the wire; (b) the potential difference between two points in the wire 50.0 m apart; (c) the resistance of a 50.0-m length of this wire.

SOLUTION

IDENTIFY: We are given the values of cross-sectional area A and current I. Our target variables are the electric-field magnitude E, potential difference V, and resistance R.

SET UP: The magnitude of the current density is $J = I/A$ and the resistivity ρ is given in Table 25.1. We find the electric-field magnitude by using Eq. (25.5), $E = \rho J$. Once we have found E, the potential difference is simply the product of E and the length of the wire. We find the resistance by using Eq. (25.11).

EXECUTE: (a) From Table 25.1, the resistivity of copper is $1.72 \times 10^{-8}\ \Omega \cdot$ m. Hence, using Eq. (25.5),

$$E = \rho J = \frac{\rho I}{A} = \frac{(1.72 \times 10^{-8}\ \Omega \cdot \text{m})(1.67\ \text{A})}{8.20 \times 10^{-7}\ \text{m}^2}$$

$$= 0.0350\ \text{V/m}$$

(b) The potential difference is given by

$$V = EL = (0.0350\ \text{V/m})(50.0\ \text{m}) = 1.75\ \text{V}$$

(c) From Eq. (25.11) the resistance of a 50.0-m length of this wire is

$$R = \frac{V}{I} = \frac{1.75\ \text{V}}{1.67\ \text{A}} = 1.05\ \Omega$$

EVALUATE: To check our result in part (c), we calculate the resistance using Eq. (25.10):

$$R = \frac{\rho L}{A} = \frac{(1.72 \times 10^{-8}\ \Omega \cdot \text{m})(50.0\ \text{m})}{8.20 \times 10^{-7}\ \text{m}^2} = 1.05\ \Omega$$

We emphasize that the resistance of the wire is *defined* to be the ratio of voltage to current. If the wire is made of nonohmic material, then R is different for different values of V but is always given by $R = V/I$. Resistance is also always given by $R = \rho L/A$; if the material is nonohmic, ρ is not constant but depends on E (or, equivalently, on $V = EL$).

Example 25.3   Temperature dependence of resistance

Suppose the resistance of the wire in Example 25.2 is 1.05 Ω at a temperature of 20°C. Find the resistance at 0°C and at 100°C.

SOLUTION

IDENTIFY: This example concerns how resistance (the target variable) depends on temperature. As Table 25.2 shows, this temperature dependence differs for different substances.

SET UP: Our target variables are the values of the wire resistance R at two temperatures, $T = 0$°C and $T = 100$°C. To find these values we use Eq. (25.12). Note that we are given the resistance $R_0 = 1.05$ Ω at a reference temperature $T_0 = 20$°C, and we know from Example 25.2 that the wire is made of copper.

EXECUTE: From Table 25.2 the temperature coefficient of resistivity of copper is $\alpha = 0.00393 \ (\text{C}°)^{-1}$. From Eq. (25.12), the resistance at $T = 0$°C is

$$R = R_0[1 + \alpha(T - T_0)]$$
$$= (1.05 \ \Omega)\{1 + [0.00393 \ (\text{C}°)^{-1}][0°\text{C} - 20°\text{C}]\}$$
$$= 0.97 \ \Omega$$

At $T = 100$°C,

$$R = (1.05 \ \Omega)\{1 + [0.00393 \ (\text{C}°)^{-1}][100°\text{C} - 20°\text{C}]\}$$
$$= 1.38 \ \Omega$$

EVALUATE: The resistance at 100°C is greater than that at 0°C by a factor of $(1.38 \ \Omega)/(0.97 \ \Omega) = 1.42$. In other words, raising the temperature of ordinary copper wire from 0°C to 100°C increases its resistance by 42%. From Eq. (25.11), $V = IR$, this means that 42% more voltage V is required to produce the same current I at 100°C than at 0°C. This is a substantial effect that must be taken into account in designing electric circuits that are to operate over a wide range of temperatures.

Example 25.4   Calculating resistance

The hollow cylinder shown in Fig. 25.11 has length L and inner and outer radii a and b. It is made of a material with resistivity ρ. A potential difference is set up between the inner and outer surfaces of the cylinder (each of which is an equipotential surface) so that current flows radially through the cylinder. What is the resistance to this radial current flow?

SOLUTION

IDENTIFY: Figure 25.11 shows that the current flows radially from the inside of the conductor toward the outside, *not* along the length of the conductor as in Fig. 25.7. Hence we must use the ideas of this section to derive a new formula for resistance (our target variable) appropriate for radial current flow.

SET UP: We can't use Eq. (25.10) directly because the cross section through which the charge travels is *not* constant; it varies from $2\pi aL$ at the inner surface to $2\pi bL$ at the outer surface. Instead, we calculate the resistance to radial current flow through a thin cylindrical shell of inner radius r and thickness dr. We then combine the resistances for all such shells between the inner and outer radii of the cylinder.

EXECUTE: The area A for the shell is $2\pi rL$, the surface area that the current encounters as it flows outward. The length of the current path through the shell is dr. The resistance dR of this shell, between inner and outer surfaces, is that of a conductor with length dr and area $2\pi rL$:

$$dR = \frac{\rho \, dr}{2\pi rL}$$

The current has to pass successively through all such shells between the inner and outer radii a and b. From Eq. (25.11) the potential difference across one shell is $dV = I \, dR$, and the total potential difference between the inner and outer surfaces is the sum of the potential differences for all shells. The total current is

the same through each shell, so the total resistance is the sum of the resistances of all the shells. If the area $2\pi rL$ were constant, we could just integrate dr from $r = a$ to $r = b$ to get the total length of the current path. But the area increases as the current passes through shells of greater radius, so we have to integrate the above expression for dR. The total resistance is thus given by

$$R = \int dR = \frac{\rho}{2\pi L} \int_a^b \frac{dr}{r} = \frac{\rho}{2\pi L} \ln \frac{b}{a}$$

EVALUATE: The conductor geometry shown in Fig. 25.11 plays an important role in your body's nervous system. Each neuron, or nerve cell, has a long extension called a nerve fiber or *axon*. An axon has a cylindrical membrane shaped much like the resistor in Fig. 25.11, with one conducting fluid inside the membrane and another outside it. Ordinarily all of the inner fluid is at the same potential, so no current tends to flow along the length of the axon. If the axon is stimulated at a certain point along its length, however, charged ions flow radially across the cylindrical membrane at that point, as in Fig. 25.11. This flow causes a potential difference between that point and other points along the length of the axon, which makes a nerve signal flow along that length.

25.11 Finding the resistance for radial current flow.

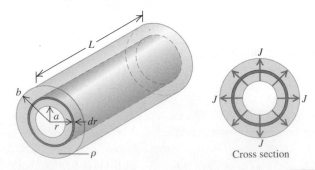

Cross section

Test Your Understanding of Section 25.3   Suppose you increase the voltage across the copper wire in Examples 25.2 and 25.3. The increased voltage causes more current to flow, which makes the temperature of the wire increase. (The same thing happens to the coils of an electric oven or a toaster when a voltage is applied to them. We'll explore this issue in more depth in Section 25.5.) If you double the voltage across the wire, the current in the wire increases. By what factor does it increase? (i) 2; (ii) greater than 2; (iii) less than 2.

25.4 Electromotive Force and Circuits

For a conductor to have a steady current, it must be part of a path that forms a closed loop or **complete circuit.** Here's why. If you establish an electric field $\vec{E}_1$ inside an isolated conductor with resistivity ρ that is *not* part of a complete circuit, a current begins to flow with current density $\vec{J} = \vec{E}_1/\rho$ (Fig. 25.12a). As a result a net positive charge quickly accumulates at one end of the conductor and a net negative charge accumulates at the other end (Fig. 25.12b). These charges themselves produce an electric field $\vec{E}_2$ in the direction opposite to $\vec{E}_1$, causing the total electric field and hence the current to decrease. Within a very small fraction of a second, enough charge builds up on the conductor ends that the total electric field $\vec{E} = \vec{E}_1 + \vec{E}_2 = 0$ inside the conductor. Then $\vec{J} = 0$ as well, and the current stops altogether (Fig. 25.12c). So there can be no steady motion of charge in such an *incomplete* circuit.

To see how to maintain a steady current in a *complete* circuit, we recall a basic fact about electric potential energy: If a charge q goes around a complete circuit and returns to its starting point, the potential energy must be the same at the end of the round trip as at the beginning. As described in Section 25.3, there is always a *decrease* in potential energy when charges move through an ordinary conducting material with resistance. So there must be some part of the circuit in which the potential energy *increases.*

The problem is analogous to an ornamental water fountain that recycles its water. The water pours out of openings at the top, cascades down over the terraces and spouts (moving in the direction of decreasing gravitational potential energy), and collects in a basin in the bottom. A pump then lifts it back to the top (increasing the potential energy) for another trip. Without the pump, the water would just fall to the bottom and stay there.

Electromotive Force

In an electric circuit there must be a device somewhere in the loop that acts like the water pump in a water fountain (Fig. 25.13). In this device a charge travels "uphill," from lower to higher potential energy, even though the electrostatic force is trying to push it from higher to lower potential energy. The direction of current in such a device is from lower to higher potential, just the opposite of what happens in an ordinary conductor. The influence that makes current flow from lower to higher potential is called **electromotive force** (abbreviated **emf** and pronounced "ee-em-eff"). This is a poor term because emf is *not* a force but an energy-per-unit-charge quantity, like potential. The SI unit of emf is the same as that for potential, the volt $(1 \text{ V} = 1 \text{ J/C})$. A typical flashlight battery has an emf of 1.5 V; this means that the battery does 1.5 J of work on every coulomb of charge that passes through it. We'll use the symbol $\mathcal{E}$ (a script capital E) for emf.

Every complete circuit with a steady current must include some device that provides emf. Such a device is called a **source of emf.** Batteries, electric generators, solar cells, thermocouples, and fuel cells are all examples of sources of emf. All such devices convert energy of some form (mechanical, chemical, thermal, and so on) into electric potential energy and transfer it into the circuit to which the device is connected. An *ideal* source of emf maintains a constant potential

25.12 If an electric field is produced inside a conductor that is *not* part of a complete circuit, current flows for only a very short time.

(a) An electric field $\vec{E}_1$ produced inside an isolated conductor causes a current.

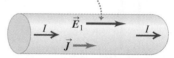

(b) The current causes charge to build up at the ends.

The charge buildup produces an opposing field $\vec{E}_2$, thus reducing the current.

(c) After a very short time $\vec{E}_2$ has the same magnitude as $\vec{E}_1$; then the total field is $\vec{E}_{\text{total}} = 0$ and the current stops completely.

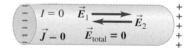

25.13 Just as a water fountain requires a pump, an electric circuit requires a source of electromotive force to sustain a steady current.

Activ
Physics ONLINE

12.1   DC Series Circuits (Qualitative)

25.14 Schematic diagram of a source of emf in an "open-circuit" situation. The electric-field force $\vec{F}_e = q\vec{E}$ and the non-electrostatic force $\vec{F}_n$ are shown for a positive charge q.

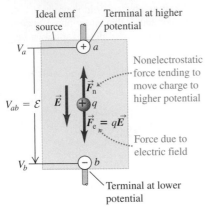

Ideal emf source

Terminal at higher potential

V_a

$V_{ab} = \mathcal{E}$ $\vec{E}$

Nonelectrostatic force tending to move charge to higher potential

$\vec{F}_n$

q

$\vec{F}_e = q\vec{E}$

Force due to electric field

V_b

Terminal at lower potential

When the emf source is not part of a closed circuit, $F_n = F_e$ and there is no net motion of charge between the terminals.

25.15 Schematic diagram of an ideal source of emf in a complete circuit. The electric-field force $\vec{F}_e = q\vec{E}$ and the non-electrostatic force $\vec{F}_n$ are shown for a positive charge q The current is in the direction from a to b in the external circuit and from b to a within the source.

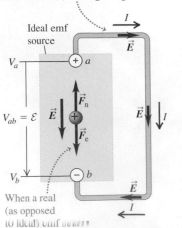

Potential across terminals creates electric field in circuit, causing charges to move.

Ideal emf source

I

$\vec{E}$

V_a

$V_{ab} = \mathcal{E}$ $\vec{E}$

$\vec{F}_n$

$\vec{F}_e$

$\vec{E}$ I

V_b

$\vec{E}$

I

When a real (as opposed to ideal) emf source is connected to a circuit, V_{ab} and thus F_e fall, so that $F_n > F_e$ and $\vec{F}_n$ does work on the charges.

difference between its terminals, independent of the current through it. We define electromotive force quantitatively as the magnitude of this potential difference. As we will see, such an ideal source is a mythical beast, like the frictionless plane and the massless rope. We will discuss later how real-life sources of emf differ in their behavior from this idealized model.

Fig. 25.14 is a schematic diagram of an ideal source of emf that maintains a potential difference between conductors a and b, called the *terminals* of the device. Terminal a, marked $+$, is maintained at *higher* potential than terminal b, marked $-$. Associated with this potential difference is an electric field $\vec{E}$ in the region around the terminals, both inside and outside the source. The electric field inside the device is directed from a to b, as shown. A charge q within the source experiences an electric force $\vec{F}_e = q\vec{E}$. But the source also provides an additional influence, which we represent as a nonelectrostatic force $\vec{F}_n$. This force, operating inside the device, pushes charge from b to a in an "uphill" direction against the electric force $\vec{F}_e$. Thus $\vec{F}_n$ maintains the potential difference between the terminals. If $\vec{F}_n$ were not present, charge would flow between the terminals until the potential difference was zero. The origin of the additional influence $\vec{F}_n$ depends on the kind of source. In a generator it results from magnetic-field forces on moving charges. In a battery or fuel cell it is associated with diffusion processes and varying electrolyte concentrations resulting from chemical reactions. In an electrostatic machine such as a Van de Graaff generator (see Fig. 22.27), an actual mechanical force is applied by a moving belt or wheel.

If a positive charge q is moved from b to a inside the source, the nonelectrostatic force $\vec{F}_n$ does a positive amount of work $W_n = q\mathcal{E}$ on the charge. This displacement is *opposite* to the electrostatic force $\vec{F}_e$, so the potential energy associated with the charge *increases* by an amount equal to qV_{ab}, where $V_{ab} = V_a - V_b$ is the (positive) potential of point a with respect to point b. For the ideal source of emf that we've described, $\vec{F}_e$ and $\vec{F}_n$ are equal in magnitude but opposite in direction, so the total work done on the charge q is zero; there is an increase in potential energy but *no* change in the kinetic energy of the charge. It's like lifting a book from the floor to a high shelf at constant speed. The increase in potential energy is just equal to the non-electrostatic work W_n, so $q\mathcal{E} = qV_{ab}$, or

$$V_{ab} = \mathcal{E} \quad \text{(ideal source of emf)} \qquad (25.13)$$

Now let's make a complete circuit by connecting a wire with resistance R to the terminals of a source (Fig. 25.15). The potential difference between terminals a and b sets up an electric field within the wire; this causes current to flow around the loop from a toward b, from higher to lower potential. Where the wire bends, equal amounts of positive and negative charge persist on the "inside" and "outside" of the bend. These charges exert the forces that cause the current to follow the bends in the wire.

From Eq. (25.11) the potential difference between the ends of the wire in Fig. 25.15 is given by $V_{ab} = IR$. Combining with Eq. (25.13), we have

$$\mathcal{E} = V_{ab} = IR \quad \text{(ideal source of emf)} \qquad (25.14)$$

That is, when a positive charge q flows around the circuit, the potential *rise* $\mathcal{E}$ as it passes through the ideal source is numerically equal to the potential *drop* $V_{ab} = IR$ as it passes through the remainder of the circuit. Once $\mathcal{E}$ and R are known, this relationship determines the current in the circuit.

CAUTION Current is not "used up" in a circuit It's a common misconception that in a closed circuit, current is something that squirts out of the positive terminal of a battery and is consumed or "used up" by the time it reaches the negative terminal. In fact the current is the *same* at every point in a simple loop circuit like that in Fig. 25.15, even if the thickness of the wires is different at different points in the circuit. This happens because charge is conserved (that is, it can be neither created nor destroyed) and because charge cannot accumulate in the circuit devices we have described. If charge did accumulate, the potential differences would change with time. It's like the flow of water in an ornamental fountain; water flows out of the top of the fountain at the same rate at which it reaches the bottom, no matter what the dimensions of the fountain. None of the water is "used up" along the way! ▮

Internal Resistance

Real sources of emf in a circuit don't behave in exactly the way we have described; the potential difference across a real source in a circuit is *not* equal to the emf as in Eq. (25.14). The reason is that charge moving through the material of any real source encounters *resistance*. We call this the **internal resistance** of the source, denoted by r. If this resistance behaves according to Ohm's law, r is constant and independent of the current I. As the current moves through r, it experiences an associated drop in potential equal to Ir. Thus, when a current is flowing through a source from the negative terminal b to the positive terminal a, the potential difference V_{ab} between the terminals is

$$V_{ab} = \mathcal{E} - Ir \qquad \begin{array}{l}\text{(terminal voltage, source} \\ \text{with internal resistance)}\end{array} \qquad (25.15)$$

The potential V_{ab}, called the **terminal voltage,** is less than the emf $\mathcal{E}$ because of the term Ir representing the potential drop across the internal resistance r. Expressed another way, the increase in potential energy qV_{ab} as a charge q moves from b to a within the source is now less than the work $q\mathcal{E}$ done by the nonelectrostatic force $\vec{F}_n$, since some potential energy is lost in traversing the internal resistance.

A 1.5-V battery has an emf of 1.5 V, but the terminal voltage V_{ab} of the battery is equal to 1.5 V only if no current is flowing through it so that $I - 0$ in Eq. (25.15). If the battery is part of a complete circuit through which current is flowing, the terminal voltage will be less than 1.5 V. *For a real source of emf, the terminal voltage equals the emf only if no current is flowing through the source* (Fig. 25.16). Thus we can describe the behavior of a source in terms of two properties: an emf $\mathcal{E}$, which supplies a constant potential difference independent of current, in series with an internal resistance r.

The current in the external circuit connected to the source terminals a and b is still determined by $V_{ab} = IR$. Combining this with Eq. (25.15), we find

$$\mathcal{E} - Ir = IR \quad \text{or} \quad I = \frac{\mathcal{E}}{R + r} \qquad \begin{array}{l}\text{(current, source with} \\ \text{internal resistance)}\end{array} \qquad (25.16)$$

That is, the current equals the source emf divided by the *total* circuit resistance $(R + r)$.

CAUTION   **A battery is not a "current source"** You might have thought that a battery or other source of emf always produces the same current, no matter what circuit it's used in. But as Eq. (25.16) shows, the current that a source of emf produces in a given circuit depends on the resistance R of the external circuit (as well as on the internal resistance r of the source). The greater the resistance, the less current the source will produce. It's analogous to pushing an object through a thick, viscous liquid such as oil or molasses; if you exert a certain steady push (emf), you can move a small object at high speed (small R, large I) or a large object at low speed (large R, small I). ▮

Symbols for Circuit Diagrams

An important part of analyzing any electric circuit is drawing a schematic *circuit diagram*. Table 25.4 shows the usual symbols used in circuit diagrams. We will use these symbols extensively in this chapter and the next. We usually assume that the wires that connect the various elements of the circuit have negligible resistance; from Eq. (25.11), $V = IR$, the potential difference between the ends of such a wire is zero.

25.16 The emf of this battery—that is, the terminal voltage when it's not connected to anything—is 12 V. But because the battery has internal resistance, the terminal voltage of the battery is less than 12 V when it is supplying current to a light bulb.

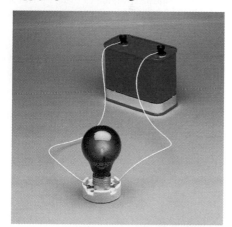

Table 25.4 includes two *meters* that are used to measure the properties of circuits. Idealized meters do not disturb the circuit in which they are connected. A **voltmeter,** introduced in Section 23.2, measures the potential difference between its terminals; an idealized voltmeter has infinitely large resistance and measures potential difference without having any current diverted through it. An ammeter measures the current passing through it; an idealized **ammeter** has zero resistance and has no potential difference between its terminals. Because meters act as part of the circuit in which they are connected, these properties are important to remember.

Table 25.4 Symbols for Circuit Diagrams

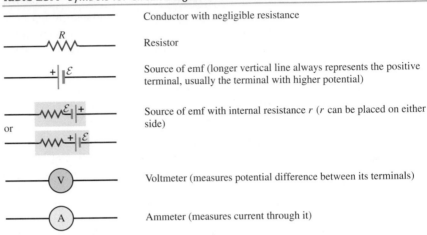

	Conductor with negligible resistance
R	Resistor
$+\ \mathcal{E}$	Source of emf (longer vertical line always represents the positive terminal, usually the terminal with higher potential)
$\mathcal{E}+$ or $+\ \mathcal{E}$	Source of emf with internal resistance r (r can be placed on either side)
V	Voltmeter (measures potential difference between its terminals)
A	Ammeter (measures current through it)

Conceptual Example 25.5 **A source in an open circuit**

Fig. 25.17 shows a source (a battery) with an emf $\mathcal{E}$ of 12 V and an internal resistance r of 2 Ω. (For comparison, the internal resistance of a commercial 12-V lead storage battery is only a few thousandths of an ohm.) The wires to the left of a and to the right of the ammeter A are not connected to anything. Determine the readings of the idealized voltmeter V and the idealized ammeter A.

SOLUTION

There is no current because there is no complete circuit. (There is no current through our idealized voltmeter, with its infinitely large resistance.) Hence the ammeter A reads $I = 0$. Because there is no current through the battery, there is no potential difference across its internal resistance. From Eq. (25.15) with $I = 0$, the potential

25.17 A source of emf in an open circuit.

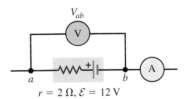

difference V_{ab} across the battery terminals is equal to the emf. So the voltmeter reads $V_{ab} = \mathcal{E} = 12$ V. The terminal voltage of a real, nonideal source equals the emf *only* if there is no current flowing through the source, as in this example.

Example 25.6 **A source in a complete circuit**

Using the battery in Conceptual Example 25.5, we add a 4-Ω resistor to form the complete circuit shown in Fig. 25.18. What are the voltmeter and ammeter readings now?

SOLUTION

IDENTIFY Our first target variable is the current I through the circuit $aa'b'b$ (equal to the ammeter reading). The second is the potential difference V_{ab} (equal to the voltmeter reading).

SET UP: We find I using Eq. (25.16). To find V_{ab}, we note that we can regard this either as the potential difference across the source or as the potential difference around the circuit through the external resistor.

25.18 A source of emf in a complete circuit.

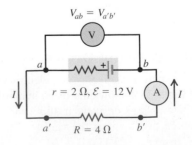

EXECUTE: The ideal ammeter has zero resistance, so the resistance external to the source is $R = 4\ \Omega$. From Eq. (25.16), the current through the circuit $aa'b'b$ is

$$I = \frac{\mathcal{E}}{R + r} = \frac{12\ \text{V}}{4\ \Omega + 2\Omega} = 2\ \text{A}$$

The ammeter A reads $I = 2$ A.

Our idealized conducting wires have zero resistance, and the idealized ammeter A also has zero resistance. So there is no potential difference between points a and a' or between points b and b'; that is, $V_{ab} = V_{a'b'}$. We can find V_{ab} by considering a and b either as the terminals of the resistor or as the terminals of the source. Considering them as terminals of the resistor, we use Ohm's law ($V = IR$):

$$V_{a'b'} = IR = (2\ \text{A})(4\ \Omega) = 8\ \text{V}$$

Considering them as the terminals of the source, we have

$$V_{ab} = \mathcal{E} - Ir = 12\ \text{V} - (2\ \text{A})(2\ \Omega) = 8\ \text{V}$$

Either way, we conclude that the voltmeter reads $V_{ab} = 8$ V.

EVALUATE: With a current flowing through the source, the terminal voltage V_{ab} is less than the emf. The smaller the internal resistance r, the less the difference between V_{ab} and $\mathcal{E}$.

Conceptual Example 25.7   Using voltmeters and ammeters

The voltmeter and ammeter in Example 25.6 are moved to different positions in the circuit. What are the voltmeter and ammeter readings in the situations shown in (a) Fig. 25.19a and (b) Fig. 25.19b?

25.19 Different placements of a voltmeter and an ammeter in a complete circuit.

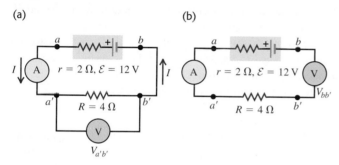

(a)   (b)

SOLUTION

(a) The voltmeter now measures the potential difference between points a' and b'. But as mentioned in Example 25.6, $V_{ab} = V_{a'b'}$, so the voltmeter reads the same as in Example 25.6: $V_{a'b'} = 8$ V.

CAUTION   **Current in a simple loop**   You might be tempted to conclude that the ammeter in Fig. 25.19a, which is located "upstream" of the resistor, would have a higher reading than the

one located "downstream" of the resistor in Fig. 25.18. But this conclusion is based on the misconception that current is somehow "used up" as it moves through a resistor. As charges move through a resistor, there is a decrease in electric potential energy, but there is *no* change in the current. *The current in a simple loop is the same at every point.* An ammeter placed as in Fig. 25.19a reads the same as one placed as in Fig. 25.18: $I = 2$ A. ▪

(b) There is no current through the voltmeter because it has infinitely large resistance. Since the voltmeter is now part of the circuit, there is no current at all in the circuit, and the ammeter reads $I = 0$.

The voltmeter measures the potential difference $V_{bb'}$ between points b and b'. Since $I = 0$, the potential difference across the resistor is $V_{a'b'} = IR = 0$, and the potential difference between the ends a and a' of the idealized ammeter is also zero. So $V_{bb'}$ is equal to V_{ab}, the terminal voltage of the source. As in Conceptual Example 25.5, there is no current flowing, so the terminal voltage equals the emf, and the voltmeter reading is $V_{ab} = \mathcal{E} = 12$ V.

This example shows that ammeters and voltmeters are circuit elements, too. Moving the voltmeter from the position in Fig. 25.19a to that in Fig. 25.19b changes the current and potential differences in the circuit—in this case rather dramatically. If you want to measure the potential difference between two points in a circuit without disturbing the circuit, use a voltmeter as in Figs. 25.18 or 25.19a, *not* as in Fig. 25.19b.

Example 25.8   A source with a short circuit

Using the same battery as in the preceding three examples, we now replace the 4-Ω resistor with a zero-resistance conductor. What are the meter readings now?

SOLUTION

IDENTIFY: Our target variables are I and V_{ab}, the same as in Example 25.6. The only difference from that example is that the external resistance is now $R = 0$.

SET UP: Figure 25.20 shows the new circuit. There is now a zero-resistance path between points a and b (through the lower loop in Fig. 25.20). Hence the potential difference between these points must be zero, which we can use to help solve the problem.

25.20 Our sketch for this problem.

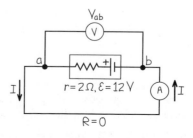

Continued

EXECUTE: We must have $V_{ab} = IR = I(0) = 0$, no matter what the current. Knowing this, we can find the current I from Eq. (25.15):

$$V_{ab} = \mathcal{E} - Ir = 0$$

$$I = \frac{\mathcal{E}}{r} = \frac{12\text{ V}}{2\text{ }\Omega} = 6\text{ A}$$

The ammeter reads $I = 6$ A and the voltmeter reads $V_{ab} = 0$.

EVALUATE: The current has a different value than in Example 25.6, even though the same battery is used. A source does *not* deliver the same current in all situations; the amount of current depends on the internal resistance r and on the resistance of the external circuit.

The situation in this example is called a *short circuit*. The terminals of the battery are connected directly to each other, with no external resistance. The short-circuit current is equal to the emf $\mathcal{E}$ divided by the internal resistance r. *Warning:* A short circuit can be an extremely dangerous situation. An automobile battery or a household power line has very small internal resistance (much less than in these examples), and the short-circuit current can be great enough to melt a small wire or cause a storage battery to explode. Don't try it!

Potential Changes Around a Circuit

The net change in potential energy for a charge q making a round trip around a complete circuit must be zero. Hence the net change in *potential* around the circuit must also be zero; in other words, the algebraic sum of the potential differences and emfs around the loop is zero. We can see this by rewriting Eq. (25.16) in the form

$$\mathcal{E} - Ir - IR = 0$$

A potential gain of $\mathcal{E}$ is associated with the emf, and potential drops of Ir and IR are associated with the internal resistance of the source and the external circuit, respectively. Fig. 25.21 is a graph showing how the potential varies as we go around the complete circuit of Fig. 25.18. The horizontal axis doesn't necessarily represent actual distances, but rather various points in the loop. If we take the potential to be zero at the negative terminal of the battery, then we have a rise $\mathcal{E}$ and a drop Ir in the battery and an additional drop IR in the external resistor, and as we finish our trip around the loop, the potential is back where it started.

In this section we have considered only situations in which the resistances are ohmic. If the circuit includes a nonlinear device such as a diode (see Fig. 25.10b), Eq. (25.16) is still valid but cannot be solved algebraically because R is not a constant. In such a situation, the current I can be found by using numerical techniques (see Challenge Problem 25.84).

Finally, we remark that Eq. (25.15) is not always an adequate representation of the behavior of a source. The emf may not be constant, and what we have

25.21 Potential rises and drops in a circuit.

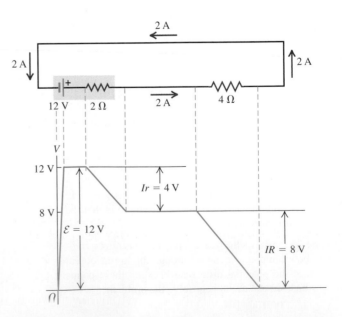

described as an internal resistance may actually be a more complex voltage–current relationship that doesn't obey Ohm's law. Nevertheless, the concept of internal resistance frequently provides an adequate description of batteries, generators, and other energy converters. The principal difference between a fresh flashlight battery and an old one is not in the emf, which decreases only slightly with use, but in the internal resistance, which may increase from less than an ohm when the battery is fresh to as much as $1000 \ \Omega$ or more after long use. Similarly, a car battery can deliver less current to the starter motor on a cold morning than when the battery is warm, not because the emf is appreciably less but because the internal resistance increases with decreasing temperature. Cold-climate dwellers take a number of measures to avoid this loss, from using special battery warmers to soaking the battery in warm water on very cold mornings.

Test Your Understanding of Section 25.4   Rank the following circuits in order from highest to lowest current. (i) a $1.4\text{-}\Omega$ resistor connected to a 1.5-V battery that has an internal resistance of $0.10 \ \Omega$; (ii) a $1.8\text{-}\Omega$ resistor connected to a 4.0-V battery that has a terminal voltage of 3.6 V but an unknown internal resistance; (iii) an unknown resistor connected to a 12.0-V battery that has an internal resistance of $0.20 \ \Omega$ and a terminal voltage of 11.0 V.

25.5 Energy and Power in Electric Circuits

Let's now look at some energy and power relationships in electric circuits. The box in Fig. 25.22 represents a circuit element with potential difference $V_a - V_b = V_{ab}$ between its terminals and current I passing through it in the direction from a toward b. This element might be a resistor, a battery, or something else; the details don't matter. As charge passes through the circuit element, the electric field does work on the charge. In a source of emf, additional work is done by the force $\vec{F}_n$ that we mentioned in Section 25.4.

As an amount of charge q passes through the circuit element, there is a change in potential energy equal to qV_{ab}. For example, if $q > 0$ and $V_{ab} = V_a - V_b$ is positive, potential energy decreases as the charge "falls" from potential V_a to lower potential V_b. The moving charges don't gain *kinetic* energy, because the rate of charge flow (that is, the current) out of the circuit element must be the same as the rate of charge flow into the element. Instead, the quantity qV_{ab} represents electrical energy transferred into the circuit element. This situation occurs in the coils of a toaster or electric oven, in which electrical energy is converted to thermal energy.

It may happen that the potential at b is higher than that at a. In this case V_{ab} is negative, and a net transfer of energy *out* of the circuit element occurs. The element then acts as a source, delivering electrical energy into the circuit to which it is attached. This is the usual situation for a battery, which converts chemical energy into electrical energy and delivers it to the external circuit. Thus qV_{ab} can denote either a quantity of energy delivered to a circuit element or a quantity of energy extracted from that element.

In electric circuits we are most often interested in the *rate* at which energy is either delivered to or extracted from a circuit element. If the current through the element is I, then in a time interval dt an amount of charge $dQ = I \, dt$ passes through the element. The potential energy change for this amount of charge is $V_{ab} \, dQ = V_{ab}I \, dt$. Dividing this expression by dt, we obtain the *rate* at which energy is transferred either into or out of the circuit element. The time rate of energy transfer is *power*, denoted by P, so we write

$$P = V_{ab}I \qquad \text{(rate at which energy is delivered to or extracted from a circuit element)} \qquad (25.17)$$

25.22 The power input to the circuit element between a and b is $P = (V_a - V_b)I = V_{ab}I$.

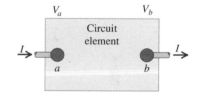

The unit of V_{ab} is one volt, or one joule per coulomb, and the unit of I is one ampere, or one coulomb per second. Hence the unit of $P = V_{ab}I$ is one watt, as it should be:

$$(1 \text{ J/C})(1 \text{ C/s}) = 1 \text{ J/s} = 1 \text{ W}$$

Let's consider a few special cases.

Power Inout to a Pure Resistance

If the circuit element in Fig. 25.22 is a resistor, the potential difference is $V_{ab} = IR$. From Eq. (25.17) the electrical power delivered to the resistor by the circuit is

$$P = V_{ab}I = I^2R = \frac{V_{ab}^2}{R} \qquad \text{(power delivered to a resistor)} \qquad (25.18)$$

In this case the potential at a (where the current enters the resistor) is always higher than that at b (where the current exits). Current enters the higher-potential terminal of the device, and Eq. (25.18) represents the rate of transfer of electric potential energy *into* the circuit element.

What becomes of this energy? The moving charges collide with atoms in the resistor and transfer some of their energy to these atoms, increasing the internal energy of the material. Either the temperature of the resistor increases or there is a flow of heat out of it, or both. In any of these cases we say that energy is *dissipated* in the resistor at a rate I^2R. Every resistor has a *power rating*, the maximum power the device can dissipate without becoming overheated and damaged. In practical applications the power rating of a resistor is often just as important a characteristic as its resistance value. Of course, some devices, such as electric heaters, are designed to get hot and transfer heat to their surroundings. But if the power rating is exceeded, even such a device may melt or even explode.

Power Output of a Source

The upper rectangle in Fig. 25.23a represents a source with emf $\mathcal{E}$ and internal resistance r, connected by ideal (resistanceless) conductors to an external circuit represented by the lower box. This could describe a car battery connected to one of the car's headlights (Fig. 25.23b). Point a is at higher potential than point b, so $V_a > V_b$ and V_{ab} is positive. Note that the current I is *leaving* the source at the higher-potential terminal (rather than entering there). Energy is being delivered to the external circuit, and the rate of its delivery to the circuit is given by Eq. (25.17):

$$P = V_{ab}I$$

For a source that can be described by an emf $\mathcal{E}$ and an internal resistance r, we may use Eq. (25.15):

$$V_{ab} = \mathcal{E} - Ir$$

Multiplying this equation by I, we find

$$P = V_{ab}I = \mathcal{E}I - I^2r \qquad (25.19)$$

What do the terms $\mathcal{E}I$ and I^2r mean? In Section 25.4 we defined the emf $\mathcal{E}$ as the work per unit charge performed on the charges by the nonelectrostatic force as the charges are pushed "uphill" from b to a in the source. In a time dt, a charge $dQ = I\,dt$ flows through the source; the work done on it by this nonelectrostatic force is $\mathcal{E}\,dQ = \mathcal{E}I\,dt$. Thus $\mathcal{E}I$ is the *rate* at which work is done on the circulating charges by whatever agency causes the nonelectrostatic force in the source. This term represents the rate of conversion of nonelectrical energy to electrical energy within the source. The term I^2r is the rate at which electrical energy is

25.23 Energy conversion in a simple circuit.

(a) Diagrammatic circuit

- The emf source converts nonelectrical to electrical energy at a rate $\mathcal{E}I$.
- Its internal resistance *dissipates* energy at a rate I^2r.
- The difference $\mathcal{E}I - I^2r$ is its power output.

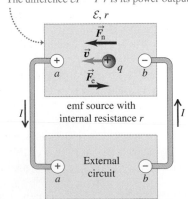

(b) A real circuit of the type shown in (a)

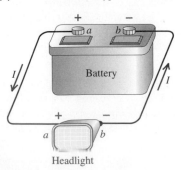

dissipated in the internal resistance of the source. The difference $\mathcal{E}I - I^2r$ is the *net* electrical power output of the source—that is, the rate at which the source delivers electrical energy to the remainder of the circuit.

Power Input to a Source

Suppose that the lower rectangle in Fig. 25.23a is itself a source, with an emf *larger* than that of the upper source and with its emf opposite to that of the upper source. Fig. 25.24 shows a practical example, an automobile battery (the upper circuit element) being charged by the car's alternator (the lower element). The current I in the circuit is then *opposite* to that shown in Fig. 25.23; the lower source is pushing current backward through the upper source. Because of this reversal of current, instead of Eq. (25.15) we have for the upper source

$$V_{ab} = \mathcal{E} + Ir$$

and instead of Eq. (25.19), we have

$$P = V_{ab}I = \mathcal{E}I + I^2R \qquad (25.20)$$

Work is being done *on,* rather than *by,* the agent that causes the nonelectrostatic force in the upper source. There is a conversion of electrical energy into non-electrical energy in the upper source at a rate $\mathcal{E}I$. The term I^2r in Eq. (25.20) is again the rate of dissipation of energy in the internal resistance of the upper source, and the sum $\mathcal{E}I + I^2r$ is the total electrical power *input* to the upper source. This is what happens when a rechargeable battery (a storage battery) is connected to a charger. The charger supplies electrical energy to the battery; part of it is converted to chemical energy, to be reconverted later, and the remainder is dissipated (wasted) in the battery's internal resistance, warming the battery and causing a heat flow out of it. If you have a power tool or laptop computer with a rechargeable battery, you may have noticed that it gets warm while it is charging.

25.24 When two sources are connected in a simple loop circuit, the source with the larger emf delivers energy to the other source.

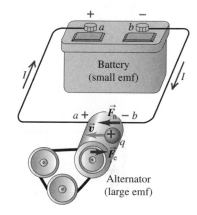

| **Problem-Solving Strategy 25.1** | **Power and Energy in Circuits** | |

IDENTIFY *the relevant concepts:*
The ideas of electric power input and output can be applied to any electric circuit. In most cases you'll know when these concepts are needed because the problem will ask you explicitly to consider power or energy.

SET UP *the problem* using the following steps:
1. Make a drawing of the circuit.
2. Identify the circuit elements, including sources of emf and resistors. In later chapters we will add other kinds of circuit elements, including capacitors and inductors (described in Chapter 30).
3. Determine the target variables. Typically they will be the power input or output for each circuit element, or the total amount of energy put into or taken out of a circuit element in a given time.

EXECUTE *the solution* as follows:
1. A source of emf $\mathcal{E}$ delivers power $\mathcal{E}I$ into a circuit when the current I runs through the source from $-$ to $+$. The energy is converted from chemical energy in a battery, from mechanical energy in a generator, or whatever. In this case the source has a *positive* power output to the circuit or, equivalently, a *negative* power input to the source.
2. A source of emf takes power $\mathcal{E}I$ from a circuit—that is, it has a *negative* power output or, equivalently, a *positive* power input— when current passes through the source in the direction from $+$

to $-$. This occurs in charging a storage battery, when electrical energy is converted back to chemical energy. In this case the source has a *negative* power output to the circuit or, equivalently, a *positive* power input to the source.
3. No matter what the direction of the current through a resistor, there is always a *positive* power input to the resistor. It removes energy from a circuit at a rate given by $VI = I^2R = V^2/R$, where V is the potential difference across the resistor.
4. There is also a *positive* power input to the internal resistance r of a source, irrespective of the direction of the current. The internal resistance always removes energy from the circuit, converting it into heat at a rate I^2r.
5. You may need to calculate the total energy delivered to or extracted from a circuit element in a given amount of time. If the power into or out of a circuit element is constant, this integral is just the product of power and elapsed time. (In Chapter 26 we will encounter situations in which the power is not constant. In such cases, calculating the total energy requires an integral.)

EVALUATE *your answer:* Check your results, including a check that energy is conserved. This conservation can be expressed in either of two forms: "net power input = net power output" or "the algebraic sum of the power inputs to the circuit elements is zero."

Example 25.9   Power input and output in a complete circuit

For the situation that we analyzed in Example 25.6, find the rate of energy conversion (chemical to electrical) and the rate of dissipation of energy in the battery and the net power output of the battery.

SOLUTION

IDENTIFY: Our target variables are the power output of the source of emf, the power input to the internal resistance, and the net power output of the source.

SET UP: Fig. 25.25 shows the circuit. We use Eq. (25.17) to find the power input or output of a circuit element and Eq. (25.19) to find the source's net power output.

25.25 Our sketch for this problem.

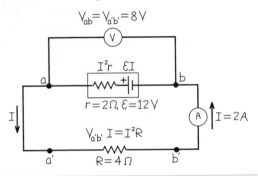

EXECUTE: From Example 25.6 the current in the circuit is $I = 2$ A. The rate of energy conversion in the battery is

$$\mathcal{E}I = (12 \text{ V})(2 \text{ A}) = 24 \text{ W}$$

The rate of dissipation of energy in the battery is

$$I^2r = (2 \text{ A})^2(2 \text{ } \Omega) = 8 \text{ W}$$

The electrical power *output* of the source is the difference between these: $\mathcal{E}I - I^2r = 16$ W.

EVALUATE: The power output is also given by the terminal voltage $V_{ab} = 8$ V (calculated in Example 25.6) multiplied by the current:

$$V_{ab}I = (8 \text{ V})(2 \text{ A}) = 16 \text{ W}$$

The electrical power input to the resistor is

$$V_{a'b'}I = (8 \text{ V})(2 \text{ A}) = 16 \text{ W}$$

This equals the rate of dissipation of electrical energy in the resistor:

$$I^2R = (2 \text{ A})^2(4 \text{ } \Omega) = 16 \text{ W}$$

Note that our results agree with Eq. (25.19), which states that $V_{ab}I = \mathcal{E}I - I^2R$; the left side of this equation equals 16 W, and the right side equals 24 W − 8 W = 16 W. This verifies the consistency of the various power quantities.

Example 25.10   Increasing the resistance

Suppose the 4-Ω resistor in Fig. 25.25 is replaced by an 8-Ω resistor. How does this affect the electrical power dissipated in the resistor?

SOLUTION

IDENTIFY: Our target variable is the power dissipated in the resistor to which the source of emf is connected.

SET UP: The situation is the same as that in Example 25.9, but with a different value of the external resistance R.

EXECUTE: According to Eq. (25.18), the power dissipated in the resistor is given by $P = I^2R$. If you were in a hurry, you might conclude that since R now has twice the value that it had in Example 25.9, the power should also be twice as great, or $2(16 \text{ W}) = 32$ W. Or you might instead try to use the formula $P = V_{ab}^2/R$; this formula would lead you to conclude that the power should be one-half as great as in the preceding example, or $(16 \text{ W})/2 = 8$ W. Which answer is correct?

In fact, *both* of these conclusions are *incorrect*. The first is incorrect because changing the resistance R also changes the current in the circuit (remember, a source of emf does *not* generate the same current in all situations). The second conclusion is also incorrect because the potential difference V_{ab} across the resistor changes when the current changes. To get the correct answer, we first use the same technique as in Example 25.6 to find the current:

$$I = \frac{\mathcal{E}}{R + r} = \frac{12 \text{ V}}{8 \text{ } \Omega + 2 \text{ } \Omega} = 1.2 \text{ A}$$

The greater resistance causes the current to decrease. The potential difference across the resistor is

$$V_{ab} = IR = (1.2 \text{ A})(8 \text{ } \Omega) = 9.6 \text{ V}$$

which is greater than that with the 4-Ω resistor. We can then find the power dissipated in the resistor in either of two ways:

$$P = I^2R = (1.2 \text{ A})^2(8 \text{ } \Omega) = 12 \text{ W} \quad \text{or}$$

$$P = \frac{V_{ab}^2}{R} = \frac{(9.6 \text{ V})^2}{8 \text{ } \Omega} = 12 \text{ W}$$

EVALUATE: Increasing the resistance R causes a *reduction* in the power input to the resistor. In the expression $P = I^2R$ the decrease in current is more important than the increase in resistance; in the expression $P = V_{ab}^2/R$ the increase in resistance is more important than the increase in V_{ab}. This same principle applies to ordinary light bulbs; a 50-W light bulb has a greater resistance than does a 100-W light bulb.

Can you show that replacing the 4-Ω resistor with an 8-Ω resistor decreases both the rate of energy conversion (chemical to electrical) in the battery and the rate of energy dissipation in the battery?

| Example 25.11 | **Power in a short circuit** |

For the circuit that we analyzed in Example 25.8, find the rates of energy conversion and energy dissipation in the battery and the net power output of the battery.

SOLUTION

IDENTIFY: Our target variables are again the power inputs and outputs associated with the battery.

SET UP: Fig. 25.26 shows the circuit. This is once again the same situation as in Example 25.9, but now the external resistance R is zero.

EXECUTE: We found in Example 25.8 that the current in this situation is $I = 6$ A. The rate of energy conversion (chemical to electrical) in the battery is

$$\mathcal{E}I = (12\text{ V})(6\text{ A}) = 72\text{ W}$$

The rate of dissipation of energy in the battery is

$$I^2r = (6\text{ A})^2(2\ \Omega) = 72\text{ W}$$

The net power output of the source, given by $V_{ab}I$, is zero because the terminal voltage V_{ab} is zero.

25.26 Our sketch for this problem.

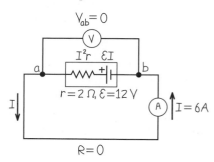

EVALUATE: With ideal wires and an ideal ammeter so that $R = 0$, *all* of the converted energy is dissipated within the source. This is why a short-circuited battery is quickly ruined and in some cases may even explode.

Test Your Understanding of Section 25.5 Rank the following circuits in order from highest to lowest values of the net power output of the battery. (i) a 1.4-Ω resistor connected to a 1.5-V battery that has an internal resistance of 0.10 Ω; (ii) a 1.8-Ω resistor connected to a 4.0-V battery that has a terminal voltage of 3.6 V but an unknown internal resistance; (iii) an unknown resistor connected to a 12.0-V battery that has an internal resistance of 0.20 Ω; and a terminal voltage of 11.0 V.

*25.6 Theory of Metallic Conduction

We can gain additional insight into electrical conduction by looking at the microscopic origin of conductivity. We'll consider a very simple model that treats the electrons as classical particles and ignores their quantum-mechanical, wavelike behavior in solids. Using this model, we'll derive an expression for the resistivity of a metal. Even though this model is not entirely correct conceptually, it will still help you to develop an intuitive idea of the microscopic basis of conduction.

In the simplest microscopic model of conduction in a metal, each atom in the metallic crystal gives up one or more of its outer electrons. These electrons are then free to move through the crystal, colliding at intervals with the stationary positive ions. The motion of the electrons is analogous to the motion of molecules of a gas moving through a porous bed of sand, and they are often referred to as an "electron gas."

If there is no electric field, the electrons move in straight lines between collisions, the directions of their velocities are random, and on average they never get anywhere (Fig. 25.27a). But if an electric field is present, the paths curve slightly because of the acceleration caused by electric-field forces. Figure 25.27b shows a few paths of an electron in an electric field directed from right to left. As we mentioned in Section 25.1, the average speed of random motion is of the order of 10^6 m/s, while the average drift speed is *much* slower, of the order of 10^{-4} m/s.

25.27 Random motions of an electron in a metallic crystal (a) with zero electric field and (b) with an electric field that causes drift. The curvatures of the paths are greatly exaggerated.

(a) Typical trajectory for an electron in a metallic crystal *without* an internal $\vec{E}$ field

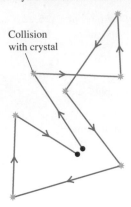

Collision with crystal

(a) Typical trajectory for an electron in a metallic crystal *with* an internal $\vec{E}$ field

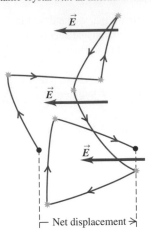

$\vec{E}$

$\vec{E}$

$\vec{E}$

|← Net displacement →|

25.28 The motion of a ball rolling down an inclined plane and bouncing off pegs in its path is analogous to the motion of an electron in a metallic conductor with an electric field present.

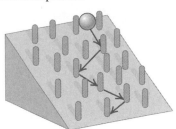

The average time between collisions is called the **mean free time,** denoted by τ. Figure 25.28 shows a mechanical analog of this electron motion.

We would like to derive from this model an expression for the resistivity ρ of a material, defined by Eq. (25.5):

$$\rho = \frac{E}{J} \tag{25.21}$$

where E and J are the magnitudes of electric field and current density. The current density $\vec{J}$ is in turn given by Eq. (25.4):

$$\vec{J} = nq\vec{v}_d \tag{25.22}$$

where n is the number of free electrons per unit volume, q is the charge of each, and $\vec{v}_d$ is their average drift velocity. (We also know that $q = -e$ in an ordinary metal; we'll use that fact later.)

We need to relate the drift velocity $\vec{v}_d$ to the electric field $\vec{E}$. The value of $\vec{v}_d$ is determined by a steady-state condition in which, on average, the velocity *gains* of the charges due to the force of the $\vec{E}$ field are just balanced by the velocity *losses* due to collisions.

To clarify this process, let's imagine turning on the two effects one at a time. Suppose that before time $t = 0$ there is no field. The electron motion is then completely random. A typical electron has velocity $\vec{v}_0$ at time $t = 0$, and the value of $\vec{v}_0$ averaged over many electrons (that is, the initial velocity of an average electron) is zero: $(\vec{v}_0)_{av} = \mathbf{0}$. Then at time $t = 0$ we turn on a constant electric field $\vec{E}$. The field exerts a force $\vec{F} = q\vec{E}$ on each charge, and this causes an acceleration $\vec{a}$ in the direction of the force, given by

$$\vec{a} = \frac{\vec{F}}{m} = \frac{q\vec{E}}{m}$$

where m is the electron mass. *Every* electron has this acceleration.

We wait for a time τ, the average time between collisions, and then "turn on" the collisions. An electron that has velocity $\vec{v}_0$ at time $t = 0$ has a velocity at time $t = \tau$ equal to

$$\vec{v} = \vec{v}_0 + \vec{a}\tau$$

The velocity $\vec{v}_{av}$ of an *average* electron at this time is the sum of the averages of the two terms on the right. As we have pointed out, the initial velocity $\vec{v}_0$ is zero for an average electron, so

$$\vec{v}_{av} = \vec{a}\tau = \frac{q\tau}{m}\vec{E} \qquad (25.23)$$

After time $t = \tau$, the tendency of the collisions to decrease the velocity of an average electron (by means of randomizing collisions) just balances the tendency of the $\vec{E}$ field to increase this velocity. Thus the velocity of an average electron, given by Eq. (25.23), is maintained over time and is equal to the drift velocity $\vec{v}_d$:

$$\vec{v}_d = \frac{q\tau}{m}\vec{E}$$

Now we substitute this equation for the drift velocity $\vec{v}_d$ into Eq. (25.22):

$$\vec{J} = nq\vec{v}_d = \frac{nq^2\tau}{m}\vec{E}$$

Comparing this with Eq. (25.21), which we can rewrite as $\vec{J} = \vec{E}/\rho$, and substituting $q = -e$, we see that the resistivity ρ is given by

$$\rho = \frac{m}{ne^2\tau} \qquad (25.24)$$

If n and τ are independent of $\vec{E}$, then the resistivity is independent of $\vec{E}$ and the conducting material obeys Ohm's law.

Turning the interactions on one at a time may seem artificial. But the derivation would come out the same if each electron had its own clock and the $t = 0$ times were different for different electrons. If τ is the average time between collisions, then $\vec{v}_d$ is still the average electron drift velocity, even though the motions of the various electrons aren't actually correlated in the way we postulated.

What about the temperature dependence of resistivity? In a perfect crystal with no atoms out of place, a correct quantum-mechanical analysis would let the free electrons move through the crystal with no collisions at all. But the atoms vibrate about their equilibrium positions. As the temperature increases, the amplitudes of these vibrations increase, collisions become more frequent, and the mean free time τ decreases. So this theory predicts that the resistivity of a metal increases with temperature. In a superconductor, roughly speaking, there are no inelastic collisions, τ is infinite, and the resistivity ρ is zero.

In a pure semiconductor such as silicon or germanium, the number of charge carriers per unit volume, n, is not constant but increases very rapidly with increasing temperature. This increase in n far outweighs the decrease in the mean free time, and in a semiconductor the resistivity always decreases rapidly with increasing temperature. At low temperatures, n is very small, and the resistivity becomes so large that the material can be considered an insulator.

Electrons gain energy between collisions through the work done on them by the electric field. During collisions they transfer some of this energy to the atoms of the material of the conductor. This leads to an increase in the material's internal energy and temperature; that's why wires carrying current get warm. If the electric field in the material is large enough, an electron can gain enough energy between collisions to knock off electrons that are normally bound to atoms in the material. These can then knock off more electrons, and so on, possibly leading to an avalanche of current. This is the microscopic basis of dielectric breakdown in insulators.

| Example 25.12 | **Mean free time in copper** |

Calculate the mean free time between collisions in copper at room temperature.

SOLUTION

IDENTIFY: This problem uses the ideas developed in this section.

SET UP: We can find an expression for mean free time τ in terms of n, ρ, e, and m by rearranging Eq. (25.24). From Example 25.1 and Table 25.1, for copper $n = 8.5 \times 10^{28} \text{ m}^{-3}$ and $\rho = 1.72 \times 10^{-8} \, \Omega \cdot \text{m}$. Also, $e = 1.60 \times 10^{-19} \text{ C}$ and $m = 9.11 \times 10^{-31} \text{ kg}$ for electrons.

EXECUTE: From Eq. (25.24), we get

$$\tau = \frac{m}{ne^2\rho}$$

$$= \frac{9.11 \times 10^{-31} \text{ kg}}{(8.5 \times 10^{28} \text{ m}^{-3})(1.60 \times 10^{-19} \text{ C})^2(1.72 \times 10^{-8} \, \Omega \cdot \text{m})}$$

$$= 2.4 \times 10^{-14} \text{ s}$$

EVALUATE: Taking the reciprocal of this time, we find that each electron averages about 4×10^{13} collisions every second!

Test Your Understanding of Section 25.6 Which of the following factors will, if increased, make it more difficult to produce a certain amount of current in a conductor? (There may be more than one correct answer.) (i) the mass of the moving charged particles in the conductor; (ii) the number of moving charged particles per cubic meter; (iii) the amount of charge on each moving particle; (iv) the average time between collisions for a typical moving charged particle.

Current and current density: Current is the amount of charge flowing through a specified area, per unit time. The SI unit of current is the ampere, equal to one coulomb per second ($1 \text{ A} = 1 \text{ C/s}$). The current I through an area A depends on the concentration n and charge q of the charge carriers, as well as on the magnitude of their drift velocity $\vec{v}_d$. The current density is current per unit cross-sectional area. Current is conventionally described in terms of a flow of positive charge, even when the actual charge carriers are negative or of both signs. (See Example 25.1.)

$$I = \frac{dQ}{dt} = n|q|v_d A \quad (25.2)$$

$$\vec{J} = nq\vec{v}_d \quad (25.4)$$

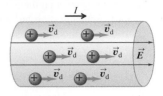

Resistivity: The resistivity ρ of a material is the ratio of the magnitudes of electric field and current density. Good conductors have small resistivity; good insulators have large resistivity. Ohm's law, obeyed approximately by many materials, states that ρ is a constant independent of the value of E. Resistivity usually increases with temperature; for small temperature changes this variation is represented approximately by Eq. (25.6), where α is the temperature coefficient of resistivity.

$$\rho = \frac{E}{J} \quad (25.5)$$

$$\rho(T) = \rho_0[1 + \alpha(T - T_0)] \quad (25.6)$$

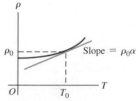

Metal: ρ increases with increasing T.

Resistors: For materials obeying Ohm's law, the potential difference V across a particular sample of material is proportional to the current I through the material. The ratio $V/I = R$ is the resistance of the sample. The SI unit of resistance is the ohm ($1 \ \Omega = 1 \text{ V/A}$). The resistance of a cylindrical conductor is related to its resistivity ρ, length L, and cross-sectional area A. (See Examples 25.2–25.4.)

$$V = IR \quad (25.11)$$

$$R = \frac{\rho L}{A} \quad (25.10)$$

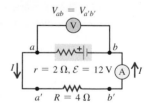

Circuits and emf: A complete circuit has a continuous current-carrying path. A complete circuit carrying a steady current must contain a source of electromotive force (emf) $\mathcal{E}$. The SI unit of electromotive force is the volt (1 V). An ideal source of emf maintains a constant potential difference, independent of current through the device, but every real source of emf has some internal resistance r. The terminal potential difference V_{ab} then depends on current. (See Examples 25.5–25.8.)

$$V_{ab} = \mathcal{E} - Ir \quad (25.15)$$
(source with internal resistance)

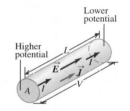

Energy and power in circuits: A circuit element with a potential difference $V_a - V_b = V_{ab}$ and a current I puts energy into a circuit if the current direction is from lower to higher potential in the device, and it takes energy out of the circuit if the current is opposite. The power P (rate of energy transfer) is equal to the product of the potential difference and the current. A resistor always takes electrical energy out of a circuit. (See Examples 25.9–25.11.)

$$P = V_{ab}I \quad (25.17)$$
(general circuit element)

$$P = V_{ab}I = I^2R = \frac{V_{ab}^2}{R} \quad (25.18)$$
(power into a resistor)

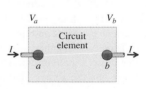

Conduction in metals: The microscopic basis of conduction in metals is the motion of electrons that move freely through the metallic crystal, bumping into ion cores in the crystal. In a crude classical model of this motion, the resistivity of the material can be related to the electron mass, charge, speed of random motion, density, and mean free time between collisions. (See Example 25.12.)

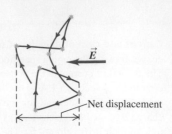

Net displacement

Key Terms

Answer to Chapter Opening Question **?**

The current out equals the current in. In other words, charge must enter the bulb at the same rate as it exits the bulb. It is not "used up" or consumed as it flows through the bulb.

Answers to Test Your Understanding Questions

25.1 Answer: (v) Doubling the diameter increases the cross-sectional area A by a factor of 4. Hence the current density magnitude $J = I/A$ is reduced to $\frac{1}{4}$ of the value in Example 25.1, and the magnitude of the drift velocity $v_d = J/n|q|$ is reduced by the same factor. The new magnitude is $v_d = (0.15 \text{ mm/s})/4 = 0.038 \text{ mm/s}$. This behavior is the same as that of an incompressible fluid, which slows down when it moves from a narrow pipe to a broader one (see Section 14.4).

25.2 Answer (ii) Figure 25.6b shows that the resistivity ρ of a semiconductor increases as the temperature decreases. From Eq. (25.5), the magnitude of the current density is $J = E/\rho$, so the current density decreases as the temperature drops and the resistivity increases.

25.3 Answer (iii) Solving Eq. (25.11) for the current shows that $I = V/R$. If the resistance R of the wire remained the same, doubling the voltage V would make the current I double as well. However, we saw in Example 25.3 that the resistance is *not* constant: As the current increases and the temperature increases, R increases as well. Thus doubling the voltage produces a current that is *less* than double the original current. An ohmic conductor is one for which $R = V/I$ has the same value no matter what the voltage, so the

wire is *nonohmic*. (In many practical problems the temperature change of the wire is so small that it can be ignored, so we can safely regard the wire as being ohmic. We do so in almost all examples in this book.)

25.4 Answer: (iii), (ii), (i) For circuit (i), we find the current from Eq. (25.16): $I = \mathcal{E}/(R + r) = (1.5 \text{ V})/(1.4 \,\Omega + 0.10 \,\Omega) = 1.0 \text{ A}$. For circuit (ii), we note that the terminal voltage $V_{ab} = 3.6 \text{ V}$ equals the voltage IR across the 1.8-Ω resistor: $V_{ab} = IR$, so $I = V_{ab}/R = (3.6 \text{ V})/(1.8 \,\Omega) = 2.0 \text{ A}$. For circuit (iii), we use Eq. (25.15) for the terminal voltage: $V_{ab} = \mathcal{E} - Ir$, so $I = (\mathcal{E} - V_{ab})/r = (12.0 \text{ V} - 11.0 \text{ V})/(0.20 \,\Omega) = 5.0 \text{ A}$.

25.5 Answer: (iii), (ii), (i) These are the same circuits that we analyzed in Test Your Understanding of Section 25.4. In each case the net power output of the battery is $P = V_{ab}I$, where V_{ab} is the battery terminal voltage. For circuit (i), we found that $I = 1.0 \text{ A}$, so $V_{ab} = \mathcal{E} - Ir = 1.5 \text{ V} - (1.0 \text{ A})(0.10 \,\Omega) = 1.4 \text{ V}$, so $P = (1.4 \text{ V})(1.0 \text{ A}) = 1.4 \text{ W}$. For circuit (ii), we have $V_{ab} = 3.6 \text{ V}$ and found that $I = 2.0 \text{ A}$, so $P = (3.6 \text{ V})(2.0 \text{ A}) = 7.2 \text{ W}$. For circuit (iii), we have $V_{ab} = 11.0 \text{ V}$ and found that $I = 5.0 \text{ A}$, so $P = (11.0 \text{ V})(5.0 \text{ A}) = 55 \text{ A}$.

25.6 Answer: (i) The difficulty of producing a certain amount of current increases as the resistivity ρ increases. From Eq. (25.24), $\rho = m/ne^2\tau$, so increasing the mass m will increase the resistivity. That's because a more massive charged particle will respond more sluggishly to an applied electric field and hence drift more slowly. To produce the same current, a greater electric field would be needed. (Increasing n, e, or τ; would decrease the resistivity and make it easier to produce a given current.)

PROBLEMS

For instructor-assigned homework, go to **www.masteringphysics.com**

Discussion Questions

Q25.1. The definition of resistivity $(\rho = E/J)$ implies that an electric field exists inside a conductor. Yet we saw in Chapter 21

that there can be no electric field inside a conductor. Is there a contradiction here? Explain.

Q25.2. A cylindrical rod has resistance R. If we triple its length and diameter, what is its resistance, in terms of R?

Q25.3. A cylindrical rod has resistivity ρ. If we triple its length and diameter, what is its resistivity, in terms of ρ?

Q25.4. Two copper wires with different diameters are joined end to end. If a current flows in the wire combination, what happens to electrons when they move from the larger-diameter wire into the smaller-diameter wire? Does their drift speed increase, decrease, or stay the same? If the drift speed changes, what is the force that causes the change? Explain your reasoning.

Q25.5. When is a 1.5-V AAA battery *not* actually a 1.5-V battery? That is, when do its terminals provide a potential difference of less than 1.5 V?

Q25.6. Can the potential difference between the terminals of a battery ever be opposite in direction to the emf? If it can, give an example. If it cannot, explain why not.

Q25.7. A rule of thumb used to determine the internal resistance of a source is that it is the open-circuit voltage divided by the short-circuit current. Is this correct? Why or why not?

Q25.8. Batteries are always labeled with their emf; for instance, an AA flashlight battery is labeled "1.5 volts." Would it also be appropriate to put a label on batteries stating how much current they provide? Why or why not?

Q25.9. We have seen that a coulomb is an enormous amount of charge; it is virtually impossible to place a charge of 1 C on an object. Yet, a current of 10 A, 10 C/s, is quite reasonable. Explain this apparent discrepancy.

Q25.10. Electrons in an electric circuit pass through a resistor. The wire on either side of the resistor has the same diameter. (a) How does the drift speed of the electrons before entering the resistor compare to the speed after leaving the resistor? Explain your reasoning. (b) How does the potential energy for an electron before entering the resistor compare to the potential energy after leaving the resistor? Explain your reasoning.

Q25.11. Current causes the temperature of a real resistor to increase. Why? What effect does this heating have on the resistance? Explain.

Q25.12. Which of the graphs in Fig. 25.29 best illustrates the current I in a real resistor as a function of the potential difference V across it? Explain. (*Hint:* See Discussion Question Q25.11.)

Figure 25.29 Question Q25.12.

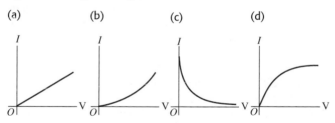

Q25.13. Why does an electric light bulb nearly always burn out just as you turn on the light, almost never while the light is shining?

Q25.14. A light bulb glows because it has resistance. The brightness of a light bulb increases with the electrical power dissipated in the bulb. (a) In the circuit shown in Fig. 25.30a, the two bulbs A

Figure 25.30 Question Q25.14.

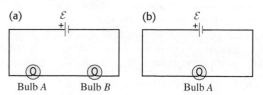

and B are identical. Compared to bulb A, does bulb B glow more brightly, just as brightly, or less brightly? Explain your reasoning. (b) Bulb B is removed from the circuit and the circuit is completed as shown in Fig. 25.30b. Compared to the brightness of bulb A in Fig. 25.30a, does bulb A now glow more brightly, just as brightly, or less brightly? Explain your reasoning.

Q25.15. (See Discussion Question Q25.14.) An ideal ammeter A is placed in a circuit with a battery and a light bulb as shown in Fig. 25.31a, and the ammeter reading is noted. The circuit is then reconnected as in Fig. 25.31b, so that the positions of the ammeter and light bulb are reversed. (a) How does the ammeter reading in the situation shown in Fig. 25.31a compare to the reading in the situation shown in Fig. 25.31b? Explain your reasoning. (b) In which situation does the light bulb glow more brightly? Explain your reasoning.

Figure 25.31 Question Q25.15.

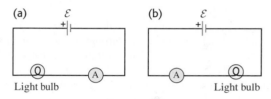

Q25.16. (See Discussion Question Q25.14.) Will a light bulb glow more brightly when it is connected to a battery as shown in Fig. 25.32a, in which an ideal ammeter A is placed in the circuit, or when it is connected as shown in Fig. 25.32b, in which an ideal voltmeter V is placed in the circuit? Explain your reasoning.

Figure 25.32 Question Q25.16.

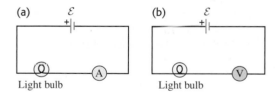

Q25.17. The energy that can be extracted from a storage battery is always less than the energy that goes into it while it is being charged. Why?

Q25.18. Eight flashlight batteries in series have an emf of about 12 V, similar to that of a car battery. Could they be used to start a car with a dead battery? Why or why not?

Q25.19. Small aircraft often have 24-V electrical systems rather than the 12-V systems in automobiles, even though the electrical power requirements are roughly the same in both applications. The explanation given by aircraft designers is that a 24-V system weighs less than a 12-V system because thinner wires can be used. Explain why this is so.

Q25.20. Long-distance, electric-power, transmission lines always operate at very high voltage, sometimes as much as 750 kV. What are the advantages of such high voltages? What are the disadvantages?

Q25.21. Ordinary household electric lines in North America usually operate at 120 V. Why is this a desirable voltage, rather than a value considerably larger or smaller? On the other hand, automobiles usually have 12-V electrical systems. Why is this a desirable voltage?

Q25.22. A fuse is a device designed to break a circuit, usually by melting when the current exceeds a certain value. What characteristics should the material of the fuse have?

Q25.23. High-voltage power supplies are sometimes designed intentionally to have rather large internal resistance as a safety precaution. Why is such a power supply with a large internal resistance safer than a supply with the same voltage but lower internal resistance?

Q25.24. The text states that good thermal conductors are also good electrical conductors. If so, why don't the cords used to connect toasters, irons, and similar heat-producing appliances get hot by conduction of heat from the heating element?

Exercises

Section 25.1 Current

25.1. A current of 3.6 A flows through an automobile headlight. How many coulombs of charge flow through the headlight in 3.0 h?

25.2. A silver wire 2.6 mm in diameter transfers a charge of 420 C in 80 min. Silver contains 5.8×10^{28} free electrons per cubic meter. (a) What is the current in the wire? (b) What is the magnitude of the drift velocity of the electrons in the wire?

25.3. A 5.00-A current runs through a 12-gauge copper wire (diameter 2.05 mm) and through a light bulb. Copper has 8.5×10^{28} free electrons per cubic meter. (a) How many electrons pass through the light bulb each second? (b) What is the current density in the wire? (c) At what speed does a typical electron pass by any given point in the wire? (d) If you were to use wire of twice the diameter, which of the above answers would change? Would they increase or decrease?

25.4. An 18-gauge wire (diameter 1.02 mm) carries a current with a current density of $1.50 \times 10^6 \text{ A/m}^2$. Calculate (a) the current in the wire and (b) the drift velocity of electrons in the wire.

25.5. Copper has 8.5×10^{28} free electrons per cubic meter. A 71.0-cm length of 12-gauge copper wire that is 2.05 mm in diameter carries 4.85 A of current. (a) How much time does it take for an electron to travel the length of the wire? (b) Repeat part (a) for 6-gauge copper wire (diameter 4.12 mm) of the same length that carries the same current. (c) Generally speaking, how does changing the diameter of a wire that carries a given amount of current affect the drift velocity of the electrons in the wire?

25.6. Consider the 18-gauge wire in Example 25.1. How many atoms are in 1.00 m^3 of copper? With the density of free electrons given in the example, how many free electrons are there per copper atom?

25.7. The current in a wire varies with time according to the relationship $I = 55 \text{ A} - (0.65 \text{ A/s}^2)t^2$. (a) How many coulombs of charge pass a cross section of the wire in the time interval between $t = 0$ and $t = 8.0$ s? (b) What constant current would transport the same charge in the same time interval?

25.8. Current passes through a solution of sodium chloride. In 1.00 s, 2.68×10^{16} Na^+ ions arrive at the negative electrode and 3.92×10^{16} Cl^- ions arrive at the positive electrode. (a) What is the current passing between the electrodes? (b) What is the direction of the current?

25.9. Assume that in silver metal there is one free electron per silver atom. Compute the free electron density for silver, and compare it to the value given in Exercise 25.2.

Section 25.2 Resistivity and Section 25.3 Resistance

25.10. (a) At room temperature what is the strength of the electric field in a 12-gauge copper wire (diameter 2.05 mm) that is needed to cause a 2.75-A current to flow? (b) What field would be needed if the wire were made of silver instead?

25.11. A 1.50-m cylindrical rod of diameter 0.500 cm is connected to a power supply that maintains a constant potential difference of 15.0 V across its ends, while an ammeter measures the current through it. You observe that at room temperature (20.0°C) the ammeter reads 18.5 A, while at 92.0°C it reads 17.2 A. You can ignore any thermal expansion of the rod. Find (a) the resistivity and (b) the temperature coefficient of resistivity at 20°C for the material of the rod.

25.12. A copper wire has a square cross section 2.3 mm on a side. The wire is 4.0 m long and carries a current of 3.6 A. The density of free electrons is $8.5 \times 10^{28}/\text{m}^3$. Find the magnitudes of (a) the current density in the wire and (b) the electric field in the wire. (c) How much time is required for an electron to travel the length of the wire?

25.13. In an experiment conducted at room temperature, a current of 0.820 A flows through a wire 3.26 mm in diameter. Find the magnitude of the electric field in the wire if the wire is made of (a) tungsten; and (b) aluminum.

25.14. A wire 6.50 m long with diameter of 2.05 mm has a resistance of 0.0290 Ω. What material is the wire most likely made of?

25.15. A cylindrical tungsten filament 15.0 cm long with a diameter of 1.00 mm is to be used in a machine for which the temperature will range from room temperature (20°C) up to 120°C. It will carry a current of 12.5 A at all temperatures (consult Tables 25.1 and 25.2). (a) What will be the maximum electric field in this filament, and (b) what will be its resistance with that field? (c) What will be the maximum potential drop over the full length of the filament?

25.16. What length of copper wire, 0.462 mm in diameter, has a resistance of 1.00 Ω?

25.17. In household wiring, copper wire 2.05 mm in diameter is often used. Find the resistance of a 24.0-m length of this wire.

25.18. What diameter must a copper wire have if its resistance is to be the same as that of an equal length of aluminum wire with diameter 3.26 mm?

25.19. You need to produce a set of cylindrical copper wires 3.50 m long that will have a resistance of 0.125 Ω each. What will be the mass of each of these wires?

25.20. A tightly coiled spring having 75 coils, each 3.50 cm in diameter, is made of insulated metal wire 3.25 mm in diameter. An ohmmeter connected across its opposite ends reads 1.74 Ω. What is the resistivity of the metal?

25.21. An aluminum cube has sides of length of 1.80 m. What is the resistance between two opposite faces of the cube?

25.22. A battery-powered light bulb has a tungsten filament. When the switch connecting the bulb to the battery is first turned on and the temperature of the bulb is 20°C, the current in the bulb is 0.860 A. After the bulb has been on for 30 s, the current is 0.220 A. What is then the temperature of the filament?

25.23. A rectangular solid of pure germanium measures 12 cm × 12 cm × 25 cm. Assuming that each of its faces is an equipotential surface, what is the resistance between opposite faces that are (a) farthest apart and (b) closest together?

25.24. You apply a potential difference of 4.50 V between the ends of a wire that is 2.50 m in length and 0.654 mm in radius. The resulting current through the wire is 17.6 A. What is the resistivity of the wire?

25.25. A current-carrying gold wire has diameter 0.84 mm. The electric field in the wire is 0.49 V/m. What are (a) the current carried by the wire; (b) the potential difference between two points in the wire 6.4 m apart; (c) the resistance of a 6.4-m length of this wire?

25.26. The potential difference between points in a wire 75.0 cm apart is 0.938 V when the current density is 4.40×10^7 A/m². What are (a) the magnitude of $\vec{E}$ in the wire and (b) the resistivity of the material of which the wire is made?

25.27. (a) What is the resistance of a Nichrome wire at 0.0°C if its resistance is 100.00 Ω at 11.5°C? (b) What is the resistance of a carbon rod at 25.8°C if its resistance is 0.0160 Ω at 0.0°C?

25.28. A carbon resistor is to be used as a thermometer. On a winter day when the temperature is 4.0°C, the resistance of the carbon resistor is 217.3 Ω. What is the temperature on a spring day when the resistance is 215.8 Ω? (Take the reference temperature T_0 to be 4.0°C.)

25.29. A strand of wire has resistance 5.60 μΩ. Find the net resistance of 120 such strands if they are (a) placed side by side to form a cable of the same length as a single strand, and (b) connected end to end to form a wire 120 times as long as a single strand.

25.30. A hollow aluminum cylinder is 2.50 m long and has an inner radius of 3.20 cm and an outer radius of 4.60 cm. Treat each surface (inner, outer, and the two end faces) as an equipotential surface. At room temperature, what will an ohmmeter read if it is connected between (a) the opposite faces and (b) the inner and outer surfaces?

Section 25.4 Electromotive Force and Circuits

25.31. A copper transmission cable 100 km long and 10.0 cm in diameter carries a current of 125 A. (a) What is the potential drop across the cable? (b) How much electrical energy is dissipated as thermal energy every hour?

25.32. Consider the circuit shown in Fig. 25.33. The terminal voltage of the 24.0-V battery is 21.2 V. What are (a) the internal resistance r of the battery and (b) the resistance R of the circuit resistor?

Figure 25.33 Exercise 25.32.

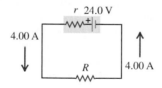

25.33. An idealized voltmeter is connected across the terminals of a battery while the current is varied. Figure 25.34 shows a graph of the voltmeter reading V as a function of the current I through the battery. Find (a) the emf $\mathcal{E}$ and (b) the internal resistance of the battery.

Figure 25.34 Exercise 25.33.

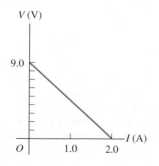

25.34. An idealized ammeter is connected to a battery as shown in Fig. 25.35. Find (a) the reading of the ammeter, (b) the current through the 4.00-Ω resistor, (c) the terminal voltage of the battery.

Figure 25.35 Exercise 25.34.

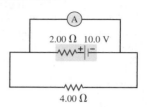

25.35. An ideal voltmeter V is connected to a 2.0-Ω resistor and a battery with emf 5.0 V and internal resistance 0.5 Ω as shown in Fig. 25.36. (a) What is the current in the 2.0-Ω resistor? (b) What is the terminal voltage of the battery? (c) What is the reading on the voltmeter? Explain your answers.

Figure 25.36 Exercise 25.35.

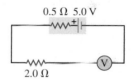

25.36. The circuit shown in Fig. 25.37 contains two batteries, each with an emf and an internal resistance, and two resistors. Find (a) the current in the circuit (magnitude *and* direction); (b) the terminal voltage V_{ab} of the 16.0-V battery; (c) the potential difference V_{ac} of point *a* with respect to point *c*. (d) Using Fig. 25.21 as a model, graph the potential rises and drops in this circuit.

Figure 25.37 Exercises 25.36, 25.38, 25.39, and 25.48.

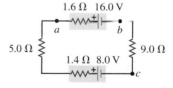

25.37. When switch S in Fig. 25.38 is open, the voltmeter V of the battery reads 3.08 V. When the switch is closed, the voltmeter reading drops to 2.97 V, and the ammeter A reads 1.65 A. Find the emf, the internal resistance of the battery, and the circuit resistance R. Assume that the two meters are ideal, so they don't affect the circuit.

Figure 25.38 Exercise 25.37.

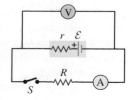

25.38. In the circuit of Fig. 25.37, the 5.0-Ω resistor is removed and replaced by a resistor of unknown resistance R. When this is done, an ideal voltmeter connected across the points b and c reads 1.9 V. Find (a) the current in the circuit and (b) the resistance R. (c) Graph the potential rises and drops in this circuit (see Fig. 25.21).

25.39. In the circuit shown in Fig. 25.37, the 16.0-V battery is removed and reinserted with the opposite polarity, so that its negative terminal is now next to point a. Find (a) the current in the circuit (magnitude *and* direction); (b) the terminal voltage V_{ba} of the 16.0-V battery; (c) the potential difference V_{ac} of point a with respect to point c. (d) Graph the potential rises and drops in this circuit (see Fig. 25.21).

25.40. The following measurements were made on a Thyrite resistor:

$I(A)$	0.50	1.00	2.00	4.00
$V_{ab}(V)$	2.55	3.11	3.77	4.58

(a) Graph V_{ab} as a function of I. (b) Does Thyrite obey Ohm's law? How can you tell? (c) Graph the resistance $R = V_{ab}/I$ as a function of I.

25.41. The following measurements of current and potential difference were made on a resistor constructed of Nichrome wire:

$I(A)$	0.50	1.00	2.00	4.00
$V_{ab}(V)$	1.94	3.88	7.76	15.52

(a) Graph V_{ab} as a function of I. (b) Does Nichrome obey Ohm's law? How can you tell? (c) What is the resistance of the resistor in ohms?

Section 25.5 Energy and Power in Electric Circuits

25.42. A resistor with a 15.0-V potential difference across its ends develops thermal energy at a rate of 327 W. (a) What is its resistance? (b) What is the current in the resistor?

25.43. Light Bulbs. The power rating of a light bulb (such as a 100-W bulb) is the power it dissipates when connected across a 120-V potential difference. What is the resistance of (a) a 100-W bulb and (b) a 60-W bulb? (c) How much current does each bulb draw in normal use?

25.44. If a "75-W" bulb (see Problem 25.43) is connected across a 220-V potential difference (as is used in Europe), how much power does it dissipate?

25.45. European Light Bulb. In Europe the standard voltage in homes is 220 V instead of the 120 V used in the United States. Therefore a "100-W" European bulb would be intended for use with a 220-V potential difference (see Problem 25.44). (a) If you bring a "100-W" European bulb home to the United States, what should be its U.S. power rating? (b) How much current will the 100-W European bulb draw in normal use in the United States?

25.46. A battery-powered global positioning system (GPS) receiver operating on 9.0 V draws a current of 0.13 A. How much electrical energy does it consume during 1.5 h?

25.47. Consider a resistor with length L, uniform cross-sectional area A, and uniform resistivity ρ that is carrying a current with uniform current density J. Use Eq. (25.18) to find the electrical power dissipated per unit volume, p. Express your result in terms of (a) E and J; (b) J and ρ; (c) E and ρ.

25.48. Consider the circuit of Fig. 25.37. (a) What is the total rate at which electrical energy is dissipated in the 5.00-Ω and 9.00-Ω resistors? (b) What is the power output of the 16.0-V battery? (c) At what rate is electrical energy being converted to other forms in the 8.0-V battery? (d) Show that the power output of the 16.0-V

battery equals the overall rate of dissipation of electrical energy in the rest of the circuit.

25.49. The capacity of a storage battery, such as those used in automobile electrical systems, is rated in ampere-hours $(A \cdot h)$. A 50-$A \cdot h$ battery can supply a current of 50 A for 1.0 h, or 25 A for 2.0 h, and so on. (a) What total energy can be supplied by a 12-V, 60-$A \cdot h$ battery if its internal resistance is negligible? (b) What volume (in liters) of gasoline has a total heat of combustion equal to the energy obtained in part (a)? (See Section 17.6; the density of gasoline is 900 kg/m^3.) (c) If a generator with an average electrical power output of 0.45 kW is connected to the battery, how much time will be required for it to charge the battery fully?

25.50. In the circuit analyzed in Example 25.9 the 4.0-Ω resistor is replaced by a 8.0-Ω resistor, as in Example 25.10. (a) Calculate the rate of conversion of chemical energy to electrical energy in the battery. How does your answer compare to the result calculated in Example 25.9? (b) Calculate the rate of electrical energy dissipation in the internal resistance of the battery. How does your answer compare to the result calculated in Example 25.9? (c) Use the results of parts (a) and (b) to calculate the net power output of the battery. How does your result compare to the electrical power dissipated in the 8.0-Ω resistor as calculated for this circuit in Example 25.10?

25.51. A 25.0-Ω bulb is connected across the terminals of a 12.0-V battery having 3.50 Ω of internal resistance. What percentage of the power of the battery is dissipated across the internal resistance and hence is not available to the bulb?

25.52. An idealized voltmeter is connected across the terminals of a 15.0-V battery, and a 75.0-Ω appliance is also connected across its terminals. If the voltmeter reads 11.3 V: (a) how much power is being dissipated by the appliance, and (b) what is the internal resistance of the battery?

25.53. In the circuit in Fig. 25.39, find (a) the rate of conversion of internal (chemical) energy to electrical energy within the battery; (b) the rate of dissipation of electrical energy in the battery; (c) the rate of dissipation of electrical energy in the external resistor.

Figure 25.39 Exercise 25.53.

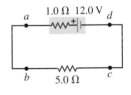

25.54. A typical small flashlight contains two batteries, each having an emf of 1.5 V, connected in series with a bulb having resistance 17 Ω. (a) If the internal resistance of the batteries is negligible, what power is delivered to the bulb? (b) If the batteries last for 5.0 h, what is the total energy delivered to the bulb? (c) The resistance of real batteries increases as they run down. If the initial internal resistance is negligible, what is the combined internal resistance of both batteries when the power to the bulb has decreased to half its initial value? (Assume that the resistance of the bulb is constant. Actually, it will change somewhat when the current through the filament changes, because this changes the temperature of the filament and hence the resistivity of the filament wire.)

25.55. A "540-W" electric heater is designed to operate from 120-V lines. (a) What is its resistance? (b) What current does it draw? (c) If the line voltage drops to 110 V, what power does the heater take? (Assume that the resistance is constant. Actually, it will change because of the change in temperature.) (d) The heater coils are metallic, so that the resistance of the heater decreases with decreasing temperature. If the change of resistance with temperature is taken into account, will the electrical power consumed by the heater be larger or smaller than what you calculated in part (c)? Explain.

*Section 25.6 Theory of Metallic Conduction

*25.56. Pure silicon contains approximately 1.0×10^{16} free electrons per cubic meter. (a) Referring to Table 25.1, calculate the mean free time τ for silicon at room temperature. (b) Your answer in part (a) is much greater than the mean free time for copper given in Example 25.12. Why, then, does pure silicon have such a high resistivity compared to copper?

Problems

25.57. An electrical conductor designed to carry large currents has a circular cross section 2.50 mm in diameter and is 14.0 m long. The resistance between its ends is 0.104 Ω. (a) What is the resistivity of the material? (b) If the electric-field magnitude in the conductor is 1.28 V/m, what is the total current? (c) If the material has 8.5×10^{28} free electrons per cubic meter, find the average drift speed under the conditions of part (b).

25.58. A plastic tube 25.0 m long and 4.00 cm in diameter is dipped into a silver solution, depositing a layer of silver 0.100 mm thick uniformly over the outer surface of the tube. If this coated tube is then connected across a 12.0-V battery, what will be the current?

25.59. On your first day at work as an electrical technician, you are asked to determine the resistance per meter of a long piece of wire. The company you work for is poorly equipped. You find a battery, a voltmeter, and an ammeter, but no meter for directly measuring resistance (an ohmmeter). You put the leads from the voltmeter across the terminals of the battery, and the meter reads 12.6 V. You cut off a 20.0-m length of wire and connect it to the battery, with an ammeter in series with it to measure the current in the wire. The ammeter reads 7.00 A. You then cut off a 40.0-m length of wire and connect it to the battery, again with the ammeter in series to measure the current. The ammeter reads 4.20 A. Even though the equipment you have available to you is limited, your boss assures you of its high quality: The ammeter has very small resistance, and the voltmeter has very large resistance. What is the resistance of 1 meter of wire?

25.60. A 2.0-mm length of wire is made by welding the end of a 120-cm-long silver wire to the end of an 80-cm-long copper wire. Each piece of wire is 0.60 mm in diameter. The wire is at room temperature, so the resistivities are as given in Table 25.1. A potential difference of 5.0 V is maintained between the ends of the 2.0-m composite wire. (a) What is the current in the copper section? (b) What is the current in the silver section? (c) What is the magnitude of $\vec{E}$ in the copper? (d) What is the magnitude of $\vec{E}$ in the silver? (e) What is the potential difference between the ends of the silver section of wire?

25.61. A 3.00-m length of copper wire at 20°C has a 1.20-m-long section with diameter 1.60 mm and a 1.80-m-long section with diameter 0.80 mm. There is a current of 2.5 mA in the 1.60-mm-diameter section. (a) What is the current in the 0.80-mm-diameter section? (b) What is the magnitude of $\vec{E}$ in the 1.60-mm-diameter section? (c) What is the magnitude of $\vec{E}$ in the 0.80-mm-diameter section? (d) What is the potential difference between the ends of the 3.00-m length of wire?

25.62. **Critical Current Density in Superconductors.** One problem with some of the newer high-temperature superconductors is getting a large enough current density for practical use without causing the resistance to reappear. The maximum current density for which the material will remain a superconductor is called the critical current density of the material. In 1987, IBM research labs had produced thin films with critical current densities of 1.0×10^{5} A/cm². (a) How much current could an 18-gauge wire (see Example 25.1 in Section 25.1) of this material carry and still remain superconducting? (b) Researchers are trying to develop superconductors with critical current densities of 1.0×10^{6} A/cm². What diameter cylindrical wire of such a material would be needed to carry 1000 A without losing its superconductivity?

25.63. A material of resistivity ρ is formed into a solid, truncated cone of height h and radii r_1 and r_2 at either end (Fig. 25.40). (a) Calculate the resistance of the cone between the two flat end faces. (Hint: Imagine slicing the cone into very many thin disks, and calculate the resistance of one such disk.) (b) Show that your result agrees with Eq. (25.10) when $r_1 = r_2$.

Figure 25.40
Problem 25.63.

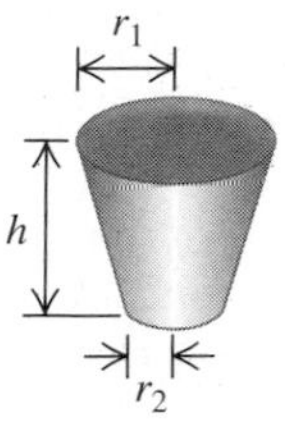

25.64. The region between two concentric conducting spheres with radii a and b is filled with a conducting material with resistivity ρ. (a) Show that the resistance between the spheres is given by

$$R = \frac{\rho}{4\pi}\left(\frac{1}{a} - \frac{1}{b}\right)$$

(b) Derive an expression for the current density as a function of radius, in terms of the potential difference V_{ab} between the spheres. (c) Show that the result in part (a) reduces to Eq. (25.10) when the separation $L = b - a$ between the spheres is small.

25.65. **Leakage in a Dielectric.** Two parallel plates of a capacitor have equal and opposite charges Q. The dielectric has a dielectric constant K and a resistivity ρ. Show that the "leakage" current I carried by the dielectric is given by $I = Q/K\epsilon_0\rho$.

25.66. In the circuit shown in Fig. 25.41, R is a variable resistor whose value can range from 0 to ∞, and a and b are the terminals of a battery having an emf $\mathcal{E} = 15.0$ V and an internal resistance of 4.00 Ω. The ammeter and voltmeter are both idealized meters. As R varies over its full range of values, what will be the largest and smallest readings of (a) the voltmeter and (b) the ammeter? (c) Sketch qualitative graphs of the readings of both meters as functions of R, as R ranges from 0 to ∞.

Figure 25.41 Problem 25.66.

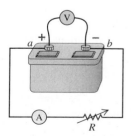

25.67. The temperature coefficient of resistance α in Eq. (25.12) equals the temperature coefficient of resistivity α in Eq. (25.6) only if the coefficient of thermal expansion is small. A cylindrical column of mercury is in a vertical glass tube. At 20°C, the length of the mercury column is 12.0 cm. The diameter of the mercury column is 1.6 mm and doesn't change with temperature because glass has a small coefficient of thermal expansion. The coefficient of volume expansion of the mercury is given in Table 17.2, its resistivity at 20°C is given in Table 25.1, and its temperature coefficient of resistivity is given in Table 25.2. (a) At 20°C, what is the resistance between the ends of the mercury column? (b) The mercury column is heated to 60°C. What is the change in its resistivity? (c) What is the change in its length? Explain why the coefficient of volume expansion, rather than the coefficient of linear expansion, determines the change in length. (d) What is the change in its resistance? (*Hint:* Since the percentage changes in ρ and L are small, you may find it helpful to derive from Eq. (25.10) an equation for ΔR in terms of $\Delta\rho$ and ΔL) (e) What is the temperature coefficient of resistance α for the mercury column, as defined in Eq. (25.12)? How does this value compare with the temperature coefficient of resistivity? Is the effect of the change in length important?

25.68. (a) What is the potential difference V_{ad} in the circuit of Fig. 25.42? (b) What is the terminal voltage of the 4.00-V battery? (c) A battery with emf 10.30z V and internal resistance 0.50 Ω is inserted in the circuit at d, with its negative terminal connected to the negative terminal of the 8.00-V battery. What is the difference of potential V_{bc} between the terminals of the 4.00-V battery now?

Figure **25.42** Problem 25.68.

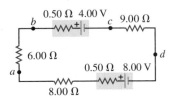

25.69. The potential difference across the terminals of a battery is 8.4 V when there is a current of 1.50 A in the battery from the negative to the positive terminal. When the current is 3.50 A in the reverse direction, the potential difference becomes 9.4 V. (a) What is the internal resistance of the battery? (b) What is the emf of the battery?

25.70. A person with body resistance between his hands of 10 kΩ accidentally grasps the terminals of a 14-kV power supply. (a) If the internal resistance of the power supply is 2000 Ω, what is the current through the person's body? (b) What is the power dissipated in his body? (c) If the power supply is to be made safe by increasing its internal resistance, what should the internal resistance be for the maximum current in the above situation to be 1.00 mA or less?

25.71. The average bulk resistivity of the human body (apart from surface resistance of the skin) is about 5.0 $\Omega \cdot$ m. The conducting path between the hands can be represented approximately as a cylinder 1.6 m long and 0.10 m in diameter. The skin resistance can be made negligible by soaking the hands in salt water. (a) What is the resistance between the hands if the skin resistance is negligible? (b) What potential difference between the hands is needed for a lethal shock current of 100 mA? (Note that your result shows that small potential differences produce dangerous currents when the skin is damp.) (c) With the current in part (b), what power is dissipated in the body?

25.72. A typical cost for electric power is 12.0¢ per kilowatt-hour. (a) Some people leave their porch light on all the time. What is the yearly cost to keep a 75-W bulb burning day and night? (b) Sup-

pose your refrigerator uses 400 W of power when it's running, and it runs 8 hours a day. What is the yearly cost of operating your refrigerator?

25.73. A 12.6-V car battery with negligible internal resistance is connected to a series combination of a 3.2-Ω resistor that obeys Ohm's law and a thermistor that does not obey Ohm's law but instead has a current–voltage relationship $V = \alpha I + \beta I^2$, with $\alpha = 3.8\ \Omega$ and $\beta = 1.3\ \Omega/$A. What is the current through the 3.2-Ω resistor?

25.74. A cylindrical copper cable 1.50 km long is connected across a 220.0-V potential difference. (a) What should be its diameter so that it produces heat at a rate of 50.0 W? (b) What is the electric field inside the cable under these conditions?

25.75. A Nonideal Ammeter. Unlike the idealized ammeter described in Section 25.4, any real ammeter has a nonzero resistance. (a) An ammeter with resistance R_A is connected in series with a resistor R and a battery of emf $\mathcal{E}$ and internal resistance r. The current measured by the ammeter is I_A. Find the current through the circuit if the ammeter is removed so that the battery and the resistor form a complete circuit. Express your answer in terms of I_A, r, R_A, and R. The more "ideal" the ammeter, the smaller the difference between this current and the current I_A. (b) If $R = 3.80\ \Omega$, $\mathcal{E} = 7.50$ V, and $r = 0.45\ \Omega$, find the maximum value of the ammeter resistance R_A so that I_A is within 1.0% of the current in the circuit when the ammeter is absent. (c) Explain why your answer in part (b) represents a *maximum* value.

25.76. A 1.50-m cylinder of radius 1.10 cm is made of a complicated mixture of materials. Its resistivity depends on the distance x from the left end and obeys the formula $\rho(x) = a + bx^2$, where a and b are constants. At the left end, the resistivity is $2.25 \times 10^{-8}\ \Omega \cdot$ m, while at the right end it is $8.50 \times 10^{-8}\ \Omega \cdot$ m. (a) What is the resistance of this rod? (b) What is the electric field at its midpoint if it carries a 1.75-A current? (c) If we cut the rod into two 75.0-cm halves, what is the resistance of each half?

25.77. According to the U.S. National Electrical Code, copper wire used for interior wiring of houses, hotels, office buildings, and industrial plants is permitted to carry no more than a specified maximum amount of current. The table below shows the maximum current I_{max} for several common sizes of wire with varnished cambric insulation. The "wire gauge" is a standard used to describe the diameter of wires. Note that the larger the diameter of the wire, the *smaller* the wire gauge.

Wire gauge	Diameter (cm)	I_{max} (A)
14	0.163	18
12	0.205	25
10	0.259	30
8	0.326	40
6	0.412	60
5	0.462	65
4	0.519	85

(a) What considerations determine the maximum current-carrying capacity of household wiring? (b) A total of 4200 W of power is to be supplied through the wires of a house to the household electrical appliances. If the potential difference across the group of appliances is 120 V, determine the gauge of the thinnest permissible wire that can be used. (c) Suppose the wire used in this house is of the gauge found in part (b) and has total length 42.0 m. At what rate is energy dissipated in the wires? (d) The house is built in a community where the consumer cost of electric energy is $0.11 per kilowatt-hour. If the house were built with wire of the next larger diameter than that found in part (b), what would be the savings in electricity costs in one year? Assume that the appliances are kept on for an average of 12 hours a day.

25.78. A toaster using a Nichrome heating element operates on 120 V. When it is switched on at 20°C, the heating element carries an initial current of 1.35 A. A few seconds later the current reaches the steady value of 1.23 A. (a) What is the final temperature of the element? The average value of the temperature coefficient of resistivity for Nichrome over the temperature range is $4.5 \times 10^{-4}\ (\text{C}°)^{-1}$. (b) What is the power dissipated in the heating element initially and when the current reaches a steady value?

25.79. In the circuit of Fig. 25.43, find (a) the current through the 8.0-Ω resistor and (b) the total rate of dissipation of electrical energy in the 8.0-Ω resistor and in the internal resistance of the batteries. (c) In one of the batteries, chemical energy is being converted into electrical energy. In which one is this happening, and at what rate? (d) In one of the batteries, electrical energy is being converted into chemical energy. In which one is this happening, and at what rate? (e) Show that the overall rate of production of electrical energy equals the overall rate of consumption of electrical energy in the circuit.

Figure 25.43 Problem 25.79.

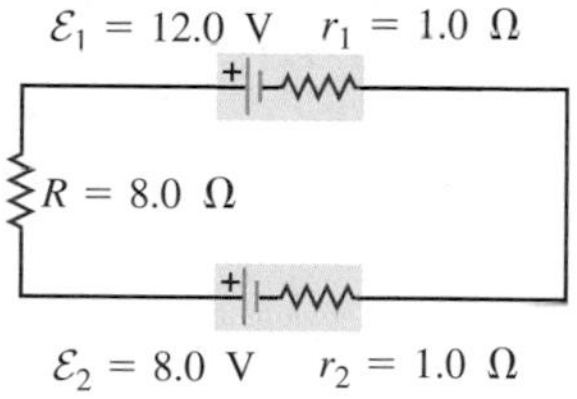

$$\mathcal{E}_1 = 12.0\ \text{V} \quad r_1 = 1.0\ \Omega$$

$$R = 8.0\ \Omega$$

$$\mathcal{E}_2 = 8.0\ \text{V} \quad r_2 = 1.0\ \Omega$$

25.80. A lightning bolt strikes one end of a steel lightning rod, producing a 15,000-A current burst that lasts for 65 μs. The rod is 2.0 m long and 1.8 cm in diameter, and its other end is connected to the ground by 35 m of 8.0-mm-diameter copper wire. (a) Find the potential difference between the top of the steel rod and the lower end of the copper wire during the current burst. (b) Find the total energy deposited in the rod and wire by the current burst.

25.81. A 12.0-V battery has an internal resistance of 0.24 Ω and a capacity of 50.0 A · h (see Exercise 25.49). The battery is charged by passing a 10-A current through it for 5.0 h. (a) What is the terminal voltage during charging? (b) What total electrical energy is supplied to the battery during charging? (c) What electrical energy is dissipated in the internal resistance during charging? (d) The battery is now completely discharged through a resistor, again with a constant current of 10 A. What is the external circuit resistance? (e) What total electrical energy is supplied to the external resistor? (f) What total electrical energy is dissipated in the internal resistance? (g) Why are the answers to parts (b) and (e) not the same?

25.82. Repeat Problem 25.81 with charge and discharge currents of 30 A. The charging and discharging times will now be 1.7 h rather than 5.0 h. What differences in performance do you see?

Challenge Problems

25.83. The *Tolman-Stewart experiment* in 1916 demonstrated that the free charges in a metal have negative charge and provided a quantitative measurement of their charge-to-mass ratio, $|q|/m$. The experiment consisted of abruptly stopping a rapidly rotating spool of wire and measuring the potential difference that this produced between the ends of the wire. In a simplified model of this experiment, consider a metal rod of length L that is given a uniform acceleration $\vec{a}$ to the right. Initially the free charges in the metal lag behind the rod's motion, thus setting up an electric field $\vec{E}$ in the rod. In the steady state this field exerts a force on the free charges that makes them accelerate along with the rod. (a) Apply $\Sigma\vec{F} = m\vec{a}$ to the free charges to obtain an expression for $|q|/m$ in terms of the magnitudes of the induced electric field $\vec{E}$ and the acceleration $\vec{a}$. (b) If all the free charges in the metal rod have the same acceleration, the electric field $\vec{E}$ is the same at all points in the rod. Use this fact to rewrite the expression for $|q|/m$ in terms of the potential V_{bc} between the ends of the rod (Fig. 25.44). (c) If the free charges have negative charge, which end of the rod, b or c, is at higher potential? (d) If the rod is 0.50 m long and the free charges are electrons (charge $q = -1.60 \times 10^{-19}$ C, mass 9.11×10^{-31} kg), what magnitude of acceleration is required to produce a potential difference of 1.0 mV between the ends of the rod? (e) Discuss why the actual experiment used a rotating spool of thin wire rather than a moving bar as in our simplified analysis.

Figure 25.44 Challenge Problem 25.83.

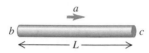

25.84. The current–voltage relationship of a semiconductor diode is given by

$$I = I_S\left[\exp\left(\frac{eV}{kT}\right) - 1\right]$$

where I and V are the current through and the voltage across the diode, respectively. I_S is a constant characteristic of the device, e is the magnitude of the electron charge, k is the Boltzmann constant, and T is the Kelvin temperature. Such a diode is connected in series with a resistor with $R = 1.00\ \Omega$ and a battery with $\mathcal{E} = 2.00$ V. The polarity of the battery is such that the current through the diode is in the forward direction (Fig. 25.45). The battery has negligible internal resistance. (a) Obtain an equation for V. Note that you cannot solve for V algebraically. (b) The value of V must be obtained by using a numerical method. One approach is to try a value of V, see how the left- and right-hand sides of the equation compare for this V, and use this to refine your guess for V. Using $I_S = 1.50$ mA and $T = 293$ K, obtain a solution (accurate to three significant figures) for the voltage drop V across the diode and the current I through it.

Figure 25.45 Challenge Problem 25.84.

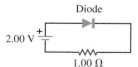

2.00 V

Diode

1.00 Ω

25.85. The resistivity of a semiconductor can be modified by adding different amounts of impurities. A rod of semiconducting material of length L and cross-sectional area A lies along the x-axis between $x = 0$ and $x = L$. The material obeys Ohm's law, and its resistivity varies along the rod according to $\rho(x) = \rho_0 \exp(-x/L)$. The end of the rod at $x = 0$ is at a potential V_0 greater than the end at $x = L$. (a) Find the total resistance of the rod and the current in the rod. (b) Find the electric-field magnitude

$E(x)$ in the rod as a function of x. (c) Find the electric potential $V(x)$ in the rod as a function of x. (d) Graph the functions $\rho(x)$, $E(x)$, and $V(x)$ for values of x between $x = 0$ and $x = L$.

25.86. A source with emf $\mathcal{E}$ and internal resistance r is connected to an external circuit. (a) Show that the power output of the source is maximum when the current in the circuit is one-half the short-circuit current of the source. (b) If the external circuit consists of a resistance R, show that the power output is maximum when $R = r$ and that the maximum power is $\mathcal{E}^2/4r$.

25.87. The temperature coefficient of resistivity α is given by

$$\alpha = \frac{1}{\rho} \frac{d\rho}{dT}$$

where ρ is the resistivity at the temperature T. Equation (25.6) then follows if α is assumed constant and much smaller than $(T - T_0)^{-1}$. (a) If α is not constant but is given by $\alpha = -n/T$, where T is the Kelvin temperature and n is a constant, show that the resistivity is given by $\rho = a/T^n$, where a is a constant. (b) From Fig. 25.10, you can see that such a relationship might be used as a rough approximation for a semiconductor. Using the values of ρ and α for carbon from Tables 25.1 and 25.2, determine a and n. (In Table 25.1, assume that "room temperature" means 293 K). (c) Using your result from part (b), determine the resistivity of carbon at $-196°C$ and $300°C$. (Remember to express T in kelvins.)

DIRECT-CURRENT CIRCUITS

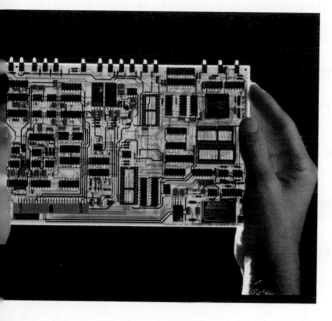

? In a complex circuit like the one on this circuit board, is it possible to connect several resistors with different resistances so that they all have the same potential difference? If so, will the current be the same through all of the resistors?

LEARNING GOALS

By studying this chapter, you will learn:

- How to analyze circuits with multiple resistors in series or parallel.

- Rules that you can apply to any circuit with more than one loop.

- How to use an ammeter, voltmeter, ohmmeter, or potentiometer in a circuit.

- How to analyze circuits that include both a resistor and a capacitor.

- How electric power is distributed in the home.

I f you look inside your TV, your computer, or your stereo receiver or under the hood of a car, you will find circuits of much greater complexity than the simple circuits we studied in Chapter 25. Whether connected by wires or integrated in a semiconductor chip, these circuits often include several sources, resistors, and other circuit elements, such as capacitors, transformers, and motors, interconnected in a *network*.

In this chapter we study general methods for analyzing such networks, including how to find unknown voltages, currents, and properties of circuit elements. We'll learn how to determine the equivalent resistance for several resistors connected in series or in parallel. For more general networks we need two rules called *Kirchhoff's rules*. One is based on the principle of conservation of charge applied to a junction; the other is derived from energy conservation for a charge moving around a closed loop. We'll discuss instruments for measuring various electrical quantities. We also look at a circuit containing resistance and capacitance, in which the current varies with time.

Our principal concern in this chapter is with **direct-current** (dc) circuits, in which the direction of the current does not change with time. Flashlights and automobile wiring systems are examples of direct-current circuits. Household electrical power is supplied in the form of **alternating current** (ac), in which the current oscillates back and forth. The same principles for analyzing networks apply to both kinds of circuits, and we conclude this chapter with a look at household wiring systems. We'll discuss alternating-current circuits in detail in Chapter 31.

26.1 Resistors in Series and Parallel

Resistors turn up in all kinds of circuits, ranging from hair dryers and space heaters to circuits that limit or divide current or reduce or divide a voltage. Such circuits often contain several resistors, so it's appropriate to consider *combinations* of resistors. A simple example is a string of light bulbs used for holiday decorations;

12.1 DC Series Circuits (Qualitative)

26.1 Four different ways of connecting three resistors.

(a) R_1, R_2, and R_3 in series

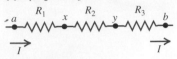

(b) R_1, R_2, and R_3 in parallel

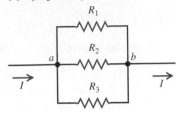

(c) R_1 in series with parallel combination of R_2 and R_3

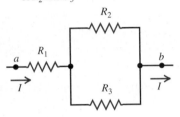

(d) R_1 in parallel with series combination of R_2 and R_3

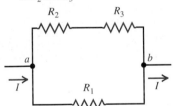

each bulb acts as a resistor, and from a circuit-analysis perspective the string of bulbs is simply a combination of resistors.

Suppose we have three resistors with resistances R_1, R_2, and R_3. Figure 26.1 shows four different ways in which they might be connected between points a and b. When several circuit elements such as resistors, batteries, and motors are connected in sequence as in Fig. 26.1a, with only a single current path between the points, we say that they are connected in **series.** We studied *capacitors* in series in Section 24.2; we found that, because of conservation of charge, capacitors in series all have the same charge if they are initially uncharged. In circuits we're often more interested in the *current,* which is charge flow per unit time.

The resistors in Fig. 26.1b are said to be connected in **parallel** between points a and b. Each resistor provides an alternative path between the points. For circuit elements that are connected in parallel, the *potential difference* is the same across each element. We studied capacitors in parallel in Section 24.2.

In Fig. 26.1c, resistors R_2 and R_3 are in parallel, and this combination is in series with R_1. In Fig. 26.1d, R_2 and R_3 are in series, and this combination is in parallel with R_1.

For any combination of resistors we can always find a *single* resistor that could replace the combination and result in the same total current and potential difference. For example, a string of holiday light bulbs could be replaced by a single, appropriately chosen light bulb that would draw the same current and have the same potential difference between its terminals as the original string of bulbs. The resistance of this single resistor is called the **equivalent resistance** of the combination. If any one of the networks in Fig. 26.1 were replaced by its equivalent resistance R_{eq}, we could write

$$V_{ab} = IR_{eq} \quad \text{or} \quad R_{eq} = \frac{V_{ab}}{I}$$

where V_{ab} is the potential difference between terminals a and b of the network and I is the current at point a or b. To compute an equivalent resistance, we assume a potential difference V_{ab} across the actual network, compute the corresponding current I, and take the ratio V_{ab}/I.

Resistors in Series

We can derive general equations for the equivalent resistance of a series or parallel combination of resistors. If the resistors are in *series,* as in Fig. 26.1a, the current I must be the same in all of them. (As we discussed in Section 25.4, current is *not* "used up" as it passes through a circuit.) Applying $V = IR$ to each resistor, we have

$$V_{ax} = IR_1 \qquad V_{xy} = IR_2 \qquad V_{yb} = IR_3$$

The potential differences across each resistor need not be the same (except for the special case in which all three resistances are equal). The potential difference V_{ab} across the entire combination is the sum of these individual potential differences:

$$V_{ab} = V_{ax} + V_{xy} + V_{yb} = I(R_1 + R_2 + R_3)$$

and so

$$\frac{V_{ab}}{I} = R_1 + R_2 + R_3$$

The ratio V_{ab}/I is, by definition, the equivalent resistance R_{eq}. Therefore

$$R_{eq} = R_1 + R_2 + R_3$$

It is easy to generalize this to any number of resistors:

$$R_{eq} = R_1 + R_2 + R_3 + \cdots \qquad \text{(resistors in series)} \qquad (26.1)$$

The equivalent resistance of *any number* of resistors in series equals the sum of their individual resistances.

The equivalent resistance is *greater than* any individual resistance.

Let's compare this result with Eq. (24.5) for *capacitors* in series. Resistors in series add directly because the voltage across each is directly proportional to its resistance and to the common current. Capacitors in series add reciprocally because the voltage across each is directly proportional to the common charge but *inversely* proportional to the individual capacitance.

Resistors in Parallel

If the resistors are in *parallel,* as in Fig. 26.1b, the current through each resistor need not be the same. But the potential difference between the terminals of each resistor must be the same and equal to V_{ab} (Fig. 26.2). (Remember that the potential difference between any two points does not depend on the path taken between the points.) Let's call the currents in the three resistors I_1, I_2, and I_3. Then from $I = V/R$,

$$I_1 = \frac{V_{ab}}{R_1} \qquad I_2 = \frac{V_{ab}}{R_2} \qquad I_3 = \frac{V_{ab}}{R_3}$$

In general, the current is different through each resistor. Because charge is not accumulating or draining out of point a, the total current I must equal the sum of the three currents in the resistors:

$$I = I_1 + I_2 + I_3 = V_{ab}\left(\frac{1}{R_1} + \frac{1}{R_2} + \frac{1}{R_3}\right) \quad \text{or}$$

$$\frac{I}{V_{ab}} = \frac{1}{R_1} + \frac{1}{R_2} + \frac{1}{R_3}$$

But by the definition of the equivalent resistance R_{eq}, $I/V_{ab} = 1/R_{eq}$, so

$$\frac{1}{R_{eq}} = \frac{1}{R_1} + \frac{1}{R_2} + \frac{1}{R_3}$$

Again it is easy to generalize to *any number* of resistors in parallel:

$$\frac{1}{R_{eq}} = \frac{1}{R_1} + \frac{1}{R_2} + \frac{1}{R_3} + \cdots \qquad \text{(resistors in parallel)} \qquad (26.2)$$

For *any number* of resistors in parallel, the *reciprocal* of the equivalent resistance equals the *sum of the reciprocals* of their individual resistances.

The equivalent resistance is always *less than* any individual resistance.

We can compare this result with Eq. (24.7) for *capacitors* in parallel. Resistors in parallel add reciprocally because the current in each is proportional to the common voltage across them and *inversely* proportional to the resistance of each. Capacitors in parallel add directly because the charge on each is proportional to the common voltage across them and *directly* proportional to the capacitance of each.

For the special case of *two* resistors in parallel,

$$\frac{1}{R_{eq}} = \frac{1}{R_1} + \frac{1}{R_2} = \frac{R_1 + R_2}{R_1 R_2} \quad \text{and}$$

$$R_{eq} = \frac{R_1 R_2}{R_1 + R_2} \qquad \text{(two resistors in parallel)} \qquad (26.3)$$

26.2 A car's headlights are connected in parallel. Hence each headlight is exposed to the full potential difference supplied by the car's electrical system, giving maximum brightness. Another advantage is that if one headlight burns out, the other one keeps shining (see Example 26.2).

Activ
ONLINE
Physics

12.2 DC Parallel Circuits

Because $V_{ab} = I_1R_1 = I_2R_2$, it follows that

$$\frac{I_1}{I_2} = \frac{R_2}{R_1} \qquad \text{(two resistors in parallel)} \qquad (26.4)$$

This shows that the currents carried by two resistors in parallel are *inversely proportional* to their resistances. More current goes through the path of least resistance.

Problem-Solving Strategy 26.1   Resistors in Series and Parallel

IDENTIFY *the relevant concepts:* Many resistor networks are made up of resistors in series, in parallel, or a combination of the two. The key concept is that such a network can be replaced by a single equivalent resistor.

SET UP *the problem* using the following steps:
1. Make a drawing of the resistor network.
2. Determine whether the resistors are connected in series or parallel. Note that you can often consider networks such as those in Figs. 26.1c and 26.1d as combinations of series and parallel arrangements.
3. Determine what the target variables are. They could include the equivalent resistance of the network, the potential difference across each resistor, or the current through each resistor.

EXECUTE *the solution* as follows:
1. Use Eq. (26.1) or (26.2) to find the equivalent resistance for a series or a parallel combination, respectively.
2. If the network is more complex, try reducing it to series and parallel combinations. For example, in Fig. 26.1c we first replace the parallel combination of R_2 and R_3 with its equivalent resistance; this then forms a series combination with R_1. In

Fig. 26.1d, the combination of R_2 and R_3 in series forms a parallel combination with R_1.
3. When calculating potential differences, remember that when resistors are connected in series, the total potential difference across the combination equals the sum of the individual potential differences. When resistors are connected in parallel, the potential difference is the same for every resistor and equals the potential difference across the parallel combination.
4. Keep in mind the analogous statements for current. When resistors are connected in series, the current is the same through every resistor and equals the current through the series combination. When resistors are connected in parallel, the total current through the combination equals the sum of the currents through the individual resistors.

EVALUATE *your answer:* Check whether your results are consistent. If resistors are connected in series, the equivalent resistance should be greater than that of any individual resistor; if they are connected in parallel, the equivalent resistance should be less than that of any individual resistor.

Example 26.1   Equivalent resistance

Compute the equivalent resistance of the network in Fig. 26.3a, and find the current in each resistor. The source of emf has negligible internal resistance.

SOLUTION

IDENTIFY: This network of three resistors is a *combination* of series and parallel resistances, just as in Fig. 26.1c. The 6-Ω and

26.3 Steps in reducing a combination of resistors to a single equivalent resistor and finding the current in each resistor.

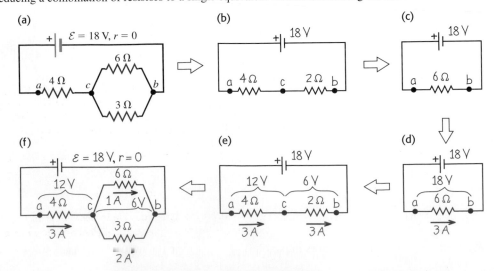

3-Ω resistors are in parallel, and their combination is in series with the 4-Ω resistor.

SET UP: We first determine the equivalent resistance R_{eq} of this network as a whole. Given this value, we find the current in the emf, which is the same as the current in the 4-Ω resistor. This same current is split between the 6-Ω and 3-Ω resistors; we determine how much goes into each resistor by using the principle that the potential difference must be the same across these two resistors (because they are connected in parallel).

EXECUTE: Figures 26.3b and 26.3c show successive steps in reducing the network to a single equivalent resistance. From Eq.(26.2) the 6-Ω and 3-Ω resistors in parallel in Fig. 26.3a are equivalent to the single 2-Ω resistor in Fig. 26.3b:

$$\frac{1}{R_{eq}} = \frac{1}{6\ \Omega} + \frac{1}{3\ \Omega} = \frac{1}{2\ \Omega}$$

[You can find the same result using Eq. (26.3).] From Eq. (26.1) the series combination of this 2-Ω resistor with the 4-Ω resistor is equivalent to the single 6-Ω resistor in Fig. 26.3c.

To find the current in each resistor of the original network, we reverse the steps by which we reduced the network. In the circuit shown in Fig. 26.3d (identical to Fig. 26.3c), the current is $I = V_{ab}/R = (18\ \text{V})/(6\ \Omega) = 3\ \text{A}$. So the current in the 4-Ω and 2-Ω resistors in Fig. 26.3e (identical to Fig. 26.3b) is also 3 A. The potential difference V_{cb} across the 2-Ω resistor is therefore $V_{cb} = IR = (3\ \text{A})(2\ \Omega) = 6\ \text{V}$. This potential difference must also be 6 V in Fig. 26.3f (identical to Fig. 26.3a). Using $I = V_{cb}/R$, the currents in the 6-Ω and 3-Ω resistors in Fig. 26.3f are $(6\ \text{V})/(6\ \Omega) = 1\ \text{A}$ and $(6\ \text{V})/(3\ \Omega) = 2\ \text{A}$, respectively.

EVALUATE: Note that for the two resistors in parallel between points c and b in Fig. 26.3f, there is twice as much current through the 3-Ω resistor as through the 6-Ω resistor; more current goes through the path of least resistance, in accordance with Eq. (26.4). Note also that the total current through these two resistors is 3 A, the same as it is through the 4-Ω resistor between points a and c.

Example 26.2   **Series versus parallel combinations**

Two identical light bulbs are to be connected to a source with $\mathcal{E} = 8\ \text{V}$ and negligible internal resistance. Each light bulb has a resistance $R = 2\ \Omega$. Find the current through each bulb, the potential difference across each bulb, and the power delivered to each bulb and to the entire network if the bulbs are connected (a) in series and (b) in parallel. (c) Suppose one of the bulbs burns out; that is, its filament breaks and current can no longer flow through it. What happens to the other bulb in the series case? In the parallel case?

SOLUTION

IDENTIFY: The light bulbs are just resistors in simple series and parallel connections.

SET UP: Figures 26.4a and 26.4b show our sketches of the series and parallel circuits, respectively. Once we have found the current

through each light bulb, we can find the power delivered to each bulb using Eq. (25.18), $P = I^2R = V^2/R$.

EXECUTE: (a) From Eq. (26.1) the equivalent resistance of the two bulbs between points a and c in Fig. 26.4a is the sum of their individual resistances:

$$R_{eq} = 2R = 2(2\ \Omega) = 4\ \Omega$$

The current is the same through either light bulb in series:

$$I = \frac{V_{ac}}{R_{eq}} = \frac{8\ \text{V}}{4\ \Omega} = 2\ \text{A}$$

Since the bulbs have the same resistance, the potential difference is the same across each bulb:

$$V_{ab} = V_{bc} = IR = (2\ \text{A})(2\ \Omega) = 4\ \text{V}$$

This is one-half of the 8-V terminal voltage of the source. From Eq.(25.18), the power delivered to each light bulb is

$$P = I^2R = (2\ \text{A})^2(2\ \Omega) = 8\ \text{W} \qquad \text{or}$$

$$P = \frac{V_{ab}^2}{R} = \frac{V_{bc}^2}{R} = \frac{(4\ \text{V})^2}{2\ \Omega} = 8\ \text{W}$$

The total power delivered to both bulbs is $P_{total} = 2P = 16\ \text{W}$. Alternatively, we can find the total power by using the equivalent resistance $R_{eq} = 4\ \Omega$, through which the current is $I = 2\ \text{A}$ and across which the potential difference is $V_{ac} = 8\ \text{V}$:

$$P_{total} = I^2R_{eq} = (2\ \text{A})^2(4\ \Omega) = 16\ \text{W} \qquad \text{or}$$

$$P_{total} = \frac{V_{ac}^2}{R_{eq}} = \frac{(8\ \text{V})^2}{4\ \Omega} = 16\ \text{W}$$

(b) If the light bulbs are in parallel, as in Fig. 26.4b, the potential difference V_{de} across each bulb is the same and equal to 8 V,

26.4 Our sketches for this problem.

(a) Light bulbs in series

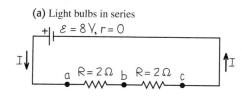

(b) Light bulbs in parallel

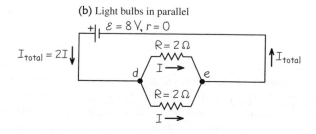

Continued

the terminal voltage of the source. Hence the current through each light bulb is

$$I = \frac{V_{de}}{R} = \frac{8 \text{ V}}{2 \text{ }\Omega} = 4 \text{ A}$$

and the power delivered to each bulb is

$$P = I^2R = (4 \text{ A})^2(2 \text{ }\Omega) = 32 \text{ W} \quad \text{or}$$

$$P = \frac{V_{de}^2}{R} = \frac{(8 \text{ V})^2}{2 \text{ }\Omega} = 32 \text{ W}$$

Both the potential difference across each bulb and the current through each bulb are twice as great as in the series case. Hence the power delivered to each bulb is *four* times greater, and each bulb glows more brightly than in the series case. If the goal is to produce the maximum amount of light from each bulb, a parallel arrangement is superior to a series arrangement.

The total power delivered to the parallel network is $P_{\text{total}} = 2P = 64 \text{ W}$, four times greater than in the series case. The increased power compared to the series case isn't obtained "for free"; energy is extracted from the source four times more rapidly in the parallel case than in the series case. If the source is a battery, it will be used up four times as fast.

We can also find the total power by using the equivalent resistance R_{eq}, given by Eq. (26.2):

$$\frac{1}{R_{\text{eq}}} = 2\left(\frac{1}{2 \text{ }\Omega}\right) = 1 \text{ }\Omega^{-1} \quad \text{or} \quad R_{\text{eq}} = 1 \text{ }\Omega$$

The total current through the equivalent resistor is $I_{\text{total}} = 2I = 2(4 \text{ A}) = 8 \text{ A}$, and the potential difference across the equivalent resistor is 8 V. Hence the total power is

$$P_{\text{total}} = I^2R_{\text{eq}} = (8 \text{ A})^2(1 \text{ }\Omega) = 64 \text{ W} \quad \text{or}$$

$$P_{\text{total}} = \frac{V_{de}^2}{R} = \frac{(8 \text{ V})^2}{1 \text{ }\Omega} = 64 \text{ W}$$

The potential difference across the equivalent resistance is the same for both the series and parallel cases, but for the parallel case the value of R_{eq} is less, and so $P_{\text{total}} = V^2/R_{\text{eq}}$ is greater.

(c) In the series case the same current flows through both bulbs. If one of the bulbs burns out, there will be no current at all in the circuit, and neither bulb will glow.

In the parallel case the potential difference across either bulb remains equal to 8 V even if one of the bulbs burns out. Hence the current through the functional bulb remains equal to 4 A, and the power delivered to that bulb remains equal to 32 W, the same as before the other bulb burned out. This is another of the merits of a parallel arrangement of light bulbs: If one fails, the other bulbs are unaffected. This principle is used in household wiring systems, which we'll discuss in Section 26.5.

EVALUATE: Our calculation isn't completely accurate, because the resistance $R = V/I$ of real light bulbs is *not* a constant independent of the potential difference V across the bulb. (The resistance of the filament increases with increasing operating temperature and hence with increasing V.) But it is indeed true that light bulbs connected in series across a source glow less brightly than when connected in parallel across the same source (Fig. 26.5).

26.5 When connected to the same source, two light bulbs in series (shown at top) draw less power and glow less brightly than when they are in parallel (shown at bottom).

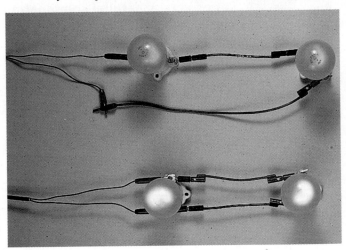

Test Your Understanding of Section 26.1 Suppose all three of the resistors shown in Fig. 26.1 have the same resistance, so $R_1 = R_2 = R_3 = R$. Rank the four arrangements shown in parts (a)–(d) of Fig. 26.1 in order of their equivalent resistance, from highest to lowest.

26.2 Kirchhoff's Rules

Many practical resistor networks cannot be reduced to simple series-parallel combinations. Figure 26.6a shows a dc power supply with emf $\mathcal{E}_1$ charging a battery with a smaller emf $\mathcal{E}_2$ and feeding current to a light bulb with resistance R. Figure 26.6b is a "bridge" circuit, used in many different types of measurement and control systems. (One important application of a "bridge" circuit is described in Problem 26.79.) We don't need any new principles to compute the currents in these networks, but there are some techniques that help us handle such problems systematically. We will describe the techniques developed by the German physicist Gustav Robert Kirchhoff (1824–1887).

First, here are two terms that we will use often. A **junction** in a circuit is a point where three or more conductors meet. Junctions are also called *nodes* or *branch points*. A **loop** is any closed conducting path. In Fig. 26.6a points *a* and *b* are junctions, but points *c* and *d* are not; in Fig. 26.6b the points *a*, *b*, *c*, and *d* are junctions, but points *e* and *f* are not. The blue lines in Figs. 26.6a and 26.6b show some possible loops in these circuits.

Kirchhoff's rules are the following two statements:

Kirchhoff's junction rule: *The algebraic sum of the currents into any junction is zero.* That is,

$$\sum I = 0 \qquad \text{(junction rule, valid at any junction)} \qquad (26.5)$$

Kirchhoff's loop rule: *The algebraic sum of the potential differences in any loop,* including those associated with emfs and those of resistive elements, *must equal zero.* That is,

$$\sum V = 0 \qquad \text{(loop rule, valid for any closed loop)} \qquad (26.6)$$

The junction rule is based on *conservation of electric charge.* No charge can accumulate at a junction, so the total charge entering the junction per unit time must equal the total charge leaving per unit time (Fig. 26.7a). Charge per unit time is current, so if we consider the currents entering a junction to be positive and those leaving to be negative, the algebraic sum of currents into a junction must be zero. It's like a T branch in a water pipe (Fig. 26.7b); if you have 1 liter per minute coming in one pipe, you can't have 3 liters per minute going out the other two pipes. We may as well confess that we used the junction rule (without saying so) in Section 26.1 in the derivation of Eq. (26.2) for resistors in parallel.

The loop rule is a statement that the electrostatic force is *conservative.* Suppose we go around a loop, measuring potential differences across successive circuit elements as we go. When we return to the starting point, we must find that the *algebraic sum* of these differences is zero; otherwise, we could not say that the potential at this point has a definite value.

Sign Conventions for the Loop Rule

In applying the loop rule, we need some sign conventions. Problem-Solving Strategy 26.2 describes in detail how to use these, but here's a quick overview. We first assume a direction for the current in each branch of the circuit and mark it on a diagram of the circuit. Then, starting at any point in the circuit, we imagine traveling around a loop, adding emfs and *IR* terms as we come to them. When we travel through a source in the direction from − to +, the emf is considered to be *positive;* when we travel from + to −, the emf is considered to be *negative* (Fig. 26.8a). When we travel through a resistor in the *same* direction as the assumed current, the *IR* term is *negative* because the current goes in the direction of decreasing potential. When we travel through a resistor in the direction *opposite* to the assumed current, the *IR* term is *positive* because this represents a rise of potential (Fig. 26.8b).

26.6 Two networks that cannot be reduced to simple series-parallel combinations of resistors.

(a)

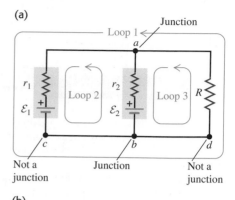

(b)

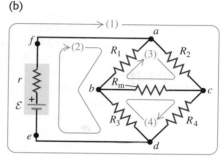

26.7 (a) Kirchhoff's junction rule states that as much current flows into a junction as flows out of it. (b) A water-pipe analogy.

(a) Kirchhoff's junction rule

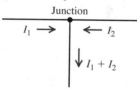

(b) Water-pipe analogy for Kirchhoff's junction rule

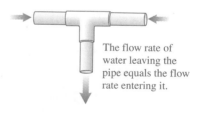

The flow rate of water leaving the pipe equals the flow rate entering it.

(a) Sign conventions for emfs   **(b)** Sign conventions for resistors

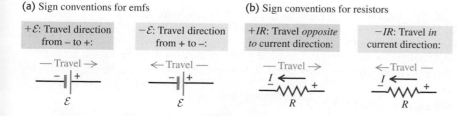

26.8 Use these sign conventions when you apply Kirchhoff's loop rule. In each part of the figure "Travel" is the direction that we imagine going around the loop, which is not necessarily the direction of the current.

Kirchhoff's two rules are all we need to solve a wide variety of network problems. Usually, some of the emfs, currents, and resistances are known, and others are unknown. We must always obtain from Kirchhoff's rules a number of independent equations equal to the number of unknowns so that we can solve the equations simultaneously. Often the hardest part of the solution is not understanding the basic principles but keeping track of algebraic signs!

Problem-Solving Strategy 26.2   Kirchhoff's Rules

IDENTIFY *the relevant concepts:*   Kirchhoff's rules are important tools for analyzing any circuit more complicated than a single loop.

SET UP *the problem* using the following steps:
1. Draw a *large* circuit diagram so you have plenty of room for labels. Label all quantities, known and unknown, including an assumed direction for each unknown current and emf. Often you will not know in advance the actual direction of an unknown current or emf, but this doesn't matter. If the actual direction of a particular quantity is opposite to your assumption, the result will come out with a negative sign. If you use Kirchhoff's rules correctly, they will give you the directions as well as the magnitudes of unknown currents and emfs.
2. When you label currents, it is usually best to use the junction rule immediately to express the currents in terms of as few quantities as possible. For example, Fig. 26.9a shows a circuit correctly labeled; Fig. 26.9b shows the same circuit, relabeled by applying the junction rule to point *a* to eliminate I_3.
3. Determine which quantities are the target variables.

EXECUTE *the solution* as follows:
1. Choose any closed loop in the network and designate a direction (clockwise or counterclockwise) to travel around the loop when applying the loop rule. The direction doesn't have to be the same as any assumed current direction.
2. Travel around the loop in the designated direction, adding potential differences as you cross them. Remember that a posi-

tive potential difference corresponds to an increase in potential and a negative potential difference corresponds to a decrease in potential. An emf is counted as positive when you traverse it from $(-)$ to $(+)$, and negative when you go from $(+)$ to $(-)$. An *IR* term is negative if you travel through the resistor in the same direction as the assumed current and positive if you pass through it in the opposite direction. Figure 26.8 summarizes these sign conventions.
3. Equate the sum in Step 2 to zero.
4. If necessary, choose another loop to get a different relationship among the unknowns, and continue until you have as many independent equations as unknowns or until every circuit element has been included in at least one of the chosen loops.
5. Solve the equations simultaneously to determine the unknowns. This step involves algebra, not physics, but it can be fairly complex. Be careful with algebraic manipulations; one sign error will prove fatal to the entire solution.
6. You can use this same bookkeeping system to find the potential V_{ab} of any point *a* with respect to any other point *b*. Start at *b* and add the potential changes you encounter in going from *b* to *a*, using the same sign rules as in Step 2. The algebraic sum of these changes is $V_{ab} = V_a - V_b$.

EVALUATE *your answer:*   Check all the steps in your algebra. A useful strategy is to consider a loop other than the ones you used to solve the problem; if the sum of potential drops around this loop isn't zero, you made an error somewhere in your calculations. As always, ask yourself whether the answers make sense.

26.9 Applying the junction rule to point *a* reduces the number of unknown currents from three to two.

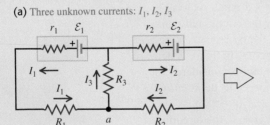

(a) Three unknown currents: I_1, I_2, I_3

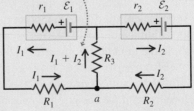

(b) Applying the junction rule to point *a* eliminates I_3.

Example 26.3   A single-loop circuit

The circuit shown in Fig. 26.10a contains two batteries, each with an emf and an internal resistance, and two resistors. Find (a) the current in the circuit, (b) the potential difference V_{ab}, and (c) the power output of the emf of each battery.

SOLUTION

IDENTIFY: This single-loop circuit has no junctions, so we don't need Kirchhoff's junction rule to solve for the target variables.

SET UP: To apply the loop rule to the single loop, we first assume a direction for the current; let's assume a counterclockwise direction, as shown in Fig. 26.10a.

EXECUTE: (a) Starting at *a* and going counterclockwise, we add potential increases and decreases and equate the sum to zero, as in Eq. (26.6). The resulting equation is

$$-I(4\,\Omega) - 4\,\text{V} - I(7\,\Omega) + 12\,\text{V} - I(2\,\Omega) - I(3\,\Omega) = 0$$

Collecting terms containing I and solving for I, we find

$$8 \text{ V} = I(16 \text{ }\Omega) \quad \text{and} \quad I = 0.5 \text{ A}$$

The result for I is positive, showing that our assumed current direction is correct. For an exercise, try assuming the opposite direction for I; you should then get $I = -0.5$ A, indicating that the actual current is opposite to this assumption.

(b) To find V_{ab}, the potential at a with respect to b, we start at b and add potential changes as we go toward a. There are two possible paths from b to a; taking the lower one first, we find

$$V_{ab} = (0.5 \text{ A})(7 \text{ }\Omega) + 4 \text{ V} + (0.5 \text{ A})(4 \text{ }\Omega) = 9.5 \text{ V}$$

Point a is at 9.5 V higher potential than b. All the terms in this sum, including the IR terms, are positive because each represents an *increase* in potential as we go from b toward a. If we use the upper path instead, the resulting equation is

$$V_{ab} = 12 \text{ V} - (0.5 \text{ A})(2 \text{ }\Omega) - (0.5 \text{ A})(3 \text{ }\Omega) = 9.5 \text{ V}$$

Here the IR terms are negative because our path goes in the direction of the current, with potential decreases through the resistors. The result is the same as for the lower path, as it must be in order for the total potential change around the complete loop to be zero. In each case, potential rises are taken to be positive and drops are taken to be negative.

(c) The power output of the emf of the 12-V battery is

$$P = \mathcal{E}I = (12 \text{ V})(0.5 \text{ A}) = 6 \text{ W}$$

and the power output of the emf of the 4-V battery is

$$P = \mathcal{E}I = (-4 \text{ V})(0.5 \text{ A}) = -2 \text{ W}$$

The negative sign in $\mathcal{E}$ for the 4-V battery appears because the current actually runs from the higher-potential side of the battery to the lower-potential side. The negative value of P means that we are *storing* energy in that battery, and it is being *recharged* by the 12-V battery.

EVALUATE: By applying the expression $P = I^2R$ to each of the four resistors in Fig. 26.10a, you should be able to show that the total power dissipated in all four resistors is 4 W. Of the 6 W provided by the emf of the 12-V battery, 2 W goes into storing energy in the 4-V battery and 4 W is dissipated in the resistances.

The circuit shown in Fig. 26.10a is very much like that used when a 12-V automobile battery is used to recharge a run-down battery in another automobile (Fig. 26.10b). The 3-Ω and 7-Ω resistors in Fig. 26.10a represent the resistances of the jumper cables and of the conducting path through the automobile with the run-down battery. (The values of the resistances in actual automobiles and jumper cables are different from those used in this example.)

26.10 (a) In this example we travel around the loop in the same direction as the assumed current, so all the IR terms are negative. The potential decreases as we travel from + to − through the bottom emf but increases as we travel from − to + through the top emf. (b) A real-life example of a circuit of this kind.

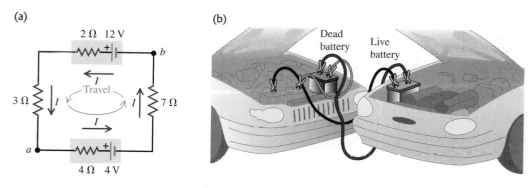

Example 26.4 Charging a battery

In the circuit shown in Fig. 26.11, a 12-V power supply with unknown internal resistance r is connected to a run-down rechargeable battery with unknown emf $\mathcal{E}$ and internal resistance 1 Ω and to an indicator light bulb of resistance 3 Ω carrying a current of 2 A. The current through the run-down battery is 1 A in the direction shown. Find the unknown current I, the internal resistance r, and the emf $\mathcal{E}$.

SOLUTION

IDENTIFY: This circuit has more than one loop, so we must apply both the junction rule and the loop rule.

SET UP: We assume the direction of the current through the 12-V power supply to be as shown. There are three target variables, so we need three equations.

26.11 In this circuit a power supply charges a run-down battery and lights a bulb. An assumption has been made about the polarity of the emf $\mathcal{E}$ of the run-down battery. Is this assumption correct?

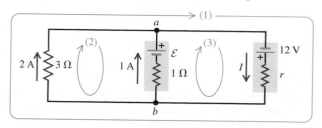

EXECUTE: First we apply the junction rule, Eq. (26.5), to point a. We find

$$-I + 1 \text{ A} + 2 \text{ A} = 0 \quad \text{so} \quad I = 3 \text{ A}$$

Continued

To determine r, we apply the loop rule, Eq. (26.6), to the outer loop labeled (1); we find

$$12 \text{ V} - (3 \text{ A})r - (2 \text{ A})(3 \text{ }\Omega) = 0 \quad \text{so} \quad r = 2 \text{ }\Omega$$

The terms containing the resistances r and $3 \text{ }\Omega$ are negative because our loop traverses those elements in the same direction as the current and hence finds potential *drops*. If we had chosen to traverse loop (1) in the opposite direction, every term would have had the opposite sign, and the result for r would have been the same.

To determine $\mathcal{E}$, we apply the loop rule to loop (2):

$$-\mathcal{E} + (1 \text{ A})(1 \text{ }\Omega) - (2 \text{ A})(3 \text{ }\Omega) = 0 \quad \text{so} \quad \mathcal{E} = -5 \text{ V}$$

The term for the 1-Ω resistor is positive because in traversing it in the direction opposite to the current, we find a potential *rise*. The negative value for $\mathcal{E}$ shows that the actual polarity of this emf is opposite to the assumption made in Fig. 26.11; the positive terminal of this source is really on the right side. As in Example 26.3, the battery is being recharged.

EVALUATE: We can check our result for $\mathcal{E}$ by using loop (3), obtaining the equation

$$12 \text{ V} - (3 \text{ A})(2 \text{ }\Omega) - (1 \text{ A})(1 \text{ }\Omega) + \mathcal{E} = 0$$

from which we again find $\mathcal{E} = -5 \text{ V}$.

As an additional consistency check, we note that $V_{ba} = V_b - V_a$ equals the voltage across the 3-Ω resistance, which is $(2 \text{ A})(3 \text{ }\Omega) = 6 \text{ V}$. Going from a to b by the top branch, we encounter potential differences $+12 \text{ V} - (3 \text{ A})(2 \text{ }\Omega) = +6 \text{ V}$, and going by the middle branch we find $-(-5 \text{ V}) + (1 \text{ A})(1 \text{ }\Omega) = +6 \text{ V}$. The three ways of getting V_{ba} give the same results. Make sure that you understand all the signs in these calculations.

Example 26.5   Power in a battery-charging circuit

In the circuit of Example 26.4 (shown in Fig. 26.11), find the power delivered by the 12-V power supply and by the battery being recharged, and find the power dissipated in each resistor.

SOLUTION

IDENTIFY: We use the results of Section 25.5, in which we found that the power delivered *from* an emf to a circuit is $\mathcal{E}I$ and the power delivered *to* a resistor from a circuit is $V_{ab}I = I^2R$.

SET UP: We know the values of each emf, each current, and each resistance from Example 26.4.

EXECUTE: The power output from the emf of the power supply is

$$P_{\text{supply}} = \mathcal{E}_{\text{supply}}I_{\text{supply}} = (12 \text{ V})(3 \text{ A}) = 36 \text{ W}$$

The power dissipated in the power supply's internal resistance r is

$$P_{r\text{-supply}} = I_{\text{supply}}{}^2 r_{\text{supply}} = (3 \text{ A})^2(2 \text{ }\Omega) = 18 \text{ W}$$

so the power supply's *net* power output is $P_{\text{net}} = 36 \text{ W} - 18 \text{ W} = 18 \text{ W}$. Alternatively, from Example 26.4 the terminal voltage of the battery is $V_{ba} = 6 \text{ V}$, so the net power output is

$$P_{\text{net}} = V_{ba}I_{\text{supply}} = (6 \text{ V})(3 \text{ A}) = 18 \text{ W}$$

The power output of the emf $\mathcal{E}$ of the battery being charged is

$$P_{\text{emf}} = \mathcal{E}I_{\text{battery}} = (-5 \text{ V})(1 \text{ A}) = -5 \text{ W}$$

This is negative because the 1-A current runs through the battery from the higher-potential side to the lower-potential side. (As we mentioned in Example 26.4, the polarity assumed for this battery in Fig. 26.11 was wrong.) We are storing energy in the battery as we charge it. Additional power is dissipated in the battery's internal resistance; this power is

$$P_{r\text{-battery}} = I_{\text{battery}}{}^2 r_{\text{battery}} = (1 \text{ A})^2(1 \text{ }\Omega) = 1 \text{ W}$$

The total power input to the battery is thus $1 \text{ W} + |-5 \text{ W}| = 6 \text{ W}$. Of this, 5 W represents useful energy stored in the battery; the remainder is wasted in its internal resistance.

The power dissipated in the light bulb is

$$P_{\text{bulb}} = I_{\text{bulb}}{}^2 R_{\text{bulb}} = (2 \text{ A})^2(3 \text{ }\Omega) = 12 \text{ W}$$

EVALUATE: As a check, note that all of the power from the supply is accounted for. Of the 18 W of net power from the power supply, 5 W goes to recharge the battery, 1 W is dissipated in the battery's internal resistance, and 12 W is dissipated in the light bulb.

Example 26.6   A complex network

Figure 26.12 shows a "bridge" circuit of the type described at the beginning of this section (see Fig. 26.6b). Find the current in each resistor and the equivalent resistance of the network of five resistors.

SOLUTION

IDENTIFY: This network cannot be represented in terms of series and parallel combinations. Hence we must use Kirchhoff's rules to find the values of the target variables.

SET UP: There are five different currents to determine, but by applying the junction rule to junctions a and b, we can represent them in terms of three unknown currents as shown in the figure. The current in the battery is $I_1 + I_2$.

26.12 A network circuit with several resistors.

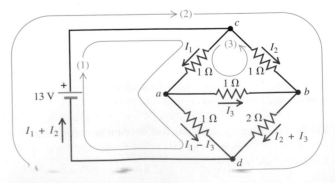

EXECUTE: We apply the loop rule to the three loops shown, obtaining the following three equations:

$$13\text{ V} - I_1(1\ \Omega) - (I_1 - I_3)(1\ \Omega) = 0 \quad (1)$$

$$-I_2(1\ \Omega) - (I_2 + I_3)(2\ \Omega) + 13\text{ V} = 0 \quad (2)$$

$$-I_1(1\ \Omega) - I_3(1\ \Omega) + I_2(1\ \Omega) = 0 \quad (3)$$

This is a set of three simultaneous equations for the three unknown currents. They may be solved by various methods; one straightforward procedure is to solve the third equation for I_2, obtaining $I_2 = I_1 + I_3$, and then substitute this expression into the second equation to eliminate I_2. When this is done, we are left with the two equations

$$13\text{ V} = I_1(2\ \Omega) - I_3(1\ \Omega) \quad (1')$$

$$13\text{ V} = I_1(3\ \Omega) + I_3(5\ \Omega) \quad (2')$$

Now we can eliminate I_3 by multiplying Eq. (1′) by 5 and adding the two equations. We obtain

$$78\text{ V} = I_1(13\ \Omega) \qquad I_1 = 6\text{ A}$$

We substitute this result back into Eq. (1′) to obtain $I_3 = -1$ A, and finally, from Eq. (3) we find $I_2 = 5$ A. The negative value of I_3 tells us that its direction is opposite to our initial assumption.

The total current through the network is $I_1 + I_2 = 11$ A, and the potential drop across it is equal to the battery emf—namely, 13 V. The equivalent resistance of the network is

$$R_{eq} = \frac{13\text{ V}}{11\text{ A}} = 1.2\ \Omega$$

EVALUATE: You can check the results $I_1 = 6$ A, $I_2 = 5$ A, and $I_3 = -1$ A by substituting these values into the three equations (1), (2), and (3). What do you find?

Example 26.7 **A potential difference within a complex network**

In the circuit of Example 26.6 (Fig. 26.12), find the potential difference V_{ab}.

SOLUTION

IDENTIFY: Our target variable is $V_{ab} = V_a - V_b$, which is the potential at point a with respect to point b.

SET UP: To find V_{ab}, we start at point b and follow a path to point a, adding potential rises and drops as we go. We can follow any of several paths from b to a; the value of V_{ab} must be independent of which path we choose, which gives us a natural way to check our result.

EXECUTE: The simplest path to follow is through the center 1-Ω resistor. We have found $I_3 = -1$ A, showing that the actual current direction in this branch is from right to left. Thus, as we go

from b to a, there is a *drop* of potential with magnitude $IR = (1\text{ A})(1\ \Omega) = 1$ V, and $V_{ab} = -1$ V. That is, the potential at point a is 1 V less than that at point b.

EVALUATE: To test our result, let's try a path from b to a that goes through the lower two resistors. The currents through these are

$$I_2 + I_3 = 5\text{ A} + (-1\text{ A}) = 4\text{ A} \quad \text{and}$$

$$I_1 - I_3 = 6\text{ A} - (-1\text{ A}) = 7\text{ A}$$

and so

$$V_{ab} = -(4\text{ A})(2\ \Omega) + (7\text{ A})(1\ \Omega) = -1\text{ V}$$

We suggest that you try some other paths from b to a to verify that they also give this result.

Test Your Understanding of Section 26.2   Subtract Eq. (1) from Eq. (2) in Example 26.6. To which loop in Fig. 26.12 does this equation correspond? Would this equation have simplified the solution of Example 26.6?

26.3 Electrical Measuring Instruments

We've been talking about potential difference, current, and resistance for two chapters, so it's about time we said something about how to *measure* these quantities. Many common devices, including car instrument panels, battery chargers, and inexpensive electrical instruments, measure potential difference (voltage), current, or resistance using a **d'Arsonval galvanometer** (Fig. 26.13). In the following discussion we'll often call it just a *meter*. A pivoted coil of fine wire is placed in the magnetic field of a permanent magnet (Fig. 26.14). Attached to the coil is a spring, similar to the hairspring on the balance wheel of a watch. In the equilibrium position, with no current in the coil, the pointer is at zero. When there is a current in the coil, the magnetic field exerts a torque on the coil that is proportional to the current. (We'll discuss this magnetic interaction in detail in Chapter 27.) As the coil turns, the spring exerts a restoring torque that is proportional to the angular displacement.

Thus the angular deflection of the coil and pointer is directly proportional to the coil current, and the device can be calibrated to measure current. The maximum deflection, typically 90° or so, is called *full-scale deflection*. The essential electrical characteristics of the meter are the current I_{fs} required for

26.13 This ammeter (top) and voltmeter (bottom) are both d'Arsonval galvanometers. The difference has to do with their internal connections (see Fig. 26.15).

26.14 A d'Arsonval galvanometer, showing a pivoted coil with attached pointer, a permanent magnet supplying a magnetic field that is uniform in magnitude, and a spring to provide restoring torque, which opposes magnetic-field torque.

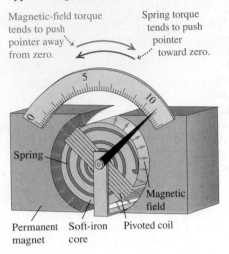

Magnetic-field torque tends to push pointer away from zero.

Spring torque tends to push pointer toward zero.

Spring

Magnetic field

Permanent magnet

Soft-iron core

Pivoted coil

Activ
Physics
ONLINE

12.4   Using Ammeters and Voltmeters

full-scale deflection (typically on the order of 10 μA to 10 mA) and the resistance R_c of the coil (typically on the order of 10 to 1000 Ω).

The meter deflection is proportional to the *current* in the coil. If the coil obeys Ohm's law, the current is proportional to the *potential difference* between the terminals of the coil, and the deflection is also proportional to this potential difference. For example, consider a meter whose coil has a resistance $R_c = 20.0 \, \Omega$ and that deflects full scale when the current in its coil is $I_{fs} = 1.00$ mA. The corresponding potential difference for full-scale deflection is

$$V = I_{fs}R_c = (1.00 \times 10^{-3} \, \text{A})(20.0 \, \Omega) = 0.0200 \, \text{V}$$

Ammeters

A current-measuring instrument is usually called an **ammeter** (or milliammeter, microammeter, and so forth, depending on the range). *An ammeter always measures the current passing through it.* An *ideal* ammeter, discussed in Section 25.4, would have *zero* resistance, so including it in a branch of a circuit would not affect the current in that branch. Real ammeters always have some finite resistance, but it is always desirable for an ammeter to have as little resistance as possible.

We can adapt any meter to measure currents that are larger than its full-scale reading by connecting a resistor in parallel with it (Fig. 26.15a) so that some of the current bypasses the meter coil. The parallel resistor is called a **shunt resistor** or simply a *shunt*, denoted as R_{sh}.

Suppose we want to make a meter with full-scale current I_{fs} and coil resistance R_c into an ammeter with full-scale reading I_a. To determine the shunt resistance R_{sh} needed, note that at full-scale deflection the total current through the parallel combination is I_a, the current through the coil of the meter is I_{fs}, and the current through the shunt is the difference $I_a - I_{fs}$. The potential difference V_{ab} is the same for both paths, so

$$I_{fs}R_c = (I_a - I_{fs})R_{sh} \qquad \text{(for an ammeter)} \qquad (26.7)$$

26.15 Using the same meter to measure (a) current and (b) voltage.

(a) A moving-coil ammeter

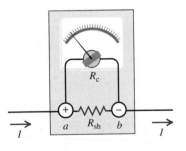

(b) A moving-coil voltmeter

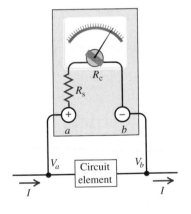

Example 26.8   Designing an ammeter

What shunt resistance is required to make the 1.00-mA, 20.0-Ω meter described above into an ammeter with a range of 0 to 50.0 mA?

SOLUTION

IDENTIFY: Since the meter is being used as an ammeter, its internal connections are as shown in Fig. 26.15a. Our target variable is the shunt resistance R_{sh}.

SET UP: We want the ammeter to be able to handle a maximum current $I_a = 50.0$ mA $= 50.0 \times 10^{-3}$ A. The resistance of the coil

is $R_c = 20.0 \, \Omega$, and the meter shows full-scale deflection when the current through the coil is $I_{fs} = 1.00 \times 10^{-3}$ A. We find the shunt resistance R_{sh} using Eq. (26.7).

EXECUTE: Solving Eq. (26.7) for R_{sh}, we find

$$R_{sh} = \frac{I_{fs}R_c}{I_a - I_{fs}} = \frac{(1.00 \times 10^{-3} \, \text{A})(20.0 \, \Omega)}{50.0 \times 10^{-3} \, \text{A} - 1.00 \times 10^{-3} \, \text{A}}$$

$$= 0.408 \, \Omega$$

EVALUATE: It's useful to consider the equivalent resistance R_{eq} of the ammeter as a whole. From Eq. (26.2),

$$\frac{1}{R_{eq}} = \frac{1}{R_c} + \frac{1}{R_{sh}} = \frac{1}{20.0\ \Omega} + \frac{1}{0.408\ \Omega}$$

$$R_{eq} = 0.400\ \Omega$$

The shunt resistance is so small in comparison to the meter resistance that the equivalent resistance is very nearly equal to the shunt resistance. The result is a low-resistance instrument with the desired range of 0 to 50.0 mA. At full-scale deflection, $I = I_a = 50.0$ mA, the current through the galvanometer is 1.00 mA, the current through the shunt resistor is 49.0 mA, and $V_{ab} = 0.0200$ V. If the current I is *less* than 50.0 mA, the coil current and the deflection are proportionally less, but the resistance R_{eq} is still 0.400 Ω.

Voltmeters

This same basic meter may also be used to measure potential difference or *voltage*. A voltage-measuring device is called a **voltmeter** (or millivoltmeter, and so forth, depending on the range). A voltmeter always measures the potential difference between two points, and its terminals must be connected to these points. (Example 25.7 in Section 25.4 described what can happen if a voltmeter is connected incorrectly.) As we discussed in Section 25.4, an ideal voltmeter would have *infinite* resistance, so connecting it between two points in a circuit would not alter any of the currents. Real voltmeters always have finite resistance, but a voltmeter should have large enough resistance that connecting it in a circuit does not change the other currents appreciably.

For the meter described in Example 26.8 the voltage across the meter coil at full-scale deflection is only $I_{fs}R_c = (1.00 \times 10^{-3}\ \text{A})(20.0\ \Omega) = 0.0200$ V. We can extend this range by connecting a resistor R_s in *series* with the coil (Fig. 26.15b). Then only a fraction of the total potential difference appears across the coil itself, and the remainder appears across R_s. For a voltmeter with full-scale reading V_V, we need a series resistor R_s in Fig. 26.15b such that

$$V_V = I_{fs}(R_c + R_s) \qquad \text{(for a voltmeter)} \qquad (26.8)$$

Example 26.9   Designing a voltmeter

How can we make a galvanometer with $R_c = 20.0\ \Omega$ and $I_{fs} = 1.00$ mA into a voltmeter with a maximum range of 10.0 V?

SOLUTION

IDENTIFY: Since this meter is being used as a voltmeter, its internal connections are as shown in Fig. 26.15b. Our target variable is the series resistance R_s.

SET UP: The maximum allowable voltage across the voltmeter is $V_V = 10.0$ V. We want this to occur when the current through the coil (of resistance $R_c = 20.0\ \Omega$) is $I_{fs} = 1.00 \times 10^{-3}$ A. We find the series resistance R_s with Eq.(26.8).

EXECUTE: From Eq. (26.8),

$$R_s = \frac{V_V}{I_{fs}} - R_c = \frac{10.0\ \text{V}}{0.00100\ \text{A}} - 20.0\ \Omega = 9980\ \Omega$$

EVALUATE: At full-scale deflection, $V_{ab} = 10.0$ V, the voltage across the meter is 0.0200 V, the voltage across R_s is 9.98 V, and the current through the voltmeter is 0.00100 A. In this case most of the voltage appears across the series resistor. The equivalent meter resistance is $R_{eq} = 20.0\ \Omega + 9980\ \Omega = 10,000\ \Omega$. Such a meter is described as a "1000 ohms-per-volt meter," referring to the ratio of resistance to full-scale deflection. In normal operation the current through the circuit element being measured (I in Fig. 26.15b) is much greater than 0.00100 A, and the resistance between points a and b in the circuit is much less than 10,000 Ω. So the voltmeter draws off only a small fraction of the current and disturbs only slightly the circuit being measured.

Ammeters and Voltmeters in Combination

A voltmeter and an ammeter can be used together to measure *resistance* and *power*. The resistance R of a resistor equals the potential difference V_{ab} between its terminals divided by the current I; that is, $R = V_{ab}/I$. The power input P to any circuit element is the product of the potential difference across it and the current through it: $P = V_{ab}I$. In principle, the most straightforward way to measure R or P is to measure V_{ab} and I simultaneously.

With practical ammeters and voltmeters this isn't quite as simple as it seems. In Fig. 26.16a, ammeter A reads the current I in the resistor R. Voltmeter V, however, reads the *sum* of the potential difference V_{ab} across the resistor and the potential difference V_{bc} across the ammeter. If we transfer the voltmeter terminal from c to b, as in Fig. 26.16b, then the voltmeter reads the potential difference V_{ab} correctly, but the ammeter now reads the *sum* of the current I in the resistor and the current I_V in the voltmeter. Either way, we have to correct the reading of one instrument or the other unless the corrections are small enough to be negligible.

26.16 Ammeter–voltmeter method for measuring resistance.

(a)

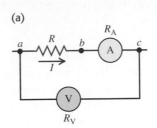

(b)

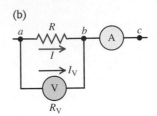

Example 26.10   Measuring resistance I

Suppose we want to measure an unknown resistance R using the circuit of Fig. 26.16a. The meter resistances are $R_V = 10,000\ \Omega$ (for the voltmeter) and $R_A = 2.00\ \Omega$ (for the ammeter). If the voltmeter reads 12.0 V and the ammeter reads 0.100 A, what are the resistance R and the power dissipated in the resistor?

SOLUTION

IDENTIFY: The ammeter reads the current $I = 0.100$ A through the resistor, and the voltmeter reads the potential difference between a and c. If the ammeter were *ideal* (that is, if $R_A = 0$), there would be zero potential difference between b and c, the voltmeter reading $V = 12.0$ V would be equal to the potential difference V_{ab} across the resistor, and the resistance would simply be equal to $R = V/I = (12.0\ \text{V})/(0.100\ \text{A}) = 120\ \Omega$. The ammeter is *not* ideal, however (its resistance is $R_A = 2.00\ \Omega$), so the voltmeter reading V is actually the sum of the potential differences V_{bc} (across the ammeter) and V_{ab} (across the resistor).

SET UP: We use Ohm's law to find the voltage V_{bc} across the ammeter from its known current and resistance. Then we solve for V_{ab} and the resistance R. Given these, we are able to calculate the power P into the resistor.

EXECUTE: From Ohm's law, $V_{bc} = IR_A = (0.100\ \text{A})(2.00\ \Omega) = 0.200$ V and $V_{ab} = IR$. The sum of these is $V = 12.0$ V, so the potential difference across the resistor is $V_{ab} = V - V_{bc} = (12.0\ \text{V}) - (0.200\ \text{V}) = 11.8$ V. Hence the resistance is

$$R = \frac{V_{ab}}{I} = \frac{11.8\ \text{V}}{0.100\ \text{A}} = 118\ \Omega$$

The power dissipated in this resistor is

$$P = V_{ab}I = (11.8\ \text{V})(0.100\ \text{A}) = 1.18\ \text{W}$$

EVALUATE: You can confirm this result for the power by using the alternative formula $P = I^2R$. Do you get the same answer?

Example 26.11   Measuring resistance II

Suppose the meters of Example 26.10 are connected to a different resistor in the circuit shown in Fig. 26.16b, and the readings obtained on the meters are the same as in Example 26.10. What is the value of this new resistance R, and what is the power dissipated in the resistor?

SOLUTION

IDENTIFY: In Example 26.10 the ammeter read the actual current through the resistor, but the voltmeter reading was not the same as the potential difference across the resistor. Now the situation is reversed: The voltmeter reading $V = 12.0$ V shows the actual potential difference V_{ab} across the resistor, but the ammeter reading $I_A = 0.100$ A is *not* equal to the current I through the resistor.

SET UP: Applying the junction rule at b in Fig. 26.16b shows that $I_A = I + I_V$, where I_V is the current through the voltmeter. We find I_V from the given values of V and the voltmeter resistance R_V, and we use this value to find the resistor current I. We then determine the resistance R from I and the voltmeter reading, and calculate the power as in Example 26.10.

EXECUTE: We have $I_V = V/R_V = (12.0\ \text{V})/(10,000\ \Omega) = 1.20$ mA. The actual current I in the resistor is $I = I_A - I_V = 0.100\ \text{A} - 0.0012\ \text{A} = 0.0988$ A, and the resistance is

$$R = \frac{V_{ab}}{I} = \frac{12.0\ \text{V}}{0.0988\ \text{A}} = 121\ \Omega$$

The power dissipated in the resistor is

$$P = V_{ab}I = (12.0\ \text{V})(0.0988\ \text{A}) = 1.19\ \text{W}$$

EVALUATE: Our results for R and P are not too different than the results of Example 26.10, in which the meters are connected in a different way. That's because the ammeter and voltmeter are nearly ideal: Compared to the resistance R under test, the ammeter resistance R_A is very small and the voltmeter resistance R_V is very large. Nonetheless, the results of the two examples *are* different, which shows that you must account for how ammeters and voltmeters are used when interpreting their readings.

Ohmmeters

An alternative method for measuring resistance is to use a d'Arsonval meter in an arrangement called an **ohmmeter.** It consists of a meter, a resistor, and a source (often a flashlight battery) connected in series (Fig. 26.17). The resistance R to be measured is connected between terminals x and y.

The series resistance R_s is variable; it is adjusted so that when terminals x and y are short-circuited (that is, when $R = 0$), the meter deflects full scale. When nothing is connected to terminals x and y, so that the circuit between x and y is *open* (that is, when $R \rightarrow \infty$), there is no current and hence no deflection. For any intermediate value of R the meter deflection depends on the value of R, and the meter scale can be calibrated to read the resistance R directly. Larger currents correspond to smaller resistances, so this scale reads backward compared to the scale showing the current.

In situations in which high precision is required, instruments containing d'Arsonval meters have been supplanted by electronic instruments with direct digital readouts. These are more precise, stable, and mechanically rugged than d'Arsonval meters. Digital voltmeters can be made with extremely high internal resistance, of the order of 100 MΩ. Figure 26.18 shows a digital *multimeter,* an instrument that can measure voltage, current, or resistance over a wide range.

The Potentiometer

The *potentiometer* is an instrument that can be used to measure the emf of a source without drawing any current from the source; it also has a number of other useful applications. Essentially, it balances an unknown potential difference against an adjustable, measurable potential difference.

The principle of the potentiometer is shown schematically in Fig. 26.19a. A resistance wire ab of total resistance R_{ab} is permanently connected to the terminals of a source of known emf $\mathcal{E}_1$. A sliding contact c is connected through the galvanometer G to a second source whose emf $\mathcal{E}_2$ is to be measured. As contact c is moved along the resistance wire, the resistance R_{cb} between points c and b varies; if the resistance wire is uniform, R_{cb} is proportional to the length of wire between c and b. To determine the value of $\mathcal{E}_2$, contact c is moved until a position is found at which the galvanometer shows no deflection; this corresponds to zero current passing through $\mathcal{E}_2$. With $I_2 = 0$, Kirchhoff's loop rule gives

$$\mathcal{E}_2 = IR_{cb}$$

With $I_2 = 0$, the current I produced by the emf $\mathcal{E}_1$ has the same value no matter what the value of the emf $\mathcal{E}_2$. We calibrate the device by replacing $\mathcal{E}_2$ by a source of known emf; then any unknown emf $\mathcal{E}_2$ can be found by measuring the length of wire cb for which $I_2 = 0$ (see Exercise 26.35). Note that for this to work, V_{ab} must be greater than $\mathcal{E}_2$.

The term *potentiometer* is also used for any variable resistor, usually having a circular resistance element and a sliding contact controlled by a rotating shaft and knob. The circuit symbol for a potentiometer is shown in Fig. 26.19b.

Test Your Understanding of Section 26.3   You want to measure the current through and the potential difference across the 2-Ω resistor shown in Fig. 26.12 (Example 26.6 in Section 26.2). (a) How should you connect an ammeter and a voltmeter to do this? (i) ammeter and voltmeter both in series with the 2-Ω resistor; (ii) ammeter in series with the 2-Ω resistor and voltmeter connected between points b and d; (iii) ammeter connected between points b and d and voltmeter in series with the 2-Ω resistor; (iv) ammeter and voltmeter both connected between points b and d. (b) What resistances should these meters have? (i) Ammeter and voltmeter resistances should both be much greater than 2 Ω; (ii) ammeter resistance should be much greater than 2 Ω and voltmeter resistance should be much less than 2 Ω; (iii) ammeter resistance should be much less than 2 Ω and voltmeter resistance should be much greater than 2 Ω; (iv) ammeter and voltmeter resistances should both be much less than 2 Ω.

26.17 Ohmmeter circuit. The resistor R_s has a variable resistance, as is indicated by the arrow through the resistor symbol. To use the ohmmeter, first connect x directly to y and adjust R_s until the meter reads zero. Then connect x and y across the resistor R and read the scale.

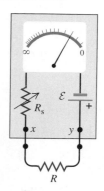

26.18 This digital multimeter can be used as a voltmeter (red arc), ammeter (yellow arc), or ohmmeter (green arc).

26.19 (a) Potentiometer circuit. (b) Circuit symbol for a potentiometer (variable resistor).

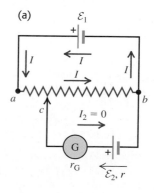

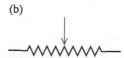

26.20 This colored x-ray image shows a pacemaker surgically implanted in a patient with a malfunctioning sinoatrial node, the part of the heart that generates the electrical signal to trigger heartbeats. To compensate, the pacemaker (located near the collarbone) sends a pulsed electrical signal along the lead to the heart to maintain regular beating.

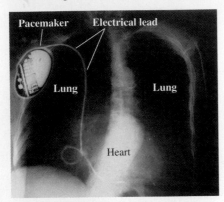

26.21 Charging a capacitor. (a) Just before the switch is closed, the charge q is zero. (b) When the switch closes (at $t = 0$), the current jumps from zero to $\mathcal{E}/R$. As time passes, q approaches Q_f and the current i approaches zero.

(a) Capacitor initially uncharged

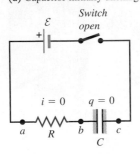

(b) Charging the capacitor

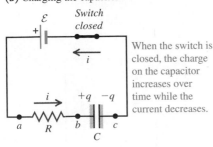

When the switch is closed, the charge on the capacitor increases over time while the current decreases.

26.4 *R-C* Circuits

In the circuits we have analyzed up to this point, we have assumed that all the emfs and resistances are *constant* (time independent) so that all the potentials, currents, and powers are also independent of time. But in the simple act of charging or discharging a capacitor we find a situation in which the currents, voltages, and powers *do* change with time.

Many important devices incorporate circuits in which a capacitor is alternately charged and discharged. These include heart pacemakers (Fig. 26.20), flashing traffic lights, automobile turn signals, and electronic flash units. Understanding what happens in such circuits is thus of great practical importance.

Charging a Capacitor

Figure 26.21 shows a simple circuit for charging a capacitor. A circuit such as this that has a resistor and a capacitor in series is called an *R-C* circuit. We idealize the battery (or power supply) to have a constant emf $\mathcal{E}$ and zero internal resistance ($r = 0$), and we neglect the resistance of all the connecting conductors.

We begin with the capacitor initially uncharged (Fig. 26.21a); then at some initial time $t = 0$ we close the switch, completing the circuit and permitting current around the loop to begin charging the capacitor (Fig. 26.21b). For all practical purposes, the current begins at the same instant in every conducting part of the circuit, and at each instant the current is the same in every part.

CAUTION Lowercase means time-varying Up to this point we have been working with constant potential differences (voltages), currents, and charges, and we have used *capital* letters V, I, and Q, respectively, to denote these quantities. To distinguish between quantities that vary with time and those that are constant, we will use *lowercase* letters v, i, and q for time-varying voltages, currents, and charges, respectively. We suggest that you follow this same convention in your own work. ∎

Because the capacitor in Fig. 26.21 is initially uncharged, the potential difference v_{bc} across it is zero at $t = 0$. At this time, from Kirchhoff's loop law, the voltage v_{ab} across the resistor R is equal to the battery emf $\mathcal{E}$. The initial ($t = 0$) current through the resistor, which we will call I_0, is given by Ohm's law: $I_0 = v_{ab}/R = \mathcal{E}/R$.

As the capacitor charges, its voltage v_{bc} increases and the potential difference v_{ab} across the resistor decreases, corresponding to a decrease in current. The sum of these two voltages is constant and equal to $\mathcal{E}$. After a long time the capacitor becomes fully charged, the current decreases to zero, and the potential difference v_{ab} across the resistor becomes zero. Then the entire battery emf $\mathcal{E}$ appears across the capacitor and $v_{bc} = \mathcal{E}$.

Let q represent the charge on the capacitor and i the current in the circuit at some time t after the switch has been closed. We choose the positive direction for the current to correspond to positive charge flowing onto the left-hand capacitor plate, as in Fig. 26.21b. The instantaneous potential differences v_{ab} and v_{bc} are

$$v_{ab} = iR \qquad v_{bc} = \frac{q}{C}$$

Using these in Kirchhoff's loop rule, we find

$$\mathcal{E} - iR - \frac{q}{C} = 0 \tag{26.9}$$

The potential drops by an amount iR as we travel from a to b and by q/C as we travel from b to c. Solving Eq. (26.9) for i, we find

$$i = \frac{\mathcal{E}}{R} - \frac{q}{RC} \tag{26.10}$$

At time $t = 0$, when the switch is first closed, the capacitor is uncharged, and so $q = 0$. Substituting $q = 0$ into Eq. (26.10), we find that the *initial* current I_0 is given by $I_0 = \mathcal{E}/R$, as we have already noted. If the capacitor were not in the circuit, the last term in Eq. (26.10) would not be present; then the current would be *constant* and equal to $\mathcal{E}/R$.

As the charge q increases, the term q/RC becomes larger and the capacitor charge approaches its final value, which we will call Q_f. The current decreases and eventually becomes zero. When $i = 0$, Eq. (26.10) gives

$$\frac{\mathcal{E}}{R} = \frac{Q_f}{RC} \qquad Q_f = C\mathcal{E} \tag{26.11}$$

Note that the final charge Q_f does not depend on R.

The current and the capacitor charge are shown as functions of time in Fig. 26.22. At the instant the switch is closed $(t = 0)$, the current jumps from zero to its initial value $I_0 = \mathcal{E}/R$; after that, it gradually approaches zero. The capacitor charge starts at zero and gradually approaches the final value given by Eq. (26.11), $Q_f = C\mathcal{E}$.

We can derive general expressions for the charge q and current i as functions of time. With our choice of the positive direction for current (Fig. 26.21b), i equals the rate at which positive charge arrives at the left-hand (positive) plate of the capacitor, so $i = dq/dt$. Making this substitution in Eq. (26.10), we have

$$\frac{dq}{dt} = \frac{\mathcal{E}}{R} - \frac{q}{RC} = -\frac{1}{RC}(q - C\mathcal{E})$$

We can rearrange this to

$$\frac{dq}{q - C\mathcal{E}} = -\frac{dt}{RC}$$

and then integrate both sides. We change the integration variables to q' and t' so that we can use q and t for the upper limits. The lower limits are $q' = 0$ and $t' = 0$:

$$\int_0^q \frac{dq'}{q' - C\mathcal{E}} = -\int_0^t \frac{dt'}{RC}$$

When we carry out the integration, we get

$$\ln\!\left(\frac{q - C\mathcal{E}}{-C\mathcal{E}}\right) = -\frac{t}{RC}$$

Exponentiating both sides (that is, taking the inverse logarithm) and solving for q, we find

$$\frac{q - C\mathcal{E}}{-C\mathcal{E}} = e^{-t/RC}$$

$$q = C\mathcal{E}(1 - e^{-t/RC}) = Q_f(1 - e^{-t/RC}) \qquad \begin{array}{l}\text{(\textit{R-C} circuit,}\\\text{charging capacitor)}\end{array} \tag{26.12}$$

The instantaneous current i is just the time derivative of Eq. (26.12):

$$i = \frac{dq}{dt} = \frac{\mathcal{E}}{R}e^{-t/RC} = I_0 e^{-t/RC} \qquad \begin{array}{l}\text{(\textit{R-C} circuit,}\\\text{charging capacitor)}\end{array} \tag{26.13}$$

The charge and current are both *exponential* functions of time. Figure 26.22a is a graph of Eq. (26.13) and Fig. 26.22b is a graph of Eq. (26.12).

26.22 Current i and capacitor charge q as functions of time for the circuit of Fig. 26.21. The initial current is I_0 and the initial capacitor charge is zero. The current asymptotically approaches zero and the capacitor charge asymptotically approaches a final value of Q_f.

(a) Graph of current versus time for a charging capacitor

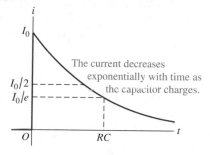

The current decreases exponentially with time as the capacitor charges.

(b) Graph of capacitor charge versus time for a charging capacitor

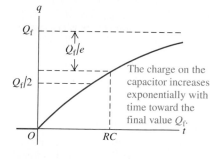

The charge on the capacitor increases exponentially with time toward the final value Q_f.

26.23 Discharging a capacitor. (a) Before the switch is closed at time $t = 0$, the capacitor charge is Q_0 and the current is zero. (b) At time t after the switch is closed, the capacitor charge is q and the current is i. The actual current direction is opposite to the direction shown; i is negative. After a long time, q and i both approach zero.

(a) Capacitor initially charged

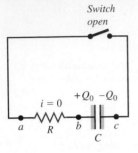

(b) Discharging the capacitor

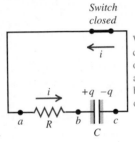

When the switch is closed, the charge on the capacitor and the current both decrease over time.

26.24 Current i and capacitor charge q as functions of time for the circuit of Fig. 26.23. The initial current is I_0 and the initial capacitor charge is Q_0. Both i and q asymptotically approach zero.

(a) Graph of current versus time for a discharging capacitor

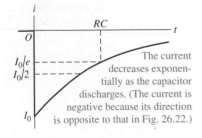

The current decreases exponentially as the capacitor discharges. (The current is negative because its direction is opposite to that in Fig. 26.22.)

(b) Graph of capacitor charge versus time for a discharging capacitor

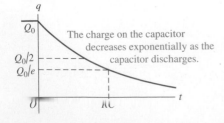

The charge on the capacitor decreases exponentially as the capacitor discharges.

Time Constant

After a time equal to RC, the current in the R-C circuit has decreased to $1/e$ (about 0.368) of its initial value. At this time, the capacitor charge has reached $(1 - 1/e) = 0.632$ of its final value $Q_f = C\mathcal{E}$. The product RC is therefore a measure of how quickly the capacitor charges. We call RC the **time constant,** or the **relaxation time,** of the circuit, denoted by τ:

$$\tau = RC \qquad \text{(time constant for } R\text{-}C \text{ circuit)} \qquad (26.14)$$

When τ is small, the capacitor charges quickly; when it is larger, the charging takes more time. If the resistance is small, it's easier for current to flow, and the capacitor charges more quickly. If R is in ohms and C in farads, τ is in seconds.

In Fig. 26.22a the horizontal axis is an *asymptote* for the curve. Strictly speaking, i never becomes exactly zero. But the longer we wait, the closer it gets. After a time equal to 10 RC, the current has decreased to 0.000045 of its initial value. Similarly, the curve in Fig. 26.22b approaches the horizontal dashed line labeled Q_f as an asymptote. The charge q never attains exactly this value, but after a time equal to $10RC$, the difference between q and Q_f is only 0.000045 of Q_f. We invite you to verify that the product RC has units of time.

Discharging a Capacitor

Now suppose that after the capacitor in Fig. 26.21b has acquired a charge Q_0, we remove the battery from our R-C circuit and connect points a and c to an open switch (Fig. 26.23a). We then close the switch and at the same instant reset our stopwatch to $t = 0$; at that time, $q = Q_0$. The capacitor then *discharges* through the resistor, and its charge eventually decreases to zero.

Again let i and q represent the time-varying current and charge at some instant after the connection is made. In Fig. 26.23b we make the same choice of the positive direction for current as in Fig. 26.21b. Then Kirchhoff's loop rule gives Eq. (26.10) but with $\mathcal{E} = 0$; that is,

$$i = \frac{dq}{dt} = -\frac{q}{RC} \qquad (26.15)$$

The current i is now negative; this is because positive charge q is leaving the left-hand capacitor plate in Fig. 26.23b, so the current is in the direction opposite to that shown in the figure. At time $t = 0$, when $q = Q_0$, the initial current is $I_0 = -Q_0/RC$.

To find q as a function of time, we rearrange Eq. (26.15), again change the names of the variables to q' and t', and integrate. This time the limits for q' are Q_0 to q. We get

$$\int_{Q_0}^{q} \frac{dq'}{q'} = -\frac{1}{RC} \int_0^t dt'$$

$$\ln \frac{q}{Q_0} = -\frac{t}{RC}$$

$$q = Q_0 e^{-t/RC} \qquad \text{(} R\text{-}C \text{ circuit, discharging capacitor)} \qquad (26.16)$$

The instantaneous current i is the derivative of this with respect to time:

$$i = \frac{dq}{dt} = -\frac{Q_0}{RC} e^{-t/RC} = I_0 e^{-t/RC} \qquad \begin{array}{l}\text{(} R\text{-}C \text{ circuit,}\\ \text{discharging capacitor)}\end{array} \qquad (26.17)$$

The current and the charge are graphed in Fig. 26.24; both quantities approach zero exponentially with time. Comparing these results with Eqs. (26.12) and (26.13), we note that the expressions for the current are identical, apart from the sign of I_0.

The capacitor charge approaches zero asymptotically in Eq. (26.16), while the *difference* between q and Q approaches zero asymptotically in Eq. (26.12).

Energy considerations give us additional insight into the behavior of an *R-C* circuit. While the capacitor is charging, the instantaneous rate at which the battery delivers energy to the circuit is $P = \mathcal{E}i$. The instantaneous rate at which electrical energy is dissipated in the resistor is i^2R and the rate at which energy is stored in the capacitor is $iv_{bc} = iq/C$. Multiplying Eq. (26.9) by i, we find

$$\mathcal{E}i = i^2R + \frac{iq}{C} \qquad (26.18)$$

This means that of the power $\mathcal{E}i$ supplied by the battery, part (i^2R) is dissipated in the resistor and part (iq/C) is stored in the capacitor.

The *total* energy supplied by the battery during charging of the capacitor equals the battery emf $\mathcal{E}$ multiplied by the total charge Q_f, or $\mathcal{E}Q_f$. The total energy stored in the capacitor, from Eq. (24.9), is $Q_f\mathcal{E}/2$. Thus, of the energy supplied by the battery, *exactly half* is stored in the capacitor, and the other half is dissipated in the resistor. It is a little surprising that this half-and-half division of energy doesn't depend on C, R, or $\mathcal{E}$. This result can also be verified in detail by taking the integral over time of each of the power quantities in Eq. (26.18). We leave this calculation for your amusement (see Problem 26.87).

Example 26.12   **Charging a capacitor**

A resistor with resistance 10 MΩ is connected in series with a capacitor with capacitance 1.0 μF and a battery with emf 12.0 V. Before the switch is closed at time $t = 0$, the capacitor is uncharged. (a) What is the time constant? (b) What fraction of the final charge is on the plates at time $t = 46$ s? (c) What fraction of the initial current remains at $t = 46$ s?

SOLUTION

IDENTIFY: This is the same situation as shown in Fig. 26.21, with $R = 10$ MΩ, $C = 1.0$ μF, and $\mathcal{E} = 12.0$ V. The charge and current vary with time as shown in Fig. 26.22. Our target variables are (a) the time constant, (b) the charge q at $t = 46$ s divided by the final charge Q_f, and (c) the current i at $t = 46$ s divided by the initial current i_0.

SET UP: For a capacitor being charged, the charge is given by Eq. (26.12) and the current by Eq. (26.13). Equation (26.14) gives the time constant.

EXECUTE: (a) From Eq. (26.14), the time constant is

$$\tau = RC = (10 \times 10^6 \, \Omega)(1.0 \times 10^{-6} \, \text{F}) = 10 \text{ s}$$

(b) From Eq. (26.12),

$$\frac{q}{Q_f} = 1 - e^{-t/RC} = 1 - e^{-(46 \text{ s})/(10 \text{ s})} = 0.99$$

The capacitor is 99% charged after a time equal to 4.6 *RC*, or 4.6 time constants.

(c) From Eq. (26.13),

$$\frac{i}{I_0} = e^{-4.6} = 0.010$$

After 4.6 time constants the current has decreased to 1.0% of its initial value.

EVALUATE: The time constant is relatively long because the resistance is very large. The circuit charges more rapidly if a smaller resistance is used.

Example 26.13   **Discharging a capacitor**

The resistor and capacitor described in Example 26.12 are reconnected as shown in Fig. 26.23. The capacitor is originally given a charge of 5.0 μC and then discharged by closing the switch at $t = 0$. (a) At what time will the charge be equal to 0.50 μC? (b) What is the current at this time?

SOLUTION

IDENTIFY: Now the capacitor is being discharged, so the charge q and current i vary with time as shown in Fig. 26.24. Our target variables are (a) the value of t at which $q = 0.50$ μC and (b) the value of i at this time.

SET UP: The charge is given by Eq. (26.16) and the current by Eq. (26.17).

EXECUTE: (a) Solving Eq. (26.16) for the time t gives

$$t = -RC \ln \frac{q}{Q_0}$$

$$= -(10 \times 10^6 \, \Omega)(1.0 \times 10^{-6} \, \text{F}) \ln \frac{0.50 \, \mu\text{C}}{5.0 \, \mu\text{C}} = 23 \text{ s}$$

Continued

This is 2.3 times the time constant $\tau = RC = 10$ s.

(b) From Eq. (26.17), with $Q_0 = 5.0 \; \mu C = 5.0 \times 10^{-6}$ C,

$$i = -\frac{Q_0}{RC}e^{-t/RC} = -\frac{5.0 \times 10^{-6} \; C}{10 \; s}e^{-2.3} = -5.0 \times 10^{-8} \; A$$

The current has the opposite sign when the capacitor is discharging than when it is charging.

EVALUATE: We could have saved the effort required to calculate $e^{-t/RC}$ by noticing that at the time in question, $q = 0.10Q_0$; from Eq. (26.16) this means $e^{-t/RC} = 0.10$.

Test Your Understanding of Section 26.4 The energy stored in a capacitor is equal to $q^2/2C$. When a capacitor is discharged, what fraction of the initial energy remains after an elapsed time of one time constant? (i) $1/e$; (ii) $1/e^2$; (iii) $1 - 1/e$; (iv) $(1 - 1/e)^2$; (v) answer depends on how much energy was stored initially.

26.5 Power Distribution Systems

We conclude this chapter with a brief discussion of practical household and automotive electric-power distribution systems. Automobiles use direct-current (dc) systems, while nearly all household, commercial, and industrial systems use alternating current (ac) because of the ease of stepping voltage up and down with transformers. Most of the same basic wiring concepts apply to both. We'll talk about alternating-current circuits in greater detail in Chapter 31.

The various lamps, motors, and other appliances to be operated are always connected in *parallel* to the power source (the wires from the power company for houses, or from the battery and alternator for a car). If appliances were connected in series, shutting one appliance off would shut them all off (see Example 26.2 in Section 26.1). The basic idea of house wiring is shown in Fig. 26.25. One side of the "line," as the pair of conductors is called, is called the *neutral* side; it is always connected to "ground" at the entrance panel. For houses, *ground* is an actual electrode driven into the earth (which is usually a good conductor) or sometimes connected to the household water pipes. Electricians speak of the "hot" side and the "neutral" side of the line. Most modern house wiring systems have *two* hot lines with opposite polarity with respect to the neutral. We'll return to this detail later.

Household voltage is nominally 120 V in the United States and Canada, and often 240 V in Europe. (For alternating current, which varies sinusoidally with time, these numbers represent the *root-mean-square* voltage, which is $1/\sqrt{2}$ times the peak voltage. We'll discuss this further in Section 31.1.) The amount of current I drawn by a given device is determined by its power input P, given by Eq. (25.17): $P = VI$. Hence $I = P/V$. For example, the current in a 100-W light bulb is

$$I = \frac{P}{V} = \frac{100 \; W}{120 \; V} = 0.83 \; A$$

26.25 Schematic diagram of part of a house wiring system. Only two branch circuits are shown; an actual system might have four to thirty branch circuits. Lamps and appliances may be plugged into the outlets. The grounding wires, which normally carry no current, are not shown.

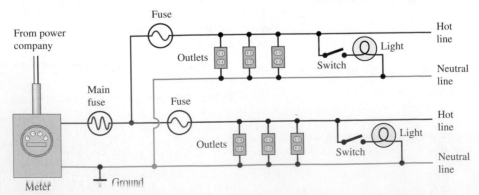

The power input to this bulb is actually determined by its resistance R. Using Eq. (25.18), which states that $P = VI = I^2R = V^2/R$ for a resistor, the resistance of this bulb at operating temperature is

$$R = \frac{V}{I} = \frac{120 \text{ V}}{0.83 \text{ A}} = 144 \ \Omega \qquad \text{or} \qquad R = \frac{V^2}{P} = \frac{(120 \text{ V})^2}{100 \text{ W}} = 144 \ \Omega$$

Similarly, a 1500-W waffle iron draws a current of $(1500 \text{ W})/(120 \text{ V}) = 12.5 \text{ A}$ and has a resistance, at operating temperature, of $9.6 \ \Omega$. Because of the temperature dependence of resistivity, the resistances of these devices are considerably less when they are cold. If you measure the resistance of a 100-W light bulb with an ohmmeter (whose small current causes very little temperature rise), you will probably get a value of about $10 \ \Omega$. When a light bulb is turned on, this low resistance causes an initial surge of current until the filament heats up. That's why a light bulb that's ready to burn out nearly always does so just when you turn it on.

Circuit Overloads and Short Circuits

The maximum current available from an individual circuit is limited by the resistance of the wires. As we discussed in Section 25.5, the I^2R power loss in the wires causes them to become hot, and in extreme cases this can cause a fire or melt the wires. Ordinary lighting and outlet wiring in houses usually uses 12-gauge wire. This has a diameter of 2.05 mm and can carry a maximum current of 20 A safely (without overheating). Larger sizes such as 8-gauge (3.26 mm) or 6-gauge (4.11 mm) are used for high-current appliances such as electric ranges and clothes dryers, and 2-gauge (6.54 mm) or larger is used for the main power lines entering a house.

Protection against overloading and overheating of circuits is provided by fuses or circuit breakers. A *fuse* contains a link of lead–tin alloy with a very low melting temperature; the link melts and breaks the circuit when its rated current is exceeded (Fig. 26.26a). A *circuit breaker* is an electromechanical device that performs the same function, using an electromagnet or a bimetallic strip to "trip" the breaker and interrupt the circuit when the current exceeds a specified value (Fig. 26.26b). Circuit breakers have the advantage that they can be reset after they are tripped, while a blown fuse must be replaced. However, fuses are somewhat more reliable in operation than circuit breakers are.

If your system has fuses and you plug too many high-current appliances into the same outlet, the fuse blows. *Do not* replace the fuse with one of larger rating; if you do, you risk overheating the wires and starting a fire. The only safe solution is to distribute the appliances among several circuits. Modern kitchens often have three or four separate 20-A circuits.

Contact between the hot and neutral sides of the line causes a *short circuit*. Such a situation, which can be caused by faulty insulation or by any of a variety of mechanical malfunctions, provides a very low-resistance current path, permitting a very large current that would quickly melt the wires and ignite their insulation if the current were not interrupted by a fuse or circuit breaker (see Example 25.11 in Section 25.5). An equally dangerous situation is a broken wire that interrupts the current path, creating an *open circuit*. This is hazardous because of the sparking that can occur at the point of intermittent contact.

In approved wiring practice, a fuse or breaker is placed *only* in the hot side of the line, never in the neutral side. Otherwise, if a short circuit should develop because of faulty insulation or other malfunction, the ground-side fuse could blow. The hot side would still be live and would pose a shock hazard if you touched the live conductor and a grounded object such as a water pipe. For similar reasons the wall switch for a light fixture is always in the hot side of the line, never the neutral side.

Further protection against shock hazard is provided by a third conductor called the *grounding wire,* included in all present-day wiring. This conductor

26.26 (a) Excess current will melt the thin wire of lead–tin alloy that runs along the length of a fuse, inside the transparent housing. (b) The switch on this circuit breaker will flip if the maximum allowable current is exceeded.

(a)

(b)

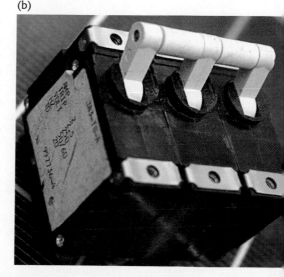

26.27 (a) If a malfunctioning electric drill is connected to a wall socket via a two-prong plug, a person may receive a shock. (b) When the drill malfunctions when connected via a three-prong plug, a person touching it receives no shock, because electric charge flows through the ground wire (shown in green) to the third prong and into the ground rather than into the person's body. If the ground current is appreciable, the fuse blows.

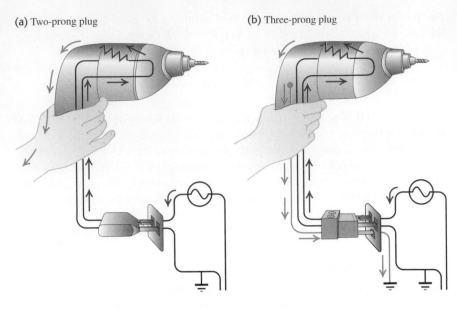

(a) Two-prong plug   (b) Three-prong plug

corresponds to the long round or U-shaped prong of the three-prong connector plug on an appliance or power tool. It is connected to the neutral side of the line at the entrance panel. The grounding wire normally carries no current, but it connects the metal case or frame of the device to ground. If a conductor on the hot side of the line accidentally contacts the frame or case, the grounding conductor provides a current path, and the fuse blows. Without the ground wire, the frame could become "live,"—that is, at a potential 120 V above ground. Then if you touched it and a water pipe (or even a damp basement floor) at the same time, you could get a dangerous shock (Fig. 26.27). In some situations, especially outlets located outdoors or near a sink or other water pipes, a special kind of circuit breaker called a *ground-fault interrupter* (GFI or GFCI) is used. This device senses the difference in current between the hot and neutral conductors (which is normally zero) and trips when this difference exceeds some very small value, typically 5 mA.

Household and Automotive Wiring

Most modern household wiring systems actually use a slight elaboration of the system described above. The power company provides *three* conductors (Fig. 26.28). One is neutral; the other two are both at 120 V with respect to the neutral but with opposite polarity, giving a voltage between them of 240 V. The power company calls this a *three-wire line,* in contrast to the 120-V two-wire (plus ground wire) line described above. With a three-wire line, 120-V lamps and appliances can be connected between neutral and either hot conductor, and high-power devices requiring 240 V, such as electric ranges and clothes dryers, are connected between the two hot lines.

To help prevent wiring errors, household wiring uses a standardized color code in which the hot side of a line has black insulation (black and red for the two sides of a 240-V line), the neutral side has white insulation, and the grounding conductor is bare or has green insulation. But in electronic devices and equipment the ground or neutral side of the line is usually black. Beware! (Our illustrations do not follow this standard code but use red for the hot line and blue for neutral.)

All of the above discussion can be applied directly to automobile wiring. The voltage is about 13 V (direct current); the power is supplied by the battery and by the alternator, which charges the battery when the engine is running. The neutral

26.28 Diagram of a typical 120–240-V wiring system in a kitchen. Grounding wires are not shown. For each line, the hot side is shown in red, and the neutral line is shown in blue. (Different colors are used in actual household wiring.)

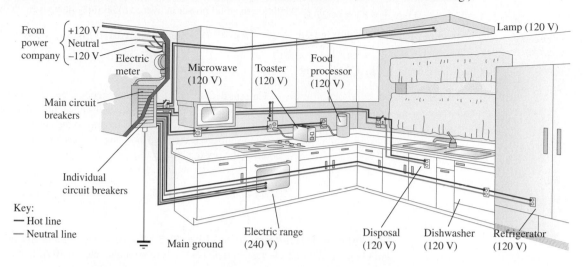

side of each circuit is connected to the body and frame of the vehicle. For this low voltage a separate grounding conductor is not required for safety. The fuse or circuit breaker arrangement is the same in principle as in household wiring. Because of the lower voltage (less energy per charge), more current (a greater number of charges per second) is required for the same power; a 100-W headlight bulb requires a current of about $(100 \text{ W})/(13 \text{ V}) = 8$ A.

Although we spoke of *power* in the above discussion, what we buy from the power company is *energy*. Power is energy transferred per unit time, so energy is average power multiplied by time. The usual unit of energy sold by the power company is the kilowatt-hour $(1 \text{ kW} \cdot \text{h})$:

$$1 \text{ kW} \cdot \text{h} = (10^3 \text{ W})(3600 \text{ s}) = 3.6 \times 10^6 \text{ W} \cdot \text{s} = 3.6 \times 10^6 \text{ J}$$

One kilowatt-hour typically costs 2 to 10 cents, depending on the location and quantity of energy purchased. To operate a 1500-W (1.5-kW) waffle iron continuously for 1 hour requires 1.5 kW · h of energy; at 10 cents per kilowatt-hour, the energy cost is 15 cents. The cost of operating any lamp or appliance for a specified time can be calculated in the same way if the power rating is known. However, many electric cooking utensils (including waffle irons) cycle on and off to maintain a constant temperature, so the average power may be less than the power rating marked on the device.

Example 26.14 **A kitchen circuit**

An 1800-W toaster, a 1.3-kW electric frying pan, and a 100-W lamp are plugged into the same 20-A, 120-V circuit. (a) What current is drawn by each device, and what is the resistance of each device? (b) Will this combination blow the fuse?

SOLUTION

IDENTIFY: When plugged into the same circuit, the three devices are in parallel. The voltage across each device is $V = 120$ V.

SET UP: We find the current I drawn by each device using the relationship $P = VI$, where P is the power input of the device. To find the resistance R for each device we use the relationship $P = V^2/R$.

EXECUTE: (a) To simplify the calculation of current and resistance, we note that $I = P/V$ and $R = V^2/P$. Hence

$$I_{\text{toaster}} = \frac{1800 \text{ W}}{120 \text{ V}} = 15 \text{ A} \qquad R_{\text{toaster}} = \frac{(120 \text{ V})^2}{1800 \text{ W}} = 8 \ \Omega$$

$$I_{\text{frying pan}} = \frac{1300 \text{ W}}{120 \text{ V}} = 11 \text{ A} \qquad R_{\text{frying pan}} = \frac{(120 \text{ V})^2}{1300 \text{ W}} = 11 \ \Omega$$

$$I_{\text{lamp}} = \frac{100 \text{ W}}{120 \text{ V}} = 0.83 \text{ A} \qquad R_{\text{lamp}} = \frac{(120 \text{ V})^2}{100 \text{ W}} = 144 \ \Omega$$

For constant voltage the device with the *least* resistance (in this case the toaster) draws the most current and receives the most power.

Continued

(b) The total current through the line is the sum of the currents drawn by the three devices:

$$I = I_{toaster} + I_{frying\ pan} + I_{lamp} = 15\ A + 11\ A + 0.83\ A = 27\ A$$

This exceeds the 20-A rating of the line, and the fuse will indeed blow.

EVALUATE: We could also find the current by first finding the equivalent resistance of the three devices in parallel:

$$\frac{1}{R_{eq}} = \frac{1}{R_{toaster}} + \frac{1}{R_{frying\ pan}} + \frac{1}{R_{lamp}}$$

$$= \frac{1}{8\ \Omega} + \frac{1}{11\ \Omega} + \frac{1}{144\ \Omega} = 0.22\ \Omega^{-1}$$

$$R_{eq} = 4.5\ \Omega$$

The total current is then $I = V/R_{eq} = (120\ V)/(4.5\ \Omega) = 27\ A$, as before. A third way to determine I is to use $I = P/V$ and simply divide the total power delivered to all three devices by the voltage:

$$I = \frac{P_{toaster} + P_{frying\ pan} + P_{lamp}}{V} = \frac{1800\ W + 1300\ W + 100\ W}{120\ V}$$

$$= 27\ A$$

Current demands like these are encountered in everyday life in kitchens, which is why modern kitchens have more than one 20-A circuit. In actual practice, the toaster and frying pan should be connected to different circuits; the current in each circuit would then be safely below the 20-A rating.

Test Your Understanding of Section 26.5   To prevent the fuse in Example 26.14 from blowing, a home electrician replaces the fuse with one rated at 40 A. Is this a reasonable thing to do?

Resistors in series and parallel: When several resistors $R_1, R_2, R_3, \ldots$, are connected in series, the equivalent resistance R_{eq} is the sum of the individual resistances. The same *current* flows through all the resistors in a series connection. When several resistors are connected in parallel, the reciprocal of the equivalent resistance R_{eq} is the sum of the reciprocals of the individual resistances. All resistors in a parallel connection have the same *potential difference* between their terminals. (See Examples 26.1 and 26.2.)

$$R_{eq} = R_1 + R_2 + R_3 + \cdots \quad \text{(26.1)}$$
(resistors in series)

$$\frac{1}{R_{eq}} = \frac{1}{R_1} + \frac{1}{R_2} + \frac{1}{R_3} + \cdots \quad \text{(26.2)}$$
(resistors in parallel)

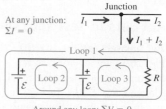

Kirchhoff's rules: Kirchhoff's junction rule is based on conservation of charge. It states that the algebraic sum of the currents into any junction must be zero. Kirchhoff's loop rule is based on conservation of energy and the conservative nature of electrostatic fields. It states that the algebraic sum of potential differences around any loop must be zero. Careful use of consistent sign rules is essential in applying Kirchhoff's rules. (See Examples 26.3–26.7)

$$\sum I = 0 \quad \text{(junction rule)} \quad \text{(26.5)}$$
$$\sum V = 0 \quad \text{(loop rule)} \quad \text{(26.6)}$$

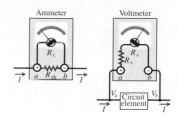

Electrical measuring instruments: In a d'Arsonval galvanometer, the deflection is proportional to the current in the coil. For a larger current range, a shunt resistor is added, so some of the current bypasses the meter coil. Such an instrument is called an ammeter. If the coil and any additional series resistance included obey Ohm's law, the meter can also be calibrated to read potential difference or voltage. The instrument is then called a voltmeter. A good ammeter has very low resistance; a good voltmeter has very high resistance. (See Examples 26.8–26.11.)

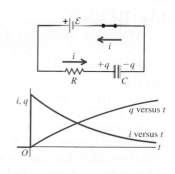

R-C circuits: When a capacitor is charged by a battery in series with a resistor, the current and capacitor charge are not constant. The charge approaches its final value asymptotically and the current approaches zero asymptotically. The charge and current in the circuit are given by Eqs. (26.12) and (26.13). After a time $\tau = RC$, the charge has approached within $1/e$ of its final value. This time is called the time constant or relaxation time of the circuit. When the capacitor discharges, the charge and current are given as functions of time by Eqs. (26.16) and (26.17). The time constant is the same for charging and discharging. (See Examples 26.12 and 26.13.)

Capacitor charging:
$$q = C\mathcal{E}(1 - e^{-t/RC})$$
$$= Q_f(1 - e^{-t/RC}) \quad \text{(26.12)}$$

$$i = \frac{dq}{dt} = \frac{\mathcal{E}}{R}e^{-t/RC}$$
$$= I_0 e^{-t/RC} \quad \text{(26.13)}$$

Capacitor discharging:
$$q = Q_0 e^{-t/RC} \quad \text{(26.16)}$$

$$i = \frac{dq}{dt} = -\frac{Q_0}{RC}e^{-t/RC}$$
$$= I_0 e^{-t/RC} \quad \text{(26.17)}$$

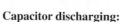

Household wiring: In household wiring systems, the various electrical devices are connected in parallel across the power line, which consists of a pair of conductors, one "hot" and the other "neutral." An additional "ground" wire is included for safety. The maximum permissible current in a circuit is determined by the size of the wires and the maximum temperature they can tolerate. Protection against excessive current and the resulting fire hazard is provided by fuses or circuit breakers. (See Example 26.14.)

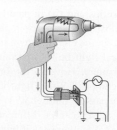

Key Terms

Answer to Chapter Opening Question ?

The potential difference V is the same across resistors connected in parallel. However, there is a different current I through each resistor if the resistances R are different: $I = V/R$.

Answers to Test Your Understanding Questions

26.1 answer: (a), (c), (d), (b) Here's why: The three resistors in Fig. 26.1a are in series, so $R_{eq} = R + R + R = 3R$. In Fig. 26.1b the three resistors are in parallel, so $1/R_{eq} = 1/R + 1/R + 1/R = 3/R$ and $R_{eq} = R/3$. In Fig. 26.1c the second and third resistors are in parallel, so their equivalent resistance R_{23} is given by $1/R_{23} = 1/R + 1/R = 2/R$; hence $R_{23} = R/2$. This combination is in series with the first resistor, so the three resistors together have equivalent resistance $R_{eq} = R + R/2 = 3R/2$. In Fig. 26.1d the second and third resistors are in series, so their equivalent resistance is $R_{23} = R + R = 2R$. This combination is in parallel with the first resistor, so the equivalent resistance of the three-resistor combination is given by $1/R_{eq} = 1/R + 1/2R = 3/2R$. Hence $R_{eq} = 2R/3$.

26.2 answer: loop *cbdac* Equation (2) minus Eq. (1) gives $-I_2(1\ \Omega) - (I_2 + I_3)(2\ \Omega) + (I_1 - I_3)(1\ \Omega) + I_1(1\ \Omega) = 0$.

We can obtain this equation by applying the loop rule around the path from *c* to *b* to *d* to *a* to *c* in Fig. 26.12. This isn't a new equation, so it would not have helped with the solution of Example 26.6.

26.3 answers: (a) (ii), (b) (iii) An ammeter must always be placed in series with the circuit element of interest, and a voltmeter must always be placed in parallel. Ideally the ammeter would have zero resistance and the voltmeter would have infinite resistance so that their presence would have no effect on either the resistor current or the voltage. Neither of these idealizations is possible, but the ammeter resistance should be much less than 2 Ω and the voltmeter resistance should be much greater than 2 Ω.

26.4 answer: (ii) After one time constant, $t = RC$ and the initial charge Q_0 has decreased to $Q_0 e^{-t/RC} = Q_0 e^{-RC/RC} = Q_0 e^{-1} = Q_0/e$. Hence the stored energy has decreased from $Q_0^2/2C$ to $(Q_0/e)^2/2C = Q_0^2/2Ce^2$, a fraction $1/e^2 = 0.135$ of its initial value. This result doesn't depend on the initial value of the energy.

26.5 answer: no This is a very dangerous thing to do. The fuse will allow currents up to 40 A, double the rated value of the wiring. The amount of power $P = I^2R$ dissipated in a section of wire can therefore be up to four times the rated value, so the wires could get very warm and start a fire.

PROBLEMS

For instructor-assigned homework, go to **www.masteringphysics.com**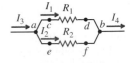

Discussion Questions

Q26.1. In which 120-V light bulb does the filament have greater resistance: a 60-W bulb or a 120-W bulb? If the two bulbs are connected to a 120-V line in series, through which bulb will there be the greater voltage drop? What if they are connected in parallel? Explain your reasoning.

Q26.2. Two 120-V light bulbs, one 25-W and one 200-W, were connected in series across a 240-V line. It seemed like a good idea at the time, but one bulb burned out almost immediately. Which one burned out, and why?

Q26.3. You connect a number of identical light bulbs to a flashlight battery. (a) What happens to the brightness of each bulb as more and more bulbs are added to the circuit if you connect them (i) in series and (ii) in parallel? (b) Will the battery last longer if the bulbs are in series or in parallel? Explain your reasoning.

Q26.4. In the circuit shown in Fig. 26.29, three identical light bulbs are connected to a flashlight battery. How do the brightnesses of the bulbs compare? Which light bulb has the greatest current passing through it? Which light bulb has the greatest potential difference between its terminals? What happens if bulb *A* is unscrewed? Bulb *B*? Bulb *C*? Explain your reasoning.

Figure 26.29
Question Q26.4.

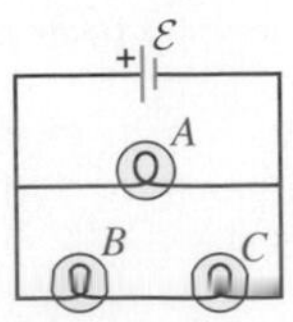

Q26.5. If two resistors R_1 and R_2 ($R_2 > R_1$) are connected in series as shown in Fig. 26.30, which of the following must be true? In each case justify your answer. (a) $I_1 = I_2 = I_3$. (b) The current is greater in R_1 than in R_2. (c) The electrical power consumption is the same for both resistors. (d) The electrical power consumption is greater in R_2 than in R_1. (e) The potential drop is the same across both resistors. (f) The potential at point *a* is the same as at point *c*. (g) The potential at point *b* is lower than at point *c*. (h) The potential at point *c* is lower than at point *b*.

Figure 26.30
Question Q26.5.

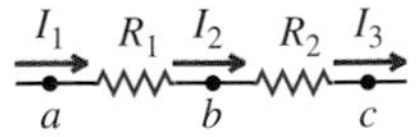

Q26.6. If two resistors R_1 and R_2 ($R_2 > R_1$) are connected in parallel as shown in Fig. 26.31, which of the following must be true? In each case justify your answer. (a) $I_1 = I_2$. (b) $I_3 = I_4$. (c) The current is greater in R_1 than in R_2. (d) The rate of electrical energy consumption is the same for both resistors. (e) The rate of electrical energy consumption is greater in R_2 than in R_1. (f) $V_{cd} = V_{ef} = V_{ab}$. (g) Point *c* is at higher potential than point *d*. (h) Point *f* is at higher potential than point *e*. (i) Point *c* is at higher potential than point *e*.

Figure 26.31
Question Q26.6.

Q26.7. Why do the lights on a car become dimmer when the starter is operated?

Q26.8. A resistor consists of three identical metal strips connected as shown in Fig. 26.32. If one of the strips is cut out, does the ammeter reading increase, decrease, or stay the same? Why?

Figure 26.32 Question Q26.8.

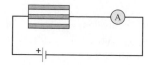

Q26.9. A light bulb is connected in the circuit shown in Fig. 26.33. If we close the switch S, does the bulb's brightness increase, decrease, or remain the same? Explain why.

Figure 26.33 Question Q26.9.

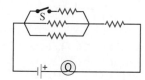

Q26.10. A real battery, having nonnegligible internal resistance, is connected across a light bulb as shown in Fig. 26.34. When the switch S is closed, what happens to the brightness of the bulb? Why?

Figure 26.34
Question Q26.10.

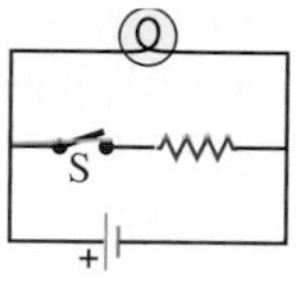

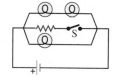

Q26.11. If the battery in Discussion Question Q26.10 is ideal with no internal resistance, what will happen to the brightness of the bulb when S is closed? Why?

Q26.12. For the circuit shown in Fig. 26.35 what happens to the brightness of the bulbs when the switch S is closed if the battery (a) has no internal resistance and (b) has nonnegligible internal resistance? Explain why.

Figure 26.35
Question Q26.12.

Q26.13. Is it possible to connect resistors together in a way that cannot be reduced to some combination of series and parallel combinations? If so, give examples. If not, state why not.

Q26.14. The direction of current in a battery can be reversed by connecting it to a second battery of greater emf with the positive terminals of the two batteries together. When the direction of current is reversed in a battery, does its emf also reverse? Why or why not?

Q26.15. In a two-cell flashlight, the batteries are usually connected in series. Why not connect them in parallel? What possible advantage could there be in connecting several identical batteries in parallel?

Q26.16. Electric rays (genus *Torpedo*) deliver electric shocks to stun their prey and to discourage predators. (In ancient Rome, physicians practiced a primitive form of electroconvulsive therapy by placing electric rays on their patients to cure headaches and gout.) Figure 26.36a shows *Torpedo* as seen from below. The voltage is produced by thin, waferlike cells called *electrocytes,* each of which acts like a battery with an emf of about 10^{-4} V. Stacks of electrocytes are arranged side by side on the underside of *Torpedo* (Fig. 26.36b); in such a stack, the positive face of each electrocyte touches the negative face of the next electrocyte (Fig. 26.36c). What is the advantage of stacking the electrocytes? Of having the stacks side by side?

Figure 26.36 Question Q26.16.

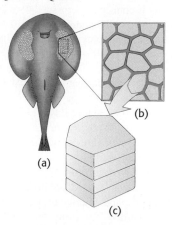

Q26.17. The emf of a flashlight battery is roughly constant with time, but its internal resistance increases with age and use. What sort of meter should be used to test the freshness of a battery?

Q26.18. Is it possible to have a circuit in which the potential difference across the terminals of a battery in the circuit is zero? If so, give an example. If not, explain why not.

Q26.19. Verify that the time constant RC has units of time.

Q26.20. For very large resistances it is easy to construct R-C circuits that have time constants of several seconds or minutes. How might this fact be used to measure very large resistances, those that are too large to measure by more conventional means?

Q26.21. Whan a capacitor, battery, and resistor are connected in series, does the resistor affect the maximum charge stores on the capacitor? Why or why not? What purpose does the resistor serve?

Q26.22. The greater the diameter of the wire used in household wiring, the greater the maximum current that can safely be carried by the wire. Why is this? Does the maximum permissible current depend on the length of the wire? Does it depend on what the wire is made of? Explain your reasoning.

Exercises

Section 26.1 Resistors in Series and Parallel

26.1. A uniform wire of resistance R is cut into three equal lengths. One of these is formed into a circle and connected between the other two (Fig. 26.37). What is the resistance between the opposite ends a and b?

Figure 26.37
Exercise 26.1.

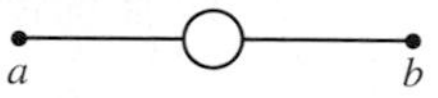

26.2. A machine part has a resistor X protruding from an opening in the side. This resistor is connected to three other resistors, as shown in Fig. 26.38. An ohmmeter connected across a and b reads 2.00 Ω. What is the resistance of X?

Figure 26.38 Exercise 26.2.

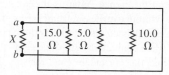

26.3. (a) Prove that when two resistors are connected in parallel, the equivalent resistance of the combination is always smaller than that of the smaller resistor. (b) Generalize your result from part (a) for N resistors.

26.4. A 32-Ω resistor and a 20-Ω resistor are connected in parallel, and the combination is connected across a 240-V dc line. (a) What is the resistance of the parallel combination? (b) What is the total current through the parallel combination? (c) What is the current through each resistor?

26.5. A triangular array of resistors is shown in Fig. 26.39. What current will this array draw from a 35.0-V battery having negligible internal resistance if we connect it across (a) ab; (b) bc; (c) ac? (d) If the battery has an internal resistance of 3.00 Ω, what current will the array draw if the battery is connected across bc?

Figure 26.39 Exercise 26.5.

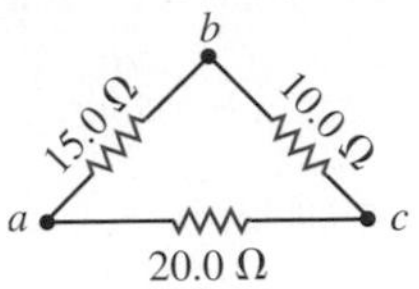

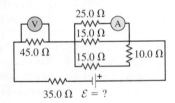

26.6. For the circuit shown in Fig. 26.40 both meters are idealized, the battery has no appreciable internal resistance, and the ammeter reads 1.25 A. (a) What does the voltmeter read? (b) What is the emf $\mathcal{E}$ of the battery?

Figure 26.40 Exercise 26.6.

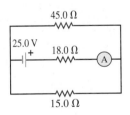

26.7. For the circuit shown in Fig. 26.41 find the reading of the idealized ammeter if the battery has an internal resistance of 3.26 Ω.

Figure 26.41 Exercise 26.7.

26.8. Three resistors having resistances of 1.60 Ω, 2.40 Ω, and 4.80 Ω are connected in parallel to a 28.0-V battery that has negligible internal resistance. Find (a) the equivalent resistance of the combination; (b) the current in each resistor; (c) the total current through the battery; (d) the voltage across each resistor; (e) the power dissipated in each resistor. (f) Which resistor dissipates the most power: the one with the greatest resistance or the least resistance? Explain why this should be.

26.9. Now the three resistors of Exercise 26.8 are connected in series to the same battery. Answer the same questions for this situation.

26.10. Power Rating of a Resistor. The *power rating* of a resistor is the maximum power the resistor can safely dissipate without too great a rise in temperature and hence damage to the resistor. (a) If the power rating of a 15-kΩ resistor is 5.0 W, what is the maximum allowable potential difference across the terminals of the resistor? (b) A 9.0-kΩ resistor is to be connected across a 120-V potential difference. What power rating is required? (c) A 100.0-Ω and a 150.0-Ω resistor, both rated at 2.00 W, are connected in series across a variable potential difference. What is the greatest this potential difference can be without overheating either resistor, and what is the rate of heat generated in each resistor under these conditions?

26.11. Compute the equivalent resistance of the network in Fig. 26.42, and find the current in each resistor. The battery has negligible internal resistance.

Figure 26.42 Exercise 26.11.

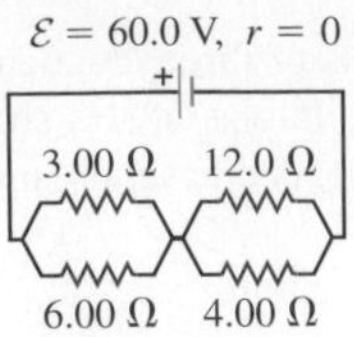

26.12. Compute the equivalent resistance of the network in Fig. 26.43, and find the current in each resistor. The battery has negligible internal resistance.

Figure 26.43 Exercise 26.12.

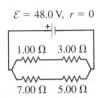

26.13. In the circuit of Fig. 26.44, each resistor represents a light bulb. Let $R_1 = R_2 = R_3 = R_4 = 4.50\ \Omega$ and $\mathcal{E} = 9.00$ V. (a) Find the current in each bulb. (b) Find the power dissipated in each bulb. Which bulb or bulbs glow the brightest? (c) Bulb R_4 is now removed from the circuit, leaving a break in the wire at its position. Now what is the current in each of the remaining bulbs R_1, R_2, and R_3? (d) With bulb R_4 removed, what is the power dissipated in each of the remaining bulbs? (e) Which light bulb(s) glow brighter as a result of removing R_4? Which bulb(s) glow less brightly? Discuss why there are different effects on different bulbs.

Figure 26.44 Exercise 26.13.

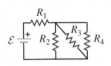

26.14. Consider the circuit shown in Fig. 26.45. The current through the 6.00-Ω resistor is 4.00 A, in the direction shown. What are the currents through the 25.0-Ω and 20.0-Ω resistors?

Figure 26.45 Exercise 26.14.

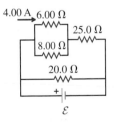

26.15. In the circuit shown in Fig. 26.46, the voltage across the 2.00-Ω resistor is 12.0 V. What are the emf of the battery and the current through the 6.00-Ω resistor?

26.16. A Three-Way Light Bulb. A three-way light bulb has three brightness settings (low, medium, and high) but only two filaments. (a) A particular three-way light bulb connected across a 120-V line can dissipate 60 W, 120 W, or 180 W. Describe how the two filaments are arranged in the bulb, and calculate the resistance of each filament. (b) Suppose the filament with the higher resistance burns out. How much power will the bulb dissipate on each of the three brightness settings? What will be the brightness (low, medium, or high) on each setting?

Figure 26.46 Exercise 26.15.

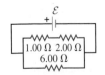

(c) Repeat part (b) for the situation in which the filament with the lower resistance burns out.

26.17. Light Bulbs in Series and in Parallel. Two light bulbs have resistances of 400 Ω and 800 Ω. If the two light bulbs are connected in series across a 120-V line, find (a) the current through each bulb; (b) the power dissipated in each bulb; (c) the total power dissipated in both bulbs. The two light bulbs are now connected in parallel across the 120-V line. Find (d) the current through each bulb; (e) the power dissipated in each bulb; (f) the total power dissipated in both bulbs. (g) In each situation, which of the two bulbs glows the brightest? (h) In which situation is there a greater total light output from both bulbs combined?

26.18. Light Bulbs in Series. A 60-W, 120-V light bulb and a 200-W, 120-V light bulb are connected in series across a 240-V line. Assume that the resistance of each bulb does not vary with current. (*Note:* This description of a light bulb gives the power it dissipates when connected to the stated potential difference; that is, a 25-W, 120-V light bulb dissipates 25 W when connected to a 120-V line.) (a) Find the current through the bulbs. (b) Find the power dissipated in each bulb. (c) One bulb burns out very quickly. Which one? Why?

26.19. In the circuit in Fig. 26.47, a 20.0-Ω resistor is inside 100 g of pure water that is surrounded by insulating styrofoam. If the water is initially at 10.0°C, how long will it take for its temperature to rise to 58.0°C?

Figure 26.47
Exercise 26.19.

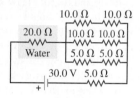

26.20. In the circuit shown in Fig. 26.48, the rate at which R_1 is dissipating electrical energy is 20.0 W. (a) Find R_1 and R_2. (b) What is the emf of the battery? (c) Find the current through both R_2 and the 10.0-Ω resistor. (d) Calculate the total electrical power consumption in all the resistors and the electrical power delivered by the battery. Show that your results are consistent with conservation of energy.

Figure 26.48
Exercise 26.20.

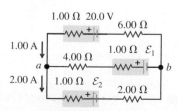

Section 26.2 Kirchhoff's Rules

26.21. In the circuit shown in Fig. 26.49 find (a) the current in resistor R; (b) the resistance R; (c) the unknown emf $\mathcal{E}$. (d) If the circuit is broken at point x, what is the current in resistor R?

Figure 26.49
Exercise 26.21.

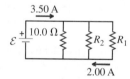

26.22. Find the emfs $\mathcal{E}_1$ and $\mathcal{E}_2$ in the circuit of Fig. 26.50, and find the potential difference of point b relative to point a.

Figure 26.50 Exercise 26.22.

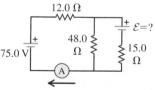

26.23. In the circuit shown in Fig. 26.51, find (a) the current in the 3.00-Ω resistor; (b) the unknown emfs $\mathcal{E}_1$ and $\mathcal{E}_2$; (c) the resistance R. Note that three currents are given.

Figure 26.51 Exercise 26.23.

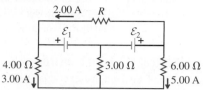

26.24. In the circuit shown in Fig. 26.52, find (a) the current in each branch and (b) the potential difference V_{ab} of point a relative to point b.

26.25. The 10.00-V battery in Fig. 26.52 is removed from the circuit and reinserted with the opposite polarity, so that its positive terminal is now next to point a. The rest of the circuit is as shown in the figure. Find (a) the current in each branch and (b) the potential difference V_{ab} of point a relative to point b.

Figure 26.52
Exercises 26.24, 26.25, and 26.26.

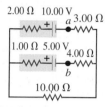

26.26. The 5.00-V battery in Fig. 26.52 is removed from the circuit and replaced by a 20.00-V battery, with its negative terminal next to point b. The rest of the circuit is as shown in the figure. Find (a) the current in each branch and (b) the potential difference V_{ab} of point a relative to point b.

26.27. In the circuit shown in Fig. 26.53 the batteries have negligible internal resistance and the meters are both idealized. With the switch S open, the voltmeter reads 15.0 V. (a) Find the emf $\mathcal{E}$ of the battery. (b) What will the ammeter read when the switch is closed?

Figure 26.53 Exercise 26.27.

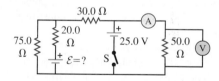

26.28. In the circuit shown in Fig. 26.54 both batteries have insignificant internal resistance and the idealized ammeter reads 1.50 A in the direction shown. Find the emf $\mathcal{E}$ of the battery. Is the polarity shown correct?

Figure 26.54 Exercise 26.28.

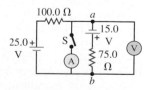

26.29. In the circuit shown in Fig. 26.55 all meters are idealized and the batteries have no appreciable internal resistance. (a) Find the reading of the voltmeter with the switch S open. Which point is at a higher potential: a or b? (b) With the switch closed, find the reading of the voltmeter and the ammeter. Which way (up or down) does the current flow through the switch?

Figure 26.55
Exercise 26.29.

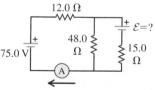

26.30. In the circuit shown in Fig. 26.12 (Example 26.6) the 2-Ω resistor is replaced by a 1-Ω resistor, and the center 1-Ω resistor (through which the current is I_3) is replaced by a resistor of unknown resistance R. The rest of the circuit is as shown in the figure. (a) Calculate the current in each resistor. Draw a diagram of the circuit, and label each resistor with the current through it. (b) Calculate the equivalent resistance of the network. (c) Calculate the potential difference V_{ab}. (d) Your answers in parts (a), (b), and (c) do not depend on the value of R. Explain why.

Section 26.3 Electrical Measuring Instruments

26.31. The resistance of a galvanometer coil is 25.0 Ω, and the current required for full-scale deflection is 500 μA. (a) Show in a diagram how to convert the galvanometer to an ammeter reading 20.0 mA full scale, and compute the shunt resistance. (b) Show how to convert the galvanometer to a voltmeter reading 500 mV full scale, and compute the series resistance.

26.32. The resistance of the coil of a pivoted-coil galvanometer is 9.36 Ω, and a current of 0.0224 A causes it to deflect full scale. We want to convert this galvanometer to an ammeter reading 20.0 A full scale. The only shunt available has a resistance of 0.0250 Ω. What resistance R must be connected in series with the coil (Fig. 26.56)?

Figure 26.56
Exercise 26.32.

26.33. A circuit consists of a series combination of 6.00-kΩ and 5.00-kΩ resistors connected across a 50.0-V battery having negligible internal resistance. You want to measure the true potential difference (that is, the potential difference without the meter present) across the 5.00-kΩ resistor using a voltmeter having an internal resistance of 10.0 kΩ. (a) What potential difference does the voltmeter measure across the 5.00-kΩ resistor? (b) What is the *true* potential difference across this resistor when the meter is not present? (c) By what percentage is the voltmeter reading in error from the true potential difference?

26.34. A galvanometer having a resistance of 25.0 Ω has a 1.00-Ω shunt resistance installed to convert it to an ammeter. It is then used to measure the current in a circuit consisting of a 15.0-Ω resistor connected across the terminals of a 25.0-V battery having no appreciable internal resistance. (a) What current does the ammeter measure? (b) What should be the *true* current in the circuit (that is, the current without the ammeter present)? (c) By what percentage is the ammeter reading in error from the *true* current?

26.35. Consider the potentiometer circuit of Fig. 26.19a. The resistor between a and b is a uniform wire with length l, with a sliding contact c at a distance x from b. An unknown emf $\mathcal{E}_2$ is measured by sliding the contact until the galvanometer G reads zero. (a) Show that under this condition the unknown emf is given by $\mathcal{E}_2 = (x/l)\mathcal{E}_1$. (b) Why is the internal resistance of the galvanometer not important? (c) Suppose $\mathcal{E}_1 = 9.15$ V and $l = 1.000$ m. The galvanometer G reads zero when $x = 0.365$ m. What is the emf $\mathcal{E}_2$?

26.36. In the ohmmeter of Fig. 26.17, the coil of the meter has resistance $R_c = 15.0$ Ω and the current required for full-scale deflection is $I_{fs} = 3.60$ mA. The source is a flashlight battery with $\mathcal{E} = 1.50$ V and negligible internal resistance. The ohmmeter is to show a meter deflection of one-half of full scale when connected to a resistor with $R = 600$ Ω. What series resistance R_s is required?

26.37. In the ohmmeter in Fig. 26.57 M is a 2.50-mA meter of resistance 65.0 Ω. (A 2.50-mA meter deflects full scale when the current through it is 2.50 mA.) The battery B has an emf of 1.52 V and negligible internal resistance. R is chosen so that when the terminals a and b are shorted $(R_x = 0)$, the meter reads full scale. When a and b are open $(R_x = \infty)$, the meter reads zero. (a) What is the resistance of the resistor R? (b) What current indi-

Figure 26.57
Exercise 26.37.

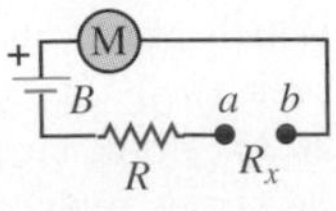

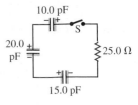

cates a resistance R_x of 200 Ω? (c) What values of R_x correspond to meter deflections of $\frac{1}{4}$, $\frac{1}{2}$, and $\frac{3}{4}$ of full scale if the deflection is proportional to the current through the galvanometer?

Section 26.4 R-C Circuits

26.38. A 4.60-μF capacitor that is initially uncharged is connected in series with a 7.50-kΩ resistor and an emf source with $\mathcal{E} = 125$ V and negligible internal resistance. Just after the circuit is completed, what are (a) the voltage drop across the capacitor; (b) the voltage drop across the resistor; (c) the charge on the capacitor; (d) the current through the resistor? (e) A long time after the circuit is completed (after many time constants) what are the values of the quantities in parts (a)–(d)?

26.39. A capacitor is charged to a potential of 12.0 V and is then connected to a voltmeter having an internal resistance of 3.40 MΩ. After a time of 4.00 s the voltmeter reads 3.0 V. What are (a) the capacitance and (b) the time constant of the circuit?

26.40. A 12.4-μF capacitor is connected through a 0.895-MΩ resistor to a constant potential difference of 60.0 V. (a) Compute the charge on the capacitor at the following times after the connections are made: 0, 5.0 s, 10.0 s, 20.0 s, and 100.0 s. (b) Compute the charging currents at the same instants. (c) Graph the results of parts (a) and (b) for t between 0 and 20 s.

26.41. In the circuit shown in Fig. 26.58 both capacitors are initially charged to 45.0 V. (a) How long after closing the switch S will the potential across each capacitor be reduced to 10.0 V, and (b) what will be the current at that time?

Figure 26.58
Exercise 26.41.

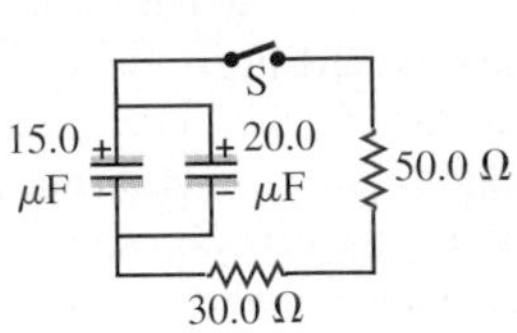

26.42. A resistor and a capacitor are connected in series to an emf source. The time constant for the circuit is 0.870 s. (a) A second capacitor, identical to the first, is added in series. What is the time constant for this new circuit? (b) In the original circuit a second capacitor, identical to the first, is connected in parallel with the first capacitor. What is the time constant for this new circuit?

26.43. An emf source with $\mathcal{E} = 120$ V, a resistor with $R = 80.0$ Ω, and a capacitor with $C = 4.00$ μF are connected in series. As the capacitor charges, when the current in the resistor is 0.900 A, what is the magnitude of the charge on each plate of the capacitor?

26.44. A 1.50-μF capacitor is charging through a 12.0-Ω resistor using a 10.0-V battery. What will be the current when the capacitor has acquired $\frac{1}{4}$ of its maximum charge? Will it be $\frac{1}{4}$ of the maximum current?

26.45. In the circuit shown in Fig. 26.59 each capacitor initially has a charge of magnitude 3.50 nC on its plates. After the switch S is closed, what will be the current in the circuit at the instant that the capacitors have lost 80.0% of their initial stored energy?

Figure 26.59
Exercise 26.45.

26.46. A 12.0-μF capacitor is charged to a potential of 50.0 V and then discharged through a 175-Ω resistor How long does it take the capacitor to lose (a) half of its charge and (b) half of its stored energy?

26.47. In the circuit in Fig. 26.60 the capacitors are all initially uncharged, the battery has no internal resistance, and the ammeter is idealized. Find the reading of the ammeter (a) just after the switch S is closed and (b) after the switch has been closed for a very long time

Figure 26.60 Exercise 26.47.

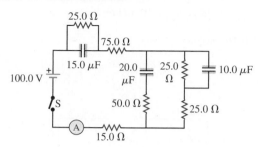

26.48. In the circuit shown in Fig. 26.61, $C = 5.90\ \mu F$, $\mathcal{E} = 28.0$ V, and the emf has negligible resistance. Initially the capacitor is uncharged and the switch S is in position 1. The switch is then moved to position 2, so that the capacitor begins to charge. (a) What will be the charge on the capacitor a long time after the switch is moved to position 2? (b) After the switch has been in position 2 for 3.00 ms, the charge on the capacitor is measured to be 110 μC. What is the value of the resistance R? (c) How long after the switch is moved to position 2 will the charge on the capacitor be equal to 99.0% of the final value found in part (a)?

Figure 26.61 Exercises 26.48 and 26.49.

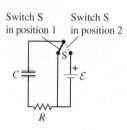

26.49. A capacitor with $C = 1.50 \times 10^{-5}$ F is connected as shown in Fig. 26.61 with a resistor with $R = 980\ \Omega$ and an emf source with $\mathcal{E} = 18.0$ V and negligible internal resistance. Initially the capacitor is uncharged and the switch S is in position 1. The switch is then moved to position 2, so that the capacitor begins to charge. After the switch has been in position 2 for 10.0 ms, the switch is moved back to position 1 so that the capacitor begins to discharge. (a) Compute the charge on the capacitor just *before* the switch is thrown from position 2 back to position 1. (b) Compute the voltage drops across the resistor and across the capacitor at the instant described in part (a). (c) Compute the voltage drops across the resistor and across the capacitor just *after* the switch is thrown from position 2 back to position 1. (d) Compute the charge on the capacitor 10.0 ms after the switch is thrown from position 2 back to position 1.

Section 26.5 Power Distribution Systems

26.50. The heating element of an electric dryer is rated at 4.1 kW when connected to a 240-V line. (a) What is the current in the heating element? Is 12-gauge wire large enough to supply this current? (b) What is the resistance of the dryer's heating element at its operating temperature? (c) At 11 cents per kWh, how much does it cost per hour to operate the dryer?

26.51. A 1500-W electric heater is plugged into the outlet of a 120-V circuit that has a 20-A circuit breaker. You plug an electric hair dryer into the same outlet. The hair dryer has power settings of 600 W, 900 W, 1200 W, and 1500 W. You start with the hair dryer on the 600-W setting and increase the power setting until the circuit breaker trips. What power setting caused the breaker to trip?

26.52. How many 90-W, 120-V light bulbs can be connected to a 20-A, 120-V circuit without tripping the circuit breaker? (See the note in Exercise 26.18.)

26.53. The heating element of an electric stove consists of a heater wire embedded within an electrically insulating material, which in turn is inside a metal casing. The heater wire has a resistance of 20 Ω at room temperature $(23.0°C)$ and a temperature coefficient of resistivity $\alpha = 2.8 \times 10^{-3}(C°)^{-1}$. The heating element operates from a 120-V line. (a) When the heating element is first turned on, what current does it draw and what electrical power does it dissipate? (b) When the heating element has reached an operating temperature of 280°C $(536°F)$, what current does it draw and what electrical power does it dissipate?

Problems

26.54. A 400-Ω, 2.4-W resistor is needed, but only several 400-Ω, 1.2-W resistors are available (see Exercise 26.10). (a) What two different combinations of the available units give the required resistance and power rating? (b) For each of the resistor networks from part (a), what power is dissipated in each resistor when 2.4 W is dissipated by the combination?

26.55. A 20.0-m-long cable consists of a solid-inner, cylindrical, nickel core 10.0 cm in diameter surrounded by a solid-outer cylindrical shell of copper 10.0 cm in inside diameter and 20.0 cm in outside diameter. The resistivity of nickel is $7.8 \times 10^{-8}\ \Omega \cdot$ m. (a) What is the resistance of this cable? (b) If we think of this cable as a single material, what is its equivalent resistivity?

26.56. Two identical 1.00-Ω wires are laid side by side and soldered together so they touch each other for half of their lengths. What is the equivalent resistance of this combination?

26.57. The two identical light bulbs in Example 26.2 (Section 26.1) are connected in parallel to a different source, one with $\mathcal{E} = 8.0$ V and internal resistance 0.8 Ω. Each light bulb has a resistance $R = 2.0\ \Omega$ (assumed independent of the current through the bulb). (a) Find the current through each bulb, the potential difference across each bulb, and the power delivered to each bulb. (b) Suppose one of the bulbs burns out, so that its filament breaks and current no longer flows through it. Find the power delivered to the remaining bulb. Does the remaining bulb glow more or less brightly after the other bulb burns out than before?

26.58. Each of the three resistors in Fig. 26.62 has a resistance of 2.4 Ω and can dissipate a maximum of 36 W without becoming excessively heated. What is the maximum power the circuit can dissipate?

Figure 26.62 Problem 26.58.

26.59. If an ohmmeter is connected between points a and b in each of the circuits shown in Fig. 26.63, what will it read?

Figure 26.63 Problem 26.59.

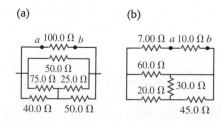

26.60. For the circuit shown in Fig. 26.64 a 20.0-Ω resistor is embedded in a large block of ice at 0.00°C, and the battery has negligible internal resistance. At what rate (in g/s) is this circuit melting the ice? (The latent heat of fusion for ice is 3.34×10^5 J/kg.)

Figure 26.64 Problem 26.60.

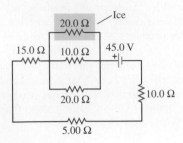

26.61. Calculate the three currents I_1, I_2, and I_3 indicated in the circuit diagram shown in Fig. 26.65.

Figure 26.65 Problem 26.61.

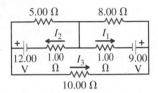

26.62. What must the emf $\mathcal{E}$ in Fig. 26.66 be in order for the current through the 7.00-Ω resistor to be 1.80 A? Each emf source has negligible internal resistance.

Figure 26.66 Problem 26.62.

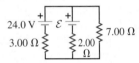

26.63. Find the current through each of the three resistors of the circuit shown in Fig. 26.67. The emf sources have negligible internal resistance.

26.64. (a) Find the current through the battery and each resistor in the circuit shown in Fig. 26.68. (b) What is the equivalent resistance of the resistor network?

Figure 26.67 Problem 26.63.

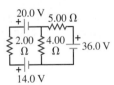

Figure 26.68 Problem 26.64.

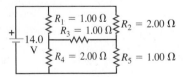

26.65. (a) Find the potential of point a with respect to point b in Fig. 26.69. (b) If points a and b are connected by a wire with negligible resistance, find the current in the 12.0-V battery.

Figure 26.69 Problem 26.65.

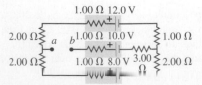

26.66. Consider the circuit shown in Fig. 26.70: (a) What must the emf $\mathcal{E}$ of the battery be in order for a current of 2.00 A to flow through the 5.00-V battery as shown? Is the polarity of the battery correct as shown? (b) How long does it take for 60.0 J of thermal energy to be produced in the 10.0-Ω resistor?

Figure 26.70 Problem 26.66.

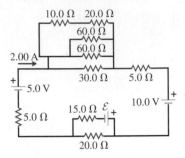

26.67. In the circuit shown in Fig. 26.71 the current through the 12.0-V battery is measured to be 70.6 mA in the direction shown. What is the terminal voltage V_{ab} of the 24.0-V battery?

Figure 26.71 Problem 26.67.

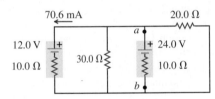

26.68. In the circuit shown in Fig. 26.72 all the resistors are rated at a maximum power of 1.00 W. What is the maximum emf $\mathcal{E}$ that the battery can have without burning up any of the resistors?

Figure 26.72 Problem 26.68.

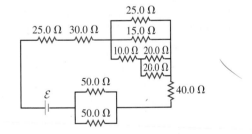

26.69. In the circuit shown in Fig. 26.73, the current in the 20.0-V battery is 5.00 A in the direction shown and the voltage across the 8.00-Ω resistor is 16.0 V, with the lower end of the resistor at higher potential. Find (a) the emf (including its polarity) of the battery X; (b) the current I through the 200.0-V battery (including its direction); (c) the resistance R.

Figure 26.73 Problem 26.69.

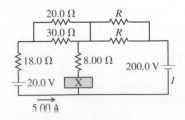

26.70. Three identical resistors are connected in series. When a certain potential difference is applied across the combination, the total power dissipated is 27 W. What power would be dissipated if the three resistors were connected in parallel across the same potential difference?

26.71. A resistor R_1 consumes electrical power P_1 when connected to an emf $\mathcal{E}$. When resistor R_2 is connected to the same emf, it consumes electrical power P_2. In terms of P_1 and P_2, what is the total electrical power consumed when they are both connected to this emf source (a) in parallel and (b) in series?

26.72. The capacitor in Fig. 26.74 is initially uncharged. The switch is closed at $t = 0$. (a) Immediately after the switch is closed, what is the current through each resistor? (b) What is the final charge on the capacitor?

Figure 26.74 Problem 26.72.

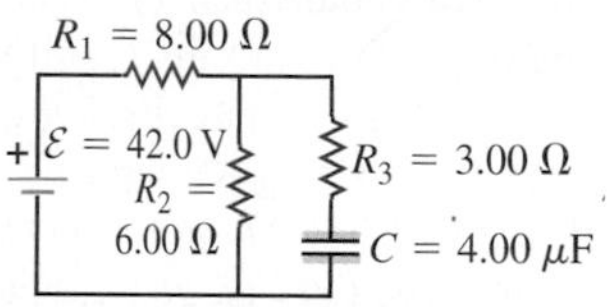

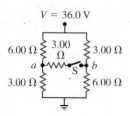

$R_1 = 8.00\ \Omega$
$+\ \mathcal{E} = 42.0\ \text{V}$
$R_2 =$
$6.00\ \Omega$
$R_3 = 3.00\ \Omega$
$C = 4.00\ \mu\text{F}$

26.73. Figure 26.75 employs a convention often used in circuit diagrams. The battery (or other power supply) is not shown explicitly. It is understood that the point at the top, labeled "36.0 V," is connected to the positive terminal of a 36.0-V battery having negligible internal resistance, and that the "ground" symbol at the bottom is connected to the negative terminal of the battery. The circuit is completed through the battery, even though it is not shown on the diagram. (a) What is the potential difference V_{ab}, the potential of point a relative to point b, when the switch S is open? (b) What is the current through switch S when it is closed? (c) What is the equivalent resistance when switch S is closed?

Figure 26.75
Problem 26.73.

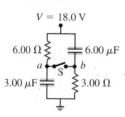

$V = 36.0\ \text{V}$
$6.00\ \Omega$ $3.00\ \Omega$ $3.00\ \Omega$
a S b
$3.00\ \Omega$ $6.00\ \Omega$

26.74. (See Problem 26.73.) (a) What is the potential of point a with respect to point b in Fig. 26.76 when switch S is open? (b) Which point, a or b, is at the higher potential? (c) What is the final potential of point b with respect to ground when switch S is closed? (d) How much does the charge on each capacitor change when S is closed?

Figure 26.76
Problem 26.74.

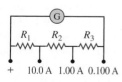

$V = 18.0\ \text{V}$
$6.00\ \Omega$ $6.00\ \mu\text{F}$
a S b
$3.00\ \mu\text{F}$ $3.00\ \Omega$

26.75. A Multirange Ammeter. The resistance of the moving coil of the galvanometer G in Fig. 26.77 is 48.0 Ω, and the galvanometer deflects full scale with a current of 0.0200 A. When the meter is connected to the circuit being measured, one connection is made to the post marked $+$ and the other to the post marked with the desired current range. Find the magnitudes of the resistances R_1, R_2, and R_3 required to convert the galvanometer to a multirange ammeter deflecting full scale with currents of 10.0 A, 1.00 A, and 0.100 A.

Figure 26.77
Problem 26.75.

G
R_1 R_2 R_3
$+$ 10.0 A 1.00 A 0.100 A

26.76. A Multirange Voltmeter. Figure 26.78 shows the internal wiring of a "three-scale" voltmeter whose binding posts are marked $+$, 3.00 V, 15.0 V, and 150 V. When the meter is connected to the circuit being meas-

Figure 26.78
Problem 26.76.

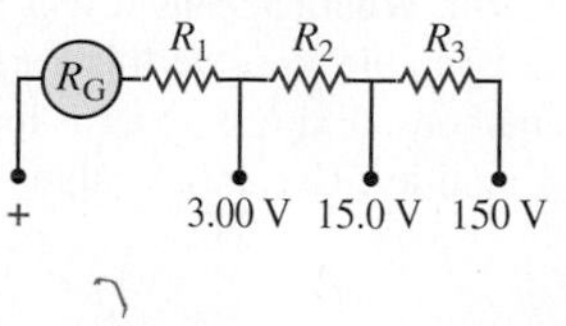

R_G R_1 R_2 R_3
$+$ 3.00 V 15.0 V 150 V

ured, one connection is made to the post marked $+$ and the other to the post marked with the desired voltage range. The resistance of the moving coil, R_G, is 40.0 Ω, and a current of 1.00 mA in the coil causes it to deflect full scale. Find the resistances R_1, R_2, and R_3, and the overall resistance of the meter on each of its ranges.

26.77. Point a in Fig. 26.79 is maintained at a constant potential of 400 V above ground. (See Problem 26.73.) (a) What is the reading of a voltmeter with the proper range and with resistance $5.00 \times 10^4\ \Omega$ when connected between point b and ground? (b) What is the reading of a voltmeter with resistance $5.00 \times 10^6\ \Omega$? (c) What is the reading of a voltmeter with infinite resistance?

Figure 26.79
Problem 26.77.

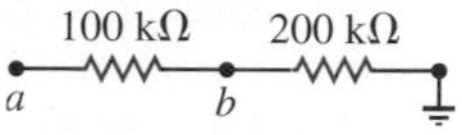

$100\ \text{k}\Omega$ $200\ \text{k}\Omega$
a b

26.78. A 150-V voltmeter has a resistance of 30,000 Ω. When connected in series with a large resistance R across a 110-V line, the meter reads 68 V. Find the resistance R.

26.79. The Wheatstone Bridge. The circuit shown in Fig. 26.80, called a *Wheatstone bridge,* is used to determine the value of an unknown resistor X by comparison with three resistors M, N, and P whose resistances can be varied. For each setting, the resistance of each resistor is precisely known. With switches K_1 and K_2 closed, these resistors are varied until the current in the galvanometer G is zero; the bridge is then said to be *balanced.* (a) Show that under this condition the unknown resistance is given by $X = MP/N$. (This method permits very high precision in comparing resistors.) (b) If the galvanometer G shows zero deflection when $M = 850.0\ \Omega$, $N = 15.00\ \Omega$, and $P = 33.48\ \Omega$, what is the unknown resistance X?

Figure 26.80
Problem 26.79.

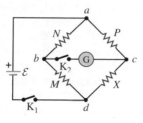

a
N P
b G c
$+\ \mathcal{E}$ K_2
M X
K_1 d

26.80. A certain galvanometer has a resistance of 65.0 Ω and deflects full scale with a current of 1.50 mA in its coil. This is to be replaced with a second galvanometer that has a resistance of 38.0 Ω and deflects full scale with a current of 3.60 μA in its coil. Devise a circuit incorporating the second galvanometer such that the equivalent resistance of the circuit equals the resistance of the first galvanometer, and the second galvanometer deflects full scale when the current through the circuit equals the full-scale current of the first galvanometer.

26.81. A 224-Ω resistor and a 589-Ω resistor are connected in series across a 90.0-V line. (a) What is the voltage across each resistor? (b) A voltmeter connected across the 224-Ω resistor reads 23.8 V. Find the voltmeter resistance. (c) Find the reading of the same voltmeter if it is connected across the 589-Ω resistor. (d) The readings on this voltmeter are lower than the "true" voltages (that is, without the voltmeter present). Would it be possible to design a voltmeter that gave readings *higher* than the "true" voltages? Explain.

26.82. A .2.36-μF capacitor that is initially uncharged is connected in series with a 4.26-Ω resistor and an emf source with $\mathcal{E} = 120$ V and negligible internal resistance. (a) Just after the connection is made, what are (i) the rate at which electrical energy is being dissipated in the resistor; (ii) the rate at which the electrical energy stored in the capacitor is increasing; (iii) the electrical power output of the source? How do the answers to parts (i), (ii), and (iii) compare? (b) Answer the same questions as in part (a) at a long time after the connection is made. (c) Answer the same questions as in part (a) at the instant when the charge on the capacitor is one-half its final value.

26.83. A capacitor that is initially uncharged is connected in series with a resistor and an emf source with $\mathcal{E} = 110$ V and negligible internal resistance. Just after the circuit is completed, the current through the resistor is 6.5×10^{-5} A. The time constant for the circuit is 6.2 s. What are the resistance of the resistor and the capacitance of the capacitor?

26.84. A resistor with $R = 850$ Ω is connected to the plates of a charged capacitor with capacitance $C = 4.62$ μF. Just before the connection is made, the charge on the capacitor is 8.10 mC. (a) What is the energy initially stored in the capacitor? (b) What is the electrical power dissipated in the resistor just after the connection is made? (c) What is the electrical power dissipated in the resistor at the instant when the energy stored in the capacitor has decreased to half the value calculated in part (a)?

26.85. Strictly speaking, Eq. (26.16) implies that an *infinite* amount of time is required to discharge a capacitor completely. Yet for practical purposes, a capacitor may be considered to be fully discharged after a finite length of time. To be specific, consider a capacitor with capacitance C connected to a resistor R to be fully discharged if its charge q differs from zero by no more than the charge of one electron. (a) Calculate the time required to reach this state if $C = 0.920$ μF, $R = 670$ kΩ, and $Q_0 = 7.00$ μC. How many time constants is this? (b) For a given Q_0, is the time required to reach this state always the same number of time constants, independent of the values of C and R? Why or why not?

26.86. An R-C circuit has a time constant RC. (a) If the circuit is discharging, how long will it take for its stored energy to be reduced to $1/e$ of its initial value? (b) If it is charging, how long will it take for the stored energy to reach $1/e$ of its maximum value?

26.87. The current in a charging capacitor is given by Eq. (26.13). (a) The instantaneous power supplied by the battery is $\mathcal{E}i$. Integrate this to find the total energy supplied by the battery. (b) The instantaneous power dissipated in the resistor is i^2R. Integrate this to find the total energy dissipated in the resistor. (c) Find the final energy stored in the capacitor, and show that this equals the total energy supplied by the battery less the energy dissipated in the resistor, as obtained in parts (a) and (b). (d) What fraction of the energy supplied by the battery is stored in the capacitor? How does this fraction depend on R?

26.88. (a) Using Eq. (26.17) for the current in a discharging capacitor, derive an expression for the instantaneous power $P = i^2R$ dissipated in the resistor. (b) Integrate the expression for P to find the total energy dissipated in the resistor, and show that this is equal to the total energy initially stored in the capacitor.

Challenge Problems

26.89. According to the theorem of superposition, the response (current) in a circuit is proportional to the stimulus (voltage) that causes it. This is true even if there are multiple sources in a circuit. This theorem can be used to analyze a circuit without resorting to Kirchhoff's rules by considering the currents in the circuit to be the superposition of currents caused by each source independently. In this way the circuit can be analyzed by computing equivalent resistances rather than by using the (sometimes) more cumbersome method of Kirchhoff's rules. Furthermore, with the superposition theorem it is possible to examine how the modification of a source in one part of the circuit will affect the currents in all parts of the circuit without having to use Kirchhoff's rules to recalculate all of the currents. Consider the circuit shown in Fig. 26.81. If the circuit were redrawn with the 55.0-V and 57.0-V sources replaced by short circuits, the circuit could be analyzed by the method of equivalent resistances without resorting to Kirchhoff's rules, and the current in each branch could be found in a simple manner. Similarly, if the circuit with the 92.0-V and the 55.0-V sources were replaced by short circuits, the circuit could again be analyzed in a simple manner. Finally, if the 92.0-V and the 57.0-V sources were replaced with a short circuit, the circuit could once again be analyzed simply. By superimposing the respective currents found in each of the branches by using the three simplified circuits, we can find the actual current in each branch. (a) Using Kirchhoff's rules, find the branch currents in the 140.0-Ω, 210.0-Ω, and 35.0-Ω resistors. (b) Using a circuit similar to the circuit of Fig. 26.81, but with the 55.0-V and 57.0-V sources replaced by a short circuit, determine the currents in each resistance. (c) Repeat part (b) by replacing the 92.0-V and 55.0-V sources by short circuits, leaving the 57.0-V source intact. (d) Repeat part (b) by replacing the 92.0-V and 57.0-V sources by short circuits, leaving the 55.0-V source intact. (e) Verify the superposition theorem by taking the currents calculated in parts (b), (c), and (d) and comparing them with the currents calculated in part (a). (f) If the 57.0-V source is replaced by an 80.0-V source, what will be the new currents in all branches of the circuit? [*Hint:* Using the superposition theorem, recalculate the partial currents calculated in part (c) using the fact that those currents are proportional to the source that is being replaced. Then superpose the new partial currents with those found in parts (b) and (d).]

Figure 26.81 Challenge Problem 26.89.

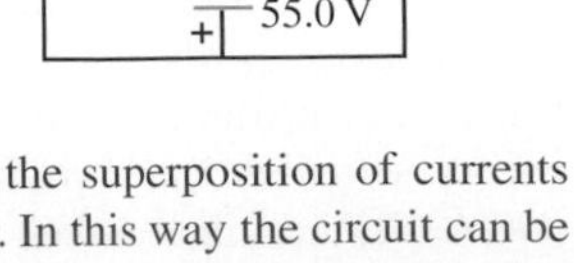

$$140.0\ \Omega \qquad 35.0\ \Omega$$

$I_1 \rightarrow \qquad \leftarrow I_3$

$I_2 \downarrow \;\; 210.0\ \Omega$

$\quad\;\; 92.0\ \text{V}\qquad\qquad 57.0\ \text{V}$

$\qquad\quad 55.0\ \text{V}$

26.90. A Capacitor Burglar Alarm. The capacitance of a capacitor can be affected by dielectric material that, although not inside the capacitor, is near enough to the capacitor to be polarized by the fringing electric field that exists near a charged capacitor. This effect is usually of the order of picofarads (pF), but it can be used with appropriate electronic circuitry to detect a change in the dielectric material surrounding the capacitor. Such a dielectric material might be the human body, and the effect described above might be used in the design of a burglar alarm. Consider the simplified circuit shown in Fig. 26.82. The voltage source has emf $\mathcal{E} = 1000$ V, and the capacitor has capacitance $C = 10.0$ pF. The electronic circuitry for detecting the current, represented as an ammeter in the diagram, has negligible resistance and is capable of detecting a current that persists at a level of at least 1.00 μA for at least 200 μs after the capacitance has changed abruptly from C to C'. The burglar alarm is designed to be activated if the capacitance changes by 10%. (a) Determine the charge on the 10.0-pF capacitor when it is fully charged. (b) If the capacitor is fully charged before the intruder is detected, assuming that the time taken for the capacitance to change by 10% is short enough to be ignored, derive an equation that expresses the current through the resistor R as a function of the time t since the capacitance has changed. (c) Determine the range of values of the resistance R that will meet the design specifications of the burglar alarm. What happens if R is too small? Too large? (*Hint:* You will not be able to solve this part analytically but must use numerical methods. Express R as a logarithmic function of R plus known quantities. Use a trial value of R and calculate from the expression

Figure 26.82 Challenge Problem 26.90.

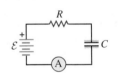

a new value. Continue to do this until the input and output values of R agree to within three significant figures.)

26.91. An Infinite Network. As shown in Fig. 26.83, a network of resistors of resistances R_1 and R_2 extends to infinity toward the right. Prove that the total resistance R_T of the infinite network is equal to

$$R_T = R_1 + \sqrt{R_1^2 + 2R_1R_2}$$

(*Hint:* Since the network is infinite, the resistance of the network to the right of points c and d is also equal to R_T.)

Figure 26.83 Challenge Problems 26.91 and 26.93.

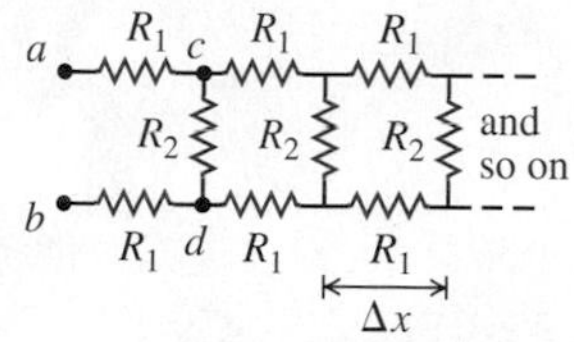

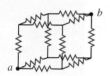

26.92. Suppose a resistor R lies along each edge of a cube (12 resistors in all) with connections at the corners. Find the equivalent resistance between two diagonally opposite corners of the cube (points a and b in Fig. 26.84).

Figure 26.84 Challenge Problem 26.92.

26.93. Attenuator Chains and Axons. The infinite network of resistors shown in Fig. 26.83 is known as an *attenuator chain,* since this chain of resistors causes the potential difference between the upper and lower wires to decrease, or attenuate, along the length of the chain. a) Show that if the potential difference between the points a and b in Fig. 26.83 is V_{ab}, then the potential difference between points c and d is $V_{cd} = V_{ab}/(1 + \beta)$, where $\beta = 2R_1(R_T + R_2)/R_TR_2$ and R_T, the

total resistance of the network, is given in Challenge Problem 26.91. (See the hint given in that problem.) (b) If the potential difference between terminals a and b at the left end of the infinite network is V_0, show that the potential difference between the upper and lower wires n segments from the left end is $V_n = V_0/(1 + \beta)^n$. If $R_1 = R_2$, how many segments are needed to decrease the potential difference V_n to less than 1.0% of V_0? (c) An infinite attenuator chain provides a model of the propagation of a voltage pulse along a nerve fiber, or axon. Each segment of the network in Fig. 26.83 represents a short segment of the axon of length Δx. The resistors R_1 represent the resistance of the fluid inside and outside the membrane wall of the axon. The resistance of the membrane to current flowing through the wall is represented by R_2. For an axon segment of length $\Delta x = 1.0 \ \mu m$, $R_1 = 6.4 \times 10^3 \ \Omega$ and $R_2 = 8.0 \times 10^8 \ \Omega$ (the membrane wall is a good insulator). Calculate the total resistance R_T and β for an infinitely long axon. (This is a good approximation, since the length of an axon is much greater than its width; the largest axons in the human nervous system are longer than 1 m but only about 10^{-7} m in radius.) (d) By what fraction does the potential difference between the inside and outside of the axon decrease over a distance of 2.0 mm? (e) The attenuation of the potential difference calculated in part (d) shows that the axon cannot simply be a passive, current-carrying electrical cable; the potential difference must periodically be reinforced along the axon's length. This reinforcement mechanism is slow, so a signal propagates along the axon at only about 30 m/s. In situations where faster response is required, axons are covered with a segmented sheath of fatty myelin. The segments are about 2 mm long, separated by gaps called the *nodes of Ranvier.* The myelin increases the resistance of a 1.0-μm-long segment of the membrane to $R_2 = 3.3 \times 10^{12} \ \Omega$. For such a myelinated axon, by what fraction does the potential difference between the inside and outside of the axon decrease over the distance from one node of Ranvier to the next? This smaller attenuation means the propagation speed is increased.

27 MAGNETIC FIELD AND MAGNETIC FORCES

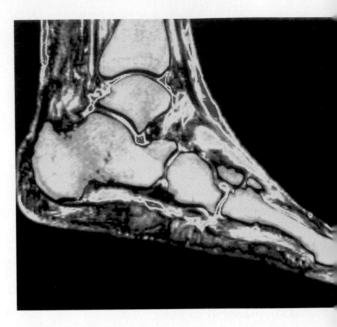

? Magnetic resonance imaging (MRI) makes it possible to see details of soft tissue (such as in the foot shown here) that aren't visible in x-ray images. Yet soft tissue isn't a magnetic material (it's not attracted to a magnet). How does MRI work?

Everybody uses magnetic forces. They are at the heart of electric motors, TV picture tubes, microwave ovens, loudspeakers, computer printers, and disk drives. The most familiar aspects of magnetism are those associated with permanent magnets, which attract unmagnetized iron objects and can also attract or repel other magnets. A compass needle aligning itself with the earth's magnetism is an example of this interaction. But the *fundamental* nature of magnetism is the interaction of moving electric charges. Unlike electric forces, which act on electric charges whether they are moving or not, magnetic forces act only on *moving* charges.

Although electric and magnetic forces are very different from each other, we use the idea of a *field* to describe both kinds of force. We saw in Chapter 21 that the electric force arises in two stages: (1) a charge produces an electric field in the space around it, and (2) a second charge responds to this field. Magnetic forces also arise in two stages. First, a *moving* charge or a collection of moving charges (that is, an electric current) produces a *magnetic* field. Next, a second current or moving charge responds to this magnetic field, and so experiences a magnetic force.

In this chapter we study the second stage in the magnetic interaction—that is, how moving charges and currents *respond* to magnetic fields. In particular, we will see how to calculate magnetic forces and torques, and we will discover why magnets can pick up iron objects like paper clips. In Chapter 28 we will complete our picture of the magnetic interaction by examining how moving charges and currents *produce* magnetic fields.

27.1 Magnetism

Magnetic phenomena were first observed at least 2500 years ago in fragments of magnetized iron ore found near the ancient city of Magnesia (now Manisa, in western Turkey). These fragments were examples of what are now called

permanent magnets; you probably have several permanent magnets on your refrigerator door at home. Permanent magnets were found to exert forces on each other as well as on pieces of iron that were not magnetized. It was discovered that when an iron rod is brought in contact with a natural magnet, the rod also becomes magnetized. When such a rod is floated on water or suspended by a string from its center, it tends to line itself up in a north-south direction. The needle of an ordinary compass is just such a piece of magnetized iron.

Before the relationship of magnetic interactions to moving charges was understood, the interactions of permanent magnets and compass needles were described in terms of *magnetic poles.* If a bar-shaped permanent magnet, or *bar magnet,* is free to rotate, one end points north. This end is called a *north pole* or *N pole;* the other end is a *south pole* or *S pole.* Opposite poles attract each other, and like poles repel each other (Fig. 27.1). An object that contains iron but is not itself magnetized (that is, it shows no tendency to point north or south) is attracted by *either* pole of a permanent magnet (Fig. 27.2). This is the attraction that acts between a magnet and the unmagnetized steel door of a refrigerator. By analogy to electric interactions, we describe the interactions in Figs. 27.1 and 27.2 by saying that a bar magnet sets up a *magnetic field* in the space around it and a second body responds to that field. A compass needle tends to align with the magnetic field at the needle's position.

The earth itself is a magnet. Its north geographic pole is close to a magnetic *south* pole, which is why the north pole of a compass needle points north. The earth's magnetic axis is not quite parallel to its geographic axis (the axis of rotation), so a compass reading deviates somewhat from geographic north. This deviation, which varies with location, is called *magnetic declination* or *magnetic variation.* Also, the magnetic field is not horizontal at most points on the earth's surface; its angle up or down is called *magnetic inclination.* At the magnetic poles the magnetic field is vertical.

Figure 27.3 is a sketch of the earth's magnetic field. The lines, called *magnetic field lines,* show the direction that a compass would point at each location; they are discussed in detail in Section 27.3. The direction of the field at any point can

27.1 (a) Two bar magnets attract when opposite poles (N and S, or S and N) are next to each other. (b) The bar magnets repel when like poles (N and N, or S and S) are next to each other.

(a) Opposite poles attract.

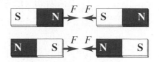

(b) Like poles repel.

27.2 (a) Either pole of a bar magnet attracts an unmagnetized object that contains iron, such as a nail. (b) A real-life example of this effect.

(a)

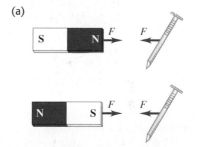

(b)

27.3 A sketch of the earth's magnetic field. The field, which is caused by currents in the earth's molten core, changes with time; geologic evidence shows that it reverses direction entirely at irregular intervals of about a half million years.

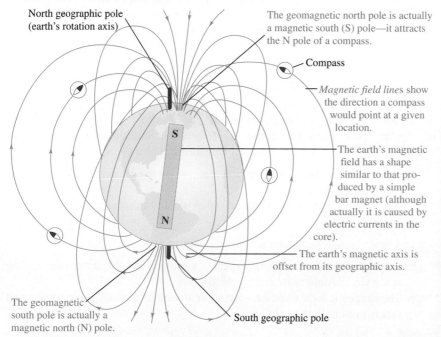

North geographic pole (earth's rotation axis)

The geomagnetic north pole is actually a magnetic south (S) pole—it attracts the N pole of a compass.

Compass

Magnetic field lines show the direction a compass would point at a given location.

The earth's magnetic field has a shape similar to that produced by a simple bar magnet (although actually it is caused by electric currents in the core).

The earth's magnetic axis is offset from its geographic axis.

The geomagnetic south pole is actually a magnetic north (N) pole.

South geographic pole

27.4 Breaking a bar magnet. Each piece has a north and south pole, even if the pieces are different sizes. (The smaller the piece, the weaker its magnetism.)

In contrast to electric charges, magnetic poles always come in pairs and can't be isolated.

Breaking a magnet in two ...

... yields two magnets, not two isolated poles.

27.5 In Oersted's experiment, a compass is placed directly over a horizontal wire (here viewed from above). When the compass is placed directly under the wire, the compass deflection is reversed.

(a)

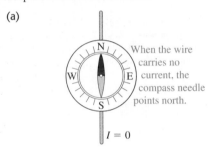

When the wire carries no current, the compass needle points north.

$I = 0$

(b)

When the wire carries a current, the compass needle deflects. The direction of deflection depends on the direction of the current.

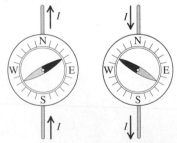

Magnetic Poles Versus Electric Charge

be defined as the direction of the force that the field would exert on a magnetic north pole. In Section 27.2 we'll describe a more fundamental way to define the direction and magnitude of a magnetic field.

The concept of magnetic poles may appear similar to that of electric charge, and north and south poles may seem analogous to positive and negative charge. But the analogy can be misleading. While isolated positive and negative charges exist, there is *no* experimental evidence that a single isolated magnetic pole exists; poles always appear in pairs. If a bar magnet is broken in two, each broken end becomes a pole (Fig. 27.4). The existence of an isolated magnetic pole, or **magnetic monopole,** would have sweeping implications for theoretical physics. Extensive searches for magnetic monopoles have been carried out, but so far without success.

The first evidence of the relationship of magnetism to moving charges was discovered in 1820 by the Danish scientist Hans Christian Oersted. He found that a compass needle was deflected by a current-carrying wire, as shown in Fig. 27.5. Similar investigations were carried out in France by André Ampère. A few years later, Michael Faraday in England and Joseph Henry in the United States discovered that moving a magnet near a conducting loop can cause a current in the loop. We now know that the magnetic forces between two bodies shown in Figs. 27.1 and 27.2 are fundamentally due to interactions between moving electrons in the atoms of the bodies. (There are also *electric* interactions between the two bodies, but these are far weaker than the magnetic interactions because the two bodies are electrically neutral.) Inside a magnetized body such as a permanent magnet, there is a *coordinated* motion of certain of the atomic electrons; in an unmagnetized body these motions are not coordinated. (We'll describe these motions further in Section 27.7, and see how the interactions shown in Figs. 27.1 and 27.2 come about.)

Electric and magnetic interactions prove to be intimately connected. Over the next several chapters we will develop the unifying principles of electromagnetism, culminating in the expression of these principles in *Maxwell's equations.* These equations represent the synthesis of electromagnetism, just as Newton's laws of motion are the synthesis of mechanics, and like Newton's laws they represent a towering achievement of the human intellect.

Test Your Understanding of Section 27.1 Suppose you cut off the part of the compass needle shown in Fig. 27.5a that is painted gray. You discard this part, drill a hole in the remaining red part, and place the red part on the pivot at the center of the compass. Will the red part still swing east and west when a current is applied as in Fig. 27.5b? ∎

27.2 Magnetic Field

To introduce the concept of magnetic field properly, let's review our formulation of *electric* interactions in Chapter 21, where we introduced the concept of *electric* field. We represented electric interactions in two steps:

1. A distribution of electric charge at rest creates an electric field $\vec{E}$ in the surrounding space.
2. The electric field exerts a force $\vec{F} = q\vec{E}$ on any other charge q that is present in the field.

We can describe magnetic interactions in a similar way:

1. A moving charge or a current creates a **magnetic field** in the surrounding space (in addition to its *electric* field).
2. The magnetic field exerts a force $\vec{F}$ on any other moving charge or current that is present in the field.

In this chapter we'll concentrate on the *second* aspect of the interaction: Given the presence of a magnetic field, what force does it exert on a moving charge or a current? In Chapter 28 we will come back to the problem of how magnetic fields are *created* by moving charges and currents.

Like electric field, magnetic field is a *vector field*—that is, a vector quantity associated with each point in space. We will use the symbol $\vec{B}$ for magnetic field. At any position the direction of $\vec{B}$ is defined as the direction in which the north pole of a compass needle tends to point. The arrows in Fig. 27.3 suggest the direction of the earth's magnetic field; for any magnet, $\vec{B}$ points out of its north pole and into its south pole.

Magnetic Forces on Moving Charges

There are four key characteristics of the magnetic force on a moving charge. First, its magnitude is proportional to the magnitude of the charge. If a 1-μC charge and a 2-μC charge move through a given magnetic field with the same velocity, experiments show that the force on the 2-μC charge is twice as great as the force on the 1-μC charge. Second, the magnitude of the force is also proportional to the magnitude, or "strength," of the field; if we double the magnitude of the field (for example, by using two identical bar magnets instead of one) without changing the charge or its velocity, the force doubles.

A third characteristic is that the magnetic force depends on the particle's velocity. This is quite different from the electric-field force, which is the same whether the charge is moving or not. A charged particle at rest experiences *no* magnetic force. And fourth, we find by experiment that the magnetic force $\vec{F}$ *does not* have the same direction as the magnetic field $\vec{B}$ but instead is always *perpendicular* to both $\vec{B}$ and the velocity $\vec{v}$. The magnitude F of the force is found to be proportional to the component of $\vec{v}$ perpendicular to the field; when that component is zero (that is, when $\vec{v}$ and $\vec{B}$ are parallel or antiparallel), the force is zero.

Figure 27.6 shows these relationships. The direction of $\vec{F}$ is always perpendicular to the plane containing $\vec{v}$ and $\vec{B}$. Its magnitude is given by

$$F = |q|v_{\perp}B = |q|vB\sin\phi \tag{27.1}$$

where $|q|$ is the magnitude of the charge and ϕ is the angle measured from the direction of $\vec{v}$ to the direction of $\vec{B}$, as shown in the figure.

This description does not specify the direction of $\vec{F}$ completely; there are always two directions, opposite to each other, that are both perpendicular to the plane of $\vec{v}$ and $\vec{B}$. To complete the description, we use the same right-hand rule that we used to define the vector product in Section 1.10. (It would be a good idea to review that section before you go on.) Draw the vectors $\vec{v}$ and $\vec{B}$ with their tails together, as in Fig. 27.7a. Imagine turning $\vec{v}$ until it points in the direction of $\vec{B}$ (turning through the smaller of the two possible angles). Wrap the fingers of your right hand around the line perpendicular to the plane of $\vec{v}$ and $\vec{B}$ so that they curl around with the sense of rotation from $\vec{v}$ to $\vec{B}$. Your thumb then points in the direction of the force $\vec{F}$ on a *positive* charge. (Alternatively, the direction of the force $\vec{F}$ on a positive charge is the direction in which a right-hand-thread screw would advance if turned the same way.)

This discussion shows that the force on a charge q moving with velocity $\vec{v}$ in a magnetic field $\vec{B}$ is given, both in magnitude and in direction, by

$$\vec{F} = q\vec{v} \times \vec{B} \qquad \text{(magnetic force on a moving charged particle)} \tag{27.2}$$

This is the first of several vector products we will encounter in our study of magnetic-field relationships. It's important to note that Eq. (27.2) was *not* deduced theoretically; it is an observation based on *experiment*.

13.4   Magnetic Force on a Particle

27.6 The magnetic force $\vec{F}$ acting on a positive charge q moving with velocity $\vec{v}$ is perpendicular to both $\vec{v}$ and the magnetic field $\vec{B}$. For given values of the speed v and magnetic field strength B, the force is greatest when $\vec{v}$ and $\vec{B}$ are perpendicular.

(a)

A charge moving **parallel** to a magnetic field experiences **zero magnetic force.**

(b)

A charge moving at an angle ϕ to a magnetic field experiences a magnetic force with magnitude $F = |q|v_{\perp}B = |q|vB\sin\phi$.

$\vec{F}$ is perpendicular to the plane containing $\vec{v}$ and $\vec{B}$.

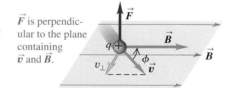

(c)

A charge moving **perpendicular** to a magnetic field experiences a maximal magnetic force with magnitude $F_{max} = qvB$.

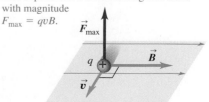

27.7 Finding the direction of the magnetic force on a moving charged particle.

(a)

Right-hand rule for the direction of magnetic force on a **positive** charge moving in a magnetic field:

(1) Place the $\vec{v}$ and $\vec{B}$ vectors tail to tail.

(2) Imagine turning $\vec{v}$ toward $\vec{B}$ in the $\vec{v}$-$\vec{B}$ plane (through the smaller angle).

(3) The force acts along a line perpendicular to the $\vec{v}$-$\vec{B}$ plane. Curl the fingers of your *right hand* around this line in the same direction you rotated $\vec{v}$. Your thumb now points in the direction the force acts.

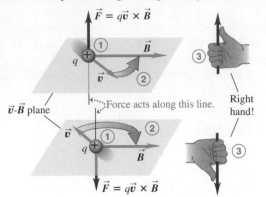

(b)

If the charge is negative, the direction of the force is *opposite* to that given by the right-hand rule.

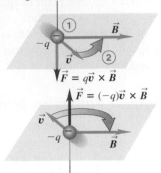

27.8 Two charges of the same magnitude but opposite sign moving with the same velocity in the same magnetic field. The magnetic forces on the charges are equal in magnitude but opposite in direction.

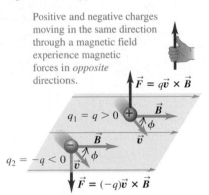

Positive and negative charges moving in the same direction through a magnetic field experience magnetic forces in *opposite* directions.

Equation (27.2) is valid for both positive and negative charges. When q is negative, the direction of the force $\vec{F}$ is opposite to that of $\vec{v} \times \vec{B}$ (Fig. 27. 7b). If two charges with equal magnitude and opposite sign move in the same $\vec{B}$ field with the same velocity (Fig. 27.8), the forces have equal magnitude and opposite direction. Figures 27.6, 27.7, and 27.8 show several examples of the relationships of the directions of $\vec{F}$, $\vec{v}$, and $\vec{B}$ for both positive and negative charges. Be sure you understand the relationships shown in these figures.

Equation (27.1) gives the magnitude of the magnetic force $\vec{F}$ in Eq. (27.2). We can express this magnitude in a different but equivalent way. Since ϕ is the angle between the directions of vectors $\vec{v}$ and $\vec{B}$, we may interpret $B \sin \phi$ as the component of $\vec{B}$ perpendicular to $\vec{v}$—that is, $B_\perp$. With this notation the force magnitude is

$$F = |q| v B_\perp \tag{27.3}$$

This form is sometimes more convenient, especially in problems involving *currents* rather than individual particles. We will discuss forces on currents later in this chapter.

From Eq. (27.1) the *units* of B must be the same as the units of F/qv. Therefore the SI unit of B is equivalent to $1 \text{ N} \cdot \text{s}/\text{C} \cdot \text{m}$, or, since one ampere is one coulomb per second $(1 \text{ A} = 1 \text{ C}/\text{s})$, $1 \text{ N}/\text{A} \cdot \text{m}$. This unit is called the **tesla** (abbreviated T), in honor of Nikola Tesla (1857–1943), the prominent Serbian-American scientist and inventor:

$$1 \text{ tesla} = 1 \text{ T} = 1 \text{ N}/\text{A} \cdot \text{m}$$

Another unit of B, the **gauss** $(1 \text{ G} = 10^{-4} \text{ T})$, is also in common use. Instruments for measuring magnetic field are sometimes called *gaussmeters*.

The magnetic field of the earth is of the order of 10^{-4} T or 1 G. Magnetic fields of the order of 10 T occur in the interior of atoms and are important in the analysis of atomic spectra. The largest steady magnetic field that can be produced at present in the laboratory is about 45 T. Some pulsed-current electromagnets can produce fields of the order of 120 T for short time intervals of the order of a millisecond. The magnetic field at the surface of a neutron star is believed to be of the order of 10^8 T.

Measuring Magnetic Fields with Test Charges

To explore an unknown magnetic field, we can measure the magnitude and direction of the force on a *moving* test charge and then use Eq. (27.2) to determine $\vec{B}$. The electron beam in a cathode-ray tube, such as that used in a television set, is a convenient device for making such measurements. The electron gun shoots out a narrow beam of electrons at a known speed. If there is no force to deflect the beam, it strikes the center of the screen.

If a magnetic field is present, in general the electron beam is deflected. But if the beam is parallel or antiparallel to the field, then $\phi = 0$ or π in Eq. (27.1) and $F = 0$; there is no force, and hence no deflection. If we find that the electron beam is not deflected when its direction is parallel to a certain axis as in Fig. 27.9a, the $\vec{B}$ vector must point either up or down along that axis.

If we then turn the tube 90° (Fig. 27.9b), $\phi = \pi/2$ in Eq. (27.1) and the magnetic force is maximum; the beam is deflected in a direction perpendicular to the plane of $\vec{B}$ and $\vec{v}$. The direction and magnitude of the deflection determine the direction and magnitude of $\vec{B}$. We can perform additional experiments in which the angle between $\vec{B}$ and $\vec{v}$ is between zero and 90° to confirm Eq. (27.1) or (27.3) and the accompanying discussion. We note that the electron has a negative charge; the force in Fig. 27.9b is opposite in direction to the force on a positive charge.

When a charged particle moves through a region of space where *both* electric and magnetic fields are present, both fields exert forces on the particle. The total force $\vec{F}$ is the vector sum of the electric and magnetic forces:

$$\vec{F} = q(\vec{E} + \vec{v} \times \vec{B}) \tag{27.4}$$

(a) If the tube axis is parallel to the y-axis, the beam is undeflected, so $\vec{B}$ is in either the $+y$- or the $-y$-direction.

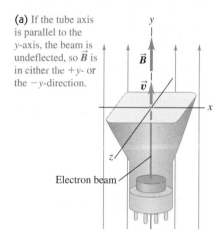

Electron beam

(b) If the tube axis is parallel to the x-axis, the beam is deflected in the $-z$-direction, so $\vec{B}$ is in the $+y$-direction.

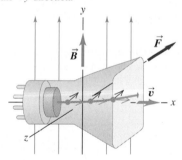

27.9 Determining the direction of a magnetic field using a cathode-ray tube. Because electrons have a negative charge, the magnetic force $\vec{F} = q\vec{v} \times \vec{B}$ in part (b) points opposite to the direction given by the right-hand rule (see Fig. 27.7b).

Problem-Solving Strategy 27.1   **Magnetic Forces**

IDENTIFY *the relevant concepts:*   The right-hand rule allows you to determine the magnetic force on a moving charged particle.

SET UP *the problem* using the following steps:
1. Draw the velocity vector $\vec{v}$ and magnetic field $\vec{B}$ with their tails together so that you can visualize the plane in which these two vectors lie.
2. Identify the angle ϕ between the two vectors.
3. Identify the target variables. This may be the magnitude and direction of the force, or it may be the magnitude or direction of $\vec{v}$ or $\vec{B}$.

EXECUTE *the solution* as follows:
1. Express the magnetic force using Eq. (27.2), $\vec{F} = q\vec{v} \times \vec{B}$. The magnitude of the force is given by Eq. (27.1), $F = qvB\sin\phi$.

2. Remember that $\vec{F}$ is perpendicular to the plane of the vectors $\vec{v}$ and $\vec{B}$. The direction of $\vec{v} \times \vec{B}$ is determined by the right-hand rule; keep referring to Fig. 27.7 until you're sure you understand this rule. If q is negative, the force is *opposite* to $\vec{v} \times \vec{B}$.

EVALUATE *your answer:*   Whenever you can, solve the problem in two ways. Do it directly from the geometric definition of the vector product. Then find the components of the vectors in some convenient axis system and calculate the vector product algebraically from the components. Verify that the results agree.

Example 27.1   Magnetic force on a proton

A beam of protons ($q = 1.6 \times 10^{-19}$ C) moves at 3.0×10^5 m/s through a uniform magnetic field with magnitude 2.0 T that is directed along the positive z-axis, as in Fig. 27.10. The velocity of each proton lies in the xz-plane at an angle of 30° to the +z-axis. Find the force on a proton.

SOLUTION

IDENTIFY: This problem uses the expression for the magnetic force on a moving charged particle.

SET UP: Figure 27.10 shows that the vectors $\vec{v}$ and $\vec{B}$ lie in the xz-plane. The angle between these vectors is 30°. The target variables are the magnitude and direction of the force $\vec{F}$.

27.10 Directions of $\vec{v}$ and $\vec{B}$ for a proton in a magnetic field.

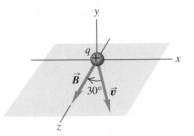

EXECUTE: The charge is positive, so the force is in the same direction as the vector product $\vec{v} \times \vec{B}$. From the right-hand rule, this direction is along the negative y-axis. The magnitude of the force, from Eq. (27.1), is

$$F = qvB\sin\phi$$
$$= (1.6 \times 10^{-19}\,\text{C})(3.0 \times 10^5\,\text{m/s})(2.0\,\text{T})(\sin 30°)$$
$$= 4.8 \times 10^{-14}\,\text{N}$$

EVALUATE: We check our result by evaluating the force using vector language and Eq. (27.2). We have

$$\vec{v} = (3.0 \times 10^5\,\text{m/s})(\sin 30°)\hat{\imath} + (3.0 \times 10^5\,\text{m/s})(\cos 30°)\hat{k}$$
$$\vec{B} = (2.0\,\text{T})\hat{k}$$
$$\vec{F} = q\vec{v} \times \vec{B}$$
$$= (1.6 \times 10^{-19}\,\text{C})(3.0 \times 10^5\,\text{m/s})(2.0\,\text{T})$$
$$\times (\sin 30°\,\hat{\imath} + \cos 30°\hat{k}) \times \hat{k}$$
$$= (-4.8 \times 10^{-14}\,\text{N})\hat{\jmath}$$

(Recall that $\hat{\imath} \times \hat{k} = -\hat{\jmath}$ and $\hat{k} \times \hat{k} = \mathbf{0}$.) We again find that the force is in the negative y-direction with magnitude 4.8×10^{-14} N.

If the beam consists of *electrons* rather than protons, the charge is negative ($q = -1.6 \times 10^{-19}$ C) and the direction of the force is reversed. The force is now directed along the *positive* y-axis, but the magnitude is the same as before, $F = 4.8 \times 10^{-14}$ N.

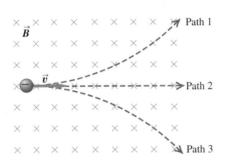

Test Your Understanding of Section 27.2   The figure at left shows a uniform magnetic field $\vec{B}$ directed into the plane of the paper (shown by the blue ×'s). A particle with a negative charge moves in the plane. Which of the three paths—1, 2, or 3—does the particle follow?   (MP)

27.11 The magnetic field lines of a permanent magnet. Note that the field lines pass through the interior of the magnet.

At each point, the field line is tangent to the magnetic field vector $\vec{B}$.

The more densely the field lines are packed, the stronger the field is at that point.

At each point, the field lines point in the same direction a compass would . . .

. . . therefore, magnetic field lines point *away from* N poles and *toward* S poles.

27.3   Magnetic Field Lines and Magnetic Flux

We can represent any magnetic field by **magnetic field lines,** just as we did for the earth's magnetic field in Fig. 27.3. The idea is the same as for the electric field lines we introduced in Section 21.6. We draw the lines so that the line through any point is tangent to the magnetic field vector $\vec{B}$ at that point (Fig. 27.11). Just as with electric field lines, we draw only a few representative lines; otherwise, the lines would fill up all of space. Where adjacent field lines are close together, the field magnitude is large; where these field lines are far apart, the field magnitude is small. Also, because the direction of $\vec{B}$ at each point is unique, field lines never intersect.

CAUTION   **Magnetic field lines are not "lines of force"**   Magnetic field lines are sometimes called "magnetic lines of force," but that's not a good name for them; unlike electric field lines, they *do not* point in the direction of the force on a charge (Fig. 27.12). Equation (27.2) shows that the force on a moving charged particle is always perpendicular to the magnetic field, and hence to the magnetic field line that passes through the particle's position. The direction of the force depends on the particle's velocity and the sign of its charge, so just looking at magnetic field lines cannot in itself tell you the direction of the force on an arbitrary moving charged particle. Magnetic field lines *do* have the direction that a compass needle would point at each location; this may help you to visualize them. ▮

Figures 27.11 and 27.13 show magnetic field lines produced by several common sources of magnetic field. In the gap between the poles of the magnet shown in Fig. 27.13a, the field lines are approximately straight, parallel, and equally spaced, showing that the magnetic field in this region is approximately *uniform* (that is, constant in magnitude and direction).

Because magnetic-field patterns are three-dimensional, it's often necessary to draw magnetic field lines that point into or out of the plane of a drawing. To do this we use a dot (·) to represent a vector directed out of the plane and a cross (×) to represent a vector directed into the plane (Fig. 27.13b). Here's a good way to remember these conventions: Think of a dot as the head of an arrow coming directly toward you, and think of a cross as the feathers of an arrow flying directly away from you.

Iron filings, like compass needles, tend to align with magnetic field lines. Hence they provide an easy way to visualize field lines (Fig. 27.14).

27.12 Magnetic field lines are *not* "lines of force."

Magnetic field lines are *not* "lines of force." The force on a charged particle is not along the direction of a field line.

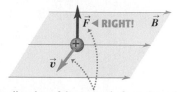

The direction of the magnetic force depends on the velocity $\vec{v}$, as expressed by the magnetic force law $\vec{F} = q\vec{v} \times \vec{B}$.

27.13 Magnetic field lines produced by several common sources of magnetic field.

(a) Magnetic field of a C-shaped magnet

Between flat, parallel magnetic poles, the magnetic field is nearly uniform.

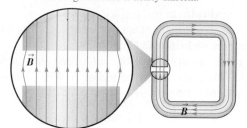

(b) Magnetic field of a straight current-carrying wire

To represent a field coming out of or going into the plane of the paper, we use dots and crosses, respectively.

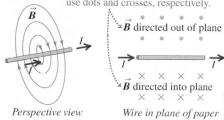

$\vec{B}$ directed out of plane

$\vec{B}$ directed into plane

Perspective view   *Wire in plane of paper*

(c) Magnetic fields of a current-carrying loop and a current-carrying coil (solenoid)

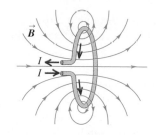

Notice that the field of the loop and, especially, that of the coil look like the field of a bar magnet (see Fig. 27.11).

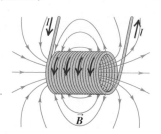

27.14 **(a)** Like little compass needles, iron filings line up tangent to magnetic field lines. **(b)** Drawing of the field lines for the situation shown in **(a)**.

(a)

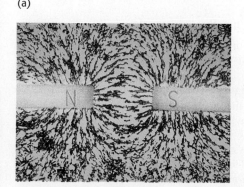

(b)

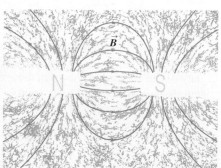

27.15 The magnetic flux through an area element dA is defined to be $d\Phi_B = B_\perp dA$.

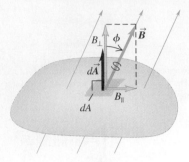

Magnetic Flux and Gauss's Law for Magnetism

We define the **magnetic flux** Φ_B through a surface just as we defined electric flux in connection with Gauss's law in Section 22.2. We can divide any surface into elements of area dA (Fig. 27.15). For each element we determine $B_\perp$, the component of $\vec{B}$ normal to the surface at the position of that element, as shown. From the figure, $B_\perp = B\cos\phi$, where ϕ is the angle between the direction of $\vec{B}$ and a line perpendicular to the surface. (Be careful not to confuse ϕ with Φ_B.) In general, this component varies from point to point on the surface. We define the magnetic flux $d\Phi_B$ through this area as

$$d\Phi_B = B_\perp dA = B\cos\phi\, dA = \vec{B} \cdot d\vec{A} \qquad (27.5)$$

The *total* magnetic flux through the surface is the sum of the contributions from the individual area elements:

$$\Phi_B = \int B_\perp dA = \int B\cos\phi\, dA = \int \vec{B} \cdot d\vec{A} \qquad \text{(magnetic flux through a surface)} \qquad (27.6)$$

(This equation uses the concepts of vector area and surface integral that we introduced in Section 22.2; you may want to review that discussion.)

Magnetic flux is a *scalar* quantity. In the special case in which $\vec{B}$ is uniform over a plane surface with total area A, $B_\perp$ and ϕ are the same at all points on the surface, and

$$\Phi_B = B_\perp A = BA\cos\phi \qquad (27.7)$$

If $\vec{B}$ happens to be perpendicular to the surface, then $\cos\phi = 1$ and Eq. (27.7) reduces to $\Phi_B = BA$. We will use the concept of magnetic flux extensively during our study of electromagnetic induction in Chapter 29.

The SI unit of magnetic flux is equal to the unit of magnetic field (1 T) times the unit of area $(1\ \text{m}^2)$. This unit is called the **weber** (1 Wb), in honor of the German physicist Wilhelm Weber (1804–1891):

$$1\ \text{Wb} = 1\ \text{T} \cdot \text{m}^2$$

Also, $1\ \text{T} = 1\ \text{N}/\text{A} \cdot \text{m}$, so

$$1\ \text{Wb} = 1\ \text{T} \cdot \text{m}^2 = 1\ \text{N} \cdot \text{m}/\text{A}$$

In Gauss's law the total *electric* flux through a closed surface is proportional to the total electric charge enclosed by the surface. For example, if the closed surface encloses an electric dipole, the total electric flux is zero because the total charge is zero. (You may want to review Section 22.3 on Gauss's law.) By analogy, if there were such a thing as a single magnetic charge (magnetic monopole), the total *magnetic* flux through a closed surface would be proportional to the total magnetic charge enclosed. But we have mentioned that no magnetic monopole has ever been observed, despite intensive searches. We conclude:

The total magnetic flux through a closed surface is always zero.

Symbolically,

$$\oint \vec{B} \cdot d\vec{A} = 0 \qquad \text{(magnetic flux through any closed surface)} \qquad (27.8)$$

This equation is sometimes called *Gauss's law for magnetism*. You can verify it by examining Figs. 27.11 and 27.13; if you draw a closed surface anywhere in any of the field maps shown in those figures, you will see that every field line that enters the surface also exits from it; the net flux through the surface is zero. It also follows from Eq. (27.8) that magnetic field lines always form closed loops.

CAUTION Magnetic field lines have no ends Unlike electric field lines that begin and end on electric charges, magnetic field lines *never* have end points; such a point would indicate the presence of a monopole. You might be tempted to draw magnetic field lines that begin at the north pole of a magnet and end at a south pole. But as Fig. 27.11 shows, the field lines of a magnet actually continue through the interior of the magnet. Like all other magnetic field lines, they form closed loops. ▮

For Gauss's law, which always deals with *closed* surfaces, the vector area element $d\vec{A}$ in Eq. (27.6) always points *out of* the surface. However, some applications of *magnetic* flux involve an *open* surface with a boundary line; there is then an ambiguity of sign in Eq. (27.6) because of the two possible choices of direction for $d\vec{A}$. In these cases we choose one of the two sides of the surface to be the "positive" side and use that choice consistently.

If the element of area dA in Eq. (27.5) is at right angles to the field lines, then $B_\perp = B$; calling the area $dA_\perp$, we have

$$B = \frac{d\Phi_B}{dA_\perp} \qquad (27.9)$$

That is, the magnitude of magnetic field is equal to *flux per unit area* across an area at right angles to the magnetic field. For this reason, magnetic field $\vec{B}$ is sometimes called **magnetic flux density.**

Example 27.2   Magnetic flux calculations

Figure 27.16a shows a perspective view of a flat surface with area 3.0 cm² in a uniform magnetic field. If the magnetic flux through this area is 0.90 mWb, calculate the magnitude of the magnetic field and find the direction of the area vector.

SOLUTION

IDENTIFY: In many problems we are asked to calculate the flux of a given magnetic field through a given area. In this example, how-

27.16 (a) A flat area A in a uniform magnetic field $\vec{B}$. (b) The area vector $\vec{A}$ makes a 60° angle with $\vec{B}$. (If we had chosen $\vec{A}$ to point in the opposite direction, ϕ would have been 120° and the magnetic flux Φ_B would have been negative.)

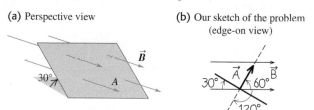

(a) Perspective view

(b) Our sketch of the problem (edge-on view)

ever, we are given the flux, the area, and the direction of the magnetic field. Our target variables are the field magnitude and the direction of the area vector.

SET UP: Because the magnetic field is uniform, B and ϕ are the same at all points on the surface. Hence we can use Eq. (27.7): $\Phi_B = BA\cos\phi$. Our target variable is B.

EXECUTE: The area A is 3.0×10^{-4} m²; the direction of $\vec{A}$ is perpendicular to the surface, so ϕ could be either 60° or 120°. But Φ_B, B, and A are all positive, so $\cos\phi$ must also be positive. This rules out 120°, so $\phi = 60°$, and we find

$$B = \frac{\Phi_B}{A\cos\phi} = \frac{0.90 \times 10^{-3}\,\text{Wb}}{(3.0 \times 10^{-4}\,\text{m}^2)(\cos 60°)} = 6.0\,\text{T}$$

The area vector $\vec{A}$ is perpendicular to the area in the direction shown in Fig. 27.16b.

EVALUATE: A good way to check our result is to calculate the product $BA\cos\phi$ to make sure that it is equal to the given value of the magnetic flux Φ_B. Is it?

Test Your Understanding of Section 27.3   Imagine moving along the axis of the current-carrying loop in Fig. 27.13c, starting at a point well to the left of the loop and ending at a point well to the right of the loop. (a) How would the magnetic field strength vary as you moved along this path? (i) It would be the same at all points along the path; (ii) it would increase and then decrease; (iii) it would decrease and then increase. (b) Would the magnetic field direction vary as you moved along the path? ▮

27.4 Motion of Charged Particles in a Magnetic Field

When a charged particle moves in a magnetic field, it is acted on by the magnetic force given by Eq. (27.2), and the motion is determined by Newton's laws. Figure 27.17 shows a simple example. A particle with positive charge q is at

27.17 A charged particle moves in a plane perpendicular to a uniform magnetic field $\vec{B}$.

(a) The orbit of a charged particle in a uniform magnetic field

A charge moving at right angles to a uniform $\vec{B}$ field moves in a circle at constant speed because $\vec{F}$ and $\vec{v}$ are always perpendicular to each other.

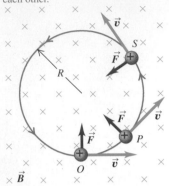

(b) An electron beam (seen as a blue arc) curving in a magnetic field

point O, moving with velocity $\vec{v}$ in a uniform magnetic field $\vec{B}$ directed into the plane of the figure. The vectors $\vec{v}$ and $\vec{B}$ are perpendicular, so the magnetic force $\vec{F} = q\vec{v} \times \vec{B}$ has magnitude $F = qvB$ and a direction as shown in the figure. The force is *always* perpendicular to $\vec{v}$, so it cannot change the *magnitude* of the velocity, only its direction. To put it differently, the magnetic force never has a component parallel to the particle's motion, so the magnetic force can never do *work* on the particle. This is true even if the magnetic field is not uniform.

> **Motion of a charged particle under the action of a magnetic field alone is always motion with constant speed.**

Using this principle, we see that in the situation shown in Fig. 27.17a the magnitudes of both $\vec{F}$ and $\vec{v}$ are constant. At points such as P and S the directions of force and velocity have changed as shown, but their magnitudes are the same. The particle therefore moves under the influence of a constant-magnitude force that is always at right angles to the velocity of the particle. Comparing these conditions with the discussion of circular motion in Sections 3.4 and 5.4, we see that the particle's path is a *circle*, traced out with constant speed v. The centripetal acceleration is v^2/R and the only force acting is the magnetic force, so from Newton's second law,

$$F = |q|vB = m\frac{v^2}{R} \tag{27.10}$$

where m is the mass of the particle. Solving Eq. (27.10) for the radius R of the circular path, we find

$$R = \frac{mv}{|q|B} \quad \text{(radius of a circular orbit in a magnetic field)} \tag{27.11}$$

We can also write this as $R = p/|q|B$, where $p = mv$ is the magnitude of the particle's momentum. If the charge q is negative, the particle moves *clockwise* around the orbit in Fig. 27.17a.

The angular speed ω of the particle can be found from Eq. (9.13), $v = R\omega$. Combining this with Eq. (27.11), we get

$$\omega = \frac{v}{R} = v\frac{|q|B}{mv} = \frac{|q|B}{m} \tag{27.12}$$

The number of revolutions per unit time is $f = \omega/2\pi$. This frequency f is independent of the radius R of the path. It is called the **cyclotron frequency;** in a particle accelerator called a *cyclotron,* particles moving in nearly circular paths are given a boost twice each revolution, increasing their energy and their orbital radii but not their angular speed or frequency. Similarly, one type of *magnetron,* a common source of microwave radiation for microwave ovens and radar systems, emits radiation with a frequency equal to the frequency of circular motion of electrons in a vacuum chamber between the poles of a magnet.

If the direction of the initial velocity is *not* perpendicular to the field, the velocity *component* parallel to the field is constant because there is no force parallel to the field. Then the particle moves in a helix (Fig. 27.18). The radius of the helix is given by Eq. (27.11), where v is now the component of velocity perpendicular to the $\vec{B}$ field.

Motion of a charged particle in a nonuniform magnetic field is more complex. Figure 27.19 shows a field produced by two circular coils separated by some distance. Particles near either coil experience a magnetic force toward the center of the region; particles with appropriate speeds spiral repeatedly from one end of the region to the other and back. Because charged particles can be trapped in such a magnetic field, it is called a *magnetic bottle.* This technique is used to confine very hot plasmas with temperatures of the order of 10^6 K. In a similar way the

27.18 The general case of a charged particle moving in a uniform magnetic field $\vec{B}$. The magnetic field does no work on the particle, so its speed and kinetic energy remain constant.

This particle's motion has components both parallel ($v_\parallel$) and perpendicular ($v_\perp$) to the magnetic field, so it moves in a helical path.

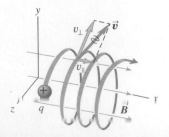

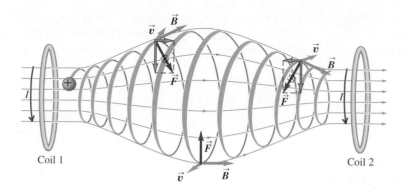

27.19 A magnetic bottle. Particles near either end of the region experience a magnetic force toward the center of the region. This is one way of containing an ionized gas that has a temperature of the order of 10^6 K, which would vaporize any material container.

(a) (b)

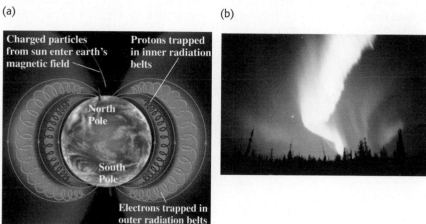

27.20 (a) The Van Allen radiation belts around the earth. Near the poles, charged particles from these belts can enter the atmosphere, producing the aurora borealis ("northern lights") and aurora australis ("southern lights"). (b) A photograph of the aurora borealis.

27.21 This bubble chamber image shows the result of a high-energy gamma ray (which does not leave a track) that collides with an electron in a hydrogen atom. This electron flies off to the right at high speed. Some of the energy in the collision is transformed into a second electron and a positron (a positively charged electron). A magnetic field is directed into the plane of the image, which makes the positive and negative particles curve off in different directions.

earth's nonuniform magnetic field traps charged particles coming from the sun in doughnut-shaped regions around the earth, as shown in Fig. 27.20. These regions, called the *Van Allen radiation belts,* were discovered in 1958 using data obtained by instruments aboard the Explorer I satellite.

Magnetic forces on charged particles play an important role in studies of elementary particles. Figure 27.21 shows a chamber filled with liquid hydrogen and with a magnetic field directed into the plane of the photograph. A high-energy gamma ray dislodges an electron from a hydrogen atom, sending it off at high speed and creating a visible track in the liquid hydrogen. The track shows the electron curving downward due to the magnetic force. The energy of the collision also produces another electron and a *positron* (a positively charged electron). Because of their opposite charges, the trajectories of the electron and the positron curve in opposite directions. As these particles plow through the liquid hydrogen, they collide with other charged particles, losing energy and speed. As a result, the radius of curvature decreases as suggested by Eq. (27.11). (The electron's speed is comparable to the speed of light, so Eq. (27.11) isn't directly applicable here.) Similar experiments allow physicists to determine the mass and charge of newly discovered particles.

	Slow-moving positron ($q > 0$)
Path of incoming gamma ray	$\vec{B}$ ×
Hydrogen atom	
Slow-moving electron ($q < 0$)	Fast-moving electron ($q < 0$)

Problem-Solving Strategy 27.2   Motion in Magnetic Fields

IDENTIFY *the relevant concepts:* In analyzing the motion of a charged particle in electric and magnetic fields, you will apply Newton's second law of motion, $\Sigma \vec{F} = m\vec{a}$, with the net force given by $\Sigma \vec{F} = q(\vec{E} + \vec{v} \times \vec{B})$. Often other forces such as gravity can be neglected. Many of the problems are similar to the trajectory and circular-motion problems in Sections 3.3, 3.4, and 5.4; it would be a good idea to review those sections.

SET UP *the problem* using the following steps:
1. Determine the target variable(s).
2. Often the use of components is the most efficient approach. Choose a coordinate system and then express all vector quantities (including $\vec{E}$, $\vec{B}$, $\vec{v}$, $\vec{F}$, and $\vec{a}$) in terms of their components in this system.

Continued

EXECUTE *the solution* as follows:

1. If the particle moves perpendicular to a uniform magnetic field, the trajectory is a circle with a radius and angular speed given by Eqs. (27.11) and (27.12), respectively.
2. If your calculation involves a more complex trajectory, use $\sum \vec{F} = m\vec{a}$ in component form: $\sum F_x = ma_x$, and so forth. This

approach is particularly useful when both electric and magnetic fields are present.

EVALUATE *your answer:* Check whether your results are reasonable.

Example 27.3   Electron motion in a microwave oven

A magnetron in a microwave oven emits electromagnetic waves with frequency $f = 2450$ MHz. What magnetic field strength is required for electrons to move in circular paths with this frequency?

SOLUTION

IDENTIFY: The problem refers to circular motion as shown in Fig. 27.17a. Our target variable is the field magnitude B.

SET UP: We use Eq. (27.12) to relate the angular speed in circular motion to the mass and charge of the particle and the magnetic field strength B.

EXECUTE: The angular speed that corresponds to the frequency f is $\omega = 2\pi f = (2\pi)(2450 \times 10^6 \text{ s}^{-1}) = 1.54 \times 10^{10} \text{ s}^{-1}$. From Eq. (27.12),

$$B = \frac{m\omega}{|q|} = \frac{(9.11 \times 10^{-31} \text{ kg})(1.54 \times 10^{10} \text{ s}^{-1})}{1.60 \times 10^{-19} \text{ C}}$$

$$= 0.0877 \text{ T}$$

EVALUATE: This is a moderate field strength, easily produced with a permanent magnet. Incidentally, 2450-MHz electromagnetic waves are strongly absorbed by water molecules, so they are useful for heating and cooking food.

Example 27.4   Helical particle motion

In a situation like that shown in Fig. 27.18, the charged particle is a proton ($q = 1.60 \times 10^{-19}$ C, $m = 1.67 \times 10^{-27}$ kg) and the uniform magnetic field is directed along the x-axis with magnitude 0.500 T. Only the magnetic force acts on the proton. At $t = 0$ the proton has velocity components $v_x = 1.50 \times 10^5$ m/s, $v_y = 0$, and $v_z = 2.00 \times 10^5$ m/s. (a) At $t = 0$, find the force on the proton and its acceleration. (b) Find the radius of the helical path, the angular speed of the proton, and the *pitch* of the helix (the distance traveled along the helix axis per revolution).

SOLUTION

IDENTIFY: The force is given by $\vec{F} = q\vec{v} \times \vec{B}$ and the acceleration is given by Newton's second law. The force is perpendicular to the velocity, so the speed of the proton does not change. Hence the radius of the helical trajectory is just as given by Eq. (27.11) for circular motion, but with v replaced by the component of velocity perpendicular to $\vec{B}$. The angular speed is given by Eq. (27.12).

SET UP: We use the coordinate system shown in Fig. 27.18. Given the angular speed, we can determine the time required for one revolution; given the velocity parallel to the magnetic field, we can determine the distance traveled along the helix in this time.

EXECUTE: (a) Since $v_y = 0$, the velocity vector is $\vec{v} = v_x\hat{\imath} + v_z\hat{k}$. Using Eq. (27.2) and recalling that $\hat{\imath} \times \hat{\imath} = 0$ and $\hat{k} \times \hat{\imath} = \hat{\jmath}$, we find

$$\vec{F} = q\vec{v} \times \vec{B} = q(v_x\hat{\imath} + v_z\hat{k}) \times B\hat{\imath} = qv_zB\hat{\jmath}$$

$$= (1.60 \times 10^{-19} \text{ C})(2.00 \times 10^5 \text{ m/s})(0.500 \text{ T})\hat{\jmath}$$

$$= (1.60 \times 10^{-14} \text{ N})\hat{\jmath}$$

(To check unit consistency, recall from Section 27.2 that $1 \text{ T} = 1 \text{ N/A} \cdot \text{m} = 1 \text{ N} \cdot \text{s/C} \cdot \text{m}$.) This may seem like a very weak force, but the resulting acceleration is tremendous because the proton mass is so small:

$$\vec{a} = \frac{\vec{F}}{m} = \frac{1.60 \times 10^{-14} \text{ N}}{1.67 \times 10^{-27} \text{ kg}}\hat{\jmath} = (9.58 \times 10^{12} \text{ m/s}^2)\hat{\jmath}$$

(b) At $t = 0$ the component of velocity perpendicular to $\vec{B}$ is v_z, so

$$R = \frac{mv_z}{|q|B} = \frac{(1.67 \times 10^{-27} \text{ kg})(2.00 \times 10^5 \text{ m/s})}{(1.60 \times 10^{-19} \text{ C})(0.500 \text{ T})}$$

$$= 4.18 \times 10^{-3} \text{ m} = 4.18 \text{ mm}$$

From Eq. (27.12) the angular speed is

$$\omega = \frac{|q|B}{m} = \frac{(1.60 \times 10^{-19} \text{ C})(0.500 \text{ T})}{1.67 \times 10^{-27} \text{ kg}} = 4.79 \times 10^7 \text{ rad/s}$$

The time required for one revolution (the period) is $T = 2\pi/\omega = 2\pi/(4.79 \times 10^7 \text{ s}^{-1}) = 1.31 \times 10^{-7}$ s. The pitch is the distance traveled along the x-axis during this time, or

$$v_xT = (1.50 \times 10^5 \text{ m/s})(1.31 \times 10^{-7} \text{ s})$$

$$= 0.0197 \text{ m} = 19.7 \text{ mm}$$

EVALUATE: The pitch of the helix is almost five times greater than the radius. This helical trajectory is much more "stretched out" than that shown in Fig. 27.18.

Test Your Understanding of Section 27.4 (a) If you double the speed of (MP) the charged particle in Fig. 27.17a while keeping the magnetic field the same (as well as the charge and the mass), how does this affect the radius of the trajectory? (i) The radius is unchanged; (ii) the radius is twice as large; (iii) the radius is four times as large; (iv) the radius is $\frac{1}{2}$ as large; (v) the radius is $\frac{1}{4}$ as large. (b) How does this affect the time required for one complete circular orbit? (i) The time is unchanged; (ii) the time is twice as long; (iii) the time is four times as long; (iv) the time is $\frac{1}{2}$ as long; (v) the time is $\frac{1}{4}$ as long.

27.5 Applications of Motion of Charged Particles

This section describes several applications of the principles introduced in this chapter. Study them carefully, watching for applications of Problem-Solving Strategy 27.2 (Section 27.4).

Velocity Selector

In a beam of charged particles produced by a heated cathode or a radioactive material, not all particles move with the same speed. Many applications, however, require a beam in which all the particle speeds are the same. Particles of a specific speed can be selected from the beam using an arrangement of electric and magnetic fields called a *velocity selector*. In Fig. 27.22a a charged particle with mass m, charge q, and speed v enters a region of space where the electric and magnetic fields are perpendicular to the particle's velocity and to each other. The electric field $\vec{E}$ is to the left, and the magnetic field $\vec{B}$ is into the plane of the figure. If q is positive, the electric force is to the left, with magnitude qE, and the magnetic force is to the right, with magnitude qvB. For given field magnitudes E and B, for a particular value of v the electric and magnetic forces will be equal in magnitude; the total force is then zero, and the particle travels in a straight line with constant velocity. For zero total force, $\Sigma F_y = 0$, we need $-qE + qvB = 0$; solving for the speed v for which there is no deflection, we find

$$v = \frac{E}{B} \tag{27.13}$$

Only particles with speeds equal to E/B can pass through without being deflected by the fields (Fig. 27.22b). By adjusting E and B appropriately, we can select particles having a particular speed for use in other experiments. Because q divides out in Eq. (27.13), a velocity selector for positively charged particles also works for electrons or other negatively charged particles.

Thomson's e/m Experiment

In one of the landmark experiments in physics at the end of the 19th century, J. J. Thomson (1856–1940) used the idea just described to measure the ratio of charge to mass for the electron. For this experiment, carried out in 1897 at the Cavendish Laboratory in Cambridge, England, Thomson used the apparatus shown in Fig. 27.23. In a highly evacuated glass container, electrons from the hot cathode are accelerated and formed into a beam by a potential difference V between the two anodes A and A'. The speed v of the electrons is determined by the accelerating potential V. The kinetic energy $\frac{1}{2}mv^2$ equals the loss of electric potential energy eV, where e is the magnitude of the electron charge:

$$\frac{1}{2}mv^2 = eV \quad \text{or} \quad v = \sqrt{\frac{2eV}{m}} \tag{27.14}$$

27.22 (a) A velocity selector for charged particles uses perpendicular $\vec{E}$ and $\vec{B}$ fields. Only charged particles with $v = E/B$ move through undeflected. (b) The electric and magnetic forces on a positive charge. The forces are reversed if the charge is negative.

(a) Schematic diagram of velocity selector

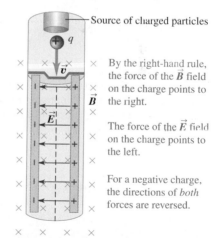

Source of charged particles

By the right-hand rule, the force of the $\vec{B}$ field on the charge points to the right.

The force of the $\vec{E}$ field on the charge points to the left.

For a negative charge, the directions of *both* forces are reversed.

(b) Free-body diagram for a positive particle

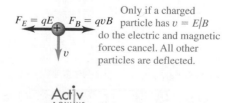

$F_E = qE \qquad F_B = qvB$

Only if a charged particle has $v = E/B$ do the electric and magnetic forces cancel. All other particles are deflected.

Activ Physics ONLINE

13.8 Velocity Selector

27.23 Thomson's apparatus for measuring the ratio e/m for the electron.

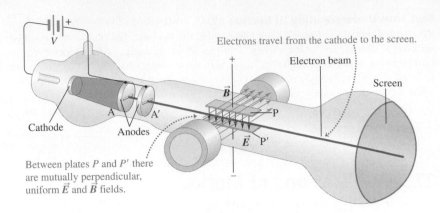

Electrons travel from the cathode to the screen.

Electron beam

Screen

$\vec{B}$

P

Cathode

Anodes

$\vec{E}$ P'

Between plates P and P' there are mutually perpendicular, uniform $\vec{E}$ and $\vec{B}$ fields.

The electrons pass between the plates P and P' and strike the screen at the end of the tube, which is coated with a material that fluoresces (glows) at the point of impact. The electrons pass straight through the plates when Eq. (27.13) is satisfied; combining this with Eq. (27.14), we get

$$\frac{E}{B} = \sqrt{\frac{2eV}{m}} \qquad \text{so} \qquad \frac{e}{m} = \frac{E^2}{2VB^2} \qquad (27.15)$$

All the quantities on the right side can be measured, so the ratio e/m of charge to mass can be determined. It is *not* possible to measure e or m separately by this method, only their ratio.

The most significant aspect of Thomson's e/m measurements was that he found a *single value* for this quantity. It did not depend on the cathode material, the residual gas in the tube, or anything else about the experiment. This independence showed that the particles in the beam, which we now call electrons, are a common constituent of all matter. Thus Thomson is credited with discovery of the first subatomic particle, the electron. He also found that the *speed* of the electrons in the beam was about one-tenth the speed of light, much greater than any previously measured speed of a material particle.

The most precise value of e/m available as of this writing is

$$e/m = 1.75882012(15) \times 10^{11} \text{ C/kg}$$

In this expression, (15) indicates the likely uncertainty in the last two digits, 12.

Fifteen years after Thomson's experiments, the American physicist Robert Millikan succeeded in measuring the charge of the electron precisely (see Challenge Problem 23.91). This value, together with the value of e/m, enables us to determine the *mass* of the electron. The most precise value available at present is

$$m = 9.1093826(16) \times 10^{-31} \text{ kg}$$

Mass Spectrometers

27.24 Bainbridge's mass spectrometer utilizes a velocity selector to produce particles with uniform speed v. In the region of magnetic field B', particles with greater mass $(m_2 > m_1)$ travel in paths with larger radius $(R_2 > R_1)$.

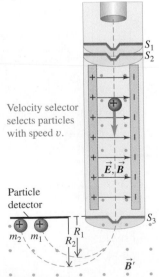

S_1
S_2

Velocity selector selects particles with speed v.

$\vec{E}, \vec{B}$

Particle detector

S_3

m_2 m_1 R_1 R_2

$\vec{B}'$

Magnetic field separates particles by mass; the greater a particle's mass, the larger is the radius of its path.

Techniques similar to Thomson's e/m experiment can be used to measure masses of ions and thus measure atomic and molecular masses. In 1919, Francis Aston (1877–1945), a student of Thomson's, built the first of a family of instruments called **mass spectrometers.** A variation built by Bainbridge is shown in Fig. 27.24. Positive ions from a source pass through the slits S_1 and S_2, forming a narrow beam. Then the ions pass through a velocity selector with crossed $\vec{E}$ and $\vec{B}$ fields, as we have described, to block all ions except those with speeds v equal to E/B. Finally, the ions pass into a region with a magnetic field $\vec{B}'$ perpendicular to the figure, where they move in circular arcs with radius R determined by Eq. (27.11): $R = mv/qB'$. Ions with different masses strike the detector (in

Bainbridge's design, a photographic plate) at different points, and the values of R can be measured. We assume that each ion has lost one electron, so the net charge of each ion is just $+e$. With everything known in this equation except m, we can compute the mass m of the ion.

One of the earliest results from this work was the discovery that neon has two species of atoms, with atomic masses 20 and 22 g/mol. We now call these species **isotopes** of the element. Later experiments have shown that many elements have several isotopes, atoms that are identical in their chemical behavior but different in mass owing to differing numbers of neutrons in their nuclei. This is just one of the many applications of mass spectrometers in chemistry and physics.

Act|v
ONLINE
Phys|cs

13.7   Mass Spectrometer

Example 27.5   An e/m experiment

You set out to reproduce Thomson's e/m experiment with an accelerating potential of 150 V and a deflecting electric field of magnitude 6.0×10^6 N/C. (a) At what fraction of the speed of light do the electrons move? (b) What magnitude of magnetic field will you need? (c) With this magnetic field, what will happen to the electron beam if you increase the accelerating potential above 150 V?

SOLUTION

IDENTIFY: This is the same situation as depicted in Fig. 27.23.

SET UP: We use Eq. (27.14) to determine the speed of the electrons and Eq. (27.13) to determine the requisite magnetic field.

EXECUTE: (a) From Eq. (27.14), the electron speed v is related to the accelerating potential by:

$$v = \sqrt{2(e/m)V} = \sqrt{2(1.76 \times 10^{11} \text{ C/kg})(150 \text{ V})}$$

$$= 7.27 \times 10^6 \text{ m/s}$$

$$\frac{v}{c} = \frac{7.27 \times 10^6 \text{ m/s}}{3.00 \times 10^8 \text{ m/s}} = 0.024$$

The electrons are traveling at 2.4% of the speed of light.
(b) From Eq. (27.13),

$$B = \frac{E}{v} = \frac{6.00 \times 10^6 \text{ N/C}}{7.27 \times 10^6 \text{ m/s}} = 0.83 \text{ T}$$

(c) Increasing the accelerating potential V increases the electron speed v. In Fig. 27.23 this doesn't change the upward electric force eE, but it increases the downward magnetic force evB. Therefore the electron beam will be bent *downward* and will hit the end of the tube below the undeflected position.

EVALUATE: The required magnetic field is relatively large. If the maximum available magnetic field B is less than 0.83 T, the electric field strength E would have to be reduced to maintain the desired ratio E/B in Eq. (27.15).

Example 27.6   Finding leaks in a vacuum system

There is almost no helium in ordinary air, so helium sprayed near a leak in a vacuum system will quickly show up in the output of a vacuum pump connected to such a system. You are designing a leak detector that uses a mass spectrometer to detect He$^+$ ions (charge $+e = +1.60 \times 10^{-19}$ C, mass 6.65×10^{-27} kg). The ions emerge from the velocity selector with a speed of 1.00×10^5 m/s. They are curved in a semicircular path by a magnetic field B' and are detected at a distance of 10.16 cm from the slit S_3 in Fig. 27.24. Calculate the magnitude of the magnetic field B'.

SOLUTION

IDENTIFY: The motion of the ion after it passes through slit S_3 in Fig. 27.24 is just motion in a circular path as described in Section 27.4 (see Fig. 27.17).

SET UP: We use Eq. (27.11) to relate the magnetic field strength B' (the target variable) to the radius of curvature of the path and to the mass, charge, and speed of the ion.

EXECUTE: The distance given is the *diameter* of the semicircular path shown in Fig. 27.24, so the radius is $R = \frac{1}{2}(10.16 \times 10^{-2} \text{ m}) = 5.08 \times 10^{-2}$ m. From Eq. (27.11), $R = mv/qB'$, we get

$$B' = \frac{mv}{qR} = \frac{(6.65 \times 10^{-27} \text{ kg})(1.00 \times 10^5 \text{ m/s})}{(1.60 \times 10^{-19} \text{ C})(5.08 \times 10^{-2} \text{ m})}$$

$$= 0.0817 \text{ T}$$

EVALUATE: Helium leak detectors are actual devices that are widely used for diagnosing problems with high-vacuum systems. Our result shows that only a small magnetic field is required, which makes it possible to build relatively compact leak detectors.

Test Your Understanding of Section 27.5   In Example 27.6 He$^+$ ions with charge $+e$ move at 1.00×10^5 m/s in a straight line through a velocity selector. Suppose the He$^+$ ions were replaced with He^{2+} ions, in which both electrons have been removed from the helium atom and the ion charge is $+2e$. At what speed must the He^{2+} ions travel through the same velocity selector in order to move in a straight line? (i) about 4.00×10^5 m/s; (ii) about 2.00×10^5 m/s; (iii) 1.00×10^5 m/s; (iv) about 0.50×10^5 m/s; (v) about 0.25×10^5 m/s.

27.6 Magnetic Force on a Current-Carrying Conductor

27.25 Forces on a moving positive charge in a current-carrying conductor.

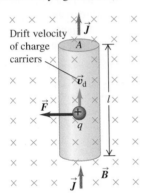

27.26 A straight wire segment of length $\vec{l}$ carries a current I in the direction of $\vec{l}$. The magnetic force on this segment is perpendicular to both $\vec{l}$ and the magnetic field $\vec{B}$.

Force $\vec{F}$ on a straight wire carrying a positive current and oriented at an angle ϕ to a magnetic field $\vec{B}$:
• Magnitude is $F = IlB_\perp = IlB \sin \phi$.
• Direction of $\vec{F}$ is given by the right-hand rule.

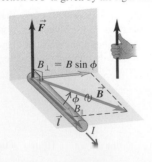

What makes an electric motor work? The forces that make it turn are forces that a magnetic field exerts on a conductor carrying a current. The magnetic forces on the moving charges within the conductor are transmitted to the material of the conductor, and the conductor as a whole experiences a force distributed along its length. The moving-coil galvanometer that we described in Section 26.3 also uses magnetic forces on conductors.

We can compute the force on a current-carrying conductor starting with the magnetic force $\vec{F} = q\vec{v} \times \vec{B}$ on a single moving charge. Figure 27.25 shows a straight segment of a conducting wire, with length l and cross-sectional area A; the current is from bottom to top. The wire is in a uniform magnetic field $\vec{B}$, perpendicular to the plane of the diagram and directed *into* the plane. Let's assume first that the moving charges are positive. Later we'll see what happens when they are negative.

The drift velocity $\vec{v}_d$ is upward, perpendicular to $\vec{B}$. The average force on each charge is $\vec{F} = q\vec{v}_d \times \vec{B}$, directed to the left as shown in the figure; since $\vec{v}_d$ and $\vec{B}$ are perpendicular, the magnitude of the force is $F = qv_dB$.

We can derive an expression for the *total* force on all the moving charges in a length l of conductor with cross-sectional area A using the same language we used in Eqs. (25.2) and (25.3) of Section 25.1. The number of charges per unit volume is n; a segment of conductor with length l has volume Al and contains a number of charges equal to nAl. The total force $\vec{F}$ on *all* the moving charges in this segment has magnitude

$$F = (nAl)(qv_dB) = (nqv_dA)(lB) \tag{27.16}$$

From Eq. (25.3) the current density is $J = nqv_d$. The product JA is the total current I, so we can rewrite Eq. (27.16) as

$$F = IlB \tag{27.17}$$

If the $\vec{B}$ field is not perpendicular to the wire but makes an angle ϕ with it, we handle the situation the same way we did in Section 27.2 for a single charge. Only the component of $\vec{B}$ perpendicular to the wire (and to the drift velocities of the charges) exerts a force; this component is $B_\perp = B \sin \phi$. The magnetic force on the wire segment is then

$$F = IlB_\perp = IlB \sin \phi \tag{27.18}$$

The force is always perpendicular to both the conductor and the field, with the direction determined by the same right-hand rule we used for a moving positive charge (Fig. 27.26). Hence this force can be expressed as a vector product, just like the force on a single moving charge. We represent the segment of wire with a vector $\vec{l}$ along the wire in the direction of the current; then the force $\vec{F}$ on this segment is

$$\vec{F} = I\vec{l} \times \vec{B} \quad \text{(magnetic force on a straight wire segment)} \quad (27.19)$$

Figure 27.27 illustrates the directions of $\vec{B}$, $\vec{l}$, and $\vec{F}$ for several cases.

If the conductor is not straight, we can divide it into infinitesimal segments $d\vec{l}$. The force $d\vec{F}$ on each segment is

$$d\vec{F} = I\,d\vec{l} \times \vec{B} \quad \text{(magnetic force on an infinitesimal wire section)} \quad (27.20)$$

Then we can integrate this expression along the wire to find the total force on a conductor of any shape. The integral is a *line integral*, the same mathematical operation we have used to define work (Section 6.3) and electric potential (Section 23.2).

CAUTION   **Current is not a vector**   Recall from Section 25.1 that the current I is not a vector. The direction of current flow is described by $d\vec{l}$, not I. If the conductor is curved, the current I is the same at all points along its length, but $d\vec{l}$ changes direction so that it is always tangent to the conductor. ▮

Finally, what happens when the moving charges are negative, such as electrons in a metal? Then in Fig. 27.25 an upward current corresponds to a downward drift velocity. But because q is now negative, the direction of the force $\vec{F}$ is the same as before. Thus Eqs. (27.17) through (27.20) are valid for *both* positive and negative charges and even when *both* signs of charge are present at once. This happens in some semiconductor materials and in ionic solutions.

A common application of the magnetic forces on a current-carrying wire is found in loudspeakers (Fig. 27.28). The radial magnetic field created by the permanent magnet exerts a force on the voice coil that is proportional to the current in the coil; the direction of the force is either to the left or to the right, depending on the direction of the current. The signal from the amplifier causes the current to oscillate in direction and magnitude. The coil and the speaker cone to which it is attached respond by oscillating with an amplitude proportional to the amplitude of the current in the coil. Turning up the volume knob on the amplifier increases the current amplitude and hence the amplitudes of the cone's oscillation and of the sound wave produced by the moving cone.

27.27 Magnetic field $\vec{B}$, length $\vec{l}$, and force $\vec{F}$ vectors for a straight wire carrying a current I.

(a)

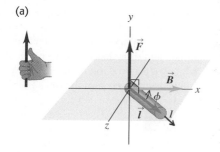

(b)

Reversing $\vec{B}$ reverses the force direction.

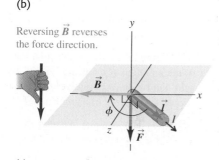

(c)

Reversing the current [relative to (b)] reverses the force direction.

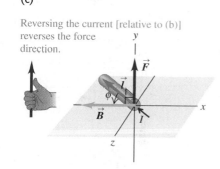

27.28 (a) Components of a loudspeaker. (b) The permanent magnet creates a magnetic field that exerts forces on the current in the voice coil; for a current I in the direction shown, the force is to the right. If the electric current in the voice coil oscillates, the speaker cone attached to the voice coil oscillates at the same frequency.

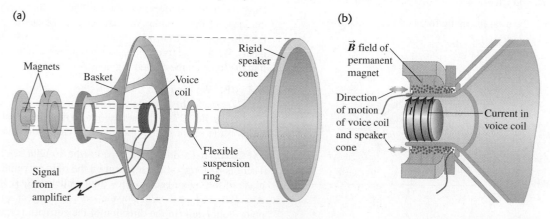

| Example 27.7 | **Magnetic force on a straight conductor** |

A straight horizontal copper rod carries a current of 50.0 A from west to east in a region between the poles of a large electromagnet. In this region there is a horizontal magnetic field toward the northeast (that is, 45° north of east) with magnitude 1.20 T. (a) Find the magnitude and direction of the force on a 1.00-m section of rod. (b) While keeping the rod horizontal, how should it be oriented to maximize the magnitude of the force? What is the force magnitude in this case?

SOLUTION

IDENTIFY: This is a straight wire segment in a uniform magnetic field, which is the same situation as shown in Fig. 27.26. Our target variables are the force $\vec{F}$ on the rod segment and the angle ϕ for which the force magnitude is greatest.

SET UP: Figure 27.29 shows the situation. We can find the magnitude of the magnetic force using Eq. (27.18) and the direction from the right-hand rule. Alternatively, we can find the force vector (magnitude and direction) using Eq. (27.19).

EXECUTE: (a) The angle ϕ between the directions of current and field is 45°. From Eq. (27.18) we obtain

$$F = IlB\sin\phi = (50.0\ \text{A})(1.00\ \text{m})(1.20\ \text{T})(\sin45°) = 42.4\ \text{N}$$

27.29 Our sketch of the copper rod as seen from overhead.

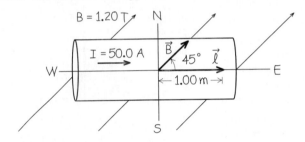

The *direction* of the force is perpendicular to the plane of the current and the field, both of which lie in the horizontal plane. Thus the force must be vertical; the right-hand rule shows that it is vertically *upward* (out of the plane of the figure).

Alternatively, we can use a coordinate system with the x-axis pointing east, the y-axis north, and the z-axis up. Then we have

$$\vec{l} = (1.00\ \text{m})\hat{\imath} \qquad \vec{B} = (1.20\ \text{T})[(\cos45°)\hat{\imath} + (\sin45°)\hat{\jmath}]$$

$$\vec{F} = I\vec{l} \times \vec{B}$$

$$= (50\ \text{A})(1.00\ \text{m})\hat{\imath} \times (1.20\ \text{T})[(\cos45°)\hat{\imath} + (\sin45°)\hat{\jmath}]$$

$$= (42.4\ \text{N})\hat{k}$$

If the conductor is in mechanical equilibrium under the action of its weight and the upward magnetic force, its weight is 42.4 N and its mass is

$$m = \frac{w}{g} = \frac{42.4\ \text{N}}{9.8\ \text{m/s}^2} = 4.33\ \text{kg}$$

(b) The magnitude of the force is maximum if $\phi = 90°$ so that $\vec{l}$ and $\vec{B}$ are perpendicular. To have the force still be upward, we rotate the rod clockwise by 45° from its orientation in Fig. 27.29 so that the current runs toward the southeast. Then the magnetic force has magnitude

$$F = IlB = (50.0\ \text{A})(1.00\ \text{m})(1.20\ \text{T}) = 60.0\ \text{N}$$

and the mass of a rod that can be held up against gravity is $m = w/g = (60.0\ \text{N})/(9.8\ \text{m/s}^2) = 6.12\ \text{kg}$.

EVALUATE: This is a simple example of magnetic levitation. Magnetic levitation is also used in special high-speed trains. Conventional electromagnetic technology is used to suspend the train over the tracks; the elimination of rolling friction allows the train to achieve speeds in excess of 400 km/h (250 mi/h).

| Example 27.8 | **Magnetic force on a curved conductor** |

In Fig. 27.30 the magnetic field $\vec{B}$ is uniform and perpendicular to the plane of the figure, pointing out. The conductor has a straight segment with length L perpendicular to the plane of the figure on the right, with the current opposite to $\vec{B}$; followed by a semicircle with radius R; and finally another straight segment with length L

27.30 What is the total magnetic force on the conductor?

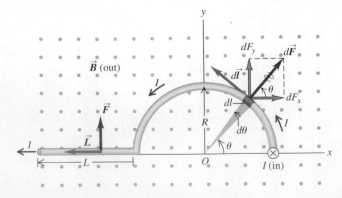

parallel to the x-axis, as shown. The conductor carries a current I. Find the total magnetic force on these three segments of wire.

SOLUTION

IDENTIFY: Two of the three segments of wire are straight and the magnetic field is uniform, so we can find the force on these using the ideas of this section. We can analyze the curved segment by first dividing it into a large number of infinitesimal straight segments. We find the force on one such segment and then integrate to find the force on the curved segment as a whole.

SET UP: We find the force on the straight segments using Eq. (27.19) and the force on an infinitesimal part of the curved segment using Eq. (27.20). The total magnetic force on all three segments is the vector sum of the forces on each individual segment.

EXECUTE: Let's do the easy parts (the straight segments) first. There is *no* force on the segment on the right perpendicular to the plane of the figure because it is antiparallel to $\vec{B}$; $\vec{L} \times \vec{B} = 0$, or $\phi = 180°$ and $\sin\phi = 0$. For the straight segment on the left, $\vec{L}$ points to the left (in the direction of the current), perpendicular to

$\vec{B}$. The force has magnitude $F = ILB$, and its direction is up (the $+y$-direction in the figure).

The fun part is the semicircle. The figure shows a segment $d\vec{l}$ with length $dl = R\,d\theta$, at angle θ. The direction of $d\vec{l} \times \vec{B}$ is radially outward from the center; make sure you can verify this direction. Because $d\vec{l}$ and $\vec{B}$ are perpendicular, the magnitude dF of the force on the segment $d\vec{l}$ is just $dF = I\,dl\,B$, so we have

$$dF = I(R\,d\theta)B$$

The components of the force $d\vec{F}$ on segment $d\vec{l}$ are

$$dF_x = IR\,d\theta\,B\cos\theta \qquad dF_y = IR\,d\theta\,B\sin\theta$$

To find the components of the total force, we integrate these expressions, letting θ vary from 0 to π to take in the whole semicircle. We find

$$F_x = IRB\int_0^\pi \cos\theta\,d\theta = 0$$

$$F_y = IRB\int_0^\pi \sin\theta\,d\theta = 2IRB$$

Finally, adding the forces on the straight and semicircular segments, we find the total force:

$$F_x = 0 \qquad F_y = IB(L + 2R)$$

or

$$\vec{F} = IB(L + 2R)\hat{\jmath}$$

EVALUATE: We could have predicted from symmetry that the x-component of force on the semicircle would be zero. On the right half of the semicircle the x-component of the force is positive (to the right) and on the left half it is negative (to the left); the positive and negative contributions to the integral cancel.

Note that the net force on all three segments together is the same force that would be exerted if we replaced the semicircle with a straight segment along the x-axis. Do you see why?

Test Your Understanding of Section 27.6 The figure at right shows a top view of two conducting rails on which a conducting bar can slide. A uniform magnetic field is directed perpendicular to the plane of the figure as shown. A battery is to be connected to the two rails so that when the switch is closed, current will flow through the bar and cause a magnetic force to push the bar to the right. In which orientation, A or B, should the battery be placed in the circuit?

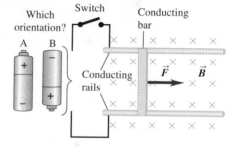

27.7 Force and Torque on a Current Loop

Current-carrying conductors usually form closed loops, so it is worthwhile to use the results of Section 27.6 to find the *total* magnetic force and torque on a conductor in the form of a loop. Many practical devices make use of the magnetic force or torque on a conducting loop, including loudspeakers (see Fig. 27.28) and galvanometers (see Section 26.3). Hence the results of this section are of substantial practical importance. These results will also help us understand the behavior of bar magnets described in Section 27.1.

As an example, let's look at a rectangular current loop in a uniform magnetic field. We can represent the loop as a series of straight line segments. We will find that the total *force* on the loop is zero but that there can be a net *torque* acting on the loop, with some interesting properties.

Figure 27.31a shows a rectangular loop of wire with side lengths a and b. A line perpendicular to the plane of the loop (i.e., a *normal* to the plane) makes an angle ϕ with the direction of the magnetic field $\vec{B}$, and the loop carries a current I. The wires leading the current into and out of the loop and the source of emf are omitted to keep the diagram simple.

The force $\vec{F}$ on the right side of the loop (length a) is to the right, in the $+x$-direction as shown. On this side, $\vec{B}$ is perpendicular to the current direction, and the force on this side has magnitude

$$F = IaB \tag{27.21}$$

A force $-\vec{F}$ with the same magnitude but opposite direction acts on the opposite side of the loop, as shown in the figure.

The sides with length b make an angle $(90° - \phi)$ with the direction of $\vec{B}$. The forces on these sides are the vectors $\vec{F}'$ and $-\vec{F}'$; their magnitude F' is given by

$$F' = IbB\sin(90° - \phi) = IbB\cos\phi$$

The lines of action of both forces lie along the y-axis.

Act**iv**
ONLINE
Physics

13.6   Magnetic Torque on a Loop

27.31 Finding the torque on a current-carrying loop in a uniform magnetic field.

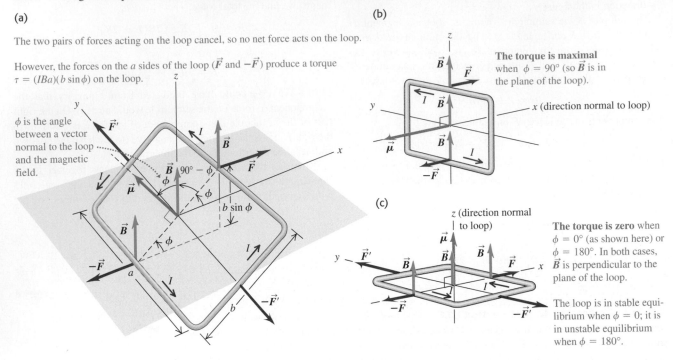

(a)

The two pairs of forces acting on the loop cancel, so no net force acts on the loop.

However, the forces on the *a* sides of the loop ($\vec{F}$ and $-\vec{F}$) produce a torque $\tau = (IBa)(b\sin\phi)$ on the loop.

ϕ is the angle between a vector normal to the loop and the magnetic field.

(b)

The torque is maximal when $\phi = 90°$ (so $\vec{B}$ is in the plane of the loop).

x (direction normal to loop)

(c)

z (direction normal to loop)

The torque is zero when $\phi = 0°$ (as shown here) or $\phi = 180°$. In both cases, $\vec{B}$ is perpendicular to the plane of the loop.

The loop is in stable equilibrium when $\phi = 0$; it is in unstable equilibrium when $\phi = 180°$.

The *total* force on the loop is zero because the forces on opposite sides cancel out in pairs.

The net force on a current loop in a uniform magnetic field is zero. However, the net torque is not in general equal to zero.

(You may find it helpful at this point to review the discussion of torque in Section 10.1.) The two forces $\vec{F}'$ and $-\vec{F}'$ in Fig. 27.31a lie along the same line and so give rise to zero net torque with respect to any point. The two forces $\vec{F}$ and $-\vec{F}$ lie along different lines, and each gives rise to a torque about the *y*-axis. According to the right-hand rule for determining the direction of torques, the vector torques due to $\vec{F}$ and $-\vec{F}$ are both in the $+y$-direction; hence the net vector torque $\vec{\tau}$ is in the $+y$-direction as well. The moment arm for each of these forces (equal to the perpendicular distance from the rotation axis to the line of action of the force) is $(b/2)\sin\phi$, so the torque due to each force has magnitude $F(b/2)\sin\phi$. If we use Eq. (27.21) for F, the magnitude of the net torque is

$$\tau = 2F(b/2)\sin\phi = (IBa)(b\sin\phi) \qquad (27.22)$$

The torque is greatest when $\phi = 90°$, $\vec{B}$ is in the plane of the loop, and the normal to this plane is perpendicular to $\vec{B}$ (Fig. 27.31b). The torque is zero when ϕ is 0° or 180° and the normal to the loop is parallel or antiparallel to the field (Fig. 27.31c). The value $\phi = 0°$ is a stable equilibrium position because the torque is zero there, and when the loop is rotated slightly from this position, the resulting torque tends to rotate it back toward $\phi = 0°$. The position $\phi = 180°$ is an *unstable* equilibrium position; if displaced slightly from this position, the loop tends to move farther away from $\phi = 180°$. Figure 27.31 shows rotation about the *y*-axis, but because the net force on the loop is zero, Eq. (27.22) for the torque is valid for *any* choice of axis.

The area A of the loop is equal to ab, so we can rewrite Eq. (27.22) as

$$\tau = IBA\sin\phi \qquad \text{(magnitude of torque on a current loop)} \qquad (27.23)$$

The product IA is called the **magnetic dipole moment** or **magnetic moment** of the loop, for which we use the symbol μ (the Greek letter mu):

$$\mu = IA \qquad (27.24)$$

It is analogous to the electric dipole moment introduced in Section 21.7. In terms of μ, the magnitude of the torque on a current loop is

$$\tau = \mu B \sin\phi \qquad (27.25)$$

where ϕ is the angle between the normal to the loop (the direction of the vector area $\vec{A}$) and $\vec{B}$. The torque tends to rotate the loop in the direction of *decreasing* ϕ—that is, toward its stable equilibrium position in which the loop lies in the xy-plane perpendicular to the direction of the field $\vec{B}$ (Fig. 27.31c). A current loop, or any other body that experiences a magnetic torque given by Eq. (27.25), is also called a **magnetic dipole.**

Magnetic Torque: Vector Form

We can also define a vector magnetic moment $\vec{\mu}$ with magnitude IA: this is shown in Fig. 27.31. The direction of $\vec{\mu}$ is defined to be perpendicular to the plane of the loop, with a sense determined by a right-hand rule, as shown in Fig. 27.32. Wrap the fingers of your right hand around the perimeter of the loop in the direction of the current. Then extend your thumb so that it is perpendicular to the plane of the loop; its direction is the direction $\vec{\mu}$ (and of the vector area $\vec{A}$ of the loop). The torque is greatest when $\vec{\mu}$ and $\vec{B}$ are perpendicular and is zero when they are parallel or antiparallel. In the stable equilibrium position, $\vec{\mu}$ and $\vec{B}$ are parallel.

Finally, we can express this interaction in terms of the torque vector $\vec{\tau}$, which we used for *electric*-dipole interactions in Section 21.7. From Eq. (27.25) the magnitude of $\vec{\tau}$ is equal to the magnitude of $\vec{\mu} \times \vec{B}$, and reference to Fig. 27.31 shows that the directions are also the same. So we have

$$\vec{\tau} = \vec{\mu} \times \vec{B} \qquad \text{(vector torque on a current loop)} \qquad (27.26)$$

This result is directly analogous to the result we found in Section 21.7 for the torque exerted by an *electric* field $\vec{E}$ on an *electric* dipole with dipole moment $\vec{p}$: $\vec{\tau} = \vec{p} \times \vec{E}$.

Potential Energy for a Magnetic Dipole

When a magnetic dipole changes orientation in a magnetic field, the field does work on it. In an infinitesimal angular displacement $d\phi$ the work dW is given by $\tau\,d\phi$, and there is a corresponding change in potential energy. As the above discussion suggests, the potential energy is least when $\vec{\mu}$ and $\vec{B}$ are parallel and greatest when they are antiparallel. To find an expression for the potential energy U as a function of orientation, we can make use of the beautiful symmetry between the electric and magnetic dipole interactions. The torque on an *electric* dipole in an *electric* field is $\vec{\tau} = \vec{p} \times \vec{E}$; we found in Section 21.7 that the corresponding potential energy is $U = -\vec{p} \cdot \vec{E}$. The torque on a *magnetic* dipole in a *magnetic* field is $\vec{\tau} = \vec{\mu} \times \vec{B}$, so we can conclude immediately that the corresponding potential energy is

$$U = -\vec{\mu} \cdot \vec{B} = -\mu B \cos\phi \qquad \text{(potential energy for a magnetic dipole)} \qquad (27.27)$$

With this definition, U is zero when the magnetic dipole moment is perpendicular to the magnetic field.

Magnetic Torque: Loops and Coils

Although we have derived Eqs. (27.21) through (27.27) for a rectangular current loop, all these relationships are valid for a plane loop of any shape at all. Any planar loop may be approximated as closely as we wish by a very large number of

27.32 The right-hand rule determines the direction of the magnetic moment of a current-carrying loop. This is also the direction of the loop's area vector $\vec{A}$; $\vec{\mu} = I\vec{A}$ is a vector equation.

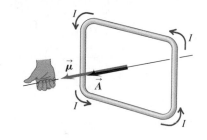

27.33 The collection of rectangles exactly matches the irregular plane loop in the limit as the number of rectangles approaches infinity and the width of each rectangle approaches zero.

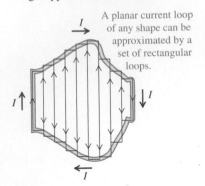

A planar current loop of any shape can be approximated by a set of rectangular loops.

27.34 The torque $\vec{\tau} = \vec{\mu} \times \vec{B}$ on this solenoid in a uniform magnetic field is directed straight into the page. An actual solenoid has many more turns, wrapped closely together.

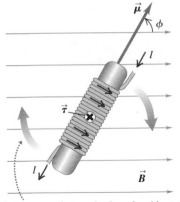

The torque tends to make the solenoid rotate clockwise in the plane of the page, aligning magnetic moment $\vec{\mu}$ with field $\vec{B}$.

rectangular loops, as shown in Fig. 27.33. If these loops all carry equal currents in the same clockwise sense, then the forces and torques on the sides of two loops adjacent to each other cancel, and the only forces and torques that do not cancel are due to currents around the boundary. Thus all the above relationships are valid for a plane current loop of any shape, with the magnetic moment $\vec{\mu}$ given by $\vec{\mu} = I\vec{A}$.

We can also generalize this whole formulation to a coil consisting of N planar loops close together; the effect is simply to multiply each force, the magnetic moment, the torque, and the potential energy by a factor of N.

An arrangement of particular interest is the **solenoid,** a helical winding of wire, such as a coil wound on a circular cylinder (Fig. 27.34). If the windings are closely spaced, the solenoid can be approximated by a number of circular loops lying in planes at right angles to its long axis. The total torque on a solenoid in a magnetic field is simply the sum of the torques on the individual turns. For a solenoid with N turns in a uniform field B, the magnetic moment is $\mu = NIA$ and

$$\tau = NIAB\sin\phi \tag{27.28}$$

where ϕ is the angle between the axis of the solenoid and the direction of the field. The magnetic moment vector $\vec{\mu}$ is along the solenoid axis. The torque is greatest when the solenoid axis is perpendicular to the magnetic field and zero when they are parallel. The effect of this torque is to tend to rotate the solenoid into a position where its axis is parallel to the field. Solenoids are also useful as *sources* of magnetic field, as we'll discuss in Chapter 28.

The d'Arsonval galvanometer, described in Section 26.3, makes use of a magnetic torque on a coil carrying a current. As Fig. 26.14 shows, the magnetic field is not uniform but is *radial,* so the side thrusts on the coil are always perpendicular to its plane. Thus the angle ϕ in Eq. (27.28) is always 90°, and the magnetic torque is directly proportional to the current, no matter what the orientation of the coil. A restoring torque proportional to the angular displacement of the coil is provided by two hairsprings, which also serve as current leads to the coil. When current is supplied to the coil, it rotates along with its attached pointer until the restoring spring torque just balances the magnetic torque. Thus the pointer deflection is proportional to the current.

An important medical application of the torque on a magnetic dipole is *magnetic resonance imaging* (MRI). A patient is placed in a magnetic field of about 1.5 T, more than 10^4 times stronger than the earth's field. The nucleus of each hydrogen atom in the tissue to be imaged has a magnetic dipole moment, which experiences a torque that aligns it with the applied field. The tissue is then illuminated with radio waves of just the right frequency to flip these magnetic moments out of alignment. The extent to which these radio waves are absorbed in the tissue is proportional to the amount of hydrogen present. Hence hydrogen-rich soft tissue looks quite different from hydrogen-deficient bone, which makes MRI ideal for analyzing details in soft tissue that cannot be seen in x-ray images (see the image that opens this chapter).

Example 27.9	**Magnetic torque on a circular coil**

A circular coil 0.0500 m in radius, with 30 turns of wire, lies in a horizontal plane. It carries a current of 5.00 A in a counterclockwise sense when viewed from above. The coil is in a uniform magnetic field directed toward the right, with magnitude 1.20 T. Find the magnitudes of the magnetic moment and the torque on the coil.

SOLUTION

IDENTIFY: This problem uses the definition of magnetic moment and the expression for the torque on a magnetic dipole in a magnetic field.

SET UP: Figure 27.35 shows the situation. The magnitude μ of the magnetic moment of a single turn of wire is given in terms of the

27.35 Our sketch for this problem.

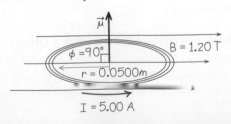

current and coil area by Eq. (27.24). For N turns, the magnetic moment is N times greater. The magnitude τ of the torque is found using Eq. (27.25).

EXECUTE: The area of the coil is

$$A = \pi r^2 = \pi (0.0500 \text{ m})^2 = 7.85 \times 10^{-3} \text{ m}^2$$

The magnetic moment of each turn of the coil is

$$\mu = IA = (5.00 \text{ A})(7.85 \times 10^{-3} \text{ m}^2) = 3.93 \times 10^{-2} \text{ A} \cdot \text{m}^2$$

and the total magnetic moment of all 30 turns is

$$\mu_{\text{total}} = (30)(3.93 \times 10^{-2} \text{ A} \cdot \text{m}^2) = 1.18 \text{ A} \cdot \text{m}^2$$

The angle ϕ between the direction of $\vec{B}$ and the direction of $\vec{\mu}$ (which is along the normal to the plane of the coil) is 90°. From Eq. (27.25),

$$\tau = \mu_{\text{total}} B \sin \phi = (1.18 \text{ A} \cdot \text{m}^2)(1.20 \text{ T})(\sin 90°)$$
$$= 1.41 \text{ N} \cdot \text{m}$$

Alternatively, from Eq. (27.23), the torque on each turn of the coil is

$$\tau = IBA \sin \phi = (5.00 \text{ A})(1.20 \text{ T})(7.85 \times 10^{-3} \text{ m}^2)(\sin 90°)$$
$$= 0.0471 \text{ N} \cdot \text{m}$$

and the total torque on the coil is

$$\tau = (30)(0.0471 \text{ N} \cdot \text{m}) = 1.41 \text{ N} \cdot \text{m}$$

EVALUATE: The torque tends to rotate the right side of the coil down and the left side up, into a position where the normal to its plane is parallel to $\vec{B}$.

Example 27.10 | Potential energy for a coil in a magnetic field

If the coil in Example 27.9 rotates from its initial position to a position where its magnetic moment is parallel to $\vec{B}$, what is the change in potential energy?

SOLUTION

IDENTIFY: The initial position is as shown in Fig. 27.35. In the final position, the coil is rotated 90° clockwise so that $\vec{\mu}$ and $\vec{B}$ are parallel ($\phi = 0$).

SET UP: We calculate the potential energy for each orientation using Eq. (27.27). We then take the difference between the final and initial values to find the change in potential energy.

EXECUTE: From Eq. (27.27), the initial potential energy U_1 is

$$U_1 = -\mu_{\text{total}} B \cos \phi_1 = -(1.18 \text{ A} \cdot \text{m}^2)(1.20 \text{ T})(\cos 90°) = 0$$

and the final potential energy U_2 is

$$U_2 = -\mu_{\text{total}} B \cos \phi_2 = -(1.18 \text{ A} \cdot \text{m}^2)(1.20 \text{ T})(\cos 0°)$$
$$= -1.41 \text{ J}$$

The change in potential energy is $\Delta U = U_2 - U_1 = -1.41 \text{ J}$.

EVALUATE: The potential energy decreases because the rotation is in the direction of the magnetic torque.

Magnetic Dipole in a Nonuniform Magnetic Field

We have seen that a current loop (that is, a magnetic dipole) experiences zero net force in a uniform magnetic field. Figure 27.36 shows two current loops in the *nonuniform* $\vec{B}$ field of a bar magnet; in both cases the net force on the loop is *not* zero. In Fig. 27.36a the magnetic moment $\vec{\mu}$ is in the direction opposite to the field, and the force $d\vec{F} = I \, d\vec{l} \times \vec{B}$ on a segment of the loop has both a radial component and a component to the right. When these forces are summed to find the net force $\vec{F}$ on the loop, the radial components cancel so that the net force is to the right, away from the magnet. Note that in this case the force is toward the region where the field lines are farther apart and the field magnitude B is less. The polarity of the bar magnet is reversed in Fig. 27.36b, so $\vec{\mu}$ and $\vec{B}$ are parallel; now the net force on the loop is to the left, toward the region of greater field magnitude near the magnet. Later in this section we'll use these observations to explain why bar magnets can pick up unmagnetized iron objects.

Magnetic Dipoles and How Magnets Work

The behavior of a solenoid in a magnetic field (see Fig. 27.34) resembles that of a bar magnet or compass needle; if free to turn, both the solenoid and the magnet orient themselves with their axes parallel to the $\vec{B}$ field. In both cases this is due to the interaction of moving electric charges with a magnetic field; the difference is that in a bar magnet the motion of charge occurs on the microscopic scale of the atom.

Think of an electron as being like a spinning ball of charge. In this analogy the circulation of charge around the spin axis is like a current loop, and so the electron has a net magnetic moment. (This analogy, while helpful, is inexact; an electron

27.36 Forces on current loops in a nonuniform $\vec{B}$ field. In each case the axis of the bar magnet is perpendicular to the plane of the loop and passes through the center of the loop.

(a) Net force on this coil is away from north pole of magnet.

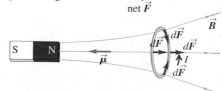

(b) Net force on same coil is toward south pole of magnet.

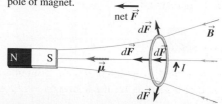

27.37 (a) An unmagnetized piece of iron. (Only a few representative atomic moments are shown.) (b) A magnetized piece of iron (bar magnet). The net magnetic moment of the bar magnet points from its south pole to its north pole. (c) A bar magnet in a magnetic field.

(a) Unmagnetized iron: magnetic moments are oriented randomly.

$\vec{\mu}_{\text{atom}}$

(b) In a bar magnet, the magnetic moments are aligned.

$\vec{\mu}$ N

S

(c) A magnetic field creates a torque on the bar magnet that tends to align its dipole moment with the $\vec{B}$ field.

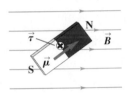

$\vec{\tau}$ N $\vec{B}$

S $\vec{\mu}$

27.38 A bar magnet attracts an unmagnetized iron nail in two steps. First, the $\vec{B}$ field of the bar magnet gives rise to a net magnetic moment in the nail. Second, because the field of the bar magnet is not uniform, this magnetic dipole is attracted toward the magnet. The attraction is the same whether the nail is closer to (a) the magnet's north pole or (b) the magnet's south pole.

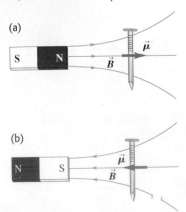

(a)

S N

$\vec{B}$ $\vec{\mu}$

(b)

N S

$\vec{\mu}$

$\vec{B}$

isn't really a spinning sphere. A full explanation of the origin of an electron's magnetic moment involves quantum mechanics, which is beyond our scope here.) In an iron atom a substantial fraction of the electron magnetic moments align with each other, and the atom has a nonzero magnetic moment. (By contrast, the atoms of most elements have little or no net magnetic moment.) In an unmagnetized piece of iron there is no overall alignment of the magnetic moments of the atoms; their vector sum is zero, and the net magnetic moment is zero (Fig. 27.37a). But in an iron bar magnet the magnetic moments of many of the atoms are parallel, and there is a substantial net magnetic moment $\vec{\mu}$ (Fig. 27.37b). If the magnet is placed in a magnetic field $\vec{B}$, the field exerts a torque given by Eq. (27.26) that tends to align $\vec{\mu}$ with $\vec{B}$ (Fig. 27.37c). A bar magnet tends to align with a $\vec{B}$ field so that a line from the south pole to the north pole of the magnet is in the direction of $\vec{B}$; hence the real significance of a magnet's north and south poles is that they represent the head and tail, respectively, of the magnet's dipole moment $\vec{\mu}$.

The torque experienced by a current loop in a magnetic field also explains how an unmagnetized iron object like that in Fig. 27.37a becomes magnetized. If an unmagnetized iron paper clip is placed next to a powerful magnet, the magnetic moments of the paper clip's atoms tend to align with the $\vec{B}$ field of the magnet. When the paper clip is removed, its atomic dipoles tend to remain aligned, and the paper clip has a net magnetic moment. The paper clip can be demagnetized by being dropped on the floor or heated; the added internal energy jostles and re-randomizes the atomic dipoles.

The magnetic-dipole picture of a bar magnet explains the attractive and repulsive forces between bar magnets shown in Fig. 27.1. The magnetic moment $\vec{\mu}$ of a bar magnet points from its south pole to its north pole, so the current loops in Figs. 27.36a and 27.36b are both equivalent to a magnet with its north pole on the left. Hence the situation in Fig. 27.36a is equivalent to two bar magnets with their north poles next to each other; the resultant force is repulsive, just as in Fig. 27.1b. In Fig. 27.36b we again have the equivalent of two bar magnets end to end, but with the south pole of the left-hand magnet next to the north pole of the right-hand magnet. The resultant force is attractive, as in Fig. 27.1a.

Finally, we can explain how a magnet can attract an unmagnetized iron object (see Fig. 27.2). It's a two-step process. First, the atomic magnetic moments of the iron tend to align with the $\vec{B}$ field of the magnet, so the iron acquires a net magnetic dipole moment $\vec{\mu}$ parallel to the field. Second, the nonuniform field of the magnet attracts the magnetic dipole. Figure 27.38a shows an example. The north pole of the magnet is closer to the nail (which contains iron), and the magnetic dipole produced in the nail is equivalent to a loop with a current that circulates in a direction opposite to that shown in Fig. 27.36a. Hence the net magnetic force on the nail is opposite to the force on the loop in Fig. 27.36a, and the nail is attracted toward the magnet. Changing the polarity of the magnet, as in Fig. 27.38b, reverses the directions of both $\vec{B}$ and $\vec{\mu}$. The situation is now equivalent to that shown in Fig. 27.36b; like the loop in that figure, the nail is attracted toward the magnet. Hence a previously unmagnetized object containing iron is attracted to *either* pole of a magnet. By contrast, objects made of brass, aluminum, or wood hardly respond at all to a magnet; the atomic magnetic dipoles of these materials, if present at all, have less tendency to align with an external field.

Our discussion of how magnets and pieces of iron interact has just scratched the surface of a diverse subject known as *magnetic properties of materials*. We'll discuss these properties in more depth in Section 28.8.

Test Your Understanding of Section 27.7 Figure 27.13c depicts the magnetic field lines due to a circular current-carrying loop. (a) What is the direction of the magnetic moment of this loop? (b) Which side of the loop is equivalent to the north pole of a magnet, and which side is equivalent to the south pole?

*27.8 The Direct-Current Motor

Electric motors play an important role in contemporary society. In a motor a magnetic torque acts on a current-carrying conductor, and electric energy is converted to mechanical energy. As an example, let's look at a simple type of direct-current (dc) motor, shown in Fig. 27.39.

The moving part of the motor is the *rotor*, a length of wire formed into an open-ended loop and free to rotate about an axis. The ends of the rotor wires are attached to circular conducting segments that form a *commutator*. In Fig. 27.39a, each of the two commutator segments makes contact with one of the terminals, or *brushes,* of an external circuit that includes a source of emf. This causes a current to flow into the rotor on one side, shown in red, and out of the rotor on the other side, shown in blue. Hence the rotor is a current loop with a magnetic moment $\vec{\mu}$. The rotor lies between opposing poles of a permanent magnet, so there is a magnetic field $\vec{B}$ that exerts a torque $\vec{\tau} = \vec{\mu} \times \vec{B}$ on the rotor. For the rotor orientation shown in Fig. 27.39a the torque causes the rotor to turn counterclockwise, in the direction that will align $\vec{\mu}$ with $\vec{B}$.

In Fig. 27.39b the rotor has rotated by 90° from its orientation in Fig. 27.39a. If the current through the rotor were constant, the rotor would now be in its equilibrium orientation; it would simply oscillate around this orientation. But here's where the commutator comes into play; each brush is now in contact with *both* segments of the commutator. There is no potential difference between the commutators, so at this instant no current flows through the rotor, and the magnetic moment is zero. The rotor continues to rotate counterclockwise because of its inertia, and current again flows through the rotor as in Fig. 27.39c. But now current enters on the *blue* side of the rotor and exits on the *red* side, just the opposite of the situation in Fig. 27.39a. While the direction of the current has reversed with respect to the rotor, the rotor itself has rotated 180° and the magnetic moment $\vec{\mu}$ is in the same direction with respect to the magnetic field. Hence the magnetic torque $\vec{\tau}$ is in the same direction in Fig. 27.39c as in Fig. 27.39a. Thanks to the commutator, the current reverses after every 180° of rotation, so the torque is always in the direction to rotate the rotor counterclockwise. When the motor has come "up to speed," the average magnetic torque is just balanced by an opposing torque due to air resistance, friction in the rotor bearings, and friction between the commutator and brushes.

The simple motor shown in Fig. 27.39 has only a single turn of wire in its rotor. In practical motors, the rotor has many turns; this increases the magnetic

27.39 Schematic diagram of a simple dc motor. The rotor is a wire loop that is free to rotate about an axis; the rotor ends are attached to the two curved conductors that form the commutator. (The rotor halves are colored red and blue for clarity.) The commutator segments are insulated from one another.

(a) Brushes are aligned with commutator segments.

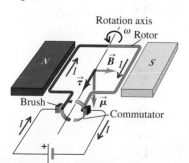

- Current flows into the red side of the rotor and out of the blue side.
- Therefore the magnetic torque causes the rotor to spin counterclockwise.

(b) Rotor has turned 90°.

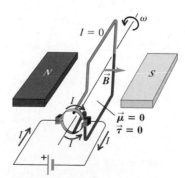

- Each brush is in contact with both commutator segments, so the current bypasses the rotor altogether.
- No magnetic torque acts on the rotor.

(c) Rotor has turned 180°.

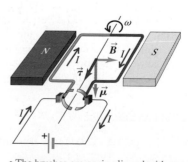

- The brushes are again aligned with commutator segments. This time the current flows into the blue side of the rotor and out of the red side.
- Therefore the magnetic torque again causes the rotor to spin counterclockwise.

27.40 This motor from a computer disk drive has 12 current-carrying coils. They interact with permanent magnets on the turntable (not shown) to make the turntable rotate. (This design is the reverse of the design in Fig. 27.39, in which the permanent magnets are stationary and the coil rotates.) Because there are multiple coils, the magnetic torque is very nearly constant and the turntable spins at a very constant rate.

Coils

moment and the torque so that the motor can spin larger loads. The torque can also be increased by using a stronger magnetic field, which is why many motor designs use electromagnets instead of a permanent magnet. Another drawback of the simple design in Fig. 27.39 is that the magnitude of the torque rises and falls as the rotor spins. This can be remedied by having the rotor include several independent coils of wire oriented at different angles (Fig. 27.40).

Power for Electric Motors

Because a motor converts electric energy to mechanical energy or work, it requires electric energy input. If the potential difference between its terminals is V_{ab} and the current is I, then the power input is $P = V_{ab}I$. Even if the motor coils have negligible resistance, there must be a potential difference between the terminals if P is to be different from zero. This potential difference results principally from magnetic forces exerted on the currents in the conductors of the rotor as they rotate through the magnetic field. The associated electromotive force $\mathcal{E}$ is called an *induced* emf; it is also called a *back* emf because its sense is opposite to that of the current. In Chapter 29 we will study induced emfs resulting from motion of conductors in magnetic fields.

In a *series* motor the rotor is connected in series with the electromagnet that produces the magnetic field; in a *shunt* motor they are connected in parallel. In a series motor with internal resistance r, V_{ab} is greater than $\mathcal{E}$, and the difference is the potential drop Ir across the internal resistance. That is,

$$V_{ab} = \mathcal{E} + Ir \qquad (27.29)$$

Because the magnetic force is proportional to velocity, $\mathcal{E}$ is *not* constant but is proportional to the speed of rotation of the rotor.

Example 27.11   A series dc motor

A dc motor with its rotor and field coils connected in series has an internal resistance of 2.00 Ω. When running at full load on a 120-V line, it draws a current of 4.00 A. (a) What is the emf in the rotor? (b) What is the power delivered to the motor? (c) What is the rate of dissipation of energy in the resistance of the motor? (d) What is the mechanical power developed? (e) What is the efficiency of the motor? (f) What happens if the machine the motor is driving jams and the rotor suddenly stops turning?

SOLUTION

IDENTIFY: This problem uses the ideas of power and potential drop in a series dc motor.

SET UP: We are given the internal resistance $r = 2.00\ \Omega$, the voltage $V_{ab} = 120$ V across the motor, and the current $I = 4.00$ A through the motor. We use Eq. (27.29) to determine the emf $\mathcal{E}$ from these quantities. The power delivered to the motor is $V_{ab}I$, the rate of energy dissipation is I^2r, and the power output by the motor is the difference between the power input and the power dissipated. The efficiency e is the ratio of mechanical power output to electric power input.

EXECUTE: (a) From Eq. (27.29), $V_{ab} = \mathcal{E} + Ir$, we have

$$120\ \text{V} = \mathcal{E} + (4.0\ \text{A})(2.0\ \Omega) \qquad \text{and so} \qquad \mathcal{E} = 112\ \text{V}$$

(b) The power delivered to the motor from the source is

$$P_{\text{input}} = V_{ab}I = (120\ \text{V})(4.0\ \text{A}) = 480\ \text{W}$$

(c) The power dissipated in the resistance r is

$$P_{\text{dissipated}} = I^2r = (4.0\ \text{A})^2(2.0\ \Omega) = 32\ \text{W}$$

(d) The mechanical power output is the electric power input minus the rate of dissipation of energy in the motor's resistance (assuming that there are no other power losses):

$$P_{\text{output}} = P_{\text{input}} - P_{\text{dissipated}} = 480\ \text{W} - 32\ \text{W} = 448\ \text{W}$$

(e) The efficiency e is the ratio of mechanical power output to electric power input:

$$e = \frac{P_{\text{output}}}{P_{\text{input}}} = \frac{448\ \text{W}}{480\ \text{W}} = 0.93 = 93\%$$

(f) With the rotor stalled, the back emf $\mathcal{E}$ (which is proportional to rotor speed) goes to zero. From Eq. (27.29) the current becomes

$$I = \frac{V_{ab}}{r} = \frac{120\ \text{V}}{2.0\ \Omega} = 60\ \text{A}$$

and the power dissipated in the resistance r becomes

$$P_{\text{dissipated}} = I^2r = (60\ \text{A})^2(2\ \Omega) = 7200\ \text{W}$$

EVALUATE: If this massive overload doesn't blow a fuse or trip a circuit breaker, the coils will quickly melt. When the motor is first turned on, there's a momentary surge of current until the motor picks up speed. This surge causes greater-than-usual voltage drops ($V = IR$) in the power lines supplying the current. Similar effects are responsible for the momentary dimming of lights in a house when an air conditioner or dishwasher motor starts.

Test Your Understanding of Section 27.8   In the circuit shown in Fig. 27.39, you add a switch in series with the source of emf so that the current can be turned on and off. When you close the switch and allow current to flow, will the rotor begin to turn no matter what its original orientation?

*27.9 The Hall Effect

The reality of the forces acting on the moving charges in a conductor in a magnetic field is strikingly demonstrated by the *Hall effect,* an effect analogous to the transverse deflection of an electron beam in a magnetic field in vacuum. (The effect was discovered by the American physicist Edwin Hall in 1879 while he was still a graduate student.) To describe this effect, let's consider a conductor in the form of a flat strip, as shown in Fig. 27.41. The current is in the direction of the $+x$-axis and there is a uniform magnetic field $\vec{B}$ perpendicular to the plane of the strip, in the $+y$-direction. The drift velocity of the moving charges (charge magnitude $|q|$) has magnitude v_d. Figure 27.41a shows the case of negative charges, such as electrons in a metal, and Fig. 27.41b shows positive charges. In both cases the magnetic force is upward, just as the magnetic force on a conductor is the same whether the moving charges are positive or negative. In either case a moving charge is driven toward the *upper* edge of the strip by the magnetic force $F_z = |q|v_d B$.

If the charge carriers are electrons, as in Fig. 27.41a, an excess negative charge accumulates at the upper edge of the strip, leaving an excess positive charge at its lower edge. This accumulation continues until the resulting transverse electrostatic field $\vec{E}_e$ becomes large enough to cause a force (magnitude $|q|E_e$) that is equal and opposite to the magnetic force (magnitude $|q|v_d B$). After that, there is no longer any net transverse force to deflect the moving charges. This electric field causes a transverse potential difference between opposite edges of the strip, called the *Hall voltage* or the *Hall emf.* The polarity depends on whether the moving charges are positive or negative. Experiments show that for metals the upper edge of the strip in Fig. 27.41a *does* become negatively charged, showing that the charge carriers in a metal are indeed negative electrons.

However, if the charge carriers are *positive,* as in Fig. 27.41b, then *positive* charge accumulates at the upper edge, and the potential difference is *opposite* to the situation with negative charges. Soon after the discovery of the Hall effect in 1879, it was observed that some materials, particularly some *semiconductors,* show a Hall emf opposite to that of the metals, as if their charge carriers were positively charged. We now know that these materials conduct by a process known as *hole conduction.* Within such a material there are locations, called *holes,* that would normally be occupied by an electron but are actually empty. A missing negative charge is equivalent to a positive charge. When an electron moves in one direction to fill a hole, it leaves another hole behind it. The hole migrates in the direction opposite to that of the electron.

In terms of the coordinate axes in Fig. 27.41b, the electrostatic field $\vec{E}_e$ for the positive-q case is in the $-z$-direction; its z-component E_z is negative. The magnetic field is in the $+y$-direction, and we write it as B_y. The magnetic force (in the $+z$-direction) is $qv_d B_y$. The current density J_x is in the $+x$-direction. In the steady state, when the forces qE_z and $qv_d B_y$ are equal in magnitude and opposite in direction,

$$qE_z + qv_d B_y = 0 \quad \text{or} \quad E_z = -v_d B_y$$

This confirms that when q is positive, E_z is negative. The current density J_x is

$$J_x = nqv_d$$

27.41 Forces on charge carriers in a conductor in a magnetic field.

(a) Negative charge carriers (electrons)

The charge carriers are pushed toward the top of the strip ...

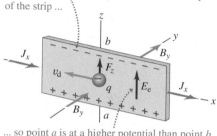

... so point *a* is at a higher potential than point *b*.

(b) Positive charge carriers

The charge carriers are again pushed toward the top of the strip ...

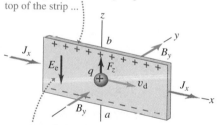

... so the polarity of the potential difference is opposite to that for negative charge carriers.

Eliminating v_d between these equations, we find

$$nq = \frac{-J_x B_y}{E_z} \quad \text{(Hall effect)} \quad (27.30)$$

Note that this result (as well as the entire derivation) is valid for both positive and negative q. When q is negative, E_z is positive, and conversely.

We can measure J_x, B_y, and E_z, so we can compute the product nq. In both metals and semiconductors, q is equal in magnitude to the electron charge, so the Hall effect permits a direct measurement of n, the concentration of current-carrying charges in the material. The *sign* of the charges is determined by the polarity of the Hall emf, as we have described.

The Hall effect can also be used for a direct measurement of electron drift speed v_d in metals. As we saw in Chapter 25, these speeds are very small, often of the order of 1 mm/s or less. If we move the entire conductor in the opposite direction to the current with a speed equal to the drift speed, then the electrons are at rest with respect to the magnetic field, and the Hall emf disappears. Thus the conductor speed needed to make the Hall emf vanish is equal to the drift speed.

Example 27.12 Using the Hall effect

You place a slab of copper, 2.0 mm thick and 1.50 cm wide, in a uniform magnetic field with magnitude 0.40 T, as shown in Fig. 27.41a. When you run a 75-A current in the +x-direction, you find by careful measurement that the potential at the bottom of the slab is 0.81 μV higher than at the top. From this measurement, determine the concentration of mobile electrons in copper.

SOLUTION

IDENTIFY: This problem describes a Hall-effect experiment.

SET UP: We use Eq. (27.30) to determine the mobile electron concentration n.

EXECUTE: First we find the current density J_x and the electric field E_z:

$$J_x = \frac{I}{A} = \frac{75 \text{ A}}{(2.0 \times 10^{-3} \text{ m})(1.50 \times 10^{-2} \text{ m})} = 2.5 \times 10^6 \text{ A/m}^2$$

$$E_z = \frac{V}{d} = \frac{0.81 \times 10^{-6} \text{ V}}{1.5 \times 10^{-2} \text{ m}} = 5.4 \times 10^{-5} \text{ V/m}$$

Then, from Eq. (27.30),

$$n = \frac{-J_x B_y}{qE_z} = \frac{-(2.5 \times 10^6 \text{ A/m}^2)(0.40 \text{ T})}{(-1.60 \times 10^{-19} \text{ C})(5.4 \times 10^{-5} \text{ V/m})}$$
$$= 11.6 \times 10^{28} \text{ m}^{-3}$$

EVALUATE: The actual value of n for copper is $8.5 \times 10^{28} \text{ m}^{-3}$, which shows that the simple model of the Hall effect in this section, ignoring quantum effects and electron interactions with the ions, must be used with caution. This example also shows that with good conductors, the Hall emf is very small even with large current densities. Hall-effect devices for magnetic-field measurements and other purposes use semiconductor materials, for which moderate current densities give much larger Hall emfs.

Test Your Understanding of Section 27.9   A copper wire of square cross section is oriented vertically. The four sides of the wire face north, south, east, and west. There is a uniform magnetic field directed from east to west, and the wire carries current downward. Which side of the wire is at the highest electric potential? (i) north side; (ii) south side; (iii) east side; (iv) west side.

Magnetic forces: Magnetic interactions are fundamentally interactions between moving charged particles. These interactions are described by the vector magnetic field, denoted by $\vec{B}$. A particle with charge q moving with velocity $\vec{v}$ in a magnetic field $\vec{B}$ experiences a force $\vec{F}$ that is perpendicular to both $\vec{v}$ and $\vec{B}$. The SI unit of magnetic field is the tesla $(1 \text{ T} = 1 \text{ N}/\text{A} \cdot \text{m})$. (See Example 27.1.)

$$\vec{F} = q\vec{v} \times \vec{B} \qquad (27.2)$$

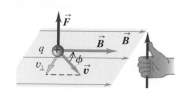

Magnetic field and flux: A magnetic field can be represented graphically by magnetic field lines. At each point a magnetic field line is tangent to the direction of $\vec{B}$ at that point. Where field lines are close together the field magnitude is large, and vice versa. Magnetic flux Φ_B through an area is defined in an analogous way to electric flux. The SI unit of magnetic flux is the weber $(1 \text{ Wb} = 1 \text{ T} \cdot \text{m}^2)$. The net magnetic flux through any closed surface is zero (Gauss's law for magnetism). As a result, magnetic field lines always close on themselves. (See Example 27.2.)

$$\Phi_B = \int B_\perp \, dA$$
$$= \int B \cos\phi \, dA \qquad (27.6)$$
$$= \int \vec{B} \cdot d\vec{A}$$

$$\oint \vec{B} \cdot d\vec{A} = 0 \quad \text{(closed surface)} \quad (27.8)$$

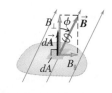

Motion in a magnetic field: The magnetic force is always perpendicular to $\vec{v}$; a particle moving under the action of a magnetic field alone moves with constant speed. In a uniform field, a particle with initial velocity perpendicular to the field moves in a circle with radius R that depends on the magnetic field strength B and the particle mass m, speed v, and charge q. (See Examples 27.3 and 27.4.)

Crossed electric and magnetic fields can be used as a velocity selector. The electric and magnetic forces exactly cancel when $v = E/B$. (See Examples 27.5 and 27.6.)

$$R = \frac{mv}{|q|B} \qquad (27.11)$$

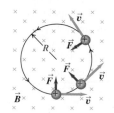

Magnetic force on a conductor: A straight segment of a conductor carrying current I in a uniform magnetic field $\vec{B}$ experiences a force $\vec{F}$ that is perpendicular to both $\vec{B}$ and the vector $\vec{l}$, which points in the direction of the current and has magnitude equal to the length of the segment. A similar relationship gives the force $d\vec{F}$ on an infinitesimal current-carrying segment $d\vec{l}$ (See Examples 27.7 and 27.8.)

$$\vec{F} = I\vec{l} \times \vec{B} \qquad (27.19)$$
$$d\vec{F} = I \, d\vec{l} \times \vec{B} \qquad (27.20)$$

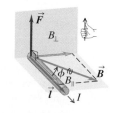

Magnetic torque: A current loop with area A and current I in a uniform magnetic field $\vec{B}$ experiences no net magnetic force, but does experience a magnetic torque of magnitude τ. The vector torque $\vec{\tau}$ can be expressed in terms of the magnetic moment $\vec{\mu} = I\vec{A}$ of the loop, as can the potential energy U of a magnetic moment in a magnetic field $\vec{B}$. The magnetic moment of a loop depends only on the current and the area; it is independent of the shape of the loop. (See Examples 27.9 and 27.10.)

$$\tau = IBA \sin\phi \qquad (27.23)$$
$$\vec{\tau} = \vec{\mu} \times \vec{B} \qquad (27.26)$$
$$U = -\vec{\mu} \cdot \vec{B} = -\mu B \cos\phi \qquad (27.27)$$

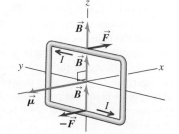

Electric motors: In a dc motor a magnetic field exerts a torque on a current in the rotor. Motion of the rotor through the magnetic field causes an induced emf called a back emf. For a series motor, in which the rotor coil is in parallel with coils that produce the magnetic field, the terminal voltage is the sum of the back emf and the drop Ir across the internal resistance. (See Example 27.11.)

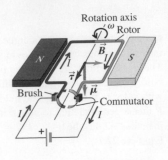

The Hall effect: The Hall effect is a potential difference perpendicular to the direction of current in a conductor, when the conductor is placed in a magnetic field. The Hall potential is determined by the requirement that the associated electric field must just balance the magnetic force on a moving charge. Hall-effect measurements can be used to determine the sign of charge carriers and their concentration n. (See Example 27.12.)

$$nq = \frac{-J_x B_y}{E_z} \qquad (27.30)$$

Key Terms

Answer to Chapter Opening Question ?

In MRI the nuclei of hydrogen atoms within soft tissue act like miniature current loops whose magnetic moments align with an applied field. See Section 27.7 for details.

Answers to Test Your Understanding Questions

27.1 Answer: yes   When a magnet is cut apart, each part has a north and south pole (see Fig. 27.4). Hence the small red part behaves much like the original, full-sized compass needle.

27.2 Answer: path 3   Applying the right-hand rule to the vectors $\vec{v}$ (which points to the right) and $\vec{B}$ (which points into the plane of the figure) says that the force $\vec{F} = q\vec{v} \times \vec{B}$ on a *positive* charge would point *upward*. Since the charge is *negative,* the force points *downward* and the particle follows a trajectory that curves downward.

27.3 Answer: (a) (ii), (b) no   The magnitude of $\vec{B}$ would increase as you moved to the right, reaching a maximum as you pass through the plane of the loop. As you moved beyond the plane of the loop, the field magnitude would decrease. You can tell this from the spacing of the field lines: The closer the field lines, the stronger the field. The direction of the field would be to the right at all points along the path, since the path is along a field line and the direction of $\vec{B}$ at any point is tangent to the field line through that point.

27.4 Answers: (a) (ii), (b) (i)   The radius of the orbit as given by Eq. (27.11) is directly proportional to the speed, so doubling the particle speed causes the radius to double as well. The particle has twice as far to travel to complete one orbit but is traveling at double the speed, so the time for one orbit is unchanged. This result

also follows from Eq. (27.12), which states that the angular speed ω is independent of the linear speed v. Hence the time per orbit, $T = 2\pi/\omega$, likewise does not depend on v.

27.5 Answer: (iii)   From Eq. (27.13), the speed $v = E/B$ at which particles travel straight through the velocity selector does not depend on the magnitude or sign of the charge or the mass of the particle. All that is required is that the particles (in this case, ions) have a nonzero charge.

27.6 Answer: A   This orientation will cause current to flow clockwise around the circuit and hence through the conducting bar in the direction from the top to the bottom of the figure. From the right-hand rule, the magnetic force $\vec{F} = I\vec{l} \times \vec{B}$ on the bar will then point to the right.

27.7 Answers: (a) to the right; (b) north pole on the right, south pole on the left   If you wrap the fingers of your right hand around the coil in the direction of the current, your right thumb points to the right (perpendicular to the plane of the coil). This is the direction of the magnetic moment $\vec{\mu}$. The magnetic moment points from the south pole to the north pole, so the right side of the loop is equivalent to a north pole and the left side is equivalent to a south pole.

27.8 Answer: no   The rotor will not begin to turn when the switch is closed if the rotor is initially oriented as shown in Fig. 27.39b. In this case there is no current through the rotor and hence no magnetic torque. This situation can be remedied by using multiple rotor coils oriented at different angles around the rotation axis. With this arrangement, there is always a magnetic torque no matter what the orientation.

27.9 Answer: (ii)   The mobile charge carriers in copper are negatively charged electrons which move upward through the wire to give a downward current. From the right-hand rule, the force on a positively charged particle moving upward in a westward-pointing magnetic field would be to the south; hence the force on a negatively charged particle is to the north. The result is an

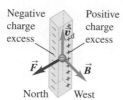

excess of negative charge on the north side of the wire, leaving an excess of positive charge—and hence a higher electric potential—on the south side.

PROBLEMS

For instructor-assigned homework, go to **www.masteringphysics.com**

Discussion Questions

Q27.1. Can a charged particle move through a magnetic field without experiencing any force? If so, how? If not, why not?

Q27.2. At any point in space, the electric field $\vec{E}$ is defined to be in the direction of the electric force on a positively charged particle at that point. Why don't we similarly define the magnetic field $\vec{B}$ to be in the direction of the magnetic force on a moving, positively charged particle?

Q27.3. Section 27.2 describes a procedure for finding the direction of the magnetic force using your right hand. If you use the same procedure, but with your left hand, will you get the correct direction for the force? Explain.

Q27.4. The magnetic force on a moving charged particle is always perpendicular to the magnetic field $\vec{B}$. Is the trajectory of a moving charged particle always perpendicular to the magnetic field lines? Explain your reasoning.

Q27.5. A charged particle is fired into a cubical region of space where there is a uniform magnetic field. Outside this region, there is no magnetic field. Is it possible that the particle will remain inside the cubical region? Why or why not?

Q27.6. If the magnetic force does no work on a charged particle, how can it have any effect on the particle's motion? Are there other examples of forces that do no work but have a significant effect on a particle's motion?

Q27.7. A charged particle moves through a region of space with constant velocity (magnitude and direction). If the external magnetic field is zero in this region, can you conclude that the external electric field in the region is also zero? Explain. (By "external" we mean fields other than those produced by the charged particle.) If the external electric field is zero in the region, can you conclude that the external magnetic field in the region is also zero?

Q27.8. How might a loop of wire carrying a current be used as a compass? Could such a compass distinguish between north and south? Why or why not?

Q27.9. How could the direction of a magnetic field be determined by making only *qualitative* observations of the magnetic force on a straight wire carrying a current?

Q27.10. A loose, floppy loop of wire is carrying current I. The loop of wire is placed on a horizontal table in a uniform magnetic field $\vec{B}$ perpendicular to the plane of the table. This causes the loop of wire to expand into a circular shape while still lying on the table. In a diagram, show all possible orientations of the current I and magnetic field $\vec{B}$ that could cause this to occur. Explain your reasoning.

Q27.11. Several charges enter a uniform magnetic field directed into the page, (a) What path would a positive charge q moving with a velocity of magnitude v follow through the field? (b) What path would a positive charge q moving with a velocity of magnitude $2v$ follow through the field? (c) What path would a negative charge $-q$ moving with a velocity of magnitude v follow through the field? (d) What path would a neutral particle follow through the field?

Q27.12. Each of the lettered points at the corners of the cube in Fig. 27.42 represents a positive charge q moving with a velocity of magnitude v in the direction indicated. The region in the figure is in a uniform magnetic field $\vec{B}$, parallel to the x-axis and directed toward the right. Which charges experience a force due to $\vec{B}$? What is the direction of the force on each charge?

Figure **27.42** Question Q27.12.

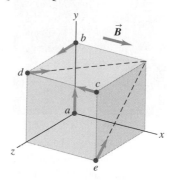

Q27.13. A student claims that if lightning strikes a metal flagpole, the force exerted by the earth's magnetic field on the current in the pole can be large enough to bend it. Typical lightning currents are of the order of 10^4 to 10^5 A. Is the student's opinion justified? Explain your reasoning.

Q27.14. Bubble Chamber I. Certain types of bubble chambers are filled with liquid hydrogen. When a particle (such as an electron or a proton) passes through the liquid, it leaves a track of bubbles, which can be photographed to show the path of the particle. The apparatus is immersed in a known magnetic field, which causes the particle to curve. Figure 27.43 is a trace of a bubble-chamber image showing the path of an electron. (a) How could you determine the *sign* of the charge of a particle from a photograph of its path? (b) How can physicists determine the *momentum* and the *speed* of this electron by using measurements made on the photograph, given that the magnetic field is known and is perpendicular to the plane of the figure? (c) The electron is obviously spiraling into smaller and smaller circles. What properties of the electron must be changing to cause this behavior? Why does this happen? (d) What would be the path of a neutron in a bubble chamber? Why?

Figure **27.43** Question Q27.14.

Q27.15. An ordinary loudspeaker such as that shown in Fig. 27.28 should not be placed next to a computer monitor or TV screen. Why not?

Q27.16. Bubble Chamber II. Figure 27.44 show the paths of several particles in a bubble chamber. (See Discussion Question Q27.14.) The two spirals near the top of the photo come from two particles that were created at the same instant due to a high-energy gamma ray. (a) What can you conclude about the *signs* of the charges of these two particles, assuming that the magnetic field is perpendicular to the plane of the photograph and pointing into the paper? (b) Which of the two particles (the right one or the left one) had more initial momentum? How do you know? (c) Why do the paths spiral inward? What causes this to happen?

Figure 27.44 Question Q27.16.

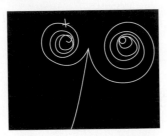

Q27.17. If an emf is produced in a dc motor, would it be possible to use the motor somehow as a generator or source, taking power out of it rather than putting power into it? How might this be done?

Q27.18. When the polarity of the voltage applied to a dc motor is reversed, the direction of motion does *not* reverse. Why not? How *could* the direction of motion be reversed?

Q27.19. In a Hall-effect experiment, is it possible that *no* transverse potential difference will be observed? Under what circumstances might this happen?

Q27.20. Hall-effect voltages are much greater for relatively poor conductors (such as germanium) than for good conductors (such as copper), for comparable currents, fields, and dimensions. Why?

Q27.21. Could an accelerator be built in which *all* the forces on the particles, for steering and for increasing speed, are magnetic forces? Why or why not?

Q27.22. The magnetic force acting on a charged particle can never do work because at every instant the force is perpendicular to the velocity. The torque exerted by a magnetic field can do work on a current loop when the loop rotates. Explain how these seemingly contradictory statements can be reconciled.

Exercises

Section 27.2 Magnetic Field

27.1. A particle with a charge of -1.24×10^{-8} C is moving with instantaneous velocity $\vec{v} = (4.19 \times 10^4 \text{ m/s})\hat{\imath} + (-3.85 \times 10^4 \text{ m/s})\hat{\jmath}$. What is the force exerted on this particle by a magnetic field (a) $\vec{B} = (1.40 \text{ T})\hat{\imath}$ and (b) $\vec{B} = (1.40 \text{ T})\hat{k}$?

27.2. A particle of mass 0.195 g carries a charge of -2.50×10^{-8} C. The particle is given an initial horizontal velocity that is due north and has magnitude 4.00×10^4 m/s. What are the magnitude and direction of the minimum magnetic field that will keep the particle moving in the earth's gravitational field in the same horizontal, northward direction?

27.3. In a 1.25 T magnetic field directed vertically upward, a particle having a charge of magnitude 8.50 μC and initially moving

northward at 4.75 km/s is deflected toward the east. (a) What is the sign of the charge of this particle? Make a sketch to illustrate how you found your answer. (b) Find the magnetic force on the particle.

27.4. A particle with mass 1.81×10^{-3} kg and a charge of 1.22×10^{-8} C has, at a given instant, a velocity $\vec{v} = (3.00 \times 10^4 \text{ m/s})\hat{\jmath}$. What are the magnitude and direction of the particle's acceleration produced by a uniform magnetic field $\vec{B} = (1.63 \text{ T})\hat{\imath} + (0.980 \text{ T})\hat{\jmath}$?

27.5. An electron experiences a magnetic force of magnitude 4.60×10^{-15} N when moving at an angle of 60.0° with respect to a magnetic field of magnitude 3.50×10^{-3} T. Find the speed of the electron.

27.6. An electron moves at 2.50×10^6 m/s through a region in which there is a magnetic field of unspecified direction and magnitude 7.40×10^{-2} T. (a) What are the largest and smallest possible magnitudes of the acceleration of the electron due to the magnetic field? (b) If the actual acceleration of the electron is one-fourth of the largest magnitude in part (a), what is the angle between the electron velocity and the magnetic field?

27.7. A particle with charge 7.80 μC is moving with velocity $\vec{v} = -(3.80 \times 10^3 \text{ m/s})\hat{\jmath}$. The magnetic force on the particle is measured to be $\vec{F} = +(7.60 \times 10^{-3}\text{N})\hat{\imath} - (5.20 \times 10^{-3}\text{ N})\hat{k}$. (a) Calculate all the components of the magnetic field you can from this information. (b) Are there components of the magnetic field that are not determined by the measurement of the force? Explain. (c) Calculate the scalar product $\vec{B} \cdot \vec{F}$ What is the angle between $\vec{B}$ and $\vec{F}$?

27.8. A particle with charge -5.60 nC is moving in a uniform magnetic field $\vec{B} = -(1.25 \text{ T})\hat{k}$. The magnetic force on the particle is measured to be $\vec{F} = -(3.40 \times 10^{-7}\text{ N})\hat{\imath} + (7.40 \times 10^{-7}\text{ N})\hat{\jmath}$. (a) Calculate all the components of the velocity of the particle that you can from this information. (b) Are there components of the velocity that are not determined by the measurement of the force? Explain. (c) Calculate the scalar product $\vec{v} \cdot \vec{F}$. What is the angle between $\vec{v}$ and $\vec{F}$?

27.9. A group of particles is traveling in a magnetic field of unknown magnitude and direction. You observe that a proton moving at 1.50 km/s in the $+x$-direction experiences a force of 2.25×10^{-16} N in the $+y$-direction, and an electron moving at 4.75 km/s in the $-z$-direction experiences a force of 8.50×10^{-16} N. (a) What are the magnitude and direction of the magnetic field? (b) What are the magnitude and direction of the magnetic force on an electron moving in the $-y$-direction at 3.2 km/s?

Section 27.3 Magnetic Field Lines and Magnetic Flux

27.10. The magnetic flux through one face of a cube is $+0.120$ Wb. (a) What must the total magnetic flux through the other five faces of the cube be? (b) Why didn't you need to know the dimensions of the cube in order to answer part (a)? (c) Suppose the magnetic flux is due to a permanent magnet like that shown in Fig. 27.11. In a sketch, show where the cube in part (a) might be located relative to the magnet.

27.11. A circular area with a radius of 6.50 cm lies in the xy-plane. What is the magnitude of the magnetic flux through this circle due to a uniform magnetic field $B = 0.230$ T (a) in the $+z$-direction; (b) at an angle of 53.1° from the $+z$-direction; (c) in the $+y$-direction?

27.12. The magnetic field $\vec{B}$ in a certain region is 0.128 T, and its direction is that of the $+z$-axis in Fig. 27.45. (a) What is the magnetic flux across the surface $abcd$ in the figure? (b) What is the magnetic flux across the surface $befc$? (c) What is the magnetic flux across the surface *aefd*? (d) What is the net flux through all five surfaces that enclose the shaded volume?

27.13. An open plastic soda bottle with an opening diameter of 2.5 cm is placed on a table. A uniform 1.75-T magnetic field directed upward and oriented 25° from vertical encompasses the bottle. What is the total magnetic flux through the plastic of the soda bottle?

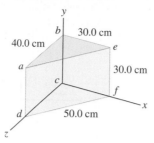

Figure **27.45** Exercise 27.12.

Section 27.4 Motion of Charged Particles in a Magnetic Field

27.14. A particle with charge 6.40×10^{-19} C travels in a circular orbit with radius 4.68 mm due to the force exerted on it by a magnetic field with magnitude 1.65 T and perpendicular to the orbit. (a) What is the magnitude of the linear momentum $\vec{p}$ of the particle? (b) What is the magnitude of the angular momentum $\vec{L}$ of the particle?

27.15. An electron at point A in Fig. 27.46 has a speed v_0 of 1.41×10^6 m/s. Find (a) the magnitude and direction of the magnetic field that will cause the electron to follow the semicircular path from A to B, and (b) the time required for the electron to move from A to B.

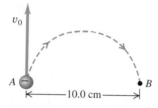

Figure **27.46** Exercise 27.15.

27.16. Repeat Exercise 27.15 for the case in which the particle is a proton rather than an electron.

27.17. A 150-g ball containing 4.00×10^8 excess electrons is dropped into a 125-m vertical shaft. At the bottom of the shaft, the ball suddenly enters a uniform horizontal magnetic field that has magnitude 0.250 T and direction from east to west. If air resistance is negligibly small, find the magnitude and direction of the force that this magnetic field exerts on the ball just as it enters the field.

27.18. An alpha particle (a He nucleus, containing two protons and two neutrons and having a mass of 6.64×10^{-27} kg) traveling horizontally at 35.6 km/s enters a uniform, vertical, 1.10-T magnetic field. (a) What is the diameter of the path followed by this alpha particle? (b) What effect does the magnetic field have on the speed of the particle? (c) What are the magnitude and direction of the acceleration of the alpha particle while it is in the magnetic field? (d) Explain why the speed of the particle does not change even though an unbalanced external force acts on it.

27.19. Fusion Reactor. If two deuterium nuclei (charge $+e$, mass 3.34×10^{-27} kg) get close enough together, the attraction of the strong nuclear force will fuse them to make an isotope of helium, releasing vast amounts of energy. The range of this force is about 10^{-15} m. This is the principle behind the fusion reactor. The deuterium nuclei are moving much too fast to be contained by physical walls, so they are confined magnetically. (a) How fast would two nuclei have to move so that in a head-on collision they would get close enough to fuse? (Treat the nuclei as point charges, and assume that a separation of 1.0×10^{-15} is required for fusion.) (b) What strength magnetic field is needed to make deuterium nuclei with this speed travel in a circle of diameter 2.50 m?

27.20. (a) An ^{16}O nucleus (charge $+8e$) moving horizontally from west to east with a speed of 500 km/s experiences a magnetic force of 0.00320 nN vertically downward. Find the magnitude and direc-

tion of the weakest magnetic field required to produce this force. Explain how this same force could be caused by a larger magnetic field. (b) An electron moves in a uniform, horizontal, 2.10-T magnetic field that is toward the west. What must the magnitude and direction of the minimum velocity of the electron be so that the magnetic force on it will be 4.60 pN, vertically upward? Explain how the velocity could be greater than this minimum value and the force still have this same magnitude and direction.

27.21. A deuteron (the nucleus of an isotope of hydrogen) has a mass of 3.34×10^{-27} kg and a charge of $+e$. The deuteron travels in a circular path with a radius of 6.96 mm in a magnetic field with magnitude 2.50 T. (a) Find the speed of the deuteron. (b) Find the time required for it to make half a revolution. (c) Through what potential difference would the deuteron have to be accelerated to acquire this speed?

27.22. In an experiment with cosmic rays, a vertical beam of particles that have charge of magnitude $3e$ and mass 12 times the proton mass enters a uniform horizontal magnetic field of 0.250 T and is bent in a semicircle of diameter 95.0 cm, as shown in Fig. 27.47. (a) Find the speed of the particles and the sign of their charge. (b) Is it reasonable to ignore the gravity force on the particles? (c) How does the speed of the particles as they enter the field compare to their speed as they exit the field?

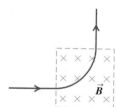

Figure **27.47** Exercise 27.22.

27.23. A physicist wishes to produce electromagnetic waves of frequency 3.0 THz (1 THz = 1 terahertz = 10^{12} Hz) using a magnetron (see Example 27.3). (a) What magnetic field would be required? Compare this field with the strongest constant magnetic fields yet produced on earth, about 45 T. (b) Would there be any advantage to using protons instead of electrons in the magnetron? Why or why not?

27.24. A beam of protons traveling at 1.20 km/s enters a uniform magnetic field, traveling perpendicular to the field. The beam exits the magnetic field, leaving the field in a direction perpendicular to its original direction (Fig. 27.48). The beam travels a distance of 1.18 cm *while in the field*. What is the magnitude of the magnetic field?

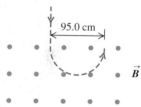

Figure **27.48** Exercise 27.24.

27.25. An electron in the beam of a TV picture tube is accelerated by a potential difference of 2.00 kV. Then it passes through a region of transverse magnetic field, where it moves in a circular arc with radius 0.180 m. What is the magnitude of the field?

27.26. A singly charged ion of ^{7}Li (an isotope of lithium) has a mass of 1.16×10^{-26} kg. It is accelerated through a potential difference of 220 V and then enters a magnetic field with magnitude 0.723 T perpendicular to the path of the ion. What is the radius of the ion's path in the magnetic field?

27.27. A proton ($q = 1.60 \times 10^{-19}$ C, $m = 1.67 \times 10^{-27}$ kg) moves in a uniform magnetic field $\vec{B} = (0.500 \text{ T})\hat{\imath}$. At $t = 0$ the proton has velocity components $v_x = 1.50 \times 10^5$ m/s, $v_y = 0$, and $v_z = 2.00 \times 10^5$ m/s (see Example 27.4). (a) What are the magnitude and direction of the magnetic force acting on the proton? In addition to the magnetic field there is a uniform electric field in the $+x$-direction, $\vec{E} = (+2.00 \times 10^4 \text{ V/m})\hat{\imath}$. (b) Will the proton have a component of acceleration in the direction of the electric field?

(c) Describe the path of the proton. Does the electric field affect the radius of the helix? Explain. (d) At $t = T/2$, where T is the period of the circular motion of the proton, what is the x-component of the displacement of the proton from its position at $t = 0$?

Section 27.5 Applications of Motion of Charged Particles

27.28. (a) What is the speed of a beam of electrons when the simultaneous influence of an electric field of 1.56×10^4 V/m and a magnetic field of 4.62×10^{-3} T, with both fields normal to the beam and to each other, produces no deflection of the electrons? (b) In a diagram, show the relative orientation of the vectors $\vec{v}, \vec{E}$, and $\vec{B}$. (c) When the electric field is removed, what is the radius of the electron orbit? What is the period of the orbit?

27.29. A 150-V battery is connected across two parallel metal plates of area 28.5 cm^2 and separation 8.20 mm. A beam of alpha particles (charge $+2e$, mass 6.64×10^{-27} kg) is accelerated from rest through a potential difference of 1.75 kV and enters the region between the plates perpendicular to the electric field. What magnitude and direction of magnetic field are needed so that the alpha particles emerge undeflected from between the plates?

27.30. Crossed $\vec{E}$ and $\vec{B}$ Fields. A particle with initial velocity $\vec{v}_0 = (5.85 \times 10^3 \text{ m/s})\hat{j}$ enters a region of uniform electric and magnetic fields. The magnetic field in the region is $\vec{B} = -(1.35 \text{ T})\hat{k}$. Calculate the magnitude and direction of the electric field in the region if the particle is to pass through undeflected, for a particle of charge (a) $+0.640$ nC and (b) -0.320 nC. You can ignore the weight of the particle.

27.31. Determining the Mass of an Isotope. The electric field between the plates of the velocity selector in a Bainbridge mass spectrometer (see Fig. 27.22) is 1.12×10^5 V/m, and the magnetic field in both regions is 0.540 T. A stream of singly charged selenium ions moves in a circular path with a radius of 31.0 cm in the magnetic field. Determine the mass of one selenium ion and the mass number of this selenium isotope. (The mass number is equal to the mass of the isotope in atomic mass units, rounded to the nearest integer. One atomic mass unit $= 1$ u $= 1.66 \times 10^{-27}$ kg.)

27.32. In the Bainbridge mass spectrometer (see Fig. 27.24), the magnetic-field magnitude in the velocity selector is 0.650 T, and ions having a speed of 1.82×10^6 m/s pass through undeflected. (a) What is the electric-field magnitude in the velocity selector? (b) If the separation of the plates is 5.20 mm, what is the potential difference between plates P and P'?

Section 27.6 Magnetic Force on a Current-Carrying Conductor

27.33. A straight 2.00-m, 150-g wire carries a current in a region where the earth's magnetic field is horizontal with a magnitude of 0.55 gauss. (a) What is the minimum value of the current in this wire so that its weight is completely supported by the magnetic force due to earth's field, assuming that no other forces except gravity act on it? Does it seem likely that such a wire could support this size of current? (b) Show how the wire would have to be oriented relative to the earth's magnetic field to be supported in this way.

27.34. An electromagnet produces a magnetic field of 0.550 T in a cylindrical region of radius 2.50 cm between its poles. A straight wire carrying a current of 10.8 A passes through the center of this region and is perpendicular to both the axis of the cylindrical region and the magnetic field. What magnitude of force is exerted on the wire?

27.35. A long wire carrying 4.50 A of current makes two 90° bends, as shown in Fig. 27.49. The bent part of the wire passes

Figure **27.49** Exercise 27.35.

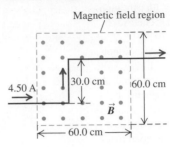

Magnetic field region

4.50 A
30.0 cm
60.0 cm
B
60.0 cm

through a uniform 0.240-T magnetic field directed as shown in the figure and confined to a limited region of space. Find the magnitude and direction of the force that the magnetic field exerts on the wire.

27.36. A straight, vertical wire carries a current of 1.20 A downward in a region between the poles of a large superconducting electromagnet, where the magnetic field has magnitude $B = 0.588$ T and is horizontal. What are the magnitude and direction of the magnetic force on a 1.00-cm section of the wire that is in this uniform magnetic field, if the magnetic field direction is (a) east; (b) south; (c) 30.0° south of west?

27.37. A horizontal rod 0.200 m long is mounted on a balance and carries a current. At the location of the rod a uniform horizontal magnetic field has magnitude 0.067 T and direction perpendicular to the rod. The magnetic force on the rod is measured by the balance and is found to be 0.13 N. What is the current?

27.38. In Fig. 27.50, a wire carrying current into the plane of the figure is between the north and south poles of two bar magnets. What is the direction of the force exerted by the magnets on the wire?

Figure **27.50** Exercise 27.38.

27.39. A thin, 50.0-cm-long metal bar with mass 750 g rests on, but is not attached to, two metallic supports in a uniform 0.450-T magnetic field, as shown in Fig. 27.51. A battery and a 25.0-Ω resistor in series are connected to the supports. (a) What

Figure **27.51** Exercise 27.39.

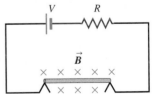

is the highest voltage the battery can have without breaking the circuit at the supports? (b) The battery voltage has the maximum value calculated in part (a). If the resistor suddenly gets partially short-circuited, decreasing its resistance to 2.0 Ω, find the initial acceleration of the bar.

27.40. Magnetic Balance. The circuit shown in Fig. 27.52 is used to make a magnetic balance to weigh objects. The mass m to be measured is hung from the center of the bar that is in a uniform magnetic field of 1.50 T, directed into the plane of the figure. The battery voltage can be adjusted to vary the current in the circuit. The horizontal bar is 60.0 cm long and is made of extremely light-weight material. It is connected to the battery by thin vertical wires that can support no appreciable tension; all the weight of the suspended mass m is supported by the magnetic force on the bar. A resistor with

Figure **27.52** Exercise 27.40.

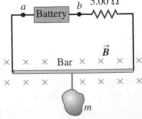

$R = 5.00 \, \Omega$ is in series with the bar; the resistance of the rest of the circuit is much less than this. (a) Which point, a or b, should be the positive terminal of the battery? (b) If the maximum terminal voltage of the battery is 175 V, what is the greatest mass m that this instrument can measure?

27.41. Consider the conductor and current in Example 27.8, but now let the magnetic field be parallel to the x-axis. (a) What are the magnitude and direction of the total magnetic force on the conductor? (b) In Example 27.8, the total force is the same as if we replaced the semicircle with a straight segment along the x-axis. Is that still true when the magnetic field is in this different direction? Can you explain why, or why not?

Section 27.7 Force and Torque on a Current Loop

27.42. The plane of a 5.0 cm × 8.0 cm rectangular loop of wire is parallel to a 0.19-T magnetic field. The loop carries a current of 6.2 A. (a) What torque acts on the loop? (b) What is the magnetic moment of the loop? (c) What is the maximum torque that can be obtained with the same total length of wire carrying the same current in this magnetic field?

27.43. Magnetic Moment of the Hydrogen Atom. In the Bohr model of the hydrogen atom (see Section 38.5), in the lowest energy state the electron orbits the proton at a speed of 2.2×10^6 m/s in a circular orbit of radius 5.3×10^{-11} m. (a) What is the orbital period of the electron? (b) If the orbiting electron is considered to be a current loop, what is the current I? (c) What is the magnetic moment of the atom due to the motion of the electron?

27.44. A rectangular coil of wire, 22.0 cm by 35.0 cm and carrying a current of 1.40 A, is oriented with the plane of its loop perpendicular to a uniform 1.50-T magnetic field, as shown in Fig. 27.53. (a) Calculate the net force and torque that the magnetic field exerts on the coil. (b) The coil is rotated through a 30.0° angle about the axis shown, with the left side coming out of the plane of the figure and the right side going into the plane. Calculate the net force and torque that the magnetic field now exerts on the coil. (*Hint:* In order to help visualize this three-dimensional problem, make a careful drawing of the coil as viewed along the rotation axis.)

Figure 27.53 Exercise 27.44.

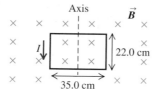

27.45. A uniform rectangular coil of total mass 210 g and dimensions 0.500 m × 1.00 m is oriented perpendicular to a uniform 3.00-T magnetic field (Fig. 27.54). A current of 2.00 A is suddenly started in the coil. (a) About which axis $(A_1$ or $A_2)$ will the coil begin to rotate? Why? (b) Find the initial angular acceleration of the coil just after the current is started.

Figure 27.54 Exercise 27.45.

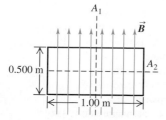

27.46. A circular coil with area A and N turns is free to rotate about a diameter that coincides with the x-axis. Current I is circu-

lating in the coil. There is a uniform magnetic field $\vec{B}$ in the positive y-direction. Calculate the magnitude and direction of the torque $\vec{\tau}$ and the value of the potential energy U, as given in Eq. (27.27), when the coil is oriented as shown in parts (a) through (d) of Fig. 27.55.

Figure 27.55 Exercise 27.46.

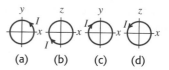

(a)   (b)   (c)   (d)

27.47. A coil with magnetic moment $1.45 \, \text{A} \cdot \text{m}^2$ is oriented initially with its magnetic moment antiparallel to a uniform 0.835-T magnetic field. What is the change in potential energy of the coil when it is rotated 180° so that its magnetic moment is parallel to the field?

*Section 27.8 The Direct-Current Motor

***27.48.** A dc motor with its rotor and field coils connected in series has an internal resistance of 3.2 Ω. When the motor is running at full load on a 120-V line, the emf in the rotor is 105 V. (a) What is the current drawn by the motor from the line? (b) What is the power delivered to the motor? (c) What is the mechanical power developed by the motor?

***27.49.** In a shunt-wound dc motor with the field coils and rotor connected in parallel (Fig. 27.56), the resistance R_f of the field coils is 106 Ω, and the resistance R_r of the rotor is 5.9 Ω. When a potential difference of 120 V is applied to the brushes and the motor is running at full speed delivering mechanical power, the current supplied to it is 4.82 A. (a) What is the current in the field coils? (b) What is the current in the rotor? (c) What is the induced emf developed by the motor? (d) How much mechanical power is developed by this motor?

Figure 27.56 Exercises 27.49 and 27.50.

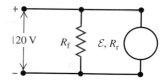

***27.50.** A shunt-wound dc motor with the field coils and rotor connected in parallel (Fig. 27.56) operates from a 120-V dc power line. The resistance of the field windings, R_f, is 218 Ω. The resistance of the rotor, R_r, is 5.9 Ω. When the motor is running, the rotor develops an emf $\mathcal{E}$. The motor draws a current of 4.82 A from the line. Friction losses amount to 45.0 W. Compute (a) the field current; (b) the rotor current; (c) the emf $\mathcal{E}$; (d) the rate of development of thermal energy in the field windings; (e) the rate of development of thermal energy in the rotor; (f) the power input to the motor; (g) the efficiency of the motor.

*Section 27.9 The Hall Effect

***27.51.** Figure 27.57 shows a portion of a silver ribbon with $z_1 = 11.8$ mm and $y_1 = 0.23$ mm, carrying a current of 120 A in the +x-direction. The ribbon lies in a uniform magnetic field, in the y-direction, with magnitude 0.95 T. Apply the simplified model of the Hall

Figure 27.57 Exercises 27.51 and 27.52.

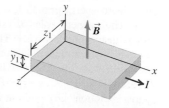

effect presented in Section 27.9. If there are 5.85×10^{28} free electrons per cubic meter, find (a) the magnitude of the drift velocity of the electrons in the x-direction; (b) the magnitude and direction of the electric field in the z-direction due to the Hall effect; (c) the Hall emf.

*27.52. Let Fig. 27.57 represent a strip of an unknown metal of the same dimensions as those of the silver ribbon in Exercise 27.51. When the magnetic field is 2.29 T and the current is 78.0 A, the Hall emf is found to be 131 μV. What does the simplified model of the Hall effect presented in Section 27.9 give for the density of free electrons in the unknown metal?

Problems

27.53. When a particle of charge $q > 0$ moves with a velocity of $\vec{v}_1$ at $45.0°$ from the $+x$-axis in the xy-plane, a uniform magnetic field exerts a force $\vec{F}_1$ along the $-z$-axis (Fig. 27.58). When the same particle moves with a velocity $\vec{v}_2$ with the same magnitude as $\vec{v}_1$ but along the $+z$-axis, a force $\vec{F}_2$ of magnitude F_2 is exerted on it along the $+x$-axis. (a) What are the magnitude (in terms of q, v_1, and F_2) and direction of the magnetic field? (b) What is the magnitude of $\vec{F}_1$ in terms of F_2?

Figure 27.58 Problem 27.53.

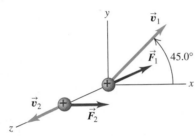

27.54. A particle with charge 9.45×10^{-8} C is moving in a region where there is a uniform magnetic field of 0.450 T in the $+x$-direction. At a particular instant of time the velocity of the particle has components $v_x = -1.68 \times 10^4$ m/s, $v_y = -3.11 \times 10^4$ m/s, and $v_z = 5.85 \times 10^4$ m/s. What are the components of the force on the particle at this time?

27.55. You wish to hit a target from several meters away with a charged coin having a mass of 5.0 g and a charge of $+2500$ μC. The coin is given an initial velocity of 12.8 m/s, and a downward, uniform electric field with field strength 27.5 N/C exists throughout the region. If you aim directly at the target and fire the coin horizontally, what magnitude and direction of uniform magnetic field are needed in the region for the coin to hit the target?

27.56. A cyclotron is to accelerate protons to an energy of 5.4 MeV. The superconducting electromagnet of the cyclotron produces a 3.5-T magnetic field perpendicular to the proton orbits. (a) When the protons have achieved a kinetic energy of 2.7 MeV, what is the radius of their circular orbit and what is their angular speed? (b) Repeat part (a) when the protons have achieved their final kinetic energy of 5.4 MeV.

27.57. The magnetic poles of a small cyclotron produce a magnetic field with magnitude 0.85 T. The poles have a radius of 0.40 m, which is the maximum radius of the orbits of the accelerated particles. (a) What is the maximum energy to which protons ($q = 1.60 \times 10^{-19}$ C, $m = 1.67 \times 10^{-27}$ kg) can be accelerated by this cyclotron? Give your answer in electron volts and in joules. (b) What is the time for one revolution of a proton orbiting at this maximum radius? (c) What would the magnetic-field magnitude have to be for the maximum energy to which a proton can be accelerated to be twice that calculated in part (a)? (d) For $B = 0.85$ T, what is the maximum energy to which alpha particles ($q = 3.20 \times 10^{-19}$ C, $m = 6.65 \times 10^{-27}$ kg) can be accelerated by this cyclotron? How does this compare to the maximum energy for protons?

27.58. The force on a charged particle moving in a magnetic field can be computed as the vector sum of the forces due to each separate component of the magnetic field. As an example, a particle with charge q is moving with speed v in the $-y$-direction. It is moving in a uniform magnetic field $\vec{B} = B_x\hat{i} + B_y\hat{j} + B_z\hat{k}$. (a) What are the components of the force $\vec{F}$ exerted on the particle by the magnetic field? (b) If $q > 0$, what must the signs of the components of $\vec{B}$ be if the components of $\vec{F}$ are all nonnegative? (c) If $q < 0$ and $B_x = B_y = B_z > 0$, find the direction of $\vec{F}$ and find the magnitude of $\vec{F}$ in terms of $|q|$, v, and B_x.

27.59. A uniform, 458-g metal bar 75.0 cm long carries a current I in a uniform, horizontal, 1.55-T magnetic field as shown in Fig. 27.59. The bar is hinged at b but rests unattached at a. What is the largest current that can flow from a to b without breaking the electrical contact at a?

Figure 27.59 Problem 27.59.

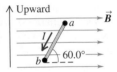

27.60. In the electron gun of a TV picture tube the electrons (charge $-e$, mass m) are accelerated by a voltage V. After leaving the electron gun, the electron beam travels a distance D to the screen; in this region there is a transverse magnetic field of magnitude B and no electric field. (a) Sketch the path of the electron beam in the tube. (b) Show that the approximate deflection of the beam due to this magnetic field is

$$d = \frac{BD^2}{2}\sqrt{\frac{e}{2mV}}$$

(*Hint*: Place the origin at the center of the electron beam's arc and compare an undeflected beam's path to the deflected beam's path.) (c) Evaluate this expression for $V = 750$ V, $D = 50$ cm, and $B = 5.0 \times 10^{-5}$ T (comparable to the earth's field). Is this deflection significant?

27.61. A particle with negative charge q and mass $m = 2.58 \times 10^{-15}$ kg is traveling through a region containing a uniform magnetic field $\vec{B} = -(0.120\text{ T})\hat{k}$. At a particular instant of time the velocity of the particle is $\vec{v} = (1.05 \times 10^6$ m/s$)(-3\hat{i} + 4\hat{j} + 12\hat{k})$ and the force $\vec{F}$ on the particle has a magnitude of 1.25 N. (a) Determine the charge q. (b) Determine the acceleration $\vec{a}$ of the particle. (c) Explain why the path of the particle is a helix, and determine the radius of curvature R of the circular component of the helical path. (d) Determine the cyclotron frequency of the particle. (e) Although helical motion is not periodic in the full sense of the word, the x- and y-coordinates do vary in a periodic way. If the coordinates of the particle at $t = 0$ are $(x, y, z) = (R, 0, 0)$, determine its coordinates at a time $t = 2T$, where T is the period of the motion in the xy-plane.

27.62. A long, straight wire containing a semicircular region of radius 0.95 m is placed in a uniform magnetic field of magnitude 2.20 T as shown in Fig. 27.60. What is the net magnetic force acting on the wire when it carries a current of 3.40 A?

Figure 27.60 Problem 27.62.

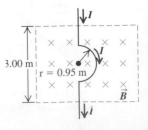

27.63. A magnetic field exerts a torque τ on a round current-carrying loop of wire. What will be the torque on this loop (in terms of τ) if its diameter is tripled?

27.64. A particle of charge $q > 0$ is moving at speed v in the $+z$-direction through a region of uniform magnetic field $\vec{B}$. The magnetic force on the particle is $\vec{F} = F_0(3\hat{\imath} + 4\hat{\jmath})$, where F_0 is a positive constant. (a) Determine the components B_x, B_y, and B_z, or at least as many of the three components as is possible from the information given. (b) If it is given in addition that the magnetic field has magnitude $6F_0/qv$, determine as much as you can about the remaining components of $\vec{B}$.

27.65. Suppose the electric field between the plates P and P' in Fig. 27.24 is 1.88×10^4 V/m and the magnetic field in both regions is 0.701 T. If the source contains the three isotopes of krypton, ^{82}Kr, ^{84}Kr, and ^{86}Kr, and the ions are singly charged, find the distance between the lines formed by the three isotopes on the photographic plate. Assume the atomic masses of the isotopes (in atomic mass units) are equal to their mass numbers, 82, 84, and 86. (One atomic mass unit = 1 u = 1.66×10^{-27} kg.)

27.66. Mass Spectrograph. A mass spectrograph is used to measure the masses of ions, or to separate ions of different masses (see Section 27.5). In one design for such an instrument, ions with mass m and charge q are accelerated through a potential difference V. They then enter a uniform magnetic field that is perpendicular to their velocity, and they are deflected in a semicircular path of radius R. A detector measures where the ions complete the semicircle and from this it is easy to calculate R. (a) Derive the equation for calculating the mass of the ion from measurements of B, V, R, and q. (b) What potential difference V is needed so that singly ionized ^{12}C atoms will have $R = 50.0$ cm in a 0.150-T magnetic field? (c) Suppose the beam consists of a mixture of ^{12}C and ^{14}C ions. If V and B have the same values as in part (b), calculate the separation of these two isotopes at the detector. Do you think that this beam separation is sufficient for the two ions to be distinguished? (Make the assumption described in Problem 27.65 for the masses of the ions.)

27.67. A straight piece of conducting wire with mass M and length L is placed on a frictionless incline tilted at an angle θ from the horizontal (Fig. 27.61). There is a uniform, vertical magnetic field $\vec{B}$ at all points (produced by an arrangement of magnets not shown in the figure). To keep the wire from sliding down the incline, a voltage source is attached to the ends of the wire. When just the right amount of current flows through the wire, the wire remains at rest. Determine the magnitude and direction of the current in the wire that will cause the wire to remain at rest. Copy the figure and draw the direction of the current on your copy. In addition, show in a free-body diagram all the forces that act on the wire.

Figure 27.61 Problem 27.67.

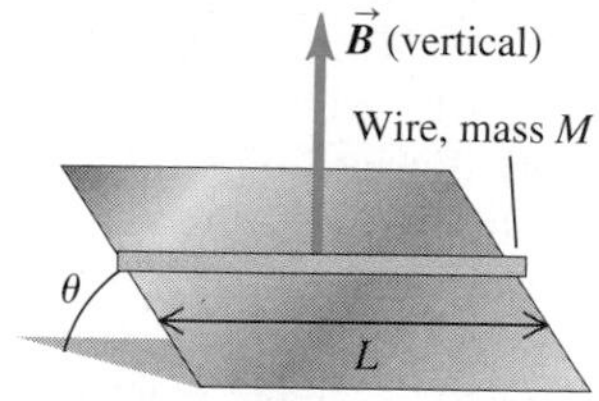

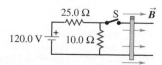

27.68. A 3.00-N metal bar, 1.50 m long and having a resistance of 10.0 Ω, rests horizontally on conducting wires connecting it to the circuit shown in Fig. 27.62. The bar is in a uniform, horizontal, 1.60-T magnetic field and is not attached to the wires in the circuit. What is the acceleration of the bar just after the switch S is closed?

Figure 27.62 Problem 27.68.

27.69. Two positive ions having the same charge q but different masses m_1 and m_2 are accelerated horizontally from rest through a

potential difference V. They then enter a region where there is a uniform magnetic field $\vec{B}$ normal to the plane of the trajectory. (a) Show that if the beam entered the magnetic field along the x-axis, the value of the y-coordinate for each ion at any time t is approximately

$$y = Bx^2 \left(\frac{q}{8mV} \right)^{1/2}$$

provided y remains much smaller than x. (b) Can this arrangement be used for isotope separation? Why or why not?

27.70. A plastic circular loop of radius R and a positive charge q is distributed uniformly around the circumference of the loop. The loop is then rotated around its central axis, perpendicular to the plane of the loop, with angular speed ω. If the loop is in a region where there is a uniform magnetic field $\vec{B}$ directed parallel to the plane of the loop, calculate the magnitude of the magnetic torque on the loop.

27.71. Determining Diet. One method for determining the amount of corn in early Native American diets is the *stable isotope ratio analysis* (SIRA) technique. As corn photosynthesizes, it concentrates the isotope carbon-13, whereas most other plants concentrate carbon-12. Overreliance on corn consumption can then be correlated with certain diseases, because corn lacks the essential amino acid lysine. Archaeologists use a mass spectrometer to separate the ^{12}C and ^{13}C isotopes in samples of human remains. Suppose you use a velocity selector to obtain singly ionized (missing one electron) atoms of speed 8.50 km/s, and you want to bend them within a uniform magnetic field in a semicircle of diameter 25.0 cm for the ^{12}C. The measured masses of these isotopes are 1.99×10^{-26} kg (^{12}C) and 2.16×10^{-26} kg (^{13}C). (a) What strength of magnetic field is required? (b) What is the diameter of the ^{13}C semicircle? (c) What is the separation of the ^{12}C and ^{13}C ions at the detector at the end of the semicircle? Is this distance large enough to be easily observed?

27.72. An Electromagnetic Rail Gun. A conducting bar with mass m and length L slides over horizontal rails that are connected to a voltage source. The voltage source maintains a constant current I in the rails and bar, and a constant, uniform, vertical magnetic field $\vec{B}$ fills the region between the rails (Fig. 27.63). (a) Find the magnitude and direction of the net force on the conducting bar. Ignore friction, air resistance, and electrical resistance. (b) If the bar has mass m, find the distance d that the bar must move along the rails from rest to attain speed v. (c) It has been suggested that rail guns based on this principle could accelerate payloads into earth orbit or beyond. Find the distance the bar must travel along the rails if it is to reach the escape speed for the earth $(11.2$ km/s$)$. Let $B = 0.50$ T, $I = 2.0 \times 10^3$ A, $m = 25$ kg, and $L = 50$ cm. For simplicity assume the net force on the object is equal to the magnetic force, as in parts (a) and (b), even though gravity plays an important role in an actual launch in space.

Figure 27.63 Problem 27.72.

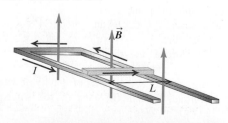

27.73. A long wire carrying a 6.00-A current reverses direction by means of two right-angle bends, as shown in Fig. 27.64. The part of the wire where the bend occurs is in a magnetic field of 0.666 T confined to the circular region of diameter 75 cm, as shown. Find the magnitude and direction of the net force that the magnetic field exerts on this wire.

Figure 27.64 Problem 27.73.

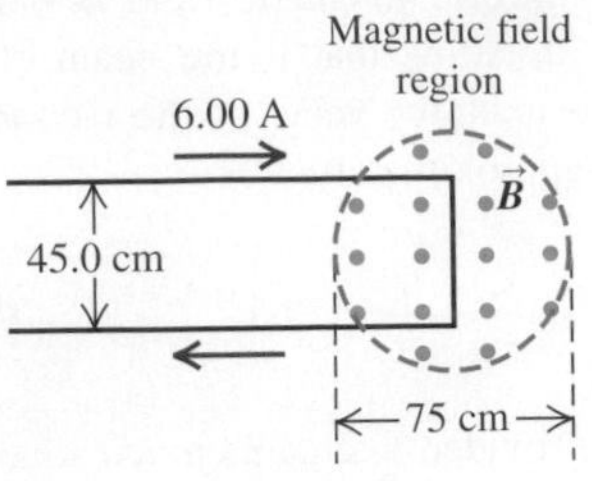

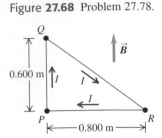

27.74. A wire 25.0 cm long lies along the z-axis and carries a current of 9.00 A in the $+z$-direction. The magnetic field is uniform and has components $B_x = -0.242$ T, $B_y = -0.985$ T, and $B_z = -0.336$ T. (a) Find the components of the magnetic force on the wire. (b) What is the magnitude of the net magnetic force on the wire?

27.75. The rectangular loop of wire shown in Fig. 27.65 has a mass of 0.15 g per centimeter of length and is pivoted about side ab on a frictionless axis. The current in the wire is 8.2 A in the direction shown. Find the magnitude and direction of the magnetic field parallel to the y-axis that will cause the loop to swing up until its plane makes an angle of 30.0° with the yz-plane.

Figure 27.65 Problem 27.75.

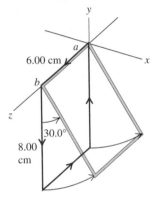

27.76. The rectangular loop shown in Fig. 27.66 is pivoted about the y-axis and carries a current of 15.0 A in the direction indicated. (a) If the loop is in a uniform magnetic field with magnitude 0.48 T in the $+x$-direction, find the magnitude and direction of the torque required to hold the loop in the position shown. (b) Repeat part (a) for the case in which the field is in the $-z$-direction. (c) For each of the above magnetic fields, what torque would be required if the loop were pivoted about an axis through its center, parallel to the y-axis?

Figure 27.66 Problem 27.76.

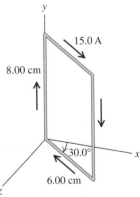

27.77. A thin, uniform rod with negligible mass and length 0.200 m is attached to the floor by a frictionless hinge at point P (Fig. 27.67). A horizontal spring with force constant $k = 4.80$ N/m connects the other end of the rod to a vertical wall. The rod is in a uniform magnetic field $B = 0.340$ T directed into the plane of the figure. There is current $I = 6.50$ A in the rod, in the direction shown. (a) Calculate the torque due to the magnetic force on the rod, for an axis at P. Is it correct to take the total magnetic force to act at the center of gravity of the rod when calculating the torque? Explain. (b) When the rod is in equilibrium

Figure 27.67 Problem 27.77.

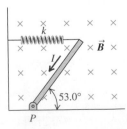

and makes an angle of 53.0° with the floor, is the spring stretched or compressed? (c) How much energy is stored in the spring when the rod is in equilibrium?

27.78. The triangular loop of wire shown in Fig. 27.68 carries a current $I = 5.00$ A in the direction shown. The loop is in a uniform magnetic field that has magnitude $B = 3.00$ T and the same direction as the current in side PQ of the loop. (a) Find the force exerted by the magnetic field on each side of the triangle. If the force is not zero, specify its direction. (b) What is the net force on the loop? (c) The loop is pivoted about an axis that lies along side PR. Use the forces calculated in part (a) to calculate the torque on each side of the loop (see Problem 27.77). (d) What is the magnitude of the net torque on the loop? Calculate the net torque from the torques calculated in part (c) and also from Eq. (27.28). Do these two results agree? (e) Is the net torque directed to rotate point Q into the plane of the figure or out of the plane of the figure?

Figure 27.68 Problem 27.78.

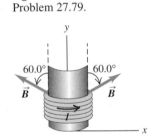

27.79. A Voice Coil. It was shown in Section 27.7 that the net force on a current loop in a *uniform* magnetic field is zero. The magnetic force on the voice coil of a loudspeaker (see Fig. 27.28) is nonzero because the magnetic field at the coil is not uniform. A voice coil in a loudspeaker has 50 turns of wire and a diameter of 1.56 cm, and the current in the coil is 0.950 A. Assume that the magnetic field at each point of the coil has a constant magnitude of 0.220 T and is directed at an angle of 60.0° outward from the normal to the plane of the coil (Fig. 27.69). Let the axis of the coil be in the y-direction. The current in the coil is in the direction shown (counterclockwise as viewed from a point above the coil on the y-axis). Calculate the magnitude and direction of the net magnetic force on the coil.

Figure 27.69 Problem 27.79.

27.80. Paleoclimate. Climatologists can determine the past temperature of the earth by comparing the ratio of the isotope oxygen-18 to the isotope oxygen-16 in air trapped in ancient ice sheets, such as those in Greenland. In one method for separating these isotopes, a sample containing both of them is first singly ionized (one electron is removed) and then accelerated from rest through a potential difference V. This beam then enters a magnetic field B at right angles to the field and is bent into a quarter-circle. A particle detector at the end of the path measures the amount of each isotope. (a) Show that the separation Δr of the two isotopes at the detector is given by

$$\Delta r = \frac{\sqrt{2eV}}{eB}\left(\sqrt{m_{18}} - \sqrt{m_{16}}\right)$$

where m_{16} and m_{18} are the masses of the two oxygen isotopes, (b) The measured masses of the two isotopes are 2.66×10^{-26} kg (^{16}O) and 2.99×10^{-26} kg (^{18}O). If the magnetic field is 0.050 T, what must be the accelerating potential V so that these two isotopes will be separated by 4.00 cm at the detector?

27.81. Force on a Current Loop in a Nonuniform Magnetic Field. It was shown in Section 27.7 that the net force on a current loop in a *uniform* magnetic field is zero. But what if $\vec{B}$ is *not* uniform? Figure 27.70 shows a square loop of wire that lies in the *xy*-plane. The loop has corners at $(0, 0)$, $(0, L)$, $(L, 0)$, and (L, L) and carries a constant current I in the clockwise direction. The magnetic field has no *x*-component but has both *y*- and *z*-components: $\vec{B} = (B_0 z/L)\hat{j} + (B_0 y/L)\hat{k}$, where B_0 is a positive constant. (a) Sketch the mag-

Figure 27.70 Problems 27.81 and 27.82.

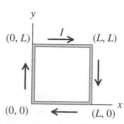

netic field lines in the *yz*-plane. (b) Find the magnitude and direction of the magnetic force exerted on each of the sides of the loop by integrating Eq. (27.20). (c) Find the magnitude and direction of the net magnetic force on the loop.

27.82. Torque on a Current Loop in a Nonuniform Magnetic Field. In Section 27.7 the expression for the torque on a current loop was derived assuming that the magnetic field $\vec{B}$ was uniform. But what if $\vec{B}$ is *not* uniform? Figure 27.70 shows a square loop of wire that lies in the *xy*-plane. The loop has corners at $(0, 0)$, $(0, L)$, $(L, 0)$, and (L, L) and carries a constant current I in the clockwise direction. The magnetic field has no *z*-component but has both *x*- and *y*-components: $\vec{B} = (B_0 y/L)\hat{i} + (B_0 x/L)\hat{j}$, where B_0 is a positive constant. (a) Sketch the magnetic field lines in the *xy*-plane. (b) Find the magnitude and direction of the magnetic force exerted on each of the sides of the loop by integrating Eq. (27.20). (c) If the loop is free to rotate about the *x*-axis, find the magnitude and direction of the magnetic torque on the loop. (d) Repeat part (c) for the case in which the loop is free to rotate about the *y*-axis. (e) Is Eq. (27.26), $\vec{\tau} = \vec{\mu} \times \vec{B}$, an appropriate description of the torque on this loop? Why or why not?

27.83. An insulated wire with mass $m = 5.40 \times 10^{-5}$ kg is bent into the shape of an inverted U such that the horizontal part has a length $l = 15.0$ cm. The bent ends of the wire are partially immersed in two pools of mercury, with 2.5 cm of each end below the mercury's surface. The entire structure is in a region containing a uniform 0.00650-T magnetic field directed into the page (Fig. 27.71). An electrical connection from the mercury pools is made through the ends of the wires. The mercury pools are connected to a 1.50-V battery and a switch S. When switch S is closed, the wire jumps 35.0 cm into the air, measured from its initial position. (a) Determine the speed v of the wire as it leaves the mercury. (b) Assuming that the current I through the wire was constant from the time the switch was closed until the wire left the mercury, determine I. (c) Ignoring the resistance of the mercury and the circuit wires, determine the resistance of the moving wire.

Figure 27.71 Problem 27.83.

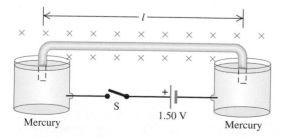

27.84. Derivation of Eq. (27.26) for a Circular Current Loop. A wire ring lies in the *xy*-plane with its center at the origin. The ring carries a counterclockwise current I (Fig. 27.72). A uniform magnetic field $\vec{B}$ is in the $+x$-direction, $\vec{B} = B_x \hat{i}$ (The result is easily extended to $\vec{B}$ in an arbitrary direction.) (a) In Fig. 27.72, show that the element $d\vec{l} = R\,d\theta(-\sin\theta\hat{i} + \cos\theta\hat{j})$, and find $d\vec{F} = I\,d\vec{l} \times \vec{B}$. (b) Integrate $d\vec{F}$ around the loop to show that the net force is zero. (c) From part (a), find $d\vec{\tau} = \vec{r} \times d\vec{F}$, where $\vec{r} = R(\cos\theta\hat{i} + \sin\theta\hat{j})$ is the vector from the center of the loop to the element $d\vec{l}$. (Note that $d\vec{l}$ is perpendicular to $\vec{r}$.) (d) Integrate $d\vec{\tau}$ over the loop to find the total torque $\vec{\tau}$ on the loop. Show that the result can be written as $\vec{\tau} = \vec{\mu} \times \vec{B}$, where $\mu = IA$. (*Note:* $\int\cos^2 x\,dx = \frac{1}{2}x + \frac{1}{4}\sin 2x$, $\int\sin^2 x\,dx = \frac{1}{2}x - \frac{1}{4}\sin 2x$, and $\int\sin x\cos x\,dx = \frac{1}{2}\sin^2 x$.)

Figure 27.72 Problem 27.84.

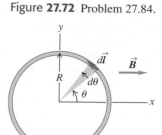

27.85. A circular loop of wire with area A lies in the *xy*-plane. As viewed along the *z*-axis looking in the $-z$-direction toward the origin, a current I is circulating clockwise around the loop. The torque produced by an external magnetic field $\vec{B}$ is given by $\vec{\tau} = D(4\hat{i} - 3\hat{j})$, where D is a positive constant, and for this orientation of the loop the magnetic potential energy $U = -\vec{\mu} \cdot \vec{B}$ is negative. The magnitude of the magnetic field is $B_0 = 13D/IA$. (a) Determine the vector magnetic moment of the current loop. (b) Determine the components B_x, B_y, and B_z of $\vec{B}$.

27.86. Quark Model of the Neutron. The neutron is a particle with zero charge. Nonetheless, it has a nonzero magnetic moment with *z*-component 9.66×10^{-27} A·m². This can be explained by the internal structure of the neutron. A substantial body of evidence indicates that a neutron is composed of three fundamental particles called *quarks*: an "up" (u) quark, of charge $+2e/3$, and two "down" (d) quarks, each of charge $-e/3$. The combination of the three quarks produces a net charge of $2e/3 - e/3 - e/3 = 0$. If the quarks are in motion, they can produce a nonzero magnetic moment. As a very simple model, suppose the u quark moves in a counterclockwise circular path and the d quarks move in a clockwise circular path, all of radius r and all with the same speed v (Fig. 27.73). (a) Determine the current due to the circulation of the u quark. (b) Determine the magnitude of the magnetic moment due to the circulating u quark. (c) Determine the magnitude of the magnetic moment of the three-quark system. (Be careful to use the correct magnetic moment directions.) (d) With what speed v must the quarks move if this model is to reproduce the magnetic moment of the neutron? Use $r = 1.20 \times 10^{-15}$ m (the radius of the neutron) for the radius of the orbits.

Figure 27.73 Problem 27.86.

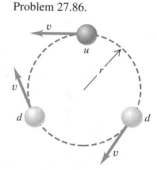

27.87. Using Gauss's Law for Magnetism. In a certain region of space, the magnetic field $\vec{B}$ is not uniform. The magnetic field has both a *z*-component and a component that points radially away from or toward the *z*-axis. The *z*-component is given by $B_z(z) = \beta z$, where β is a positive constant. The radial component B_r depends only on r, the radial distance from the *z*-axis. (a) Use Gauss's law for magnetism, Eq. (27.8), to find the radial component B_r as a function of r. (*Hint:* Try a cylindrical Gaussian surface of radius r concentric with the *z*-axis, with one end at $z = 0$ and the other at $z = L$.) (b) Sketch the magnetic field lines.

27.88. A circular ring with area 4.45 cm^2 is carrying a current of 12.5 A. The ring is free to rotate about a diameter. The ring, initially at rest, is immersed in a region of uniform magnetic field given by $\vec{B} = (1.15 \times 10^{-2}\,\text{T})(12\hat{i} + 3\hat{j} - 4\hat{k})$. The ring is positioned initially such that its magnetic moment is given by $\vec{\mu}_i = \mu(-0.800\hat{i} + 0.600\hat{j})$, where μ is the (positive) magnitude of the magnetic moment. The ring is released and turns through an angle of 90.0°, at which point its magnetic moment is given by $\vec{\mu}_f = -\mu\hat{k}$. (a) Determine the decrease in potential energy. (b) If the moment of inertia of the ring about a diameter is $8.50 \times 10^{-7}\,\text{kg} \cdot \text{m}^2$, determine the angular speed of the ring as it passes through the second position.

Challenge Problems

27.89. A particle with charge 2.15 μC and mass 3.20×10^{-11} kg is initially traveling in the +y-direction with a speed $v_0 = 1.45 \times 10^5$ m/s. It then enters a region containing a uniform magnetic field that is directed into, and perpendicular to, the page in Fig. 27.74. The magnitude of the field is 0.420 T. The region extends a distance of 25.0 cm along the initial direction of travel; 75.0 cm from the point of entry into the magnetic field region is a wall. The length of the field-free region is thus 50.0 cm. When the charged particle enters the magnetic field, it follows a curved path whose radius of curvature is R. It then leaves the magnetic field after a time t_1, having been deflected a distance Δx_1. The particle then travels in the field-free region and strikes the wall after undergoing a total deflection Δx. (a) Determine the radius R of the curved part of the path. (b) Determine t_1, the time the particle spends in the magnetic field. (c) Determine Δx_1, the horizontal deflection at the point of exit from the field. (d) Determine Δx, the total horizontal deflection.

Figure 27.74 Challenge Problem 27.89.

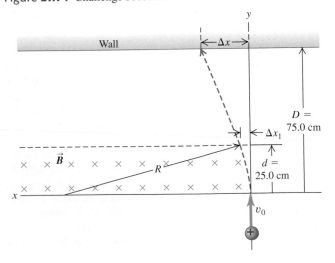

27.90.   The Electromagnetic Pump. Magnetic forces acting on conducting fluids provide a convenient means of pumping these fluids. For example, this method can be used to pump blood without the damage to the cells that can be caused by a mechanical pump. A horizontal tube with rectangular cross section (height h, width w) is placed at right angles to a uniform magnetic field with magnitude B so that a length l is in the field (Fig. 27.75). The tube is filled with a conducting liquid, and an electric current of density J is maintained in the third mutually perpendicular direction. (a) Show that the difference of pressure between a point in the liquid on a vertical plane through ab and a point in the liquid on another vertical plane through cd, under conditions in which the liquid is prevented from flowing, is $\Delta p = JlB$. (b) What current density is needed to provide a pressure difference of 1.00 atm between these two points if $B = 2.20$ T and $l = 35.0$ mm?

27.91. A Cycloidal Path. A particle with mass m and positive charge q starts from rest at the origin shown in Fig. 27.76. There is a uniform electric field $\vec{E}$ in the +y-direction and a uniform magnetic field $\vec{B}$ directed out of the page. It is shown in more advanced books that the path is a *cycloid* whose radius of curvature at the top points is twice the y-coordinate at that level. (a) Explain why the path has this general shape and why it is repetitive. (b) Prove that the speed at any point is equal to $\sqrt{2qEy/m}$. (*Hint:* Use energy conservation.) (c) Applying Newton's second law at the top point and taking as given that the radius of curvature here equals $2y$, prove that the speed at this point is $2E/B$.

Figure 27.75 Challenge Problem 27.90.

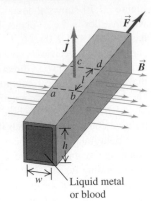

Figure 27.76 Challenge Problem 27.91.

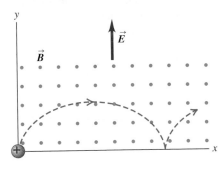

?The immense cylinder in this photograph is actually a current-carrying coil, or solenoid, that generates a uniform magnetic field in its interior as part of an experiment at CERN, the European Laboratory for Particle Physics. If two such solenoids were joined end to end, how much stronger would the magnetic field become?

LEARNING GOALS

By studying this chapter, you will learn:

- The nature of the magnetic field produced by a single moving charged particle.

- How to describe the magnetic field produced by an element of a current-carrying conductor.

- How to calculate the magnetic field produced by a long, straight, current-carrying wire.

- Why wires carrying current in the same direction attract, while wires carrying opposing currents repel.

- How to calculate the magnetic field produced by a current-carrying wire bent into a circle.

- What Ampere's law is, and what it tells us about magnetic fields.

- How to use Ampere's law to calculate the magnetic field of symmetric current distributions.

In Chapter 27 we studied the forces exerted on moving charges and on current-carrying conductors in a magnetic field. We didn't worry about how the magnetic field got there; we simply took its existence as a given fact. But how are magnetic fields *created*? We know that both permanent magnets and electric currents in electromagnets create magnetic fields. In this chapter we will study these sources of magnetic field in detail.

We've learned that a charge creates an electric field and that an electric field exerts a force on a charge. But a *magnetic* field exerts a force only on a *moving* charge. Is it also true that a charge *creates* a magnetic field only when the charge is moving? In a word, yes.

Our analysis will begin with the magnetic field created by a single moving point charge. We can use this analysis to determine the field created by a small segment of a current-carrying conductor. Once we can do that, we can in principle find the magnetic field produced by *any* shape of conductor.

Then we will introduce Ampere's law, which plays a role in magnetism analogous to the role of Gauss's law in electrostatics. Ampere's law lets us exploit symmetry properties in relating magnetic fields to their sources.

Moving charged particles within atoms respond to magnetic fields and can also act as sources of magnetic field. We'll use these ideas to understand how certain magnetic materials can be used to intensify magnetic fields as well as why some materials such as iron act as permanent magnets.

28.1 Magnetic Field of a Moving Charge

Let's start with the basics, the magnetic field of a single point charge q moving with a constant velocity $\vec{v}$. In practical applications, such as the solenoid shown in the photo that opens this chapter, magnetic fields are produced by tremendous numbers of charged particles moving together in a current. But once we understand how to calculate the magnetic field due to a single point charge, it's a small leap to calculate the field due to a current-carrying wire or collection of wires.

As we did for electric fields, we call the location of the moving charge at a given instant the **source point** and the point P where we want to find the field the **field point.** In Section 21.4 we found that at a field point a distance r from a point charge q, the magnitude of the *electric* field $\vec{E}$ caused by the charge is proportional to the charge magnitude $|q|$ and to $1/r^2$, and the direction of $\vec{E}$ (for positive q) is along the line from source point to field point. The corresponding relationship for the *magnetic* field $\vec{B}$ of a point charge q moving with constant velocity has some similarities and some interesting differences.

Experiments show that the magnitude of $\vec{B}$ is also proportional to $|q|$ and to $1/r^2$. But the *direction* of $\vec{B}$ is *not* along the line from source point to field point. Instead, $\vec{B}$ is perpendicular to the plane containing this line and the particle's velocity vector $\vec{v}$, as shown in Fig. 28.1. Furthermore, the field *magnitude B* is also proportional to the particle's speed v and to the sine of the angle ϕ. Thus the magnetic field magnitude at point P is given by

$$B = \frac{\mu_0}{4\pi} \frac{|q|v\sin\phi}{r^2} \tag{28.1}$$

where $\mu_0/4\pi$ is a proportionality constant (μ_0 is read as "mu-nought" or "mu-sub-zero"). The reason for writing the constant in this particular way will emerge shortly. We did something similar with Coulomb's law in Section 21.3.

Moving Charge: Vector Magnetic Field

We can incorporate both the magnitude and direction of $\vec{B}$ into a single vector equation using the vector product. To avoid having to say "the direction from the source q to the field point P" over and over, we introduce a *unit* vector $\hat{r}$ ("r-hat") that points from the source point to the field point. (We used $\hat{r}$ for the same purpose in Section 21.4.) This unit vector is equal to the vector $\vec{r}$ from the source to the field point divided by its magnitude: $\hat{r} = \vec{r}/r$. Then the $\vec{B}$ field of a moving point charge is

$$\vec{B} = \frac{\mu_0}{4\pi}\frac{q\vec{v} \times \hat{r}}{r^2} \qquad \text{(magnetic field of a point charge with constant velocity)} \tag{28.2}$$

Figure 28.1 shows the relationship of $\hat{r}$ to P and also shows the magnetic field $\vec{B}$ at several points in the vicinity of the charge. At all points along a line through the charge parallel to the velocity $\vec{v}$, the field is zero because $\sin\phi = 0$ at all such points. At any distance r from q, $\vec{B}$ has its greatest magnitude at points lying in the plane perpendicular to $\vec{v}$ because at all such points, $\phi = 90°$ and $\sin\phi = 1$. If the charge q is negative, the directions of $\vec{B}$ are opposite to those shown in Fig. 28.1.

Moving Charge: Magnetic Field Lines

A point charge in motion also produces an *electric* field, with field lines that radiate outward from a positive charge. The *magnetic* field lines are completely different. The above discussion shows that for a point charge moving with velocity $\vec{v}$, the magnetic field lines are *circles* centered on the line of $\vec{v}$ and lying in planes perpendicular to this line. The field-line directions for a positive charge are given by the following *right-hand rule,* one of several that we will encounter in this chapter for determining the direction of the magnetic field caused by different sources. Grasp the velocity vector $\vec{v}$ with your right hand so that your right thumb points in the direction of $\vec{v}$; your fingers then curl around the line of $\vec{v}$ in the same sense as the magnetic field lines, assuming q is positive. Figure 28.1a shows parts of a few field lines; Fig. 28.1b shows some field lines in a plane through q, perpendicular to $\vec{v}$, as seen by looking in the direction of $\vec{v}$. If the point charge is negative, the directions of the field and field lines are the opposite of those shown in Fig. 28.1.

Equations (28.1) and (28.2) describe the $\vec{B}$ field of a point charge moving with *constant* velocity. If the charge accelerates, the field can be much more compli-

28.1 (a) Magnetic-field vectors due to a moving positive point charge q. At each point, $\vec{B}$ is perpendicular to the plane of $\vec{r}$ and $\vec{v}$, and its magnitude is proportional to the sine of the angle between them. (b) Magnetic field lines in a plane containing a moving positive charge.

(a) Perspective view

Right-hand rule for the magnetic field due to a positive charge moving at constant velocity: Point the thumb of your right hand in the direction of the velocity. Your fingers now curl around the charge in the direction of the magnetic field lines. (If the charge is negative, the field lines are in the opposite direction.)

For these field points, $\vec{r}$ and $\vec{v}$ both lie in the beige plane, and $\vec{B}$ is perpendicular to this plane.

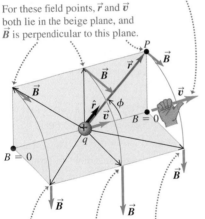

For these field points, $\vec{r}$ and $\vec{v}$ both lie in the gold plane, and $\vec{B}$ is perpendicular to this plane.

(b) View from behind the charge

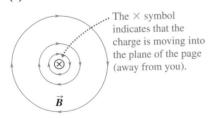

The $\times$ symbol indicates that the charge is moving into the plane of the page (away from you).

cated. We won't need these more complicated results for our purposes. (The moving charged particles that make up a current in a wire accelerate at points where the wire bends and the direction of $\vec{v}$ changes. But because the magnitude v_d of the drift velocity in a conductor is typically very small, the acceleration v_d^2/r is also very small, and the effects of acceleration can be ignored.)

As we discussed in Section 27.2, the unit of B is one tesla (1 T):

$$1\,\text{T} = 1\,\text{N} \cdot \text{s}/\text{C} \cdot \text{m} = 1\,\text{N}/\text{A} \cdot \text{m}$$

Using this with Eq. (28.1) or (28.2), we find that the units of the constant μ_0 are

$$1\,\text{N} \cdot \text{s}^2/\text{C}^2 = 1\,\text{N}/\text{A}^2 = 1\,\text{Wb}/\text{A} \cdot \text{m} = 1\,\text{T} \cdot \text{m}/\text{A}$$

In SI units the numerical value of μ_0 is exactly $4\pi \times 10^{-7}$. Thus

$$\begin{aligned} \mu_0 &= 4\pi \times 10^{-7}\,\text{N} \cdot \text{s}^2/\text{C}^2 = 4\pi \times 10^{-7}\,\text{Wb}/\text{A} \cdot \text{m} \\ &= 4\pi \times 10^{-7}\,\text{T} \cdot \text{m}/\text{A} \end{aligned} \tag{28.3}$$

It may seem incredible that μ_0 has *exactly* this numerical value! In fact this is a *defined* value that arises from the definition of the ampere, as we'll discuss in Section 28.4.

We mentioned in Section 21.3 that the constant $1/4\pi\epsilon_0$ in Coulomb's law is related to the speed of light c:

$$k = \frac{1}{4\pi\epsilon_0} = \left(10^{-7}\,\text{N} \cdot \text{s}^2/\text{C}^2\right)c^2$$

When we study electromagnetic waves in Chapter 32, we will find that their speed of propagation in vacuum, which is equal to the speed of light c, is given by

$$c^2 = \frac{1}{\epsilon_0\mu_0} \tag{28.4}$$

If we solve the equation $k = 1/4\pi\epsilon_0$ for ϵ_0, substitute the resulting expression into Eq. (28.4), and solve for μ_0, we indeed get the value of μ_0 stated above. This discussion is a little premature, but it may give you a hint that electric and magnetic fields are intimately related to the nature of light.

Example 28.1   Forces between two moving protons

Two protons move parallel to the x-axis in opposite directions (Fig. 28.2) at the same speed v (small compared to the speed of light c). At the instant shown, find the electric and magnetic forces on the upper proton and determine the ratio of their magnitudes.

SOLUTION

IDENTIFY: The electric force is given by Coulomb's law. To find the magnetic force, we must first find the magnetic field that the lower proton produces at the position of the upper proton.

SET UP: We use Eq. (21.2) for Coulomb's law. Equation (28.2) gives us the magnetic field due to the lower proton, and the magnetic force law, Eq. (27.2), gives us the resulting magnetic force on the upper proton.

EXECUTE: From Coulomb's law, the magnitude of the electric force on the upper proton is

$$F_E = \frac{1}{4\pi\epsilon_0}\frac{q^2}{r^2}$$

28.2 Electric and magnetic forces between two moving protons.

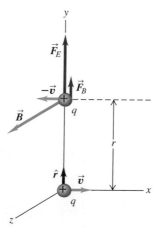

Continued

The forces are repulsive, and the force on the upper proton is vertically upward (in the $+y$-direction).

From the right-hand rule for the cross product $\vec{v} \times \hat{r}$ in Eq. (28.2), the $\vec{B}$-field due to the lower proton at the position of the upper proton is in the $+z$-direction (see Fig. 28.2). From Eq. (28.2), the magnitude of $\vec{B}$ is

$$B = \frac{\mu_0}{4\pi} \frac{qv}{r^2}$$

since $\phi = 90°$. Alternatively, from Eq. (28.2),

$$\vec{B} = \frac{\mu_0}{4\pi} \frac{q(v\hat{\imath}) \times \hat{\jmath}}{r^2} = \frac{\mu_0}{4\pi} \frac{qv}{r^2} \hat{k}$$

The velocity of the upper proton is $-\vec{v}$ and the magnetic force on it is $\vec{F} = q(-\vec{v}) \times \vec{B}$. Combining this with the expressions for $\vec{B}$, we find

$$F_B = \frac{\mu_0}{4\pi} \frac{q^2 v^2}{r^2} \quad \text{or}$$

$$\vec{F}_B = q(-\vec{v}) \times \vec{B} = q(-v\hat{\imath}) \times \frac{\mu_0}{4\pi} \frac{qv}{r^2} \hat{k} = \frac{\mu_0}{4\pi} \frac{q^2 v^2}{r^2} \hat{\jmath}$$

The magnetic interaction in this situation is also repulsive. The ratio of the magnitudes of the two forces is

$$\frac{F_B}{F_E} = \frac{\mu_0 q^2 v^2 / 4\pi r^2}{q^2 / 4\pi \epsilon_0 r^2} = \frac{\mu_0 v^2}{1/\epsilon_0} = \epsilon_0 \mu_0 v^2$$

Using the relationship $\epsilon_0 \mu_0 = 1/c^2$, Eq. (28.4), we can express our result very simply as

$$\frac{F_B}{F_E} = \frac{v^2}{c^2}$$

When v is small in comparison to c, the speed of light, the magnetic force is much smaller than the electric force.

EVALUATE: Note that it is essential to use the same frame of reference in this entire calculation. We have described the velocities and the fields as they appear to an observer who is stationary in the coordinate system of Fig. 28.2. In a coordinate system that moves with one of the charges, one of the velocities would be zero, so there would be *no* magnetic force. The explanation of this apparent paradox provided one of the paths that led to the special theory of relativity.

Test Your Understanding of Section 28.1 (a) If two protons are traveling parallel to each other in the *same* direction and at the same speed, is the magnetic force between them (i) attractive or (ii) repulsive? (b) Is the net force between them (i) attractive, (ii) repulsive, or (iii) zero? (Assume that the protons' speed is much slower than the speed of light.)

28.2 Magnetic Field of a Current Element

Just as for the electric field, there is a **principle of superposition of magnetic fields:**

The total magnetic field caused by several moving charges is the vector sum of the fields caused by the individual charges.

We can use this principle with the results of Section 28.1 to find the magnetic field produced by a current in a conductor.

We begin by calculating the magnetic field caused by a short segment $d\vec{l}$ of a current-carrying conductor, as shown in Fig. 28.3a. The volume of the segment is $A \, dl$, where A is the cross-sectional area of the conductor. If there are n moving charged particles per unit volume, each of charge q, the total moving charge dQ in the segment is

$$dQ = nqA \, dl$$

The moving charges in this segment are equivalent to a single charge dQ, traveling with a velocity equal to the *drift* velocity $\vec{v}_d$. (Magnetic fields due to the *random* motions of the charges will, on average, cancel out at every point.) From Eq. (28.1) the magnitude of the resulting field $d\vec{B}$ at any field point P is

$$dB = \frac{\mu_0}{4\pi} \frac{|dQ| v_d \sin\phi}{r^2} = \frac{\mu_0}{4\pi} \frac{n|q| v_d A \, dl \sin\phi}{r^2}$$

But from Eq. (25.2), $n|q| v_d A$ equals the current I in the element. So

$$dB = \frac{\mu_0}{4\pi} \frac{I \, dl \sin\phi}{r^2} \tag{28.5}$$

Current Element: Vector Magnectic Field

In vector form, using the unit vector $\hat{r}$ as in Section 28.1, we have

$$d\vec{B} = \frac{\mu_0}{4\pi} \frac{I\, d\vec{l} \times \hat{r}}{r^2} \quad \text{(magnetic field of a current element)} \quad (28.6)$$

where $d\vec{l}$ is a vector with length dl, in the same direction as the current in the conductor.

Equations (28.5) and (28.6) are called the **law of Biot and Savart** (pronounced "Bee-oh" and "Suh-var"). We can use this law to find the total magnetic field $\vec{B}$ at any point in space due to the current in a complete circuit. To do this, we integrate Eq. (28.6) over all segments $d\vec{l}$ that carry current; symbolically,

$$\vec{B} = \frac{\mu_0}{4\pi} \int \frac{I\, d\vec{l} \times \hat{r}}{r^2} \quad (28.7)$$

In the following sections we will carry out this vector integration for several examples.

Current Element: Magnetic Field Lines

As Fig. 28.3 shows, the field vectors $d\vec{B}$ and the magnetic field lines of a current element are exactly like those set up by a positive charge dQ moving in the direction of the drift velocity $\vec{v}_d$. The field lines are circles in planes perpendicular to $d\vec{l}$ and centered on the line of $d\vec{l}$. Their directions are given by the same right-hand rule that we introduced for point charges in Section 28.1.

We can't verify Eq. (28.5) or (28.6) directly because we can never experiment with an isolated segment of a current-carrying circuit. What we measure experimentally is the *total* $\vec{B}$ for a complete circuit. But we can still verify these equations indirectly by calculating $\vec{B}$ for various current configurations using Eq. (28.7) and comparing the results with experimental measurements.

If matter is present in the space around a current-carrying conductor, the field at a field point P in its vicinity will have an additional contribution resulting from the *magnetization* of the material. We'll return to this point in Section 28.8. However, unless the material is iron or some other ferromagnetic material, the additional field is small and is usually negligible. Additional complications arise if time-varying electric or magnetic fields are present or if the material is a superconductor; we'll return to these topics later.

28.3 (a) Magnetic-field vectors due to a current element $d\vec{l}$. (b) Magnetic field lines in a plane containing the current element $d\vec{l}$. Compare this figure to Fig. 28.1 for the field of a moving point charge.

(a) Perspective view

Right-hand rule for the magnetic field due to a current element: Point the thumb of your right hand in the direction of the current. Your fingers now curl around the current element in the direction of the magnetic field lines.

For these field points, $\vec{r}$ and $d\vec{l}$ both lie in the beige plane, and $d\vec{B}$ is perpendicular to this plane.

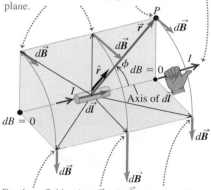

For these field points, $\vec{r}$ and $d\vec{l}$ both lie in the gold plane, and $d\vec{B}$ is perpendicular to this plane.

(b) View along the axis of the current element

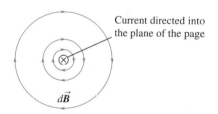

Current directed into the plane of the page

Problem-Solving Strategy 28.1 | **Magnetic-Field Calculations**

IDENTIFY *the relevant concepts:* The law of Biot and Savart allows you to calculate the magnetic field due to a current-carrying wire of any shape. The idea is to calculate the field due to a representative current element in the wire and then combine the contributions from all such elements to find the total field.

SET UP *the problem* using the following steps:
1. Make a diagram showing a representative current element and the point P at which the field is to be determined (the field point).
2. Draw the current element $d\vec{l}$, being careful that it points in the direction of the current.
3. Draw the unit vector $\hat{r}$. Note that it is always directed *from* the current element (the source point) to the field point P.
4. Identify the target variables. Usually they will be the magnitude and direction of the magnetic field $\vec{B}$.

EXECUTE *the solution* as follows:
1. Use Eq. (28.5) or (28.6) to express the magnetic field $d\vec{B}$ at P from the representative current element.
2. Add up all the $d\vec{B}$'s to find the total field at point P. In some situations the $d\vec{B}$'s at point P have the same direction for all the current elements; then the magnitude of the total $\vec{B}$ field is the sum of the magnitudes of the $d\vec{B}$'s. But often the $d\vec{B}$'s have different directions for different current elements. Then you have to set up a coordinate system and represent each $d\vec{B}$ in terms of its components. The integral for the total $\vec{B}$ is then expressed in terms of an integral for each component.
3. Sometimes you can use the symmetry of the situation to prove that one component of $\vec{B}$ must vanish. Always be alert for ways to use symmetry to simplify the problem.

Continued

4. Look for ways to use the principle of superposition of magnetic fields. Later in this chapter we'll determine the fields produced by certain simple conductor shapes; if you encounter a conductor of a complex shape that can be represented as a combination of these simple shapes, you can use superposition to find the field of the complex shape. Examples include a rectangular loop and a semicircle with straight line segments on both sides.

EVALUATE *your answer:*   Often your answer will be a mathematical expression for $\vec{B}$ as a function of the position of the field point. Check the answer by examining its behavior in as many limits as you can.

Example 28.2 | Magnetic field of a current segment

A copper wire carries a steady current of 125 A to an electroplating tank. Find the magnetic field caused by a 1.0-cm segment of this wire at a point 1.2 m away from it, if the point is (a) point P_1, straight out to the side of the segment, and (b) point P_2, on a line at 30° to the segment, as shown in Fig. 28.4.

SOLUTION

IDENTIFY: Although Eqs. (28.5) and (28.6) are strictly to be used with infinitesimal current elements only, we may use them here since the segment's 1.0-cm length is much smaller than the 1.2-m distance to the field point.

SET UP: The current element is shown in red in Fig. 28.4 and points in the $-x$-direction (the direction of the current). The unit vector $\hat{r}$ for each field point is directed from the current element toward that point: $\hat{r}$ is in the $+y$-direction for point P_1 and at an angle of 30° above the $-x$-direction for point P_2.

EXECUTE: (a) From the right-hand rule, the direction of $\vec{B}$ at P_1 is *into* the xy-plane of Fig. 28.4. Or, using unit vectors, we note that $d\vec{l} = dl(-\hat{\imath})$. At point P_1, $\hat{r} = \hat{\jmath}$, so in Eq. (28.6),

$$d\vec{l} \times \hat{r} = dl(-\hat{\imath}) \times \hat{\jmath} = dl(-\hat{k})$$

The negative z-direction is *into* the plane.

To find the magnitude of $\vec{B}$, we use Eq. (28.5). At point P_1, the angle between $d\vec{l}$ and $\hat{r}$ is 90°, so

$$B = \frac{\mu_0}{4\pi} \frac{I\,dl\sin\phi}{r^2}$$

$$= (10^{-7}\ \text{T} \cdot \text{m/A}) \frac{(125\ \text{A})(1.0 \times 10^{-2}\ \text{m})(\sin 90°)}{(1.2\ \text{m})^2}$$

$$= 8.7 \times 10^{-8}\ \text{T}$$

28.4 Finding the magnetic field at two points due to a 1.0-cm segment of current-carrying wire (not shown to scale).

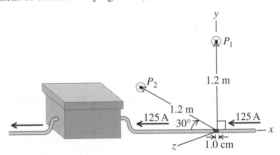

(b) At point P_2 the direction of $\vec{B}$ is again into the xy-plane of the figure. The angle between $d\vec{l}$ and $\hat{r}$ is 30°, and

$$B = (10^{-7}\ \text{T} \cdot \text{m/A}) \frac{(125\ \text{A})(1.0 \times 10^{-2}\ \text{m})(\sin 30°)}{(1.2\ \text{m})^2}$$

$$= 4.3 \times 10^{-8}\ \text{T}$$

EVALUATE: You can check our results for the direction of $\vec{B}$ by comparing them with Fig. 28.3. The xy-plane in Fig. 28.4 corresponds to the beige plane in Fig. 28.3. However, in the present example the direction of the current and hence of $d\vec{l}$ is the reverse of the direction shown in Fig. 28.3, so the direction of the magnetic field is reversed as well. Hence the field at points in the xy-plane in Fig. 28.4 must point *into*, not out of, that plane. This is just what we concluded above.

Note that these magnetic-field magnitudes are very small; for comparison the magnetic field of the earth is of the order of 10^{-4} T. Note also that the values are not the *total* fields at points P_1 and P_2, but only the contributions from the short segment of conductor described.

Test Your Understanding of Section 28.2   An infinitesimal current element located at the origin $(x = y = z = 0)$ carries current I in the positive y-direction. Rank the following locations in order of the strength of the magnetic field that the current element produces at that location, from largest to smallest value. (i) $x = L, y = 0, z = 0$; (ii) $x = 0, y = L, z = 0$; (iii) $x = 0, y = 0, z = L$; (iv) $x = L/\sqrt{2}, y = L/\sqrt{2}, z = 0$. ∎

28.3 Magnetic Field of a Straight Current-Carrying Conductor

An important application of the law of Biot and Savart is finding the magnetic field produced by a straight current-carrying conductor. This result is useful because straight conducting wires are found in essentially all electric and electronic devices. Fig. 28.5 shows such a conductor with length $2a$ carrying a current I. We will find $\vec{B}$ at a point a distance x from the conductor on its perpendicular bisector.

We first use the law of Biot and Savart, Eq. (28.5), to find the field $d\vec{B}$ caused by the element of conductor of length $dl = dy$ shown in Fig. 28.5. From the figure, $r = \sqrt{x^2 + y^2}$ and $\sin\phi = \sin(\pi - \phi) = x/\sqrt{x^2 + y^2}$. The right-hand rule for the vector product $d\vec{l} \times \hat{r}$ shows that the *direction* of $d\vec{B}$ is into the plane of the figure, perpendicular to the plane; furthermore, the directions of the $d\vec{B}$'s from *all* elements of the conductor are the same. Thus in integrating Eq. (28.7), we can just add the *magnitudes* of the $d\vec{B}$'s, a significant simplification.

Putting the pieces together, we find that the magnitude of the total $\vec{B}$ field is

$$B = \frac{\mu_0 I}{4\pi} \int_{-a}^{a} \frac{x\, dy}{(x^2 + y^2)^{3/2}}$$

We can integrate this by trigonometric substitution or by using an integral table. The final result is

$$B = \frac{\mu_0 I}{4\pi} \frac{2a}{x\sqrt{x^2 + a^2}} \qquad (28.8)$$

When the length $2a$ of the conductor is very great in comparison to its distance x from point P, we can consider it to be infinitely long. When a is much larger than x, $\sqrt{x^2 + a^2}$ is approximately equal to a; hence in the limit $a \to \infty$, Eq. (28.8) becomes

$$B = \frac{\mu_0 I}{2\pi x}$$

The physical situation has axial symmetry about the y-axis. Hence $\vec{B}$ must have the same *magnitude* at all points on a circle centered on the conductor and lying in a plane perpendicular to it, and the *direction* of $\vec{B}$ must be everywhere tangent to such a circle. Thus, at all points on a circle of radius r around the conductor, the magnitude B is

$$B = \frac{\mu_0 I}{2\pi r} \qquad \text{(near a long, straight, current-carrying conductor)} \quad (28.9)$$

Part of the magnetic field around a long, straight, current-carrying conductor is shown in Fig. 28.6.

The geometry of this problem is similar to that of Example 21.11 (Section 21.5), in which we solved the problem of the *electric* field caused by an infinite line of charge. The same integral appears in both problems, and the field magnitudes in both problems are proportional to $1/r$. But the lines of $\vec{B}$ in the magnetic problem have completely different shapes than the lines of $\vec{E}$ in the analogous electrical problem. Electric field lines radiate outward from a positive line charge distribution (inward for negative charges). By contrast, magnetic field lines *encircle* the current that acts as their source. Electric field lines due to charges begin and end at those charges, but magnetic field lines always form closed loops and *never* have end points, irrespective of the shape of the current-carrying conductor that sets up the field. As we discussed in Section 27.3, this is a consequence of Gauss's law for magnetism, which states that the total magnetic flux through *any* closed surface is always zero:

$$\oint \vec{B} \cdot d\vec{A} = 0 \qquad \text{(magnetic flux through any closed surface)} \quad (28.10)$$

This implies that there are no isolated magnetic charges or magnetic monopoles. Any magnetic field line that enters a closed surface must also emerge from that surface.

28.5 Magnetic field produced by a straight current-carrying conductor of length $2a$.

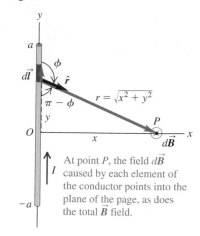

At point P, the field $d\vec{B}$ caused by each element of the conductor points into the plane of the page, as does the total $\vec{B}$ field.

28.6 Magnetic field around a long, straight, current-carrying conductor. The field lines are circles, with directions determined by the right-hand rule.

Right-hand rule for the magnetic field around a current-carrying wire: Point the thumb of your right hand in the direction of the current. Your fingers now curl around the wire in the direction of the magnetic field lines.

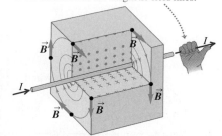

Example 28.3 Magnetic field of a single wire

A long, straight conductor carries a current of 1.0 A. At what distance from the axis of the conductor is the magnetic field caused by the current equal in magnitude to the earth's magnetic field in Pittsburgh (about 0.5×10^{-4} T)?

SOLUTION

IDENTIFY: The straight conductor is described as being long, which means that its length is much greater than the distance from the conductor at which we measure the field. Hence we can use the ideas of this section.

SET UP: The geometry is the same as that in Fig. 28.6, so we use Eq. (28.8). All of the quantities in this equation are known except the target variable, the distance r.

EXECUTE: We solve Eq. (28.8) for r and insert the appropriate numbers:

$$r = \frac{\mu_0 I}{2\pi B}$$

$$= \frac{(4\pi \times 10^{-7}\ \text{T}\cdot\text{m/A})(1.0\ \text{A})}{(2\pi)(0.5 \times 10^{-4}\ \text{T})} = 4 \times 10^{-3}\ \text{m} = 4\ \text{mm}$$

EVALUATE: Currents of an ampere or so are typical of those found in the wiring of home appliances. This example shows that the magnetic fields produced by these appliances are very weak even at points very close to the wire. At greater distances the field becomes even weaker; for example, at five times the distance ($r = 20\ \text{mm} = 2\ \text{cm} = 2 \times 10^{-2}\ \text{m}$) the field is one-fifth as great ($B = 0.1 \times 10^{-4}\ \text{T}$).

Example 28.4 Magnetic field of two wires

Fig. 28.7a is an end-on view of two long, straight, parallel wires perpendicular to the xy-plane, each carrying a current I but in opposite directions. (a) Find the magnitude and direction of $\vec{B}$ at points P_1, P_2, and P_3. (b) Find the magnitude and direction of $\vec{B}$ at any point on the x-axis to the right of wire 2 in terms of the x-coordinate of the point.

SOLUTION

IDENTIFY: We can find the magnetic fields $\vec{B}_1$ and $\vec{B}_2$ due to each wire using the ideas of this section. The principle of superposition of magnetic fields says that the total magnetic field $\vec{B}$ is the vector sum of $\vec{B}_1$ and $\vec{B}_2$.

SET UP: We use Eq. (28.9) to find the magnitude of the fields $\vec{B}_1$ (due to wire 1) and $\vec{B}_2$ (due to wire 2) at any point. We find the directions of these fields using the right-hand rule. The total magnetic field at the point in question is $\vec{B}_{\text{total}} = \vec{B}_1 + \vec{B}_2$.

EXECUTE: (a) Point P_1 is closer to wire 1 (distance $2d$) than to wire 2 (distance $4d$), so at this point the field magnitude B_1 is greater than the magnitude B_2:

$$B_1 = \frac{\mu_0 I}{2\pi(2d)} = \frac{\mu_0 I}{4\pi d} \qquad B_2 = \frac{\mu_0 I}{2\pi(4d)} = \frac{\mu_0 I}{8\pi d}$$

The right-hand rule shows that $\vec{B}_1$ is in the negative y-direction and $\vec{B}_2$ is in the positive y-direction. Since B_1 is the larger magnitude, the total field $\vec{B}_{\text{total}} = \vec{B}_1 + \vec{B}_2$ is in the negative y-direction, with magnitude

$$B_{\text{total}} = B_1 - B_2 = \frac{\mu_0 I}{4\pi d} - \frac{\mu_0 I}{8\pi d} = \frac{\mu_0 I}{8\pi d} \qquad \text{(point } P_1\text{)}$$

At point P_2, a distance d from both wires, $\vec{B}_1$ and $\vec{B}_2$ are both in the positive y-direction, and both have the same magnitude:

$$B_1 = B_2 = \frac{\mu_0 I}{2\pi d}$$

so $\vec{B}_{\text{total}}$ is also in the positive y-direction and has magnitude

$$B_{\text{total}} = B_1 + B_2 = \frac{\mu_0 I}{\pi d} \qquad \text{(point } P_2\text{)}$$

Finally, at point P_3 the right-hand rule shows that $\vec{B}_1$ is in the positive y-direction and $\vec{B}_2$ is in the negative y-direction. This point is farther from wire 1 (distance $3d$) than from wire 2 (distance d), so B_1 is less than B_2:

$$B_1 = \frac{\mu_0 I}{2\pi(3d)} = \frac{\mu_0 I}{6\pi d} \qquad B_2 = \frac{\mu_0 I}{2\pi d}$$

28.7 (a) Two long, straight conductors carrying equal currents in opposite directions. The conductors are seen end-on. (b) Map of the magnetic field produced by the two conductors. The field lines are closest together between the conductors, where the field is strongest.

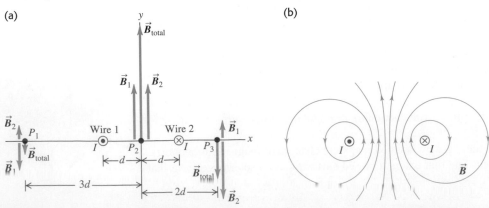

The total field is in the negative y-direction, the same as $\vec{B}_2$, and has magnitude

$$B_{total} = B_2 - B_1 = \frac{\mu_0 I}{2\pi d} - \frac{\mu_0 I}{6\pi d} = \frac{\mu_0 I}{3\pi d} \qquad \text{(point } P_3\text{)}$$

You should be able to use the right-hand rule to verify for yourself the directions of $\vec{B}_1$ and $\vec{B}_2$ for each point.

The fields $\vec{B}_1$, $\vec{B}_2$, and $\vec{B}_{total}$ at each of the three points are shown in Fig. 28.7a. The same technique can be used to find $\vec{B}_{total}$ at any point; for points off the x-axis, caution must be taken in vector addition, since $\vec{B}_1$ and $\vec{B}_2$ need no longer be simply parallel or antiparallel (see Problem 28.60). Figure 28.7b shows some of the magnetic field lines due to this combination of wires.

(b) At any point to the right of wire 2 (that is, for $x > d$), $\vec{B}_1$ and $\vec{B}_2$ are in the same directions as at P_3. As x increases, both $\vec{B}_1$ and $\vec{B}_2$ decrease in magnitude, so $\vec{B}_{total}$ must decrease as well. The magnitudes of the fields due to each wire are

$$B_1 = \frac{\mu_0 I}{2\pi(x+d)} \qquad \text{and} \qquad B_2 = \frac{\mu_0 I}{2\pi(x-d)}$$

At any field point to the right of wire 2, wire 2 is closer than wire 1, and so $B_2 > B_1$. Hence $\vec{B}_{total}$ is in the negative y-direction, the same as $\vec{B}_2$, and has magnitude

$$B_{total} = B_2 - B_1 = \frac{\mu_0 I}{2\pi(x-d)} - \frac{\mu_0 I}{2\pi(x+d)} = \frac{\mu_0 I d}{\pi(x^2-d^2)}$$

where we combined the two terms using a common denominator.

EVALUATE: At points very far from the wires, so that x is much larger than d, the d^2 term in the denominator can be neglected, and

$$B_{total} = \frac{\mu_0 I d}{\pi x^2}$$

The magnetic-field magnitude for a single wire decreases with distance in proportion to $1/x$, as shown by Eq. (28.9); for two wires carrying opposite currents, $\vec{B}_1$ and $\vec{B}_2$ partially cancel each other, and so the magnitude of $\vec{B}_{total}$ decreases more rapidly, in proportion to $1/x^2$. This effect is used in communication systems such as telephone or computer networks. The wiring is arranged so that a conductor carrying a signal in one direction and the conductor carrying the return signal are side by side, as in Fig. 28.7a, or twisted around each other (Fig. 28.8). As a result, the magnetic field caused *outside* the conductors by these signals is greatly reduced and is less likely to exert unwanted forces on other information-carrying currents.

28.8 Computer cables, or cables for audio-video equipment, create little or no magnetic field. This is because within each cable, closely spaced wires carry current in both directions along the length of the cable. The magnetic fields from these opposing currents cancel each other.

Test Your Understanding of Section 28.3 The figure at right shows a circuit that lies on a horizontal table. A compass is placed on top of the circuit as shown. A battery is to be connected to the circuit so that when the switch is closed, the compass needle deflects counterclockwise. In which orientation, A or B, should the battery be placed in the circuit?

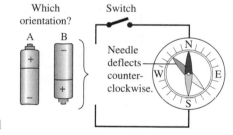

28.4 Force Between Parallel Conductors

In Example 28.4 (Section 28.3) we showed how to use the principle of superposition of magnetic fields to find the total field due to two long current-carrying conductors. Another important aspect of this configuration is the *interaction force* between the conductors. This force plays a role in many practical situations in which current-carrying wires are close to each other, and it also has fundamental significance in connection with the definition of the ampere. Figure 28.9 shows segments of two long, straight, parallel conductors separated by a distance r and carrying currents I and I' in the same direction. Each conductor lies in the magnetic field set up by the other, so each experiences a force. The diagram shows some of the field lines set up by the current in the lower conductor.

From Eq. (28.9) the lower conductor produces a $\vec{B}$ field that, at the position of the upper conductor, has magnitude

$$B = \frac{\mu_0 I}{2\pi r}$$

From Eq. (27.19) the force that this field exerts on a length L of the upper conductor is $\vec{F} = I'\vec{L} \times \vec{B}$, where the vector $\vec{L}$ is in the direction of the current I' and

28.9 Parallel conductors carrying currents in the same direction attract each other. The diagrams show how the magnetic field $\vec{B}$ caused by the current in the lower conductor exerts a force $\vec{F}$ on the upper conductor.

The magnetic field of the lower wire exerts an attractive force on the upper wire. By the same token, the upper wire attracts the lower one.

If the wires had currents in *opposite* directions, they would *repel* each other.

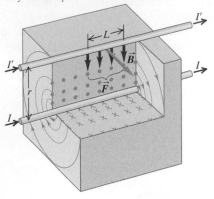

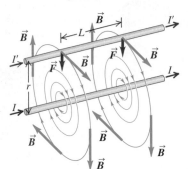

has magnitude L. Since $\vec{B}$ is perpendicular to the length of the conductor and hence to $\vec{L}$, the magnitude of this force is

$$F = I'LB = \frac{\mu_0 II'L}{2\pi r}$$

and the force *per unit length* F/L is

$$\frac{F}{L} = \frac{\mu_0 II'}{2\pi r} \quad \text{(two long, parallel, current-carrying conductors)} \quad (28.11)$$

Applying the right-hand rule to $\vec{F} = I'\vec{L} \times \vec{B}$ shows that the force on the upper conductor is directed *downward*.

The current in the upper conductor also sets up a field at the position of the lower one. Two successive applications of the right-hand rule for vector products (one to find the direction of the $\vec{B}$ field due to the upper conductor, as in Section 28.2, and one to find the direction of the force that this field exerts on the lower conductor, as in Section 27.6) show that the force on the lower conductor is *upward*. Thus *two parallel conductors carrying current in the same direction attract each other*. If the direction of either current is reversed, the forces also reverse. *Parallel conductors carrying currents in opposite directions repel each other.*

Magnetic Forces and Defining the Ampere

The attraction or repulsion between two straight, parallel, current-carrying conductors is the basis of the official SI definition of the **ampere:**

> *One ampere* is that unvarying current that, if present in each of two parallel conductors of infinite length and one meter apart in empty space, causes each conductor to experience a force of exactly 2×10^{-7} newtons per meter of length.

From Eq. (28.11) you can see that this definition of the ampere is what leads us to choose the value of $4\pi \times 10^{-7}$ T · m/A for μ_0. It also forms the basis of the SI definition of the coulomb, which is the amount of charge transferred in one second by a current of one ampere.

This is an *operational definition;* it gives us an actual experimental procedure for measuring current and defining a unit of current. In principle we could use this definition to calibrate an ammeter, using only a meter stick and a spring balance. For high-precision standardization of the ampere, coils of wire are used instead of straight wires, and their separation is only a few centimeters. Even more precise measurements of the standardized ampere are possible using a version of the Hall effect (see Section 27.9).

Mutual forces of attraction exist not only between *wires* carrying currents in the same direction, but also between the longitudinal elements of a single current-carrying conductor. If the conductor is a liquid or an ionized gas (a plasma), these forces result in a constriction of the conductor, as if its surface were acted on by an inward pressure. The constriction of the conductor is called the *pinch effect*. The high temperature produced by the pinch effect in a plasma has been used in one technique to bring about nuclear fusion.

Example 28.5 Forces between parallel wires

Two straight, parallel, superconducting wires 4.5 mm apart carry equal currents of 15,000 A in opposite directions. Should we worry about the mechanical strength of these wires?

SOLUTION

IDENTIFY: Whether or not we need to worry about the wires' mechanical strength depends on how much magnetic force each wire exerts on the other.

28.10 Our sketch for this problem.

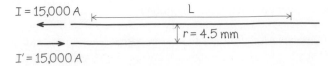

SET UP: Figure 28.10 shows the situation. Our target variable is the magnetic force per unit length of wire, which we find using Eq. (28.11).

EXECUTE: Because the currents are in opposite directions, the two conductors repel each other. From Eq. (28.11) the force per unit length is

$$\frac{F}{L} = \frac{\mu_0 I I'}{2\pi r} = \frac{(4\pi \times 10^{-7}\ \text{T} \cdot \text{m/A})(15{,}000\ \text{A})^2}{(2\pi)(4.5 \times 10^{-3}\ \text{m})}$$

$$= 1.0 \times 10^4\ \text{N/m}$$

EVALUATE: This is a large force, more than one ton per meter, so the mechanical strengths of the conductors and insulating materials are certainly a significant consideration. Currents and separations of this magnitude are used in superconducting electromagnets in particle accelerators, and mechanical stress analysis is a crucial part of the design process.

Test Your Understanding of Section 28.4   A solenoid is a wire wound into a helical coil. The figure at right shows a solenoid that carries a current I. (a) Is the *magnetic* force that one turn of the coil exerts on an adjacent turn (i) attractive, (ii) repulsive, or (iii) zero? (b) Is the *electric* force that one turn of the coil exerts on an adjacent turn (i) attractive, (ii) repulsive, or (iii) zero? (c) Is the *magnetic* force between opposite sides of the same turn of the coil (i) attractive, (ii) repulsive, or (iii) zero? (d) Is the *electric* force between opposite sides of the same turn of the coil (i) attractive, (ii) repulsive, or (iii) zero?

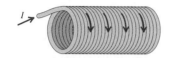

28.5 Magnetic Field of a Circular Current Loop

If you look inside a doorbell, a transformer, an electric motor, or an electromagnet (Fig. 28.11), you will find coils of wire with a large number of turns, spaced so closely that each turn is very nearly a planar circular loop. A current in such a coil is used to establish a magnetic field. So it is worthwhile to derive an expression for the magnetic field produced by a single circular conducting loop carrying a current or by N closely spaced circular loops forming a coil. In Section 27.7 we considered the force and torque on such a current loop placed in an external magnetic field produced by other currents; we are now about to find the magnetic field produced by the loop itself.

Figure 28.12 shows a circular conductor with radius a that carries a current I. The current is led into and out of the loop through two long, straight wires side by side; the currents in these straight wires are in opposite directions, and their magnetic fields very nearly cancel each other (see Example 28.4 in Section 28.3).

We can use the law of Biot and Savart, Eq. (28.5) or (28.6), to find the magnetic field at a point P on the axis of the loop, at a distance x from the center. As the figure shows, $d\vec{l}$ and $\hat{r}$ are perpendicular, and the direction of the field $d\vec{B}$ caused by this particular element $d\vec{l}$ lies in the xy-plane. Since $r^2 = x^2 + a^2$, the magnitude dB of the field due to element $d\vec{l}$ is

$$dB = \frac{\mu_0 I}{4\pi} \frac{dl}{(x^2 + a^2)} \qquad (28.12)$$

The components of the vector $d\vec{B}$ are

$$dB_x = dB\cos\theta = \frac{\mu_0 I}{4\pi} \frac{dl}{(x^2 + a^2)} \frac{a}{(x^2 + a^2)^{1/2}} \qquad (28.13)$$

$$dB_y = dB\sin\theta = \frac{\mu_0 I}{4\pi} \frac{dl}{(x^2 + a^2)} \frac{x}{(x^2 + a^2)^{1/2}} \qquad (28.14)$$

The situation has rotational symmetry about the x-axis, so there cannot be a component of the total field $\vec{B}$ perpendicular to this axis. For every element $d\vec{l}$ there is a corresponding element on the opposite side of the loop, with opposite direction. These two elements give equal contributions to the x-component of $d\vec{B}$, given by Eq. (28.13), but *opposite* components perpendicular to the

28.11 This electromagnet contains a current-carrying coil with numerous turns of wire. The resulting magnetic field can pick up large quantities of steel bars and other iron-bearing items.

28.12 Magnetic field on the axis of a circular loop. The current in the segment $d\vec{l}$ causes the field $d\vec{B}$, which lies in the xy-plane. The currents in other $d\vec{l}$'s cause $d\vec{B}$'s with different components perpendicular to the x-axis; these components add to zero. The x-components of the $d\vec{B}$'s combine to give the total $\vec{B}$ field at point P.

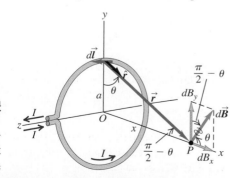

Act**i**v
ONLINE
Physics
13.2   Magnetic Field of a Loop

x-axis. Thus all the perpendicular components cancel and only the *x*-components survive.

To obtain the *x*-component of the total field $\vec{B}$, we integrate Eq. (28.13), including all the $d\vec{l}$'s around the loop. Everything in this expression except dl is constant and can be taken outside the integral, and we have

$$B_x = \int \frac{\mu_0 I}{4\pi} \frac{a\, dl}{(x^2 + a^2)^{3/2}} = \frac{\mu_0 Ia}{4\pi(x^2 + a^2)^{3/2}} \int dl$$

The integral of dl is just the circumference of the circle, $\int dl = 2\pi a$, and we finally get

$$B_x = \frac{\mu_0 Ia^2}{2(x^2 + a^2)^{3/2}} \qquad \text{(on the axis of a circular loop)} \qquad (28.15)$$

28.13 The right-hand rule for the direction of the magnetic field produced on the axis of a current-carrying coil.

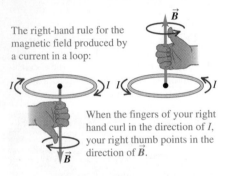

The right-hand rule for the magnetic field produced by a current in a loop:

I I I

When the fingers of your right hand curl in the direction of I, your right thumb points in the direction of $\vec{B}$.

The *direction* of the magnetic field on the axis of a current-carrying loop is given by a right-hand rule. If you curl the fingers of your right hand around the loop in the direction of the current, your right thumb points in the direction of the field (Fig. 28.13).

Magnetic Field on the Axis of a Coil

Now suppose that instead of the single loop in Fig. 28.12 we have a coil consisting of N loops, all with the same radius. The loops are closely spaced so that the plane of each loop is essentially the same distance x from the field point P. Each loop contributes equally to the field, and the total field is N times the field of a single loop:

$$B_x = \frac{\mu_0 NIa^2}{2(x^2 + a^2)^{3/2}} \qquad \text{(on the axis of } N \text{ circular loops)} \qquad (28.16)$$

The factor N in Eq. (28.16) is the reason coils of wire, not single loops, are used to produce strong magnetic fields; for a desired field strength, using a single loop might require a current I so great as to exceed the rating of the loop's wire.

Figure 28.14 shows a graph of B_x as a function of x. The maximum value of the field is at $x = 0$, the center of the loop or coil:

28.14 Graph of the magnetic field along the axis of a circular coil with N turns. When x is much larger than a, the field magnitude decreases approximately as $1/x^3$.

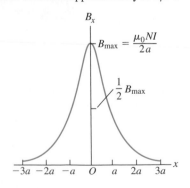

B_x

$B_{\max} = \dfrac{\mu_0 NI}{2a}$

$\dfrac{1}{2} B_{\max}$

$-3a \quad -2a \quad -a \quad O \quad a \quad 2a \quad 3a \qquad x$

$$B_x = \frac{\mu_0 NI}{2a} \qquad \text{(at the center of } N \text{ circular loops)} \qquad (28.17)$$

As we go out along the axis, the field decreases in magnitude.

In Section 27.7 we defined the *magnetic dipole moment* μ (or *magnetic moment*) of a current-carrying loop to be equal to IA, where A is the cross-sectional area of the loop. If there are N loops, the total magnetic moment is NIA. The circular loop in Fig. 28.12 has area $A = \pi a^2$, so the magnetic moment of a single loop is $\mu = I\pi a^2$; for N loops, $\mu = NI\pi a^2$. Substituting these results into Eqs. (28.15) and (28.16), we find that both of these expressions can be written as

$$B_x = \frac{\mu_0 \mu}{2\pi(x^2 + a^2)^{3/2}} \qquad \begin{array}{l}\text{(on the axis of any number} \\ \text{of circular loops)}\end{array} \qquad (28.18)$$

We described a magnetic dipole in Section 27.7 in terms of its response to a magnetic field produced by currents outside the dipole. But a magnetic dipole is also a *source* of magnetic field; Eq. (28.18) describes the magnetic field *produced* by a magnetic dipole for points along the dipole axis. This field is directly proportional to the magnetic dipole moment μ. Note that the field along the *x*-axis is in the same direction as the vector magnetic moment $\vec{\mu}$; this is true on both the positive and negative x-axis.

CAUTION **Magnetic field of a coil** Equations (28.15), (28.16), and (28.18) are valid only on the *axis* of a loop or coil. Don't attempt to apply these equations at other points! ∎

Figure 28.15 shows some of the magnetic field lines surrounding a circular current loop (magnetic dipole) in planes through the axis. The directions of the field lines are given by the same right-hand rule as for a long, straight conductor. Grab the conductor with your right hand, with your thumb in the direction of the current; your fingers curl around in the same direction as the field lines. The field lines for the circular current loop are closed curves that encircle the conductor; they are *not* circles, however.

28.15 Magnetic field lines produced by the current in a circular loop. At points on the axis the $\vec{B}$ field has the same direction as the magnetic moment of the loop.

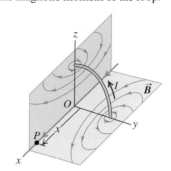

Example 28.6   Magnetic field of a coil

A coil consisting of 100 circular loops with radius 0.60 m carries a current of 5.0 A. (a) Find the magnetic field at a point along the axis of the coil, 0.80 m from the center. (b) Along the axis, at what distance from the center of the coil is the field magnitude $\frac{1}{8}$ as great as it is at the center?

SOLUTION

IDENTIFY: This problem asks about the magnetic field along the axis of a current-carrying coil, so we can use the ideas of this section.

SET UP: We want the field on the axis of the coil, not necessarily at its center, so we use Eq. (28.16). We are given $N = 100$, $I = 5.0$ A, and $a = 0.60$ m. In part (a) our target variable is the magnetic field at a given value of the coordinate x. In part (b) the target variable is the value of x at which the field has $\frac{1}{8}$ of the magnitude that it has at $x = 0$.

EXECUTE: (a) Using $x = 0.80$ m, from Eq. (28.16) we have

$$B_x = \frac{(4\pi \times 10^{-7}\,\text{T}\cdot\text{m/A})(100)(5.0\,\text{A})(0.60\,\text{m})^2}{2[(0.80\,\text{m})^2 + (0.60\,\text{m})^2]^{3/2}}$$

$$= 1.1 \times 10^{-4}\,\text{T}$$

(b) Considering Eq. (28.16), we want to find a value of x such that

$$\frac{1}{(x^2 + a^2)^{3/2}} = \frac{1}{8}\frac{1}{(0^2 + a^2)^{3/2}}$$

To solve this for x, we take the reciprocal of the whole thing and then take the $2/3$ power of both sides; the result is

$$x = \pm\sqrt{3}\,a = \pm 1.04\,\text{m}$$

At a distance of about 1.7 radii from the center, the field has dropped off to $\frac{1}{8}$ its value at the center.

EVALUATE: We can check our answer in part (a) by first finding the magnetic moment and then substituting the result into Eq. (28.18):

$$\mu = NI\pi a^2 = (100)(5.0\,\text{A})\pi(0.60\,\text{m})^2 = 5.7 \times 10^2\,\text{A}\cdot\text{m}^2$$

$$B_x = \frac{(4\pi \times 10^{-7}\,\text{T}\cdot\text{m/A})(5.7 \times 10^2\,\text{A}\cdot\text{m}^2)}{2\pi[(0.80\,\text{m})^2 + (0.60\,\text{m})^2]^{3/2}} = 1.1 \times 10^{-4}\,\text{T}$$

The magnetic moment μ is relatively large, yet this is a rather small field, comparable in magnitude to the earth's magnetic field. This example may give you some idea of the difficulty of producing a field of 1 T or more.

Test Your Understanding of Section 28.5   Figure 28.12 shows the magnetic field $d\vec{B}$ produced at point P by a segment $d\vec{l}$ that lies on the positive y-axis (at the top of the loop). This field has components $dB_x > 0$, $dB_y > 0$, $dB_z = 0$. (a) What are the signs of the components of the field $d\vec{B}$ produced at P by a segment $d\vec{l}$ on the negative y-axis (at the bottom of the loop)? (i) $dB_x > 0$, $dB_y > 0$, $dB_z = 0$; (ii) $dB_x > 0$, $dB_y < 0$, $dB_z = 0$; (iii) $dB_x < 0$, $dB_y > 0$, $dB_z = 0$; (iv) $dB_x < 0$, $dB_y < 0$, $dB_z = 0$; (v) none of these. (b) What are the signs of the components of the field $d\vec{B}$ produced at P by a segment $d\vec{l}$ on the negative z-axis (at the right-hand side of the loop)? (i) $dB_x > 0$, $dB_y > 0$, $dB_z = 0$; (ii) $dB_x > 0$, $dB_y < 0$, $dB_z = 0$; (iii) $dB_x < 0$, $dB_y > 0$, $dB_z = 0$; (iv) $dB_x < 0$, $dB_y < 0$, $dB_z = 0$; (v) none of these. ∎

28.6 Ampere's Law

So far our calculations of the magnetic field due to a current have involved finding the infinitesimal field $d\vec{B}$ due to a current element and then summing all the $d\vec{B}$'s to find the total field. This approach is directly analogous to our *electric-field* calculations in Chapter 21.

28.16 Three integration paths for the line integral of $\vec{B}$ in the vicinity of a long, straight conductor carrying current I *out* of the plane of the page (as indicated by the circle with a dot). The conductor is seen end-on.

(a) Integration path is a circle centered on the conductor; integration goes around the circle counterclockwise.

Result: $\oint \vec{B} \cdot d\vec{l} = \mu_0 I$

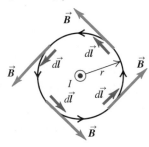

(b) Same integration path as in (a), but integration goes around the circle clockwise.

Result: $\oint \vec{B} \cdot d\vec{l} = -\mu_0 I$

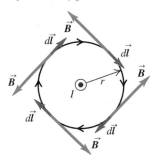

(c) An integration path that does not enclose the conductor.

Result: $\oint \vec{B} \cdot dl = 0$

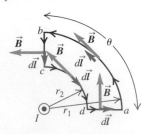

For the electric-field problem we found that in situations with a highly symmetric charge distribution, it was often easier to use Gauss's law to find $\vec{E}$. There is likewise a law that allows us to more easily find the *magnetic* fields caused by highly symmetric *current* distributions. But the law that allows us to do this, called *Ampere's law,* is rather different in character from Gauss's law.

Gauss's law for electric fields involves the flux of $\vec{E}$ through a closed surface; it states that this flux is equal to the total charge enclosed within the surface, divided by the constant ϵ_0. Thus this law relates electric fields and charge distributions. By contrast, Gauss's law for *magnetic* fields, Eq. (28.10), is *not* a relationship between magnetic fields and current distributions; it states that the flux of $\vec{B}$ through *any* closed surface is always zero, whether or not there are currents within the surface. So Gauss's law for $\vec{B}$ can't be used to determine the magnetic field produced by a particular current distribution.

Ampere's law is formulated not in terms of magnetic flux, but rather in terms of the *line integral* of $\vec{B}$ around a closed path, denoted by

$$\oint \vec{B} \cdot d\vec{l}$$

We used line integrals to define work in Chapter 6 and to calculate electric potential in Chapter 23. To evaluate this integral, we divide the path into infinitesimal segments $d\vec{l}$, calculate the scalar product of $\vec{B} \cdot d\vec{l}$ for each segment, and sum these products. In general, $\vec{B}$ varies from point to point, and we must use the value of $\vec{B}$ at the location of each $d\vec{l}$. An alternative notation is $\oint B_{\parallel}\, dl$, where $B_{\parallel}$ is the component of $\vec{B}$ parallel to $d\vec{l}$ at each point. The circle on the integral sign indicates that this integral is always computed for a *closed* path, one whose beginning and end points are the same.

Ampere's Law for a Long, Straight Conductor

To introduce the basic idea of Ampere's law, let's consider again the magnetic field caused by a long, straight conductor carrying a current I. We found in Section 28.3 that the field at a distance r from the conductor has magnitude

$$B = \frac{\mu_0 I}{2\pi r}$$

and that the magnetic field lines are circles centered on the conductor. Let's take the line integral of $\vec{B}$ around one such circle with radius r, as in Figure 28.16a. At every point on the circle, $\vec{B}$ and $d\vec{l}$ are parallel, and so $\vec{B} \cdot d\vec{l} = B\, dl$; since r is constant around the circle, B is constant as well. Alternatively, we can say that $B_{\parallel}$ is constant and equal to B at every point on the circle. Hence we can take B outside of the integral. The remaining integral $\oint dl$ is just the circumference of the circle, so

$$\oint \vec{B} \cdot d\vec{l} = \oint B_{\parallel}\, dl = B \oint dl = \frac{\mu_0 I}{2\pi r}(2\pi r) = \mu_0 I$$

The line integral is thus independent of the radius of the circle and is equal to μ_0 multiplied by the current passing through the area bounded by the circle.

In Fig. 28.16b the situation is the same, but the integration path now goes around the circle in the opposite direction. Now $\vec{B}$ and $d\vec{l}$ are antiparallel, so $\vec{B} \cdot d\vec{l} = -B\, dl$ and the line integral equals $-\mu_0 I$. We get the same result if the integration path is the same as in Fig. 28.16a, but the direction of the current is reversed. Thus the line integral $\oint \vec{B} \cdot d\vec{l}$ equals μ_0 multiplied by the current passing through the area bounded by the integration path, with a positive or negative sign depending on the direction of the current relative to the direction of integration.

There's a simple rule for the sign of the current; you won't be surprised to learn that it uses your right hand. Curl the fingers of your right hand around the integration path so that they curl in the direction of integration (that is, the direction that you use to evaluate $\oint \vec{B} \cdot d\vec{l}$). Then your right thumb indicates the positive current direction. Currents that pass through the integration path in this direction are positive; those in the opposite direction are negative. Using this rule, you should be able to convince yourself that the current is positive in Fig. 28.16a and negative in Fig. 28.16b. Here's another way to say the same thing: Looking at the surface bounded by the integration path, integrate counterclockwise around the path as in Fig. 28.16a. Currents moving toward you through the surface are positive, and those going away from you are negative.

An integration path that does *not* enclose the conductor is used in Fig. 28.16c. Along the circular arc ab of radius r_1, $\vec{B}$ and $d\vec{l}$ are parallel, and $B_\parallel = B_1 = \mu_0 I/2\pi r_1$; along the circular arc cd of radius r_2, $\vec{B}$ and $d\vec{l}$ are antiparallel and $B_\parallel = -B_2 = -\mu_0 I/2\pi r_2$. The $\vec{B}$ field is perpendicular to $d\vec{l}$ at each point on the straight sections bc and da, so $B_\parallel = 0$ and these sections contribute zero to the line integral. The total line integral is then

$$\oint \vec{B} \cdot d\vec{l} = \oint B_\parallel \, dl = B_1 \int_a^b dl + (0) \int_b^c dl + (-B_2) \int_c^d dl + (0) \int_d^a dl$$

$$= \frac{\mu_0 I}{2\pi r_1}(r_1\theta) + 0 - \frac{\mu_0 I}{2\pi r_2}(r_2\theta) + 0 = 0$$

The magnitude of $\vec{B}$ is greater on arc cd than on arc ab, but the arc length is less, so the contributions from the two arcs exactly cancel. Even though there is a magnetic field everywhere along the integration path, the line integral $\oint \vec{B} \cdot d\vec{l}$ is zero if there is no current passing through the area bounded by the path.

We can also derive these results for more general integration paths, such as the one in Figure 28.17. At the position of the line element $d\vec{l}$, the angle between $d\vec{l}$ and $\vec{B}$ is ϕ, and

$$\vec{B} \cdot d\vec{l} = B \, dl \cos\phi$$

From the figure, $dl\cos\phi = r \, d\theta$, where $d\theta$ is the angle subtended by $d\vec{l}$ at the position of the conductor and r is the distance of $d\vec{l}$ from the conductor. Thus

$$\oint \vec{B} \cdot d\vec{l} = \oint \frac{\mu_0 I}{2\pi r}(r \, d\theta) = \frac{\mu_0 I}{2\pi} \oint d\theta$$

But $\oint d\theta$ is just equal to 2π, the total angle swept out by the radial line from the conductor to $d\vec{l}$ during a complete trip around the path. So we get

$$\oint \vec{B} \cdot d\vec{l} = \mu_0 I \qquad (28.19)$$

This result doesn't depend on the shape of the path or on the position of the wire inside it. If the current in the wire is opposite to that shown, the integral has the opposite sign. But if the path doesn't enclose the wire (Fig. 28.17b), then the net change in θ during the trip around the integration path is zero; $\oint d\theta$ is zero instead of 2π and the line integral is zero.

Ampere's Law: General Statement

Equation (28.19) is almost, but not quite, the general statement of Ampere's law. To generalize it even further, suppose *several* long, straight conductors pass through the surface bounded by the integration path. The total magnetic field $\vec{B}$ at any point on the path is the vector sum of the fields produced by the individual conductors. Thus the line integral of the total $\vec{B}$ equals μ_0 times the *algebraic sum* of the currents. In calculating this sum, we use the sign rule for currents described above. If the integration path does not enclose a particular wire, the

28.17 (a) A more general integration path for the line integral of $\vec{B}$ around a long, straight conductor carrying current I *out of* the plane of the page. The conductor is seen end-on. (b) A more general integration path that does not enclose the conductor.

(a)

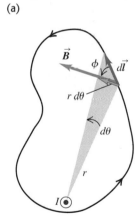

(b)

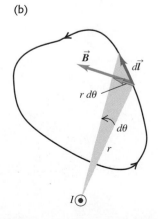

28.18 Ampere's law.

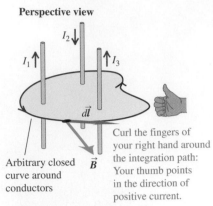

Perspective view

Curl the fingers of your right hand around the integration path: Your thumb points in the direction of positive current.

Arbitrary closed curve around conductors

Top view

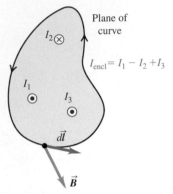

Plane of curve

$$I_{encl} = I_1 - I_2 + I_3$$

Ampere's law: If we calculate the line integral of the magnetic field around a closed curve, the result equals μ_0 times the total enclosed current: $\oint \vec{B} \cdot d\vec{l} = \mu_0 I_{encl}$

28.19 Two long, straight conductors carrying equal currents in opposite directions. The conductors are seen end-on, and the integration path is counterclockwise. The line integral $\oint \vec{B} \cdot d\vec{l}$ gets zero contribution from the upper and lower segments, a positive contribution from the left segment, and a negative contribution from the right segment; the net integral is zero.

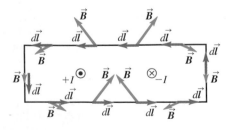

line integral of the $\vec{B}$ field of that wire is zero, because the angle θ for that wire sweeps through a net change of zero rather than 2π during the integration. Any conductors present that are not enclosed by a particular path may still contribute to the value of $\vec{B}$ at every point, but the *line integrals* of their fields around the path are zero.

Thus we can replace I in Eq. (28.19) with I_{encl}, the algebraic sum of the currents *enclosed* or *linked* by the integration path, with the sum evaluated by using the sign rule just described (Fig. 28.18). Our statement of **Ampere's law** is then

$$\oint \vec{B} \cdot d\vec{l} = \mu_0 I_{encl} \qquad \text{(Ampere's law)} \qquad (28.20)$$

While we have derived Ampere's law only for the special case of the field of several long, straight, parallel conductors, Eq. (28.20) is in fact valid for conductors and paths of *any* shape. The general derivation is no different in principle from what we have presented, but the geometry is more complicated.

If $\oint \vec{B} \cdot d\vec{l} = 0$, it *does not* necessarily mean that $\vec{B} = 0$ everywhere along the path, only that the total current through an area bounded by the path is zero. In Figs. 28.16c and 28.17b, the integration paths enclose no current at all; in Fig. 28.19 there are positive and negative currents of equal magnitude through the area enclosed by the path. In both cases, $I_{encl} = 0$ and the line integral is zero.

CAUTION **Line integrals of electric and magnetic fields** In Chapter 23 we saw that the line integral of the electrostatic field $\vec{E}$ around any closed path is equal to zero; this is a statement that the electrostatic force $\vec{F} = q\vec{E}$ on a point charge q is conservative, so this force does zero work on a charge that moves around a closed path that returns to the starting point. You might think that the value of the line integral $\oint \vec{B} \cdot d\vec{l}$ is similarly related to the question of whether the *magnetic* force is conservative. This isn't the case at all. Remember that the magnetic force $\vec{F} = q\vec{v} \times \vec{B}$ on a moving charged particle is always *perpendicular* to $\vec{B}$, so $\oint \vec{B} \cdot d\vec{l}$ is *not* related to the work done by the magnetic force; as stated in Ampere's law, this integral is related only to the total current through a surface bounded by the integration path. In fact, the magnetic force on a moving particle is *not* conservative. A conservative force depends only on the position of the body on which the force is exerted, but the magnetic force on a moving charged particle also depends on the *velocity* of the particle. ∎

In the form we have stated it, Ampere's law turns out to be valid only if the currents are steady and if no magnetic materials or time-varying electric fields are present. In Chapter 29 we will see how to generalize Ampere's law for time-varying fields.

Test Your Understanding of Section 28.6 The figure below shows magnetic field lines through the center of a permanent magnet. The magnet is not connected to a source of emf. One of the field lines is colored red. What can you conclude about the currents inside the permanent magnet within the region enclosed by this field line? (i) There are no currents inside the magnet; (ii) there are currents directed out of the plane of the page; (iii) there are currents directed into the plane of the page; (iv) not enough information given to decide.

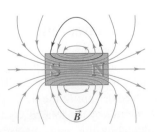

28.7 Applications of Ampere's Law

Ampere's law is useful when we can exploit the symmetry of a situation to evaluate the line integral of $\vec{B}$. Several examples are given below. Problem-Solving Strategy 28.2 is directly analogous to Problem Solving Strategy 22.1 (Section 22.4) for applications of Gauss's law; we suggest you review that strategy now and compare the two methods.

Problem-Solving Strategy 28.2 — Ampere's Law

IDENTIFY *the relevant concepts:* Like Gauss's law for electricity, Ampere's law is always true but is most useful in situations where the magnetic field pattern is highly symmetrical. In such situations you can use Ampere's law to find a relationship between the magnetic field as a function of position and the current that generates the field.

SET UP *the problem* using the following steps:

1. Select the integration path you will use with Ampere's law. If you want to determine the magnetic field at a certain point, then the path must pass through that point. The integration path doesn't have to be any actual physical boundary. Usually it is a purely geometric curve; it may be in empty space, embedded in a solid body, or some of each. The integration path has to have enough *symmetry* to make evaluation of the integral possible. If the problem itself has cylindrical symmetry, the integration path will usually be a circle coaxial with the cylinder axis.

2. Determine the target variable(s). Usually this will be the magnitude of the $\vec{B}$ field as a function of position.

EXECUTE *the solution* as follows:

1. Carry out the integral $\oint \vec{B} \cdot d\vec{l}$ along your chosen integration path. If $\vec{B}$ is tangent to all or some portion of the integration path and has the same magnitude B at every point, then its line integral equals B multiplied by the length of that portion of the path. If $\vec{B}$ is perpendicular to some portion of the path, that portion makes no contribution to the integral.

2. In the integral $\oint \vec{B} \cdot d\vec{l}$, $\vec{B}$ is always the *total* magnetic field at each point on the path. This field can be caused partly by currents enclosed by the path and partly by currents outside the path. If *no* net current is enclosed by the path, the field at points on the path need not be zero, but the integral $\oint \vec{B} \cdot d\vec{l}$ is always zero.

3. Determine the current I_{encl} enclosed by the integration path. The sign of this current is given by a right-hand rule. Curl the fingers of your right hand so that they follow the integration path in the direction that you carry out the integration. Your right thumb then points in the direction of positive current. If $\vec{B}$ is tangent to the integration at all points along the path and I_{encl} is positive, then the direction of $\vec{B}$ is the same as the direction of the integration path; if instead I_{encl} is negative, $\vec{B}$ is in the direction opposite to that of the integration.

4. Use Ampere's law $\oint \vec{B} \cdot d\vec{l} = \mu_0 I$ to solve for the target variable.

EVALUATE *your answer:* If your result is an expression for the field magnitude as a function of position, you can check it by examining how the expression behaves in different limits.

Example 28.7 — Field of a long, straight, current-carrying conductor

In Section 28.6 we derived Ampere's law using Eq. (28.9) for the field of a long, straight, current-carrying conductor. Reverse this process, and use Ampere's law to find the magnitude *and* direction of $\vec{B}$ for this situation.

SOLUTION

IDENTIFY: This situation has cylindrical symmetry, so we can use Ampere's law to find the magnetic field at all points a distance r from the conductor

SET UP: We take as our integration path a circle with radius r centered on the conductor and in a plane perpendicular to it, as in Fig. 28.16a (Section 28.6). At each point, $\vec{B}$ is tangent to this circle.

EXECUTE: With our choice of integration path, Ampere's law [Eq. (28.20)] becomes

$$\oint \vec{B} \cdot d\vec{l} = \oint B_{\parallel}\, dl = B(2\pi r) = \mu_0 I$$

Equation (28.9), $B = \mu_0 I / 2\pi r$, follows immediately.

Ampere's law determines the direction of $\vec{B}$ as well as its magnitude. Since we go around the integration path in the counterclockwise direction, the positive direction for current is out of the plane of Fig. 28.16a; this is the same as the actual current direction in the figure, so I is positive and the integral $\oint \vec{B} \cdot d\vec{l}$ is also positive. Since the $d\vec{l}$'s run counterclockwise, the direction of $\vec{B}$ must be counterclockwise as well, as shown in Fig. 28.16a.

EVALUATE: Our results are consistent with those in Section 28.6, as they must be.

Example 28.8 Field inside a long cylindrical conductor

A cylindrical conductor with radius R carries a current I. (Fig. 28.20). The current is uniformly distributed over the cross-sectional area of the conductor. Find the magnetic field as a function of the distance r from the conductor axis for points both inside $(r < R)$ and outside $(r > R)$ the conductor.

SOLUTION

IDENTIFY: Once again we have a current distribution with cylindrical symmetry. As for a long, straight, skinny current-carrying conductor, the magnetic field lines must be circles concentric with the conductor axis.

SET UP: To find the magnetic field *inside* the conductor, we take as our integration path a circle with radius $r < R$ as shown in Fig. 28.20. *Outside* the conductor, we again use a circle but with a radius $r > R$. In either case, the integration path takes advantage of the circular symmetry of the magnetic field pattern.

EXECUTE: Inside the conductor, $\vec{B}$ has the same magnitude at every point on the circular integration path and is tangent to the path. Thus the magnitude of the line integral is simply $B(2\pi r)$. If we use the right-hand rule for determining the sign of the current, the current through the brown area enclosed by the path is positive; hence $\vec{B}$ points in the same direction as the integration path, as shown. To find the current I_{encl} enclosed by the path, note that the current density (current per unit area) is $J = I/\pi R^2$, so $I_{encl} = J(\pi r^2) = Ir^2/R^2$. Finally, Ampere's law gives

$$B(2\pi r) = \mu_0 \frac{Ir^2}{R^2}$$

$$B = \frac{\mu_0 I}{2\pi} \frac{r}{R^2} \qquad \begin{array}{l}\text{(inside the conductor,} \\ r < R)\end{array} \qquad (28.21)$$

For the circular integration path outside the conductor $(r > R)$, the same symmetry arguments apply and the magnitude of $\oint \vec{B} \cdot d\vec{l}$ is again $B(2\pi r)$. The right-hand rule gives the direction of $\vec{B}$ as shown in Fig. 28.20. For this path, $I_{encl} = I$, the total current in the conductor. Applying Ampere's law gives the same equation as in Example 28.7, with the same result for B:

$$B = \frac{\mu_0 I}{2\pi r} \qquad \begin{array}{l}\text{(outside the conductor,} \\ r > R)\end{array} \qquad (28.22)$$

Outside the conductor, the magnetic field is the same as that of a long, straight conductor carrying current I, independent of the

28.20 To find the magnetic field at radius $r < R$, we apply Ampere's law to the circle enclosing the red area. The current through the red area is $(r^2/R^2)I$. To find the magnetic field at radius $r > R$, we apply Ampere's law to the circle enclosing the entire conductor.

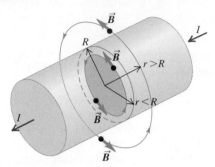

radius R over which the current is distributed. Indeed, the magnetic field outside *any* cylindrically symmetric current distribution is the same as if the entire current were concentrated along the axis of the distribution. This is analogous to the results of Examples 22.5 and 22.9 (Section 22.4), in which we found that the *electric* field outside a spherically symmetric *charged* body is the same as though the entire charge were concentrated at the center.

EVALUATE: Note that at the surface of the conductor $(r = R)$, Eq. (28.21) for $r < R$ and Eq. (28.22) for $r > R$ agree (as they must). Figure 28.21 shows a graph of B as a function of r, both inside and outside the conductor.

28.21 Magnitude of the magnetic field inside and outside a long, straight cylindrical conductor with radius R carrying a current I.

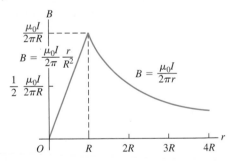

Example 28.9 Field of a solenoid

A solenoid consists of a helical winding of wire on a cylinder, usually circular in cross section. There can be hundreds or thousands of closely spaced turns, each of which can be regarded as a circular loop. There may be several layers of windings. For simplicity, Fig. 28.22 shows a solenoid with only a few turns. All turns carry the same current I, and the total $\vec{B}$ field at every point is the vector sum of the fields caused by the individual turns. The figure shows field lines in the *xy*- and *xz*-planes. We draw a set of field lines that are uniformly spaced at the center of the solenoid. Exact calculations show that for a long, closely wound solenoid, half of these field lines emerge from the ends and half "leak out" through the windings between the center and the end.

The field lines near the center of the solenoid are approximately parallel, indicating a nearly uniform $\vec{B}$; outside the solenoid, the

28.22 Magnetic field lines produced by the current in a solenoid. For clarity, only a few turns are shown.

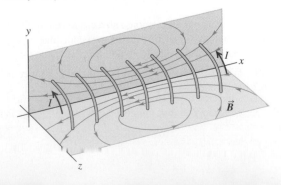

field lines are spread apart, and the magnetic field is weak. If the solenoid is long in comparison with its cross-sectional diameter and the coils are tightly wound, the *internal* field near the midpoint of the solenoid's length is very nearly uniform over the cross section and parallel to the axis, and the *external* field near the midpoint is very small.

Use Ampere's law to find the field at or near the center of such a long solenoid. The solenoid has n turns of wire per unit length and carries a current I.

SOLUTION

IDENTIFY: This is a highly symmetrical situation, with a uniform $\vec{B}$ field inside the solenoid and zero field outside. Hence we can use Ampere's law to find the field inside by using an appropriate choice of integration path.

SET UP: Fig. 28.23 shows the situation and our integration path, rectangle *abcd*. Side *ab*, with length L, is parallel to the axis of the solenoid. Sides *bc* and *da* are taken to be very long so that side *cd* is far from the solenoid; then the field at side *cd* is negligibly small.

EXECUTE: By symmetry, the $\vec{B}$ field along side *ab* is parallel to this side and is constant. In carrying out the Ampere's-law integration, we go along side *ab* in the same direction as $\vec{B}$. So for this side, $B_\parallel = +B$ and

$$\int_a^b \vec{B} \cdot d\vec{l} = BL$$

Along sides *bc* and *da*, $B_\parallel = 0$ because $\vec{B}$ is perpendicular to these sides; along side *cd*, $B_\parallel = 0$ because $\vec{B} = 0$. The integral $\oint \vec{B} \cdot d\vec{l}$ around the entire closed path therefore reduces to BL.

28.23 Our sketch for this problem.

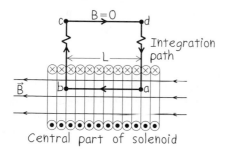

The number of turns in length L is nL. Each of these turns passes once through the rectangle *abcd* and carries a current I, where I is the current in the windings. The total current enclosed by the rectangle is then $I_{encl} = nLI$. From Ampere's law, since the integral $\oint \vec{B} \cdot d\vec{l}$ is positive, I_{encl} must be positive as well; hence the current passing through the surface bounded by the integration path must be in the direction shown in Fig. 28.23. Ampere's law then gives the magnitude B:

$$BL = \mu_0 nLI$$
$$B = \mu_0 nI \qquad \text{(solenoid)} \qquad (28.23)$$

Side *ab* need not lie on the axis of the solenoid, so this calculation also proves that the field is uniform over the entire cross section at the center of the solenoid's length.

EVALUATE: Note that the *direction* of $\vec{B}$ inside the solenoid is in the same direction as the solenoid's vector magnetic moment $\vec{\mu}$. This is the same result that we found in Section 28.5 for a single current-carrying loop.

For points along the axis, the field is strongest at the center of the solenoid and drops off near the ends. For a solenoid that is very long in comparison to its diameter, the field at each end is exactly half as strong as the field at the center. For a short, fat solenoid the relationship is more complicated. Fig. 28.24 shows a graph of B as a function of x for points on the axis of a short solenoid.

28.24 Magnitude of the magnetic field at points along the axis of a solenoid with length $4a$, equal to four times its radius a. The field magnitude at each end is about half its value at the center. (Compare with Fig. 28.14 for the field of N circular loops.)

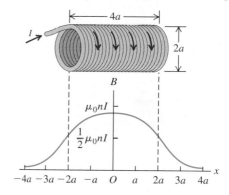

Example 28.10 | Field of a toroidal solenoid

Figure 28.25a shows a doughnut-shaped **toroidal solenoid,** also called a *toroid,* wound with N turns of wire carrying a current I. In a practical version the turns would be more closely spaced than they are in the figure. Find the magnetic field at all points.

SOLUTION

IDENTIFY: The flow of current around the toroid's circumference produces a magnetic field component perpendicular to the plane of the figure, just as for the current loop discussed in Section 28.5. But if the coils are very tightly wound, we can consider them as circular loops that carry current between the inner and outer radii of the toroidal solenoid; the flow of current around the toroid's circumference is then negligible, and the perpendicular component of $\vec{B}$ is likewise negligible. In this idealized approximation the circular symmetry of the situation tells us that the

magnetic field lines must be circles concentric with the axis of the toroid.

SET UP: To take advantage of this symmetry in finding the field, we choose circular integration paths for use with Ampere's law. Three such paths are shown as black lines in Fig. 28.25b.

EXECUTE: First consider integration path 1 in Fig. 28.25b. If the toroidal solenoid produces any field at all in this region, it must be *tangent* to the path at all points, and $\oint \vec{B} \cdot d\vec{l}$ will equal the product of B and the circumference $l = 2\pi r$ of the path. But the total current enclosed by the path is zero, so from Ampere's law the field $\vec{B}$ must be zero everywhere on this path.

Similarly, if the toroidal solenoid produces any field along path 3, it must also be tangent to the path at all points. Each turn of the winding passes *twice* through the area bounded by this path,

Continued

28.25 (a) A toroidal solenoid. For clarity, only a few turns of the winding are shown. (b) Integration paths (black circles) used to compute the magnetic field $\vec{B}$ set up by the current (shown as dots and crosses).

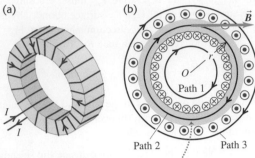

(a)   (b)

$\vec{B}$

O

r

Path 1

Path 2   Path 3

The magnetic field is confined almost entirely to the space enclosed by the windings (in blue).

carrying equal currents in opposite directions. The *net* current I_{encl} enclosed within this area is therefore zero, and hence $\vec{B} = 0$ at all points of the path. Conclusion: *The field of an idealized toroidal solenoid is confined completely to the space enclosed by the windings.* We can think of such an idealized toroidal solenoid as a tightly wound solenoid that has been bent into a circle.

Finally, we consider path 2, a circle with radius r. Again by symmetry we expect the $\vec{B}$ field to be tangent to the path, and $\oint \vec{B} \cdot d\vec{l}$ equals $2\pi r B$. Each turn of the winding passes *once* through the area bounded by path 2. The total current enclosed by the path is $I_{encl} = NI$, where N is the total number of turns in the winding; I_{encl} is

positive for the clockwise direction of integration in Fig. 28.25b, so $\vec{B}$ is in the direction shown. Then, from Ampere's law,

$$2\pi r B = \mu_0 NI$$

$$B = \frac{\mu_0 NI}{2\pi r} \qquad \text{(toroidal solenoid)} \qquad (28.24)$$

EVALUATE: The magnetic field is *not* uniform over a cross section of the core, because the radius r is larger at the outer side of the section than at the inner side. However, if the radial thickness of the core is small in comparison to r, the field varies only slightly across a section. In that case, considering that $2\pi r$ is the circumferential length of the toroid and that $N/2\pi r$ is the number of turns per unit length n, the field may be written as

$$B = \mu_0 nI$$

just as it is at the center of a long, *straight* solenoid.

In a real toroidal solenoid the turns are not precisely circular loops but rather segments of a bent helix. As a result, the field outside is not strictly zero. To estimate its magnitude, we imagine Fig. 28.25a as being roughly equivalent, for points outside the torus, to a circular loop with a single turn and radius r. Then we can use Eq. (28.17) to show that the field at the *center* of the torus is smaller than the field inside by approximately a factor of N/π.

The equations we have derived for the field in a closely wound straight or toroidal solenoid are strictly correct only for windings in *vacuum*. For most practical purposes, however, they can be used for windings in air or on a core of any nonmagnetic, nonsuperconducting material. In the next section we will show how they are modified if the core is a magnetic material.

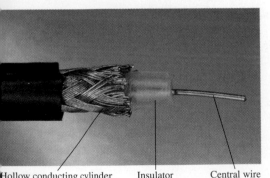

Hollow conducting cylinder   Insulator   Central wire

Test Your Understanding of Section 28.7   Consider a conducting wire that runs along the central axis of a hollow conducting cylinder. Such an arrangement, called a *coaxial cable,* has many applications in telecommunications. (The cable that connects a television set to a local cable provider is an example of a coaxial cable.) In such a cable a current I runs in one direction along the hollow conducting cylinder and is spread uniformly over the cylinder's cross-sectional area. An equal current runs in the opposite direction along the central wire. How does the magnitude B of the magnetic field outside such a cable depend on the distance r from the central axis of the cable? (i) B is proportional to $1/r$; (ii) B is proportional to $1/r^2$; (iii) B is zero at all points outside the cable.

*28.8 Magnetic Materials

In discussing how currents cause magnetic fields, we have assumed that the conductors are surrounded by vacuum. But the coils in transformers, motors, generators, and electromagnets nearly always have iron cores to increase the magnetic field and confine it to desired regions. Permanent magnets, magnetic recording tapes, and computer disks depend directly on the magnetic properties of materials; when you store information on a computer disk, you are actually setting up an array of microscopic permanent magnets on the disk. So it is worthwhile to examine some aspects of the magnetic properties of materials. After describing the atomic origins of magnetic properties, we will discuss three broad classes of magnetic behavior that occur in materials; these are called *paramagnetism, diamagnetism,* and *ferromagnetism.*

The Bohr Magneton

As we discussed briefly in Section 27.7, the atoms that make up all matter contain moving electrons, and these electrons form microscopic current loops that produce magnetic fields of their own. In many materials these currents are randomly oriented and cause no net magnetic field. But in some materials an external field (a field produced by currents outside the material) can cause these loops to become oriented preferentially with the field, so their magnetic fields *add* to the external field. We then say that the material is *magnetized.*

Let's look at how these microscopic currents come about. Figure 28.26 shows a primitive model of an electron in an atom. We picture the electron (mass m, charge $-e$) as moving in a circular orbit with radius r and speed v. This moving charge is equivalent to a current loop. In Section 27.7 we found that a current loop with area A and current I has a magnetic dipole moment μ given by $\mu = IA$; for the orbiting electron the area of the loop is $A = \pi r^2$. To find the current associated with the electron, we note that the orbital period T (the time for the electron to make one complete orbit) is the orbit circumference divided by the electron speed: $T = 2\pi r/v$. The equivalent current I is the total charge passing any point on the orbit per unit time, which is just the magnitude e of the electron charge divided by the orbital period T:

$$I = \frac{e}{T} = \frac{ev}{2\pi r}$$

The magnetic moment $\mu = IA$ is then

$$\mu = \frac{ev}{2\pi r}(\pi r^2) = \frac{evr}{2} \tag{28.25}$$

It is useful to express μ in terms of the *angular momentum L* of the electron. For a particle moving in a circular path, the magnitude of angular momentum equals the magnitude of momentum mv multiplied by the radius r, that is, $L = mvr$ (see Section 10.5). Comparing this with Eq. (28.25), we can write

$$\mu = \frac{e}{2m}L \tag{28.26}$$

Equation (28.26) is useful in this discussion because atomic angular momentum is *quantized;* its component in a particular direction is always an integer multiple of $h/2\pi$, where h is a fundamental physical constant called *Planck's constant.* (We will discuss the quantization of angular momentum in more detail in Chapter 41.) The numerical value of h is

$$h = 6.626 \times 10^{-34} \text{ J} \cdot \text{s}$$

The quantity $h/2\pi$ thus represents a fundamental unit of angular momentum in atomic systems, just as e is a fundamental unit of charge. Associated with the quantization of $\vec{L}$ is a fundamental uncertainty in the *direction* of $\vec{L}$ and therefore of $\vec{\mu}$. In the following discussion, when we speak of the magnitude of a magnetic moment, a more precise statement would be "maximum component in a given direction." Thus, to say that a magnetic moment $\vec{\mu}$ is aligned with a magnetic field $\vec{B}$ really means that $\vec{\mu}$ has its maximum possible component in the direction of $\vec{B}$; such components are always quantized.

Equation (28.26) shows that associated with the fundamental unit of angular momentum is a corresponding fundamental unit of magnetic moment. If $L = h/2\pi$, then

$$\mu = \frac{e}{2m}\left(\frac{h}{2\pi}\right) = \frac{eh}{4\pi m} \tag{28.27}$$

This quantity is called the **Bohr magneton,** denoted by μ_B. Its numerical value is

$$\mu_\text{B} = 9.274 \times 10^{-24} \text{ A} \cdot \text{m}^2 = 9.274 \times 10^{-24} \text{ J/T}$$

You should verify that these two sets of units are consistent. The second set is useful when we compute the potential energy $U = -\vec{\mu} \cdot \vec{B}$ for a magnetic moment in a magnetic field.

Electrons also have an intrinsic angular momentum, called *spin,* that is not related to orbital motion but that can be pictured in a classical model as spinning

28.26 An electron moving with speed v in a circular orbit of radius r has an angular momentum $\vec{L}$ and an oppositely directed orbital magnetic dipole moment $\vec{\mu}$. It also has a spin angular momentum and an oppositely directed spin magnetic dipole moment.

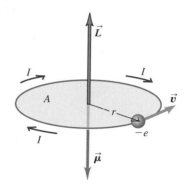

on an axis. This angular momentum also has an associated magnetic moment, and its magnitude turns out to be almost exactly one Bohr magneton. (Effects having to do with quantization of the electromagnetic field cause the spin magnetic moment to be about $1.001 \, \mu_B$.)

Paramagnetism

In an atom, most of the various orbital and spin magnetic moments of the electrons add up to zero. However, in some cases the atom has a net magnetic moment that is of the order of μ_B. When such a material is placed in a magnetic field, the field exerts a torque on each magnetic moment, as given by Eq. (27.26): $\vec{\tau} = \vec{\mu} \times \vec{B}$. These torques tend to align the magnetic moments with the field, the position of minimum potential energy, as we discussed in Section 27.7. In this position, the directions of the current loops are such as to *add* to the externally applied magnetic field.

We saw in Section 28.5 that the $\vec{B}$ field produced by a current loop is proportional to the loop's magnetic dipole moment. In the same way, the additional $\vec{B}$ field produced by microscopic electron current loops is proportional to the total magnetic moment $\vec{\mu}_{\text{total}}$ per unit volume V in the material. We call this vector quantity the **magnetization** of the material, denoted by $\vec{M}$:

$$\vec{M} = \frac{\vec{\mu}_{\text{total}}}{V} \tag{28.28}$$

The additional magnetic field due to magnetization of the material turns out to be equal simply to $\mu_0 \vec{M}$, where μ_0 is the same constant that appears in the law of Biot and Savart and Ampere's law. When such a material completely surrounds a current-carrying conductor, the total magnetic field $\vec{B}$ in the material is

$$\vec{B} = \vec{B}_0 + \mu_0 \vec{M} \tag{28.29}$$

where $\vec{B}_0$ is the field caused by the current in the conductor.

To check that the units in Eq. (28.29) are consistent, note that magnetization $\vec{M}$ is magnetic moment per unit volume. The units of magnetic moment are current times area $(A \cdot m^2)$, so the units of magnetization are $(A \cdot m^2)/m^3 = A/m$. From Section 28.1, the units of the constant μ_0 are $T \cdot m/A$. So the units of $\mu_0 \vec{M}$ are the same as the units of $\vec{B}$: $(T \cdot m/A)(A/m) = T$.

A material showing the behavior just described is said to be **paramagnetic.** The result is that the magnetic field at any point in such a material is greater by a dimensionless factor K_m, called the **relative permeability** of the material, than it would be if the material were replaced by vacuum. The value of K_m is different for different materials; for common paramagnetic solids and liquids at room temperature, K_m typically ranges from 1.00001 to 1.003.

All of the equations in this chapter that relate magnetic fields to their sources can be adapted to the situation in which the current-carrying conductor is embedded in a paramagnetic material. All that need be done is to replace μ_0 by $K_m \mu_0$. This product is usually denoted as μ and is called the **permeability** of the material:

$$\mu = K_m \mu_0 \tag{28.30}$$

CAUTION **Two meanings of the symbol μ** Equation (28.30) involves some really dangerous notation because we have also used μ for magnetic dipole moment. It's customary to use μ for both quantities, but beware: From now on, every time you see a μ, make sure you know whether it is permeability or magnetic moment. You can usually tell from the context. ▮

The amount by which the relative permeability differs from unity is called the **magnetic susceptibility,** denoted by χ_m:

$$\chi_m = K_m - 1 \tag{28.31}$$

Both K_m and χ_m are dimensionless quantities. Values of magnetic susceptibility for several materials are given in Table 28.1. For example, for aluminum, $\chi_m = 2.2 \times 10^{-5}$ and $K_m = 1.000022$. The first group of materials in the table are paramagnetic; we'll discuss the second group of materials, which are called *diamagnetic,* very shortly.

The tendency of atomic magnetic moments to align themselves parallel to the magnetic field (where the potential energy is minimum) is opposed by random thermal motion, which tends to randomize their orientations. For this reason, paramagnetic susceptibility always decreases with increasing temperature. In many cases it is inversely proportional to the absolute temperature T, and the magnetization M can be expressed as

$$M = C\frac{B}{T} \tag{28.32}$$

This relationship is called *Curie's law,* after its discoverer, Pierre Curie (1859–1906). The quantity C is a constant, different for different materials, called the *Curie constant.*

As we described in Section 27.7, a body with atomic magnetic dipoles is attracted to the poles of a magnet. In most paramagnetic substances this attraction is very weak due to thermal randomization of the atomic magnetic moments. That's why a magnet can't be used to pick up objects made of aluminum (a paramagnetic substance). But at very low temperatures the thermal effects are reduced, the magnetization increases in accordance with Curie's law, and the attractive forces are greater.

Table 28.1 Magnetic Susceptibilities of Paramagnetic and Diamagnetic Materials at $T = 20°C$

Material	$\chi_m = K_m - 1$ ($\times 10^{-5}$)
Paramagnetic	
Iron ammonium alum	66
Uranium	40
Platinum	26
Aluminum	2.2
Sodium	0.72
Oxygen gas	0.19
Diamagnetic	
Bismuth	−16.6
Mercury	−2.9
Silver	−2.6
Carbon (diamond)	−2.1
Lead	−1.8
Sodium chloride	−1.4
Copper	−1.0

Example 28.11 Magnetic dipoles in a paramagnetic material

Nitric oxide (NO) is a paramagnetic compound. Its molecules have a magnetic moment with a maximum component in any direction of about one Bohr magneton each. In a magnetic field with magnitude $B = 1.5$ T, compare the interaction energy of the magnetic moments with the field to the average translational kinetic energy of the molecules at a temperature of 300 K.

SOLUTION

IDENTIFY: This problem involves both the energy of a magnetic moment in a magnetic field (Chapter 27) and the average translational kinetic energy due to temperature (Chapter 18).

SET UP: In Section 27.7 we derived the equation $U = -\vec{\mu} \cdot \vec{B}$ for the interaction energy of a magnetic moment $\vec{\mu}$ with a $\vec{B}$ field. From Section 18.3 the average translational kinetic energy of a molecule at temperature T is $K = \frac{3}{2}kT$, where k is the Boltzmann constant.

EXECUTE: We can write the interaction energy as $U = -(\mu\cos\phi)B$, where $\mu\cos\phi$ is the component of the magnetic moment $\vec{\mu}$ in the direction of the $\vec{B}$ field. In our case the maximum value of the component $\mu\cos\phi$ is about μ_B, so

$$|U|_{max} \approx \mu_B B = (9.27 \times 10^{-24} \text{ J/T})(1.5 \text{ T})$$
$$= 1.4 \times 10^{-23} \text{ J} = 8.7 \times 10^{-5} \text{ eV}$$

The average translational kinetic energy K is

$$K = \frac{3}{2}kT = \frac{3}{2}(1.38 \times 10^{-23} \text{ J/K})(300 \text{ K})$$
$$= 6.2 \times 10^{-21} \text{ J} = 0.039 \text{ eV}$$

EVALUATE: At a temperature of 300 K the magnetic interaction energy is much *smaller* than the random kinetic energy, so we expect only a slight degree of alignment. This is why paramagnetic susceptibilities at ordinary temperature are usually very small.

Diamagnetism

In some materials the total magnetic moment of all the atomic current loops is zero when no magnetic field is present. But even these materials have magnetic effects because an external field alters electron motions within the atoms, causing additional current loops and induced magnetic dipoles comparable to the induced *electric* dipoles we studied in Section 28.5. In this case the additional field caused by these current loops is always *opposite* in direction to that of the external field. (This behavior is explained by Faraday's law of induction, which we will study in Chapter 29. An induced current always tends to cancel the field change that caused it.)

28.27 In this drawing adapted from a magnified photo, the arrows show the directions of magnetization in the domains of a single crystal of nickel. Domains that are magnetized in the direction of an applied magnetic field grow larger.

(a) No field

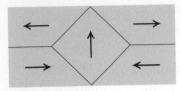

(b) Weak field

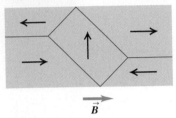

(c) Stronger field

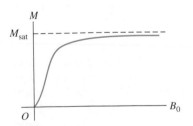

28.28 A magnetization curve for a ferromagnetic material. The magnetization M approaches its saturation value M_{sat} as the magnetic field B_0 (caused by external currents) becomes large.

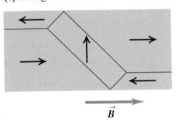

Such materials are said to be **diamagnetic.** They always have negative susceptibility, as shown in Table 28.1, and relative permeability K_m slightly *less* than unity, typically of the order of 0.99990 to 0.99999 for solids and liquids. Diamagnetic susceptibilities are very nearly temperature independent.

Ferromagnetism

There is a third class of materials, called **ferromagnetic** materials, that includes iron, nickel, cobalt, and many alloys containing these elements. In these materials, strong interactions between atomic magnetic moments cause them to line up parallel to each other in regions called **magnetic domains,** even when no external field is present. Figure 28.27 shows an example of magnetic domain structure. Within each domain, nearly all of the atomic magnetic moments are parallel.

When there is no externally applied field, the domain magnetizations are randomly oriented. But when a field $\vec{B}_0$ (caused by external currents) is present, the domains tend to orient themselves parallel to the field. The domain boundaries also shift; the domains that are magnetized in the field direction grow, and those that are magnetized in other directions shrink. Because the total magnetic moment of a domain may be many thousands of Bohr magnetons, the torques that tend to align the domains with an external field are much stronger than occur with paramagnetic materials. The relative permeability K_m is *much* larger than unity, typically of the order of 1,000 to 100,000. As a result, an object made of a ferromagnetic material such as iron is strongly magnetized by the field from a permanent magnet and is attracted to the magnet (see Fig. 27.38). A paramagnetic material such as aluminum is also attracted to a permanent magnet, but K_m for paramagnetic materials is so much smaller for such a material than for ferromagnetic materials that the attraction is very weak. Thus a magnet can pick up iron nails, but not aluminum cans.

As the external field is increased, a point is eventually reached at which nearly *all* the magnetic moments in the ferromagnetic material are aligned parallel to the external field. This condition is called *saturation magnetization;* after it is reached, further increase in the external field causes no increase in magnetization or in the additional field caused by the magnetization.

Figure 28.28 shows a "magnetization curve," a graph of magnetization M as a function of external magnetic field B_0, for soft iron. An alternative description of this behavior is that K_m is not constant but decreases as B_0 increases. (Paramagnetic materials also show saturation at sufficiently strong fields. But the magnetic fields required are so large that departures from a linear relationship between M and B_0 in these materials can be observed only at very low temperatures, 1 K or so.)

For many ferromagnetic materials the relationship of magnetization to external magnetic field is different when the external field is increasing from when it is decreasing. Figure 28.29a shows this relationship for such a material. When the material is magnetized to saturation and then the external field is reduced to zero, some magnetization remains. This behavior is characteristic of permanent magnets, which retain most of their saturation magnetization when the magnetizing field is removed. To reduce the magnetization to zero requires a magnetic field in the reverse direction.

This behavior is called **hysteresis,** and the curves in Fig. 28.29 are called *hysteresis loops.* Magnetizing and demagnetizing a material that has hysteresis involve the dissipation of energy, and the temperature of the material increases during such a process.

Ferromagnetic materials are widely used in electromagnets, transformer cores, and motors and generators, in which it is desirable to have as large a magnetic field as possible for a given current. Because hysteresis dissipates energy, materials that are used in these applications should usually have as narrow a hysteresis loop as possible. Soft iron is often used; it has high permeability without appreciable hysteresis. For permanent magnets a broad hysteresis loop is usually desirable, with large zero-field magnetization and large reverse field needed to demagnetize. Many kinds of steel and many alloys, such as Alnico, are commonly used for permanent magnets. The remaining magnetic field in such a material, after it has been magnetized to near saturation, is typically of the order of 1 T, corresponding to a remaining magnetization $M = B/\mu_0$ of about 800,000 A/m.

28.29 Hysteresis loops. The materials of both (a) and (b) remain strongly magnetized when B_0 is reduced to zero. Since (a) is also hard to demagnetize, it would be good for permanent magnets. Since (b) magnetizes and demagnetizes more easily, it could be used as a computer memory material. The material of (c) would be useful for transformers and other alternating-current devices where zero hysteresis would be optimal.

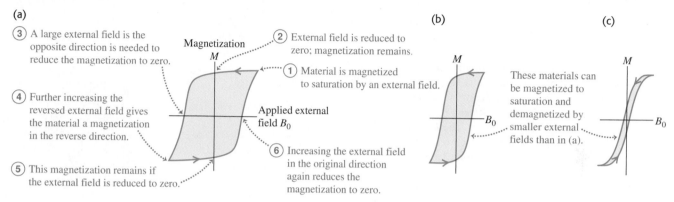

(a)

(3) A large external field is the opposite direction is needed to reduce the magnetization to zero.

(4) Further increasing the reversed external field gives the material a magnetization in the reverse direction.

(5) This magnetization remains if the external field is reduced to zero.

Magnetization M

(2) External field is reduced to zero; magnetization remains.

(1) Material is magnetized to saturation by an external field.

Applied external field B_0

(6) Increasing the external field in the original direction again reduces the magnetization to zero.

(b)

M

These materials can be magnetized to saturation and demagnetized by smaller external fields than in (a).

B_0

(c)

M

B_0

Example 28.12   **A ferromagnetic material**

A permanent magnet is made of a ferromagnetic material with a magnetization M of about 8×10^5 A/m. The magnet is in the shape of a cube of side 2 cm. (a) Find the magnetic dipole moment of the magnet. (b) Estimate the magnetic field due to the magnet at a point 10 cm from the magnet along its axis.

SOLUTION

IDENTIFY: This problem uses the relationship between magnetization and magnetic dipole moment, as well as the idea that a magnetic dipole produces a magnetic field.

SET UP: We find the magnetic dipole moment from the magnetization, which equals magnetic moment per unit volume. To estimate the magnetic field, we approximate the magnet as a current loop with the same magnetic moment and use the results of Section 28.5.

EXECUTE: (a) The total magnetic moment is the magnetization multiplied by the volume:

$$\mu_{total} = MV = (8 \times 10^5 \text{ A/m})(2 \times 10^{-2} \text{ m})^3 = 6 \text{ A} \cdot \text{m}^2$$

(b) We found in Section 28.5 that the magnetic field on the axis of a current loop with magnetic moment μ_{total} is given by Eq. (28.18),

$$B = \frac{\mu_0\mu_{total}}{2\pi(x^2 + a^2)^{3/2}}$$

where x is the distance from the loop and a is its radius. We can use this same expression here, except that a refers to the size of the permanent magnet. Strictly speaking, there are complications because our magnet does not have the same geometry as a circular current loop. But because $x = 10$ cm is fairly large in comparison to the 2-cm size of the magnet, the term a^2 is negligible in comparison to x^2 and can be ignored. So

$$B \approx \frac{\mu_0\mu_{total}}{2\pi x^3} = \frac{(4\pi \times 10^{-7} \text{ T} \cdot \text{m/A})(6 \text{ A} \cdot \text{m}^2)}{2\pi(0.1 \text{ m})^3}$$
$$= 1 \times 10^{-3} \text{ T} = 10 \text{ G}$$

which is about ten times stronger than the magnetic field of the earth. Such a magnet can easily deflect a compass needle.

EVALUATE: Note that we used μ_0, not the permeability μ of the magnetic material, in calculating B. The reason is that we are calculating B at a point *outside* the magnetic material. You would substitute permeability μ for μ_0 only if you were calculating B *inside* a material with relative permeability K_m, for which $\mu = K_m\mu_0$.

Test Your Understanding of Section 28.8   Which of the following materials are attracted to a magnet? (i) sodium; (ii) bismuth; (iii) lead; (iv) uranium.

Magnetic field of a moving charge: The magnetic field $\vec{B}$ created by a charge q moving with velocity $\vec{v}$ depends on the distance r from the source point (the location of q) to the field point (where $\vec{B}$ is measured). The $\vec{B}$ field is perpendicular to $\vec{v}$ and to $\hat{r}$, the unit vector directed from the source point to the field point. The principle of superposition of magnetic fields states that the total $\vec{B}$ field produced by several moving charges is the vector sum of the fields produced by the individual charges. (See Example 28.1.)

$$\vec{B} = \frac{\mu_0}{4\pi} \frac{q\vec{v} \times \hat{r}}{r^2} \tag{28.2}$$

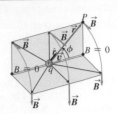

Magnetic field of a current-carrying conductor: The law of Biot and Savart gives the magnetic field $d\vec{B}$ created by an element $d\vec{l}$ of a conductor carrying current I. The field $d\vec{B}$ is perpendicular to both $d\vec{l}$ and $\hat{r}$, the unit vector from the element to the field point. The $\vec{B}$ field created by a finite current-carrying conductor is the integral of $d\vec{B}$ over the length of the conductor. (See Example 28.2.)

$$d\vec{B} = \frac{\mu_0}{4\pi} \frac{I\, d\vec{l} \times \hat{r}}{r^2} \tag{28.6}$$

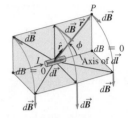

Magnetic field of a long, straight, current-carrying conductor: The magnetic field $\vec{B}$ at a distance r from a long, straight conductor carrying a current I has a magnitude that is inversely proportional to r. The magnetic field lines are circles coaxial with the wire, with directions given by the right-hand rule. (See Examples 28.3 and 28.4.)

$$B = \frac{\mu_0 I}{2\pi r} \tag{28.9}$$

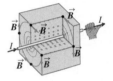

Magnetic force between current-carrying conductors: Two long, parallel, current-carrying conductors attract if the currents are in the same direction and repel if the currents are in opposite directions. The magnetic force per unit length between the conductors depends on their currents I and I' and their separation r. The definition of the ampere is based on this relationship. (See Example 28.5.)

$$\frac{F}{L} = \frac{\mu_0 I I'}{2\pi r} \tag{28.11}$$

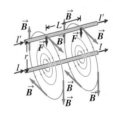

Magnetic field of a current loop: The law of Biot and Savart allows us to calculate the magnetic field produced along the axis of a circular conducting loop of radius a carrying current I. The field depends on the distance x along the axis from the center of the loop to the field point. If there are N loops, the field is multiplied by N. At the center of the loop, $x = 0$. (See Example 28.6.)

$$B_x = \frac{\mu_0 I a^2}{2(x^2 + a^2)^{3/2}} \tag{28.15}$$
(circular loop)

$$B_x = \frac{\mu_0 N I}{2a} \tag{28.17}$$
(center of N circular loops)

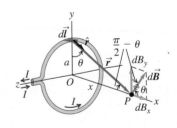

Ampere's law: Ampere's law states that the line integral of $\vec{B}$ around any closed path equals μ_0 times the net current through the area enclosed by the path. The positive sense of current is determined by a right-hand rule. (See Examples 28.7–28.10.)

$$\oint \vec{B} \cdot d\vec{l} = \mu_0 I_{encl} \tag{28.20}$$

Magnetic fields due to current distributions: The table lists magnetic fields caused by several current distributions. In each case the conductor is carrying current I.

Current Distribution	Point in Magnetic Field	Magnetic-Field Magnitude
Long, straight conductor	Distance r from conductor	$B = \dfrac{\mu_0 I}{2\pi r}$
Circular loop of radius a	On axis of loop	$B = \dfrac{\mu_0 I a^2}{2(x^2 + a^2)^{3/2}}$
	At center of loop	$B = \dfrac{\mu_0 I}{2a}$ (for N loops, multiply these expressions by N)
Long cylindrical conductor of radius R	Inside conductor, $r < R$	$B = \dfrac{\mu_0 I}{2\pi} \dfrac{r}{R^2}$
	Outside conductor, $r > R$	$B = \dfrac{\mu_0 I}{2\pi r}$
Long, closely wound solenoid with n turns per unit length, near its midpoint	Inside solenoid, near center	$B = \mu_0 n I$
	Outside solenoid	$B \approx 0$
Tightly wound toroidal solenoid (toroid) with N turns	Within the space enclosed by the windings, distance r from symmetry axis	$B = \dfrac{\mu_0 N I}{2\pi r}$
	Outside the space enclosed by the windings	$B \approx 0$

*Magnetic materials: When magnetic materials are present, the magnetization of the material causes an additional contribution to $\vec{B}$. For paramagnetic and diamagnetic materials, μ_0 is replaced in magnetic-field expressions by $\mu = K_m \mu_0$, where μ is the permeability of the material and K_m is its relative permeability. The magnetic susceptibility χ_m is defined as $\chi_m = K_m - 1$. Magnetic susceptibilities for paramagnetic materials are small positive quantities; those for diamagnetic materials are small negative quantities. For ferromagnetic materials, K_m is much larger than unity and is not constant. Some ferromagnetic materials are permanent magnets, retaining their magnetization even after the external magnetic field is removed. (See Examples 28.11 and 28.12.)

Key Terms

Answer to Chapter Opening Question ?

There would be *no* change in the magnetic field strength. From Example 28.9 (Section 28.7), the field inside a solenoid has magnitude $B = \mu_0 n I$, where n is the number of turns of wire per unit length. Joining two solenoids end to end doubles both the number of turns and the length, so the number of turns per unit length is unchanged.

Answers to Test Your Understanding Questions

28.1 Answer: (a) (i), (b) (ii) The situation is the same as shown in Fig. 28.2 except that the upper proton has velocity $\vec{v}$ rather than $-\vec{v}$. The magnetic field due to the lower proton is the same as shown in Fig. 28.2, but the direction of the magnetic force $\vec{F} = q\vec{v} \times \vec{B}$ on the upper proton is reversed. Hence the magnetic force is attractive. Since the speed v is small compared to c, the

magnetic force is much smaller in magnitude than the repulsive electric force and the net force is still repulsive.

28.2 Answer: (i) and (iii) (tie), (iv), (ii) From Eq. (28.5), the magnitude of the field dB due to a current element of length dl carrying current I is $dB = (\mu/4\pi)(I\,dl\sin\phi/r^2)$. In this expression r is the distance from the element to the field point, and ϕ is the angle between the direction of the current and a vector from the current element to the field point. All four points are the same distance $r = L$ from the current element, so the value of dB is proportional to the value of $\sin\phi$. For the four points the angle is (i) $\phi = 90°$, (ii) $\phi = 0$, (iii) $\phi = 90°$, and (iv) $\phi = 45°$, so the values of $\sin\phi$ are (i) 1, (ii) 0, (iii) 1, and (iv) $1/\sqrt{2}$.

28.3 Answer: A This orientation will cause current to flow clockwise around the circuit. Hence current will flow south through the wire that lies under the compass. From the right-hand rule for the magnetic field produced by a long, straight, current-carrying conductor, this will produce a magnetic field that points to the left at the position of the compass (which lies atop the wire). The combination of the northward magnetic field of the earth and the westward field produced by the current gives a net magnetic field to the northwest, so the compass needle will swing counterclockwise to align with this field.

28.4 Answers: (a) (i), (b) (iii), (c) (ii), (d) (iii)   Current flows in the same direction in adjacent turns of the coil, so the magnetic forces between these turns are attractive. Current flows in opposite directions on opposite sides of the same turn, so the magnetic forces between these sides are repulsive. Thus the magnetic forces on the solenoid turns squeeze them together in the direction along its axis but push them apart radially. The *electric* forces are zero because the wire is electrically neutral, with as much positive charge as there is negative charge.

28.5 Answers: (a) (ii), (b) (v)   The vector $d\vec{B}$ is in the direction of $d\vec{l} \times \vec{r}$. For a segment on the negative y-axis, $d\vec{l} = -\hat{k}\,dl$ points in the negative z-direction and $\vec{r} = x\hat{i} + a\hat{j}$. Hence $d\vec{l} \times \vec{r} = (a\,dl)\hat{i} - (x\,dl)\hat{j}$, which has a positive x-component, a negative y-component and zero z-component. For a segment on the negative z-axis, $d\vec{l} = \hat{j}\,dl$ points in the positive y-direction and $\vec{r} = x\hat{i} + a\hat{k}$. Hence $d\vec{l} \times \vec{r} = (a\,dl)\hat{i} - (x\,dl)\hat{k}$, which has a positive x-component, zero y-component, and a negative z-component.

28.6 Answer: (ii)   Imagine carrying out the integral $\oint \vec{B} \cdot d\vec{l}$ along an integration path that goes clockwise around the red magnetic field line. At each point along the path the magnetic field $\vec{B}$ and the infinitesimal segment $d\vec{l}$ are both tangent to the path, so $\vec{B} \cdot d\vec{l}$ is positive at each point and the integral $\oint \vec{B} \cdot d\vec{l}$ is likewise positive. It follows from Ampere's law $\oint \vec{B} \cdot d\vec{l} = \mu_0 I_{encl}$ and the right-hand rule that the integration path encloses a current directed out of the plane of the page. There are no currents in the empty space outside the magnet, so there must be currents inside the magnet (see Section 28.8).

28.7 Answer: (iii)   By symmetry, any $\vec{B}$ field outside the cable must circulate around the cable, with circular field lines like those surrounding the solid cylindrical conductor in Fig. 28.20. Choose an integration path like the one shown in Fig. 28.20 with radius $r > R$, so that the path completely encloses the cable. As in Example 28.8, the integral $\oint \vec{B} \cdot d\vec{l}$ for this path has magnitude $B(2\pi r)$. From Ampere's law this is equal to $\mu_0 I_{encl}$. The net enclosed current I_{encl} is zero because it includes two currents of equal magnitude but opposite direction: one in the central wire and one in the hollow cylinder. Hence $B(2\pi r) = 0$, and so $B = 0$ for any value of r outside the cable. (The field is nonzero *inside* the cable; see Exercise 28.37.)

28.8 Answer: (i), (iv)   Sodium and uranium are paramagnetic materials and hence are attracted to a magnet, while bismuth and lead are diamagnetic materials that are repelled by a magnet. (See Table 28.1.)

PROBLEMS

For instructor-assigned homework, go to **www.masteringphysics.com**

Discussion Questions

Q28.1. A topic of current interest in physics research is the search (thus far unsuccessful) for an isolated magnetic pole, or magnetic *monopole*. If such an entity were found, how could it be recognized? What would its properties be?

Q28.2. Streams of charged particles emitted from the sun during periods of solar activity create a disturbance in the earth's magnetic field. How does this happen?

Q28.3. The text discussed the magnetic field of an infinitely long, straight conductor carrying a current. Of course, there is no such thing as an infinitely long *anything*. How do you decide whether a particular wire is long enough to be considered infinite?

Q28.4. Two parallel conductors carrying current in the same direction attract each other. If they are permitted to move toward each other, the forces of attraction do work. From where does the energy come? Does this contradict the assertion in Chapter 27 that magnetic forces on moving charges do no work? Explain.

Q28.5. Pairs of conductors carrying current into or out of the power-supply components of electronic equipment are sometimes twisted together to reduce magnetic-field effects. Why does this help?

Q28.6. Suppose you have three long, parallel wires arranged so that in cross section they are at the corners of an equilateral triangle. Is there any way to arrange the currents so that all three wires attract each other? So that all three wires repel each other? Explain.

Q28.7. In deriving the force on one of the long, current-carrying conductors in Section 28.4, why did we use the magnetic field due to only one of the conductors? That is, why didn't we use the *total* magnetic field due to *both* conductors?

Q28.8. Two concentric, coplanar, circular loops of wire of different diameter carry currents in the same direction. Describe the nature of the force exerted on the inner loop by the outer loop and on the outer loop by the inner loop.

Q28.9. A current was sent through a helical coil spring. The spring contracted, as though it had been compressed. Why?

Q28.10. What are the relative advantages and disadvantages of Ampere's law and the law of Biot and Savart for practical calculations of magnetic fields?

Q28.11. Magnetic field lines never have a beginning or an end. Use this to explain why it is reasonable for the field of a toroidal solenoid to be confined entirely to its interior, while a straight solenoid *must* have some field outside.

Q28.12. If the magnitude of the magnetic field a distance R from a very long, straight, current-carrying wire is B, at what distance from the wire will the field have magnitude $3B$?

Q28.13. Two very long, parallel wires carry equal currents in opposite directions. (a) Is there any place that their magnetic fields completely cancel? If so, where? If not, why not? (b) How would the answer to part (a) change if the currents were in the same direction?

Q28.14. In the circuit shown in Figure 28.30, when switch S is suddenly closed, the wire L is pulled toward the lower wire carrying current I. Which (a or b) is the positive terminal of the battery? How do you know?

Figure 28.30
Question Q28.14.

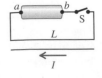

Q28.15. A metal ring carries a current that causes a magnetic field B_0 at the center of the ring and a field B at point P a distance r

from the center along the axis of the ring. If the radius of the ring is doubled, find the magnetic field at the center. Will the field at point P change by the same factor? Why?

*Q28.16. Why should the permeability of a paramagnetic material be expected to decrease with increasing temperature?

*Q28.17. If a magnet is suspended over a container of liquid air, it attracts droplets to its poles. The droplets contain only liquid oxygen; even though nitrogen is the primary constituent of air, it is not attracted to the magnet. Explain what this tells you about the magnetic susceptibilities of oxygen and nitrogen, and explain why a magnet in ordinary, room-temperature air doesn't attract molecules of oxygen *gas* to its poles.

*Q28.18. What features of atomic structure determine whether an element is diamagnetic or paramagnetic? Explain.

*Q28.19. The magnetic susceptibility of paramagnetic materials is quite strongly temperature dependent, but that of diamagnetic materials is nearly independent of temperature Why the difference?

*Q28.20. A cylinder of iron is placed so that it is free to rotate around its axis. Initially the cylinder is at rest, and a magnetic field is applied to the cylinder so that it is magnetized in a direction parallel to its axis. If the direction of the *external* field is suddenly reversed, the direction of magnetization will also reverse and the cylinder will begin rotating around its axis. (This is called the *Einstein-de Haas effect.*) Explain why the cylinder begins to rotate.

*Q28.21. The discussion of magnetic forces on current loops in Section 27.7 commented that no net force is exerted on a complete loop in a uniform magnetic field, only a torque. Yet magnetized materials that contain atomic current loops certainly *do* experience net forces in magnetic fields. How is this discrepancy resolved?

*Q28.22. Show that the units $A \cdot m^2$ and J/T for the Bohr magneton are equivalent.

Exercises

Section 26.1 Magnetic Field of a Moving Charge

28.1. A $+6.00\text{-}\mu C$ point charge is moving at a constant 8.00×10^6 m/s in the $+y$-direction, relative to a reference frame. At the instant when the point charge is at the origin of this reference frame, what is the magnetic-field vector $\vec{B}$ it produces at the following points: (a) $x = 0.500$ m, $y = 0$, $z = 0$; (b) $x = 0$, $y = -0.500$ m, $z = 0$; (c) $x = 0$, $y = 0$, $z = +0.500$ m; (d) $x = 0$, $y = -0.500$ m, $z = +0.500$ m?

28.2. Fields Within the Atom. In the Bohr model of the hydrogen atom, the electron moves in a circular orbit of radius 5.3×10^{-11} m with a speed of 2.2×10^6 m/s. If we are viewing the atom in such a way that the electron's orbit is in the plane of the paper with the electron moving clockwise, find the magnitude and direction of the electric and magnetic fields that the electron produces at the location of the nucleus (treated as a point).

28.3. An electron moves at $0.100c$ as shown in Fig. 28.31. Find the magnitude and direction of the magnetic field this electon produces at the following points, each $2.00\,\mu m$ from the electron: (a) points A and B; (b) point C; (c) point D.

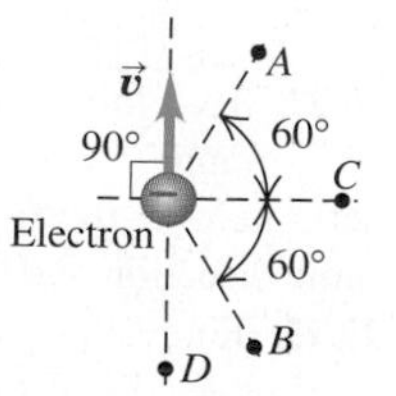

28.4. An alpha particle (charge $+2e$) and an electron move in opposite directions from the same point, each with the speed of 2.50×10^5 m/s (Fig. 28.32). Find the magnitude and direction of the total magnetic field these charges produce at point P, which is 1.75 nm from each of them.

Figure **28.31** Exercise 28.3.

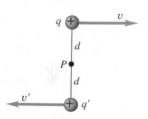

Figure **28.32** Exercise 28.4.

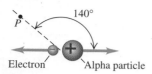

28.5. A $-4.80\text{-}\mu C$ charge is moving at a constant speed of 6.80×10^5 m/s in the $+x$-direction relative to a reference frame. At the instant when the point charge is at the origin, what is the magnetic-field vector it produces at the following points: (a) $x = 0.500$ m, $y = 0$, $z = 0$; (b) $x = 0$, $y = 0.500$ m, $z = 0$; (c) $x = 0.500$ m, $y = 0.500$ m, $z = 0$; (d) $x = 0$, $y = 0$, $z = 0.500$ m?

28.6. Positive point charges $q = +8.00\,\mu C$ and $q' = +3.00\,\mu C$ are moving relative to an observer at point P, as shown in Fig. 28.33. The distance d is 0.120 m, $v = 4.50 \times 10^6$ m/s, and $v' = 9.00 \times 10^6$ m/s. (a) When the two charges are at the locations shown in the figure, what are the magnitude and direction of the net magnetic field they produce at point P? (b) What are the magnitude and direction of the electric and magnetic forces that each charge exerts on the other, and what is the ratio of the magnitude of the electric force to the magnitude of the magnetic force? (c) If the direction of $\vec{v}'$ is reversed, so both charges are moving in the same direction, what are the magnitude and direction of the magnetic forces that the two charges exert on each other?

Figure **28.33** Exercises 28.6 and 28.7.

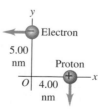

28.7. Figure 28.33 shows two point charges, q and q', moving relative to an observer at point P. Suppose that the lower charge is actually *negative*, with $q' = -q$. (a) Find the magnetic field (magnitude and direction) produced by the two charges at point P if (i) $v' = v/2$; (ii) $v' = v$; (iii) $v' = 2v$. (b) Find the direction of the magnetic force that q exerts on q', and find the direction of the magnetic force that q' exerts on q. (c) If $v = v' = 3.00 \times 10^5$ m/s, what is the ratio of the magnitude of the magnetic force acting on each charge to that of the Coulomb force acting on each charge?

28.8. An electron and a proton are each moving at 845 km/s in perpendicular paths as shown in Fig. 28.34. At the instant when they are at the positions shown in the figure, find the magnitude and direction of (a) the total magnetic field they produce at the origin; (b) the magnetic field the electron produces at the location of the proton; (c) the total electrical force and the total magnetic force that the electron exerts on the proton.

Figure **28.34** Exercise 28.8.

Section 28.2 Magnetic Field of a Current Element

28.9. A straight wire caries a 10.0-A current (Fig. 28.35). $ABCD$ is a rectangle with point D in the middle of a 1.10-mm segment of the wire and point C in the wire. Find the magnitude and direction of the magnetic field due to this segment at (a) point A; (b) point B; (c) point C.

Figure **28.35** Exercise 28.9.

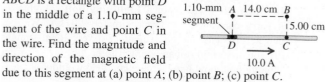

28.10. A long, straight wire, carrying a current of 200 A, runs through a cubical wooden box, entering and leaving through holes in the centers of opposite faces (Fig. 28.36). The length of each side of the box is 20.0 cm. Consider an element dl of the wire 0.100 cm long at the center of the box. Compute the magnitude dB of the magnetic field produced by this element at the points a, b, c, d, and e in Fig. 28.36. Points a, c, and d are at the centers of the faces of the cube; point b is at the midpoint of one edge; and point e is at a corner. Copy the figure and show the directions and relative magnitudes of the field vectors. (*Note:* Assume that the length dl is small in comparison to the distances from the current element to the points where the magnetic field is to be calculated.)

Figure **28.36** Exercise 28.10.

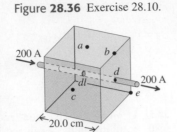

28.11. A long, straight wire lies along the z-axis and carries a 4.00-A current in the $+z$-direction. Find the magnetic field (magnitude and direction) produced at the following points by a 0.500-mm segment of the wire centered at the origin: (a) $x = 2.00$ m, $y = 0$, $z = 0$; (b) $x = 0$, $y = 2.00$ m, $z = 0$; (c) $x = 2.00$ m, $y = 2.00$ m, $z = 0$; (d) $x = 0$, $y = 0$, $z = 2.00$ m.

28.12. Two parallel wires are 5.00 cm apart and carry currents in opposite directions, as shown in Fig. 28.37. Find the magnitude and direction of the magnetic field at point P due to two 1.50-mm segments of wire that are opposite each other and each 8.00 cm from P.

Figure **28.37** Exercise 28.12.

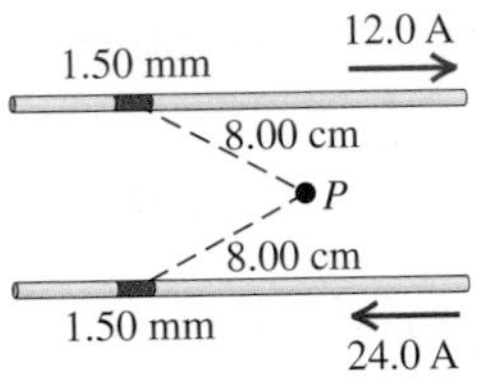

28.13. A wire carrying a 28.0-A current bends through a right angle. Consider two 2.00-mm segments of wire, each 3.00 cm from the bend (Fig. 28.38). Find the magnitude and direction of the magnetic field these two segments produce at point P, which is midway between them.

Figure **28.38** Exercise 28.13.

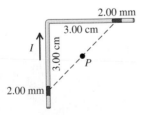

28.14. A square wire loop 10.0 cm on each side carries a clockwise current of 15.0 A. Find the magnitude and direction of the magnetic field at its center due to the four 1.20-mm wire segments at the midpoint of each side.

Section 28.3 Magnetic Field of a Straight Current-Carrying Conductor

28.15. The Magnetic Field from a Lightning Bolt. Lightning bolts can carry currents up to approximately 20 kA. We can model such a current as the equivalent of a very long, straight wire. (a) If you were unfortunate enough to be 5.0 m away from such a lightning bolt, how large a magnetic field would you expe-

rience? (b) How does this field compare to one you would experience by being 5.0 cm from a long, straight household current of 10 A?

28.16. A very long, straight horizontal wire carries a current such that 3.50×10^{18} electrons per second pass any given point going from west to east. What are the magnitude and direction of the magnetic field this wire produces at a point 4.00 cm directly above it?

28.17. (a) How large a current would a very long, straight wire have to carry so that the magnetic field 2.00 cm from the wire is equal to 1.00 G (comparable to the earth's northward-pointing magnetic field)? (b) If the wire is horizontal with the current running from east to west, at what locations would the magnetic field of the wire point in the same direction as the horizontal component of the earth's magnetic field? (c) Repeat part (b) except the wire is vertical with the current going upward.

28.18. Two long, straight wires, one above the other, are seperated by a distance $2a$ and are parallel to the x-axis. Let the $+y$-axis be in the plane of the wires in the direction from the lower wire to the upper wire. Each wire carries current I in the $+x$-direction. What are the magnitude and direction of the net magnetic field of the two wires at a point in the plane of the wires (a) midway between them; (b) at a distance a above the upper wire; (c) at a distance a below the lower wire?

28.19. A long, straight wire lies along the y-axis and carries a current $I = 8.00$ A in the $-y$-direction (Fig. 28.39). In addition to the magnetic field due to the current in the wire, a uniform magnetic field $\vec{B}_0$ with magnitude 1.50×10^{-6} T is in the $+x$-direction What is the total field (magnitude and direction) at the following points in the xz-plane: (a) $x = 0$, $z = 1.00$ m; (b) $x = 1.00$ m, $z = 0$; (c) $x = 0$, $z = -0.25$ m?

Figure **28.39** Exercise 28.19.

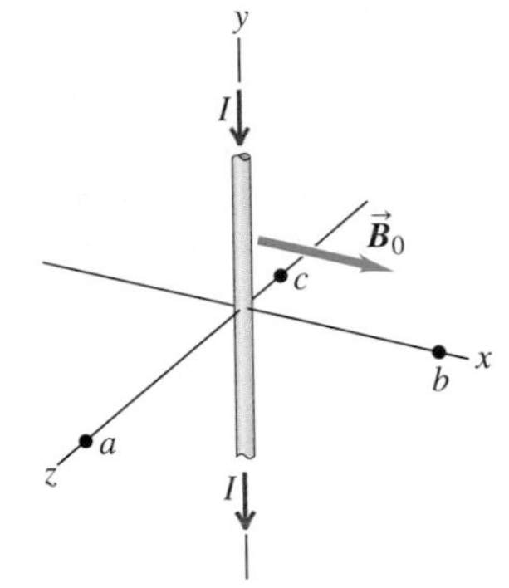

28.20. Effect of Transmission Lines. Two hikers are reading a compass under an overhead transmission line that is 5.50 m above the ground and carries a current of 800 A in a horizontal direction from north to south. (a) Find the magnitude and direction of the magnetic field at a point on the ground directly under the conductor. (b) One hiker suggests they walk on another 50 m to avoid inaccurate compass readings caused by the current. Considering that the magnitude of the earth's field is of the order of 0.5×10^{-4} T, is the current really a problem?

28.21. Two long, straight, parallel wires, 10.0 cm apart, carry equal 4.00-A currents in the same direction, as shown in Fig. 28.40. Find the magnitude and direction of the magnetic field at (a) point P_1, midway between the wires; (b) point P_2, 25.0 cm to the right of P_1; (c) point P_3, 20.0 cm directly above P_1.

Figure **28.40** Exercise 28.21.

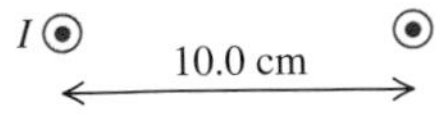

28.22. Two long, parallel transmission lines, 40.0 cm apart, carry 25.0-A and 75.0-A currents. Find all locations where the net magnetic field of the two wires is zero if these currents are in (a) the same direction and (b) the opposite direction.

28.23. Four, long, parallel power lines each carry 100-A currents. A cross-sectional diagram of these lines is a square, 20.0 cm on each side. For each of the three cases shown in Fig. 28.41, calculate the magnetic field at the center of the square.

Figure **28.41** Exercise 28.23.

(a)   (b)   (c)

28.24. Four very long, current-carrying wires in the same plane intersect to form a square 40.0 cm on each side, as shown in Fig. 28.42. Find the magnitude and direction of the current I so that the magnetic field at the center of the square is zero.

Figure **28.42** Exercise 28.24.

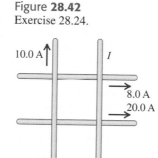

Section 28.4 Force Between Parallel Conductors

28.25. Two long, parallel wires are separated by a distance of 0.400 m (Fig. 28.43). The currents I_1 and I_2 have the directions shown. (a) Calculate the magnitude of the force exerted by each wire on a 1.20-m length of the other. Is

Figure **28.43** Exercise 28.25.

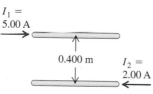

the force attractive or repulsive? (b) Each current is doubled, so that I_1 becomes 10.0 A and I_2 becomes 4.00 A. Now what is the magnitude of the force that each wire exerts on a 1.20-m length of the other?

28.26. Two long, parallel wires are separated by a distance of 2.50 cm. The force per unit length that each wire exerts on the other is 4.00×10^{-5} N/m, and the wires repel each other. The current in one wire is 0.600 A. (a) What is the current in the second wire? (b) Are the two currents in the same direction or in opposite directions?

28.27. Lamp Cord Wires. The wires in a household lamp cord are typically 3.0 mm apart center to center and carry equal currents in opposite directions. If the cord carries current to a 100-W light bulb connected across a 120-V potential difference, what force per meter does each wire of the cord exert on the other? Is the force attractive or repulsive? Is this force large enough so it should be considered in the design of lamp cord? (Model the lamp cord as a very long straight wire.)

28.28. Three parallel wires each carry current I in the directions shown in Fig. 28.44. If the separation between adjacent wires is d, calculate the magnitude and direction of the net magnetic force per unit length on each wire.

Figure **28.44** Exercise 28.28.

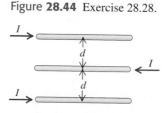

28.29. A long, horizontal wire AB rests on the surface of a table and carries a current I. Horizontal wire CD is vertically above wire AB and is free to slide up and down on the two vertical metal guides C and D (Fig. 28.45). Wire CD is connected through the sliding contacts to another wire that also carries a current I, opposite in direction to the current in wire AB. The mass per unit length of the wire CD is λ. To what equilibrium height h will the wire CD rise, assuming that the magnetic force on it is due entirely to the current in the wire AB?

Figure **28.45** Exercise 28.29.

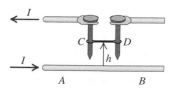

Section 28.5 Magnetic Field of a Circular Current Loop

28.30. Calculate the magnitude and direction of the magnetic field at point P due to the current in the semicircular section of wire shown in Fig. 28.46. (*Hint:* Does the current in the long, straight section of the wire produce any field at P?)

Figure **28.46** Exercise 28.30.

28.31. Calculate the magnitude of the magnetic field at point P of Fig. 28.47 in terms of R, I_1, and I_2. What does your expression give when $I_1 = I_2$?

Figure **28.47** Exercise 28.31.

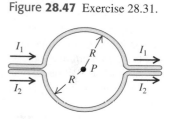

28.32. A closely wound, circular coil with radius 2.40 cm has 800 turns. a) What must the current in the coil be if the magnetic field at the center of the coil is 0.0580 T? b) At what distance x from the center of the coil, on the axis of the coil, is the magnetic field half its value at the center?

28.33. A closely wound, circular coil with a diameter of 4.00 cm has 600 turns and carries a current of 0.500 A. What is the magnitude of the magnetic field (a) at the center of the coil and (b) at a point on the axis of the coil 8.00 cm from its center?

28.34. A closely wound coil has a radius of 6.00 cm and carries a current of 2.50 A. How many turns must it have if, at a point on the coil axis 6.00 cm from the center of the coil, the magnetic field is 6.39×10^{-4} T?

Section 28.6 Ampere's Law

28.35. A closed curve encircles several conductors. The line integral $\oint \vec{B} \cdot d\vec{l}$ around this curve is 3.83×10^{-4} T·m. (a) What is the net current in the conductors? (b) If you were to integrate around the curve in the opposite direction, what would be the value of the line integral? Explain.

28.36. Figure 28.48 shows, in cross section, several conductors that carry currents through the plane of the figure. The currents have the magnitudes $I_1 = 4.0$ A, $I_2 = 6.0$ A, and $I_3 = 2.0$ A, and the directions shown. Four paths, labeled a through d, are shown. What is the line integral $\oint \vec{B} \cdot d\vec{l}$ for each path? Each integral involves going around the path in the counterclockwise direction. Explain your answers.

Figure **28.48** Exercise 28.36.

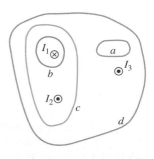

Section 28.7 Applications of Ampere's Law

28.37. Coaxial Cable. A solid conductor with radius a is supported by insulating disks on the axis of a conducting tube with inner radius b and outer radius c (Fig. 28.49). The central conductor and tube carry equal currents I in opposite directions. The currents are distributed uniformly over the cross sections of each conductor. Derive an expression for the magnitude of the magnetic field (a) at points outside the central, solid conductor but inside the tube $(a < r < b)$ and (b) at points outside the tube $(r > c)$.

Figure 28.49
Exercise 28.37.

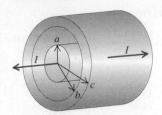

28.38. Repeat Exercise 28.37 for the case in which the current in the central, solid conductor is I_1, the current in the tube is I_2, and these currents are in the same direction rather than in opposite directions.

28.39. A long, straight, cylindrical wire of radius R carries a current uniformly distributed over its cross section. At what location is the magnetic field produced by this current equal to half of its largest value? Consider points inside and outside the wire.

28.40. A 15.0-cm-long solenoid with radius 2.50 cm is closely wound with 600 turns of wire. The current in the windings is 8.00 A. Compute the magnetic field at a point near the center of the solenoid.

28.41. A solenoid is designed to produce a magnetic field of 0.0270 T at its center. It has radius 1.40 cm and length 40.0 cm, and the wire can carry a maximum current of 12.0 A. (a) What minimum number of turns per unit length must the solenoid have? (b) What total length of wire is required?

28.42. As a new electrical technician, you are designing a large solenoid to produce a uniform 0.150 T magnetic field near the center of the solenoid. You have enough wire for 4000 circular turns. This solenoid must be 1.40 m long and 20.0 cm in diameter. What current will you need to produce the necessary field?

28.43. A magnetic field of 37.2 T has been achieved at the MIT Francis Bitter National Magnetic Laboratory. Find the current needed to achieve such a field (a) 2.00 cm from a long, straight wire; (b) at the center of a circular coil of radius 42.0 cm that has 100 turns; (c) near the center of a solenoid with radius 2.40 cm, length 32.0 cm, and 40,000 turns.

28.44. A toroidal solenoid (see Example 28.10) has inner radius $r_1 = 15.0$ cm and outer radius $r_2 = 18.0$ cm. The solenoid has 250 turns and carries a current of 8.50 A. What is the magnitude of the magnetic field at the following distances from the center of the torus: (a) 12.0 cm; (b) 16.0 cm; (c) 20.0 cm?

28.45. A wooden ring whose mean diameter is 14.0 cm is wound with a closely spaced toroidal winding of 600 turns. Compute the magnitude of the magnetic field at the center of the cross section of the windings when the current in the windings is 0.650 A.

*Section 28.8 Magnetic Materials

*28.46. A toroidal solenoid with 400 turns of wire and a mean radius of 6.0 cm carries a current of 0.25 A. The relative permeability of the core is 80. (a) What is the magnetic field in the core? (b) What part of the magnetic field is due to atomic currents?

*28.47. A toroidal solenoid with 500 turns is wound on a ring with a mean radius of 2.90 cm. Find the current in the winding that is required to set up a magnetic field of 0.350 T in the ring (a) if the ring is made of annealed iron $(K_m = 1400)$ and (b) if the ring is made of silicon steel $(K_m = 3200)$.

*28.48. The current in the windings of a toroidal solenoid is 2.400 A. There are 500 turns, and the mean radius is 25.00 cm. The toroidal solenoid is filled with a magnetic material. The magnetic field inside the windings is found to be 1.940 T. Calculate (a) the relative permeability and (b) the magnetic susceptibility of the material that fills the toroid.

*28.49. A long solenoid with 60 turns of wire per centimeter carries a current of 0.15 A. The wire that makes up the solenoid is wrapped around a solid core of silicon steel $(K_m = 5200)$. (The wire of the solenoid is jacketed with an insulator so that none of the current flows into the core.) (a) For a point inside the core, find the magnitudes of (i) the magnetic field $\vec{B}_0$ due to the solenoid current; (ii) the magnetization $\vec{M}$; (iii) the total magnetic field $\vec{B}$. (b) In a sketch of the solenoid and core, show the directions of the vectors $\vec{B}$, $\vec{B}_0$, and $\vec{M}$ inside the core.

*28.50. Curie's Law. Experimental measurements of the magnetic susceptibility of iron ammonium alum are given in the table. Graph values of $1/\chi_m$ against Kelvin temperature. Does the material obey Curie's law? If so, what is the Curie constant?

T (°C)	χ_m
−258.15	129×10^{-4}
−173	19.4×10^{-4}
−73	9.7×10^{-4}
27	6.5×10^{-4}

Problems

28.51. A pair of point charges, $q = +8.00\ \mu\text{C}$ and $q' = -5.00\ \mu\text{C}$, are moving as shown in Fig 28.50 with speeds $v = 9.00 \times 10^4$ m/s and $v' = 6.50 \times 10^4$ m/s. When the charges are at the locations shown in the figure, what are the magnitude and direction of (a) the magnetic field produced at the origin and (b) the magnetic force that q' exerts on q?

Figure 28.50
Problem 28.51.

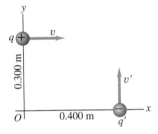

28.52. A long, straight wire carries a current of 2.50 A. An electron is traveling in the vicinity of the wire. At the instant when the electron is 4.50 cm from the wire and traveling with a speed of 6.00×10^4 m/s directly toward the wire, what are the magnitude and direction (relative to the direction of the current) of the force that the magnetic field of the current exerts on the electron?

28.53. A long, straight wire carries a 25.0-A current. An electron is fired parallel to this wire with a velocity of 250 km/s in the same direction as the current, 2.00 cm from the wire. (a) Find the magnitude and direction of the electron's initial acceleration. (b) What should be the magnitude and direction of a uniform electric field that will allow the electron to continue to travel parallel to the wire? (c) Is it necessary to include the effects of gravity? Justify your answer.

28.54. In Fig. 28.51 the battery branch of the circuit is very far from the two horizontal segments containing two resistors. These horizontal segments are separated by 5.00 cm, and they are much longer than 5.00 cm. A proton (charge $+e$) is fired at 650 km/s from a point midway between the upper two horizontal segments of the circuit. The initial velocity of the proton is in the plane of the

Figure **28.51** Problem 28.54.

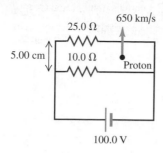

circuit and is directed toward the upper wire. Find the magnitude and direction of the initial magnetic force on the proton.

28.55. Two identical circular, wire loops 40.0 cm in diameter each carry a current of 1.50 A in the same direction. These loops are parallel to each other and are 25.0 cm apart. Line *ab* is normal to the plane of the loops and passes through their centers. A proton is fired at 2400 km/s perpendicular to line *ab* from a point midway between the centers of the loops. Find the magnitude and direction of the magnetic force these loops exert on the proton just after it is fired.

28.56. Two very long, straight wires carry currents as shown in Fig. 28.52. For each case, find all locations where the net magnetic field is zero.

Figure **28.52** Problem 28.56.

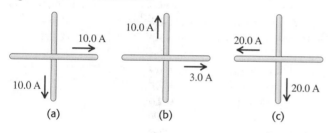

(a)   (b)   (c)

28.57. A negative point charge $q = -7.20$ mC is moving in a reference frame. When the point charge is at the origin, the magnetic field it produces at the point $x = 25.0$ cm, $y = 0$, $z = 0$ is $\vec{B} = (6.00\ \mu\text{T})\hat{j}$, and its speed is 800 km/s. (a) What are the x-, y-, and z-components of the velocity $\vec{v}_0$ of the charge? (b) At this same instant, what is the magnitude of the magnetic field that the charge produces at the point $x = 0$, $y = 25.0$ cm, $z = 0$?

28.58. A neophyte magnet designer tells you that he can produce a magnetic field $\vec{B}$ in vacuum that points everywhere in the x-direction and that increases in magnitude with increasing x. That is, $\vec{B} = B_0(x/a)\hat{i}$, where B_0 and a are constants with units of teslas and meters, respectively. Use Gauss's law for magnetic fields to show that this claim is *impossible*. (*Hint:* Use a Gaussian surface in the shape of a rectangular box, with edges parallel to the x-, y-, and z-axes.)

28.59. Two long, straight, parallel wires are 1.00 m apart (Fig. 28.53). The wire on the left carries a current I_1 of 6.00 A into the plane of the paper. (a) What must the magnitude and direction of the current I_2 be for the net field at point P to be zero? (b) Then what are the magnitude and direction of the net field at Q? (c) Then what is the magnitude of the net field at S?

Figure **28.53** Problem 28.59.

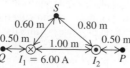

28.60. Figure 28.54 shows an end view of two long, parallel wires perpendicular to the xy-plane, each carrying a current I but in opposite directions. (a) Copy the diagram, and draw vectors to show the $\vec{B}$ field of each wire and the net $\vec{B}$ field at point P. (b) Derive the expression for the magnitude of $\vec{B}$ at any point on the x-axis in terms of the x-coordinate of the point. What is the direction of $\vec{B}$? (c) Graph the magnitude of $\vec{B}$ at points on the x-axis. (d) At what value of x is the magnitude of $\vec{B}$ a maximum? (e) What is the magnitude of $\vec{B}$ when $x \gg a$?

28.61. Refer to the situation in Problem 28.60. Suppose that a third long, straight wire, parallel to the other two, passes through point P (see Fig. 28.54) and that each wire carries a current $I = 6.00$ A. Let $a = 40.0$ cm and $x = 60.0$ cm. Find the magnitude and direction of the force per unit length on the third wire, (a) if the current in it is directed into the plane of the figure, and (b) if the current in it is directed out of the plane of the figure.

28.62. A pair of long, rigid metal rods, each of length L, lie parallel to each other on a perfectly smooth table. Their ends are connected by identical, very light conducting springs of force constant k (Fig. 28.55) and negligible unstretched length. If a current I runs through this circuit, the springs will stretch. At what separation will the rods remain at rest? Assume that k is large enough so that the separation of the rods will be much less than L.

28.63. Two long, parallel wires hang by 4.00-cm-long cords from a common axis (Fig. 28.56). The wires have a mass per unit length of 0.0125 kg/m and carry the same current in opposite directions. What is the current in each wire if the cords hang at an angle of $6.00°$ with the vertical?

Figure **28.54** Problems 28.60 and 28.61.

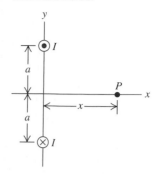

Figure **28.55** Problem 28.62.

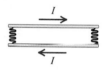

Figure **28.56** Problem 28.63.

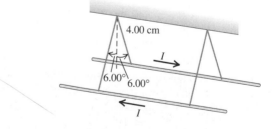

28.64. The long, straight wire AB shown in Fig. 28.57 carries a current of 14.0 A. The rectangular loop whose long edges are parallel to the wire carries a current of 5.00 A. Find the magnitude and direction of the net force exerted on the loop by the magnetic field of the wire.

Figure **28.57** Problem 28.64.

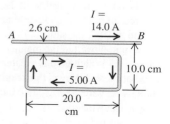

28.65. A circular wire loop of radius a has N turns and carries a current I. A second loop with N' turns of radius a' carries current I' and is located on the axis of the first loop, a distance x from the center of the first loop. The second loop is tipped so that its axis is at an angle θ from the axis of the first loop. The distance x is large compared to both a and a'. (a) Find the magnitude of the torque exerted on the second loop by the first loop. (b) Find the potential energy for the second loop due to this interaction. (c) What simplifications result from having x much larger than a? From having x much larger than a'?

28.66. The wire semicircles shown in Fig. 28.58 have radii a and b. Calculate the net magnetic field (magnitude and direction) that the current in the wires produces at point P.

Figure 28.58 Problem 28.66.

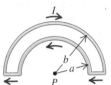

28.67. Helmholtz Coils. Fig. 28.59 is a sectional view of two circular coils with radius a, each wound with N turns of wire carrying a current I, circulating in the same direction in both coils. The coils are separated by a distance a equal to their radii. In this configuration the coils are called Helmholtz coils; they produce a very uniform magnetic field in the region between them. (a) Derive the expression for the magnitude B of the magnetic field at a point on the axis a distance x to the right of point P, which is midway between the coils. (b) Graph B versus x for $x = 0$ to $x = a/2$. Compare this graph to one for the magnetic field due to the right-hand coil alone. (c) From part (a), obtain an expression for the magnitude of the magnetic field at point P. (d) Calculate the magnitude of the magnetic field at P if $N = 300$ turns, $I = 6.00$ A, and $a = 8.00$ cm. (e) Calculate dB/dx and d^2B/dx^2 at P $(x = 0)$. Discuss how your results show that the field is very uniform in the vicinity of P.

Figure 28.59 Problem 28.67.

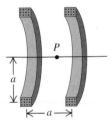

28.68. A circular wire of diameter D lies on a horizontal table and carries a current I. In Fig. 28.60 point A marks the center of the circle and point C is on its rim. (a) Find the magnitude and direction of the magnetic field at point A. (b) The wire is now unwrapped so it is straight, centered on point C, and perpendicular to the line AC, but the same current is maintained in it. Now find the magnetic field at point A. (c) Which field is greater: the one in part (a) or in part (b)? By what factor? Why is this result physically reasonable?

Figure 28.60 Problem 28.68.

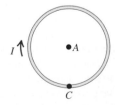

28.69. The wire in Fig. 28.61 carries current I in the direction shown. The wire consists of a very long, straight section, a quarter-circle with radius R, and another long, straight section. What are the magnitude and direction of the net magnetic field at the center of curvature of the quarter-circle section (point P)?

Figure 28.61 Problem 28.69.

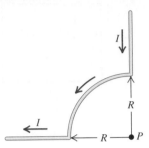

28.70. The wire shown in Fig. 28.62 is infinitely long and carries a current I. Calculate the magnitude and direction of the magnetic field that this current produces at point P.

Figure 28.62 Problem 28.70.

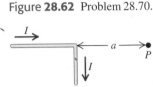

28.71. A long, straight wire with a circular cross section of radius R carries a current I. Assume that the current density is not constant across the cross section of the wire, but rather varies as $J = \alpha r$, where α is a constant. (a) By the requirement that J integrated over the cross section of the wire gives the total current I, calculate the constant α in terms of I and R. (b) Use Ampere's law to calculate the magnetic field $B(r)$ for (i) $r \leq R$ and (ii) $r \geq R$. Express your answers in terms of I.

28.72. (a) For the coaxial cable of Exercise 28.37, derive an expression for the magnitude of the magnetic field at points inside the central solid conductor $(r < a)$. Compare your result when $r = a$ to the results of part (a) of Exercise 28.37 at that same point. (b) For this coaxial cable derive an expression for the field within the tube $(b < r < c)$. Compare your result when $r = b$ to part (a) of Exercise 28.37 at that same point. Compare your result when $r = c$ to part (b) of Exercise 28.37 at that same point.

28.73. The electric field of an infinite line of positive charge is directed radially outward from the wire and can be calculated using Gauss's law for the electric field (see Example 22.6 in Section 22.4). Use Gauss's law for magnetism to show that the *magnetic* field of a straight, infinitely long, current-carrying *conductor* cannot have a radial component.

28.74. A conductor is made in the form of a hollow cylinder with inner and outer radii a and b, respectively. It carries a current I uniformly distributed over its cross section. Derive expressions for the magnitude of the magnetic field in the regions (a) $r < a$; (b) $a < r < b$; (c) $r > b$.

28.75. Knowing Magnetic Fields Inside and Out. You are given a hollow copper cylinder with inner radius a and outer radius $3a$. The cylinder's length is $200a$ and its electrical resistance to current flowing down its length is R. To test its suitability for use in a circuit, you connect the ends of the cylinder to a voltage source, causing a current I to flow down the length of the cylinder. The current is spread uniformly over the cylinder's cross section. You are interested in knowing the strength of the magnetic field that the current produces within the solid part of the cylinder, at a radius $2a$ from the cylinder axis. But since it's not easy to insert a magnetic-field probe into the solid metal, you decide instead to measure the field at a point outside the cylinder where the field should be as strong as at radius $2a$. At what distance from the axis of the cylinder should you place the probe?

28.76. A circular loop has radius R and carries current I_2 in a clockwise direction (Fig. 28.63). The center of the loop is a distance D above a long, straight wire. What are the magnitude and direction of the current I_1 in the wire if the magnetic field at the center of the loop is zero?

Figure **28.63** Problem 28.76.

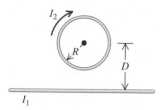

28.77. A long, straight, solid cylinder, oriented with its axis in the z-direction, carries a current whose current density is $\vec{J}$. The current density, although symmetrical about the cylinder axis, is not constant but varies according to the relationship

$$\vec{J} = \frac{2I_0}{\pi a^2}\left[1 - \left(\frac{r}{a}\right)^2\right]\hat{k} \quad \text{for } r \leq a$$
$$= 0 \quad \text{for } r \geq a$$

where a is the radius of the cylinder, r is the radial distance from the cylinder axis, and I_0 is a constant having units of amperes. (a) Show that I_0 is the total current passing through the entire cross section of the wire. (b) Using Ampere's law, derive an expression for the magnitude of the magnetic field $\vec{B}$ in the region $r \geq a$. (c) Obtain an expression for the current I contained in a circular cross section of radius $r \leq a$ and centered at the cylinder axis. (d) Using Ampere's law, derive an expression for the magnitude of the magnetic field $\vec{B}$ in the region $r \leq a$. How do your results in parts (b) and (d) compare for $r = a$?

28.78. A long, straight, solid cylinder, oriented with its axis in the z-direction, carries a current whose current density is $\vec{J}$. The current density, although symmetrical about the cylinder axis, is not constant and varies according to the relationship

$$\vec{J} = \left(\frac{b}{r}\right)e^{(r-a)/\delta}\hat{k} \quad \text{for } r \leq a$$
$$= 0 \quad \text{for } r \geq a$$

where the radius of the cylinder is $a = 5.00$ cm, r is the radial distance from the cylinder axis, b is a constant equal to 600 A/m, and δ is a constant equal to 2.50 cm. (a) Let I_0 be the total current passing through the entire cross section of the wire. Obtain an expression for I_0 in terms of b, δ, and a. Evaluate your expression to obtain a numerical value for I_0. (b) Using Ampere's law, derive an expression for the magnetic field $\vec{B}$ in the region $r \geq a$. Express your answer in terms of I_0 rather than b. (c) Obtain an expression for the current I contained in a circular cross section of radius $r \leq a$ and centered at the cylinder axis. Express your answer in terms of I_0 rather than b. (d) Using Ampere's law, derive an expression for the magnetic field $\vec{B}$ in the region $r \leq a$. (e) Evaluate the magnitude of the magnetic field at $r = \delta$, $r = a$, and $r = 2a$.

28.79. Integrate B_x as given in Eq. (28.15) from $-\infty$ to $+\infty$; that is, calculate $\int_{-\infty}^{+\infty} B_x\, dx$. Explain the significance of your result.

28.80. In a region of space where there are no conduction or displacement currents, it is impossible to have a uniform magnetic field that abruptly drops to zero. To prove this statement, use the method of contradiction: Assume that such a case *is* possible, and

then show that your assumption contradicts a law of nature. (a) In the bottom half of a piece of paper, draw evenly spaced, horizontal lines representing a uniform magnetic field to your right. Use dashed lines to draw a rectangle $abcda$ with horizontal side ab in the magnetic field region and horizontal side cd in the top half of your paper where $B = 0$. (b) Show that integration around your rectangle contradicts Ampere's law.

28.81. An Infinite Current Sheet. Long, straight conductors with square cross sections and each carrying current I are laid side by side to form an infinite current sheet (Fig. 28.64). The conductors lie in the xy-plane, are parallel to the y-axis, and carry current in the $+y$-direction. There are n conductors per unit length measured along the x-axis. (a) What are the magnitude and direction of the magnetic field a distance a below the current sheet? (b) What are the magnitude and direction of the magnetic field a distance a above the current sheet?

Figure **28.64** Problem 28.81.

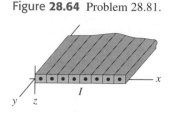

28.82. Long, straight conductors with square cross section, each carrying current I, are laid side by side to form an infinite current sheet with current directed out of the plane of the page (Fig. 28.65). A second infinite current sheet is a distance d below the first and is parallel to it. The second sheet carries current into the plane of the page. Each sheet has n conductors per unit length. (Refer to Problem 28.81.) Calculate the magnitude and direction of the net magnetic field at (a) point P (above the upper sheet); (b) point R (midway between the two sheets); (c) point S (below the lower sheet).

Figure **28.65** Problem 28.82.

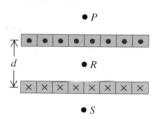

***28.83.** A piece of iron has magnetization $M = 6.50 \times 10^4$ A/m. Find the average magnetic dipole moment *per atom* in this piece of iron. Express your answer both in A · m^2 and in Bohr magnetons. The density of iron is given in Table 14.1, and the atomic mass of iron (in grams per mole) is given in Appendix D. The chemical symbol for iron is Fe.

***28.84.** (a) In Section 27.7 we discussed how a magnetic dipole, such as a current loop or a magnetized object, can be attracted or repelled by a permanent magnet. Use this to explain why *either* pole of a magnet *attracts* both paramagnetic materials and (initially unmagnetized) ferromagnetic materials, but *repels* diamagnetic materials. (b) The force that a magnet exerts on an object is directly proportional to the object's magnetic moment. A particular magnet is just strong enough to pick up a cube of annealed iron $(K_m = 1400)$ 2.00 cm on a side so that the iron sticks to one of the magnet's poles; that is, the magnet exerts an upward force on the iron cube equal to the cube's weight. If you tried to use this magnet to pick up a 2.00-cm cube of aluminum instead, what would be the upward force on the cube? How does this compare to the weight of the cube? Could the magnet pick up the cube? (*Hint:* You will need to use information from Tables 14.1 and 28.1.) (c) If you tried to use the magnet to pick up a 2.00-cm cube of silver, what would be the magnitude and direction of the force on the cube? How does this magnitude compare to the weight of the cube? Would the effects of the magnetic force be noticeable?

Challenge Problems

28.85. Two long, straight conducting wires with linear mass density λ are suspended from cords so that they are each horizontal, parallel to each other, and a distance d apart. The back ends of the wires are connected to each other by a slack, low-resistance connecting wire. A charged capacitor (capacitance C) is now added to the system; the positive plate of the capacitor (initial charge $+Q_0$) is connected to the front end of one of the wires, and the negative plate of the capacitor (initial charge $-Q_0$) is connected to the front end of the other wire (Fig. 28.66). Both of these connections are also made by slack, low-resistance wires. When the connection is made, the wires are pushed aside by the repulsive force between the wires, and each wire has an initial horizontal velocity of magnitude v_0. Assume that the time constant for the capacitor to discharge is negligible compared to the time it takes for any appreciable displacement in the position of the wires to occur. (a) Show that the initial speed v_0 of either wire is given by

$$v_0 = \frac{\mu_0 Q_0^2}{4\pi \lambda RCd}$$

where R is the total resistance of the circuit. (b) To what height h will each wire rise as a result of the circuit connection?

Figure 28.66 Challenge Problem 28.85.

28.86. A wide, long, insulating belt has a uniform positive charge per unit area σ on its upper surface. Rollers at each end move the belt to the right at a constant speed v. Calculate the magnitude and direction of the magnetic field produced by the moving belt at a point just above its surface. (*Hint:* At points near the surface and far from its edges or ends, the moving belt can be considered to be an infinite current sheet like that in Problem 28.81.)

28.87. A Charged Dielectric Disk. A thin disk of dielectric material with radius a has a total charge $+Q$ distributed uniformly over its surface. It rotates n times per second about an axis perpendicular to the surface of the disk and passing through its center. Find the magnetic field at the center of the disk. (*Hint:* Divide the disk into concentric rings of infinitesimal width.)

28.88. A wire in the shape of a semicircle with radius a is oriented in the yz-plane with its center of curvature at the origin (Fig. 28.67). If the current in the wire is I, calculate the magnetic-field components produced at point P, a distance x out along the x-axis. (*Note:* Do not forget the contribution from the straight wire at the bottom of the semicircle that runs from $z = -a$ to $z = +a$. You may use the fact that the fields of the two antiparallel currents at $z > a$ cancel, but you must explain *why* they cancel.)

Figure 28.67 Challenge Problem 28.88.

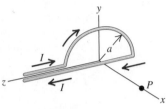

ELECTROMAGNETIC INDUCTION

? When a credit card is "swiped" through a card reader, the information coded in a magnetic pattern on the back of the card is transmitted to the card-holder's bank. Why is it necessary to swipe the card rather than holding it motionless in the card reader's slot?

LEARNING GOALS

By studying this chapter, you will learn:

- The experimental evidence that a changing magnetic field induces an emf.

- How Faraday's law relates the induced emf in a loop to the change in magnetic flux through the loop.

- How to determine the direction of an induced emf.

- How to calculate the emf induced in a conductor moving through a magnetic field.

- How a changing magnetic flux generates an electric field that is very different from that produced by an arrangement of charges.

- The four fundamental equations that completely describe both electricity and magnetism.

Almost every modern device or machine, from a computer to a washing machine to a power drill, has electric circuits at its heart. We learned in Chapter 25 that an electromotive force (emf) is required for a current to flow in a circuit; in Chapter 25 and 26 we almost always took the source of emf to be a battery. But for the vast majority of electric devices that are used in industry and in the home (including any device that you plug into a wall socket), the source of emf is *not* a battery but an electrical generating station. Such a station produces electric energy by converting other forms of energy: gravitational potential energy at a hydroelectric plant, chemical energy in a coal- or oil-fired plant, nuclear energy at a nuclear plant. But how is this energy conversion done? In other words, what is the physics behind the production of almost all of our electric energy needs?

The answer is a phenomenon known as *electromagnetic induction:* If the magnetic flux through a circuit changes, an emf and a current are induced in the circuit. In a power-generating station, magnets move relative to coils of wire to produce a changing magnetic flux in the coils and hence an emf. Other key components of electric power systems, such as transformers, also depend on magnetically induced emfs. Indeed, thanks to its key role in electric power generation, electromagnetic induction is one of the foundations of our technological society.

The central principle of electromagnetic induction, and the keystone of this chapter, is *Faraday's law.* This law relates induced emf to changing magnetic flux in any loop, including a closed circuit. We also discuss Lenz's law, which helps us to predict the directions of induced emfs and currents. This chapter provides the principles we need to understand electrical energy-conversion devices such as motors, generators, and transformers.

Electromagnetic induction tells us that a time-varying magnetic field can act as a source of electric field. We will also see how a time-varying *electric* field can act as a source of *magnetic* field. These remarkable results form part of a neat package of formulas, called *Maxwell's equations,* that describe the behavior of electric and magnetic fields in *any* situation. Maxwell's equations pave the way toward an understanding of electromagnetic waves, the topic of Chapter 32.

29.1 Induction Experiments

During the 1830s, several pioneering experiments with magnetically induced emf were carried out in England by Michael Faraday and in the United States by Joseph Henry (1797–1878), later the first director of the Smithsonian Institution. Figure 29.1 shows several examples. In Figure 29.1a, a coil of wire is connected to a galvanometer. When the nearby magnet is stationary, the meter shows no current. This isn't surprising; there is no source of emf in the circuit. But when we *move* the magnet either toward or away from the coil, the meter shows current in the circuit, but *only* while the magnet is moving (Fig. 29.1b). If we keep the magnet stationary and move the coil, we again detect a current during the motion. We call this an **induced current,** and the corresponding emf required to cause this current is called an **induced emf.**

In Fig. 29.1c we replace the magnet with a second coil connected to a battery. When the second coil is stationary, there is no current in the first coil. However, when we move the second coil toward or away from the first or move the first toward or away from the second, there is current in the first coil, but again *only* while one coil is moving relative to the other.

Finally, using the two-coil setup in Fig. 29.1d, we keep both coils stationary and vary the current in the second coil, either by opening and closing the switch or by changing the resistance of the second coil with the switch closed (perhaps by changing the second coil's temperature). We find that as we open or close the switch, there is a momentary current pulse in the first circuit. When we vary the resistance (and thus the current) in the second coil, there is an induced current in the first circuit, but only while the current in the second circuit is changing.

To explore further the common elements in these observations, let's consider a more detailed series of experiments with the situation shown in Figure 29.2. We connect a coil of wire to a galvanometer, then place the coil between the

Activ
ONLINE
Physics

13.9   Electomagnetic Induction

29.1 Demonstrating the phenomenon of induced current.

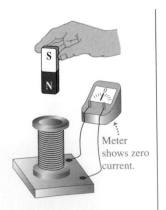

(a) A stationary magnet does NOT induce a current in a coil.

Meter shows zero current.

All these actions DO induce a current in the coil. What do they have in common?*

(b) Moving the magnet toward or away from the coil

Meter shows induced current.

(c) Moving a second, current-carrying coil toward or away from the coil

(d) Varying the current in the second coil (by closing or opening a switch)

* They cause the magnetic field through the coil to change.

poles of an electromagnet whose magnetic field we can vary. Here's what we observe:

1. When there is no current in the electromagnet, so that $\vec{B} = 0$, the galvanometer shows no current.
2. When the electromagnet is turned on, there is a momentary current through the meter as $\vec{B}$ increases.
3. When $\vec{B}$ levels off at a steady value, the current drops to zero, no matter how large $\vec{B}$ is.
4. With the coil in a horizontal plane, we squeeze it so as to decrease the cross-sectional area of the coil. The meter detects current only *during* the deformation, not before or after. When we increase the area to return the coil to its original shape, there is current in the opposite direction, but only while the area of the coil is changing.
5. If we rotate the coil a few degrees about a horizontal axis, the meter detects current during the rotation, in the same direction as when we decreased the area. When we rotate the coil back, there is a current in the opposite direction during this rotation.
6. If we jerk the coil out of the magnetic field, there is a current during the motion, in the same direction as when we decreased the area.
7. If we decrease the number of turns in the coil by unwinding one or more turns, there is a current during the unwinding, in the same direction as when we decreased the area. If we wind more turns onto the coil, there is a current in the opposite direction during the winding.
8. When the magnet is turned off, there is a momentary current in the direction opposite to the current when it was turned on.
9. The faster we carry out any of these changes, the greater the current.
10. If all these experiments are repeated with a coil that has the same shape but different material and different resistance, the current in each case is inversely proportional to the total circuit resistance. This shows that the induced emfs that are causing the current do not depend on the material of the coil but only on its shape and the magnetic field.

29.2 A coil in a magnetic field. When the $\vec{B}$ field is constant and the shape, location, and orientation of the coil do not change, no current is induced in the coil. A current is induced when any of these factors change.

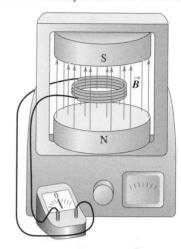

The common element in all these experiments is changing *magnetic flux* Φ_B through the coil connected to the galvanometer. In each case the flux changes either because the magnetic field changes with time or because the coil is moving through a nonuniform magnetic field. Check back through the list to verify this statement. Faraday's law of induction, the subject of the next section, states that in all of these situations the induced emf is proportional to the *rate of change* of magnetic flux Φ_B through the coil. The *direction* of the induced emf depends on whether the flux is increasing or decreasing. If the flux is constant, there is no induced emf.

Induced emfs are not mere laboratory curiosities but have a tremendous number of practical applications. If you are reading these words indoors, you are making use of induced emfs right now! At the power plant that supplies your neighborhood, an electric generator produces an emf by varying the magnetic flux through coils of wire. (In the next section we'll see in detail how this is done.) This emf supplies the voltage between the terminals of the wall sockets in your home, and this voltage supplies the power to your reading lamp. Indeed, any appliance that you plug into a wall socket makes use of induced emfs.

Magnetically induced emfs, just like the emfs discussed in Section 25.4, are always the result of the action of *nonelectrostatic* forces. When these forces are the result of additional electric fields induced by changing magnetic fields, we have to distinguish carefully between electric fields produced by charges (according to Coulomb's law) and those produced by changing magnetic fields. We'll denote these by $\vec{E}_c$ (where c stands for Coulomb or conservative) and $\vec{E}_n$ (where n stands for non-Coulomb or nonconservative), respectively. We'll return to this distinction later in this chapter and the next.

29.3 Calculating the magnetic flux through an area element.

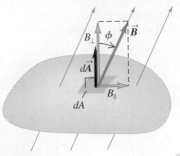

Magnetic flux through element of area $d\vec{A}$:
$d\Phi_B = \vec{B} \cdot d\vec{A} = B_\perp dA = B\,dA\cos\phi$

29.2 Faraday's Law

The common element in all induction effects is changing magnetic flux through a circuit. Before stating the simple physical law that summarizes all of the kinds of experiments described in Section 29.1, let's first review the concept of magnetic flux Φ_B (which we introduced in Section 27.3). For an infinitesimal-area element $d\vec{A}$ in a magnetic field $\vec{B}$ (Figure 29.3), the magnetic flux $d\Phi_B$ through the area is

$$d\Phi_B = \vec{B} \cdot d\vec{A} = B_\perp\,dA = B\,dA\cos\phi$$

where $B_\perp$ is the component of $\vec{B}$ perpendicular to the surface of the area element and ϕ is the angle between $\vec{B}$ and $d\vec{A}$. (As in Chapter 27, be careful to distinguish between two quantities named "phi," ϕ and Φ_B.) The total magnetic flux Φ_B through a finite area is the integral of this expression over the area:

$$\Phi_B = \int \vec{B} \cdot d\vec{A} = \int B\,dA\cos\phi \qquad (29.1)$$

If $\vec{B}$ is uniform over a flat area $\vec{A}$, then

$$\Phi_B = \vec{B} \cdot \vec{A} = BA\cos\phi \qquad (29.2)$$

Figure 29.4 reviews the rules for using Eq. (29.2).

CAUTION **Choosing the direction of $d\vec{A}$ or $\vec{A}$** In Eqs. (29.1) and (29.2) we have to be careful to define the direction of the vector area $d\vec{A}$ or $\vec{A}$ unambiguously. There are always two directions perpendicular to any given area, and the sign of the magnetic flux through the area depends on which one we choose to be positive. For example, in Fig. 29.3 we chose $d\vec{A}$ to point upward so ϕ is less than 90° and $\vec{B} \cdot d\vec{A}$ is positive. We could have chosen instead to have $d\vec{A}$ point downward, in which case ϕ would have been greater than 90° and $\vec{B} \cdot d\vec{A}$ would have been negative. Either choice is equally good, but once we make a choice we must stick with it. ∎

Faraday's law of induction states:

The induced emf in a closed loop equals the negative of the time rate of change of magnetic flux through the loop.

In symbols, Faraday's law is

$$\mathcal{E} = -\frac{d\Phi_B}{dt} \qquad \text{(Faraday's law of induction)} \qquad (29.3)$$

29.4 Calculating the flux of a uniform magnetic field through a flat area. (Compare to Fig. 22.6, which shows the rules for calculating the flux of a uniform *electric* field.)

Surface is face-on to magnetic field:
• $\vec{B}$ and $\vec{A}$ are parallel (the angle between $\vec{B}$ and $\vec{A}$ is $\phi = 0$).
• The magnetic flux $\Phi_B = \vec{B} \cdot \vec{A} = BA$.

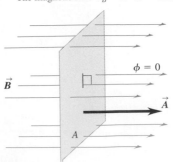

Surface is tilted from a face-on orientation by an angle ϕ:
• The angle between $\vec{B}$ and $\vec{A}$ is ϕ.
• The magnetic flux $\Phi_B = \vec{B} \cdot \vec{A} = BA\cos\phi$.

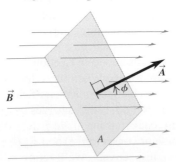

Surface is edge-on to magnetic field:
• $\vec{B}$ and $\vec{A}$ are perpendicular (the angle between $\vec{B}$ and $\vec{A}$ is $\phi = 90°$).
• The magnetic flux $\Phi_B = \vec{B} \cdot \vec{A} = BA\cos 90° = 0$.

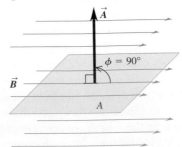

To understand the negative sign, we have to introduce a sign convention for the induced emf $\mathcal{E}$. But first let's look at a simple example of this law in action.

Example 29.1 Emf and current induced in a loop

The magnetic field between the poles of the electromagnet in Figure 29.5 is uniform at any time, but its magnitude is increasing at the rate of 0.020 T/s. The area of the conducting loop in the field is 120 cm², and the total circuit resistance, including the meter, is 5.0 Ω. (a) Find the induced emf and the induced current in the circuit. (b) If the loop is replaced by one made of an insulator, what effect does this have on the induced emf and induced current?

SOLUTION

IDENTIFY: The magnetic flux through the loop changes as the magnetic field changes. Hence there will be an induced emf in the loop, and we can find its value (one of our target variables) using Faraday's law. We can determine the current produced in the loop by this emf (our other target variable) using the same techniques as in Chapter 25.

SET UP: We calculate the magnetic flux using Eq. (29.2) and then use Faraday's law given by Eq. (29.3) to determine the resulting induced emf $\mathcal{E}$. Then we calculate the induced current produced by this emf using the relationship $\mathcal{E} = IR$, where R is the total resistance of the circuit that includes the loop.

29.5 A stationary conducting loop in an increasing magnetic field.

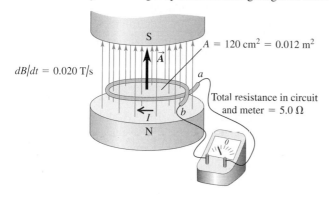

$dB/dt = 0.020 \text{ T/s}$

S

$\vec{A}$

$A = 120 \text{ cm}^2 = 0.012 \text{ m}^2$

a

b

I

N

Total resistance in circuit and meter = 5.0 Ω

EXECUTE: (a) The vector area of the loop is perpendicular to the plane of the loop; we choose it to be vertically upward. Then the vectors $\vec{A}$ and $\vec{B}$ are parallel. Since $\vec{B}$ is uniform, the magnetic flux through the loop is $\Phi_B = \vec{B} \cdot \vec{A} = BA\cos 0 = BA$. The area $A = 0.012 \text{ m}^2$ is constant, so the rate of change of magnetic flux is

$$\frac{d\Phi_B}{dt} = \frac{d(BA)}{dt} = \frac{dB}{dt}A = (0.020 \text{ T/s})(0.012 \text{ m}^2)$$

$$= 2.4 \times 10^{-4} \text{ V} = 0.24 \text{ mV}$$

This, apart from a sign that we haven't discussed yet, is the induced emf $\mathcal{E}$. The corresponding induced current is

$$I = \frac{\mathcal{E}}{R} = \frac{2.4 \times 10^{-4} \text{ V}}{5.0 \text{ Ω}} = 4.8 \times 10^{-5} \text{ A} = 0.048 \text{ mA}$$

(b) By changing to a loop made of insulator, we've made the resistance of the loop very high. Faraday's law, Eq. (29.3), does not involve the resistance of the circuit in any way, so the induced *emf* does not change. But the *current* will be smaller, as given by the equation $I = \mathcal{E}/R$. If the loop is made of a perfect insulator with infinite resistance, the induced current is zero even though an emf is present. This situation is analogous to an isolated battery whose terminals aren't connected to anything: There is an emf present, but no current flows.

EVALUATE: It's worthwhile to verify unit consistency in this calculation. There are many ways to do this; one is to note that because of the magnetic force relationship $\vec{F} = q\vec{v} \times \vec{B}$, the units of magnetic field are the units of force divided by the units of (charge times velocity): $1 \text{ T} = (1 \text{ N})/(1 \text{ C} \cdot \text{m/s})$. The units of magnetic flux can then be expressed as $(1 \text{ T})(1 \text{ m}^2) = 1 \text{ N} \cdot \text{s} \cdot \text{m/C}$, and the rate of change of magnetic flux as $1 \text{ N} \cdot \text{m/C} = 1 \text{ J/C} = 1 \text{ V}$. Thus the unit of $d\Phi_B/dt$ is the volt, as required by Eq. (29.3). Also recall that the unit of magnetic flux is the weber (Wb): $1 \text{ T} \cdot \text{m}^2 = 1 \text{ Wb}$, so $1 \text{ V} = 1 \text{ Wb/s}$.

Direction of Induced EMF

We can find the direction of an induced emf or current by using Eq. (29.3) together with some simple sign rules. Here's the procedure:

1. Define a positive direction for the vector area $\vec{A}$.

2. From the directions of $\vec{A}$ and the magnetic field $\vec{B}$, determine the sign of the magnetic flux Φ_B and its rate of change $d\Phi_B/dt$. Figure 29.6 shows several examples.

3. Determine the sign of the induced emf or current. If the flux is increasing, so $d\Phi_B/dt$ is positive, then the induced emf or current is negative; if the flux is decreasing, $d\Phi_B/dt$ is negative and the induced emf or current is positive.

29.6 The magnetic flux is becoming (a) more positive, (b) less positive, (c) more negative, and (d) less negative. Therefore Φ_B is increasing in (a) and (d) and decreasing in (b) and (c). In (a) and (d) the emfs are negative (they are opposite to the direction of the curled fingers of your right hand when your right thumb points along $\vec{A}$). In (b) and (c) the emfs are positive (in the same direction as the curled fingers).

(a)

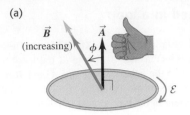

- Flux is positive ($\Phi_B > 0$) ...
- ... and becoming more positive ($d\Phi_B/dt > 0$).
- Induced emf is negative ($\mathcal{E} < 0$).

(b)

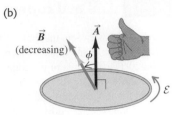

- Flux is positive ($\Phi_B > 0$) ...
- ... and becoming less positive ($d\Phi_B/dt < 0$).
- Induced emf is positive ($\mathcal{E} > 0$).

(c)

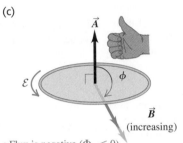

- Flux is negative ($\Phi_B < 0$) ...
- ... and becoming more negative ($d\Phi_B/dt < 0$).
- Induced emf is positive ($\mathcal{E} > 0$).

(d)

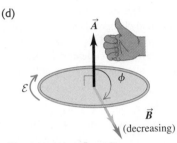

- Flux is negative ($\Phi_B < 0$) ...
- ... and becoming less negative ($d\Phi_B/dt > 0$).
- Induced emf is negative ($\mathcal{E} < 0$).

4. Finally, determine the direction of the induced emf or current using your right hand. Curl the fingers of your right hand around the $\vec{A}$ vector, with your right thumb in the direction of $\vec{A}$. If the induced emf or current in the circuit is *positive,* it is in the same direction as your curled fingers; if the induced emf or current is *negative,* it is in the opposite direction.

In Example 29.1, in which $\vec{A}$ is upward, a positive $\mathcal{E}$ would be directed counterclockwise around the loop, as seen from above. Both $\vec{A}$ and $\vec{B}$ are upward in this example, so Φ_B is positive; the magnitude B is increasing, so $d\Phi_B/dt$ is positive. Hence by Eq. (29.3), $\mathcal{E}$ in Example 29.1 is *negative.* Its actual direction is thus *clockwise* around the loop, as seen from above.

If the loop in Fig. 29.5 is a conductor, an induced current results from this emf; this current is also clockwise, as Fig. 29.5 shows. This induced current produces an additional magnetic field through the loop, and the right-hand rule described in Section 28.6 shows that this field is *opposite* in direction to the increasing field produced by the electromagnet. This is an example of a general rule called *Lenz's law,* which says that any induction effect tends to oppose the change that caused it; in this case the change is the increase in the flux of the electromagnet's field through the loop. (We'll study this law in detail in the next section.)

You should check out the signs of the induced emfs and currents for the list of experiments in Section 29.1. For example, when the loop in Fig. 29.2 is in a constant field and we tilt it or squeeze it to *decrease* the flux through it, the induced emf and current are counterclockwise, as seen from above.

CAUTION   **Induced emfs are caused by changes in flux** Since magnetic flux plays a central role in Faraday's law, it's tempting to think that *flux* is the cause of induced emf and that an induced emf will appear in a circuit whenever there is a magnetic field in the region bordered by the circuit. But Eq. (29.3) shows that only a *change* in flux through a circuit, not flux itself, can induce an emf in a circuit. If the flux through a circuit has a constant value, whether positive, negative, or zero, there is no induced emf.

If we have a coil with N identical turns, and if the flux varies at the same rate through each turn, the *total* rate of change through all the turns is N times as large as for a single turn. If Φ_B is the flux through each turn, the total emf in a coil with N turns is

$$\mathcal{E} = -N\frac{d\Phi_B}{dt} \qquad (29.4)$$

As we discussed in this chapter's introduction, induced emfs play an essential role in the generation of electric power for commercial use. Several of the following examples explore different methods of producing emfs by the motion of a conductor relative to a magnetic field, giving rise to a changing flux through a circuit.

Problem-Solving Strategy 29.1   Faraday's Law

IDENTIFY: *the relevant concepts:* Faraday's law applies when there is a changing magnetic flux. To use the law, make sure you can identify an area through which there is a flux of magnetic field. This will usually be the area enclosed by a loop, usually made of a conducting material (though not always—see part (b) of Example 29.1). As always, identify the target variable(s).

SET UP *the problem* using the following steps:

1. Faraday's law relates the induced emf to the rate of change of magnetic flux. To calculate this rate of change, you first have to understand what is making the flux change. Is the conductor moving? Is it changing orientation? Is the magnetic field changing? Remember that it's not the flux itself that counts, but its *rate of change*.

2. Choose a direction for the area vector $\vec{A}$ or $d\vec{A}$. The direction must always be perpendicular to the plane of the area. Note that you always have two choices of direction. For instance, if the plane of the area is horizontal, $\vec{A}$ could point straight up or straight down. It's like choosing which direction is the positive one in a problem involving motion in a straight line; it doesn't matter which direction you choose, just so you use it consistently throughout the problem.

EXECUTE *the solution* as follows:

1. Calculate the magnetic flux using Eq. (29.2) if $\vec{B}$ is uniform over the area of the loop or Eq. (29.1) if it isn't uniform, being mindful of the direction you chose for the area vector.

2. Calculate the induced emf using Eq. (29.3) or (29.4). If your conductor has N turns in a coil, don't forget to multiply by N. Remember the sign rule for the positive direction of emf and use it consistently.

3. If the circuit resistance is known, you can calculate the magnitude of the induced current I using $\mathcal{E} = IR$.

EVALUATE *your answer:* Check your results for the proper units, and double-check that you have properly implemented the sign rules for calculating magnetic flux and induced emf.

Example 29.2   Magnitude and direction of an induced emf

A coil of wire containing 500 circular loops with radius 4.00 cm is placed between the poles of a large electromagnet, where the magnetic field is uniform and at an angle of 60° with the plane of the coil. The field decreases at a rate of 0.200 T/s. What are the magnitude and direction of the induced emf?

CAUTION   **Remember how ϕ is defined** You may have been tempted to say that $\phi = 60°$ in this problem. If so, remember that ϕ is the angle between $\vec{A}$ and $\vec{B}$, *not* the angle between $\vec{B}$ and the plane of the loop. ▮

SOLUTION

IDENTIFY: Our target variable is the emf induced by a varying magnetic flux through the coil. The flux varies because the magnetic field decreases in amplitude.

SET UP: We choose the area vector $\vec{A}$ to be in the direction shown in Figure 29.7. With this choice, the geometry is very similar to Fig. 29.6b. That figure will help us determine the direction of the induced emf.

EXECUTE: The magnetic field is uniform over the loop, so we can calculate the flux using Eq. (29.2): $\Phi_B = BA\cos\phi$, where $\phi = 30°$. In this expression, the only quantity that changes with time is the magnitude B of the field.

29.7 Our sketch for this problem.

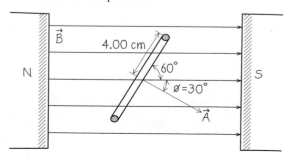

Continued

The rate of change of the flux is $d\Phi_B/dt = (dB/dt)A\cos\phi$. In our problem, $dB/dt = -0.200$ T/s and $A = \pi(0.0400$ m$)^2 = 0.00503$ m^2, so

$$\frac{d\Phi_B}{dt} = \frac{dB}{dt}A\cos 30°$$

$$= (-0.200 \text{ T/s})(0.00503 \text{ m}^2)(0.866)$$

$$= -8.71 \times 10^{-4} \text{ T} \cdot \text{m}^2/\text{s} = -8.71 \times 10^{-4} \text{ Wb/s}$$

From Eq. (29.4), the induced emf in the coil of $N = 500$ turns is

$$\mathcal{E} = -N\frac{d\Phi_B}{dt}$$

$$= -(500)(-8.71 \times 10^{-4} \text{ Wb/s}) = 0.435 \text{ V}$$

Note that the answer is positive. This means that when you point your right thumb in the direction of the area vector $\vec{A}$ (30° above the magnetic field $\vec{B}$), the positive direction for $\mathcal{E}$ is in the direction of the curled fingers of your right hand. Hence the emf in this example is in this same direction (compare Fig. 29.6b). If you were viewing the coil from the left side in Fig. 29.7a and looking in the direction of $\vec{A}$, the emf would be clockwise.

EVALUATE: If the ends of the wire are connected together, the direction of current in the coil is in the same direction as the emf— that is, clockwise as seen from the left side of the coil. A clockwise current gives added magnetic flux through the coil in the same direction as the flux from the electromagnet, and therefore tends to oppose the decrease in total flux. We'll see more examples of this in Section 29.3.

Conceptual Example 29.3   **The search coil**

One practical way to measure magnetic field strength uses a small, closely wound coil with N turns called a *search coil*. The coil, of area A, is initially held so that its area vector $\vec{A}$ is aligned with a magnetic field with magnitude B. The coil is then either quickly rotated a quarter-turn about a diameter or quickly pulled out of the field. Explain how this device can be used to measure the value of B.

SOLUTION

Initially, the flux through the coil is $\Phi_B = NBA$; when the coil is rotated or pulled from the field, the flux decreases rapidly from

NBA to zero. While the flux is decreasing, there is a momentary induced emf, and a momentary induced current occurs in an external circuit connected to the coil. The rate of change of flux through the coil is proportional to the current, or rate of flow of charge, so it is easy to show that the *total* flux change is proportional to the total charge that flows around the circuit. We can build an instrument that measures this total charge, and from this we can compute B. We leave the details as a problem (see Exercise 29.3). Strictly speaking, this method gives only the *average* field over the area of the coil. But if the area is small, this average field is very nearly equal to the field at the center of the coil.

Example 29.4   **Generator I: A simple alternator**

Figure 29.8a shows a simple version of an *alternator*, a device that generates an emf. A rectangular loop is made to rotate with constant angular speed ω about the axis shown. The magnetic field $\vec{B}$ is uniform and constant. At time $t = 0$, $\phi = 0$. Determine the induced emf.

SOLUTION

IDENTIFY: Again the emf (our target variable) is produced by a varying magnetic flux. In this situation, however, the magnetic field $\vec{B}$ is constant; the flux changes because the direction of $\vec{A}$ changes as the loop rotates.

29.8 (a) Schematic diagram of an alternator. A conducting loop rotates in a magnetic field, producing an emf. Connections from each end of the loop to the external circuit are made by means of that end's slip ring. The system is shown at the time when the angle $\phi = \omega t = 90°$. (b) Graph of the flux through the loop and the resulting emf at terminals ab, along with corresponding positions of the loop during one complete rotation.

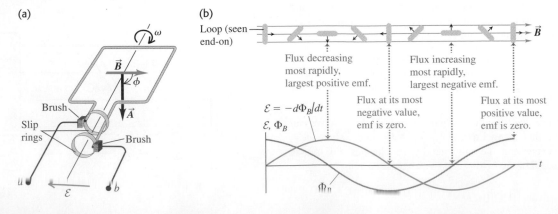

SET UP: Figure 29.8a shows the direction of the area vector $\vec{A}$. Note that as the loop rotates, the angle ϕ between $\vec{A}$ and $\vec{B}$ increases at a constant rate.

EXECUTE: Again the magnetic field is uniform over the loop, so the magnetic flux is easy to calculate. The rate of change of the angle ϕ is equal to ω, the angular speed of the loop, so we can write $\phi = \omega t$. Hence

$$\Phi_B = BA\cos\phi = BA\cos\omega t$$

The derivative of $\cos\omega t$ is $(d/dt)\cos\omega t = -\omega\sin\omega t$. Hence, by Faraday's law [Eq. (29.3)] the induced emf is

$$\mathcal{E} = -\frac{d\Phi_B}{dt} = \omega BA\sin\omega t$$

EVALUATE: The induced emf $\mathcal{E}$ varies sinusoidally with time (Fig. 29.8b). When the plane of the loop is perpendicular to $\vec{B}$ ($\phi = 0$ or $180°$), Φ_B reaches its maximum and minimum values. At these times, its instantaneous rate of change is zero and $\mathcal{E}$ is zero. Also, $\mathcal{E}$ is greatest in absolute value when the plane of the loop is parallel to $\vec{B}$ ($\phi = 90°$ or $270°$) and Φ_B is changing most rapidly. Finally, we note that the induced emf does not depend on the *shape* of the loop, but only on its area. Because $\mathcal{E}$ is directly proportional to ω and B, some tachometers use the emf in a rotating coil to measure rotational speed. Other devices use an emf of this kind to measure magnetic field.

We can use the alternator as a source of emf in an external circuit by use of two *slip rings,* which rotate with the loop, as shown in Fig. 29.8a. The rings slide against stationary contacts called *brushes,* which are connected to the output terminals *a* and *b*. Since the emf varies sinusoidally, the current that results in the circuit is an *alternating* current that also varies sinusoidally in magnitude and direction. An alternator is also called an *alternating-current* (ac) *generator* for this reason. The amplitude of the emf can be increased by increasing the rotation speed, the field magnitude, or the loop area or by using *N* loops instead of one, as in Eq. (29.4).

Alternators are used in automobiles to generate the currents in the ignition, the lights, and the entertainment system. The arrangement is a little different than in this example; rather than having a rotating loop in a magnetic field, the loop stays fixed and an electromagnet rotates. (The rotation is provided by a mechanical connection between the alternator and the engine.) But the result is the same; the flux through the loop varies sinusoidally, producing a sinusoidally varying emf. Larger alternators of this same type are used in electric power plants (Figure 29.9).

29.9 A commercial alternator uses many loops of wire wound around a barrel-like structure called an armature. The armature and wire remain stationary while electromagnets rotate on a shaft (not shown) through the center of the armature. The resulting induced emf is far larger than would be possible with a single loop of wire.

Example 29.5 **Generator II: A DC generator and back emf in a motor**

The alternator in Example 29.4 produces a sinusoidally varying emf and hence an alternating current. We can use a similar scheme to make a *direct-current* (dc) *generator* that produces an emf that always has the same sign. A prototype dc generator is shown in Fig. 29.10a. The arrangement of split rings is called a *commutator;* it reverses the connections to the external circuit at angular positions where the emf reverses. The resulting emf is shown in Fig. 29.10b. Commercial dc generators have a large number of coils and commutator segments; this arrangement smooths out the bumps in the emf, so the terminal voltage is not only one-directional but also practically constant. This brush-and-commutator arrangement is the same as that in the direct-current motor we discussed in Section 27.8. The motor's *back emf* is just the emf induced by the changing magnetic flux through its rotating coil. Consider a motor with a square coil 10.0 cm on a side, with 500 turns of wire. If the magnetic field has magnitude 0.200 T, at what rotation speed is the *average* back emf of the motor equal to 112 V?

29.10 (a) Schematic diagram of a dc generator, using a split-ring commutator. The ring halves are attached to the loop and rotate with it. (b) Graph of the resulting induced emf at terminals *ab*. Compare to Fig. 29.8b.

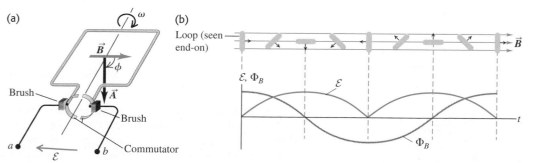

Continued

SOLUTION

IDENTIFY: As far as the rotating loop is concerned, the situation is the same as in Example 29.4 except that we now have N turns of wire. Without the commutator, the emf would alternate between positive and negative values and have an average value of zero (Fig. 29.8b). But with the commutator added, the emf is never negative and its average value is positive (Fig. 29.10b). Using our result from Example 29.4, we'll determine an expression for this average value and solve that expression for the rotational speed ω (our target variable).

SET UP: The setup is the same as in Example 29.4.

EXECUTE: Comparing Figs. 29.8b and 29.10b shows that the back emf of the motor is just the absolute value of the emf found for an alternator in Example 29.4, multiplied by the number of turns N in the coil as in Eq. (29.4):

$$|\mathcal{E}| = N\omega BA |\sin \omega t|$$

To find the *average* back emf, we replace $|\sin \omega t|$ by its average value. The average value of the sine function is found by integrating $\sin \omega t$ over half a cycle, from $t = 0$ to $t = T/2 = \pi/\omega$, and then dividing by the elapsed time π/ω. During this half cycle, the sine function is positive, so $|\sin \omega t| = \sin \omega t$, and we find

$$(|\sin \omega t|)_{av} = \frac{\int_0^{\pi/\omega} \sin \omega t \, dt}{\pi/\omega} = \frac{2}{\pi}$$

or about 0.64. The average back emf is then

$$\mathcal{E}_{av} = \frac{2N\omega BA}{\pi}$$

The back emf is proportional to the rotation speed ω, as was stated without proof in Section 27.8. Solving for ω, we obtain

$$\omega = \frac{\pi \mathcal{E}_{av}}{2NBA}$$

$$= \frac{\pi (112 \text{ V})}{2(500)(0.200 \text{ T})(0.100 \text{ m})^2} = 176 \text{ rad/s}$$

We used the relationships $1 \text{ V} = 1 \text{ Wb/s} = 1 \text{ T} \cdot \text{m}^2/\text{s}$ from Example 29.1. We were able to add "radians" to the units of the answer because it is a dimensionless quantity, as we discussed in Chapter 9. The rotation speed can also be written as

$$\omega = 176 \text{ rad/s} \frac{1 \text{ rev}}{2\pi \text{ rad}} \frac{60 \text{ s}}{1 \text{ min}} = 1680 \text{ rev/min}$$

EVALUATE: The average back emf is directly proportional to ω. Hence the slower the rotation speed, the less the back emf and the greater the possibility of burning out the motor, as we described in Example 27.11 (Section 27.8).

While we have used a very simple model of a generator in this and the preceding example, the same principles apply to the operation of commercial generators.

| Example 29.6 | **Generator III: The slidewire generator** |

Figure 29.11 shows a U-shaped conductor in a uniform magnetic field $\vec{B}$ perpendicular to the plane of the figure, directed *into* the page. We lay a metal rod with length L across the two arms of the conductor, forming a circuit, and move the rod to the right with constant velocity $\vec{v}$. This induces an emf and a current, which is why this device is called a *slidewire generator*. Find the magnitude and direction of the resulting induced emf.

29.11 A slidewire generator. The magnetic field $\vec{B}$ and the vector area $\vec{A}$ are both directed into the figure. The increase in magnetic flux (caused by an increase in area) induces the emf and current.

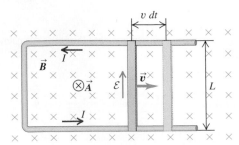

SOLUTION

IDENTIFY: The magnetic flux changes because the area of the loop—bounded on the right by the moving rod—is increasing. Our target variable is the emf $\mathcal{E}$ induced in this expanding loop.

SET UP: The magnetic field is uniform over the area of the loop, so we can again calculate the magnetic flux using $\Phi_B = BA\cos\phi$. We choose the area vector $\vec{A}$ to point straight into the plane of the picture, in the same direction as $\vec{B}$. With this choice a positive emf will be one that is directed clockwise around the loop. (You can check this with the right-hand rule. Using your right hand, point your thumb into the page and curl your fingers as in Fig. 29.6.)

EXECUTE: Since $\vec{B}$ and $\vec{A}$ point in the same direction, the angle $\phi = 0$ and $\Phi_B = BA$. The magnetic field magnitude B is constant, so the induced emf is

$$\mathcal{E} = -\frac{d\Phi_B}{dt} = -B\frac{dA}{dt}$$

To calculate dA/dt, note that in a time dt the sliding rod moves a distance $v \, dt$ (Fig. 29.11) and the loop area increases by an amount $dA = Lv \, dt$. Hence the induced emf is

$$\mathcal{E} = -B\frac{Lv \, dt}{dt} = -BLv$$

The minus sign tells us that the emf is directed *counterclockwise* around the loop. The induced current is also counterclockwise, as shown in the figure.

EVALUATE: Note that the emf is constant if the velocity $\vec{v}$ of the rod is constant. In this case the slidewire generator acts as a *direct-current* generator. It's not a very practical device because the rod eventually moves beyond the U-shaped conductor and loses contact, after which the current stops.

Example 29.7 Work and power in the slidewire generator

In the slidewire generator of Example 29.6, energy is dissipated in the circuit owing to its resistance. Let the resistance of the circuit (made up of the moving slidewire and the U-shaped conductor that connects the ends of the slidewire) at a given point in the slidewire's motion be R. Show that the rate at which energy is dissipated in the circuit is exactly equal to the rate at which work must be done to move the rod through the magnetic field.

SOLUTION

IDENTIFY: Our target variables are the *rates* at which energy is dissipated and at which work is done. This means that we'll be working with the concept of power (recall Section 6.4). Energy is dissipated in the circuit because there is resistance; to describe this we'll need the ideas of Section 25.5. It takes work to move the rod because there is an induced current flowing through it. The magnetic field exerts a force on this current-carrying rod, and whoever is pushing the rod has to do work against this force.

SET UP: We found the induced emf $\mathcal{E}$ in this circuit in Example 29.6. The current I in the circuit equals the absolute value of $\mathcal{E}$ divided by the resistance R, and the rate at which energy is dissipated in the rod is $P_{\text{dissipated}} = I^2R$. The magnetic force on the rod is $\vec{F} = I\vec{L} \times \vec{B}$; the vector $\vec{L}$ points along the rod in the direction of the current. Figure 29.12 shows that this force is opposite to the velocity of the rod, and so to maintain the motion a force of equal magnitude must be applied in the direction of the rod's motion (that is, in the direction of $\vec{v}$). The rate of doing work is equal to

29.12 The magnetic force $\vec{F} = I\vec{L} \times \vec{B}$ that acts on the rod due to the induced current is to the left, opposite to $\vec{v}$.

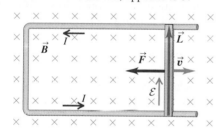

the product of the applied force and the speed of the rod: $P_{\text{applied}} = Fv$.

EXECUTE: First we'll calculate $P_{\text{dissipated}}$. From Example 29.6, $\mathcal{E} = -BLv$. Hence the current in the rod is

$$I = \frac{|\mathcal{E}|}{R} = \frac{BLv}{R}$$

and the rate of energy dissipation is

$$P_{\text{dissipated}} = I^2R = \left(\frac{BLv}{R}\right)^2 R = \frac{B^2L^2v^2}{R}$$

To calculate P_{applied}, we first calculate the magnitude of $\vec{F} = I\vec{L} \times \vec{B}$. Since $\vec{L}$ and $\vec{B}$ are perpendicular, this magnitude is

$$F = ILB = \frac{BLv}{R}LB = \frac{B^2L^2v}{R}$$

Hence the rate at which work is done by this applied force is

$$P_{\text{applied}} = Fv = \frac{B^2L^2v^2}{R}$$

EVALUATE: The rate at which work is done is just equal to the rate at which energy is dissipated in the resistance.

CAUTION **You can't violate energy conservation** You might think that reversing the direction of $\vec{B}$ or of $\vec{v}$ might make it possible to have the magnetic force $\vec{F} = I\vec{L} \times \vec{B}$ be in the *same* direction as $\vec{v}$. This would be a pretty neat trick. Once the rod was moving, the changing magnetic flux would induce an emf and a current, and the magnetic force on the rod would make it move even faster, increasing the emf and current; this would go on until the rod was moving at tremendous speed and producing electric power at a prodigious rate. If this seems too good to be true, not to mention a violation of energy conservation, that's because it is. Reversing $\vec{B}$ also reverses the sign of the induced emf and current and hence the direction of $\vec{L}$, so the magnetic force still opposes the motion of the rod; a similar result holds true if we reverse $\vec{v}$. This behavior is part of Lenz's law, to be discussed in Section 29.3. ∎

Generators As Energy Converters

Example 29.7 shows that the slidewire generator doesn't produce electric energy out of nowhere; the energy is supplied by whatever body exerts the force that keeps the rod moving. All that the generator does is to *convert* that energy into a different form. The equality between the rate at which *mechanical* energy is supplied to a generator and the rate at which *electric* energy is generated holds for all types of generators. This is true in particular for the alternator described in Example 29.4. (We are neglecting the effects of friction in the bearings of an alternator or between the rod and the U-shaped conductor of a slidewire generator. If these are included, the conservation of energy demands that the energy lost to friction is not available for conversion to electric energy. In real generators the friction is kept to a minimum to keep the energy-conversion process as efficient as possible.)

In Chapter 27 we stated that the magnetic force on moving charges can never do work. But you might think that the magnetic force $\vec{F} = I\vec{L} \times \vec{B}$ in Example 29.7 *is* doing (negative) work on the current-carrying rod as it moves, contradicting our earlier statement. In fact, the work done by the magnetic force is actually zero. The moving charges that make up the current in the rod in Fig. 29.12 have a vertical component of velocity, causing a horizontal component of force on these charges. As a result, there is a horizontal displacement of charge within the rod, the left side acquiring a net positive charge and the right side a net negative charge. The result is a horizontal component of electric field, perpendicular to the length of the rod (analogous to the Hall effect, described in Section 27.9). It is this field, in the direction of motion of the rod, that does work on the mobile charges in the rod and hence indirectly on the atoms making up the rod.

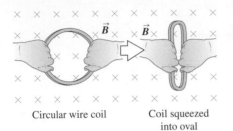

Circular wire coil   Coil squeezed
                            into oval

Test Your Understanding of Section 29.2   The figure at left shows a wire coil being squeezed in a uniform magnetic field. (a) While the coil is being squeezed, is the induced emf in the coil (i) clockwise, (ii) counterclockwise, or (iii) zero? (b) Once the coil has reached its final squeezed shape, is the induced emf in the coil (i) clockwise, (ii) counterclockwise, or (iii) zero?

29.3 Lenz's Law

Lenz's law is a convenient alternative method for determining the direction of an induced current or emf. Lenz's law is not an independent principle; it can be derived from Faraday's law. It always gives the same results as the sign rules we introduced in connection with Faraday's law, but it is often easier to use. Lenz's law also helps us gain intuitive understanding of various induction effects and of the role of energy conservation. H. F. E. Lenz (1804–1865) was a Russian scientist who duplicated independently many of the discoveries of Faraday and Henry. **Lenz's law** states:

> **The direction of any magnetic induction effect is such as to oppose the cause of the effect.**

The "cause" may be changing flux through a stationary circuit due to a varying magnetic field, changing flux due to motion of the conductors that make up the circuit, or any combination. If the flux in a stationary circuit changes, as in Examples 29.1 and 29.2, the induced current sets up a magnetic field of its own. Within the area bounded by the circuit, this field is *opposite* to the original field if the original field is *increasing* but is in the *same* direction as the original field if the latter is *decreasing*. That is, the induced current opposes the *change in flux* through the circuit (*not* the flux itself).

If the flux change is due to motion of the conductors, as in Examples 29.3 through 29.7, the direction of the induced current in the moving conductor is such that the direction of the magnetic-field force on the conductor is opposite in direction to its motion. Thus the motion of the conductor, which caused the induced current, is opposed. We saw this explicitly for the slidewire generator in Example 29.7. In all these cases the induced current tries to preserve the *status quo* by opposing motion or a change of flux.

Lenz's law is also directly related to energy conservation. If the induced current in Example 29.7 were in the direction opposite to that given by Lenz's law, the magnetic force on the rod would accelerate it to ever-increasing speed with no external energy source, even though electric energy is being dissipated in the circuit. This would be a clear violation of energy conservation and doesn't happen in nature.

Conceptual Example 29.8   **The slidewire generator, revisited**

In Fig. 29.11, the induced current in the loop causes an additional magnetic field in the area bounded by the loop. The direction of the induced current is counterclockwise. From the discussion of Section 28.2, we see that the direction of the additional magnetic field caused by this current is *out of* the plane of the figure. Its direction is opposite that of the original magnetic field, so it tends to cancel the effect of that field. This is consistent with the prediction of Lenz's law.

| Conceptual Example 29.9 | **Finding the direction of induced current** |

In Fig. 29.13 there is a uniform magnetic field $\vec{B}$ through the coil. The magnitude of the field is increasing, and the resulting induced emf causes an induced current. Use Lenz's law to determine the direction of the induced current.

29.13 The induced current due to the change in $\vec{B}$ is clockwise, as seen from above the loop. The added field $\vec{B}_{induced}$ that it causes is downward, opposing the change in the upward field $\vec{B}$.

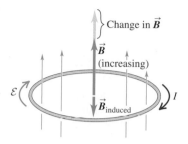

SOLUTION

This situation is the same as in Example 29.1 (Section 29.2). By Lenz's law the induced current must produce a magnetic field $\vec{B}_{induced}$ inside the coil that is downward, opposing the change in flux. Using the right-hand rule we described in Section 28.5 for the direction of the magnetic field produced by a circular loop, $\vec{B}_{induced}$ will be in the desired direction if the induced current flows as shown in Fig. 29.13.

Figure 29.14 shows several applications of Lenz's law to the similar situation of a magnet moving near a conducting loop. In each of the four cases shown, the induced current produces a mag-netic field of its own, in a direction that opposes the change in flux through the loop due to the magnet's motion.

29.14 Directions of induced currents as a bar magnet moves along the axis of a conducting loop. If the bar magnet is stationary, there is no induced current.

(a) Motion of magnet causes *increasing downward* flux through loop.

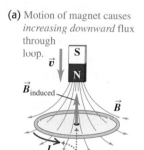

(b) Motion of magnet causes *decreasing upward* flux through loop.

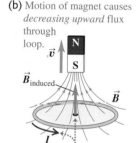

(c) Motion of magnet causes *decreasing downward* flux through loop.

(d) Motion of magnet causes *increasing upward* flux through loop.

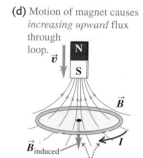

The induced magnetic field is *upward* to oppose the flux change. To produce this induced field, the induced current must be *counterclockwise* as seen from above the loop.

The induced magnetic field is *downward* to oppose the flux change. To produce this induced field, the induced current must be *clockwise* as seen from above the loop.

Lenz's Law and the Response to Flux Changes

Since an induced current always opposes any change in magnetic flux through a circuit, how is it possible for the flux to change at all? The answer is that Lenz's law gives only the *direction* of an induced current; the *magnitude* of the current depends on the resistance of the circuit. The greater the circuit resistance, the less the induced current that appears to oppose any change in flux and the easier it is for a flux change to take effect. If the loop in Fig. 29.14 were made out of wood (an insulator), there would be almost no induced current in response to changes in the flux through the loop.

Conversely, the less the circuit resistance, the greater the induced current and the more difficult it is to change the flux through the circuit. If the loop in Fig. 29.14 is a good conductor, an induced current flows as long as the magnet moves relative to the loop. Once the magnet and loop are no longer in relative motion, the induced current very quickly decreases to zero because of the nonzero resistance in the loop.

The extreme case occurs when the resistance of the circuit is *zero*. Then the induced current in Fig. 29.14 will continue to flow even after the induced emf has disappeared—that is, even after the magnet has stopped moving relative to the loop. Thanks to this *persistent current,* it turns out that the flux through the loop is exactly the same as it was before the magnet started to move, so the flux through a loop of zero resistance *never* changes. Exotic materials called *superconductors* do indeed have zero resistance; we discuss these further in Section 29.8.

29.4 Motional Electromotive Force

29.15 A conducting rod moving in a uniform magnetic field. (a) The rod, the velocity, and the field are mutually perpendicular. (b) Direction of induced current in the circuit.

(a) Isolated moving rod

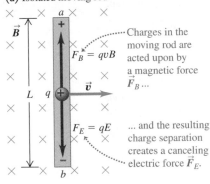

Charges in the moving rod are acted upon by a magnetic force $\vec{F}_B$...

... and the resulting charge separation creates a canceling electric force $\vec{F}_E$.

(b) Rod connected to stationary conductor

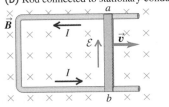

The motional emf $\mathcal{E}$ in the moving rod creates an electric field in the stationary conductor.

We've seen several situations in which a conductor moves in a magnetic field, as in the generators discussed in Examples 29.4 through 29.7. We can gain additional insight into the origin of the induced emf in these situations by considering the magnetic forces on mobile charges in the conductor. Figure 29.15a shows the same moving rod that we discussed in Example 29.6, separated for the moment from the U-shaped conductor. The magnetic field $\vec{B}$ is uniform and directed into the page, and we move the rod to the right at a constant velocity $\vec{v}$. A charged particle q in the rod then experiences a magnetic force $\vec{F} = q\vec{v} \times \vec{B}$ with magnitude $F = |q|vB$. We'll assume in the following discussion that q is positive; in that case the direction of this force is upward along the rod, from b toward a.

This magnetic force causes the free charges in the rod to move, creating an excess of positive charge at the upper end a and negative charge at the lower end b. This in turn creates an electric field $\vec{E}$ within the rod, in the direction from a toward b (opposite to the magnetic force). Charge continues to accumulate at the ends of the rod until $\vec{E}$ becomes large enough for the downward electric force (with magnitude qE) to cancel exactly the *upward* magnetic force (with magnitude qvB). Then $qE = qvB$ and the charges are in equilibrium.

The magnitude of the potential difference $V_{ab} = V_a - V_b$ is equal to the electric field magnitude E multiplied by the length L of the rod. From the above discussion, $E = vB$, so

$$V_{ab} = EL = vBL \tag{29.5}$$

with point a at higher potential than point b.

Now suppose the moving rod slides along a stationary U-shaped conductor, forming a complete circuit (Fig. 29.15b). No *magnetic* force acts on the charges in the stationary U-shaped conductor, but the charge that was near points a and b redistributes itself along the stationary conductor, creating an *electric* field within it. This field establishes a current in the direction shown. The moving rod has become a source of electromotive force; within it, charge moves from lower to higher potential, and in the remainder of the circuit, charge moves from higher to lower potential. We call this emf a **motional electromotive force,** denoted by $\mathcal{E}$. From the above discussion, the magnitude of this emf is

$$\mathcal{E} = vBL \qquad \text{(motional emf; length and velocity perpendicular to uniform } \vec{B}) \tag{29.6}$$

corresponding to a force per unit charge of magnitude vB acting for a distance L along the moving rod. If the total circuit resistance of the U-shaped conductor and the sliding rod is R, the induced current I in the circuit is given by $vBL = IR$. This is the same result we obtained in Section 29.2 using Faraday's law, and indeed motional emf is a particular case of Faraday's law, one of the several examples described in Section 29.2.

The emf associated with the moving rod in Fig. 29.15 is analogous to that of a battery with its positive terminal at a and its negative terminal at b, although the origins of the two emfs are quite different. In each case a nonelectrostatic force on the charges in the device, in the direction from b to a, and the emf is the work per unit charge done by this force when a charge moves from b to a in the device. When the device is connected to an external circuit, the direction of cur rent is from b to a in the device and from a to b in the external circuit. While we have discussed motional emf in terms of a closed circuit like that in Fig. 29.15b, a motional emf is also present in the isolated moving rod in Fig. 29.15a, in the same way that a battery has an emf even when it's not part of a circuit.

The direction of the induced emf in Fig. 29.15 can be deduced by using Lenz's law, even if (as in Fig. 29.15a) the conductor does not form a complete circuit. In this case we can mentally complete the circuit between the ends of the conductor and use Lenz's law to determine the direction of the current. From this we can deduce the polarity of the ends of the open-circuit conductor. The direction from the $-$ end to the $+$ end within the conductor is the direction the current would have if the circuit were complete.

You should verify that if we express v in meters per second, B in teslas, and L in meters, then $\mathcal{E}$ is in volts. (Recall that $1\ \text{V} = 1\ \text{J/C}$.)

Motional emf: General Form

We can generalize the concept of motional emf for a conductor with *any* shape, moving in any magnetic field, uniform or not (assuming that the magnetic field at each point does not vary with time). For an element $d\vec{l}$ of conductor, the contribution $d\mathcal{E}$ to the emf is the magnitude dl multiplied by the component of $\vec{v} \times \vec{B}$ (the magnetic force per unit charge) parallel to $d\vec{l}$; that is,

$$d\mathcal{E} = (\vec{v} \times \vec{B}) \cdot d\vec{l}$$

For any closed conducting loop, the total emf is

$$\mathcal{E} = \oint (\vec{v} \times \vec{B}) \cdot d\vec{l} \qquad \text{(motional emf: closed conducting loop)} \quad (29.7)$$

This expression looks very different from our original statement of Faraday's law, Eq. (29.3), which stated that $\mathcal{E} = -d\Phi_B/dt$. In fact, though, the two statements are equivalent. It can be shown that the rate of change of magnetic flux through a moving conducting loop is always given by the negative of the expression in Eq. (29.7). Thus this equation gives us an alternative formulation of Faraday's law. This alternative is often more convenient than the original one in problems with *moving* conductors. But when we have *stationary* conductors in changing magnetic fields, Eq. (29.7) *cannot* be used; in this case, $\mathcal{E} = -d\Phi_B/dt$ is the only correct way to express Faraday's law.

Example 29.10   Calculating motional emf

Suppose the moving rod in Fig. 29.15b is 0.10 m long, the velocity v is 2.5 m/s, the total resistance of the loop is 0.030 Ω, and B is 0.60 T. Find $\mathcal{E}$, the induced current, and the force acting on the rod.

SOLUTION

IDENTIFY: The first target variable is the *motional* emf $\mathcal{E}$ due to the rod's motion. We'll find the current from the values of $\mathcal{E}$ and the resistance R. The force on the rod is actually a magnetic force exerted by $\vec{B}$ on the current in the rod.

SET UP: We'll use the motional emf expression developed in this section, the familiar relationship $\mathcal{E} = IR$, and the formula $\vec{F} = I\vec{L} \times \vec{B}$ for the magnetic force on a current-carrying rod of length $L = 0.10$ m.

EXECUTE: From Eq. (29.6) the emf is

$$\mathcal{E} = vBL = (2.5\ \text{m/s})(0.60\ \text{T})(0.10\ \text{m}) = 0.15\ \text{V}$$

The resulting induced current in the loop is

$$I = \frac{\mathcal{E}}{R} = \frac{0.15\ \text{V}}{0.030\ \Omega} = 5.0\ \text{A}$$

The magnetic force on the rod carrying this current is directed *opposite* to the rod's motion. You can see this by applying the right-hand rule for vector products to the formula $\vec{F} = I\vec{L} \times \vec{B}$. The vector $\vec{L}$ points from b to a in Fig. 29.15, in the same direction as the induced current in the rod. Since $\vec{L}$ and $\vec{B}$ are perpendicular, this force has magnitude

$$F = ILB = (5.0\ \text{A})(0.10\ \text{m})(0.60\ \text{T}) = 0.30\ \text{N}$$

EVALUATE: We can check our answer for the direction of $\vec{F}$ by using Lenz's law. If we take the area vector $\vec{A}$ to point into the plane of the loop, the magnetic flux is positive and increasing as the rod moves to the right and increases the area of the loop. Lenz's law tells us that a force appears to oppose this increase in flux. Hence the force on the rod is to the left, opposite its motion.

Example 29.11   The Faraday disk dynamo

A conducting disk with radius R, shown in Fig. 29.16, lies in the xy-plane and rotates with constant angular velocity ω about the z-axis. The disk is in a uniform, constant $\vec{B}$ field parallel to the z-axis. Find the induced emf between the center and the rim of the disk.

SOLUTION

IDENTIFY: A motional emf is present because the conducting disk moves relative to the $\vec{B}$ field. The complication is that different parts of the disk move at different speeds v, depending on their distance from the rotation axis. We'll address this by considering small segments of the disk and adding (actually integrating) their contributions to determine our target variable, the emf between the center and the rim.

SET UP: Consider the small segment of the disk labeled by its velocity vector $\vec{v}$. The magnetic force per unit charge on this segment is $\vec{v} \times \vec{B}$, which points radially outward from the center of the disk. Hence the induced emf tends to make a current flow radially outward, which tells us that the moving conducting path to think about here is a straight line from the center to the rim. We can find the emf from each small disk segment along this line using the expression $d\mathcal{E} = (\vec{v} \times \vec{B}) \cdot d\vec{l}$ and then integrate to find the total emf.

CAUTION **Speed in a rotating disk** You might be tempted to use Eq. (29.5) and simply multiply vB times the length of the moving conducting path, which is just the radius R. That wouldn't be right, because v has different values at different points along the path.

EXECUTE: Let's consider the motional emf $d\mathcal{E}$ due to a small radial segment at a distance r from the rotation axis. The associated length vector $d\vec{l}$ (of length dr) points radially outward, in the same direction as $\vec{v} \times \vec{B}$. The vectors $\vec{v}$ and $\vec{B}$ are perpendicular, and the magnitude of $\vec{v}$ is $v = \omega r$. Hence the total emf between center and rim is the sum of all such contributions:

$$\mathcal{E} = \int_0^R \omega B r \, dr = \frac{1}{2}\omega B R^2$$

EVALUATE: We can use this device as a source of emf in a circuit by completing the circuit through stationary brushes (b in the figure) that contact the disk and its conducting shaft as shown. The emf in such a disk was studied by Faraday; the device is called *a Faraday disk dynamo* or a *homopolar generator*. Unlike the alternator in Example 29.4, the Faraday disk dynamo is a direct-current generator; it produces an emf that is constant in time. Can you use Lenz's law to show that for the direction of rotation in Fig. 29.16, the current in the external circuit must be in the direction shown?

29.16 A conducting disk with radius R rotating at an angular speed ω in a magnetic field $\vec{B}$. The emf is induced along radial lines of the disk and is applied to an external circuit through the two sliding contacts labeled b.

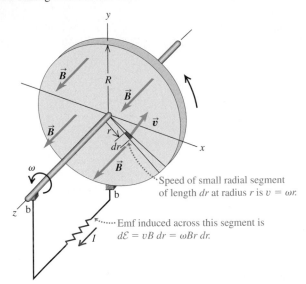

Speed of small radial segment of length dr at radius r is $v = \omega r$.

Emf induced across this segment is $d\mathcal{E} = vB \, dr = \omega B r \, dr$.

Test Your Understanding of Section 29.4   The earth's magnetic field points toward (magnetic) north. For simplicity, assume that the field has no vertical component (as is the case near the earth's equator). (a) If you hold a metal rod in your hand and walk toward the east, how should you orient the rod to get the maximum motional emf between its ends? (i) east-west; (ii) north-south; (iii) up-down; (iv) you get the same motional emf with all of these orientations. (b) How should you hold it to get *zero* emf as you walk toward the east? (i) east-west; (ii) north-south; (iii) up-down; (iv) none of these. (c) In which direction should you travel so that the motional emf across the rod is zero no matter how the rod is oriented? (i) west; (ii) north; (iii) south; (iv) straight up; (v) straight down.

29.5 Induced Electric Fields

When a conductor moves in a magnetic field, we can understand the induced emf on the basis of magnetic forces on charges in the conductor, as described in Section 29.4. But an induced emf also occurs when there is a changing flux through a stationary conductor. What is it that pushes the charges around the circuit in this type of situation?

As an example, let's consider the situation shown in Fig. 29.17. A long, thin solenoid with cross-sectional area A and n turns per unit length is encircled at its center by a circular conducting loop. The galvanometer G measures the current in the loop. A current I in the winding of the solenoid sets up a magnetic field $\vec{B}$ along the solenoid axis, as shown, with magnitude B as calculated in Example 28.9 (Section 28.7): $B = \mu_0 nI$, where n is the number of turns per unit length. If we neglect the small field outside the solenoid and take the area vector $\vec{A}$ to point in the same direction as $\vec{B}$, then the magnetic flux Φ_B through the loop is

$$\Phi_B = BA = \mu_0 nIA$$

When the solenoid current I changes with time, the magnetic flux Φ_B also changes, and according to Faraday's law the induced emf in the loop is given by

$$\mathcal{E} = -\frac{d\Phi_B}{dt} = -\mu_0 nA\frac{dI}{dt} \qquad (29.8)$$

If the total resistance of the loop is R, the induced current in the loop, which we may call I', is $I' = \mathcal{E}/R$.

But what *force* makes the charges move around the loop? It can't be a magnetic force because the conductor isn't moving in a magnetic field and in fact isn't even *in* a magnetic field. We are forced to conclude that there has to be an **induced electric field** in the conductor *caused by the changing magnetic flux.* This may be a little jarring; we are accustomed to thinking about electric field as being caused by electric charges, and now we are saying that a changing magnetic field somehow acts as a source of electric field. Furthermore, it's a strange sort of electric field. When a charge q goes once around the loop, the total work done on it by the electric field must be equal to q times the emf $\mathcal{E}$. That is, the electric field in the loop *is not conservative,* as we used the term in Chapter 23, because the line integral of $\vec{E}$ around a closed path is not zero. Indeed, this line integral, representing the work done by the induced $\vec{E}$ field per unit charge, is equal to the induced emf $\mathcal{E}$:

$$\oint \vec{E} \cdot d\vec{l} = \mathcal{E} \qquad (29.9)$$

From Faraday's law the emf $\mathcal{E}$ is also the negative of the rate of change of magnetic flux through the loop. Thus for this case we can restate Faraday's law as

$$\oint \vec{E} \cdot d\vec{l} = -\frac{d\Phi_B}{dt} \qquad \text{(stationary integration path)} \qquad (29.10)$$

Note that Faraday's law is always true in the form $\mathcal{E} = -d\Phi_B/dt$; the form given in Eq. (29.10) is valid *only* if the path around which we integrate is *stationary.*

As an example of a situation to which Eq. (29.10) can be applied, consider the stationary circular loop in Fig. 29.17b, which we take to have radius r. Because of cylindrical symmetry, the electric field $\vec{E}$ has the same magnitude at every point on the circle and is tangent to it at each point. (Symmetry would also permit the field to be *radial,* but then Gauss's law would require the presence of a net charge inside the circle, and there is none.) The line integral in Eq. (29.10) becomes simply the magnitude E times the circumference $2\pi r$ of the loop, $\oint \vec{E} \cdot d\vec{l} = 2\pi rE$, and Eq. (29.10) gives

$$E = \frac{1}{2\pi r}\left|\frac{d\Phi_B}{dt}\right| \qquad (29.11)$$

The directions of $\vec{E}$ at points on the loop are shown in Fig. 29.17b. We know that $\vec{E}$ has to have the direction shown when $\vec{B}$ in the solenoid is increasing, because

29.17 (a) The windings of a long solenoid carry a current I that is increasing at a rate dI/dt. The magnetic flux in the solenoid is increasing at a rate $d\Phi_B/dt$, and this changing flux passes through a wire loop. An emf $\mathcal{E} = -d\Phi_B/dt$ is induced in the loop, inducing a current I' that is measured by the galvanometer G. (b) Cross-sectional view.

(a)

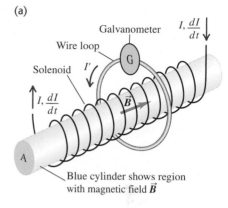

(b)

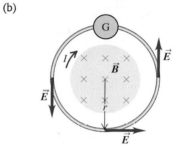

$\oint \vec{E} \cdot d\vec{l}$ has to be negative when $d\Phi_B/dt$ is positive. The same approach can be used to find the induced electric field *inside* the solenoid when the solenoid $\vec{B}$ field is changing; we leave the details to you (see Exercise 29.29).

Nonelectrostatic Electric Fields

Now let's summarize what we've learned. Faraday's law, Eq. (29.3), is valid for two rather different situations. In one, an emf is induced by magnetic forces on charges when a conductor moves through a magnetic field. In the other, a time-varying magnetic field induces an electric field in a stationary conductor and hence induces an emf; in fact, the $\vec{E}$ field is induced even when no conductor is present. This $\vec{E}$ field differs from an electro*static* field in an important way. It is *nonconservative;* the line integral $\oint \vec{E} \cdot d\vec{l}$ around a closed path is not zero, and when a charge moves around a closed path, the field does a nonzero amount of work on it. It follows that for such a field the concept of *potential* has no meaning. We call such a field a **nonelectrostatic field.** In contrast, an electro*static* field is *always* conservative, as we discussed in Section 23.1, and always has an associated potential function. Despite this difference, the fundamental effect of *any* electric field is to exert a force $\vec{F} = q\vec{E}$ on a charge q. This relationship is valid whether $\vec{E}$ is a conservative field produced by a charge distribution or a nonconservative field caused by changing magnetic flux.

So a changing magnetic field acts as a source of electric field of a sort that we *cannot* produce with any static charge distribution. This may seem strange, but it's the way nature behaves. What's more, we'll see in Section 29.7 that a changing *electric* field acts as a source of *magnetic* field. We'll explore this symmetry between the two fields in greater detail in our study of electromagnetic waves in Chapter 32.

If any doubt remains in your mind about the reality of magnetically induced electric fields, consider a few of the many practical applications (Fig. 29.18). In the playback head of a tape deck, currents are induced in a stationary coil as the variously magnetized regions of the tape move past it. Computer disk drives operate on the same principle. Pickups in electric guitars use currents induced in stationary pickup coils by the vibration of nearby ferromagnetic strings. Alternators in most cars use rotating magnets to induce currents in stationary coils. The list goes on and on; whether we realize it or not, magnetically induced electric fields play an important role in everyday life.

29.18 Applications of induced electric fields. (a) Data are stored on a computer hard disk in a pattern of magnetized areas on the surface of the disk. To read these data, a coil on a movable arm is placed next to the spinning disk. The coil experiences a changing magnetic flux, inducing a current whose characteristics depend on the pattern coded on the disk. (b) This hybrid automobile has both a gasoline engine and an electric motor. As the car comes to a halt, the spinning wheels run the motor backward so that it acts as a generator. The resulting induced current is used to recharge the car's batteries. (c) The rotating crankshaft of a piston-engine airplane spins a magnet, inducing an emf in an adjacent coil and generating the spark that ignites fuel in the engine cylinders. This keeps the engine running even if the airplane's other electrical systems fail.

Example 29.12 | Induced electric fields

Suppose the long solenoid in Fig. 29.17a is wound with 500 turns per meter and the current in its windings is increasing at the rate of 100 A/s. The cross-sectional area of the solenoid is 4.0 cm² = 4.0×10^{-4} m². (a) Find the magnitude of the induced emf in the wire loop outside the solenoid. (b) Find the magnitude of the induced electric field within the loop if its radius is 2.0 cm.

SOLUTION

IDENTIFY: As in Fig. 29.17b, the increasing magnetic field inside the solenoid causes a change in the magnetic flux through the wire loop and hence induces an electric field $\vec{E}$ around the loop. Our target variables are the induced emf $\mathcal{E}$ and the magnitude of $\vec{E}$.

SET UP: We use Eq. (29.8) to determine the emf. Determining the field magnitude E is simplified because the loop and the solenoid share the same central axis. Hence, by symmetry, the electric field is tangent to the loop and has the same magnitude all the way around its circumference. This makes it easy to find E from the emf $\mathcal{E}$ using Eq. (29.9).

EXECUTE: (a) From Eq. (29.8), the induced emf is

$$\mathcal{E} = -\frac{d\Phi_B}{dt} = -\mu_0 nA \frac{dI}{dt}$$
$$= -(4\pi \times 10^{-7} \text{ Wb/A} \cdot \text{m})(500 \text{ turns/m})$$
$$\times (4.0 \times 10^{-4} \text{ m}^2)(100 \text{ A/s})$$
$$= -25 \times 10^{-6} \text{ Wb/s} = -25 \times 10^{-6} \text{ V} = -25 \text{ μV}$$

(b) By symmetry the line integral $\oint \vec{E} \cdot d\vec{l}$ has absolute value $2\pi rE$ (disregarding the direction in which we integrate around the loop). This is equal to the absolute value of the emf, so

$$E = \frac{|\mathcal{E}|}{2\pi r} = \frac{25 \times 10^{-6} \text{ V}}{2\pi(2.0 \times 10^{-2} \text{ m})} = 2.0 \times 10^{-4} \text{ V/m}$$

EVALUATE: In Fig. 29.17b the magnetic flux *into* the plane of the figure is increasing. According to the right-hand rule for induced emf (illustrated in Fig. 29.6), a positive emf would be clockwise around the loop; the negative sign of $\mathcal{E}$ shows that the emf is in the counterclockwise direction. Can you also show this using Lenz's law?

Test Your Understanding of Section 29.5 If you wiggle a magnet back and forth in your hand, are you generating an electric field? If so, is this electric field conservative?

*29.6 Eddy Currents

In the examples of induction effects that we have studied, the induced currents have been confined to well-defined paths in conductors and other components forming a circuit. However, many pieces of electrical equipment contain masses of metal moving in magnetic fields or located in changing magnetic fields. In situations like these we can have induced currents that circulate throughout the volume of a material. Because their flow patterns resemble swirling eddies in a river, we call these **eddy currents.**

As an example, consider a metallic disk rotating in a magnetic field perpendicular to the plane of the disk but confined to a limited portion of the disk's area, as shown in Fig. 29.19a. Sector *Ob* is moving across the field and has an emf induced in it. Sectors *Oa* and *Oc* are not in the field, but they provide return conducting paths for charges displaced along *Ob* to return from *b* to *O*. The result is a circulation of eddy currents in the disk, somewhat as sketched in Fig. 29.19b.

We can use Lenz's law to decide on the direction of the induced current in the neighborhood of sector *Ob*. This current must experience a magnetic force $\vec{F} = I\vec{L} \times \vec{B}$ that *opposes* the rotation of the disk, and so this force must be to the right in Fig. 29.19b. Since $\vec{B}$ is directed into the plane of the disk, the current and hence $\vec{L}$ have downward components. The return currents lie outside the field, so they do not experience magnetic forces. The interaction between the eddy currents

29.19 Eddy currents induced in a rotating metal disk.

(a) Metal disk rotating through a magnetic field

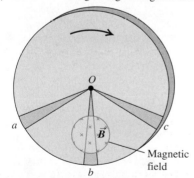

(b) Resulting eddy currents and braking force

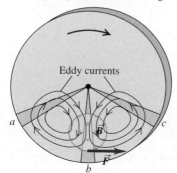

29.20 (a) A metal detector at an airport security checkpoint generates an alternating magnetic field $\vec{B}_0$. This induces eddy currents in a conducting object carried through the detector. The eddy currents in turn produce an alternating magnetic field $\vec{B}'$, and this field induces a current in the detector's receiver coil. (b) Portable metal detectors work on the same principle.

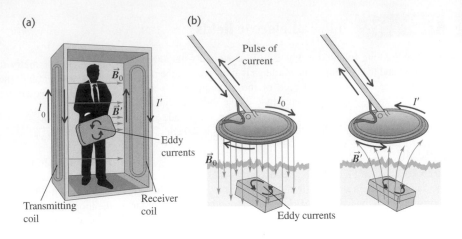

29.21 As Jupiter's moon Io moves around its orbit, the planet's powerful magnetic field induces eddy currents within Io. The lower closeup image shows two simultaneous volcanic eruptions on Io, triggered in part by eddy current heating.

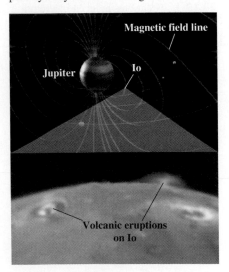

and the field causes a braking action on the disk. Such effects can be used to stop the rotation of a circular saw quickly when the power is turned off. Some sensitive balances use this effect to damp out vibrations. Eddy current braking is used on some electrically powered rapid-transit vehicles. Electromagnets mounted in the cars induce eddy currents in the rails; the resulting magnetic fields cause braking forces on the electromagnets and thus on the cars.

Eddy currents have many other practical uses. The shiny metal disk in the electric power company's meter outside your house rotates as a result of eddy currents. These currents are induced in the disk by magnetic fields caused by sinusoidally varying currents in a coil. In induction furnaces, eddy currents are used to heat materials in completely sealed containers for processes in which it is essential to avoid the slightest contamination of the materials. The metal detectors used at airport security checkpoints (Fig. 29.20a) operate by detecting eddy currents induced in metallic objects. Similar devices (Fig. 29.20b) are used to find buried treasure such as bottlecaps and lost pennies.

A particularly dramatic example of eddy currents in action is Jupiter's moon Io, which is slightly larger than the earth's moon (Fig. 29.21a). Io moves rapidly through Jupiter's intense magnetic field, and this sets up strong eddy currents within Io's interior. These currents dissipate energy at a rate of 10^{12} W, equivalent to setting off a one-kiloton nuclear weapon inside Io every four seconds! This dissipated energy helps to keep Io's interior hot and so helps to cause volcanic eruptions on its surface, like those in Fig. 29.21b. (Gravitational effects from Jupiter cause even more heating.)

Eddy currents also have undesirable effects. In an alternating-current transformer, coils wrapped around an iron core carry a sinusoidally varying current. The resulting eddy currents in the core waste energy through I^2R heating and themselves set up an unwanted opposing emf in the coils. To minimize these effects, the core is designed so that the paths for eddy currents are as narrow as possible. We'll describe how this is done when we discuss transformers in detail in Section 31.6.

Test Your Understanding of Section 29.6   Suppose that the magnetic field in Fig. 29.19 were directed out of the plane of the figure and the disk were rotating counterclockwise. Compared to the directions of the force $\vec{F}$ and the eddy currents shown in Fig. 29.19b, what would the new directions be? (i) The force $\vec{F}$ and the eddy currents would both be in the same direction; (ii) the force $\vec{F}$ would be in the same direction, but the eddy currents would be in the opposite direction; (iii) the force $\vec{F}$ would be in the opposite direction, but the eddy currents would be in the same direction; (iv) the force $\vec{F}$ and the eddy currents would be in the opposite directions.

29.7 Displacement Current and Maxwell's Equations

We have seen that a varying magnetic field gives rise to an induced electric field. In one of the more remarkable examples of the symmetry of nature, it turns out that a varying *electric* field gives rise to a *magnetic* field. This effect is of tremendous importance, for it turns out to explain the existence of radio waves, gamma rays, and visible light, as well as all other forms of electromagnetic waves.

Generalizing Ampere's Law

To see the origin of the relationship between varying electric fields and magnetic fields, let's return to Ampere's law as given in Section 28.6, Eq. (28.20):

$$\oint \vec{B} \cdot d\vec{l} = \mu_0 I_{\text{encl}}$$

The problem with Ampere's law in this form is that it is *incomplete*. To see why, let's consider the process of charging a capacitor (Fig. 29.22). Conducting wires lead current i_C into one plate and out of the other; the charge Q increases, and the electric field $\vec{E}$ between the plates increases. The notation i_C indicates *conduction* current to distinguish it from another kind of current we are about to encounter, called *displacement* current i_D. We use lowercase i's and v's to denote instantaneous values of currents and potential differences, respectively, that may vary with time.

Let's apply Ampere's law to the circular path shown. The integral $\oint \vec{B} \cdot d\vec{l}$ around this path equals $\mu_0 I_{\text{encl}}$. For the plane circular area bounded by the circle, I_{encl} is just the current i_C in the left conductor. But the surface that bulges out to the right is bounded by the same circle, and the current through that surface is zero. So $\oint \vec{B} \cdot d\vec{l}$ is equal to $\mu_0 i_C$, and at the same time it is equal to zero! This is a clear contradiction.

But something else is happening on the bulged-out surface. As the capacitor charges, the electric field $\vec{E}$ and the electric *flux* Φ_E through the surface are increasing. We can determine their rates of change in terms of the charge and current. The instantaneous charge is $q = Cv$, where C is the capacitance and v is the instantaneous potential difference. For a parallel-plate capacitor, $C = \epsilon_0 A/d$, where A is the plate area and d is the spacing. The potential difference v between plates is $v = Ed$, where E is the electric field magnitude between plates. (We neglect fringing and assume that $\vec{E}$ is uniform in the region between the plates.) If this region is filled with a material with permittivity ϵ, we replace ϵ_0 by ϵ everywhere; we'll use ϵ in the following discussion.

Substituting these expressions for C and v into $q = Cv$, we can express the capacitor charge q as

$$q = Cv = \frac{\epsilon A}{d}(Ed) = \epsilon EA = \epsilon \Phi_E \qquad (29.12)$$

where $\Phi_E = EA$ is the electric flux through the surface.

As the capacitor charges, the rate of change of q is the conduction current, $i_C = dq/dt$. Taking the derivative of Eq. (29.12) with respect to time, we get

$$i_C = \frac{dq}{dt} = \epsilon \frac{d\Phi_E}{dt} \qquad (29.13)$$

Now, stretching our imagination a little, we invent a fictitious **displacement current** i_D in the region between the plates, defined as

$$i_D = \epsilon \frac{d\Phi_E}{dt} \qquad \text{(displacement current)} \qquad (29.14)$$

29.22 Parallel-plate capacitor being charged. The conduction current through the plane surface is i_C, but there is no conduction current through the surface that bulges out to pass between the plates. The two surfaces have a common boundary, so this difference in I_{encl} leads to an apparent contradiction in applying Ampere's law.

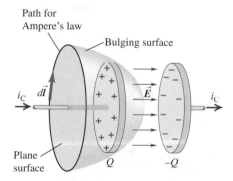

Path for Ampere's law

Bulging surface

Plane surface

i_C $d\vec{l}$ $\vec{E}$ i_C

Q $-Q$

That is, we imagine that the changing flux through the curved surface in Fig. 29.22 is somehow equivalent, in Ampere's law, to a conduction current through that surface. We include this fictitious current, along with the real conduction current i_C, in Ampere's law:

$$\oint \vec{B} \cdot d\vec{l} = \mu_0 (i_C + i_D)_{\text{encl}} \qquad \text{(generalized Ampere's law)} \qquad (29.15)$$

Ampere's law in this form is obeyed no matter which surface we use in Fig. 29.22. For the flat surface, i_D is zero; for the curved surface, i_C is zero; and i_C for the flat surface equals i_D for the curved surface. Equation (29.15) remains valid in a magnetic material, provided that the magnetization is proportional to the external field and we replace μ_0 by μ.

The fictitious current i_D was invented in 1865 by the Scottish physicist James Clerk Maxwell (1831–1879), who called it displacement current. There is a corresponding *displacement current density* $j_D = i_D/A$; using $\Phi_E = EA$ and dividing Eq. (29.14) by A, we find

$$j_D = \epsilon \frac{dE}{dt} \qquad (29.16)$$

We have pulled the concept out of thin air, as Maxwell did, but we see that it enables us to save Ampere's law in situations such as that in Fig. 29.22.

Another benefit of displacement current is that it lets us generalize Kirchhoff's junction rule, discussed in Section 26.2. Considering the left plate of the capacitor plate, we have conduction current into it but none out of it. But when we include the displacement current, we have conduction current coming in one side and an equal displacement current coming out the other side. With this generalized meaning of the term "current," we can speak of current going *through* the capacitor.

The Reality of Displacement Current

29.23 A capacitor being charged by a current i_C has a displacement current equal to i_C between the plates, with displacement-current density $j_D = \epsilon \, dE/dt$. This can be regarded as the source of the magnetic field between the plates.

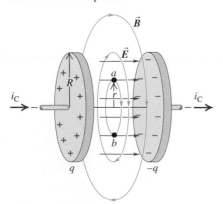

You might well ask at this point whether displacement current has any real physical significance or whether it is just a ruse to satisfy Ampere's law and Kirchhoff's junction rule. Here's a fundamental experiment that helps to answer that question. We take a plane circular area between the capacitor plates, as shown in Fig. 29.23. If displacement current really plays the role in Ampere's law that we have claimed, then there ought to be a magnetic field in the region between the plates while the capacitor is charging. We can use our generalized Ampere's law, including displacement current, to predict what this field should be.

To be specific, let's picture round capacitor plates with radius R. To find the magnetic field at a point in the region between the plates at a distance r from the axis, we apply Ampere's law to a circle of radius r passing through the point, with $r < R$. This circle passes through points a and b in Fig. 29.23. The total current enclosed by the circle is j_D times its area, or $(i_D/\pi R^2)(\pi r^2)$. The integral $\oint \vec{B} \cdot d\vec{l}$ in Ampere's law is just B times the circumference $2\pi r$ of the circle, and because $i_D = i_C$ for the charging capacitor, Ampere's law becomes

$$\oint \vec{B} \cdot d\vec{l} = 2\pi r B = \mu_0 \frac{r^2}{R^2} i_C \qquad \text{or}$$

$$B = \frac{\mu_0}{2\pi} \frac{r}{R^2} i_C \qquad (29.17)$$

This result predicts that in the region between the plates $\vec{B}$ is zero at the axis and increases linearly with distance from the axis. A similar calculation shows that *outside* the region between the plates (that is, for $r > R$), $\vec{B}$ is the same as though the wire were continuous and the plates not present at all.

When we *measure* the magnetic field in this region, we find that it really is there and that it behaves just as Eq. (29.17) predicts. This confirms directly the role of displacement current as a source of magnetic field. It is now established beyond reasonable doubt that displacement current, far from being just an artifice, is a fundamental fact of nature. Maxwell's discovery was the bold step of an extraordinary genius.

Maxwell's Equations of Electromagnetism

We are now in a position to wrap up in a single package *all* of the relationships between electric and magnetic fields and their sources. This package consists of four equations, called **Maxwell's equations.** Maxwell did not discover all of these equations single-handedly (though he did develop the concept of displacement current). But he did put them together and recognized their significance, particularly in predicting the existence of electromagnetic waves.

For now we'll state Maxwell's equations in their simplest form, for the case in which we have charges and currents in otherwise empty space. In Chapter 32 we'll discuss how to modify these equations if a dielectric or a magnetic material is present.

Two of Maxwell's equations involve an integral of $\vec{E}$ or $\vec{B}$ over a closed surface. The first is simply Gauss's law for electric fields, Eq. (22.8), which states that the surface integral of $E_\perp$ over any closed surface equals $1/\epsilon_0$ times the total charge Q_{encl} enclosed within the surface:

$$\oint \vec{E} \cdot d\vec{A} = \frac{Q_{encl}}{\epsilon_0} \qquad \text{(Gauss's law for } \vec{E}\text{)} \qquad (29.18)$$

The second is the analogous relationship for *magnetic* fields, Eq. (27.8), which states that the surface integral of $B_\perp$ over any closed surface is always zero:

$$\oint \vec{B} \cdot d\vec{A} = 0 \qquad \text{(Gauss's law for } \vec{B}\text{)} \qquad (29.19)$$

This statement means, among other things, that there are no magnetic monopoles (single magnetic charges) to act as sources of magnetic field.

The third equation is Ampere's law including displacement current. This states that both conduction current i_C and displacement current $\epsilon_0 d\Phi_E/dt$, where Φ_E is electric flux, act as sources of magnetic field:

$$\oint \vec{B} \cdot d\vec{l} = \mu_0 \left(i_C + \epsilon_0 \frac{d\Phi_E}{dt} \right)_{encl} \qquad \text{(Ampere's law)} \qquad (29.20)$$

The fourth and final equation is Faraday's law. It states that a changing magnetic field or magnetic flux induces an electric field:

$$\oint \vec{E} \cdot d\vec{l} = -\frac{d\Phi_B}{dt} \qquad \text{(Faraday's law)} \qquad (29.21)$$

If there is a changing magnetic flux, the line integral in Eq. (29.21) is not zero, which shows that the $\vec{E}$ field produced by a changing magnetic flux is not conservative. Recall that this line integral must be carried out over a *stationary* closed path.

It's worthwhile to look more carefully at the electric field $\vec{E}$ and its role in Maxwell's equations. In general, the total $\vec{E}$ field at a point in space can be the superposition of an electrostatic field $\vec{E}_c$ caused by a distribution of charges at rest and a magnetically induced, nonelectrostatic field $\vec{E}_n$. (The subscript c stands for Coulomb or conservative; the subscript n stands for non-Coulomb, nonelectrostatic, or nonconservative.) That is,

$$\vec{E} = \vec{E}_{\rm c} + \vec{E}_{\rm n}$$

The electrostatic part $\vec{E}_{\rm c}$ is *always* conservative, so $\oint \vec{E}_{\rm c} \cdot d\vec{l} = 0$. This conservative part of the field does not contribute to the integral in Faraday's law, so we can take $\vec{E}$ in Eq. (29.21) to be the total electric field $\vec{E}$, including both the part $\vec{E}_{\rm c}$ due to charges and the magnetically induced part $\vec{E}_{\rm n}$. Similarly, the nonconservative part $\vec{E}_{\rm n}$ of the $\vec{E}$ field does not contribute to the integral in Gauss's law, because this part of the field is not caused by static charges. Hence $\oint \vec{E}_{\rm n} \cdot d\vec{A}$ is always zero. We conclude that in all the Maxwell equations, $\vec{E}$ is the total electric field; these equations don't distinguish between conservative and nonconservative fields.

Symmetry in Maxwell's Equations

There is a remarkable symmetry in Maxwell's four equations. In empty space where there is no charge, the first two equations (Eqs. (29.18) and (29.19)) are identical in form, one containing $\vec{E}$ and the other containing $\vec{B}$. When we compare the second two equations, Eq. (29.20) says that a changing electric flux creates a magnetic field, and Eq. (29.21) says that a changing magnetic flux creates an electric field. In empty space, where there is no conduction current, $i_C = 0$ and the two equations have the same form, apart from a numerical constant and a negative sign, with the roles of $\vec{E}$ and $\vec{B}$ exchanged in the two equations.

We can rewrite Eqs. (29.20) and (29.21) in a different but equivalent form by introducing the definitions of electric and magnetic flux, $\Phi_E = \int \vec{E} \cdot d\vec{A}$ and $\Phi_B = \int \vec{B} \cdot d\vec{A}$, respectively. In empty space, where there is no charge or conduction current, $i_C = 0$ and $Q_{\rm encl} = 0$, and we have

$$\oint \vec{B} \cdot d\vec{l} = \epsilon_0 \mu_0 \frac{d}{dt} \int \vec{E} \cdot d\vec{A} \tag{29.22}$$

$$\oint \vec{E} \cdot d\vec{l} = -\frac{d}{dt} \int \vec{B} \cdot d\vec{A} \tag{29.23}$$

Again we notice the symmetry between the roles of $\vec{E}$ and $\vec{B}$ in these expressions.

The most remarkable feature of these equations is that a time-varying field of *either* kind induces a field of the other kind in neighboring regions of space. Maxwell recognized that these relationships predict the existence of electromagnetic disturbances consisting of time-varying electric and magnetic fields that travel or *propagate* from one region of space to another, even if no matter is present in the intervening space. Such disturbances, called *electromagnetic waves,* provide the physical basis for light, radio and television waves, infrared, ultraviolet, x rays, and the rest of the electromagnetic spectrum. We will return to this vitally important topic in Chapter 32.

Although it may not be obvious, *all* the basic relationships between fields and their sources are contained in Maxwell's equations. We can derive Coulomb's law from Gauss's law, we can derive the law of Biot and Savart from Ampere's law, and so on. When we add the equation that defines the $\vec{E}$ and $\vec{B}$ fields in terms of the forces that they exert on a charge q, namely,

$$\vec{F} = q(\vec{E} + \vec{v} \times \vec{B}) \tag{29.24}$$

we have *all* the fundamental relationships of electromagnetism!

Finally, we note that Maxwell's equations would have even greater symmetry between the $\vec{E}$ and $\vec{B}$ fields if single magnetic charges (magnetic monopoles) existed. The right side of Eq. (29.19) would contain the total *magnetic* charge enclosed by the surface, and the right side of Eq. (29.21) would include a magnetic monopole current term. Perhaps you can begin to see why some physicists wish that magnetic monopoles existed; they would help to perfect the mathematical poetry of Maxwell's equations.

The discovery that electromagnetism can be wrapped up so neatly and elegantly is a very satisfying one. In conciseness and generality, Maxwell's equations are in the same league with Newton's laws of motion and the laws of thermodynamics. Indeed, a major goal of science is learning how to express very broad and general relationships in a concise and compact form. Maxwell's synthesis of electromagnetism stands as a towering intellectual achievement, comparable to the Newtonian synthesis we described at the end of Section 12.5 and to the development of relativity and quantum mechanics in the 20th century.

Test Your Understanding of Section 29.7 (a) Which of Maxwell's equations explains how a credit card reader works? (b) Which one describes how a wire carrying a steady current generates a magnetic field?

---

*29.8 Superconductivity

The most familiar property of a superconductor is the sudden disappearance of all electrical resistance when the material is cooled below a temperature called the *critical temperature,* denoted by T_c. We discussed this behavior and the circumstances of its discovery in Section 25.2. But superconductivity is far more than just the absence of measurable resistance. Superconductors also have extraordinary *magnetic* properties. We'll explore some of these properties in this section.

The first hint of unusual magnetic properties was the discovery that for any superconducting material the critical temperature T_c changes when the material is placed in an externally produced magnetic field $\vec{B}_0$. Figure 29.24 shows this dependence for mercury, the first element in which superconductivity was observed. As the external field magnitude B_0 increases, the superconducting transition occurs at lower and lower temperature. When B_0 is greater than 0.0412 T, *no* superconducting transition occurs. The minimum magnitude of magnetic field that is needed to eliminate superconductivity at a temperature below T_c is called the *critical field,* denoted by B_c.

The Meissner Effect

Another aspect of the magnetic behavior of superconductors appears if we place a homogeneous sphere of a superconducting material in a uniform applied magnetic field $\vec{B}_0$ at a temperature T greater than T_c. The material is then in the normal phase, not the superconducting phase. The field is as shown in Figure 29.25a. Now we lower the temperature until the superconducting transition occurs. (We assume that the magnitude of $\vec{B}_0$ is not large enough to prevent the phase transition.) What happens to the field?

Measurements of the field outside the sphere show that the field lines become distorted as in Fig. 29.25b. There is no longer any field inside the material, except possibly in a very thin surface layer a hundred or so atoms thick. If a coil is wrapped around the sphere, the emf induced in the coil shows that during the superconducting transition the magnetic flux through the coil decreases from its initial value to zero; this is consistent with the absence of field inside the material. Finally, if the field is now turned off while the material is still in its superconducting phase, no emf is induced in the coil, and measurements show no field outside the sphere (Fig. 29.25c).

We conclude that during a superconducting transition in the presence of the field $\vec{B}_0$, all of the magnetic flux is expelled from the bulk of the sphere, and the

29.24 Phase diagram for pure mercury, showing the critical magnetic field B_c and its dependence on temperature. Superconductivity is impossible above the critical temperature T_c. The curves for other superconducting materials are similar but with different numerical values.

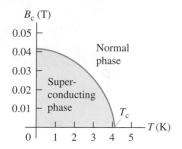

29.25 A superconducting material (a) above the critical temperature and (b), (c) below the critical temperature.

(a) Superconducting material in an external magnetic field $\vec{B}_0$ at $T > T_c$.

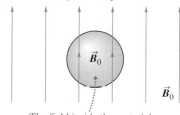

The field inside the material is very nearly equal to $\vec{B}_0$.

(b) The temperature is lowered to $T < T_c$, so the material becomes superconducting.

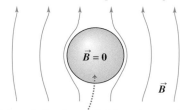

Magnetic flux is expelled from the material, and the field inside it is zero (Meissner effect).

(c) When the external field is turned off at $T < T_c$, the field is zero everywhere.

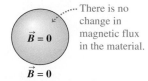

There is no change in magnetic flux in the material.

magnetic flux Φ_B through the coil becomes zero. This expulsion of magnetic flux is called the *Meissner effect*. As shown in Fig. 29.25b, this expulsion crowds the magnetic field lines closer together to the side of the sphere, increasing $\vec{B}$ there.

Superconductor Levitation and Other Applications

The diamagnetic nature of a superconductor has some interesting *mechanical* consequences. A paramagnetic or ferromagnetic material is attracted by a permanent magnet because the magnetic dipoles in the material align with the nonuniform magnetic field of the permanent magnet. (We discussed this in Section 27.7.) For a diamagnetic material the magnetization is in the opposite sense, and a diamagnetic material is *repelled* by a permanent magnet. By Newton's third law the magnet is also repelled by the diamagnetic material. Figure 29.26 shows the repulsion between a specimen of a high-temperature superconductor and a magnet; the magnet is supported ("levitated") by this repulsive magnetic force.

The behavior we have described is characteristic of what are called *type-I superconductors*. There is another class of superconducting materials called *type-II superconductors*. When such a material in the superconducting phase is placed in a magnetic field, the bulk of the material remains superconducting, but thin filaments of material, running parallel to the field, may return to the normal phase. Currents circulate around the boundaries of these filaments, and there *is* magnetic flux inside them. Type-II superconductors are used for electromagnets because they usually have much larger values of B_c than do type-I materials, permitting much larger magnetic fields without destroying the superconducting state. Type-II superconductors have *two* critical magnetic fields: the first, B_{c1}, is the field at which magnetic flux begins to enter the material, forming the filaments just described, and the second, B_{c2}, is the field at which the material becomes normal.

Many important and exciting applications of superconductors are under development. Superconducting electromagnets have been used in research laboratories for several years. Their advantages compared to conventional electromagnets include greater efficiency, compactness, and greater field magnitudes. Once a current is established in the coil of a superconducting electromagnet, no additional power input is required because there is no resistive energy loss. The coils can also be made more compact because there is no need to provide channels for the circulation of cooling fluids. Superconducting magnets routinely attain steady fields of the order of 10 T, much larger than the maximum fields that are available with ordinary electromagnets.

Superconductors are attractive for long-distance electric power transmission and for energy-conversion devices, including generators, motors, and transformers. Very sensitive measurements of magnetic fields can be made with superconducting quantum interference devices (SQUIDs), which can detect changes in magnetic flux of less than 10^{-14} Wb; these devices have applications in medicine, geology, and other fields. The number of potential uses for superconductors has increased greatly since the discovery in 1987 of high-temperature superconductors. These materials have critical temperatures that are above the temperature of liquid nitrogen (about 77 K) and so are comparatively easy to attain. Development of practical applications of superconductor science promises to be an exciting chapter in contemporary technology.

29.26 A superconductor (the black slab) exerts a repulsive force on a magnet (the metallic cylinder), supporting the magnet in midair.

Faraday's law: Faraday's law states that the induced emf in a closed loop equals the negative of the time rate of change of magnetic flux through the loop. This relationship is valid whether the flux change is caused by a changing magnetic field, motion of the loop, or both. (See Examples 29.1–29.7.)

$$\mathcal{E} = -\frac{d\Phi_B}{dt} \qquad (29.3)$$

The magnet's motion causes a *changing* magnetic field through the coil, inducing a current in the coil.

Lenz's law: Lenz's law states that an induced current or emf always tends to oppose or cancel out the change that caused it. Lenz's law can be derived from Faraday's law and is often easier to use. (See Examples 29.8 and 29.9.)

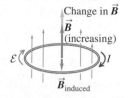

Motional emf: If a conductor moves in a magnetic field, a motional emf is induced. (See Examples 29.10 and 29.11.)

$$\mathcal{E} = vBL \qquad (29.6)$$

(conductor with length L moves in uniform $\vec{B}$ field, $\vec{L}$ and $\vec{v}$ both perpendicular to $\vec{B}$ and to each other)

$$\mathcal{E} = \oint (\vec{v} \times \vec{B}) \cdot d\vec{l} \qquad (29.7)$$

(all or part of a closed loop moves in a $\vec{B}$ field)

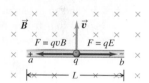

Induced electric fields: When an emf is induced by a changing magnetic flux through a stationary conductor, there is an induced electric field $\vec{E}$ of nonelectrostatic origin. This field is nonconservative and cannot be associated with a potential. (See Example 29.12.)

$$\oint \vec{E} \cdot d\vec{l} = -\frac{d\Phi_B}{dt} \qquad (29.10)$$

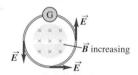

Displacement current and Maxwell's equations: A time-varying electric field generates a displacement current i_D, which acts as a source of magnetic field in exactly the same way as conduction current. The relationships between electric and magnetic fields and their sources can be stated compactly in four equations, called Maxwell's equations. Together they form a complete basis for the relationship of $\vec{E}$ and $\vec{B}$ fields to their sources.

$$i_D = \epsilon \frac{d\Psi_E}{dt} \qquad (29.14)$$

(displacement current)

$$\oint \vec{E} \cdot d\vec{A} = \frac{Q_{encl}}{\epsilon_0} \qquad (29.18)$$

(Gauss's law for $\vec{E}$ fields)

$$\oint \vec{B} \cdot d\vec{A} = 0 \qquad (29.19)$$

(Gauss's law for $\vec{B}$ fields)

$$\oint \vec{B} \cdot d\vec{l} = \mu_0 \left(i_C + \epsilon_0 \frac{d\Phi_E}{dt} \right)_{encl} \qquad (29.20)$$

(Ampere's law including displacement current)

$$\oint \vec{E} \cdot d\vec{l} = -\frac{d\Phi_B}{dt} \qquad (29.21)$$

(Faraday's law)

Key Terms

Answer to Chapter Opening Question ?

As the magnetic stripe moves through the card reader, the coded pattern of magnetization in the stripe causes a varying magnetic flux and hence an induced current in the reader's circuits. If the card does not move, there is no induced emf or current and none of the credit card's information is read.

Answers to Test Your Understanding Questions

29.2 Answers: (a) (i), (b) (iii)   (a) Initially there is magnetic flux into the plane of the page, which we call positive. While the loop is being squeezed, the flux is becoming less positive ($d\Phi_B/dt < 0$) and so the induced emf is positive as in Fig. 29.6b ($\mathcal{E} = -d\Phi_B/dt > 0$). If you point the thumb of your right hand into the page, your fingers curl clockwise, so this is the direction of positive induced emf. (b) Since the coil's shape is no longer changing, the magnetic flux is not changing and there is no induced emf.

29.3 Answers: (a) (i), (b) (iii)   In (a), as in the original situation, the magnet and loop are approaching each other and the downward flux through the loop is increasing. Hence the induced emf and induced current are the same. In (b), since the magnet and loop are moving together, the flux through the loop is not changing and no emf is induced.

29.4 Answers: (a) (iii); (b) (i) or (ii); (c) (ii) or (iii)   You will get the maximum motional emf if you hold the rod vertically, so that its length is perpendicular to both the magnetic field and the direction of motion. With this orientation, $\vec{L}$ is parallel to $\vec{v} \times \vec{B}$. If you hold the rod in any horizontal orientation, $\vec{L}$ will be perpendicular to $\vec{v} \times \vec{B}$ and no emf will be induced. If you walk due north or south, $\vec{v} \times \vec{B} = 0$ and no emf will be induced for any orientation of the rod.

29.5 Answers: yes, no   The magnetic field at a fixed position changes as you move the magnet. Such induced electric fields are *not* conservative.

29.6 Answer: (iii)   By Lenz's law, the force must oppose the motion of the disk through the magnetic field. Since the disk material is now moving to the right through the field region, the force $\vec{F}$ is to the left—that is, in the opposite direction to that shown in Fig. 29.19b. To produce a leftward magnetic force $\vec{F} = I\vec{L} \times \vec{B}$ on currents moving through a magnetic field $\vec{B}$ directed out of the plane of the figure, the eddy currents must be moving downward in the figure—that is, in the same direction shown in Fig. 29.19b.

29.7 Answers: (a) Faraday's law, (b) Ampere's law   A credit card reader works by inducing currents in the reader's coils as the card's magnetized stripe is swiped (see the answer to the chapter opening question). Ampere's law describes how currents of all kinds (both conduction currents and displacement currents) give rise to magnetic fields.

PROBLEMS

For instructor-assigned homework, go to **www.masteringphysics.com**

Discussion Questions

Q29.1. A sheet of copper is placed between the poles of an electromagnet with the magnetic field perpendicular to the sheet. When the sheet is pulled out, a considerable force is required, and the force required increases with speed. Explain.

Q29.2. In Fig. 29.8, if the angular speed ω of the loop is doubled, then the frequency with which the induced current changes direction doubles, and the maximum emf also doubles. Why? Does the torque required to turn the loop change? Explain.

Q29.3. Two circular loops lie side by side in the same plane. One is connected to a source that supplies an increasing current; the other is a simple closed ring. Is the induced current in the ring in the same direction as the current in the loop connected to the source, or opposite? What if the current in the first loop is decreasing? Explain.

Q29.4. A farmer claimed that the high-voltage transmission lines running parallel to his fence induced dangerously high voltages on the fence. Is this within the realm of possibility? Explain. (The lines carry alternating current that changes direction 120 times each second.)

Q29.5. A long, straight conductor passes through the center of a metal ring, perpendicular to its plane. If the current in the conductor increases, is a current induced in the ring? Explain.

Q29.6. A student asserted that if a permanent magnet is dropped down a vertical copper pipe, it eventually reaches a terminal velocity even if there is no air resistance. Why should this be? Or should it?

Q29.7. An airplane is in level flight over Antarctica, where the magnetic field of the earth is mostly directed upward away from the ground. As viewed by a passenger facing toward the front of the plane, is the left or the right wingtip at higher potential? Does your answer depend on the direction the plane is flying?

Q29.8. Consider the situation in Exercise 29.19. In part (a), find the direction of the force that the large circuit exerts on the small one. Explain how this result is consistent with Lenz's law.

Q29.9. A metal rectangle is close to a long, straight, current-carrying wire, with two of its sides parallel to the wire. If the current in the long wire is decreasing, is the rectangle repelled by or attracted to the wire? Explain why this result is consistent with Lenz's law.

Q29.10. A square conducting loop is in a region of uniform, constant magnetic field. Can the loop be rotated about an axis along one side and no emf be induced in the loop? Discuss, in terms of the orientation of the rotation axis relative to the magnetic-field direction.

Q29.11. Example 29.7 discusses the external force that must be applied to the slidewire to move it at constant speed. If there were a break in the left-hand end of the U-shaped conductor, how much force would be needed to move the slidewire at constant speed? As in the example, you can ignore friction.

Q29.12. In the situation shown in Fig. 29.16, would it be appropriate to ask how much *energy* an electron gains during a complete trip around the wire loop with current I'? Would it be appropriate to ask what *potential difference* the electron moves through during such a complete trip? Explain your answers.

Q29.13. A metal ring is oriented with the plane of its area perpendicular to a spatially uniform magnetic field that increases at a steady rate. If the radius of the ring is doubled, by what factor do (a) the emf induced in the ring and (b) the electric field induced in the ring change?

Q29.14. For Eq. (29.6), show that if v is in meters per second, B in teslas, and L in meters, then the units of the right-hand side of the equation are joules per coulomb or volts (the correct SI units for $\mathcal{E}$).

Q29.15. Can one have a displacement current as well as a conduction current within a conductor? Explain.

Q29.16. Your physics study partner asks you to consider a parallel-plate capacitor that has a dielectric completely filling the volume between the plates. He then claims that Eqs. (29.13) and (29.14) show that the conduction current in the dielectric equals the displacement current in the dielectric. Do you agree? Explain.

Q29.17. Match the mathematical statements of Maxwell's equations as given in Section 29.7 to these verbal statements. (a) Closed electric field lines are evidently produced only by changing magnetic flux. (b) Closed magnetic field lines are produced both by the motion of electric charge and by changing electric flux. (c) Electric field lines can start on positive charges and end on negative charges. (d) Evidently there are no magnetic monopoles on which to start and end magnetic field lines.

Q29.18. If magnetic monopoles existed, the right-hand side of Eq. (29.21) would include a term proportional to the current of magnetic monopoles. Suppose a steady monopole current is moving in a long straight wire. Sketch the *electric* field lines that such a current would produce.

Q29.19. If magnetic monopoles existed, the right-hand side of Eq. (29.19) would be proportional to the total enclosed *magnetic* charge. Suppose an infinite line of magnetic monopoles were on the *x*-axis. Sketch the magnetic field lines that this line of monopoles would produce.

Exercises

Section 29.2 Faraday's Law

29.1. A flat, rectangular coil consisting of 50 turns measures 25.0 cm by 30.0 cm. It is in a uniform, 1.20-T, magnetic field, with the plane of the coil parallel to the field. In 0.222 s, it is rotated so that the plane of the coil is perpendicular to the field. (a) What is the change in the magnetic flux through the coil due to this rotation? (b) Find the magnitude of the average emf induced in the coil during this rotation.

29.2. In a physics laboratory experiment, a coil with 200 turns enclosing an area of 12 cm² is rotated in 0.040 s from a position where its plane is perpendicular to the earth's magnetic field to a position where its plane is parallel to the field. The earth's magnetic field at the lab location is 6.0×10^{-5} T. (a) What is the total magnetic flux through the coil before it is rotated? After it is rotated? b) What is the average emf induced in the coil?

29.3. Search Coils and Credit Cards. (a) Derive the equation relating the total charge Q that flows through a search coil (Conceptual Example 29.3) to the magnetic-field magnitude B. The search

coil has N turns, each with area A, and the flux through the coil is decreased from its initial maximum value to zero in a time Δt. The resistance of the coil is R, and the total charge is $Q = I\Delta t$, where I is the average current induced by the change in flux. (b) In a credit card reader, the magnetic strip on the back of a credit card is rapidly "swiped" past a coil within the reader. Explain, using the same ideas that underlie the operation of a search coil, how the reader can decode the information stored in the pattern of magnetization on the strip. (c) Is it necessary that the credit card be "swiped" through the reader at exactly the right speed? Why or why not?

29.4. A closely wound search coil (Exercise 29.3) has an area of 3.20 cm², 120 turns, and a resistance of 60.0 Ω. It is connected to a charge-measuring instrument whose resistance is 45.0 Ω. When the coil is rotated quickly from a position parallel to a uniform magnetic field to a position perpendicular to the field, the instrument indicates a charge of 3.56×10^{-5} C. What is the magnitude of the field?

29.5. A circular loop of wire with a radius of 12.0 cm and oriented in the horizontal *xy*-plane is located in a region of uniform magnetic field. A field of 1.5 T is directed along the positive *z*-direction, which is upward. (a) If the loop is removed from the field region in a time interval of 2.0 ms, find the average emf that will be induced in the wire loop during the extraction process. (b) If the coil is viewed looking down on it from above, is the induced current in the loop clockwise or counterclockwise?

29.6. A coil 4.00 cm in radius, containing 500 turns, is placed in a uniform magnetic field that varies with time according to $B = (0.0120 \text{ T/s})t + (3.00 \times 10^{-5} \text{ T/s}^4)t^4$. The coil is connected to a 600-Ω resistor, and its plane is perpendicular to the magnetic field. You can ignore the resistance of the coil. (a) Find the magnitude of the induced emf in the coil as a function of time. (b) What is the current in the resistor at time $t = 5.00$ s?

29.7. The current in the long, straight wire *AB* shown in Fig. 29.27 is upward and is increasing steadily at a rate di/dt. (a) At an instant when the current is i, what are the magnitude and direction of the field $\vec{B}$ at a distance r to the right of the wire? (b) What is the flux $d\Phi_B$ through the narrow, shaded strip? (c) What is the total flux through the loop? (d) What is the induced emf in the loop? (e) Evaluate the numerical value of the induced emf if $a = 12.0$ cm, $b = 36.0$ cm, $L = 24.0$ cm, and $di/dt = 9.60$ A/s.

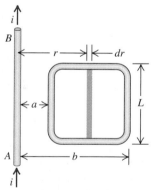

Figure 29.27 Exercise 29.7.

29.8. A flat, circular, steel loop of radius 75 cm is at rest in a uniform magnetic field, as shown in an edge-on view in Fig. 29.28. The field is changing with time, according to $B(t) = (1.4 \text{ T})e^{-(0.057 \text{ s}^{-1})t}$. (a) Find the emf induced in the loop as a function of time. (b) When is the induced emf equal to $\frac{1}{10}$ of its initial value? (c) Find the direction of the current induced in the loop, as viewed from above the loop.

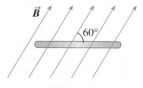

Figure 29.28 Exercise 29.8.

29.9. Shrinking Loop. A circular loop of flexible iron wire has an initial circumference of 165.0 cm, but its circumference is decreasing at a constant rate of 12.0 cm/s due to a tangential pull on the wire. The loop is in a constant, uniform magnetic field oriented perpendicular to the plane of the loop and with magnitude 0.500 T. (a) Find the emf induced in the loop at the instant when 9.0 s have passed. (b) Find the direction of the induced current in the loop as viewed looking along the direction of the magnetic field.

29.10. A rectangle measuring 30.0 cm by 40.0 cm is located inside a region of a spatially uniform magnetic field of 1.25 T, with the field perpendicular to the plane of the coil (Fig. 29.29). The coil is pulled out at a steady rate of 2.00 cm/s traveling perpendicular to the field lines. The region of the field ends abruptly as shown. Find the emf induced in this coil when it is (a) all inside the field; (b) partly inside the field; (c) all outside the field.

Figure 29.29
Exercise 29.10.

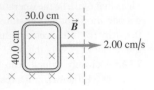

29.11. In a region of space, a magnetic field points in the $+x$-direction (toward the right). Its magnitude varies with position according to the formula $B_x = B_0 + bx$, where B_0 and b are positive constants, for $x \geq 0$. A flat coil of area A moves with uniform speed v from right to left with the plane of its area always perpendicular to this field. (a) What is the emf induced in this coil while it is to the right of the origin? (b) As viewed from the origin, what is the direction (clockwise or counterclockwise) of the current induced in the coil? (c) If instead the coil moved from left to right, what would be the answers to parts (a) and (b)?

29.12. Back emf. A motor with a brush-and-commutator arrangement, as described in Example 29.5, has a circular coil with radius 2.5 cm and 150 turns of wire. The magnetic field has magnitude 0.060 T, and the coil rotates at 440 rev/min. (a) What is the maximum emf induced in the coil? (b) What is the average back emf?

29.13. The armature of a small generator consists of a flat, square coil with 120 turns and sides with a length of 1.60 cm. The coil rotates in a magnetic field of 0.0750 T. What is the angular speed of the coil if the maximum emf produced is 24.0 mV?

29.14. A flat, rectangular coil of dimensions l and w is pulled with uniform speed v through a uniform magnetic field B with the plane of its area perpendicular to the field (Fig. 29.30). (a) Find the emf induced in this coil. (b) If the speed and magnetic field are both tripled, what is the induced emf?

Figure 29.30
Exercise 29.14.

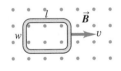

Section 29.3 Lenz's Law

29.15. A circular loop of wire is in a region of spatially uniform magnetic field, as shown in Fig. 29.31. The magnetic field is directed into the plane of the figure. Determine the direction (clockwise or counterclockwise) of the induced current in the loop when (a) B is increasing; (b) B is decreasing; (c) B is constant with value B_0. Explain your reasoning.

29.16. The current in Fig. 29.32 obeys the equation $I(t) = I_0 e^{-bt}$, where $b > 0$. Find the direction (clockwise or counterclockwise) of the current induced in the round coil for $t > 0$.

29.17 Using Lenz's law, determine the direction of the current in resistor ab of

Figure 29.31 Exercise 29.15 and 29.30.

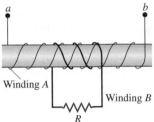

Figure 29.32
Exercise 29.16.

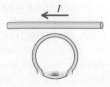

Fig. 29.33 when (a) switch S is opened after having been closed for several minutes; (b) coil B is brought closer to coil A with the switch closed; (c) the resistance of R is decreased while the switch remains closed.

Figure 29.33 Exercise 29.17.

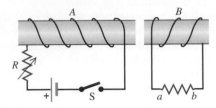

29.18. A cardboard tube is wrapped with two windings of insulated wire wound in opposite directions, as shown in Fig. 29.34. Terminals a and b of winding A may be connected to a battery through a reversing switch. State whether the induced current in the resistor R is from left to right or from right to left in the following circumstances: (a) the current in winding A is from a to b and is increasing; (b) the current in winding A is from b to a and is decreasing; (c) the current in winding A is from b to a and is increasing.

Figure 29.34 Exercise 29.18.

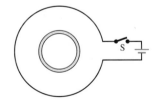

29.19. A small, circular ring is inside a larger loop that is connected to a battery and a switch, as shown in Fig. 29.35. Use Lenz's law to find the direction of the current induced in the small ring (a) just after switch S is closed; (b) after S has been closed a long time; (c) just after S has been reopened after being closed a long time.

Figure 29.35
Exercise 29.19.

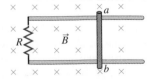

29.20. A 1.50-m-long metal bar is pulled to the right at a steady 5.0 m/s perpendicular to a uniform, 0.750-T magnetic field. The bar rides on parallel metal rails connected through a 25.0-Ω resistor, as shown in Fig. 29.36, so the apparatus makes a complete circuit. You can ignore the resistance of the bar and the rails. (a) Calculate the magnitude of the emf induced in the circuit. (b) Find the direction of the current induced in the circuit (i) using the magnetic force on the charges in the moving bar; (ii) using Faraday's law; (iii) using Lenz's law. (c) Calculate the current through the resistor.

Figure 29.36 Exercise 29.20 and Problem 29.64.

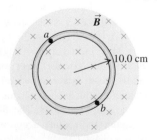

Section 29.4 Motional Electromotive Force

29.21. In Fig. 29.37 a conducting rod of length $L = 30.0$ cm moves in a magnetic field $\vec{B}$ of magnitude 0.450 T directed into the plane of the figure. The rod moves with speed $v = 5.00$ m/s in the direction shown. (a) what is the potential difference between the ends of the rod? (b) Which point, a to b, is at higher potential? (c) When the charges in the rod are in equilibrium, what are the magnitude and direction of the electric field within the rod? (d) When the charges in the rod are in equilibrium, which point, a or b, has an excess of positive charge? (e) What is the potential difference across the rod if it moves (i) parallel to ab and (ii) directly out of the page?

Figure 29.37 Exercise 29.21.

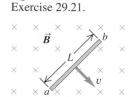

29.22. For the situation in Exercise 29.20, find (a) the motional emf in the bar and (b) the current through the resistor.

29.23. Are Motional emfs a Practical Source of Electricity? How fast (in m/s and mph) would a 5.00-cm copper bar have to move at right angles to a 0.650-T magnetic field to generate 1.50 V (the same as a AA battery) across its ends? Does this seem like a practical way to generate electricity?

29.24. Motional emfs in Transportation. Airplanes and trains move through the earth's magnetic field at rather high speeds, so it is reasonable to wonder whether this field can have a substantial effect on them. We shall use a typical value of 0.50 G for the earth's field (a) The French TGV train and the Japanese "bullet train" reach speeds of up to 180 mph moving on tracks about 1.5 m apart. At top speed moving perpendicular to the earth's magnetic field, what potential difference is induced across the tracks as the wheels roll? Does this seem large enough to produce noticeable effects? (b) The Boeing 747-400 aircraft has a wingspan of 64.4 m and a cruising speed of 565 mph. If there is no wind blowing (so that this is also their speed relative to the ground), what is the maximum potential difference that could be induced between the opposite tips of the wings? Does this seem large enough to cause problems with the plane?

29.25. The conducting rod ab shown in Fig. 29.38 makes contact with metal rails ca and db. The apparatus is in a uniform magnetic field of 0.800 T, perpendicular to the plane of the figure (a) Find the magnitude of the emf induced in the rod when it is moving toward the right with a speed 7.50 m/s. (b) In what direction does the current flow in the rod? (c) If the resistance of the circuit abdc is 1.50 Ω (assumed to be constant), find the force (magnitude and direction) required to keep the rod moving to the right with a constant speed of 7.50 m/s. You can ignore friction. (d) Compare the rate at which mechanical work is done by the force (Fv) with the rate at which thermal energy is developed in the circuit $(I^2 R)$.

Figure 29.38 Exercise 29.25.

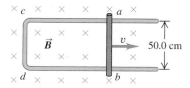

29.26. A square loop of wire with side length L and resistance R is moved at constant speed v across a uniform magnetic field confined to a square region whose sides are twice the length of those of the square loop (Fig. 29.39). (a) Graph the external force F needed to move the loop at constant speed as a function of the coordinate x from $x = -2L$ to $x = +2L$. (The coordinate x is measured from the center of the magnetic-field region to the center of the loop. It is negative when the center of the loop is to the left

Figure 29.39 Exercise 29.26.

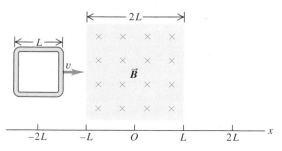

of the center of the magnetic-field region. Take positive force to be to the right.) (b) Graph the induced current in the loop as a function of x. Take counterclockwise currents to be positive.

29.27. A 1.41-m bar moves through a uniform, 1.20-T magnetic field with a speed of 2.50 m/s (Fig. 29.40). In each case, find the emf induced between the ends of this bar and identify which, if any, end (a or b) is at the higher potential. The bar moves in the direction of (a) the $+x$-axis; (b) the $-y$-axis; (c) the $+z$-axis. (d) How should this bar move so that the emf across its ends has the greatest possible value with b at a higher potential than a, and what is this maximum emf?

Figure 29.40 Exercise 29.27.

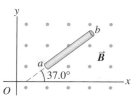

Section 29.5 Induced Electric Fields

29.28. A long, thin solenoid has 900 turns per meter and radius 2.50 cm. The current in the solenoid is increasing at a uniform rate of 60.0 A/s. What is the magnitude of the induced electric field at a point near the center of the solenoid and (a) 0.500 cm from the axis of the solenoid; (b) 1.00 cm from the axis of the solenoid?

29.29. The magnetic field within a long, straight solenoid with a circular cross section and radius R is increasing at a rate of dB/dt. (a) What is the rate of change of flux through a circle with radius r_1 inside the solenoid, normal to the axis of the solenoid, and with center on the solenoid axis? (b) Find the magnitude of the induced electric field inside the solenoid, at a distance r_1 from its axis. Show the direction of this field in a diagram. (c) What is the magnitude of the induced electric field *outside* the solenoid, at a distance r_2 from the axis? (d) Graph the magnitude of the induced electric field as a function of the distance r from the axis from $r = 0$ to $r = 2R$. (e) What is the magnitude of the induced emf in a circular turn of radius $R/2$ that has its center on the solenoid axis? (f) What is the magnitude of the induced emf if the radius in part (e) is R? (g) What is the induced emf if the radius in part (e) is $2R$?

29.30. The magnetic field $\vec{B}$ at all points within the colored circle shown in Fig. 29.31 has an initial magnitude of 0.750 T. (The circle could represent approximately the space inside a long, thin solenoid.) The magnetic field is directed into the plane of the diagram and is decreasing at the rate of -0.0350 T/s. (a) What is the shape of the field lines of the induced electric field shown in Fig. 29.31, within the colored circle? (b) What are the magnitude and direction of this field at any point on the circular conducting ring with radius 0.100 m? (c) What is the current in the ring if its resistance is 4.00 Ω? (d) What is the emf between points a and b on the ring? (e) If the ring is cut at some point and the ends are separated slightly, what will be the emf between the ends?

29.31. A long, thin solenoid has 400 turns per meter and radius 1.10 cm. The current in the solenoid is increasing at a uniform rate

di/dt. The induced electric field at a point near the center of the solenoid and 3.50 cm from its axis is 8.00×10^{-6} V/m. Calculate di/dt.

29.32. A metal ring 4.50 cm in diameter is placed between the north and south poles of large magnets with the plane of its area perpendicular to the magnetic field. These magnets produce an initial uniform field of 1.12 T between them but are gradually pulled apart, causing this field to remain uniform but decrease steadily at 0.250 T/s. (a) What is the magnitude of the electric field induced in the ring? (b) In which direction (clockwise or counterclockwise) does the current flow as viewed by someone on the south pole of the magnet?

29.33. A long, straight solenoid with a cross-sectional area of 8.00 cm^2 is wound with 90 turns of wire per centimeter, and the windings carry a current of 0.350 A. A second winding of 12 turns encircles the solenoid at its center. The current in the solenoid is turned off such that the magnetic field of the solenoid becomes zero in 0.0400 s. What is the average induced emf in the second winding?

Section 29.7 Displacement Current and Maxwell's Equations

29.34. A dielectric of permittivity 3.5×10^{-11} F/m completely fills the volume between two capacitor plates. For $t > 0$ the electric flux through the dielectric is $(8.0 \times 10^3 \text{ V} \cdot \text{m/s}^3)t^3$. The dielectric is ideal and nonmagnetic; the conduction current in the dielectric is zero. At what time does the displacement current in the dielectric equal 21 μA?

29.35. The electric flux through a certain area of a dielectric is $(8.76 \times 10^3 \text{ V} \cdot \text{m/s}^4)t^4$. The displacement current through that area is 12.9 pA at time $t = 26.1$ ms. Calculate the dielectric constant for the dielectric.

29.36. A parallel-plate, air-filled capacitor is being charged as in Fig. 29.23. The circular plates have radius 4.00 cm, and at a particular instant the conduction current in the wires is 0.280 A. (a) What is the displacement current density j_D in the air space between the plates? (b) What is the rate at which the electric field between the plates is changing? (c) What is the induced magnetic field between the plates at a distance of 2.00 cm from the axis? (d) At 1.00 cm from the axis?

29.37. Displacement Current in a Dielectric. Suppose that the parallel plates in Fig. 29.23 have an area of 3.00 cm^2 and are separated by a 2.50-mm-thick sheet of dielectric that completely fills the volume between the plates. The dielectric has dielectric constant 4.70. (You can ignore fringing effects.) At a certain instant, the potential difference between the plates is 120 V and the conduction current i_C equals 6.00 mA. At this instant, what are (a) the charge q on each plate; (b) the rate of change of charge on the plates; (c) the displacement current in the dielectric?

29.38. In Fig. 29.23 the capacitor plates have area 5.00 cm^2 and separation 2.00 mm. The plates are in vacuum. The charging current i_C has a *constant* value of 1.80 mA. At $t = 0$ the charge on the plates is zero. (a) Calculate the charge on the plates, the electric field between the plates, and the potential difference between the plates when $t = 0.500$ μs. (b) Calculate dE/dt, the time rate of change of the electric field between the plates. Does dE/dt vary in time? (c) Calculate the displacement current density j_D between the plates, and from this the total displacement current i_D. How do i_C and i_D compare?

29.39. Displacement Current in a Wire. A long, straight, copper wire with a circular cross-sectional area of 2.1 mm^2 carries a current of 16 A. The resistivity of the material is 2.0×10^{-8} $\Omega \cdot$ m.

(a) What is the uniform electric field in the material? (b) If the current is changing at the rate of 4000 A/s, at what rate is the electric field in the material changing? (c) What is the displacement current density in the material in part (b)? (*Hint:* Since K for copper is very close to 1, use $\epsilon = \epsilon_0$.) (d) If the current is changing as in part (b), what is the magnitude of the magnetic field 6.0 cm from the center of the wire? Note that both the conduction current and the displacement current should be included in the calculation of B. Is the contribution from the displacement current significant?

*Section 29.8 Superconductivity

*29.40. A long, straight wire made of a type-I superconductor carries a constant current I along its length. Show that the current cannot be uniformly spread over the wire's cross section but instead must all be at the surface.

*29.41. A type-II superconductor in an external field between B_{c1} and B_{c2} has regions that contain magnetic flux and have resistance, and also has superconducting regions. What is the resistance of a long, thin cylinder of such material?

*29.42. At temperatures near absolute zero, B_c approaches 0.142 T for vanadium, a type-I superconductor. The normal phase of vanadium has a magnetic susceptibility close to zero. Consider a long, thin vanadium cylinder with its axis parallel to an external magnetic field $\vec{B}_0$ in the $+x$-direction. At points far from the ends of the cylinder, by symmetry, all the magnetic vectors are parallel to the x-axis. At temperatures near absolute zero, what are the resultant magnetic field $\vec{B}$ and the magnetization $\vec{M}$ inside and outside the cylinder (far from the ends) for (a) $\vec{B}_0 = (0.130 \text{ T})\hat{\imath}$ and (b) $\vec{B}_0 = (0.260 \text{ T})\hat{\imath}$?

*29.43. The compound SiV$_3$ is a type-II superconductor. At temperatures near absolute zero the two critical fields are $B_{c1} = 55.0$ mT and $B_{c2} = 15.0$ T. The normal phase of SiV$_3$ has a magnetic susceptibility close to zero. A long, thin SiV$_3$ cylinder has its axis parallel to an external magnetic field $\vec{B}_0$ in the $+x$-direction. At points far from the ends of the cylinder, by symmetry, all the magnetic vectors are parallel to the x-axis. At a temperature near absolute zero the external magnetic field is slowly increased from zero. What are the resultant magnetic field $\vec{B}$ and the magnetization $\vec{M}$ inside the cylinder at points far from its ends (a) just before the magnetic flux begins to penetrate the material, and (b) just after the material becomes completely normal?

Problems

29.44. A Changing Magnetic Field. You are testing a new data-acquisition system. This system allows you to record a graph of the current in a circuit as a function of time. As part of the test, you are using a circuit made up of a 4.00-cm-radius, 500-turn coil of copper wire connected in series to a 600-Ω resistor. Copper has resistivity 1.72×10^{-8} $\Omega \cdot$ m, and the wire used for the coil has diameter 0.0300 mm. You place the coil on a table that is tilted 30.0° from the horizontal and that lies between the poles of an electromagnet. The electromagnet generates a vertically upward magnetic field that is zero for $t < 0$, equal to $(0.120 \text{ T}) \times (1 - \cos \pi t)$ for $0 \le t \le 1.00$ s, and equal to 0.240 T for $t > 1.00$ s. (a) Draw the graph that should be produced by your data-acquisition system. (This is a full-featured system, so the graph will include labels and numerical values on its axes.) (b) If you were looking vertically downward at the coil, would the current be flowing clockwise or counterclockwise?

29.45. In the circuit shown in Fig. 29.41 the capacitor has capacitance $C = 20\ \mu F$ and is initially charged to 100 V with the polarity shown. The resistor R_0 has resistance $10\ \Omega$. At time $t = 0$ the switch is closed. The small circuit is not connected in any way to the large one. The wire of the small circuit has a resistance of $1.0\ \Omega/m$ and contains 25 loops. The large circuit is a rectangle 2.0 m by 4.0 m, while the small one has dimensions $a = 10.0$ cm and $b = 20.0$ cm. The distance c is 5.0 cm. (The figure is not drawn to scale.) Both circuits are held stationary. Assume that only the wire nearest the small circuit produces an appreciable magnetic field through it. (a) Find the current in the large circuit 200 μs after S is closed. (b) Find the current in the small circuit 200 μs after S is closed. (*Hint:* See Problem 29.7.) (c) Find the direction of the current in the small circuit. (d) Justify why we can ignore the magnetic field from all the wires of the large circuit except for the wire closest to the small circuit.

Figure 29.41 Problem 29.45.

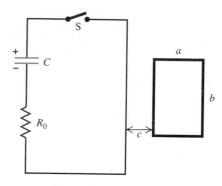

29.46. A flat coil is oriented with the plane of its area at right angles to a spatially uniform magnetic field. The magnitude of this field varies with time according to the graph in Fig. 29.42. Sketch a qualitative (but accurate!) graph of the emf induced in the coil as a function of time. Be sure to identify the times t_1, t_2, and t_3 on your graph.

Figure 29.42 Problem 29.46.

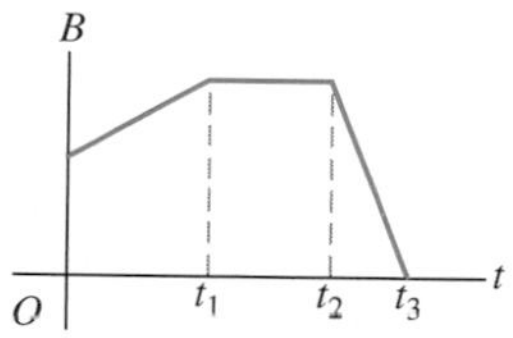

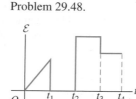

29.47. A circular wire loop of radius a and resistance R initially has a magnetic flux through it due to an external magnetic field. The external field then decreases to zero. A current is induced in the loop while the external field is changing; however, this current does not stop at the instant that the external field stops changing. The reason is that the current itself generates a magnetic field, which gives rise to a flux through the loop. If the current changes, the flux through the loop changes as well, and an induced emf appears in the loop to oppose the change. (a) The magnetic field at the center of the loop of radius a produced by a current i in the loop is given by $B = \mu_0 i/2a$. If we use the crude approximation that the field has this same value at all points within the loop, what is the flux of this field through the loop? (b) By using Faraday's law, Eq. (29.3), and the relationship $\mathcal{E} = iR$, show that after the external field has stopped changing, the current in the loop obeys the differential equation

$$\frac{di}{dt} = -\left(\frac{2R}{\pi\mu_0 a}\right)i$$

(c) If the current has the value i_0 at $t = 0$, the instant that the external field stops changing, solve the equation in part (b) to find i as a

function of time for $t > 0$. (*Hint:* In Section 26.4 we encountered a similar differential equation, Eq. (26.15), for the quantity q. This equation for i may be solved in the same way.) (d) If the loop has radius $a = 50$ cm and resistance $R = 0.10\ \Omega$, how long after the external field stops changing will the current be equal to $0.010 i_0$ (that is, $\frac{1}{100}$ of its initial value)? (e) In solving the examples in this chapter, we ignored the effects described in this problem. Explain why this is a good approximation.

29.48. A coil is stationary in a spatially uniform, external, time-varying magnetic field. The emf induced in this coil as a function of time is shown if Fig. 29.43. Sketch a clear qualitative graph of the external magnetic field as a function of time, given that it started from zero. Include the points t_1, t_2, t_3, and t_4 on your graph.

Figure 29.43 Problem 29.48.

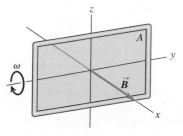

29.49. In Fig. 29.44 the loop is being pulled to the right at constant speed v. A constant current I flows in the long wire, in the direction shown. (a) Calculate the magnitude of the net emf $\mathcal{E}$ induced in the loop. Do this two ways: (i) by using Faraday's law of induction (*Hint:* See Problem 29.7) and (ii) by looking at the emf induced in each segment of the loop due to its motion. (b) Find the direction (clockwise or counterclockwise) of the current induced in the loop. Do this two ways: (i) using Lenz's law and (ii) using the magnetic force on charges in the loop. (c) Check your answer for the emf in part (a) in the following special cases to see whether it is physically reasonable: (i) The loop is stationary; (ii) the loop is very thin, so $a \to 0$; (iii) the loop gets very far from the wire.

Figure 29.44 Problem 29.49.

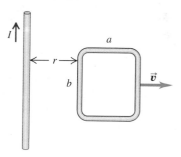

29.50. Suppose the loop in Fig. 29.45 is (a) rotated about the y-axis; (b) rotated about the x-axis; (c) rotated about an edge parallel to the z-axis. What is the maximum induced emf in each case if $A = 600$ cm^2, $\omega = 35.0$ rad/s, and $B = 0.450$ T?

Figure 29.45 Problem 29.50.

29.51. As a new electrical engineer for the local power company, you are assigned the project of designing a generator of sinusoidal ac voltage with a maximum voltage of 120 V. Besides plenty of wire, you have two strong magnets that can produce a constant uniform magnetic field of 1.5 T over a square area of 10.0 cm on a side when they are 12.0 cm apart. The basic design should consist of a square coil turning in the uniform magnetic field. To have an acceptable coil resistance, the coil can have at most 400 loops. What is the minimum rotation rate (in rpm) of the coil so it will produce the required voltage?

29.52. Make a Generator?   You are shipwrecked on a deserted tropical island. You have some electrical devices that you could operate using a generator but you have no magnets. The earth's magnetic field at your location is horizontal and has magnitude 8.0×10^{-5} T, and you decide to try to use this field for a generator by rotating a large circular coil of wire at a high rate. You need to produce a peak emf of 9.0 V and estimate that you can rotate the coil at 30 rpm by turning a crank handle. You also decide that to have an acceptable coil resistance, the maximum number of turns the coil can have is 2000. (a) What area must the coil have? (b) If the coil is circular, what is the maximum translational speed of a point on the coil as it rotates? Do you think this device is feasible? Explain.

29.53. A flexible circular loop 6.50 cm in diameter lies in a magnetic field with magnitude 0.950 T, directed into the plane of the page as shown in Fig. 29.46. The loop is pulled at the points indicated by the arrows, forming a loop of zero area in 0.250 s. (a) Find the average induced emf in the circuit. (b) What is the direction of the current in R: from a to b or from b to a? Explain your reasoning.

Figure **29.46** Problem 29.53.

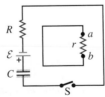

29.54. A Circuit Within a Circuit. Fig. 29.47 shows a small circuit within a larger one, both lying on the surface of a table. The switch is closed at $t = 0$ with the capacitor initially uncharged. Assume that the small circuit has no appreciable effect on the larger one. (a) What is the direction (a to b or to a) of the current in the resistor r (i) the instant after the switch is closed and (ii) one time constant after the switch is closed? (b) Sketch a graph of the current in the small circuit as a function of time, calling clockwise positive.

Figure **29.47** Problem 29.54.

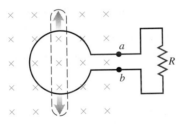

29.55. Terminal Speed. A conducting rod with length L, mass m, and resistance R moves without friction on metal rails as shown in Fig. 29.11. A uniform magnetic field $\vec{B}$ is directed into the plane of the figure. The rod starts from rest and is acted on by a constant force $\vec{F}$ directed to the right. The rails are infinitely long and have negligible resistance. (a) Graph the speed of the rod as a function of time. (b) Find an expression for the terminal speed (the speed when the acceleration of the rod is zero).

29.56. Terminal Speed. A bar of length $L = 0.8$ m is free to slide without friction on horizontal rails, as shown in Fig. 29.48. There is a uniform magnetic field B 1.6 T directed into the plane

of the figure. At one end of the rails there is a battery with emf $\mathcal{E} = 12$ V and a switch. The bar has mass 0.90 kg and resistance 5.0 Ω, and all other resistance in the circuit can be ignored. The switch is closed at time $t = 0$. (a) Sketch the speed of the bar as a function of time. (b) Just after the switch is closed, what is the acceleration of the bar? (c) What is the acceleration of the bar when its speed is 2.0 m/s? (d) What is the terminal speed of the bar?

29.57. Antenna emf. A satellite, orbiting the earth at the equator at an altitude of 400 km, has an antenna that can be modeled as a 2.0-m-long rod. The antenna is oriented perpendicular to the earth's surface. At the equator, the earth's magnetic field is essentially horizontal and has a value of 8.0×10^{-5} T; ignore any changes in B with altitude. Assuming the orbit is circular, determine the induced emf between the tips of the antenna.

29.58. emf in a Bullet. At the equator, the earth's magnetic field is approximately horizontal, is directed toward the north, and has a value of 8×10^{-5} T. (a) Estimate the emf induced between the top and bottom of a bullet shot horizontally at a target on the equator if the bullet is shot toward the east. Assume the bullet has a length of 1 cm and a diameter of 0.4 cm and is traveling at 300 m/s. Which is at higher potential: the top or bottom of the bullet? (b) What is the emf if the bullet travels south? (c) What is the emf induced between the front and back of the bullet for any horizontal velocity?

29.59. A very long, cylindrical wire of radius R carries a current I_0 uniformly distributed across the cross section of the wire. Calculate the magnetic flux through a rectangle that has one side of length W running down the center of the wire and another side of length R, as shown in Fig. 29.49 (see Problem 29.7).

Figure **29.49** Problem 29.59.

Figure **29.48** Problem 29.56.

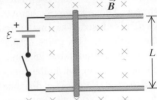

29.60. A circular conducting ring with radius $r_0 = 0.0420$ m lies in the xy-plane in a region of uniform magnetic field $\vec{B} = B_0[1 - 3(t/t_0)^2 + 2(t/t_0)^3]\hat{k}$. In this expression, $t_0 = 0.0100$ s and is constant, t is time, $\hat{k}$ is the unit vector in the $+z$-direction, and $B_0 = 0.0800$ T and is constant. At points a and b (Fig. 29.50) there is a small gap in the ring with wires leading to an external circuit of resistance $R = 12.0$ Ω. There is no magnetic field at the location of the external circuit. (a) Derive an expression, as a function of time, for the total magnetic flux Φ_B through the ring. (b) Determine the emf induced in the ring at time $t = 5.00 \times 10^{-3}$ s. What is the polarity of the emf? (c) Because of the internal resistance of the ring, the current through R at the time given in part (b) is only 3.00 mA. Determine the internal resist-

Figure **29.50** Problem 29.60.

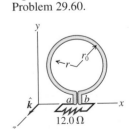

ance of the ring. (d) Determine the emf in the ring at a time $t = 1.21 \times 10^{-2}$ s. What is the polarity of the emf? (e) Determine the time at which the current through R reverses its direction.

29.61. The long, straight wire shown in Fig. 29.51a carries constant current I. A metal bar with length L is moving at constant velocity $\vec{v}$, as shown in the figure. Point a is a distance d from the wire. (a) Calculate the emf induced in the bar. (b) Which point, a or b, is at higher potential? (c) If the bar is replaced by a rectangular wire loop of resistance R (Fig. 29.51b), what is the magnitude of the current induced in the loop?

Figure 29.51 Problem 29.61.

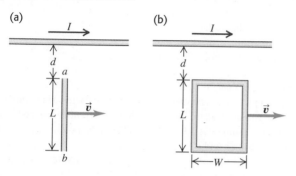

(a)
(b)

29.62. The cube shown in Fig. 29.52, 50.0 cm on a side, is in a uniform magnetic field of 0.120 T, directed along the positive y-axis. Wires A, C, and D move in the directions indicated, each with a speed of 0.350 m/s. (Wire A moves parallel to the xy-plane, C moves at an angle of 45.0° below the xy-plane, and D moves parallel to the xz-plane.) What is the potential difference between the ends of each wire?

Figure 29.52 Problem 29.62.

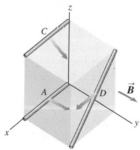

29.63. A slender rod, 0.240 m long, rotates with an angular speed of 8.80 rad/s about an axis through one end and perpendicular to the rod. The plane of rotation of the rod is perpendicular to a uniform magnetic field with a magnitude of 0.650 T. (a) What is the induced emf in the rod? (b) What is the potential difference between its ends? (c) Suppose instead the rod rotates at 8.80 rad/s about an axis through its center and perpendicular to the rod. In this case, what is the potential difference between the ends of the rod? Between the center of the rod and one end?

29.64. A Magnetic Exercise Machine. You have designed a new type of exercise machine with an extremely simple mechanism (Fig. 29.36). A vertical bar of silver (chosen for its low resistivity and because it makes the machine look cool) with length $L = 3.0$ m is free to move left or right without friction on silver rails. The entire apparatus is placed in a horizontal, uniform magnetic field of strength 0.25 T. When you push the bar to the left or right, the bar's motion sets up a current in the circuit that includes the bar. The resistance of the bar and the rails can be neglected. The magnetic field exerts a force on the current-carrying bar, and this force opposes the bar's motion. The health benefit is from the exercise that you do in working against this force. (a) Your design goal is that the person doing the exercise is to do work at the rate of 25 watts when moving the bar at a steady 2.0 m/s. What should be the resistance R? (b) You decide you want to be able to vary the power required from the person, to adapt

the machine to the person's strength and fitness. If the power is to be increased to 50 W by altering R while leaving the other design parameters constant, should R be increased or decreased? Calculate the value of R for 50 W. (c) When you start to construct a prototype machine, you find it is difficult to produce a 0.25-T magnetic field over such a large area. If you decrease the length of the bar to 0.20 m while leaving B, v, and R the same as in part (a), what will be the power required of the person?

29.65. A rectangular loop with width L and a slide wire with mass m are as shown in Fig. 29.53. A uniform magnetic field $\vec{B}$ is directed perpendicular to the plane of the loop into the plane of the figure. The slide wire is given an initial speed of v_0 and then released. There is no friction between the slide wire and the loop, and the resistance of the loop is negligible in comparison to the resistance R of the slide wire. (a) Obtain an expression for F, the magnitude of the force exerted on the wire while it is moving at speed v. (b) Show that the distance x that the wire moves before coming to rest is $x = mv_0R/a^2B^2$.

Figure 29.53 Problem 29.65.

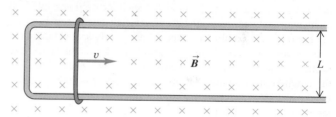

29.66. A 25.0-cm-long metal rod lies in the xy-plane and makes an angle of 36.9° with the positive x-axis and an angle of 53.1° with the positive y-axis. The rod is moving in the $+x$-direction with a speed of 4.20 m/s. The rod is in a uniform magnetic field $\vec{B} = (0.120 \text{ T})\hat{\imath} - (0.220 \text{ T})\hat{\jmath} - (0.0900 \text{ T})\hat{k}$. (a) What is the magnitude of the emf induced in the rod? (b) Indicate in a sketch which end of the rod is at higher potential.

29.67. The magnetic field $\vec{B}$, at all points within a circular region of radius R, is uniform in space and directed into the plane of the page as shown in Fig. 29.54. (The region could be a cross section inside the windings of a long, straight solenoid.) If the magnetic field is increasing at a rate dB/dt, what are the magnitude and direction of the force on a stationary positive point charge q located at points a, b, and c? (Point a is a distance r above the center of the region, point b is a distance r to the right of the center, and point c is at the center of the region.)

Figure 29.54 Problem 29.67.

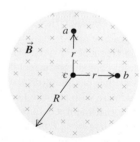

29.68. An airplane propeller of total length L rotates around its center with angular speed ω in a magnetic field that is perpendicular to the plane of rotation. Modeling the propeller as a thin, uniform bar, find the potential difference between (a) the center and either end of the propeller and (b) the two ends. (c) If the field is the earth's field of 0.50 G and the propeller turns at 220 rpm and is 2.0 m long, what is the potential difference between the middle and either end? It this large enough to be concerned about?

29.69. It is impossible to have a uniform electric field that abruptly drops to zero in a region of space in which the magnetic field is constant and in which there are no electric charges. To prove this statement, use the method of contradiction: Assume that such a case *is* possible and then show that your assumption contradicts a law of nature. (a) In the bottom half of a piece of paper, draw evenly spaced horizontal lines representing a uniform electric field to your right. Use dashed lines to draw a rectangle *abcda* with horizontal side *ab* in the electric-field region and horizontal side *cd* in the top half of your paper where $E = 0$. (b) Show that integration around your rectangle contradicts Faraday's law, Eq. (29.21).

29.70. Falling Square Loop. A vertically oriented, square loop of copper wire falls from a region where the field $\vec{B}$ is horizontal, uniform, and perpendicular to the plane of the loop, into a region where the field is zero. The loop is released from rest and initially is entirely within the magnetic-field region. Let the side length of the loop be *s* and let the diameter of the wire be *d*. The resistivity of copper is ρ_R and the density of copper is ρ_m. If the loop reaches its terminal speed while its upper segment is still in the magnetic-field region, find an expression for the terminal speed.

29.71. In a region of space where there are no conduction or displacement currents, it is impossible to have a uniform magnetic field that abruptly drops to zero. To prove this statement, use the method of contradiction: Assume that such a case *is* possible, and then show that your assumption contradicts a law of nature. (a) In the bottom half of a piece of paper, draw evenly spaced horizontal lines representing a uniform magnetic field to your right. Use dashed lines to draw a rectangle *abcda* with horizontal side *ab* in the magnetic-field region and horizontal side *cd* in the top half of your paper where $B = 0$. (b) Show that integration around your rectangle contradicts Ampere's law, Eq. (29.15).

29.72. A capacitor has two parallel plates with area *A* separated by a distance *d*. The space between plates is filled with a material having dielectric constant *K*. The material is not a perfect insulator but has resistivity ρ. The capacitor is initially charged with charge of magnitude Q_0 on each plate that gradually discharges by conduction through the dielectric. (a) Calculate the conduction current density $j_C(t)$ in the dielectric. (b) Show that at any instant the displacement current density in the dielectric is equal in magnitude to the conduction current density but opposite in direction, so the *total* current density is zero at every instant.

29.73. A rod of pure silicon (resistivity $\rho = 2300\ \Omega \cdot m$) is carrying a current. The electric field varies sinusoidally with time according to $E = E_0 \sin \omega t$, where $E_0 = 0.450\ V/m$, $\omega = 2\pi f$, and the frequency $f = 120\ Hz$. (a) Find the magnitude of the maximum conduction current density in the wire. (b) Assuming $\epsilon = \epsilon_0$, find the maximum displacement current density in the wire, and compare with the result of part (a). (c) At what frequency *f* would the maximum conduction and displacement densities become equal if $\epsilon = \epsilon_0$ (which is not actually the case)? (d) At the frequency determined in part (c), what is the relative *phase* of the conduction and displacement currents?

Challenge Problems

29.74. A square, conducting, wire loop of side *L*, total mass *m*, and total resistance *R* initially lies in the horizontal *xy*-plane, with corners at $(x, y, z) = (0, 0, 0)$, $(0, L, 0)$, $(L, 0, 0)$, and $(L, L, 0)$. There is a uniform, upward magnetic field $\vec{B} = B\hat{k}$ in the space within and around the loop. The side of the loop that extends from $(0, 0, 0)$ to $(L, 0, 0)$ is held in place on the *x*-axis; the rest of the loop is free to pivot around this axis. When the loop is released, it begins to rotate due to the gravitational torque. (a) Find the *net* torque (magnitude and direction) that acts on the loop when it has rotated through an angle ϕ from its original orientation and is

rotating downward at an angular speed ω. (b) Find the angular acceleration of the loop at the instant described in part (a). (c) Compared to the case with zero magnetic field, does it take the loop a longer or shorter time to rotate through 90°? Explain. (d) Is mechanical energy conserved as the loop rotates downward? Explain.

29.75. A square conducting loop, 20.0 cm on a side, is placed in the same magnetic field as shown in Exercise 29.30. (See Fig. 29.55; the center of the square loop is at the center of the magnetic-field region.) (a) Copy Fig. 29.55, and draw vectors to show the directions and relative magnitudes of the induced electric field $\vec{E}$ at points *a*, *b*, and *c*. (b) Prove that the component of $\vec{E}$ along the loop has the same value at every point of the loop and is equal to that of the ring shown in Fig. 29.31 (see Exercise 29.30). (c) What current is induced in the loop if its resistance is 1.90 Ω? (d) What is the potential difference between points *a* and *b*?

Figure 29.55 Challenge Problem 29.75.

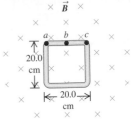

29.76. A uniform, square, conducting loop, 20.0 cm on a side, is placed in the same magnetic field as shown in Exercise 29.30, with side *ac* along a diameter and with point *b* at the center of the field (Fig. 29.56). (a) Copy Fig. 29.56, and draw vectors to show the direction and relative magnitude of the induced electric field $\vec{E}$ at the lettered points. (b) What is the induced emf in side *ac*? (c) What is the induced emf in the loop? (d) What is the current in the loop if its resistance is 1.90 Ω? (e) What is the potential difference between points *a* and *c*? Which is at higher potential?

Figure 29.56 Challenge Problem 29.76.

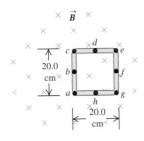

29.77. A metal bar with length *L*, mass *m*, and resistance *R* is placed on frictionless metal rails that are inclined at an angle ϕ above the horizontal. The rails have negligible resistance. A uniform magnetic field of magnitude *B* is directed downward as shown in Fig. 29.57. The bar is released from rest and slides down the rails. (a) Is the direction of the current induced in the bar from *a* to *b* or from *b* to *a*? (b) What is the terminal speed of the bar? (c) What is the induced current in the bar when the terminal speed has been reached? (d) After the terminal speed has been reached, at what rate is electrical energy being converted to thermal energy in the resistance of the bar? (e) After the terminal speed has been reached, at what rate is work being done on the bar by gravity? Compare your answer to that in part (d).

Figure 29.57 Challenge Problem 29.77.

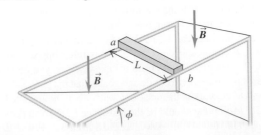

29.78. Consider a uniform metal disk rotating through a perpendicular magnetic field $\vec{B}$, as shown in Fig. 29.19a. The disk has mass m, radius R, and thickness t, is made of a material with resistivity ρ, and is rotating clockwise in Fig. 29.19a with angular speed ω. The magnetic field is directed into the plane of the disk. Suppose that the region to which the magnetic field is confined is not circular, as shown in Fig. 29.19a, but is a small square with sides of length L ($L \ll R$) centered a distance d from the point O (the center of the disk). The sides of this square are horizontal and vertical in Fig. 29.19a. (a) Show that the current induced within the square is approximately equal to $I = \omega dBLt/\rho$. In which direction does this current flow? (*Hint:* Assume that the resistance to the current is confined to the region of the square. The current also encounters resistance as it flows outside the region to which the magnetic field is confined, as shown in Fig. 29.19b; however, this resistance is relatively small, since the current can flow through such a wide area. Recall Eq. (25.10) for resistance, given in Section 25.3.) (b) Show that the induced current gives rise to a torque of approximate magnitude $\tau = \omega d^2 B^2 L^2 t/\rho$ that opposes the rotation of the disk (that is, a counterclockwise torque). (c) What would be the magnitudes and directions of the induced current and torque if the direction of $\vec{B}$ were still into the plane of the disk but the disk rotated counterclockwise? What if the direction of $\vec{B}$ were out of the plane and the disk rotated counterclockwise?

30 INDUCTANCE

? Many traffic lights change when a car rolls up to the intersection. How does the light sense the presence of the car?

Take a length of copper wire and wrap it around a pencil to form a coil. If you put this coil in a circuit, does it behave any differently than a straight piece of wire? Remarkably, the answer is yes. In an ordinary gasoline-powered car, a coil of this kind makes it possible for the 12-volt car battery to provide thousands of volts to the spark plugs, which in turn makes it possible for the plugs to fire and make the engine run. Other coils of this type are used to keep fluorescent light fixtures shining. Larger coils placed under city streets are used to control the operation of traffic signals. All of these applications, and many others, involve the *induction* effects that we studied in Chapter 29.

A changing current in a coil induces an emf in an adjacent coil. The coupling between the coils is described by their *mutual inductance*. A changing current in a coil also induces an emf in that same coil. Such a coil is called an *inductor,* and the relationship of current to emf is described by the *inductance* (also called *self-inductance*) of the coil. If a coil is initially carrying a current, energy is released when the current decreases; this principle is used in automotive ignition systems. We'll find that this released energy was stored in the magnetic field caused by the current that was initially in the coil, and we'll look at some of the practical applications of magnetic-field energy.

We'll also take a first look at what happens when an inductor is part of a circuit. In Chapter 31 we'll go on to study how inductors behave in alternating-current circuits; in that chapter we'll learn why inductors play an essential role in modern electronics, including communication systems, power supplies, and many other devices.

30.1 Mutual Inductance

In Section 28.4 we considered the magnetic interaction between two wires carrying *steady* currents; the current in one wire causes a magnetic field, which exerts a force on the current in the second wire. But an additional interaction arises between two circuits when there is a *changing* current in one of the circuits. Consider two neighboring coils of wire, as in Fig. 30.1. A current flowing in coil 1 produces a magnetic field $\vec{B}$ and hence a magnetic flux through coil 2. If the current in coil 1 changes, the flux through coil 2 changes as well; according to Faraday's law, this induces an emf in coil 2. In this way, a change in the current in one circuit can induce a current in a second circuit.

Let's analyze the situation shown in Fig. 30.1 in more detail. We will use lowercase letters to represent quantities that vary with time; for example, a time-varying current is i, often with a subscript to identify the circuit. In Fig. 30.1 a current i_1 in coil 1 sets up a magnetic field (as indicated by the blue lines), and some of these field lines pass through coil 2. We denote the magnetic flux through *each* turn of coil 2, caused by the current i_1 in coil 1, as Φ_{B2}. (If the flux is different through different turns of the coil, then Φ_{B2} denotes the *average* flux.) The magnetic field is proportional to i_1, so Φ_{B2} is also proportional to i_1. When i_1 changes, Φ_{B2} changes; this changing flux induces an emf $\mathcal{E}_2$ in coil 2, given by

$$\mathcal{E}_2 = -N_2 \frac{d\Phi_{B2}}{dt} \tag{30.1}$$

We could represent the proportionality of Φ_{B2} and i_1 in the form $\Phi_{B2} =$ (constant)i_1, but instead it is more convenient to include the number of turns N_2 in the relationship. Introducing a proportionality constant M_{21}, called the **mutual inductance** of the two coils, we write

$$N_2 \Phi_{B2} = M_{21} i_1 \tag{30.2}$$

where Φ_{B2} is the flux through a *single* turn of coil 2. From this,

$$N_2 \frac{d\Phi_{B2}}{dt} = M_{21} \frac{di_1}{dt}$$

and we can rewrite Eq. (30.1) as

$$\mathcal{E}_2 = -M_{21} \frac{di_1}{dt} \tag{30.3}$$

That is, a change in the current i_1 in coil 1 induces an emf in coil 2 that is directly proportional to the rate of change of i_1 (Fig. 30.2).

We may also write the definition of mutual inductance, Eq. (30.2), as

$$M_{21} = \frac{N_2 \Phi_{B2}}{i_1}$$

If the coils are in vacuum, the flux Φ_{B2} through each turn of coil 2 is directly proportional to the current i_1. Then the mutual inductance M_{21} is a constant that depends only on the geometry of the two coils (the size, shape, number of turns, and orientation of each coil and the separation between the coils). If a magnetic material is present, M_{21} also depends on the magnetic properties of the material. If the material has nonlinear magnetic properties, that is, if the relative permeability K_m (defined in Section 28.8) is not constant and magnetization is not proportional to magnetic field, then Φ_{B2} is no longer directly proportional to i_1. In that case the mutual inductance also depends on the value of i_1. In this discussion we will assume that any magnetic material present has constant K_m so that flux *is* directly proportional to current and M_{21} depends on geometry only.

We can repeat our discussion for the opposite case in which a changing current i_2 in coil 2 causes a changing flux Φ_{B1} and an emf $\mathcal{E}_1$ in coil 1. We might expect that the corresponding constant M_{12} would be different from M_{21} because in general the two coils are not identical and the flux through them is not the same. It turns out, however, that M_{12} is *always* equal to M_{21}, even when the two coils are not symmetric. We call this common value simply the mutual inductance,

30.1 A current i_1 in coil 1 gives rise to a magnetic flux through coil 2.

Mutual inductance: If the current in coil 1 is changing, the changing flux through coil 2 induces an emf in coil 2.

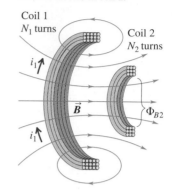

30.2 This electric toothbrush makes use of mutual inductance. The base contains a coil that is supplied with alternating current from a wall socket. This varying current induces an emf in a coil within the toothbrush itself, which is used to recharge the toothbrush battery.

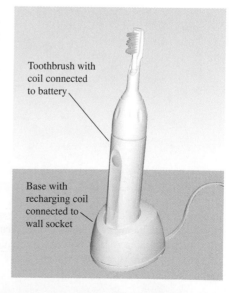

Toothbrush with coil connected to battery

Base with recharging coil connected to wall socket

denoted by the symbol M without subscripts; it characterizes completely the induced-emf interaction of two coils. Then we can write

$$\mathcal{E}_2 = -M\frac{di_1}{dt} \quad \text{and} \quad \mathcal{E}_1 = -M\frac{di_2}{dt} \qquad \text{(mutually induced emfs)} \quad (30.4)$$

where the mutual inductance M is

$$M = \frac{N_2\Phi_{B2}}{i_1} = \frac{N_1\Phi_{B1}}{i_2} \qquad \text{(mutual inductance)} \qquad (30.5)$$

The negative signs in Eq. (30.4) are a reflection of Lenz's law. The first equation says that a change in current in coil 1 causes a change in flux through coil 2, inducing an emf in coil 2 that opposes the flux change; in the second equation the roles of the two coils are interchanged.

CAUTION **Only a time-varying current induces an emf** Note that only a *time-varying* current in a coil can induce an emf and hence a current in a second coil. Equations (30.4) show that the induced emf in each coil is directly proportional to the *rate of change* of the current in the other coil, not to the value of the current. A steady current in one coil, no matter how strong, cannot induce a current in a neighboring coil. ∎

The SI unit of mutual inductance is called the **henry** (1 H), in honor of the American physicist Joseph Henry (1797–1878), one of the discoverers of electromagnetic induction. From Eq. (30.5), one henry is equal to *one weber per ampere*. Other equivalent units, obtained by using Eq. (30.4), are *one volt-second per ampere, one ohm-second,* or *one joule per ampere squared:*

$$1 \text{ H} = 1 \text{ Wb}/\text{A} = 1 \text{ V} \cdot \text{s}/\text{A} = 1 \ \Omega \cdot \text{s} = 1 \text{ J}/\text{A}^2$$

Just as the farad is a rather large unit of capacitance (see Section 24.1), the henry is a rather large unit of mutual inductance. As Example 30.1 shows, typical values of mutual inductance can be in the millihenry (mH) or microhenry (μH) range.

Drawbacks and Uses of Mutual Inductance

Mutual inductance can be a nuisance in electric circuits, since variations in current in one circuit can induce unwanted emfs in other nearby circuits. To minimize these effects, multiple-circuit systems must be designed so that M is as small as possible; for example, two coils would be placed far apart or with their planes perpendicular.

Happily, mutual inductance also has many useful applications. A *transformer,* used in alternating-current circuits to raise or lower voltages, is fundamentally no different from the two coils shown in Fig. 30.1. A time-varying alternating current in one coil of the transformer produces an alternating emf in the other coil; the value of M, which depends on the geometry of the coils, determines the amplitude of the induced emf in the second coil and hence the amplitude of the output voltage. (We'll describe transformers in more detail in Chapter 31 after we've discussed alternating current in greater depth.)

Example 30.1   **Calculating mutual inductance**

In one form of Tesla coil (a high-voltage generator that you may have seen in a science museum), a long solenoid with length l and cross-sectional area A is closely wound with N_1 turns of wire. A coil with N_2 turns surrounds it at its center (Fig. 30.3). Find the mutual inductance.

SOLUTION

IDENTIFY: Mutual inductance occurs in this situation because a current in one of the coils sets up a magnetic field that causes a flux through the other coil.

30.3 A long solenoid with cross-sectional area A and N_1 turns (shown in black) is surrounded at its center by a coil with N_2 turns (shown in blue).

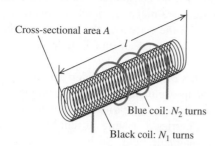

Cross-sectional area A

l

Blue coil: N_2 turns

Black coil: N_1 turns

SET UP: We use Eq. (30.5) to determine the mutual inductance M. According to that equation, we need to know either (a) the flux Φ_{B2} through each turn of the outer coil due to a current i_1 in the solenoid or (b) the flux Φ_{B1} through each turn of the solenoid due to a current i_2 in the outer coil. We choose option (a) since from Example 28.9 (Section 28.7) we have a simple expression for the field at the center of a long current-carrying solenoid, given by Eq. (28.23). Note that we are not given a value for the current i_1 in the solenoid. This omission is not cause for alarm, however: The value of the mutual inductance doesn't depend on the value of the current, so the quantity i_1 should cancel out when we calculate M.

EXECUTE: From Example 28.9, a long solenoid carrying current i_1 produces a magnetic field $\vec{B}_1$ that points along the axis of the solenoid. The field magnitude B_1 is proportional to i_1 and to n_1, the number of turns per unit length:

$$B_1 = \mu_0 n_1 i_1 = \frac{\mu_0 N_1 i_1}{l}$$

The flux through a cross section of the solenoid equals $B_1 A$. Since a very long solenoid produces no magnetic field outside of its coil, this is also equal to the flux Φ_{B2} through each turn of the outer, surrounding coil, no matter what the cross-sectional area of the outer coil. From Eq. (30.5) the mutual inductance M is

$$M = \frac{N_2 \Phi_{B2}}{i_1} = \frac{N_2 B_1 A}{i_1} = \frac{N_2}{i_1} \frac{\mu_0 N_1 i_1}{l} A = \frac{\mu_0 A N_1 N_2}{l}$$

EVALUATE: The mutual inductance of any two coils is always proportional to the product $N_1 N_2$ of their numbers of turns. Notice that the mutual inductance M depends only on the geometry of the two coils, not on the current.

Here's a numerical example to give you an idea of magnitudes. Suppose $l = 0.50$ m, $A = 10$ cm$^2 = 1.0 \times 10^{-3}$ m^2, $N_1 = 1000$ turns, and $N_2 = 10$ turns. Then

$$M = \frac{(4\pi \times 10^{-7}\ \text{Wb}/\text{A}\cdot\text{m})(1.0 \times 10^{-3}\ \text{m}^2)(1000)(10)}{0.50\ \text{m}}$$

$$= 25 \times 10^{-6}\ \text{Wb}/\text{A} = 25 \times 10^{-6}\ \text{H} = 25\ \mu\text{H}$$

Example 30.2   Emf due to mutual inductance

In Example 30.1, suppose the current i_2 in the outer, surrounding coil is given by $i_2 = (2.0 \times 10^6\ \text{A}/\text{s})t$ (currents in wires can indeed increase this rapidly for brief periods). (a) At time $t = 3.0\ \mu$s, what average magnetic flux through each turn of the solenoid is caused by the current in the outer, surrounding coil? (b) What is the induced emf in the solenoid?

SOLUTION

IDENTIFY: In Example 30.1 we found the mutual inductance by relating the current in the solenoid to the flux produced in the outer coil. In this example we are given the current in the outer coil and want to find the resulting flux in the solenoid. The key point is that the mutual inductance is the *same* in either case.

SET UP: Given the value of the mutual inductance $M = 25\ \mu$H from Example 30.1, we use Eq. (30.5) to determine the flux Φ_{B1} through each turn of the solenoid caused by a given current i_2 in the outer coil. We then use Eq. (30.4) to determine the emf induced in the solenoid by the time variation of the outer coil's current.

EXECUTE: (a) At time $t = 3.0\ \mu$s $= 3.0 \times 10^{-6}$ s, the current in the outer coil (coil 2) is $i_2 = (2.0 \times 10^6\ \text{A}/\text{s})(3.0 \times 10^{-6}\ \text{s}) =$

6.0 A. To find the average flux through each turn of the solenoid (coil 1), we solve Eq. (30.5) for Φ_{B1}:

$$\Phi_{B1} = \frac{M i_2}{N_1} = \frac{(25 \times 10^{-6}\ \text{H})(6.0\ \text{A})}{1000} = 1.5 \times 10^{-7}\ \text{Wb}$$

Note that this is an *average* value; the flux can vary considerably between the center and the ends of the solenoid.

(b) The induced emf $\mathcal{E}_1$ is given by Eq. (30.4):

$$\mathcal{E}_1 = -M\frac{di_2}{dt} = -(25 \times 10^{-6}\ \text{H})\frac{d}{dt}[(2.0 \times 10^6\ \text{A}/\text{s})t]$$

$$= -(25 \times 10^{-6}\ \text{H})(2.0 \times 10^6\ \text{A}/\text{s}) = -50\ \text{V}$$

EVALUATE: This is a substantial induced emf in response to a very rapid rate of change of current. In an operating Tesla coil, there is a high-frequency alternating current rather than a continuously increasing current as in this example; both di_2/dt and $\mathcal{E}_1$ alternate as well, with amplitudes that can be thousands of times larger than in this example.

Test Your Understanding of Section 30.1   Consider the Tesla coil described in Example 30.1. If you make the solenoid out of twice as much wire, so that it has twice as many turns and is twice as long, how much larger is the mutual inductance? (i) M is four times greater; (ii) M is twice as great; (iii) M is unchanged; (iv) M is $\frac{1}{2}$ as great; (v) M is $\frac{1}{4}$ as great.

(MP)

30.2 Self-Inductance and Inductors

In our discussion of mutual inductance we considered two separate, independent circuits: A current in one circuit creates a magnetic field and this field gives rise to a flux through the second circuit. If the current in the first circuit changes, the flux through the second circuit changes and an emf is induced in the second circuit.

An important related effect occurs even if we consider only a *single* isolated circuit. When a current is present in a circuit, it sets up a magnetic field that causes a magnetic flux through the *same* circuit; this flux changes when the current changes. Thus any circuit that carries a varying current has an emf induced in it by the variation in *its own* magnetic field. Such an emf is called a **self-induced emf.** By Lenz's law, a self-induced emf always opposes the change in the current that caused the emf and so tends to make it more difficult for variations in current to occur. For this reason, self-induced emfs can be of great importance whenever there is a varying current.

Self-induced emfs can occur in *any* circuit, since there is always some magnetic flux through the closed loop of a current-carrying circuit. But the effect is greatly enhanced if the circuit includes a coil with N turns of wire (Fig. 30.4). As a result of the current i, there is an average magnetic flux Φ_B through each turn of the coil. In analogy to Eq. (30.5) we define the **self-inductance** L of the circuit as

$$L = \frac{N\Phi_B}{i} \qquad \text{(self-inductance)} \tag{30.6}$$

30.4 The current i in the circuit causes a magnetic field $\vec{B}$ in the coil and hence a flux through the coil.

Self-inductance: If the current i in the coil is changing, the changing flux through the coil induces an emf in the coil.

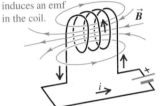

When there is no danger of confusion with mutual inductance, the self-inductance is called simply the **inductance.** Comparing Eqs. (30.5) and (30.6), we see that the units of self-inductance are the same as those of mutual inductance; the SI unit of self-inductance is one henry.

If the current i in the circuit changes, so does the flux Φ_B; from rearranging Eq. (30.6) and taking the derivative with respect to time, the rates of change are related by

$$N\frac{d\Phi_B}{dt} = L\frac{di}{dt}$$

From Faraday's law for a coil with N turns, Eq. (29.4), the self-induced emf is $\mathcal{E} = -N\,d\Phi_B/dt$, so it follows that

$$\mathcal{E} = -L\frac{di}{dt} \qquad \text{(self-induced emf)} \tag{30.7}$$

The minus sign in Eq. (30.7) is a reflection of Lenz's law; it says that the self-induced emf in a circuit opposes any change in the current in that circuit. (Later in this section we'll explore in greater depth the significance of this minus sign.)

Equation (30.7) also states that the self-inductance of a circuit is the magnitude of the self-induced emf per unit rate of change of current. This relationship makes it possible to measure an unknown self-inductance in a relatively simple way: Change the current in the circuit at a known rate di/dt, measure the induced emf, and take the ratio to determine L.

Inductors As Circuit Elements

A circuit device that is designed to have a particular inductance is called an **inductor,** or a *choke*. The usual circuit symbol for an inductor is

Like resistors and capacitors, inductors are among the indispensable circuit elements of modern electronics. Their purpose is to oppose any variations in the current through the circuit. An inductor in a direct-current circuit helps to maintain a steady current despite any fluctuations in the applied emf; in an alternating-current circuit, an inductor tends to suppress variations of the current that are more rapid than desired. In this chapter and the next we will explore the behavior and applications of inductors in circuits in more detail.

To understand the behavior of circuits containing inductors, we need to develop a general principle analogous to Kirchhoff's loop rule (discussed in Section 26.2). To apply that rule, we go around a conducting loop, measuring potential differences across successive circuit elements as we go. The algebraic sum of these differences around any closed loop must be zero because the electric field produced by charges distributed around the circuit is *conservative*. In Section 29.7 we denoted such a conservative field as $\vec{E}_c$.

When an inductor is included in the circuit, the situation changes. The magnetically induced electric field within the coils of the inductor is *not* conservative; as in Section 29.7, we'll denote it by $\vec{E}_n$. We need to think very carefully about the roles of the various fields. Let's assume we are dealing with an inductor whose coils have negligible resistance. Then a negligibly small electric field is required to make charge move through the coils, so the *total* electric field $\vec{E}_c + \vec{E}_n$ within the coils must be zero, even though neither field is individually zero. Because $\vec{E}_c$ is nonzero, we know there have to be accumulations of charge on the terminals of the inductor and the surfaces of its conductors, to produce this field.

Consider the circuit shown in Fig. 30.5; the box contains some combination of batteries and variable resistors that enables us to control the current i in the circuit. According to Faraday's law, Eq. (29.10), the line integral of $\vec{E}_n$ around the circuit is the negative of the rate of change of flux through the circuit, which in turn is given by Eq. (30.7). Combining these two relationships, we get

$$\oint \vec{E}_n \cdot d\vec{l} = -L\frac{di}{dt}$$

where we integrate clockwise around the loop (the direction of the assumed current). But $\vec{E}_n$ is different from zero only within the inductor. Therefore the integral of $\vec{E}_n$ around the whole loop can be replaced by its integral only from a to b through the inductor; that is,

$$\int_a^b \vec{E}_n \cdot d\vec{l} = -L\frac{di}{dt}$$

Next, because $\vec{E}_c + \vec{E}_n = 0$ at each point within the inductor coils, we can rewrite this as

$$\int_a^b \vec{E}_c \cdot d\vec{l} = L\frac{di}{dt}$$

But this integral is just the potential V_{ab} of point a with respect to point b, so we finally obtain

$$V_{ab} = V_a - V_b = L\frac{di}{dt} \tag{30.8}$$

We conclude that there is a genuine potential difference between the terminals of the inductor, associated with conservative, electrostatic forces, despite the fact that the electric field associated with the magnetic induction effect is nonconservative. Thus we are justified in using Kirchhoff's loop rule to analyze circuits that include inductors. Equation (30.8) gives the potential difference across an inductor in a circuit.

30.5 A circuit containing a source of emf and an inductor. The source is variable, so the current i and its rate of change di/dt can be varied.

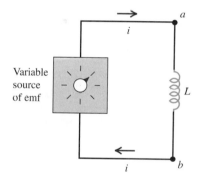

30.6 (a) The potential difference across a resistor depends on the current. (b), (c), (d) The potential difference across an inductor depends on the rate of change of the current.

(a) Resistor with current i flowing from a to b: potential drops from a to b.

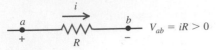

$V_{ab} = iR > 0$

(b) Inductor with *constant* current i flowing from a to b: no potential difference.

i constant: $di/dt = 0$

$\mathcal{E} = 0$

$V_{ab} = L\dfrac{di}{dt} = 0$

(c) Inductor with *increasing* current i flowing from a to b: potential drops from a to b.

i increasing: $di/dt > 0$

$\mathcal{E}$

$V_{ab} = L\dfrac{di}{dt} > 0$

(d) Inductor with *decreasing* current i flowing from a to b: potential increases from a to b.

i decreasing: $di/dt < 0$

$\mathcal{E}$

$V_{ab} = L\dfrac{di}{dt} < 0$

30.7 These fluorescent light tubes are wired in series with an inductor, or ballast, that helps to sustain the current flowing through the tubes.

CAUTION   **Self-induced emf opposes changes in current** Note that the self-induced emf does not oppose the current i itself; rather, it opposes any *change* (di/dt) in the current. Thus the circuit behavior of an inductor is quite different from that of a resistor. Figure 30.6 compares the behaviors of a resistor and an inductor and summarizes the sign relationships. ∎

Applications of Inductors

Because an inductor opposes changes in current, it plays an important role in fluorescent light fixtures (Fig. 30.7). In such fixtures, current flows from the wiring into the gas that fills the tube, ionizing the gas and causing it to glow. However, an ionized gas or *plasma* is a highly nonohmic conductor: The greater the current, the more highly ionized the plasma becomes and the lower its resistance. If a sufficiently large voltage is applied to the plasma, the current can grow so much that it damages the circuitry outside the fluorescent tube. To prevent this problem, an inductor or *magnetic ballast* is put in series with the fluorescent tube to keep the current from growing out of bounds.

The ballast also makes it possible for the fluorescent tube to work with the alternating voltage provided by household wiring. This voltage oscillates sinusoidally with a frequency of 60 Hz, so that it goes momentarily to zero 120 times per second. If there were no ballast, the plasma in the fluorescent tube would rapidly deionize when the voltage went to zero and the tube would shut off. With a ballast present, a self-induced emf sustains the current and keeps the tube lit. Magnetic ballasts are also used for this purpose in streetlights (which obtain their light from a glowing vapor of mercury or sodium atoms) and in neon lights. (In compact fluorescent lamps, the magnetic ballast is replaced by a more complicated scheme for regulating current. This scheme utilizes transistors, discussed in Chapter 42.)

The self-inductance of a circuit depends on its size, shape, and number of turns. For N turns close together, it is always proportional to N^2. It also depends on the magnetic properties of the material enclosed by the circuit. In the following examples we will assume that the circuit encloses only vacuum (or air, which from the standpoint of magnetism is essentially vacuum). If, however, the flux is concentrated in a region containing a magnetic material with permeability μ, then in the expression for B we must replace μ_0 (the permeability of vacuum) by $\mu = K_m\mu_0$, as discussed in Section 28.8. If the material is diamagnetic or paramagnetic, this replacement makes very little difference, since K_m is very close to 1. If the material is *ferromagnetic,* however, the difference is of crucial importance. A solenoid wound on a soft iron core having $K_m = 5000$ can have an inductance approximately 5000 times as great as that of the same solenoid with an air core. Ferromagnetic-core inductors are very widely used in a variety of electronic and electric-power applications.

An added complication is that with ferromagnetic materials the magnetization is in general not a linear function of magnetizing current, especially as saturation is approached. As a result, the inductance is not constant but can depend on current in a fairly complicated way. In our discussion we will ignore this complication and assume always that the inductance is constant. This is a reasonable assumption even for a ferromagnetic material if the magnetization remains well below the saturation level.

Because automobiles contain steel, a ferromagnetic material, driving an automobile over a coil causes an appreciable increase in the coil's inductance. This effect is used in traffic light sensors, which use a large, current-carrying coil embedded under the road surface near an intersection. The circuitry connected to the coil detects the inductance change as a car drives over. When a preprogrammed number of cars have passed over the coil, the light changes to green to allow the cars through the intersection.

?

Example 30.3   Calculating self-inductance

A toroidal solenoid with cross-sectional area A and mean radius r is closely wound with N turns of wire (Fig. 30.8). The toroid is wound on a nonmagnetic core. Determine its self-inductance L. Assume that B is uniform across a cross section (that is, neglect the variation of B with distance from the toroid axis).

SOLUTION

IDENTIFY: Our target variable is the self-inductance L of the toroidal solenoid.

SET UP: We can determine L in one of two ways: either with Eq. (30.6), which requires knowing the flux Φ_B through each turn and the current i in the coil, or from Eq. (30.7), which requires knowing the self-induced emf $\mathcal{E}$ due to a given rate of change of

30.8 Determining the self-inductance of a closely wound toroidal solenoid. For clarity, only a few turns of the winding are shown. Part of the toroid has been cut away to show the cross-sectional area A and radius r.

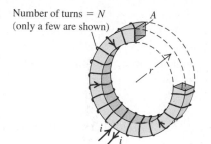

Number of turns = N
(only a few are shown)

current di/dt. We are not given any information about the emf, so we must use the first approach. We use the results of Example 28.10 (Section 28.7), in which we found the magnetic field in the interior of a toroidal solenoid.

EXECUTE: From Eq. (30.6), the self-inductance is $L = N\Phi_B/i$. From Example 28.10, the field magnitude at a distance r from the toroid axis is $B = \mu_0 Ni/2\pi r$. If we assume that the field has this magnitude over the entire cross-sectional area A, then the magnetic flux through the cross section is

$$\Phi_B = BA = \frac{\mu_0 NiA}{2\pi r}$$

The flux Φ_B is the same through each turn, and the self-inductance L is

$$L = \frac{N\Phi_B}{i} = \frac{\mu_0 N^2 A}{2\pi r} \qquad \text{(self-inductance of a toroidal solenoid)}$$

EVALUATE: Suppose $N = 200$ turns, $A = 5.0 \text{ cm}^2 = 5.0 \times 10^{-4} \text{ m}^2$, and $r = 0.10$ m; then

$$L = \frac{(4\pi \times 10^{-7} \text{ Wb/A} \cdot \text{m})(200)^2(5.0 \times 10^{-4} \text{ m}^2)}{2\pi(0.10 \text{ m})}$$
$$= 40 \times 10^{-6} \text{ H} = 40 \ \mu\text{H}$$

Later in this chapter we will use the expression $L = \mu_0 N^2 A/2\pi r$ for the inductance of a toroidal solenoid to help develop an expression for the energy stored in a magnetic field.

Example 30.4   Calculating self-induced emf

If the current in the toroidal solenoid in Example 30.3 increases uniformly from 0 to 6.0 A in 3.0 μs, find the magnitude and direction of the self-induced emf.

SOLUTION

IDENTIFY: We are given L, the self-inductance, and di/dt, the rate of change of the current. Our target variable is the self-induced emf.

SET UP: We calculate the emf using Eq. (30.7).

EXECUTE: The rate of change of the solenoid current is $di/dt = (6.0 \text{ A})/(3.0 \times 10^{-6} \text{ s}) = 2.0 \times 10^6 \text{ A/s}$. From Eq. (30.7), the magnitude of the induced emf is

$$|\mathcal{E}| = L\left|\frac{di}{dt}\right| = (40 \times 10^{-6} \text{ H})(2.0 \times 10^6 \text{ A/s}) = 80 \text{ V}$$

The current is increasing, so according to Lenz's law the direction of the emf is opposite to that of the current. This corresponds to the situation in Fig. 30.6c; the emf is in the direction from b to a, like a battery with a as the $+$ terminal and b the $-$ terminal, tending to oppose the current increase from the external circuit.

EVALUATE: This example shows that even a small inductance L can give rise to a substantial induced emf if the current changes rapidly.

Test Your Understanding of Section 30.2   Rank the following inductors in order of the potential difference V_{ab}, from most positive to most negative. In each case the inductor has zero resistance and the current flows from point a through the inductor to point b. (i) The current through a 2.0-μH inductor increases from 1.0 A to 2.0 A in 0.50 s; (ii) the current through a 4.0-μH inductor decreases from 3.0 A to 0 in 2.0 s; (iii) the current through a 1.0-μH inductor remains constant at 4.0 A; (iv) the current through a 1.0-μH inductor increases from 0 to 4.0 A in 0.25 s.

30.3 Magnetic-Field Energy

Establishing a current in an inductor requires an input of energy, and an inductor carrying a current has energy stored in it. Let's see how this comes about. In Fig. 30.5, an increasing current i in the inductor causes an emf $\mathcal{E}$ between its terminals, and a corresponding potential difference V_{ab} between the terminals of the source, with point a at higher potential than point b. Thus the source must be adding energy to the inductor, and the instantaneous power P (rate of transfer of energy into the inductor) is $P = V_{ab}i$.

Energy Stored in an Inductor

We can calculate the total energy input U needed to establish a final current I in an inductor with inductance L if the initial current is zero. We assume that the inductor has zero resistance, so no energy is dissipated within the inductor. Let the current at some instant be i and let its rate of change be di/dt; the current is increasing, so $di/dt > 0$. The voltage between the terminals a and b of the inductor at this instant is $V_{ab} = L\,di/dt$, and the rate P at which energy is being delivered to the inductor (equal to the instantaneous power supplied by the external source) is

$$P = V_{ab}i = Li\frac{di}{dt}$$

The energy dU supplied to the inductor during an infinitesimal time interval dt is $dU = P\,dt$, so

$$dU = Li\,di$$

The total energy U supplied while the current increases from zero to a final value I is

$$U = L\int_0^I i\,di = \frac{1}{2}LI^2 \qquad \text{(energy stored in an inductor)} \qquad (30.9)$$

After the current has reached its final steady value I, $di/dt = 0$ and no more energy is input to the inductor. When there is no current, the stored energy U is zero; when the current is I, the energy is $\frac{1}{2}LI^2$.

When the current decreases from I to zero, the inductor acts as a source that supplies a total amount of energy $\frac{1}{2}LI^2$ to the external circuit. If we interrupt the circuit suddenly by opening a switch or yanking a plug from a wall socket, the current decreases very rapidly, the induced emf is very large, and the energy may be dissipated in an arc across the switch contacts. This large emf is the electrical analog of the large force exerted by a car running into a brick wall and stopping very suddenly.

30.9 A resistor is a device in which energy is irrecoverably dissipated. By contrast, energy stored in a current-carrying inductor can be recovered when the current decreases to zero.

Resistor with current i: energy is *dissipated*.

Inductor with current i: energy is *stored*.

CAUTION **Energy, resistors, and inductors** It's important not to confuse the behavior of resistors and inductors where energy is concerned (Fig. 30.9). Energy flows into a resistor whenever a current passes through it, whether the current is steady or varying; this energy is dissipated in the form of heat. By contrast, energy flows into an ideal, zero-resistance inductor only when the current in the inductor *increases*. This energy is not dissipated; it is stored in the inductor and released when the current *decreases*. When a steady current flows through an inductor, there is no energy flow in or out. ▌

Magnetic Energy Density

The energy in an inductor is actually stored in the magnetic field within the coil, just as the energy of a capacitor is stored in the electric field between its plates. We can develop relationships for magnetic-field energy analogous to those we obtained for electric-field energy in Section 24.3 [Eqs. (24.9) and (24.11)]. We will concentrate on one simple case, the ideal toroidal solenoid. This system has the advantage that its magnetic field is confined completely to a finite region of space within its core. As in Example 30.3, we assume that the cross-sectional area A is small enough that we can pretend that the magnetic field is uniform over the area. The volume V enclosed by the toroidal solenoid is approximately equal to the circumference $2\pi r$ multiplied by the area A: $V = 2\pi rA$. From Example 30.3, the self-inductance of the toroidal solenoid with vacuum within its coils is

$$L = \frac{\mu_0 N^2 A}{2\pi r}$$

From Eq. (30.9), the energy U stored in the toroidal solenoid when the current is I is

$$U = \frac{1}{2}LI^2 = \frac{1}{2}\frac{\mu_0 N^2 A}{2\pi r}I^2$$

The magnetic field and therefore this energy are localized in the volume $V = 2\pi rA$ enclosed by the windings. The energy *per unit volume*, or *magnetic energy density*, is $u = U/V$:

$$u = \frac{U}{2\pi rA} = \frac{1}{2}\mu_0 \frac{N^2 I^2}{(2\pi r)^2}$$

We can express this in terms of the magnitude B of the magnetic field inside the toroidal solenoid. From Eq. (28.24) in Example 28.10 (Section 28.7), this is

$$B = \frac{\mu_0 NI}{2\pi r}$$

and so

$$\frac{N^2 I^2}{(2\pi r)^2} = \frac{B^2}{\mu_0^2}$$

When we substitute this into the above equation for u, we finally find the expression for **magnetic energy density** in vacuum:

$$u = \frac{B^2}{2\mu_0} \qquad \text{(magnetic energy density in vacuum)} \qquad (30.10)$$

This is the magnetic analog of the energy per unit volume in an *electric* field in vacuum, $u = \frac{1}{2}\epsilon_0 E^2$, which we derived in Section 24.3.

When the material inside the toroid is not vacuum but a material with (constant) magnetic permeability $\mu = K_m\mu_0$, we replace μ_0 by μ in Eq. (30.10). The energy per unit volume in the magnetic field is then

$$u = \frac{B^2}{2\mu} \qquad \text{(magnetic energy density in a material)} \qquad (30.11)$$

Although we have derived Eq. (30.11) only for one special situation, it turns out to be the correct expression for the energy per unit volume associated with *any* magnetic-field configuration in a material with constant permeability. For vacuum, Eq. (30.11) reduces to Eq. (30.10). We will use the expressions for electric-field and magnetic-field energy in Chapter 32 when we study the energy associated with electromagnetic waves.

30.10 The energy required to fire an automobile spark plug is derived from magnetic-field energy stored in the ignition coil.

Magnetic-field energy plays an important role in the ignition systems of gasoline-powered automobiles. A primary coil of about 250 turns is connected to the car's battery and produces a strong magnetic field. This coil is surrounded by a secondary coil with some 25,000 turns of very fine wire. When it is time for a spark plug to fire (see Fig. 20.5 in Section 20.3), the current to the primary coil is interrupted, the magnetic field quickly drops to zero, and an emf of tens of thousands of volts is induced in the secondary coil. The energy stored in the magnetic field thus goes into a powerful pulse of current that travels through the secondary coil to the spark plug, generating the spark that ignites the fuel–air mixture in the engine's cylinders (Fig. 30.10).

Example 30.5   Storing energy in an inductor

The electric-power industry would like to find efficient ways to store surplus energy generated during low-demand hours to help meet customer requirements during high-demand hours. Perhaps a large inductor can be used. What inductance would be needed to store $1.00 \ \text{kW} \cdot \text{h}$ of energy in a coil carrying a 200-A current?

SOLUTION

IDENTIFY: We are given the required amount of stored energy U and the current I. Our target variable is the self-inductance L.

SET UP: We solve for L using Eq. (30.9)

EXECUTE: We have $I = 200 \ \text{A}$ and $U = 1.00 \ \text{kW} \cdot \text{h} = (1.00 \times 10^3 \ \text{W})(3600 \ \text{s}) = 3.60 \times 10^6 \ \text{J}$. Solving Eq. (30.9) for L, we find

$$L = \frac{2U}{I^2} = \frac{2(3.60 \times 10^6 \ \text{J})}{(200 \ \text{A})^2} = 180 \ \text{H}$$

This is more than a *million* times greater than the self-inductance of the toroidal solenoid of Example 30.3 (Section 30.2).

EVALUATE: Conventional wires that are to carry 200 A would have to be of large diameter to keep the resistance low and avoid unacceptable energy losses due to I^2R heating. As a result, a 180-H inductor using conventional wire would be very large (room-size). A superconducting inductor could be much smaller, since the resistance of a superconductor is zero and much thinner wires could be used; one drawback is that the wires would have to be kept at low temperature to remain superconducting, and energy would have to be used to maintain this low temperature. As a result, this scheme is impractical with present technology.

Example 30.6   Magnetic energy density

In a proton accelerator used in elementary particle physics experiments, the trajectories of protons are controlled by bending magnets that produce a magnetic field of 6.6 T. What is the energy density in this field in the vacuum between the poles of such a magnet?

SOLUTION

IDENTIFY: Our target variable is the magnetic energy density u. we are given the magnitude B of the magnetic field.

SET UP: In a vacuum, $\mu = \mu_0$ and the energy density is given by Eq. (30.10).

EXECUTE: The energy density in the magnetic field is

$$u = \frac{B^2}{2\mu_0} = \frac{(6.6 \ \text{T})^2}{2(4\pi \times 10^{-7} \ \text{T} \cdot \text{m/A})} = 1.73 \times 10^7 \ \text{J/m}^3$$

EVALUATE: As an interesting comparison, the heat of combustion of natural gas, expressed on an energy per unit volume basis, is about $3.8 \times 10^7 \ \text{J/m}^3$.

Test Your Understanding of Section 30.3   The current in a solenoid is reversed in direction while keeping the same magnitude. (a) Does this change the magnetic field within the solenoid? (b) Does this change the magnetic energy density in the solenoid?

30.4 The *R-L* Circuit

Let's look at some examples of the circuit behavior of an inductor. One thing is clear already; an inductor in a circuit makes it difficult for rapid changes in current to occur, thanks to the effects of self-induced emf. Equation (30.7) shows that the greater the rate of change of current di/dt, the greater the self-induced emf and the greater the potential difference between the inductor terminals. This equation, together with Kirchhoff's rules (see Section 26.2), gives us the principles we need to analyze circuits containing inductors.

Act|v
PHYSICS
ONLINE

14.1   The *RL* Circuit

Problem-Solving Strategy 30.1   **Inductors in Circuits**

IDENTIFY *the relevant concepts:*   An inductor is just another circuit element, like a source of emf, a resistor, or a capacitor. One key difference is that when an inductor is included in a circuit, all the voltages, currents, and capacitor charges are in general functions of time, not constants as they have been in most of our previous circuit analysis. But Kirchhoff's rules, which we studied in Section 26.2, are still valid. When the voltages and currents vary with time, Kirchhoff's rules hold at each instant of time.

SET UP *the problem* using the following steps:
1. Follow the same procedure described in Problem-Solving Strategy 26.2 in Section 26.2. (Now would be an excellent time to review that strategy.) Draw a large circuit diagram and label all quantities, known and unknown. Apply the junction rule immediately at any junction.
2. Determine which quantities are the target variables.

EXECUTE *the solution* as follows:
1. As in Problem-Solving Strategy 26.2, apply Kirchhoff's loop rule to each loop in the circuit.

2. As in all circuit analysis, getting the correct sign for each potential difference is essential. (You should review the rules given in Problem-Solving Strategy 26.2.) To get the correct sign for the potential difference between the terminals of an inductor, remember Lenz's law and the sign rule described in Section 30.2 in conjunction with Eq. (30.7) and Fig. 30.6. In Kirchhoff's loop rule, when we go through an inductor in the *same* direction as the assumed current, we encounter a voltage *drop* equal to $L\,di/dt$, so the corresponding term in the loop equation is $-L\,di/dt$. When we go through an inductor in the *opposite* direction from the assumed current, the potential difference is reversed and the term to use in the loop equation is $+L\,di/dt$.
3. As always, solve for the target variables.

EVALUATE *your answer:*   Check whether your answer is consistent with the way that inductors behave. If the current through an inductor is changing, your result should indicate that the potential difference across the inductor opposes the change. If not, you probably used an incorrect sign somewhere in your calculation.

Current Growth in an *R-L* Circuit

We can learn several basic things about inductor behavior by analyzing the circuit of Fig. 30.11. A circuit that includes both a resistor and an inductor, and possibly a source of emf, is called an **R-L circuit.** The inductor helps to prevent rapid changes in current, which can be useful if a steady current is required but the external source has a fluctuating emf. The resistor R may be a separate circuit element, or it may be the resistance of the inductor windings; every real-life inductor has some resistance unless it is made of superconducting wire. By closing switch S_1, we can connect the *R-L* combination to a source with constant emf $\mathcal{E}$. (We assume that the source has zero internal resistance, so the terminal voltage equals the emf.)

Suppose both switches are open to begin with, and then at some initial time $t = 0$ we close switch S_1. The current cannot change suddenly from zero to some final value, since di/dt and the induced emf in the inductor would both be infinite. Instead, the current begins to grow at a rate that depends only on the value of L in the circuit.

Let i be the current at some time t after switch S_1 is closed, and let di/dt be its rate of change at that time. The potential difference v_{ab} across the resistor at that time is

$$v_{ab} = iR$$

and the potential difference v_{bc} across the inductor is

$$v_{bc} = L\frac{di}{dt}$$

30.11 An *R-L* circuit.

Closing switch S_1 connects the *R-L* combination in series with a source of emf $\mathcal{E}$.

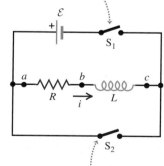

Closing switch S_2 while opening switch S_1 disconnnects the combination from the source.

Note that if the current is in the direction shown in Fig. 30.11 and is increasing, then both v_{ab} and v_{bc} are positive; a is at a higher potential than b, which in turn is at a higher potential than c. (Compare to Figs. 30.6a and c.) We apply Kirchhoff's loop rule, starting at the negative terminal and proceeding counterclockwise around the loop:

$$\mathcal{E} - ir - L\frac{di}{dt} = 0 \qquad (30.12)$$

Solving this for di/dt, we find that the rate of increase of current is

$$\frac{di}{dt} = \frac{\mathcal{E} - iR}{L} = \frac{\mathcal{E}}{L} - \frac{R}{L}i \qquad (30.13)$$

At the instant that switch S_1 is first closed, $i = 0$ and the potential drop across R is zero. The initial rate of change of current is

$$\left(\frac{di}{dt}\right)_{\text{initial}} = \frac{\mathcal{E}}{L}$$

As we would expect, the greater the inductance L, the more slowly the current increases.

As the current increases, the term $(R/L)i$ in Eq. (30.13) also increases, and the *rate* of increase of current given by Eq. (30.13) becomes smaller and smaller. This means that the current is approaching a final, steady-state value I. When the current reaches this value, its rate of increase is zero. Then Eq. (30.13) becomes

$$\left(\frac{di}{dt}\right)_{\text{final}} = 0 = \frac{\mathcal{E}}{L} - \frac{R}{L}I \quad \text{and}$$

$$I = \frac{\mathcal{E}}{R}$$

The *final* current I does not depend on the inductance L; it is the same as it would be if the resistance R alone were connected to the source with emf $\mathcal{E}$.

Figure 30.12 shows the behavior of the current as a function of time. To derive the equation for this curve (that is, an expression for current as a function of time), we proceed just as we did for the charging capacitor in Section 26.4. First we rearrange Eq. (30.13) to the form

$$\frac{di}{i - (\mathcal{E}/R)} = -\frac{R}{L}dt$$

This separates the variables, with i on the left side and t on the right. Then we integrate both sides, renaming the integration variables i' and t' so that we can use i and t as the upper limits. (The lower limit for each integral is zero, corresponding to zero current at the initial time $t = 0$.) We get

$$\int_0^i \frac{di'}{i' - (\mathcal{E}/R)} = -\int_0^t \frac{R}{L}dt'$$

$$\ln\left(\frac{i - (\mathcal{E}/R)}{-\mathcal{E}/R}\right) = -\frac{R}{L}t$$

Now we take exponentials of both sides and solve for i. We leave the details for you to work out; the final result is

$$i = \frac{\mathcal{E}}{R}\left(1 - e^{-(R/L)t}\right) \qquad \text{(current in an R-L circuit with emf)} \qquad (30.14)$$

This is the equation of the curve in Fig. 30.12. Taking the derivative of Eq. (30.14), we find

$$\frac{di}{dt} = \frac{\mathcal{E}}{L}e^{-(R/L)t} \qquad (30.15)$$

30.12 Graph of i versus t for growth of current in an R-L circuit with an emf in series. The final current is $I = \mathcal{E}/R$; after one time constant τ, the current is $1 - 1/e$ of this value.

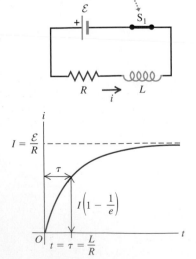

At time $t = 0$, $i = 0$ and $di/dt = \mathcal{E}/L$. As $t \to \infty$, $i \to \mathcal{E}/R$ and $di/dt \to 0$, as we predicted.

As Fig. 30.12 shows, the instantaneous current i first rises rapidly, then increases more slowly and approaches the final value $I = \mathcal{E}/R$ asymptotically. At a time equal to L/R the current has risen to $(1 - 1/e)$, or about 63%, of its final value. The quantity L/R is therefore a measure of how quickly the current builds toward its final value; this quantity is called the **time constant** for the circuit, denoted by τ:

$$\tau = \frac{L}{R} \quad \text{(time constant for an } R\text{-}L \text{ circuit)} \tag{30.16}$$

In a time equal to 2τ, the current reaches 86% of its final value; in 5τ, 99.3%; and in 10τ, 99.995%. (Compare the discussion in Section 26.4 of charging a capacitor of capacitance C that was in series with a resistor of resistance R; the time constant for that situation was the product RC.)

The graphs of i versus t have the same general shape for all values of L. For a given value of R, the time constant τ is greater for greater values of L. When L is small, the current rises rapidly to its final value; when L is large, it rises more slowly. For example, if $R = 100 \; \Omega$ and $L = 10 \; H$,

$$\tau = \frac{L}{R} = \frac{10 \; H}{100 \; \Omega} = 0.10 \; s$$

and the current increases to about 63% of its final value in 0.10 s. (Recall that $1 \; H = 1 \; \Omega \cdot s$.) But if $L = 0.010 \; H$, $\tau = 1.0 \times 10^{-4} \; s = 0.10 \; ms$, and the rise is much more rapid.

Energy considerations offer us additional insight into the behavior of an *R-L* circuit. The instantaneous rate at which the source delivers energy to the circuit is $P = \mathcal{E}i$. The instantaneous rate at which energy is dissipated in the resistor is $i^2 R$, and the rate at which energy is stored in the inductor is $iv_{bc} = Li\,di/dt$ [or, equivalently, $(d/dt)(\frac{1}{2}Li^2) = Li\,di/dt$]. When we multiply Eq. (30.12) by i and rearrange, we find

$$\mathcal{E}i = i^2 R + Li\frac{di}{dt} \tag{30.17}$$

Of the power $\mathcal{E}i$ supplied by the source, part $(i^2 R)$ is dissipated in the resistor and part $(Li\,di/dt)$ goes to store energy in the inductor. This discussion is completely analogous to our power analysis for a charging capacitor, given at the end of Section 26.4.

Example 30.7 Analyzing an *R-L* circuit

A sensitive electronic device of resistance 175 Ω is to be connected to a source of emf by a switch. The device is designed to operate with a current of 36 mA, but to avoid damage to the device, the current can rise to no more than 4.9 mA in the first 58 μs after the switch is closed. To protect the device, it is connected in series with an inductor as in Fig. 30.11; the switch in question is S_1. (a) What emf must the source have? Assume negligible internal resistance. (b) What inductance is required? (c) What is the time constant?

SOLUTION

IDENTIFY: This problem concerns current growth in an *R-L* circuit, so we can use the ideas of this section.

SET UP: Figure 30.12 shows that the final current is $I = \mathcal{E}/R$. Since the resistance is given, the emf is determined by the require-

ment that the final current is to be 36 mA. The other requirement is that the current be no more than $i = 4.9$ mA at $t = 58$ μs; to satisfy this, we use Eq. (30.14) for the current as a function of time and solve for the inductance, which is the only unknown quantity. Equation (30.16) then tells us the time constant.

EXECUTE: (a) Using $I = 36$ mA $= 0.036$ A and $R = 175$ Ω in the expression $I = \mathcal{E}/R$ for the final current and solving for the emf, we find

$$\mathcal{E} = IR = (0.036 \; A)(175 \; \Omega) = 6.3 \; V$$

(b) To find the required inductance, we solve Eq. (30.14) for L. First we multiply through by $(-R/\mathcal{E})$ and then add 1 to both sides to obtain

$$1 - \frac{iR}{\mathcal{E}} = e^{-(R/L)t}$$

Continued

Then we take natural logs of both sides, solve for L, and insert the numbers:

$$L = \frac{-Rt}{\ln(1 - iR/\mathcal{E})}$$

$$= \frac{-(175\ \Omega)(58 \times 10^{-6}\ \text{s})}{\ln[1 - (4.9 \times 10^{-3}\ \text{A})(175\ \Omega)/(6.3\ \text{V})]} = 69\ \text{mH}$$

(c) From Eq. (30.16),

$$\tau = \frac{L}{R} = \frac{69 \times 10^{-3}\ \text{H}}{175\ \Omega} = 3.9 \times 10^{-4}\ \text{s} = 390\ \mu\text{s}$$

EVALUATE: We note that 58 μs is much less than the time constant. In 58 μs the current builds up only from zero to 4.9 mA, a small fraction of its final value of 36 mA; after 390 μs the current equals $(1 - 1/e)$ of its final value, or about $(0.63)(36\ \text{mA}) = 23\ \text{mA}$.

Current Decay in an *R-L* Circuit

30.13 Graph of i versus t for decay of current in an *R-L* circuit. After one time constant τ, the current is $1/e$ of its initial value.

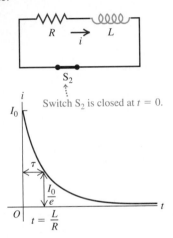

Now suppose switch S_1 in the circuit of Fig. 30.11 has been closed for a while and the current has reached the value I_0. Resetting our stopwatch to redefine the initial time, we close switch S_2 at time $t = 0$, bypassing the battery. (At the same time we should open S_1 to save the battery from ruin.) The current through R and L does not instantaneously go to zero but decays smoothly, as shown in Fig. 30.13. The Kirchhoff's-rule loop equation is obtained from Eq. (30.12) by simply omitting the $\mathcal{E}$ term. We challenge you to retrace the steps in the above analysis and show that the current i varies with time according to

$$i = I_0 e^{-(R/L)t} \tag{30.18}$$

where I_0 is the initial current at time $t = 0$. The time constant, $\tau = L/R$, is the time for current to decrease to $1/e$, or about 37%, of its original value. In time 2τ it has dropped to 13.5%, in time 5τ to 0.67%, and in 10τ to 0.0045%.

The energy that is needed to maintain the current during this decay is provided by the energy stored in the magnetic field of the inductor. The detailed energy analysis is simpler this time. In place of Eq. (30.17) we have

$$0 = i^2 R + Li\frac{di}{dt} \tag{30.19}$$

In this case, $Li\,di/dt$ is negative; Eq. (30.19) shows that the energy stored in the inductor *decreases* at a rate equal to the rate of dissipation of energy $i^2 R$ in the resistor.

This entire discussion should look familiar; the situation is very similar to that of a charging and discharging capacitor, analyzed in Section 26.4. It would be a good idea to compare that section with our discussion of the *R-L* circuit.

Example 30.8   Energy in an *R-L* circuit

When the current in an *R-L* circuit is decaying, what fraction of the original energy stored in the inductor has been dissipated after 2.3 time constants?

SOLUTION

IDENTIFY: This problem concerns current decay in an *R-L* circuit as well as the relationship between the current in an inductor and the amount of stored energy.

SET UP: The current i at any time t for this situation is given by Eq. (30.18). The stored energy associated with this current is given by Eq. (30.9), $U = \frac{1}{2}Li^2$.

EXECUTE: From Eq. (30.18), the current i at any time t is

$$i = I_0 e^{-(R/L)t}$$

The energy U in the inductor at *any* time is obtained by substituting this expression into $U = \frac{1}{2}Li^2$. We obtain

$$U = \frac{1}{2}LI_0^2 e^{-2(R/L)t} = U_0 e^{-2(R/L)t}$$

where $U_0 = \frac{1}{2}LI_0^2$ is the energy at the initial time $t = 0$. When $t = 2.3\tau = 2.3L/R$, we have

$$U = U_0 e^{-2(2.3)} = U_0 e^{-4.6} = 0.010\ U_0$$

That is, only 0.010 or 1.0% of the energy initially stored in the inductor remains, so 99.0% has been dissipated in the resistor.

EVALUATE: To get a sense of what this result means, consider the *R-L* circuit we analyzed in Example 30.7, for which the time constant is 390 μs. With $L = 69$ mH $= 0.069$ H and an initial current $I_0 = 36$ mA $= 0.036$ A, the amount of energy in the inductor initially is $U_0 = \frac{1}{2}LI_0^2 = \frac{1}{2}(0.069$ H$)(0.036$ A$)^2 = 4.5 \times 10^{-5}$ J. Of this, 99.0% or 4.4×10^{-5} J is dissipated in $2.3(390 \, \mu s) =$

9.0×10^{-4} s $= 0.90$ ms. In other words, this circuit can be powered off almost completely in 0.90 ms, and can be powered on in the same amount of time. The minimum time for a complete on-off cycle is therefore 1.8 ms. For many purposes, such as in fast switching networks for telecommunication, an even shorter cycle time is required. In such cases a smaller time constant $\tau = L/R$ is needed.

Test Your Understanding of Section 30.4 (a) In Fig. 30.11, what are the algebraic signs of the potential differences v_{ab} and v_{bc} when switch S_1 is closed and switch S_2 is open? (i) $v_{ab} > 0$, $v_{bc} > 0$; (ii) $v_{ab} > 0$, $v_{bc} < 0$; (iii) $v_{ab} < 0$, $v_{bc} > 0$; (iv) $v_{ab} < 0$, $v_{bc} < 0$. (b) What are the signs of v_{ab} and v_{bc} when S_1 is open, S_2 is closed, and current is flowing in the direction shown? (i) $v_{ab} > 0$, $v_{bc} > 0$; (ii) $v_{ab} > 0$, $v_{bc} < 0$; (iii) $v_{ab} < 0$, $v_{bc} > 0$; (iv) $v_{ab} < 0$, $v_{bc} < 0$.

30.5 The *L-C* Circuit

A circuit containing an inductor and a capacitor shows an entirely new mode of behavior, characterized by *oscillating* current and charge. This is in sharp contrast to the *exponential* approach to a steady-state situation that we have seen with both *R-C* and *R-L* circuits. In the **L-C circuit** in Fig. 30.14a we charge the

Act|v
Physics ONLINE

14.2 AC Circuits: The *RLC* Oscillator (Questions 1–6)

30.14 In an oscillating *L-C* circuit, the charge on the capacitor and the current through the inductor both vary sinusoidally with time. Energy is transferred between magnetic energy in the inductor (U_B) and electric energy in the capacitor (U_E). As in simple harmonic motion, the total energy E remains constant. (Compare Fig. 13.14 in Section 13.3.)

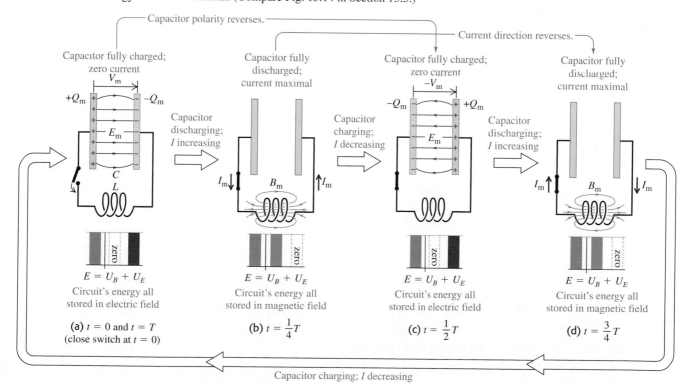

capacitor to a potential difference V_m and initial charge $Q = CV_m$ on its left-hand plate and then close the switch. What happens?

The capacitor begins to discharge through the inductor. Because of the induced emf in the inductor, the current cannot change instantaneously; it starts at zero and eventually builds up to a maximum value I_m. During this buildup the capacitor is discharging. At each instant the capacitor potential equals the induced emf, so as the capacitor discharges, the *rate of change* of current decreases. When the capacitor potential becomes zero, the induced emf is also zero, and the current has leveled off at its maximum value I_m. Figure 30.14b shows this situation; the capacitor has completely discharged. The potential difference between its terminals (and those of the inductor) has decreased to zero, and the current has reached its maximum value I_m.

During the discharge of the capacitor, the increasing current in the inductor has established a magnetic field in the space around it, and the energy that was initially stored in the capacitor's electric field is now stored in the inductor's magnetic field.

Although the capacitor is completely discharged in Fig. 30.14b, the current persists (it cannot change instantaneously), and the capacitor begins to charge with polarity opposite to that in the initial state. As the current decreases, the magnetic field also decreases, inducing an emf in the inductor in the *same* direction as the current; this slows down the decrease of the current. Eventually, the current and the magnetic field reach zero, and the capacitor has been charged in the sense *opposite* to its initial polarity (Fig. 30.14c), with potential difference $-V_m$ and charge $-Q$ on its left-hand plate.

The process now repeats in the reverse direction; a little later, the capacitor has again discharged, and there is a current in the inductor in the opposite direction (Fig. 30.14d). Still later, the capacitor charge returns to its original value (Fig. 30.14a), and the whole process repeats. If there are no energy losses, the charges on the capacitor continue to oscillate back and forth indefinitely. This process is called an **electrical oscillation.**

From an energy standpoint the oscillations of an electrical circuit transfer energy from the capacitor's electric field to the inductor's magnetic field and back. The *total* energy associated with the circuit is constant. This is analogous to the transfer of energy in an oscillating mechanical system from potential energy to kinetic energy and back, with constant total energy. As we will see, this analogy goes much further.

Electrical Oscillations in an *L-C* Circuit

To study the flow of charge in detail, we proceed just as we did for the *R-L* circuit. Figure 30.15 shows our definitions of q and i.

CAUTION **Positive current in an *L-C* circuit** After examining Fig. 30.14, the positive direction for current in Fig. 30.15 may seem backward to you. In fact we've chosen this direction to simplify the relationship between current and capacitor charge. We define the current at each instant to be $i = dq/dt$, the rate of change of the charge on the left-hand capacitor plate. Hence if the capacitor is initially charged and begins to discharge as in Figs. 30.14a and 30.14b, then $dq/dt < 0$ and the initial current i is negative; the direction of the current is then opposite to the (positive) direction shown in Fig. 30.15. ▪

We apply Kirchhoff's loop rule to the circuit in Fig. 30.15. Starting at the lower-right corner of the circuit and adding voltages as we go clockwise around the loop, we obtain

$$-L\frac{di}{dt} - \frac{q}{C} = 0$$

30.15 Applying Kirchhoff's loop rule to the *L-C* circuit. The direction of travel around the loop in the loop equation is shown. Just after the circuit is completed and the capacitor first begins to discharge, as in Fig. 30.14a, the current is negative (opposite to the direction shown).

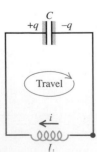

Since $i = dq/dt$, it follows that $di/dt = d^2q/dt^2$. We substitute this expression into the above equation and divide by $-L$ to obtain

$$\frac{d^2q}{dt^2} + \frac{1}{LC}q = 0 \qquad \text{(\textit{L-C} circuit)} \qquad (30.20)$$

Equation (30.20) has exactly the same form as the equation we derived for simple harmonic motion in Section 13.2, Eq. (13.4). That equation is $d^2x/dt^2 = -(k/m)x$, or

$$\frac{d^2x}{dt^2} + \frac{k}{m}x = 0$$

(You should review Section 13.2 before going on with this discussion.) In the *L-C* circuit the capacitor charge q plays the role of the displacement x, and the current $i = dq/dt$ is analogous to the particle's velocity $v_x = dx/dt$. The inductance L is analogous to the mass m, and the reciprocal of the capacitance, $1/C$, is analogous to the force constant k.

Pursuing this analogy, we recall that the angular frequency $\omega = 2\pi f$ of the harmonic oscillator is equal to $(k/m)^{1/2}$, and the position is given as a function of time by Eq. (13.13),

$$x = A\cos(\omega t + \phi)$$

where the amplitude A and the phase angle ϕ depend on the initial conditions. In the analogous electrical situation the capacitor charge q is given by

$$q = Q\cos(\omega t + \phi) \qquad (30.21)$$

and the angular frequency ω of oscillation is given by

$$\omega = \sqrt{\frac{1}{LC}} \qquad \begin{array}{l}\text{(angular frequency of oscillation} \\ \text{in an \textit{L-C} circuit)}\end{array} \qquad (30.22)$$

You should verify that Eq. (30.21) satisfies the loop equation, Eq. (30.20), when ω has the value given by Eq. (30.22). In doing this, you will find that the instantaneous current $i = dq/dt$ is given by

$$i = -\omega Q\sin(\omega t + \phi) \qquad (30.23)$$

Thus the charge and current in an *L-C* circuit oscillate sinusoidally with time, with an angular frequency determined by the values of L and C. The ordinary frequency f, the number of cycles per second, is equal to $\omega/2\pi$ as always. The constants Q and ϕ in Eqs. (30.21) and (30.23) are determined by the initial conditions. If at time $t = 0$ the left-hand capacitor plate in Fig. 30.15 has its maximum charge Q and the current i is zero, then $\phi = 0$. If $q = 0$ at time $t = 0$, then $\phi = \pm\pi/2$ rad.

Energy in an *L-C* Circuit

We can also analyze the *L-C* circuit using an energy approach. The analogy to simple harmonic motion is equally useful here. In the mechanical problem a body with mass m is attached to a spring with force constant k. Suppose we displace the body a distance A from its equilibrium position and release it from rest at time $t = 0$. The kinetic energy of the system at any later time is $\frac{1}{2}mv_x^2$, and its elastic potential energy is $\frac{1}{2}kx^2$. Because the system is conservative, the sum of these energies equals the initial energy of the system, $\frac{1}{2}kA^2$. We find the velocity v_x at any position x just as we did in Section 13.3, Eq. (13.22):

$$v_x = \pm\sqrt{\frac{k}{m}}\sqrt{A^2 - x^2} \qquad (30.24)$$

The L-C circuit is also a conservative system. Again let Q be the maximum capacitor charge. The magnetic-field energy $\frac{1}{2}Li^2$ in the inductor at any time corresponds to the kinetic energy $\frac{1}{2}mv^2$ of the oscillating body, and the electric-field energy $q^2/2C$ in the capacitor corresponds to the elastic potential energy $\frac{1}{2}kx^2$ of the spring. The sum of these energies equals the total energy $Q^2/2C$ of the system:

$$\frac{1}{2}Li^2 + \frac{q^2}{2C} = \frac{Q^2}{2C} \tag{30.25}$$

Table 30.1 Oscillation of a Mass-Spring System Compared with Electrical Oscillation in an L-C Circuit

Mass-Spring System

Kinetic energy $= \frac{1}{2}mv_x^2$

Potential energy $= \frac{1}{2}kx^2$

$\frac{1}{2}mv_x^2 + \frac{1}{2}kx^2 = \frac{1}{2}kA^2$

$v_x = \pm\sqrt{k/m}\sqrt{A^2 - x^2}$

$v_x = dx/dt$

$\omega = \sqrt{\dfrac{k}{m}}$

$x = A\cos(\omega t + \phi)$

Inductor-Capacitor Circuit

Magnetic energy $= \frac{1}{2}Li^2$

Electric energy $= q^2/2C$

$\frac{1}{2}Li^2 + q^2/2C = Q^2/2C$

$i = \pm\sqrt{1/LC}\sqrt{Q^2 - q^2}$

$i = dq/dt$

$\omega = \sqrt{\dfrac{1}{LC}}$

$q = Q\cos(\omega t + \phi)$

The total energy in the L-C circuit is *constant;* it oscillates between the magnetic and the electric forms, just as the constant total mechanical energy in simple harmonic motion is constant and oscillates between the kinetic and potential forms.

Solving Eq. (30.25) for i, we find that when the charge on the capacitor is q, the current i is

$$i = \pm\sqrt{\frac{1}{LC}}\sqrt{Q^2 - q^2} \tag{30.26}$$

You can verify this equation by substituting q from Eq. (30.21) and i from Eq. (30.23). Comparing Eqs. (30.24) and (30.26), we see that current $i = dq/dt$ and charge q are related in the same way as are velocity $v_x = dx/dt$ and position x in the mechanical problem.

The analogies between simple harmonic motion and L-C circuit oscillations are summarized in Table 30.1. The striking parallel shown there between mechanical and electrical oscillations is one of many such examples in physics. This parallel is so close that we can solve complicated mechanical and acoustical problems by setting up analogous electrical circuits and measuring the currents and voltages that correspond to the mechanical and acoustical quantities to be determined. This is the basic principle of many analog computers. This analogy can be extended to *damped* oscillations, which we consider in the next section. In Chapter 31 we will extend the analogy further to include *forced* electrical oscillations, which occur in all alternating-current circuits.

Example 30.9   An oscillating circuit

A 300-V dc power supply is used to charge a 25-μF capacitor. After the capacitor is fully charged, it is disconnected from the power supply and connected across a 10-mH inductor. The resistance in the circuit is negligible. (a) Find the frequency and period of oscillation of the circuit. (b) Find the capacitor charge and the circuit current 1.2 ms after the inductor and capacitor are connected.

SOLUTION

IDENTIFY: Our target variables are the frequency f and period T, as well as the values of charge q and current i at a given time t.

SET UP: We are given the capacitance C and the inductance L, from which we can calculate the frequency and period using Eq. (30.22). We find the charge and current using Eqs. (30.21) and (30.23). Initially the capacitor is fully charged and the current is zero, as in Fig. 30.1 (a), so the phase angle is $\phi = 0$ [see the discussion that follows Eq. (30.23)].

EXECUTE: (a) The natural *angular* frequency is

$$\omega = \sqrt{\frac{1}{LC}} = \sqrt{\frac{1}{(10 \times 10^{-3}\text{ H})(25 \times 10^{-6}\text{ F})}}$$
$$= 2.0 \times 10^3 \text{ rad/s}$$

The frequency f is $1/2\pi$ times this:

$$f = \frac{\omega}{2\pi} = \frac{2.0 \times 10^3 \text{ rad/s}}{2\pi \text{ rad/cycle}} = 320 \text{ Hz}$$

The period is the reciprocal of the frequency:

$$T = \frac{1}{f} = \frac{1}{320 \text{ Hz}} = 3.1 \times 10^{-3}\text{ s} = 3.1 \text{ ms}$$

(b) Since the period of the oscillation is $T = 3.1$ ms, $t = 1.2$ ms equals $0.38T$; this corresponds to a situation intermediate between

Fig. 30.14b $(t = T/4)$ and Fig. 30.14c $(t = T/2)$. Comparing those figures to Fig. 30.15, we expect the capacitor charge q to be negative (that is, there will be negative charge on the left-hand plate of the capacitor) and the current i to be negative as well (that is, current will be traveling in a counterclockwise direction).

To find the value of q, we use Eq. (30.21). The charge is maximum at $t = 0$, so $\phi = 0$ and $Q = C\mathcal{E} = (25 \times 10^{-6}\,\text{F})(300\,\text{V}) = 7.5 \times 10^{-3}\,\text{C}$. The charge q at any time is

$$q = (7.5 \times 10^{-3}\,\text{C})\cos\omega t$$

At time $t = 1.2 \times 10^{-3}$ s,

$$\omega t = (2.0 \times 10^3\,\text{rad/s})(1.2 \times 10^{-3}\,\text{s}) = 2.4\,\text{rad}$$
$$q = (7.5 \times 10^{-3}\,\text{C})\cos(2.4\,\text{rad}) = -5.5 \times 10^{-3}\,\text{C}$$

The current i at any time is

$$i = -\omega Q \sin \omega t$$

At time $t = 1.2 \times 10^{-3}$ s,

$$i = -(2.0 \times 10^3\,\text{rad/s})(7.5 \times 10^{-3}\,\text{C})\sin(2.4\,\text{rad}) = -10\,\text{A}$$

EVALUATE: Note that the signs of q and i are both negative, as we predicted.

Example 30.10 **Energy in an oscillating circuit**

Consider again the *L-C* circuit of Example 30.9. 9 (a) Find the magnetic energy and electric energy at $t = 0$. (b) Find the magnetic energy and electric energy at $t = 1.2$ ms.

SOLUTION

IDENTIFY: This problem asks for the magnetic energy (stored in the inductor) and the electric energy (stored in the capacitor) at two different times during the oscillation of the *L-C* circuit.

SET UP: From Example 30.9 we know the values of the capacitor charge q and circuit current i for both of the times of interest. We use them to calculate the magnetic energy stored in the inductor, given by $U_B = \frac{1}{2}Li^2$, and the electric energy stored in the capacitor, given by $U_E = q^2/2C$.

EXECUTE: (a) At $t = 0$ there is no current and $q = Q$. Hence there is no magnetic energy, and all the energy in the circuit is in the form of electric energy in the capacitor:

$$U_B = \frac{1}{2}Li^2 = 0 \qquad U_E = \frac{Q^2}{2C} = \frac{(7.5 \times 10^{-3}\,\text{C})^2}{2(25 \times 10^{-6}\,\text{F})} = 1.1\,\text{J}$$

(b) As we mentioned in Example 30.9, $t = 1.2$ ms corresponds to a situation intermediate between Fig. 30.14b $(t = T/4)$ and Fig. 30.14c $(t = T/2)$. So we expect the energy to be part magnetic and part electric at this time. From Example 30.9, $i = -10$ A and $q = -5.5 \times 10^{-3}$ C, so

$$U_B = \frac{1}{2}Li^2 = \frac{1}{2}(10 \times 10^{-3}\,\text{H})(-10\,\text{A})^2 = 0.5\,\text{J}$$

$$U_E = \frac{q^2}{2C} = \frac{(-5.5 \times 10^{-3}\,\text{C})^2}{2(25 \times 10^{-6}\,\text{F})} = 0.6\,\text{J}$$

EVALUATE: The magnetic and electric energies are the same at $t = 3T/8 = 0.375T$, exactly halfway between the situations in Figs. 30.14b and 30.14c. The time we are considering here is slightly later and U_B is slightly less than U_E, as we would expect. We emphasize that at *all* times, the *total* energy $E = U_B + U_E$ has the same value, 1.1 J. An *L-C* circuit without resistance is a conservative system; no energy is dissipated.

Test Your Understanding of Section 30.5   One way to think about the energy stored in an *L-C* circuit is to say that the circuit elements do positive or negative work on the charges that move back and forth through the circuit. (a) Between stages (a) and (b) in Fig. 30.14, does the capacitor do positive work or negative work on the charges? (b) What kind of force (electric or magnetic) does the capacitor exert on the charges to do this work? (c) During this process, does the inductor do positive or negative work on the charges? (d) What kind of force (electric or magnetic) does the inductor exert on the charges?

30.6 The *L-R-C* Series Circuit

In our discussion of the *L-C* circuit we assumed that there was no *resistance* in the circuit. This is an idealization, of course; every real inductor has resistance in its windings, and there may also be resistance in the connecting wires. Because of resistance, the electromagnetic energy in the circuit is dissipated and converted to other forms, such as internal energy of the circuit materials. Resistance in an electric circuit is analogous to friction in a mechanical system.

Suppose an inductor with inductance L and a resistor of resistance R are connected in series across the terminals of a charged capacitor, forming an **L-R-C series circuit.** As before, the capacitor starts to discharge as soon as the circuit

Activ
ONLINE
Physics

14.2   AC Circuits: The *RLC* Oscillator (Questions 7–10)

30.16 Graphs of capacitor charge as a function of time in an *L-R-C* series circuit with initial charge *Q*.

(a) Underdamped circuit (small resistance *R*)

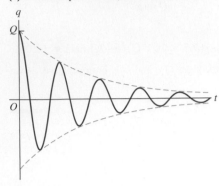

(b) Critically damped circuit (larger resistance *R*)

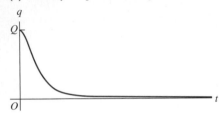

(c) Overdamped circuit (very large resistance *R*)

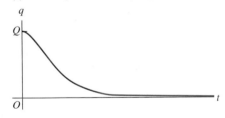

30.17 An *L-R-C* series circuit.

When switch S is in this position, the emf charges the capacitor.

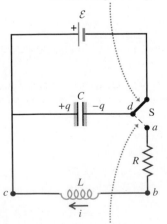

When switch S is moved to this position, the capacitor discharges through the resistor and inductor.

is completed. But because of i^2R losses in the resistor, the magnetic-field energy acquired by the inductor when the capacitor is completely discharged is *less* than the original electric-field energy of the capacitor. In the same way, the energy of the capacitor when the magnetic field has decreased to zero is still smaller, and so on.

If the resistance *R* is relatively small, the circuit still oscillates, but with **damped harmonic motion** (Fig. 30.16a), and we say that the circuit is **underdamped.** If we increase *R*, the oscillations die out more rapidly. When *R* reaches a certain value, the circuit no longer oscillates; it is **critically damped** (Fig. 30.16b). For still larger values of *R*, the circuit is **overdamped** (Fig. 30.16c), and the capacitor charge approaches zero even more slowly. We used these same terms to describe the behavior of the analogous mechanical system, the damped harmonic oscillator, in Section 13.7.

Analyzing an *L-R-C* Circuit

To analyze *L-R-C* circuit behavior in detail, we consider the circuit shown in Fig. 30.17. It is like the *L-C* circuit of Fig. 30.15 except for the added resistor *R*; we also show the source that charges the capacitor initially. The labeling of the positive senses of *q* and *i* are the same as for the *L-C* circuit.

First we close the switch in the upward position, connecting the capacitor to a source of emf $\mathcal{E}$ for a long enough time to ensure that the capacitor acquires its final charge $Q = C\mathcal{E}$ and any initial oscillations have died out. Then at time $t = 0$ we flip the switch to the downward position, removing the source from the circuit and placing the capacitor in series with the resistor and inductor. Note that the initial current is negative, opposite in direction to the direction of *i* shown in the figure.

To find how *q* and *i* vary with time, we apply Kirchhoff's loop rule. Starting at point *a* and going around the loop in the direction *abcda*, we obtain the equation

$$-iR - L\frac{di}{dt} - \frac{q}{C} = 0$$

Replacing *i* with dq/dt and rearranging, we get

$$\frac{d^2q}{dt^2} + \frac{R}{L}\frac{dq}{dt} + \frac{1}{LC}q = 0 \tag{30.27}$$

Note that when $R = 0$, this reduces to Eq. (30.20) for an *L-C* circuit.

There are general methods for obtaining solutions of Eq. (30.27). The form of the solution is different for the underdamped (small *R*) and overdamped (large *R*) cases. When R^2 is less than $4L/C$, the solution has the form

$$q = Ae^{-(R/2L)t}\cos\left(\sqrt{\frac{1}{LC} - \frac{R^2}{4L^2}}\,t + \phi\right) \tag{30.28}$$

where *A* and ϕ are constants. We invite you to take the first and second derivatives of this function and show by direct substitution that it does satisfy Eq. (30.27).

This solution corresponds to the *underdamped* behavior shown in Fig. 30.16a; the function represents a sinusoidal oscillation with an exponentially decaying amplitude. (Note that the exponential factor $e^{-(R/2L)t}$ is *not* the same as the factor $e^{-(R/L)t}$ that we encountered in describing the *R-L* circuit in Section 30.4.) When $R = 0$, Eq. (30.28) reduces to Eq. (30.21) for the oscillations in an *L-C* circuit. If *R* is not zero, the angular frequency of the oscillation is less than $1/(LC)^{1/2}$

because of the term containing R. The angular frequency ω' of the damped oscillations is given by

$$\omega' = \sqrt{\frac{1}{LC} - \frac{R^2}{4L^2}} \quad \text{(underdamped } L\text{-}R\text{-}C \text{ series circuit)} \quad (30.29)$$

When $R = 0$, this reduces to Eq. (30.22), $\omega = (1/LC)^{1/2}$. As R increases, ω' becomes smaller and smaller. When $R^2 = 4L/C$, the quantity under the radical becomes zero; the system no longer oscillates, and the case of *critical damping* (Fig. 30.16b) has been reached. For still larger values of R the system behaves as in Fig. 30.16c. In this case the circuit is *overdamped,* and q is given as a function of time by the sum of two decreasing exponential functions.

In the *underdamped* case the phase constant ϕ in the cosine function of Eq. (30.28) provides for the possibility of both an initial charge and an initial current at time $t = 0$, analogous to an underdamped harmonic oscillator given both an initial displacement and an initial velocity (see Exercise 30.38).

We emphasize once more that the behavior of the *L-R-C* series circuit is completely analogous to that of the damped harmonic oscillator studied in Section 13.7. We invite you to verify, for example, that if you start with Eq. (13.41) and substitute q for x, L for m, $1/C$ for k, and R for the damping constant b, the result is Eq. (30.27). Similarly, the cross-over point between underdamping and overdamping occurs at $b^2 = 4km$ for the mechanical system and at $R^2 = 4L/C$ for the electrical one. Can you find still other aspects of this analogy?

The practical applications of the *L-R-C* series circuit emerge when we include a sinusoidally varying source of emf in the circuit. This is analogous to the *forced oscillations* that we discussed in Section 13.7, and there are analogous *resonance* effects. Such a circuit is called an *alternating-current (ac) circuit;* the analysis of ac circuits is the principal topic of the next chapter.

Example 30.11   An underdamped *L-R-C* series circuit

What resistance R is required (in terms of L and C) to give an *L-R-C* circuit a frequency that is one-half the undamped frequency?

SOLUTION

IDENTIFY: This problem concerns an underdamped *L-R-C* series circuit (Fig. 30.16a): we want the resistance to be great enough to reduce the oscillation frequency to one-half of the undamped value, but not so great that the oscillator become criticaly damped (Fig. 30.1b) or overdamped (Fig. 30.16c).

SET UP: The angular frequency of an underdamped *L-R-C* series circuit is given by Eq. (30.29); the angular frequency of an undamped *L-C* circuit is given by Eq. (30.22). We use these to solve for the target variable R.

EXECUTE: We want ω' given by Eq. (30.29) to be equal to one-half of ω given by Eq. (30.22):

$$\sqrt{\frac{1}{LC} - \frac{R^2}{4L^2}} = \frac{1}{2}\sqrt{\frac{1}{LC}}$$

When we square both sides and solve for R, we get

$$R = \sqrt{\frac{3L}{C}}$$

For example, adding 35 Ω to the circuit of Example 30.9 would reduce the frequency from 320 Hz to 160 Hz.

EVALUATE: The circuit becomes critically damped with no oscillations when $R = \sqrt{4L/C}$. Our result for R is smaller than that, as it should be; we want the circuit to be underdamped.

Test Your Understanding of Section 30.6   An *L-R-C* series circuit includes a 2.0-Ω resistor. At $t = 0$ the capacitor charge is 2.0 μC. for which of the following values of the inductance and capacitance will the charge on the capacitor *not* oscillate? (i) $L = 3.0\ \mu$H, $C = 6.0\ \mu$F; (ii) $L = 6.0\ \mu$H, $C = 3.0\ \mu$F; (iii) $L = 3.0\ \mu$H, $C = 3.0\ \mu$F.

Mutual inductance When a changing current i_1 in one circuit causes a changing magnetic flux in a second circuit, an emf $\mathcal{E}_2$ is induced in the second circuit. Likewise, a changing current i_2 in the second circuit induces an emf $\mathcal{E}_1$ in the first circuit. The mutual inductance M depends on the geometry of the two coils and the material between them. If the circuits are coils of wire with N_1 and N_2 turns, M can be expressed in terms of the average flux Φ_{B2} through each turn of coil 2 that is caused by the current i_1 in coil 1, or in terms of the average flux Φ_{B1} through each turn of coil 1 that is caused by the current i_2 in coil 2. The SI unit of mutual inductance is the henry, abbreviated H. (See Examples 30.1 and 30.2.)

$$\mathcal{E}_2 = -M\frac{di_1}{dt} \quad \text{and} \quad \mathcal{E}_1 = -M\frac{di_2}{dt} \quad (30.4)$$

$$M = \frac{N_2\Phi_{B2}}{i_1} = \frac{N_1\Phi_{B1}}{i_2} \quad (30.5)$$

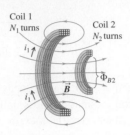

Self-inductance A changing current i in any circuit causes a self-induced emf $\mathcal{E}$. The inductance (or self-inductance) L depends on the geometry of the circuit and the material surrounding it. The inductance of a coil of N turns is related to the average flux Φ_B through each turn caused by the current i in the coil. An inductor is a circuit device, usually including a coil of wire, intended to have a substantial inductance. (See Examples 30.3 and 30.4.)

$$\mathcal{E} = -L\frac{di}{dt} \quad (30.7)$$

$$L = \frac{N\Phi_B}{i} \quad (30.6)$$

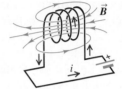

Magnetic-field energy An inductor with inductance L carrying current I has energy U associated with the inductor's magnetic field. The magnetic energy density u (energy per unit volume) is proportional to the square of the magnetic field magnitude. (See Examples 30.5 and 30.6.)

$$U = \frac{1}{2}LI^2 \quad (30.9)$$

$$u = \frac{B^2}{2\mu_0} \quad \text{(in vacuum)} \quad (30.10)$$

$$u = \frac{B^2}{2\mu} \quad (30.11)$$

(in a material with magnetic permeability μ)

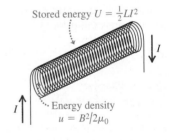

R-L circuits In a circuit containing a resistor R, an inductor L, and a source of emf, the growth and decay of current are exponential. The time constant τ is the time required for the current to approach within a fraction $1/e$ of its final value. (See Examples 30.7 and 30.8.)

$$\tau = \frac{L}{R} \quad (30.16)$$

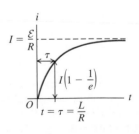

L-C circuits: A circuit that contains inductance L and capacitance C undergoes electrical oscillations with an angular frequency ω that depends on L and C. Such a circuit is analogous to a mechanical harmonic oscillator, with inductance L analogous to mass m, the reciprocal of capacitance $1/C$ to force constant k, charge q to displacement x, and current i to velocity v_x. (See Examples 30.9 and 30.10.)

$$\omega = \sqrt{\frac{1}{LC}} \quad (30.22)$$

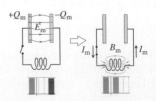

L-R-C series circuits: A circuit that contains inductance, resistance, and capacitance undergoes damped oscillations for sufficiently small resistance. The frequency ω' of damped oscillations depends on the values of L, R, and C. As R increases, the damping increases; if R is greater than a certain value, the behavior becomes over-damped and no longer oscillates. The cross-over between underdamping and overdamping occurs when $R^2 = 4L/C$; when this condition is satisfied, the oscillations are critically damped. (See Example 30.11.)

$$\omega' = \sqrt{\frac{1}{LC} - \frac{R^2}{4L^2}} \qquad (30.29)$$

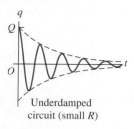

Underdamped circuit (small R)

Key Terms

mutual inductance, *1031*

henry, *1032*

self-induced emf, *1034*

inductance (self-inductance), *1034*

inductor, *1034*

magnetic energy density, *1040*

R-L circuit, *1041*

time constant, *1043*

L-C circuit, *1045*

electrical oscillation, *1046*

L-R-C series circuit, *1050*

damped harmonic motion, *1050*

underdamped, *1050*

critically damped, *1050*

overdamped, *1050*

Answer to Chapter Opening Question   ?

As explained in Section 30.2, traffic light sensors work by measuring the change in inductance of a coil embedded under the road surface when a car drives over it.

Answers to Test Your Understanding Questions

30.1 Answer: (iii) Doubling both the length of the solenoid (l) and the number of turns of wire in the solenoid (N_1) would have *no* effect on the mutual inductance M. Example 30.1 shows that M depends on the ratio of these quantities, which would remain unchanged. This is because the magnetic field produced by the solenoid depends on the number of turns *per unit length,* and the proposed change has no effect on this quantity.

30.2 Answer: (iv), (i), (iii), (ii) From Eq. (30.8), the potential difference across the inductor is $V_{ab} = L \, di/dt$. For the four cases we find (i) $V_{ab} = (2.0 \, \mu\text{H})(2.0 \, \text{A} - 1.0 \, \text{A})/(0.50 \, \text{s}) = 4.0 \, \mu\text{V}$; (ii) $V_{ab} = (4.0 \, \mu\text{H})(0 - 3.0 \, \text{A})/(2.0 \, \text{s}) = -6.0 \, \mu\text{V}$; (iii) $V_{ab} = 0$ because the rate of change of current is zero; and (iv) $V_{ab} = (1.0 \, \mu\text{H})(4.0 \, \text{A} - 0)/(0.25 \, \text{s}) = 16 \, \mu\text{V}$.

30.3 Answers: (a) yes, (b) no Reversing the direction of the current has no effect on the magnetic field magnitude, but it causes the direction of the magnetic field to reverse. It has no effect on the magnetic-field energy density, which is proportional to the square of the *magnitude* of the magnetic field.

30.4 Answers: (a) (i), (b) (ii) Recall that v_{ab} is the potential at a minus the potential at b, and similarly for v_{bc}. For either arrange-

ment of the switches, current flows through the resistor from a to b. The upstream end of the resistor is always at the higher potential, so v_{ab} is positive. With S_1 closed and S_2 open, the current through the inductor flows from b to c and is increasing. The self-induced emf opposes this increase and is therefore directed from c toward b, which means that b is at the higher potential. Hence v_{bc} is positive. With S_1 open and S_2 closed, the inductor current again flows from b to c but is now decreasing. The self-induced emf is directed from b to c in an effort to sustain the decaying current, so c is at the higher potential and v_{bc} is negative.

30.5 Answers: (a) positive, (b) electric, (c) negative, (d) electric The capacitor loses energy between stages (a) and (b), so it does positive work on the charges. It does this by exerting an electric force that pushes current away from the positively charged left-hand capacitor plate and toward the negatively charged right-hand plate. At the same time, the inductor gains energy and does negative work on the moving charges. Although the inductor stores magnetic energy, the force that the inductor exerts is *electric*. This force comes about from the inductor's self-induced emf (see Section 30.2).

30.6 Answers: (i), (iii) There are no oscillations if $R^2 \geq 4L/C$. In each case $R^2 = (2.0 \, \Omega)^2 = 4.0 \, \Omega^2$. In case (i) $4L/C = 4(3.0 \, \mu\text{H})/(6.0 \, \mu\text{F}) = 2.0 \, \Omega^2$, so there are no oscillations (the system is overdamped); in case (ii) $4L/C = 4(6.0 \, \mu\text{H})/(3.0 \, \mu\text{F}) = 8.0 \, \Omega^2$, so there are oscillations (the system is underdamped); and in case (iii) $4L/C = 4(3.0 \, \mu\text{H})/(3.0 \, \mu\text{F}) = 4.0 \, \Omega^2$, so there are no oscillations (the system is critically damped).

PROBLEMS

For instructor-assigned homework, go to **www.masteringphysics.com**

Discussion Questions

Q30.1. In an electric trolley or bus system, the vehicle's motor draws current from an overhead wire by means of a long arm with an attachment at the end that slides along the overhead wire. A brilliant electric spark is often seen when the attachment crosses a junction in the wires where contact is momentarily lost. Explain this phenomenon.

Q30.2. A transformer consists basically of two coils in close proximity but not in electrical contact. A current in one coil magnetically induces an emf in the second coil, with properties that can be controlled by adjusting the geometry of the two coils. Such a device will work only with alternating current, however, and not with direct current. Explain.

Q30.3. In Fig. 30.1, if coil 2 is turned 90° so that its axis is vertical, does the mutual inductance increase or decrease? Explain.

Q30.4. The tightly wound toroidal solenoid is one of the few configurations for which it is easy to calculate self-inductance. What features of the toroidal solenoid give it this simplicity?

Q30.5. Two identical, closely wound, circular coils, each having self-inductance L, are placed next to each other, so that they are coaxial and almost touching. If they are connected in series, what is the self-inductance of the combination? What if they are connected in parallel? Can they be connected so that the total inductance is zero? Explain.

Q30.6. Two closely wound circular coils have the same number of turns, but one has twice the radius of the other. How are the self-inductances of the two coils related? Explain your reasoning.

Q30.7. You are to make a resistor by winding a wire around a cylindrical form. To make the inductance as small as possible, it is proposed that you wind half the wire in one direction and the other half in the opposite direction. Would this achieve the desired result? Why or why not?

Q30.8. For the same magnetic field strength B, is the energy density greater in vacuum or in a magnetic material? Explain. Does Eq. (30.11) imply that for a long solenoid in which the current is I the energy stored is proportional to $1/\mu$? And does this mean that for the same current less energy is stored when the solenoid is filled with a ferromagnetic material rather than with air? Explain.

Q30.9. In Section 30.5 Kirchhoff's loop rule is applied to an L-C circuit where the capacitor is initially fully charged and the equation $-L\,di/dt - q/C = 0$ is derived. But as the capacitor starts to discharge, the current increases from zero. The equation says $L\,di/dt = -q/C$, so it says $L\,di/dt$ is negative. Explain how $L\,di/dt$ can be negative when the current is increasing.

Q30.10. In Section 30.5 the relationship $i = dq/dt$ is used in deriving Eq. (30.20). But a flow of current corresponds to a decrease in the charge on the capacitor. Explain, therefore, why this is the correct equation to use in the derivation, rather than $i = -dq/dt$.

Q30.11. In the R-L circuit shown in Fig. 30.11, when switch S_1 is closed, the potential v_{ab} changes suddenly and discontinuously, but the current does not. Explain why the voltage can change suddenly but the current can't.

Q30.12. In the R-L circuit shown in Fig. 30.11, is the current in the resistor always the same as the current in the inductor? How do you know?

Q30.13. Suppose there is a steady current in an inductor. If you attempt to reduce the current to zero instantaneously by quickly opening a switch, an arc can appear at the switch contacts. Why? Is it physically possible to stop the current instantaneously? Explain.

Q30.14. In an R-L-C circuit, what criteria could be used to decide whether the system is overdamped or underdamped? For example, could we compare the maximum energy stored during one cycle to the energy dissipated during one cycle? Explain.

Exercises

Section 30.1 Mutual Inductance

30.1. Two coils have mutual inductance $M = 3.25 \times 10^{-4}$ H. The current i_1 in the first coil increases at a uniform rate of 830 A/s. (a) What is the magnitude of the induced emf in the second coil? Is it constant? (b) Suppose that the current described is in the second coil rather than the first. What is the magnitude of the induced emf in the first coil?

30.2. Two coils are wound around the same cylindrical form, like the coils in Example 30.1. When the current in the first coil is decreasing at a rate of -0.242 A/s, the induced emf in the second

coil has magnitude 1.65×10^{-3} V. (a) What is the mutual inductance of the pair of coils? (b) If the second coil has 25 turns, what is the flux through each turn when the current in the first coil equals 1.20 A? (c) If the current in the second coil increases at a rate of 0.360 A/s, what is the magnitude of the induced emf in the first coil?

30.3. From Eq. (30.5) $1\ \text{H} = 1\ \text{Wb/A}$, and from Eq. (30.4) $1\ \text{H} = 1\ \Omega \cdot \text{s}$. Show that these two definitions are equivalent.

30.4. A solenoidal coil with 25 turns of wire is wound tightly around another coil with 300 turns (see Example 30.1). The inner solenoid is 25.0 cm long and has a diameter of 2.00 cm. At a certain time, the current in the inner solenoid is 0.120 A and is increasing at a rate of 1.75×10^3 A/s. For this time, calculate; (a) the average magnetic flux through each turn of the inner solenoid; (b) the mutual inductance of the two solenoids; (c) the emf induced in the outer solenoid by the changing current in the inner solenoid.

30.5. Two toroidal solenoids are wound around the same form so that the magnetic field of one passes through the turns of the other. Solenoid 1 has 700 turns, and solenoid 2 has 400 turns. When the current in solenoid 1 is 6.52 A, the average flux through each turn of solenoid 2 is 0.0320 Wb. (a) What is the mutual inductance of the pair of solenoids? (b) When the current in solenoid 2 is 2.54 A, what is the average flux through each turn of solenoid 1?

Section 30.2 Self-Inductance and Inductors

30.6. A toroidal solenoid has 500 turns, cross-sectional area 6.25 cm^2, and mean radius 4.00 cm. (a) Calcualte the coil's self-inductance. (b) If the current decreases uniformly from 5.00 A to 2.00 A in 3.00 ms, calculate the self-induced emf in the coil. (c) The current is directed from terminal a of the coil to terminal b. Is the direction of the induced emf from a to b or from b to a?

30.7. At the instant when the current in an inductor is increasing at a rate of 0.0640 A/s, the magnitude of the self-induced emf is 0.0160 V. (a) What is the inductance of the inductor? (b) If the inductor is a solenoid with 400 turns, what is the average magnetic flux through each turn when the current is 0.720 A?

30.8. When the current in a toroidal solenoid is changing at a rate of 0.0260 A/s, the magnitude of the induced emf is 12.6 mV. When the current equals 1.40 A, the average flux through each turn of the solenoid is 0.00285 Wb. How many turns does the solenoid have?

30.9. The inductor in Fig. 30.18 has inductance 0.260 H and carries a current in the direction shown that is decreasing at a uniform rate, $di/dt = -0.0180$ A/s. (a) Find the self-induced emf. (b) Which end of the inductor, a or b, is at a higher potential?

Figure 30.18
Exercises 30.9 and 30.10.

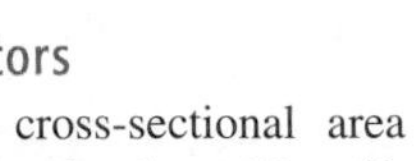

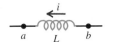

30.10. The inductor shown in Fig. 30.18 has inductance 0.260 H and carries a current in the direction shown. The current is changing at a constant rate. (a) The potential between points a and b is $V_{ab} = 1.04$ V, with point a at higher potential. Is the current increasing or decreasing? b) If the current at $t = 0$ is 12.0 A, what is the current at $t = 2.00$ s?

30.11. Inductance of a Solenoid. A long, straight solenoid has N turns, uniform cross-sectional area A, and length l. Show that the inductance of this solenoid is given by the equation $L = \mu_0 A N^2/l$. Assume that the magnetic field is uniform inside the solenoid and zero outside. (Your answer is approximate because B is actually smaller at the ends than at the center. For this reason your answer is actually an upper limit on the inductance.)

Section 30.3 Magnetic-Field Energy

30.12. An inductor used in a dc power supply has an inductance of 12.0 H and a resistance of 180 Ω. It carries a current of 0.300 A. (a) What is the energy stored in the magnetic field? (b) At what rate is thermal energy developed in the inductor? (c) Does your answer to part (b) mean that the magnetic-field energy is decreasing with time? Explain.

30.13. An air-filled toroidal solenoid has a mean radius of 15.0 cm and a cross-sectional area of 5.00 cm^2. When the current is 12.0 A, the energy stored is 0.390 J. How many turns does the winding have?

30.14. An air-filled toroidal solenoid has 300 turns of wire, a mean radius of 12.0 cm, and a cross-sectional area of 4.00 cm^2. If the current is 5.00 A, calculate: (a) the magnetic field in the solenoid; (b) the self-inductance of the solenoid; (c) the energy stored in the magnetic field; (d) the energy density in the magnetic field. (e) Check your answer for part (d) by dividing your answer to part (c) by the volume of the solenoid.

30.15. A solenoid 25.0 cm long and with a cross-sectional area of 0.500 cm^2 contains 400 turns of wire and carries a current of 80.0 A. Calculate: (a) the magnetic field in the solenoid; (b) the energy density in the magnetic field if the solenoid is filled with air; (c) the total energy contained in the coil's magnetic field (assume the field is uniform); (d) the inductance of the solenoid.

30.16. It has been proposed to use large inductors as energy storage devices. (a) How much electrical energy is converted to light and thermal energy by a 200-W light bulb in one day? (b) If the amount of energy calculated in part (a) is stored in an inductor in which the current is 80.0 A, what is the inductance?

30.17. Starting from Eq. (30.9), derive in detail Eq. (30.11) for the energy density in a toroidal solenoid filled with a magnetic material.

30.18. It is proposed to store 1.00 kW $\cdot$ h = 3.60×10^6 J of electrical energy in a uniform magnetic field with magnitude 0.600 T. (a) What volume (in vacuum) must the magnetic field occupy to store this amount of energy? (b) If instead this amount of energy is to be stored in a volume (in vacuum) equivalent to a cube 40.0 cm on a side, what magnetic field is required?

Section 30.4 The R-L Circuit

30.19. An inductor with an inductance of 2.50 H and a resistance of 8.00 Ω is connected to the terminals of a battery with an emf of 6.00 V and negligible internal resistance. Find (a) the initial rate of increase of current in the circuit; (b) the rate of increase of current at the instant when the current is 0.500 A; (c) the current 0.250 s after the circuit is closed; (d) the final steady-state current.

30.20. A 15.0-Ω resistor and a coil are connected in series with a 6.30-V battery with negligible internal resistance and a closed switch. (a) At 2.00 ms after the switch is opened the current has decayed to 0.210 A. Calculate the inductance of the coil. (b) Calculate the time constant of the circuit. (c) How long after the switch is closed will the current reach 1.00% of its original value?

30.21. A 35.0-V battery with negligible internal resistance, a 50.0-Ω resistor, and a 1.25-mH inductor with negligible resistance are all connected in series with an open switch. The switch is suddenly closed. (a) How long after closing the switch will the current through the inductor reach one-half of its maximum value? (b) How long after closing the switch will the energy stored in the inductor reach one-half of its maximum value?

30.22. In Fig. 30.11, switch S_1 is closed while switch S_2 is kept open. The inductance is $L = 0.115$ H, and the resistance is $R = 120$ Ω. (a) When the current has reached its final value, the energy stored in the inductor is 0.260 J. What is the emf $\mathcal{E}$ of the battery? (b) After the current has reached its final value, S_1 is opened and S_2 is closed. How much time does it take for the energy stored in the inductor to decrease to 0.130 J, half the original value?

30.23. Show that L/R has units of time.

30.24. Write an equation corresponding to Eq. (30.13) for the current shown in Fig. 30.11 just after switch S_2 is closed and switch S_1 is opened, if the initial current is I_0. Use integration methods to verify Eq. (30.18).

30.25. In Fig. 30.11, suppose that $\mathcal{E} = 60.0$ V, $R = 240$ Ω, and $L = 0.160$ H. With switch S_2 open, switch S_1 is left closed until a constant current is established. Then S_2 is closed and S_1 opened, taking the battery out of the circuit. (a) What is the initial current in the resistor, just after S_2 is closed and S_1 is opened? (b) What is the current in the resistor at $t = 4.00 \times 10^{-4}$ s? (c) What is the potential difference between points b and c at $t = 4.00 \times 10^{-4}$ s? Which point is at a higher potential? (d) How long does it take the current to decrease to half its initial value?

30.26. In Fig. 30.11, suppose that $\mathcal{E} = 60.0$ V, $R = 240$ Ω, and $L = 0.160$ H. Initially there is no current in the circuit. Switch S_2 is left open, and switch S_1 is closed. (a) Just after S_1 is closed, what are the potential differences v_{ab} and v_{bc}? (b) A long time (many time constants) after S_1 is closed, what are v_{ab} and v_{bc}? (c) What are v_{ab} and v_{bc} at an intermediate time when $i = 0.150$ A?

30.27. Refer to Exercise 30.19. (a) What is the power input to the inductor from the battery as a function of time if the circuit is completed at $t = 0$? (b) What is the rate of dissipation of energy in the resistance of the inductor as a function of time? (c) What is the rate at which the energy of the magnetic field in the inductor is increasing, as a function of time? (d) Compare the results of parts (a), (b), and (c).

Section 30.5 The L-C Circuit

30.28. A 20.0-μF capacitor is charged by a 150.0-V power supply, then disconnected from the power and connected in series with a 0.280-mH inductor. Calculate: (a) the oscillation frequency of the circuit; (b) the energy stored in the capacitor at time $t = 0$ ms (the moment of connection with the inductor); (c) the energy stored in the inductor at $t = 1.30$ ms.

30.29. A 7.50-nF capacitor is charged up to 12.0 V, then disconnected from the power supply and connected in series through a coil. The period of oscillation of the circuit is then measured to be 8.60×10^{-5} s. Calculate: (a) the inductance of the coil; (b) the maximum charge on the capacitor; (c) the total energy of the circuit; (d) the maximum current in the circuit.

30.30. A 18.0-μF capacitor is placed across a 22.5-V battery for several seconds and is then connected across a 12.0-mH inductor that has no appreciable resistance. (a) After the capacitor and inductor are connected together, find the maximum current in the circuit. When the current is a maximum, what is the charge on the capacitor? (b) How long after the capacitor and inductor are connected together does it take for the capacitor to be completely discharged for the first time? For the second time? (c) Sketch graphs of the charge on the capacitor plates and the current through the inductor as functions of time.

30.31. L-C Oscillations. A capacitor with capacitance 6.00×10^{-5} F is charged by connecting it to a 12.0-V battery. The capacitor is disconnected from the battery and connected across an inductor with $L = 1.50$ H. (a) What are the angular frequency ω of the electrical oscillations and the period of these oscillations (the time for one oscillation)? (b) What is the initial charge on the capacitor? (c) How much energy is initially stored in the capacitor? (d) What is the charge on the capacitor 0.0230 s after the connection to the inductor is made? Interpret the sign of your answer.

(e) At the time given in part (d), what is the current in the inductor? Interpret the sign of your answer. (f) At the time given in part (d), how much electrical energy is stored in the capacitor and how much is stored in the inductor?

30.32. A Radio Tuning Circuit. The minimum capacitance of a variable capacitor in a radio is 4.18 pF. (a) What is the inductance of a coil connected to this capacitor if the oscillation frequency of the L-C circuit is 1600×10^3 Hz, corresponding to one end of the AM radio broadcast band, when the capacitor is set to its minimum capacitance? (b) The frequency at the other end of the broadcast band is 540×10^3 Hz. What is the maximum capacitance of the capacitor if the oscillation frequency is adjustable over the range of the broadcast band?

30.33. An L-C circuit containing an 80.0-mH inductor and a 1.25-nF capacitor oscillates with a maximum current of 0.750 A. Calculate: (a) the maximum charge on the capacitor and (b) the oscillation frequency of the circuit. (c) Assuming the capacitor had its maximum charge at time $t = 0$, calculate the energy stored in the inductor after 2.50 ms of oscillation.

30.34. In an L-C circuit, $L = 85.0$ mH and $C = 3.20$ μF. During the oscillations the maximum current in the inductor is 0.850 mA. (a) What is the maximum charge on the capacitor? (b) What is the magnitude of the charge on the capacitor at an instant when the current in the inductor has magnitude 0.500 mA.

30.35. (a) Using Eqs. (30.21) and (30.23) for an L-C circuit, write expressions for the energy stored in the capacitor as a function of time and for the energy stored in the inductor as a function of time. (b) Using Eq. (30.22) and the trigonometric identity $\sin^2 x + \cos^2 x = 1$, show that the total energy in the L-C circuit is constant and equal to $Q^2/2C$.

30.36. Show that the differential equation of Eq. (30.20) is satisfied by the function $q = Q\cos(\omega t + \phi)$, with ω given by $1/\sqrt{LC}$.

30.37. Show that $\sqrt{LC}$ has units of time.

Section 30.6 The L-R-C Series Circuit

30.38. For the circuit of Fig. 30.17, let $C = 15.0$ nF, $L = 22$ mH, and $R = 75.0$ Ω (a) Calculate the oscillation frequency of the circuit once the capacitor has been charged and the switch has been connected to point a (b) How long will it take for the amplitude of the oscillation to decay to 10.0% of its original value? (c) What value of R would result in a critically damped circuit?

30.39. (a) In Eq. (13.41), substitute q for x, L for m, $1/C$ for k, and R for the damping constant b. Show that the result is Eq. (30.27). (b) Make these same substitutions in Eq. (13.43) and show that Eq. (30.29) results. (c) Make these same substitutions in Eq. (13.42) and show that Eq. (30.28) results.

30.40. (a) Take first and second derivatives with respect to time of q given in Eq. (30.28), and show that it is a solution of Eq. (30.27). (b) At $t = 0$ the switch shown in Fig. 30.17 is thrown so that it connects points d and a; at this time, $q = Q$ and $i = dq/dt = 0$. Show that the constants ϕ and A in Eq. (30.28) are given by

$$\tan\phi = -\frac{R}{2L\sqrt{(1/LC) - (R^2/4L^2)}} \quad \text{and} \quad A = \frac{Q}{\cos\phi}$$

30.41. An L-R-C circuit has $L = 0.450$ H, $C = 2.50 \times 10^{-5}$ F, and resistance R. (a) What is the angular frequency of the circuit when $R = 0$? (b) What value must R have to give a 5.0% decrease in angular frequency compared to the value calculated in part (a)?

30.42. Show that the quantity $\sqrt{L/C}$ has units of resistance (ohms).

Problems

30.43. One solenoid is centered inside another. The outer one has a length of 50.0 cm and contains 6750 coils, while the coaxial inner solenoid is 3.0 cm long and 0.120 cm in diameter and contains 15 coils. The current in the outer solenoid is changing at 37.5 A/s. (a) what is the mutual inductance of these solenoids? (b) Find the emf induced in the innner solenoid.

30.44. A coil has 400 turns and self-inductance 3.50 mH. The current in the coil varies with time according to $i = (680 \text{ mA})\cos(\pi t/0.0250 \text{ s})$. (a) What is the maximum emf induced in the coil? (b) What is the maximum average flux through each turn of the coil? (c) At $t = 0.0180$ s, what is the magnitude of the induced emf?

30.45. A Differentiating Circuit. The current in a resistanceless inductor is caused to vary with time as shown in the graph of Fig. 30.19. (a) Sketch the pattern that would be observed on the screen of an oscilloscope connected to the terminals of the inductor. (The oscilloscope spot sweeps horizontally across the screen at a constant speed, and its vertical deflection is proportional to the potential difference between the inductor terminals.) (b) Explain why a circuit with an inductor can be described as a "differentiating circuit."

Figure 30.19 Problem 30.45

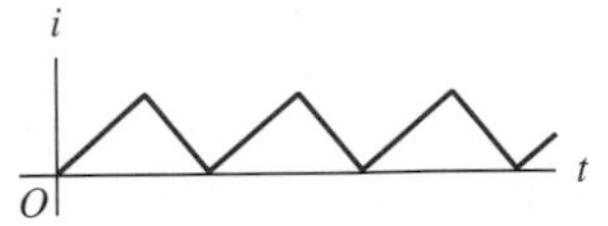

30.46. A 0.250-H inductor carries a time-varying current given by the expression $i = (124 \text{ mA})\cos[(240\pi/s) t]$. (a) Find an expression for the induced emf as a function of time. Graph the current and induced emf as functions of time for $t = 0$ to $t = \frac{1}{60}$ s. (b) What is the maximum emf? What is the current when the induced emf is a maximum? (c) What is the maximum current? What is the induced emf when the current is a maximum?

30.47. Inductors in Series and Parallel. You are given two inductors, one of self-inductance L_1 and the other of self-inductance L_2. (a) You connect the two inductors in series and arrange them so that their mutual inductance is negligible. Show that the equivalent inductance of the combination is $L_{eq} = L_1 + L_2$. (b) You now connect the two inductors in parallel, again arranging them so that their mutual inductance is negligible. Show that the equivalent inductance of the combination is $L_{eq} = (1/L_1 + 1/L_2)^{-1}$. (*Hint:* For either a series or a parallel combination, the potential difference across the combination is $L_{eq}(di/dt)$, where i is the current through the combination. For a parallel combination, i is the sum of the currents through the two inductors.)

30.48. A Coaxial Cable. A small solid conductor with radius a is supported by insulating, nonmagnetic disks on the axis of a thin-walled tube with inner radius b. The inner and outer conductors carry equal currents i in opposite directions. (a) Use Ampere's law to find the magnetic field at any point in the volume between the conductors. (b) Write the expression for the flux $d\Phi_B$ through a narrow strip of length l parallel to the axis, of width dr, at a distance r from the axis of the cable and lying in a plane containing the axis. (c) Integrate your expression from part (b) over the volume between the two conductors to find the total flux produced by a current i in the central conductor. (d) Show that the inductance of a length l of the cable is

$$L = l\frac{\mu_0}{2\pi}\ln\left(\frac{b}{a}\right)$$

(e) Use Eq. (30.9) to calculate the energy stored in the magnetic field for a length l of the cable.

30.49. Consider the coaxial cable of Problem 30.48. The conductors carry equal currents i in opposite directions. (a) Use Ampere's law to find the magnetic field at any point in the volume between the conductors. (b) Use the energy density for a magnetic field, Eq. (30.10), to calculate the energy stored in a thin, cylindrical shell between the two conductors. Let the cylindrical shell have inner radius r, outer radius $r + dr$, and length l. (c) integrate your result in part (b) over the volume between the conductors to find the total energy stored in the magnetic field for a length l of the cable. (d) Use your result in part (c) and Eq. (30.9) to calculate the inductance L of a length l of the cable. Compare your result to L calculated in part (d) of Problem 30.48.

30.50. A toroidal solenoid has a mean radius r and a cross-sectional area A and is wound uniformly with N_1 turns. A second toroidal solenoid with N_2 turns is wound uniformly around the first. The two coils are wound in the same direction. (a) Derive an expression for the inductance L_1 when only the first coil is used and an expression for L_2 when only the second coil is used. (b) Show that $M^2 = L_1 L_2$.

30.51. (a) What would have to be the self-inductance of a solenoid for it to store 10.0 J of energy when a 1.50-A current runs throught it? (b) If this solenoid's cross-sectional diameter is 4.00 cm, and if you could wrap its coils to a density of 10 coils/mm, how long would the solenoid be? (See Exercise 30.11.) Is this a realistic length for ordinary laboratory usc?

30.52. An inductor is connected to the terminals of a battery that has an emf of 12.0 V and negligible internal resistance. The current is 4.86 mA at 0.725 ms after the connection is completed. After a long time the current is 6.45 mA. What are (a) the resistance R of the inductor and (b) the inductance L of the inductor?

30.53. Continuation of Exercises 30.19 and 30.27. (a) How much energy is stored in the magnetic field of thc inductor one time constant after the battery has been connected? Compute this both by integrating the expression in Exercise 30.27(c) and by using Eq. (30.9), and compare the results. (b) Integrate the expression obtained in Exercise 30.27(a) to find the *total* energy supplied by the battery during the time interval considered in part (a). (c) Integrate the expression obtained in Exercise 30.27(b) to find the *total* energy dissipated in the resistance of the inductor during the same time period. (d) Compare the results obtained in parts (a), (b), and (c).

30.54. Continuation of Exercise 30.25. (a) What is the total energy initially stored in the inductor? (b) At $t = 4.00 \times 10^{-4}$ s, at what rate is the energy stored in the inductor decreasing? (c) At $t = 4.00 \times 10^{-4}$ s, at what rate is electrical energy being converted into thermal energy in the resistor? (d) Obtain an expression for the rate at which electrical energy is being converted into thermal energy in the resistor as a function of time. Integrate this expression from $t = 0$ to $t = \infty$ to obtain the total electrical energy dissipated in the resistor. Compare your result to that of part (a).

30.55. The equation preceding Eq. (30.27) may be converted into an energy relationship. Multiply both sides of this equation by $-i = -dq/dt$. The first term then becomes $i^2 R$. Show that the second term can be written as $d(\frac{1}{2}Li^2)/dt$, and that the third term can be written as $d(q^2/2C)/dt$. What does the resulting equation say about energy conservation in the circuit?

30.56. A 5.00-μF capacitor is initially charged to a potential of 16.0 V. It is then connected in series with a 3.75-mH inductor. (a) What is the total energy stored in this circuit? (b) What is the maximum current in the inductor? What is the charge on the capacitor plates at the instant the current in the inductor is maximal?

30.57. An Electromagnetic Car Alarm. Your latest invention is a car alarm that produces sound at a particularly annoying frequency of 3500 Hz. To do this, the car-alarm circuitry must produce an alternating electric current of the same frequency. That's why your design includes an inductor and a capacitor in series. The maximum voltage across the capacitor is to be 12.0 V (the same voltage as the car battery). To produce a sufficiently loud sound, the capacitor must store 0.0160 J of energy. What values of capacitance and inductance should you choose for your car-alarm circuit?

30.58. An L-C circuit consists of a 60.0-mH inductor and a 250-μF capacitor. The initial charge on the capacitor is 6.00 μC, and the initial current in the inductor is zero. (a) What is the maximum voltage across the capacitor? (b) What is the maximum current in the inductor? (c) What is the maximum energy stored in the inductor? (d) When the current in the inductor has half its maximum value, what is the charge on the capacitor and what is the energy stored in the inductor?

30.59. Solar Magnetic Energy. Magnetic fields within a sunspot can be as strong as 0.4 T. (By comparison, the earth's magnetic field is about $1/10,000$ as strong.) Sunspots can be as large as 25,000 km in radius. The material in a sunspot has a density of about 3×10^{-4} kg/m^3. Assume μ for the sunspot material is μ_0. If 100% of the magnetic-field energy stored in a sunspot could be used to eject the sunspot's material away from the sun's surface, at what speed would that material be ejected? Compare to the sun's escape speed, which is about 6×10^5 m/s. (*Hint:* Calcualte the kinetic energy the magnetic field could supply to 1 m^3 of sunspot material.)

30.60. While studying a coil of unknown inductance and internal resistance, you connect it in series with a 25.0-V battery and a 150-Ω resistor. You then place an oscilloscope across one of these circuit elements and use the oscilloscope to measure the voltage across the circuit element as a function of time. The result is shown in Fig. 30.20. (a) Across which circuit element (coil or resistor) is the oscilloscope connected? How do you know this? (b) Find the inductance and the internal resistance of the coil. (c) Carefully make a quantitative sketch showing the voltage versus time you would observe if you put the oscilloscope across the other circuit element (resistor or coil).

Figure 30.20 Problem 30.60.

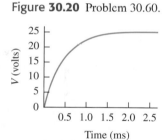

30.61. In the lab, you are trying to find the inductance and internal resistance of a solenoid. You place it in series with a battery of negligible internal resistance, a 10.0-Ω resistor, and a switch. You then put an oscilloscope across one of these circuit elements to measure the voltage across that circuit element as a function of time. You close the switch, and the oscilloscope shows voltage versus time as shown in Fig. 30.21. (a) Across which circuit element (solenoid or resistor) is the oscilloscope connected? How do you know this? (b) Why doesn't the graph approach zero as $t \to \infty$? (c) What is the emf of the battery? (d) Find the maximum current in the circuit. (e) What are the internal resistance and self-inductance of the solenoid?

Figure 30.21 Problem 30.61.

30.62. In the circuit shown in Fig. 30.22, find the reading in each ammeter and voltmeter (a) just after switch S is closed and (b) after S has been closed a very long time.

Figure 30.22 Problem 30.62.

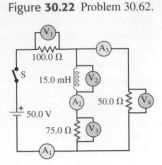

30.63. In the circuit shown in Fig. 30.23, switch S is closed at time $t = 0$ with no charge initially on the capacitor. (a) Find the reading of each ammeter and each voltmeter just after S is closed. (b) Find the reading of each meter after a long time has elapsed. (c) Find the maximum charge on the capacitor. (d) Draw a qualitative graph of the reading of voltmeter V_2 as a function of time.

Figure 30.23 Problem 30.63.

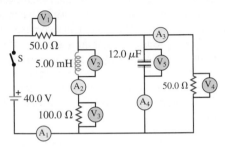

30.64. In the circuit shown in Fig. 30.24 the battery and the inductor have no appreciable internal resistance and there is no current in the circuit. After the switch is closed, find the readings of the ammeter (A) and voltmeters (V_1 and V_2) (a) the instant after the switch is closed and (b) after the switch has been closed for a very long time. (c) Which answers in parts (a) and (b) would change if the inductance were 24.0 mH instead?

Figure 30.24 Problem 30.64.

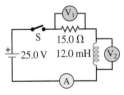

30.65. In the circuit shown in Fig. 30.25, switch S is closed at time $t = 0$. (a) Find the reading of each meter just after S is closed. (b) What does each meter read long after S is closed?

Figure 30.25 Problem 30.65.

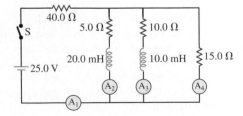

30.66. In the circuit shown in Fig. 30.26, switch S has been closed for a long enough time so that the current reads a steady 3.50 A. Suddenly, switch S_2 is closed and S_1 is opened at the same instant. (a) What is the maximum charge that the capacitor will receive? (b) What is the current in the inductor at this time?

Figure 30.26 Problem 30.66.

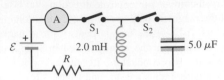

30.67. In the circuit shown in Fig. 30.27, $\mathcal{E} = 60.0$ V, $R_1 = 40.0\ \Omega$, $R_2 = 25.0\ \Omega$, and $L = 0.300$ H. Switch S is closed at $t = 0$. Just after the switch is closed, (a) what is the potential difference v_{ab} across the resistor R_1; (b) which point, a or b, is at a higher potential; (c) what is the potential difference v_{cd} across the inductor L; (d) which point, c or d, is at a higher potential? The switch is left closed a long time and then opened. Just after the switch is opened, (e) what is the potential difference v_{ab} across the resistor R_1; (f) which point, a or b, is at a higher potential; (g) what is the potential difference v_{cd} across the inductor L; (h) which point, c or d, is at a higher potential?

Figure 30.27 Problems 30.67, 30.68, and 30.75.

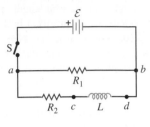

30.68. In the circuit shown in Fig. 30.27, $\mathcal{E} = 60.0$ V, $R_1 = 40.0\ \Omega$, $R_2 = 25.0\ \Omega$, and $L = 0.300$ H. (a) Switch S is closed. At some time t afterward the current in the inductor is increasing at a rate of $di/dt = 50.0$ A/s. At this instant, what are the current i_1 through R_1 and the current i_2 through R_2? (*Hint:* Analyze two separate loops: one containing $\mathcal{E}$ and R_1 and the other containing $\mathcal{E}, R_2$, and L.) (b) After the switch has been closed a long time, it is opened again. Just after it is opened, what is the current through R_1?

30.69. Consider the circuit shown in Fig. 30.28. Let $\mathcal{E} = 36.0$ V, $R_0 = 50.0\ \Omega$, $R = 150\ \Omega$, and $L = 4.00$ H. (a) Switch S_1 is closed and switch S_2 is left open. Just after S_1 is closed, what are the current i_0 through R_0 and the potential differences v_{ac} and v_{cb}? (b) After S_1 has been closed a long time (S_2 is still open) so that the current has reached its final, steady value, what are i_0, v_{ac}, and v_{cb}? (c) Find the expressions for i_0, v_{ac}, and v_{cb} as functions of the time t since S_1 was closed. Your results should agree with part (a) when $t = 0$ and with part (b) when $t \to \infty$. Graph i_0, v_{ac}, and v_{cb} versus time.

Figure 30.28 Problems 30.69 and 30.70.

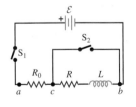

30.70. After the current in the circuit of Fig. 30.28 has reached its final, steady value with switch S_1 closed and S_2 open, switch S_2 is closed, thus short-circuiting the inductor. (Switch S_1 remains closed. See Problem 30.69 for numerical values of the circuit elements.) (a) Just after S_2 is closed, what are v_{ac} and v_{cb}, and what are the currents through R_0, R, and S_2? (b) A long time after S_2 is closed, what are v_{ac} and v_{cb}, and what are the currents through R_0, R, and S_2? (c) Derive expressions for the currents through R_0, R, and S_2 as functions of the time t that has elapsed since S_2 was closed. Your results should agree with part (a) when $t = 0$ and with part (b) when $t \to \infty$. Graph these three currents versus time.

30.71. In the circuit shown in Fig. 30.29, the switch has been open for a long time and is suddenly closed. Neither the battery nor the inductors have any appreciable resistance. Review the results of Problem 30.47. (a) What do the ammeter and voltmeter read just after S is closed? (b) What do the ammeter and the voltmeter read after S has been closed a very long time? (c) What do the ammeter and the voltmeter read 0.115 ms after S is closed?

30.72. In the circuit shown in Fig. 30.30, neither the battery nor the inductors have any appreciable resistance, the capacitors are initially uncharged, and the switch S has been in position 1 for a very long time. Review the results of Problem 30.47. (a) What is the current in the circuit? (b) The switch is now suddenly flipped to position 2. Find the maximum charge that each capacitor will receive, and how much time after the switch is flipped it will take them to acquire this charge.

30.73. We have ignored the variation of the magnetic field across the cross section of a toroidal solenoid. Let's now examine the validity of that approximation. A certain toroidal solenoid has a rectangular cross section (Fig. 30.31). It has N uniformly spaced turns, with air inside. The magnetic field at a point inside the toroid is given by the equation derived in Example 28.11 (Section 28.7). *Do not* assume the field is uniform over the cross section. (a) Show that the magnetic flux through a cross section of the toroid is

$$\Phi_B = \frac{\mu_0 Nih}{2\pi}\ln\left(\frac{b}{a}\right)$$

(b) Show that the inductance of the toroidal solenoid is given by

$$L = \frac{\mu_0 N^2 h}{2\pi}\ln\left(\frac{b}{a}\right)$$

(c) The fraction b/a may be written as

$$\frac{b}{a} = \frac{a+b-a}{a} = 1 + \frac{b-a}{a}$$

Use the power series expansion $\ln(1+z) = z + z^2/2 + \cdots$, valid for $|z| < 1$, to show that when $b - a$ is much less than a, the inductance is approximately equal to

$$L = \frac{\mu_0 N^2 h(b-a)}{2\pi a}$$

Compare this result with the result given in Example 30.3 (Section 30.2).

30.74. In Fig. 30.32 the switch is closed, with the capacitor having the polarity shown. Find the direction (clockwise or counter-clockwise) of the current induced in the rectangular wire loop A.

30.75. Demonstrating Inductance. A common demonstration of induc-

Figure **30.29** Problem 30.71.

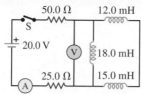

Figure **30.30** Problem 30.72.

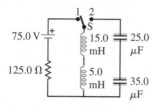

Figure **30.31** Problem 30.73.

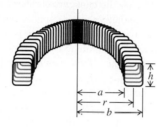

Figure **30.32** Problem 30.74.

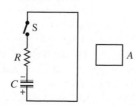

tance employs a circuit such as the one shown in Fig. 30.27. Switch S is closed, and the light bulb (represented by resistance R_1) just barely glows. After a period of time, switch S is opened, and the bulb lights up brightly for a short period of time. To understand this effect, think of an inductor as a device that imparts an "inertia" to the current, preventing a discontinuous change in the current through it. (a) Derive, as explicit functions of time, expressions for i_1 (the current through the light bulb) and i_2 (the current through the inductor) after switch S is closed. (b) After a long period of time, the currents i_1 and i_2 reach their steady-state values. Obtain expressions for these steady-state currents. (c) Switch S is now opened. Obtain an expression for the current through the inductor and light bulb as an explicit function of time. (d) You have been asked to design a demonstration apparatus using the circuit shown in Fig. 30.27 with a 22.0-H inductor and a 40.0-W light bulb. You are to connect a resistor in series with the inductor, and R_2 represents the sum of that resistance plus the internal resistance of the inductor. When switch S is opened, a transient current is to be set up that starts at 0.600 A and is not to fall below 0.150 A until after 0.0800 s. For simplicity, assume that the resistance of the light bulb is constant and equals the resistance the bulb must have to dissipate 40.0 W at 120 V. Determine R_2 and $\mathcal{E}$ for the given design considerations. (e) With the numerical values determined in part (d), what is the current through the light bulb just before the switch is opened? Does this result confirm the qualitative description of what is observed in the demonstration?

Challenge Problems

30.76. Consider the circuit shown in Fig. 30.33. The circuit elements are as follows: $\mathcal{E} = 32.0$ V, $L = 0.640$ H, $C = 2.00\ \mu$F, and $R = 400\ \Omega$. At time $t = 0$, switch S is closed. The current through the inductor is i_1, the current through the capacitor branch is i_2, and the charge on the capacitor is q_2. (a) Using Kirchhoff's rules, verify the circuit equations

Figure **30.33** Challenge Problem 30.76.

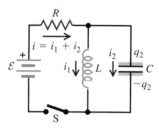

$$R(i_1 + i_2) + L\left(\frac{di_1}{dt}\right) = \mathcal{E}$$

$$R(i_2 + i_2) + \frac{q_2}{C} = \mathcal{E}$$

(b) What are the initial values of i_1, i_2, and q_2? (c) Show by direct substitution that the following solutions for i_1 and q_2 satisfy the circuit equations from part (a). Also, show that they satisfy the initial conditions

$$i_1 = \left(\frac{\mathcal{E}}{R}\right)\left[1 - e^{-\beta t}(2\omega RC)^{-1}\sin(\omega t) + \cos(\omega t)\right]$$

$$q_2 = \left(\frac{\mathcal{E}}{\omega R}\right)e^{-\beta t}\sin(\omega t)$$

where $\beta = (2RC)^{-1}$ and $\omega = [(LC)^{-1} - (2RC)^{-2}]^{1/2}$. (d) Determine the time t_1 at which i_2 first becomes zero.

30.77. A Volume Gauge. A tank containing a liquid has turns of wire wrapped around it, causing it to act like an inductor. The liquid content of the tank can be measured by using its inductance to determine the height of the liquid in the tank. The inductance of the tank changes from a value of L_0 corresponding to a relative permeability of 1 when the tank is empty to a value of L_f corresponding to a

Figure 30.34 Challenge Problem 30.77.

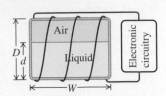

relative permeability of K_m (the relative permeability of the liquid) when the tank is full. The appropriate electronic circuitry can determine the inductance to five significant figures and thus the effective relative permeability of the combined air and liquid within the rectangular cavity of the tank. The four sides of the tank each have width W and height D (Fig. 30.34). The height of the liquid in the tank is d. You can ignore any fringing effects and assume that the relative permeability of the material of which the tank is made can be ignored. (a) Derive an expression for d as a function of L, the inductance corresponding to a certain fluid height, L_0, L_f, and D. (b) What is the inductance (to five significant figures) for a tank $\frac{1}{4}$ full, $\frac{1}{2}$ full, $\frac{3}{4}$ full, and completely full if the tank contains liquid oxygen? Take $L_0 = 0.63000$ H. The magnetic susceptibility of liquid oxygen is $\chi_m = 1.52 \times 10^{-3}$. (c) Repeat part (b) for mercury. The magnetic susceptibility of mercury is given in Table 28.1. (d) For which material is this volume gauge more practical?

30.78. Two coils are wrapped around each other as shown in Fig. 30.3. The current travels in the same sense around each coil. One coil has self-inductance L_1, and the other coil has self-inductance L_2. The mutual inductance of the two coils is M. (a) Show that if the two coils are connected in series, the equivalent inductance of the combination is $L_{eq} = L_1 + L_2 + 2M$.

(b) Show that if the two coils are connected in parallel, the equivalent inductance of the combination is

$$L_{eq} = \frac{L_1 L_2 - M^2}{L_1 + L_2 - 2M}$$

(*Hint:* See the hint for Problem 30.47.)

30.79. Consider the circuit shown in Fig. 30.35. Switch S is closed at time $t = 0$, causing a current i_1 through the inductive branch and a current i_2 through the capacitive branch. The initial charge on the capacitor is zero, and the charge at time t is q_2. (a) Derive expressions for i_1, i_2, and q_2 as functions of time. Express your answers in terms of $\mathcal{E}$, L, C, R_1, R_2, and t. For the remainder of the problem let the

Figure 30.35 Challenge Problem 30.79.

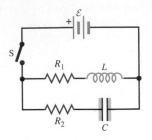

circuit elements have the following values: $\mathcal{E} = 48$ V, $L = 8.0$ H, $C = 20$ μF, $R_1 = 25$ Ω, and $R_2 = 5000$ Ω. (b) What is the initial current through the inductive branch? What is the initial current through the capacitive branch? (c) What are the currents through the inductive and capacitive branches a long time after the switch has been closed? How long is a "long time"? Explain. (d) At what time t_1 (accurate to two significant figures) will the currents i_1 and i_2 be equal? (*Hint:* You might consider using series expansions for the exponentials.) (e) For the conditions given in part (d), determine i_1. (f) The total current through the battery is $i = i_1 + i_2$. At what time t_2 (accurate to two significant figures) will i equal one-half of its final value? (*Hint:* The numerical work is greatly simplified if one makes suitable approximations. A sketch of i_1 and i_2 versus t may help you decide what approximations are valid.)

ALTERNATING CURRENT

31

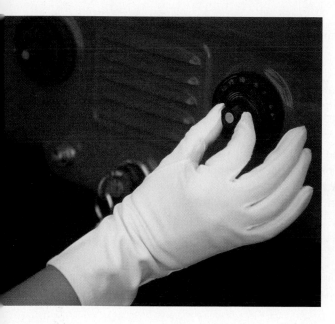

? Waves from a broadcasting station produce an alternating current in the circuits of a radio (like the one in this classic car). If a radio is tuned to a station at a frequency of 1000 kHz, does it also detect the transmissions from a station broadcasting at 600 kHz?

LEARNING GOALS

By studying this chapter, you will learn:

- How phasors make it easy to describe sinusoidally varying quantities.

- How to use reactance to describe the voltage across a circuit element that carries an alternating current.

- How to analyze an *L-R-C* series circuit with a sinusoidal emf.

- What determines the amount of power flowing into or out of an alternating-current circuit.

- How an *L-R-C* series circuit responds to sinusoidal emfs of different frequencies.

- Why transformers are useful, and how they work.

During the 1880s in the United States there was a heated and acrimonious debate between two inventors over the best method of electric-power distribution. Thomas Edison favored direct current (dc)—that is, steady current that does not vary with time. George Westinghouse favored **alternating current (ac),** with sinusoidally varying voltages and currents. He argued that transformers (which we will study in this chapter) can be used to step the voltage up and down with ac but not with dc; low voltages are safer for consumer use, but high voltages and correspondingly low currents are best for long-distance power transmission to minimize i^2R losses in the cables.

Eventually, Westinghouse prevailed, and most present-day household and industrial power-distribution systems operate with alternating current. Any appliance that you plug into a wall outlet uses ac, and many battery-powered devices such as radios and cordless telephones make use of the dc supplied by the battery to create or amplify alternating currents. Circuits in modern communication equipment, including pagers and television, also make extensive use of ac.

In this chapter we will learn how resistors, inductors, and capacitors behave in circuits with sinusoidally varying voltages and currents. Many of the principles that we found useful in Chapters 25, 28, and 30 are applicable, along with several new concepts related to the circuit behavior of inductors and capacitors. A key concept in this discussion is *resonance,* which we studied in Chapter 13 for mechanical systems.

31.1 Phasors and Alternating Currents

To supply an alternating current to a circuit, a source of alternating emf or voltage is required. An example of such a source is a coil of wire rotating with constant angular velocity in a magnetic field, which we discussed in Example 29.4 (Section 29.2). This develops a sinusoidal alternating emf and is the prototype of the commercial alternating-current generator or *alternator* (see Fig. 29.8).

We use the term **ac source** for any device that supplies a sinusoidally varying voltage (potential difference) v or current i. The usual circuit-diagram symbol for an ac source is

A sinusoidal voltage might be described by a function such as

$$v = V\cos\omega t \tag{31.1}$$

In this expression, v (lowercase) is the *instantaneous* potential difference; V (uppercase) is the maximum potential difference, which we call the **voltage amplitude;** and ω is the *angular frequency,* equal to 2π times the frequency f (Fig. 31.1).

In the United States and Canada, commercial electric-power distribution systems always use a frequency of $f = 60\ \text{Hz}$, corresponding to $\omega = (2\pi\ \text{rad})(60\ \text{s}^{-1}) = 377\ \text{rad/s}$; in much of the rest of the world, $f = 50\ \text{Hz}$ ($\omega = 314\ \text{rad/s}$) is used. Similarly, a sinusoidal current might be described as

$$i = I\cos\omega t \tag{31.2}$$

where i (lowercase) is the instantaneous current and I (uppercase) is the maximum current or **current amplitude.**

31.1 The voltage across a sinusoidal ac source.

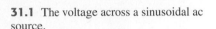

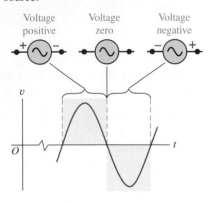

Phasor Diagrams

To represent sinusoidally varying voltages and currents, we will use rotating vector diagrams similar to those we used in the study of simple harmonic motion in Section 13.2 (see Figs. 13.5b and 13.6). In these diagrams the instantaneous value of a quantity that varies sinusoidally with time is represented by the *projection* onto a horizontal axis of a vector with a length equal to the amplitude of the quantity. The vector rotates counterclockwise with constant angular speed ω. These rotating vectors are called **phasors,** and diagrams containing them are called **phasor diagrams.** Figure 31.2 shows a phasor diagram for the sinusoidal current described by Eq. (31.2). The projection of the phasor onto the horizontal axis at time t is $I\cos\omega t$; this is why we chose to use the cosine function rather than the sine in Eq. (31.2).

31.2 A phasor diagram.

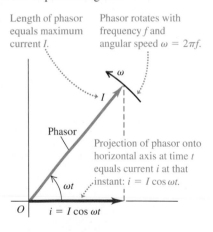

> **CAUTION** **Just what is a phasor?** A phasor is not a real physical quantity with a direction in space, such as velocity, momentum, or electric field. Rather, it is a *geometric* entity that helps us to describe and analyze physical quantities that vary sinusoidally with time. In Section 13.2 we used a single phasor to represent the position of a point mass undergoing simple harmonic motion. In this chapter we will use phasors to *add* sinusoidal voltages and currents. Combining sinusoidal quantities with phase differences then becomes a matter of vector addition. We will find a similar use for phasors in Chapters 35 and 36 in our study of interference effects with light. ▮

Rectified Alternating Current

How do we measure a sinusoidally varying current? In Section 26.3 we used a d'Arsonval galvanometer to measure steady currents. But if we pass a *sinusoidal* current through a d'Arsonval meter, the torque on the moving coil varies sinusoidally, with one direction half the time and the opposite direction the other half. The needle may wiggle a little if the frequency is low enough, but its average deflection is zero. Hence a d'Arsonval meter by itself isn't very useful for measuring alternating currents.

To get a measurable one-way current through the meter, we can use *diodes,* which we described in Section 25.3. A diode (or rectifier) is a device that conducts better in one direction than in the other; an ideal diode has zero resistance for one direction of current and infinite resistance for the other. One possible arrangement is shown in Fig. 31.3a. The current through the galvanometer G is always upward, regardless of the direction of the current from the ac source (i.e., which part of the cycle the source is in). The current through G is as shown by the graph in Fig. 31.2b. It pulsates but always has the same direction, and the average meter deflection is *not* zero. This arrangement of diodes is called a *full-wave rectifier circuit.*

The **rectified average current** I_{rav} is defined so that during any whole number of cycles, the total charge that flows is the same as though the current were constant with a value equal to I_{rav}. The notation I_{rav} and the name *rectified average current* emphasize that this is *not* the average of the original sinusoidal current. In Fig. 31.3b the total charge that flows in time t corresponds to the area under the curve of i versus t (recall that $i = dq/dt$, so q is the integral of t); this area must equal the rectangular area with height I_{rav}. We see that I_{rav} is less than the maximum current I; the two are related by

$$I_{rav} = \frac{2}{\pi}I = 0.637I \qquad \text{(rectified average value of a sinusoidal current)} \qquad (31.3)$$

(The factor of $2/\pi$ is the average value of $|\cos\omega t|$ or of $|\sin\omega t|$; see Example 29.5 in Section 29.2.) The galvanometer deflection is proportional to I_{rav}. The galvanometer scale can be calibrated to read I, I_{rav}, or, most commonly, I_{rms} (discussed below).

Root-Mean-Square (rms) Values

A more useful way to describe a quantity that can be either positive or negative is the *root-mean-square (rms) value*. We used rms values in Section 18.3 in connection with the speeds of molecules in a gas. We *square* the instantaneous current i, take the *average* (mean) value of i^2, and finally take the *square root* of that average. This procedure defines the **root-mean-square current,** denoted as I_{rms} (Fig. 31.4). Even when i is negative, i^2 is always positive, so I_{rms} is never zero (unless i is zero at every instant).

Here's how we obtain I_{rms} for a sinusoidal current, like that shown in Fig. 31.4. If the instantaneous current is given by $i = I\cos\omega t$, then

$$i^2 = I^2\cos^2\omega t$$

Using a double-angle formula from trigonometry,

$$\cos^2 A = \frac{1}{2}(1 + \cos 2A)$$

we find

$$i^2 = I^2\frac{1}{2}(1 + \cos 2\omega t) = \frac{1}{2}I^2 + \frac{1}{2}I^2\cos 2\omega t$$

The average of $\cos 2\omega t$ is zero because it is positive half the time and negative half the time. Thus the average of i^2 is simply $I^2/2$. The square root of this is I_{rms}:

$$I_{rms} = \frac{I}{\sqrt{2}} \qquad \text{(root-mean-square value of a sinusoidal current)} \qquad (31.4)$$

31.3 (a) A full-wave rectifier circuit. (b) Graph of the resulting current through the galvanometer G.

(a) A full-wave rectifier circuit

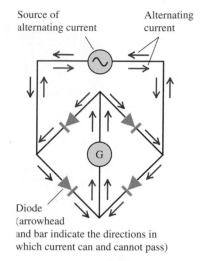

(b) Graph of the full-wave rectified current and its average value, the rectified average current I_{rav}

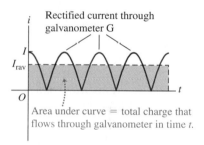

31.4 Calculating the root-mean-square (rms) value of an alternating current.

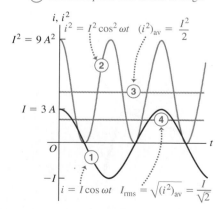

31.5 This wall socket delivers a root-mean-square voltage of 120 V. Sixty times per second, the instantaneous voltage across its terminals varies from $(\sqrt{2})(120 \text{ V}) = 170 \text{ V}$ to -170 V and back again.

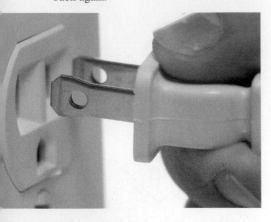

In the same way, the root-mean-square value of a sinusoidal voltage with amplitude (maximum value) V is

$$V_{rms} = \frac{V}{\sqrt{2}} \qquad \text{(root-mean-square value of a sinusoidal voltage)} \quad (31.5)$$

We can convert a rectifying ammeter into a voltmeter by adding a series resistor, just as for the dc case discussed in Section 26.3. Meters used for ac voltage and current measurements are nearly always calibrated to read rms values, not maximum or rectified average. Voltages and currents in power distribution systems are always described in terms of their rms values. The usual household power supply, "120-volt ac," has an rms voltage of 120 V (Fig. 31.5). The voltage amplitude is

$$V = \sqrt{2}\,V_{rms} = \sqrt{2}\,(120 \text{ V}) = 170 \text{ V}$$

| Example 31.1 | **Current in a personal computer** |

The plate on the back of a personal computer says that it draws 2.7 A from a 120-V, 60-Hz line. For this computer, what are (a) the average current, (b) the average of the square of the current, and (c) the current amplitude?

SOLUTION

IDENTIFY: This example is about alternating current.

SET UP: In parts (b) and (c) we use the idea that the root-mean-square current, given by Eq. (31.4), is the *square root* of the *mean* (average) of the *square* of the current.

EXECUTE: (a) The average of *any* sinusoidal alternating current, over any whole number of cycles, is zero.

(b) The current given is the rms value: $I_{rms} = 2.7$ A. The target variable $(i^2)_{av}$ is the *mean* of the *square* of the current. The rms current is the square root of this target variable, so

$$I_{rms} = \sqrt{(i^2)_{av}} \quad \text{or} \quad (i^2)_{av} = (I_{rms})^2 = (2.7 \text{ A})^2 = 7.3 \text{ A}^2$$

(c) From Eq. (31.4) the current amplitude I is

$$I = \sqrt{2}\,I_{rms} = \sqrt{2}\,(2.7 \text{ A}) = 3.8 \text{ A}$$

Figure 31.6 shows our graphs of i and i^2.

EVALUATE: Why would we be interested in the average of the square of the current? Recall that the rate at which energy is dissipated in a resistor R equals i^2R. This rate varies if the current is alternating, so it is best described by its average value $(i^2)_{av}R = I_{rms}^2R$. We make use of this idea in Section 31.4.

31.6 Our graphs of the current i and the square of the current i^2 versus time t.

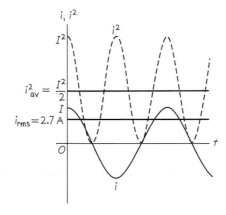

Test Your Understanding of Section 31.1   The figure at left shows four different current phasors with the same angular frequency ω. At the time shown, which phasor corresponds to (a) a positive current that is becoming more positive; (b) a positive current that is decreasing toward zero; (c) a negative current that is becoming more negative; (d) a negative current that is decreasing in magnitude toward zero?

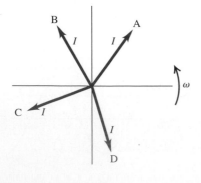

31.2 **Resistance and Reactance**

In this section we will derive voltage–current relationships for individual circuit elements carrying a sinusoidal current. We'll consider resistors, inductors, and capacitors.

Resistor in an ac Circuit

First let's consider a resistor with resistance R through which there is a sinusoidal current given by Eq. (31.2): $i = I\cos\omega t$. The positive direction of current is counterclockwise around the circuit, as in Fig. 31.7a. The current amplitude (maximum current) is I. From Ohm's law the instantaneous potential v_R of point a with respect to point b (that is, the instantaneous voltage across the resistor) is

$$v_R = iR = (IR)\cos\omega t \qquad (31.6)$$

The maximum voltage V_R, the *voltage amplitude,* is the coefficient of the cosine function:

$$V_R = IR \qquad \text{(amplitude of voltage across a resistor, ac circuit)} \qquad (31.7)$$

Hence we can also write

$$v_R = V_R\cos\omega t \qquad (31.8)$$

The current i and voltage v_R are both proportional to $\cos\omega t$, so the current is *in phase* with the voltage. Equation (31.7) shows that the current and voltage amplitudes are related in the same way as in a dc circuit.

Figure 31.7b shows graphs of i and v_R as functions of time. The vertical scales for current and voltage are different, so the relative heights of the two curves are not significant. The corresponding phasor diagram is given in Fig. 31.7c. Because i and v_R are *in phase* and have the same frequency, the current and voltage phasors rotate together; they are parallel at each instant. Their projections on the horizontal axis represent the instantaneous current and voltage, respectively.

Inductor in an ac Circuit

Next, we replace the resistor in Fig. 31.7 with a pure inductor with self-inductance L and zero resistance (Fig. 31.8a). Again we assume that the current is $i = I\cos\omega t$, with the positive direction of current taken as counterclockwise around the circuit.

Although there is no resistance, there is a potential difference v_L between the inductor terminals a and b because the current varies with time, giving rise to a self-induced emf. The induced emf in the direction of i is given by Eq. (30.7), $\mathcal{E} = -L\,di/dt$; however, the voltage v_L is *not* simply equal to $\mathcal{E}$. To see why, notice that if the current in the inductor is in the positive (counterclockwise) direction from a to b and is increasing, then di/dt is positive and the induced emf is directed to the left to oppose the increase in current; hence point a is at higher potential than is point b. Thus the potential of point a with respect to point b is positive and is given by $v_L = +L\,di/dt$, the *negative* of the induced emf. (You should convince

31.7 Resistance R connected across an ac source.

(a) Circuit with ac source and resistor

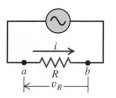

(b) Graphs of current and voltage versus time

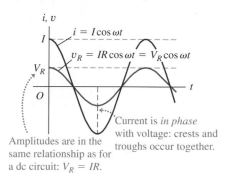

Amplitudes are in the same relationship as for a dc circuit: $V_R = IR$.

Current is *in phase* with voltage: crests and troughs occur together.

(c) Phasor diagram

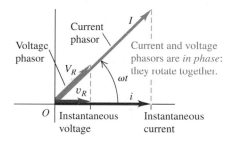

Current and voltage phasors are *in phase:* they rotate together.

31.8 Inductance L connected across an ac source.

(a) Circuit with ac source and inductor

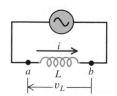

(b) Graphs of current and voltage versus time

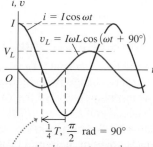

Voltage curve *leads* current curve by a quarter-cycle (corresponding to $\phi = \pi/2$ rad $= 90°$).

(c) Phasor diagram

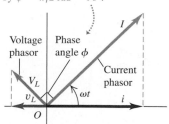

Voltage phasor *leads* current phasor by $\phi = \pi/2$ rad $= 90°$.

Act|v
Phys|cs
ONLINE

14.3   AC Circuits: The Driven Oscillator
        (Questions 1–5)

yourself that this expression gives the correct sign of v_L in *all* cases, including i counterclockwise and decreasing, i clockwise and increasing, and i clockwise and decreasing; you should also review Section 30.2.) So we have

$$v_L = L\frac{di}{dt} = L\frac{d}{dt}(I\cos\omega t) = -I\omega L\sin\omega t \qquad (31.9)$$

The voltage v_L across the inductor at any instant is proportional to the *rate of change* of the current. The points of maximum voltage on the graph correspond to maximum steepness of the current curve, and the points of zero voltage are the points where the current curve instantaneously levels off at its maximum and minimum values (Fig. 31.8b). The voltage and current are "out of step" or *out of phase* by a quarter-cycle. Since the voltage peaks occur a quarter-cycle earlier than the current peaks, we say that the voltage *leads* the current by 90°. The phasor diagram in Fig. 31.8c also shows this relationship; the voltage phasor is ahead of the current phasor by 90°.

We can also obtain this phase relationship by rewriting Eq. (31.9) using the identity $\cos(A + 90°) = -\sin A$:

$$v_L = I\omega L\cos(\omega t + 90°) \qquad (31.10)$$

This result shows that the voltage can be viewed as a cosine function with a "head start" of 90° relative to the current.

As we have done in Eq. (31.10), we will usually describe the phase of the *voltage* relative to the *current,* not the reverse. Thus if the current i in a circuit is

$$i = I\cos\omega t$$

and the voltage v of one point with respect to another is

$$v = V\cos(\omega t + \phi)$$

we call ϕ the **phase angle;** it gives the phase of the *voltage* relative to the *current.* For a pure resistor, $\phi = 0$, and for a pure inductor, $\phi = 90°$.

From Eq. (31.9) or (31.10) the amplitude V_L of the inductor voltage is

$$V_L = I\omega L \qquad (31.11)$$

We define the **inductive reactance** X_L of an inductor as

$$X_L = \omega L \qquad \text{(inductive reactance)} \qquad (31.12)$$

Using X_L, we can write Eq. (31.11) in a form similar to Eq. (31.7) for a resistor $(V_R = IR)$:

$$V_L = IX_L \qquad \text{(amplitude of voltage across an inductor, ac circuit)} \qquad (31.13)$$

Because X_L is the ratio of a voltage and a current, its SI unit is the ohm, the same as for resistance.

CAUTION   **Inductor voltage and current are not in phase** Keep in mind that Eq. (31.13) is a relationship between the *amplitudes* of the oscillating voltage and current for the inductor in Fig. 31.8a. It does *not* say that the voltage at any instant is equal to the current at that instant multiplied by X_L. As Fig. 31.8b shows, the voltage and current are 90° out of phase. Voltage and current are in phase only for resistors, as in Eq. (31.6). ∎

The Meaning of Inductive Reactance

The inductive reactance X_L is really a description of the self-induced emf that opposes any change in the current through the inductor. From Eq. (31.13), for a given current amplitude I the voltage $v_L = +L\,di/dt$ across the inductor and the self-induced emf $\mathcal{E} = -L\,di/dt$ both have an amplitude V_L that is directly proportional to X_L. According to Eq. (31.12), the inductive reactance and self-induced emf increase with more rapid variation in current (that is, increasing angular frequency ω) and increasing inductance L.

If an oscillating voltage of a given amplitude V_L is applied across the inductor terminals, the resulting current will have a smaller amplitude I for larger values of X_L. Since X_L is proportional to frequency, a high-frequency voltage applied to the inductor gives only a small current, while a lower-frequency voltage of the same amplitude gives rise to a larger current. Inductors are used in some circuit applications, such as power supplies and radio-interference filters, to block high frequencies while permitting lower frequencies or dc to pass through. A circuit device that uses an inductor for this purpose is called a *low-pass filter* (see Problem 31.50).

Example 31.2 | **An inductor in an ac circuit**

Suppose you want the current amplitude in a pure inductor in a radio receiver to be 250 μA when the voltage amplitude is 3.60 V at a frequency of 1.60 MHz (corresponding to the upper end of the AM broadcast band). (a) What inductive reactance is needed? What inductance? (b) If the voltage amplitude is kept constant, what will be the current amplitude through this inductor at 16.0 MHz? At 160 kHz?

SOLUTION

IDENTIFY: We are not told about any other elements of the circuit of which the inductor is part. Nor should we care about those other elements, since from the perspective of this example, all they do is provide the inductor with an oscillating voltage. Hence all of those other circuit elements are lumped into the ac source shown in Fig. 31.8a.

SET UP: We are given the current amplitude I and the voltage amplitude V. Our target variables in part (a) are the inductive reactance X_L at 1.60 MHz and the inductance L, which we find using Eqs. (31.13) and (31.12). Once we know L, we use these same two equations to find the inductive reactance and current amplitude at any other frequency.

EXECUTE: (a) From Eq. (31.13),

$$X_L = \frac{V_L}{I} = \frac{3.60 \text{ V}}{250 \times 10^{-6} \text{ A}} = 1.44 \times 10^4 \ \Omega = 14.4 \text{ k}\Omega$$

From Eq. (31.12), with $\omega = 2\pi f$, we find

$$L = \frac{X_L}{2\pi f} = \frac{1.44 \times 10^4 \ \Omega}{2\pi(1.60 \times 10^6 \text{ Hz})} = 1.43 \times 10^{-3} \text{ H} = 1.43 \text{ mH}$$

(b) Combining Eqs. (31.12) and (31.13), we find that the current amplitude is $I = V_L/X_L = V_L/\omega L = V_L/2\pi f L$. Thus the current amplitude is inversely proportional to the frequency f. Since $I = 250$ μA at $f = 1.60$ MHz, the current amplitude at 16.0 MHz (ten times the original frequency) will be one-tenth as great, or 25.0 μA; at 160 kHz = 0.160 MHz (one-tenth of the original frequency) the current amplitude is ten times as great, or 2500 μA = 2.50 mA.

EVALUATE: In general, the lower the frequency of an oscillating voltage applied across an inductor, the greater the amplitude of the oscillating current that results.

Capacitor in an ac Circuit

Finally, we connect a capacitor with capacitance C to the source, as in Fig. 31.9a, producing a current $i = I\cos\omega t$ through the capacitor. Again, the positive direction of current is counterclockwise around the circuit.

CAUTION **Alternating current through a capacitor** You may object that charge can't really move through the capacitor because its two plates are insulated from each other. True enough, but as the capacitor charges and discharges, there is at each instant a current i into one plate, an equal current out of the other plate, and an equal *displacement* current between the plates just as though the charge were being conducted through the capacitor. (You may want to review the discussion of displacement current in Section 29.7.) Thus we often speak about alternating current *through* a capacitor. ▮

To find the instantaneous voltage v_C across the capacitor—that is, the potential of point a with respect to point b—we first let q denote the charge on the left-hand plate of the capacitor in Fig. 31.9a (so $-q$ is the charge on the right-hand plate). The current i is related to q by $i = dq/dt$; with this definition, positive current corresponds to an increasing charge on the left-hand capacitor plate. Then

$$i = \frac{dq}{dt} = I\cos\omega t$$

Integrating this, we get

$$q = \frac{I}{\omega}\sin\omega t \qquad\qquad (31.14)$$

31.9 Capacitor C connected across an ac source.

(a) Circuit with ac source and capacitor

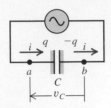

(b) Graphs of current and voltage versus time

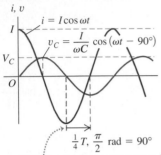

Voltage curve *lags* current curve by a quarter-cycle (corresponding to $\phi = \pi/2$ rad $= 90°$).

(c) Phasor diagram

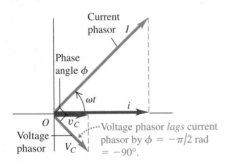

Voltage phasor *lags* current phasor by $\phi = -\pi/2$ rad $= -90°$.

Also, from Eq. (24.1) the charge q equals the voltage v_C multiplied by the capacitance, $q = Cv_C$. Using this in Eq. (31.14), we find

$$v_C = \frac{I}{\omega C} \sin \omega t \qquad (31.15)$$

The instantaneous current i is equal to the rate of change dq/dt of the capacitor charge q; since $q = Cv_C$, i is also proportional to the rate of change of voltage. (Compare to an inductor, for which the situation is reversed and v_L is proportional to the rate of change of i.) Figure 31.9b shows v_C and i as functions of t. Because $i = dq/dt = C\, dv_C/dt$, the current has its greatest magnitude when the v_C curve is rising or falling most steeply and is zero when the v_C curve instantaneously levels off at its maximum and minimum values.

The capacitor voltage and current are out of phase by a quarter-cycle. The peaks of voltage occur a quarter-cycle *after* the corresponding current peaks, and we say that the voltage *lags* the current by 90°. The phasor diagram in Fig. 31.9c shows this relationship; the voltage phasor is behind the current phasor by a quarter-cycle, or 90°.

We can also derive this phase difference by rewriting Eq. (31.15), using the identity $\cos(A - 90°) = \sin A$:

$$v_C = \frac{I}{\omega C} \cos(\omega t - 90°) \qquad (31.16)$$

This corresponds to a phase angle $\phi = -90°$. This cosine function has a "late start" of 90° compared with the current $i = I\cos\omega t$.

Equations (31.15) and (31.16) show that the *maximum* voltage V_C (the voltage amplitude) is

$$V_C = \frac{I}{\omega C} \qquad (31.17)$$

To put this expression in a form similar to Eq. (31.7) for a resistor, $V_R = IR$, we define a quantity X_C, called the **capacitive reactance** of the capacitor, as

$$X_C = \frac{1}{\omega C} \qquad \text{(capacitive reactance)} \qquad (31.18)$$

Then

$$V_C = IX_C \qquad \text{(amplitude of voltage across a capacitor, ac circuit)} \qquad (31.19)$$

The SI unit of X_C is the ohm, the same as for resistance and inductive reactance, because X_C is the ratio of a voltage and a current.

> **CAUTION** **Capacitor voltage and current are not in phase** Remember that Eq. (31.19) for a capacitor, like Eq. (31.13) for an inductor, is *not* a statement about the instantaneous values of voltage and current. The instantaneous values are actually 90° out of phase, as Fig. 31.9b shows. Rather, Eq. (31.19) relates the *amplitudes* of the voltage and current. ▮

The Meaning of Capacitive Reactance

The capacitive reactance of a capacitor is inversely proportional both to the capacitance C and to the angular frequency ω; the greater the capacitance and the higher the frequency, the *smaller* the capacitive reactance X_C. Capacitors tend to pass high-frequency current and to block low-frequency currents and dc, just the opposite of inductors. A device that preferentially passes signals of high frequency is called a *high-pass filter* (see Problem 31.49).

Example 31.3 **A resistor and a capacitor in an ac circuit**

A 200-Ω resistor is connected in series with a 5.0-μF capacitor. The voltage across the resistor is $v_R = (1.20 \text{ V}) \cos(2500 \text{ rad/s})t$. (a) Derive an expression for the circuit current. (b) Determine the capacitive reactance of the capacitor. (c) Derive an expression for the voltage across the capacitor.

SOLUTION

IDENTIFY: Since this is a series circuit, the current is the same through the capacitor as through the resistor. Our target variables are the current i, capacitive reactance X_C, and capacitor voltage v_C.

SET UP: Figure 31.10 shows the circuit. We find the current through the resistor, and hence through the circuit as a whole, using Eq. (31.6). We use Eq. (31.18) to find the capacitive reactance X_C, Eq. (31.19) to find the voltage amplitude, and Eq. (31.16) to write an expression for the instantaneous voltage across the capacitor.

EXECUTE: (a) Using $v_R = iR$, we find that the current i in the resistor and through the circuit as a whole is

$$i = \frac{v_R}{R} = \frac{(1.20 \text{ V}) \cos(2500 \text{ rad/s})t}{200 \ \Omega}$$

$$= (6.0 \times 10^{-3} \text{ A}) \cos(2500 \text{ rad/s})t$$

(b) From Eq. (31.18), the capacitive reactance at $\omega = 2500 \text{ rad/s}$ is

$$X_C = \frac{1}{\omega C} = \frac{1}{(2500 \text{ rad/s})(5.0 \times 10^{-6} \text{ F})} = 80 \ \Omega$$

31.10 Our sketch for this problem.

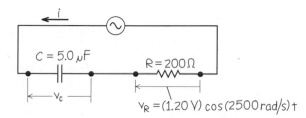

(c) From Eq. (31.19), the amplitude V_C of the voltage across the capacitor is

$$V_C = IX_C = (6.0 \times 10^{-3} \text{ A})(80 \ \Omega) = 0.48 \text{ V}$$

The 80-Ω reactance of the capacitor is 40% of the resistor's 200-Ω resistance, so the value of V_C is 40% of V_R. The instantaneous capacitor voltage v_C is given by Eq. (31.16):

$$v_C = V_C \cos(\omega t - 90°)$$

$$= (0.48 \text{ V}) \cos[(2500 \text{ rad/s})t - \pi/2 \text{ rad}]$$

EVALUATE: Although the *current* through the capacitor is the same as through the resistor, the *voltages* across these two devices are different in both amplitude and phase. Note that in the expression for v_C we converted the 90° to $\pi/2$ rad so that all the angular quantities have the same units. In ac circuit analysis, phase angles are often given in degrees, so be careful to convert to radians when necessary.

Comparing ac Circuit Elements

Table 31.1 summarizes the relationships of voltage and current amplitudes for the three circuit elements we have discussed. Note again that *instantaneous* voltage and current are proportional in a resistor, where there is zero phase difference between v_R and i (see Fig. 31.7b). The instantaneous voltage and current are *not* proportional in an inductor or capacitor, because there is a 90° phase difference in both cases (see Figs. 31.8b and 31.9b).

Figure 31.11 shows how the resistance of a resistor and the reactances of an inductor and a capacitor vary with angular frequency ω. Resistance R is independent of frequency, while the reactances X_L and X_C are not. If $\omega = 0$, corresponding to a dc circuit, there is *no* current through a capacitor because $X_C \rightarrow \infty$, and there is no inductive effect because $X_L = 0$. In the limit $\omega \rightarrow \infty$, X_L also approaches infinity, and the current through an inductor becomes vanishingly small; recall that the self-induced emf opposes rapid changes in current. In this same limit, X_C and the voltage across a capacitor both approach zero; the current changes direction so rapidly that no charge can build up on either plate.

Figure 31.12 shows an application of the above discussion to a loudspeaker system. Low-frequency sounds are produced by the *woofer*, which is a speaker

31.11 Graphs of R, X_L, and X_C as functions of angular frequency ω.

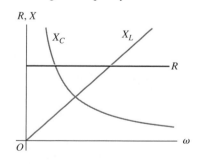

Table 31.1 Circuit Elements with Alternating Current

Circuit Element	Amplitude Relationship	Circuit Quantity	Phase of v
Resistor	$V_R = IR$	R	In phase with i
Inductor	$V_L = IX_L$	$X_L = \omega L$	Leads i by 90°
Capacitor	$V_C = IX_C$	$X_C = 1/\omega C$	Lags i by 90°

31.12 (a) The two speakers in this loud speaker system are connected in parallel to the amplifier. (b) Graphs of current amplitude in the tweeter and woofer as functions of frequency for a given amplifier voltage amplitude.

(a) A crossover network in a loudspeaker system

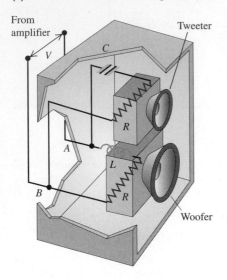

From amplifier

Tweeter

Woofer

(b) Graphs of rms current as functions of frequency for a given amplifier voltage

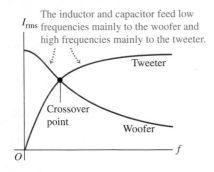

The inductor and capacitor feed low frequencies mainly to the woofer and high frequencies mainly to the tweeter.

I_{rms}

Tweeter

Crossover point

Woofer

O f

with large diameter; the *tweeter*, a speaker with smaller diameter, produces high-frequency sounds. In order to route signals of different frequency to the appropriate speaker, the woofer and tweeter are connected in parallel across the amplifier output. The capacitor in the tweeter branch blocks the low-frequency components of sound but passes the higher frequencies; the inductor in the woofer branch does the opposite.

Test Your Understanding of Section 31.2 An oscillating voltage of fixed amplitude is applied across a circuit element. If the frequency of this voltage is increased, will the amplitude of the current through the element (i) increase, (ii) decrease, or (iii) remain the same if it is (a) a resistor, (b) an inductor, or (c) a capacitor?

31.3 **The *L-R-C* Series Circuit**

Many ac circuits used in practical electronic systems involve resistance, inductive reactance, and capacitive reactance. A simple example is a series circuit containing a resistor, an inductor, a capacitor, and an ac source, as shown in Fig. 31.13a. (In Section 30.6 we considered the behavior of the current in an *L-R-C* series circuit *without* a source.)

To analyze this and similar circuits, we will use a phasor diagram that includes the voltage and current phasors for each of the components. In this circuit, because of Kirchhoff's loop rule, the instantaneous *total* voltage v_{ad} across all three components is equal to the source voltage at that instant. We will show that the phasor representing this total voltage is the *vector sum* of the phasors for the individual voltages. Complete phasor diagrams for this circuit are shown in Figs. 31.13b and 31.13c. These may appear complex, but we'll explain them one step at a time.

Let's assume that the source supplies a current i given by $i = I\cos\omega t$. Because the circuit elements are connected in series, the current at any instant is the same at every point in the circuit. Thus a *single phasor I*, with length proportional to the current amplitude, represents the current in *all* circuit elements.

As in Section 31.2, we use the symbols v_R, v_L, and v_C for the instantaneous voltages across R, L, and C, and the symbols V_R, V_L, and V_C for the maximum voltages. We denote the instantaneous and maximum *source* voltages by v and V. Then, in Fig. 31.13a, $v = v_{ad}$, $v_R = v_{ab}$, $v_L = v_{bc}$, and $v_C = v_{cd}$.

We have shown that the potential difference between the terminals of a resistor is *in phase* with the current in the resistor and that its maximum value V_R is given by Eq. (31.7):

$$V_R = IR$$

31.13 An *L-R-C* series circuit with an ac source.

(a) Series *R-L-C* circuit

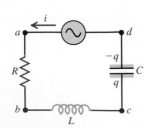

(b) Phasor diagram for the case $X_L > X_C$

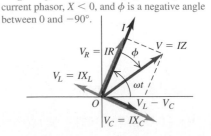

Source voltage phasor is the vector sum of the V_R, V_L, and V_C phasors.

Inductor voltage phasor leads current phasor by 90°.

$V_L = IX_L$

All circuit elements have the same current phasor.

$V = IZ$

$V_L - V_C$

ϕ

I

ωt

$V_R = IR$

Capacitor voltage phasor lags current phasor $V_C = IX_C$ by 90°. It is thus always antiparallel to the V_L phasor.

Resistor voltage phasor is in phase with current phasor.

(c) Phasor diagram for the case $X_L < X_C$

If $X_L < X_C$, the source voltage phasor lags the current phasor, $X < 0$, and ϕ is a negative angle between 0 and $-90°$.

I

$V_R = IR$ ϕ $V = IZ$

$V_L = IX_L$

ωt

O $V_L - V_C$

$V_C = IX_C$

The phasor V_R in Fig. 31.13b, in phase with the current phasor I, represents the voltage across the resistor. Its projection onto the horizontal axis at any instant gives the instantaneous potential difference v_R.

The voltage across an inductor *leads* the current by 90°. Its voltage amplitude is given by Eq. (31.13):

$$V_L = IX_L$$

The phasor V_L in Fig. 31.13b represents the voltage across the inductor, and its projection onto the horizontal axis at any instant equals v_L.

The voltage across a capacitor *lags* the current by 90°. Its voltage amplitude is given by Eq. (31.19):

$$V_C = IX_C$$

The phasor V_C in Fig. 31.13b represents the voltage across the capacitor, and its projection onto the horizontal axis at any instant equals v_C.

The instantaneous potential difference v between terminals a and d is equal at every instant to the (algebraic) sum of the potential differences v_R, v_L, and v_C. That is, it equals the sum of the *projections* of the phasors V_R, V_L, and V_C. But the sum of the projections of these phasors is equal to the *projection* of their *vector sum*. So the vector sum V must be the phasor that represents the source voltage v and the instantaneous total voltage v_{ad} across the series of elements.

To form this vector sum, we first subtract the phasor V_C from the phasor V_L. (These two phasors always lie along the same line, with opposite directions.) This gives the phasor $V_L - V_C$. This is always at right angles to the phasor V_R, so from the Pythagorean theorem the magnitude of the phasor V is

$$V = \sqrt{V_R^2 + (V_L - V_C)^2} = \sqrt{(IR)^2 + (IX_L - IX_C)^2} \quad \text{or}$$

$$V = I\sqrt{R^2 + (X_L - X_C)^2} \tag{31.20}$$

We define the **impedance** Z of an ac circuit as the ratio of the voltage amplitude across the circuit to the current amplitude in the circuit. From Eq. (31.20) the impedance of the *L-R-C* series circuit is

$$Z = \sqrt{R^2 + (X_L - X_C)^2} \tag{31.21}$$

so we can rewrite Eq. (31.20) as

$$V = IZ \qquad \text{(amplitude of voltage across an ac circuit)} \tag{31.22}$$

While Eq. (31.21) is valid only for an *L-R-C* series circuit, we can use Eq. (31.22) to define the impedance of *any* network of resistors, inductors, and capacitors as the ratio of the amplitude of the voltage across the network to the current amplitude. The SI unit of impedance is the ohm.

The Meaning of Impedance and Phase Angle

Equation (31.22) has a form similar to $V = IR$, with impedance Z in an ac circuit playing the role of resistance R in a dc circuit. Just as direct current tends to follow the path of least resistance, so alternating current tends to follow the path of lowest impedance (Fig. 31.14). Note, however, that impedance is actually a function of R, L, and C, as well as of the angular frequency ω. We can see this by substituting Eq. (31.12) for X_L and Eq. (31.18) for X_C into Eq. (31.21), giving the following complete expression for Z for a series circuit:

$$Z = \sqrt{R^2 + (X_L - X_C)^2}$$
$$= \sqrt{R^2 + [\omega L - (1/\omega C)]^2} \qquad \text{(impedance of an } L\text{-}R\text{-}C \text{ series circuit)} \tag{31.23}$$

Act!v
Physics ONLINE

14.3 AC Circuits: The Driven Oscillator
(Questions 6, 7, and 10)

31.14 This gas-filled glass sphere has an alternating voltage between its surface and the electrode at its center. The glowing streamers show the resulting alternating current that passes through the gas. When you touch the outside of the sphere, your fingertips and the inner surface of the sphere act as the plates of a capacitor, and the sphere and your body together form an *L-R-C* series circuit. The current (which is low enough to be harmless) is drawn to your fingers because the path through your body has a low impedance.

Hence for a given amplitude V of the source voltage applied to the circuit, the amplitude $I = V/Z$ of the resulting current will be different at different frequencies. We'll explore this frequency dependence in detail in Section 31.5.

In the phasor diagram shown in Fig. 31.13b, the angle ϕ between the voltage and current phasors is the phase angle of the source voltage v with respect to the current i; that is, it is the angle by which the source voltage leads the current. From the diagram,

$$\tan\phi = \frac{V_L - V_C}{V_R} = \frac{I(X_L - X_C)}{IR} = \frac{X_L - X_C}{R}$$

$$\tan\phi = \frac{\omega L - 1/\omega C}{R} \qquad \text{(phase angle of an L-R-C series circuit)} \qquad (31.24)$$

If the current is $i = I\cos\omega t$, then the source voltage v is

$$v = V\cos(\omega t + \phi) \qquad (31.25)$$

Figure 31.13b shows the behavior of a circuit in which $X_L > X_C$. Figure 31.13c shows the behavior when $X_L < X_C$; the voltage phasor V lies on the opposite side of the current phasor I and the voltage *lags* the current. In this case, $X_L - X_C$ is *negative,* $\tan\phi$ is negative, and ϕ is a negative angle between 0 and $-90°$. Since X_L and X_C depend on frequency, the phase angle ϕ depends on frequency as well. We'll examine the consequences of this in Section 31.5.

All of the expressions that we've developed for an L-R-C series circuit are still valid if one of the circuit elements is missing. If the resistor is missing, we set $R = 0$; if the inductor is missing, we set $L = 0$. But if the capacitor is missing, we set $C = \infty$, corresponding to the absence of any potential difference $(v_C = q/C = 0)$ or any capacitive reactance $(X_C = 1/\omega C = 0)$.

In this entire discussion we have described magnitudes of voltages and currents in terms of their *maximum* values, the voltage and current *amplitudes*. But we remarked at the end of Section 31.1 that these quantities are usually described in terms of rms values, not amplitudes. For any sinusoidally varying quantity the rms value is always $1/\sqrt{2}$ times the amplitude. All the relationships between voltage and current that we have derived in this and the preceding sections are still valid if we use rms quantities throughout instead of amplitudes. For example, if we divide Eq. (31.22) by $\sqrt{2}$, we get

$$\frac{V}{\sqrt{2}} = \frac{I}{\sqrt{2}}Z$$

which we can rewrite as

$$V_{\text{rms}} = I_{\text{rms}}Z \qquad (31.26)$$

We can translate Eqs. (31.7), (31.13), and (31.19) in exactly the same way.

We have considered only ac circuits in which an inductor, a resistor, and a capacitor are in series. You can do a similar analysis for a *parallel L-R-C* circuit; see Problem 31.54.

Finally, we remark that in this section we have been describing the *steady-state* condition of a circuit, the state that exists after the circuit has been connected to the source for a long time. When the source is first connected, there may be additional voltages and currents, called *transients,* whose nature depends on the time in the cycle when the circuit is initially completed. A detailed analysis of transients is beyond our scope. They always die out after a sufficiently long time, and they do not affect the steady-state behavior of the circuit. But they can cause dangerous and damaging surges in power lines, which is why delicate electronic systems such as computers are often provided with power-line surge protectors.

Problem-Solving Strategy 31.1 | Alternating-Current Circuits

IDENTIFY *the relevant concepts:* All of the concepts that we used to analyze direct-current circuits also apply to alternating-current circuits. However, we must be careful to distinguish between the amplitudes of alternating currents and voltages and their instantaneous values. We must also keep in mind the distinctions between resistance (for resistors), reactance (for inductors or capacitors), and impedance (for composite circuits).

SET UP *the problem* using the following steps:
1. Draw a diagram of the circuit and label all known and unknown quantities.
2. Determine the target variables.

EXECUTE *the solution* as follows:
1. Use the relationships derived in Sections 31.2 and 31.3 to solve for the target variables, using the following hints.
2. In ac circuit problems it is nearly always easiest to work with angular frequency ω. If you are given the ordinary frequency f, expressed in Hz, convert it using the relationship $\omega = 2\pi f$.
3. Keep in mind a few basic facts about phase relationships. For a resistor, voltage and current are always *in phase*, and the two corresponding phasors in a phasor diagram always have the same direction. For an inductor, the voltage always *leads* the current by 90° (i.e., $\phi = +90°$), and the voltage phasor is always turned 90° counterclockwise from the current phasor. For a capacitor, the voltage always *lags* the current by 90° (i.e., $\phi = -90°$), and the voltage phasor is always turned 90° clockwise from the current phasor.

4. Remember that with ac circuits, all voltages and currents are sinusoidal functions of time instead of being constant, but Kirchhoff's rules hold nonetheless at each instant. Thus, in a series circuit, the instantaneous current is the same in all circuit elements; in a parallel circuit, the instantaneous potential difference is the same across all circuit elements.
5. Inductive reactance, capacitive reactance, and impedance are analogous to resistance; each represents the ratio of voltage amplitude V to current amplitude I in a circuit element or combination of elements. Keep in mind, however, that phase relationships play an essential role. The effects of resistance and reactance have to be combined by *vector* addition of the corresponding voltage phasors, as in Figs. 31.13b and 31.13c. When you have several circuit elements in series, for example, you can't just *add* all the numerical values of resistance and reactance to get the impedance; that would ignore the phase relationships.

EVALUATE *your answer:* When working with a series *L-R-C* circuit, you can check your results by comparing the values of the inductive reactance X_L and the capacitive reactance X_C. If $X_L > X_C$, then the voltage amplitude across the inductor is greater than that across the capacitor and the phase angle ϕ is positive (between 0 and 90°). If $X_L < X_C$, then the voltage amplitude across the inductor is less than that across the capacitor and the phase angle ϕ is negative (between 0 and −90°).

Example 31.4 | An *L-R-C* series circuit I

In the series circuit of Fig. 31.13a, suppose $R = 300\,\Omega$, $L = 60$ mH, $C = 0.50\,\mu$F, $V = 50$ V, and $\omega = 10{,}000$ rad/s. Find the reactances X_L and X_C, the impedance Z, the current amplitude I, the phase angle ϕ, and the voltage amplitude across each circuit element.

SOLUTION

IDENTIFY: This problem uses the ideas developed in Section 31.2 and this section about the behavior of circuit elements in an ac circuit.

SET UP: We use Eqs. (31.12) and (31.18) to determine the reactances and Eq. (31.23) to find the impedance. We then use Eq. (31.22) to find the current amplitude and Eq. (31.24) to calculate the phase angle. Given this information, the relationships in Table 31.1 tell us the voltage amplitudes.

EXECUTE: The inductive and capacitive reactances are

$$X_L = \omega L = (10{,}000 \text{ rad/s})(60 \text{ mH}) = 600\,\Omega$$

$$X_C = \frac{1}{\omega C} = \frac{1}{(10{,}000 \text{ rad/s})(0.50 \times 10^{-6}\text{ F})} = 200\,\Omega$$

The impedance Z of the circuit is

$$Z = \sqrt{R^2 + (X_L - X_C)^2} = \sqrt{(300\,\Omega)^2 + (600\,\Omega - 200\,\Omega)^2}$$
$$= 500\,\Omega$$

With source voltage amplitude $V = 50$ V the current amplitude is

$$I = \frac{V}{Z} = \frac{50 \text{ V}}{500\,\Omega} = 0.10 \text{ A}$$

The phase angle ϕ is

$$\phi = \arctan\frac{X_L - X_C}{R} = \arctan\frac{400\,\Omega}{300\,\Omega} = 53°$$

From Table 31.1, the voltage amplitudes V_R, V_L, and V_C across the resistor, inductor, and capacitor, respectively, are

$$V_R = IR = (0.10 \text{ A})(300\,\Omega) = 30 \text{ V}$$
$$V_L = IX_L = (0.10 \text{ A})(600\,\Omega) = 60 \text{ V}$$
$$V_C = IX_C = (0.10 \text{ A})(200\,\Omega) = 20 \text{ V}$$

EVALUATE: Note that $X_L > X_C$ and hence the voltage amplitude across the inductor is greater than across the capacitor and ϕ is negative. The value $\phi = -53°$ means that the voltage *leads* the current by 53°; this is like the situation shown in Fig. 31.13b.

Note that the source voltage amplitude $V = 50$ V is *not* equal to the sum of the voltage amplitudes across the separate circuit elements. (That is, 50 V ≠ 30 V + 60 V + 20 V.) Make sure you understand why not!

Example 31.5   **An *L-R-C* series circuit II**

For the *L-R-C* series circuit described in Example 31.4, describe the time dependence of the instantaneous current and each instantaneous voltage.

SOLUTION

IDENTIFY: In Example 31.4 we found the *amplitudes* of the current and voltages. Now our task is to find expressions for the *instantaneous values* of the current and voltages. As we learned in Section 31.2, the voltage across a resistor is in phase with the current but the voltages across an inductor or capacitor are not. We also learned in this section that ϕ is the phase angle between the source voltage and the current.

SET UP: If we describe the current using Eq. (31.2), the voltages are given by Eq. (31.8) for the resistor, Eq. (31.10) for the inductor, Eq. (31.16) for the capacitor, and Eq. (31.25) for the source.

EXECUTE: The current and all of the voltages oscillate with the same angular frequency, $\omega = 10{,}000$ rad/s, and hence with the same period, $2\pi/\omega = 2\pi/(10{,}000 \text{ rad/s}) = 6.3 \times 10^{-4}$ s $= 0.63$ ms. Using Eq. (31.2), the current is

$$i = I\cos\omega t = (0.10 \text{ A})\cos(10{,}000 \text{ rad/s})t$$

This choice simply means that we choose $t = 0$ to be an instant when the current is maximum. The resistor voltage is *in phase* with the current, so

$$v_R = V_R\cos\omega t = (30 \text{ V})\cos(10{,}000 \text{ rad/s})t$$

The inductor voltage *leads* the current by 90°, so

$$v_L = V_L\cos(\omega t + 90°) = -V_L\sin\omega t$$
$$= -(60 \text{ V})\sin(10{,}000 \text{ rad/s})t$$

The capacitor voltage *lags* the current by 90°, so

$$v_C = V_C\cos(\omega t - 90°) = V_C\sin\omega t$$
$$= (20 \text{ V})\sin(10{,}000 \text{ rad/s})t$$

31.15 Graphs of the source voltage v, resistor voltage v_R, inductor voltage v_L, and capacitor voltage v_C as functions of time for the situation of Example 31.4. The current, which is not shown, is in phase with the resistor voltage.

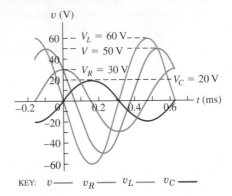

KEY: v —— v_R —— v_L —— v_C ——

Finally, the source voltage (equal to the voltage across the entire combination of resistor, inductor, and capacitor) *leads* the current by $\phi = 53°$, so

$$v = V\cos(\omega t + \phi)$$
$$= (50 \text{ V})\cos\left[(10{,}000 \text{ rad/s})t + \left(\frac{2\pi \text{ rad}}{360°}\right)(53°)\right]$$
$$= (50 \text{ V})\cos[(10{,}000 \text{ rad/s})t + 0.93 \text{ rad}]$$

EVALUATE: Figure 31.15 graphs the various voltages versus time. The inductor voltage has a larger amplitude than the capacitor voltage because $X_L > X_C$. While the source voltage amplitude V is not equal to the sum of the individual voltage amplitudes V_R, V_L, and V_C, the *instantaneous* source voltage v is always equal to the sum of the instantaneous voltages v_R, v_L, and v_C. You should verify this by measuring the values of the voltages shown in the graph at different values of the time t.

Test Your Understanding of Section 31.3   Rank the following ac circuits in order of their current amplitude, from highest to lowest value. (i) the circuit in Example 31.4; (ii) the circuit in Example 31.4 with the capacitor and inductor both removed; (iii) the circuit in Example 31.4 with the resistor and capacitor both removed; (iv) the circuit in Example 31.4 with the resistor and inductor both removed.

31.4 Power in Alternating-Current Circuits

Alternating currents play a central role in systems for distributing, converting, and using electrical energy, so it's important to look at power relationships in ac circuits. For an ac circuit with instantaneous current i and current amplitude I, we'll consider an element of that circuit across which the instantaneous potential difference is v with voltage amplitude V. The instantaneous power p delivered to this circuit element is

$$p = vi$$

Let's first see what this means for individual circuit elements. We'll assume in each case that $i = I\cos\omega t$.

Power in a Resistor

Suppose first that the circuit element is a *pure resistor R*, as in Fig. 31.7a; then $v = v_R$ and i are *in phase*. We obtain the graph representing p by multiplying the heights of the graphs of v and i in Fig. 31.7b at each instant. This graph is shown by the black curve in Fig. 31.16a. The product vi is always positive because v and i are always either both positive or both negative. Hence energy is supplied *to* the resistor at every instant for both directions of i, although the power is not constant.

The power curve for a pure resistor is symmetrical about a value equal to one-half its maximum value VI, so the *average power* P_{av} is

$$P_{av} = \frac{1}{2}VI \qquad \text{(for a pure resistor)} \qquad (31.27)$$

An equivalent expression is

$$P_{av} = \frac{V}{\sqrt{2}}\frac{I}{\sqrt{2}} = V_{rms}I_{rms} \qquad \text{(for a pure resistor)} \qquad (31.28)$$

Also, $V_{rms} = I_{rms}R$, so we can express P_{av} by any of the equivalent forms

$$P_{av} = I_{rms}{}^2R = \frac{V_{rms}{}^2}{R} = V_{rms}I_{rms} \qquad \text{(for a pure resistor)} \qquad (31.29)$$

Note that the expressions in Eq. (31.29) have the same form as the corresponding relationships for a dc circuit, Eq. (25.18). Also note that they are valid only for pure resistors, not for more complicated combinations of circuit elements.

Power in an Inductor

Next we connect the source to a pure inductor L, as in Fig. 31.8a. The voltage $v = v_L$ leads the current i by 90°. When we multiply the curves of v and i, the product vi is *negative* during the half of the cycle when v and i have *opposite* signs. The power curve, shown in Fig. 31.16b, is symmetrical about the horizontal axis; it is positive half the time and negative the other half, and the average power is zero. When p is positive, energy is being supplied to set up the magnetic field in the inductor; when p is negative, the field is collapsing and the inductor is returning energy to the source. The net energy transfer over one cycle is zero.

31.16 Graphs of current, voltage, and power as functions of time for **(a)** a pure resistor, **(b)** a pure inductor, **(c)** a pure capacitor, and **(d)** an arbitrary ac circuit that can have resistance, inductance, and capacitance.

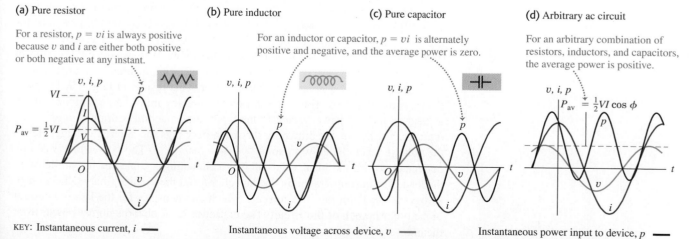

(a) Pure resistor

For a resistor, $p = vi$ is always positive because v and i are either both positive or both negative at any instant.

(b) Pure inductor

(c) Pure capacitor

For an inductor or capacitor, $p = vi$ is alternately positive and negative, and the average power is zero.

(d) Arbitrary ac circuit

For an arbitrary combination of resistors, inductors, and capacitors, the average power is positive.

$$P_{av} = \tfrac{1}{2}VI\cos\phi$$

KEY: Instantaneous current, i ——   Instantaneous voltage across device, v ——   Instantaneous power input to device, p ——

Power in a Capacitor

Finally, we connect the source to a pure capacitor C, as in Fig. 31.9a. The voltage $v = v_C$ lags the current i by 90°. Figure 31.16c shows the power curve; the average power is again zero. Energy is supplied to charge the capacitor and is returned to the source when the capacitor discharges. The net energy transfer over one cycle is again zero.

Power in a General ac Circuit

In *any* ac circuit, with any combination of resistors, capacitors, and inductors, the voltage v across the entire circuit has some phase angle ϕ with respect to the current i. Then the instantaneous power p is given by

$$p = vi = [V\cos(\omega t + \phi)][I\cos\omega t] \tag{31.30}$$

The instantaneous power curve has the form shown in Fig. 31.16d. The area between the positive loops and the horizontal axis is greater than the area between the negative loops and the horizontal axis, and the average power is positive.

We can derive from Eq. (31.30) an expression for the *average* power P_{av} by using the identity for the cosine of the sum of two angles:

$$p = [V(\cos\omega t\cos\phi - \sin\omega t\sin\phi)][I\cos\omega t]$$
$$= VI\cos\phi\cos^2\omega t - VI\sin\phi\cos\omega t\sin\omega t$$

From the discussion in Section 31.1 that led to Eq. (31.4), we see that the average value of $\cos^2\omega t$ (over one cycle) is $\frac{1}{2}$. The average value of $\cos\omega t\sin\omega t$ is zero because this product is equal to $\frac{1}{2}\sin2\omega t$, whose average over a cycle is zero. So the average power P_{av} is

$$P_{av} = \frac{1}{2}VI\cos\phi = V_{rms}I_{rms}\cos\phi \qquad \begin{array}{l}\text{(average power into a}\\ \text{general ac circuit)}\end{array} \tag{31.31}$$

31.17 Using phasors to calculate the average power for an arbitrary ac circuit.

Average power $= \frac{1}{2}I(V\cos\phi)$, where $V\cos\phi$ is the component of V in phase with I.

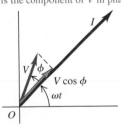

When v and i are in phase, so $\phi = 0$, the average power equals $\frac{1}{2}VI = V_{rms}I_{rms}$; when v and i are 90° out of phase, the average power is zero. In the general case, when v has a phase angle ϕ with respect to i, the average power equals $\frac{1}{2}I$ multiplied by $V\cos\phi$, the component of the voltage phasor that is *in phase* with the current phasor. Figure 31.17 shows the general relationship of the current and voltage phasors. For the L-R-C series circuit, Figs. 31.13b and 31.13c show that $V\cos\phi$ equals the voltage amplitude V_R for the resistor; hence Eq. (31.31) is the average power dissipated in the resistor. On average there is no energy flow into or out of the inductor or capacitor, so none of P_{av} goes into either of these circuit elements.

The factor $\cos\phi$ is called the **power factor** of the circuit. For a pure resistance, $\phi = 0$, $\cos\phi = 1$, and $P_{av} = V_{rms}I_{rms}$. For a pure inductor or capacitor, $\phi = \pm90°$, $\cos\phi = 0$, and $P_{av} = 0$. For an L-R-C series circuit the power factor is equal to R/Z; we leave the proof of this statement to you (see Exercise 31.27).

A low power factor (large angle ϕ of lag or lead) is usually undesirable in power circuits. The reason is that for a given potential difference, a large current is needed to supply a given amount of power. This results in large i^2R losses in the transmission lines. Your electric power company may charge a higher rate to a client with a low power factor. Many types of ac machinery draw a *lagging* current; that is, the current drawn by the machinery lags the applied voltage. Hence the voltage leads the current, so $\phi > 0$ and $\cos\phi < 1$. The power factor can be corrected toward the ideal value of 1 by connecting a capacitor in parallel with the load. The current drawn by the capacitor *leads* the voltage (that is, the voltage across the capacitor lags the current), which compensates for the lagging current in the other branch of the circuit. The capacitor itself absorbs no net power from the line.

Example 31.6 **Power in a hair dryer**

An electric hair dryer is rated at 1500 W at 120 V. The rated power of this hair dryer, or of any other ac device, is the *average* power drawn by the device, and the rated voltage is the *rms* voltage. Calculate (a) the resistance, (b) the rms current, and (c) the maximum instantaneous power. Assume that the hair dryer is a pure resistor. (The hair dryer's heating element acts as a resistor.)

SOLUTION

IDENTIFY: We assume that the hair dryer is a pure resistor. We are given the average power $P_{av} = 1500$ W and the rms voltage $V_{rms} = 120$ V. Our target variables are the resistance R, the rms current I_{rms}, and the maximum value of the instantaneous power p.

SET UP: We solve Eq. (31.29) to determine the resistance R. We find the rms current from V_{rms} and P_{av} using Eq. (31.28), and we find the maximum instantaneous power from Eq. (31.30).

EXECUTE: (a) From Eq. (31.29), the resistance is

$$R = \frac{V_{rms}^2}{P_{av}} = \frac{(120 \text{ V})^2}{1500 \text{ W}} = 9.6 \ \Omega$$

(b) From Eq. (31.28),

$$I_{rms} = \frac{P_{av}}{V_{rms}} = \frac{1500 \text{ W}}{120 \text{ V}} = 12.5 \text{ A}$$

(c) For a pure resistor, the voltage and current are in phase and the phase angle ϕ is zero. Hence from Eq. (31.30), the instantaneous power is $p = VI\cos^2 \omega t$ and the maximum instantaneous power is $p_{max} = VI$. From Eq. (31.27), this is twice the average power P_{av}, so

$$p_{max} = VI = 2P_{av} = 2(1500 \text{ W}) = 3000 \text{ W}$$

EVALUATE: We can confirm our result in part (b) by using Eq. (31.7): $I_{rms} = V_{rms}/R = (120 \text{ V})/(9.6 \ \Omega) = 12.5 \text{ A}$. Note that some manufacturers of stereo amplifiers state power outputs in terms of the peak value rather than the lower average value, to mislead the unwary consumer.

Example 31.7 **Power in an *L-R-C* series circuit**

For the *L-R-C* series circuit of Example 31.4, (a) calculate the power factor; and (b) calculate the average power delivered to the entire circuit and to each circuit element.

SOLUTION

IDENTIFY: We can use all of the results found in Example 31.4.

SET UP: The power factor is simply the cosine of the phase angle ϕ, and Eq. (31.31) allows us to find the average power delivered in terms of ϕ and the amplitudes of voltage and current.

EXECUTE: (a) The power factor is $\cos\phi = \cos 53° = 0.60$.

(b) From Eq. (31.31) the average power delivered to the circuit is

$$P_{av} = \frac{1}{2}VI\cos\phi = \frac{1}{2}(50 \text{ V})(0.10 \text{ A})(0.60) = 1.5 \text{ W}$$

EVALUATE: While P_{av} is the average power delivered to the *L-R-C* combination, all of this power is dissipated in the resistor. The average power delivered to a pure inductor or pure capacitor is always zero (see Figs. 31.16b and 31.16c).

Test Your Understanding of Section 31.4   Figure 31.16d shows that during part of a cycle of oscillation, the instantaneous power delivered to the circuit is negative. This means that energy is being extracted from the circuit. (a) Where is the energy extracted from? (i) the resistor; (ii) the inductor; (iii) the capacitor; (iv) the ac source; (v) more than one of these. (b) Where does the energy go? (i) the resistor; (ii) the inductor; (iii) the capacitor; (iv) the ac source; (v) more than one of these.

31.5 **Resonance in Alternating-Current Circuits**

Much of the practical importance of *L-R-C* series circuits arises from the way in which such circuits respond to sources of different angular frequency ω. For example, one type of tuning circuit used in radio receivers is simply an *L-R-C* series circuit. A radio signal of any given frequency produces a current of the same frequency in the receiver circuit, but the amplitude of the current is *greatest* if the signal frequency equals the particular frequency to which the receiver circuit is "tuned." This effect is called *resonance*. The circuit is designed so that signals at other than the tuned frequency produce currents that are too small to make an audible sound come out of the radio's speakers.

Act|v
ONLINE
Physics

14.3 AC Circuits: The Driven Oscillator
(Questions 8, 9, and 11)

31.18 How variations in the angular frequency of an ac circuit affect (a) reactances, resistance, and impedance, and (b) impedance, current amplitude, and phase angle.

(a) Reactance, resistance, and impedance as functions of angular frequency

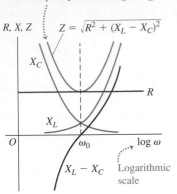

Impedance Z is least at the angular frequency at which $X_C = X_L$.

(b) Impedance, current, and phase angle as functions of angular frequency

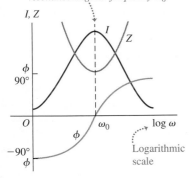

Current peaks at the angular frequency at which impedance is least. This is the *resonance angular frequency ω_0.*

To see how an *L-R-C* series circuit can be used in this way, suppose we connect an ac source with constant voltage amplitude V but adjustable angular frequency ω across an *L-R-C* series circuit. The current that appears in the circuit has the same angular frequency as the source and a current amplitude $I = V/Z$, where Z is the impedance of the *L-R-C* series circuit. This impedance depends on the frequency, as Eq. (31.23) shows. Figure 31.18a shows graphs of R, X_L, X_C, and Z as functions of ω. We have used a logarithmic angular frequency scale so that we can cover a wide range of frequencies. As the frequency increases, X_L increases and X_C decreases; hence there is always one frequency at which X_L and X_C are equal and $X_L - X_C$ is zero. At this frequency the impedance $Z = \sqrt{R^2 + (X_L - X_C)^2}$ has its *smallest* value, equal simply to the resistance R.

Circuit Behavior at Resonance

As we vary the angular frequency ω of the source, the current amplitude $I = V/Z$ varies as shown in Fig. 31.18b; the *maximum* value of I occurs at the frequency at which the impedance Z is *minimum*. This peaking of the current amplitude at a certain frequency is called **resonance.** The angular frequency ω_0 at which the resonance peak occurs is called the **resonance angular frequency.** This is the angular frequency at which the inductive and capacitive reactances are equal, so at resonance,

$$X_L = X_C \qquad \omega_0 L = \frac{1}{\omega_0 C} \qquad \omega_0 = \frac{1}{\sqrt{LC}} \qquad \begin{matrix}(\textit{L-R-C} \text{ series circuit} \\ \text{at resonance})\end{matrix} \qquad (31.32)$$

Note that this is equal to the natural angular frequency of oscillation of an *L-C* circuit, which we derived in Section 30.5, Eq. (30.22). The **resonance frequency** f_0 is $\omega_0/2\pi$. This is the frequency at which the greatest current appears in the circuit for a given source voltage amplitude; in other words, f_0 is the frequency to which the circuit is "tuned."

It's instructive to look at what happens to the *voltages* in an *L-R-C* series circuit at resonance. The current at any instant is the same in L and C. The voltage across an inductor always *leads* the current by 90°, or $\frac{1}{4}$ cycle, and the voltage across a capacitor always *lags* the current by 90°. Therefore the instantaneous voltages across L and C always differ in phase by 180°, or $\frac{1}{2}$ cycle; they have opposite signs at each instant. At the resonance frequency, and *only* at the resonance frequency, $X_L = X_C$ and the voltage amplitudes $V_L = IX_L$ and $V_C = IX_C$ are *equal;* then the instantaneous voltages across L and C add to zero at each instant, and the *total* voltage v_{bd} across the *L-C* combination in Fig. 31.13a is exactly zero. The voltage across the resistor is then equal to the source voltage. So at the resonance frequency the circuit behaves as if the inductor and capacitor weren't there at all!

The *phase* of the voltage relative to the current is given by Eq. (31.24). At frequencies below resonance, X_C is greater than X_L; the capacitive reactance dominates, the voltage *lags* the current, and the phase angle ϕ is between zero and $-90°$. Above resonance, the inductive reactance dominates; the voltage *leads* the current, and the phase angle is between zero and $+90°$. This variation of ϕ with angular frequency is shown in Fig. 31.18b.

Tailoring an ac Circuit

If we can vary the inductance L or the capacitance C of a circuit, we can also vary the resonance frequency. This is exactly how a radio or television receiving set is "tuned" to receive a particular station. In the early days of radio this was accomplished by use of capacitors with movable metal plates whose overlap could be varied to change C. (This is what is being done with the radio tuning knob shown in the photograph that opens this chapter.) A more modern approach is to vary L by using a coil with a ferrite core that slides in or out.

In a series L-R-C circuit the impedance reaches its minimum value and the current its maximum value at the resonance frequency. The middle curve in Fig. 31.19 is a graph of current as a function of frequency for such a circuit, with source voltage amplitude $V = 100$ V, $L = 2.0$ H, $C = 0.50$ μF, and $R = 500$ Ω. This curve is called a *response curve* or a *resonance curve*. The resonance angular frequency is $\omega_0 = (LC)^{-1/2} = 1000$ rad/s. As we expect, the curve has a peak at this angular frequency.

The resonance frequency is determined by L and C; what happens when we change R? Figure 31.19 also shows graphs of I as a function of ω for $R = 200$ Ω and for $R = 2000$ Ω. The curves are similar for frequencies far away from resonance, where the impedance is dominated by X_L or X_C. But near resonance, where X_L and X_C nearly cancel each other, the curve is higher and more sharply peaked for small values of R and broader and flatter for large values of R. At resonance, $Z = R$ and $I = V/R$, so the maximum height of the curve is inversely proportional to R.

The shape of the response curve is important in the design of radio and television receiving circuits. The sharply peaked curve is what makes it possible to discriminate between two stations broadcasting on adjacent frequency bands. But if the peak is *too* sharp, some of the information in the received signal is lost, such as the high-frequency sounds in music. The shape of the resonance curve is also related to the overdamped and underdamped oscillations that we described in Section 30.6. A sharply peaked resonance curve corresponds to a small value of R and a lightly damped oscillating system; a broad, flat curve goes with a large value of R and a heavily damped system.

In this section we have discussed resonance in an L-R-C *series* circuit. Resonance can also occur in an ac circuit in which the inductor, resistor, and capacitor are connected in *parallel*. We leave the details to you (see Problem 31.55).

Resonance phenomena occur not just in ac circuits, but in all areas of physics. We discussed examples of resonance in *mechanical* systems in Sections 13.8 and 16.5. The amplitude of a mechanical oscillation peaks when the driving-force frequency is close to a natural frequency of the system; this is analogous to the peaking of the current in an L-R-C series circuit. We suggest that you review the sections on mechanical resonance now, looking for the analogies. Other important examples of resonance occur in atomic and nuclear physics and in the study of fundamental particles (high-energy physics).

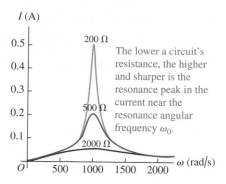

31.19 Graph of current amplitude I as a function of angular frequency ω for an L-R-C series circuit with $V = 100$ V, $L = 2.0$ H, $C = 0.50$ μF, and three different values of the resistance R.

The lower a circuit's resistance, the higher and sharper is the resonance peak in the current near the resonance angular frequency ω_0.

Example 31.8	**Tuning a radio**

The series circuit in Fig. 31.20 is similar to arrangements that are sometimes used in radio tuning circuits. This circuit is connected to the terminals of an ac source with a constant rms terminal voltage of 1.0 V and a variable frequency. Find (a) the resonance frequency; (b) the inductive reactance, the capacitive reactance, and the impedance at the resonance frequency; (c) the rms current at resonance; and (d) the rms voltage across each circuit element at resonance.

SOLUTION

IDENTIFY: The circuit in Fig. 31.20 is a series L-R-C circuit, but with meters added to measure the rms current and voltages (which are our target variables).

SET UP: Equation (31.32) includes the formula for the resonance angular frequency ω_0, from which we find the resonance frequency f_0. We find the remaining target variables using the results of Sections 31.2 and 31.3.

31.20 A radio tuning circuit at resonance. The circles denote rms current and voltages.

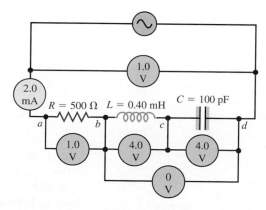

Continued

EXECUTE: (a) The resonance angular frequency is

$$\omega_0 = \frac{1}{\sqrt{LC}} = \frac{1}{\sqrt{(0.40 \times 10^{-3}\,\text{H})(100 \times 10^{-12}\,\text{F})}}$$

$$= 5.0 \times 10^6\,\text{rad/s}$$

The corresponding frequency $f_0 = \omega_0/2\pi$ is

$$f_0 = 8.0 \times 10^5\,\text{Hz} = 800\,\text{kHz}$$

This corresponds to the lower part of the AM radio band.

(b) At this frequency,

$$X_L = \omega L = (5.0 \times 10^6\,\text{rad/s})(0.40 \times 10^{-3}\,\text{H}) = 2000\,\Omega$$

$$X_C = \frac{1}{\omega C} = \frac{1}{(5.0 \times 10^6\,\text{rad/s})(100 \times 10^{-12}\,\text{F})} = 2000\,\Omega$$

Since $X_L = X_C$ and $X_L - X_C = 0$, Eq. (31.23) shows that the impedance Z at resonance is equal to the resistance: $Z = R = 500\,\Omega$.

(c) From Eq. (31.26) the rms current at resonance is

$$I_{\text{rms}} = \frac{V_{\text{rms}}}{Z} = \frac{V_{\text{rms}}}{R} = \frac{1.0\,\text{V}}{500\,\Omega} = 0.0020\,\text{A} = 2.0\,\text{mA}$$

(d) The rms potential difference across the resistor is

$$V_{R\text{-rms}} = I_{\text{rms}}R = (0.0020\,\text{A})(500\,\Omega) = 1.0\,\text{V}$$

The rms potential differences across the inductor and capacitor are, respectively:

$$V_{L\text{-rms}} = I_{\text{rms}}X_L = (0.0020\,\text{A})(2000\,\Omega) = 4.0\,\text{V}$$

$$V_{C\text{-rms}} = I_{\text{rms}}X_C = (0.0020\,\text{A})(2000\,\Omega) = 4.0\,\text{V}$$

EVALUATE: The potential differences across the inductor and the capacitor have equal rms values and amplitudes, but are 180° out of phase and so add to zero at each instant. Note also that at resonance, $V_{R\text{-rms}}$ is equal to the source voltage V_{rms}, while in this example, $V_{L\text{-rms}}$ and $V_{C\text{-rms}}$ are both considerably *larger* than V_{rms}.

Test Your Understanding of Section 31.5   How does the resonance frequency of an *L-R-C* series circuit change if the plates of the capacitor are brought closer together? (i) It increases; (ii) it decreases; (iii) it is unaffected. ∎

31.6 Transformers

One of the great advantages of ac over dc for electric-power distribution is that it is much easier to step voltage levels up and down with ac than with dc. For long-distance power transmission it is desirable to use as high a voltage and as small a current as possible; this reduces i^2R losses in the transmission lines, and smaller wires can be used, saving on material costs. Present-day transmission lines routinely operate at rms voltages of the order of 500 kV. On the other hand, safety considerations and insulation requirements dictate relatively low voltages in generating equipment and in household and industrial power distribution. The standard voltage for household wiring is 120 V in the United States and Canada and 240 V in many other countries. The necessary voltage conversion is accomplished by the use of **transformers.**

How Transformers Work

Figure 31.21 shows an idealized transformer. The key components of the transformer are two coils or *windings,* electrically insulated from each other but wound on the same core. The core is typically made of a material, such as iron, with a very large relative permeability K_m. This keeps the magnetic field lines due to a current in one winding almost completely within the core. Hence almost all of these field lines pass through the other winding, maximizing the *mutual inductance* of the two windings (see Section 30.1). The winding to which power is supplied is called the **primary;** the winding from which power is delivered is called the **secondary.** The circuit symbol for a transformer with an iron core, such as those used in power distribution systems, is

31.21 Schematic diagram of an idealized step-up transformer. The primary is connected to an ac source; the secondary is connected to a device with resistance R.

The induced emf *per turn* is the same in both coils, so we adjust the ratio of terminal voltages by adjusting the ratio of turns:

$$\frac{V_2}{V_1} = \frac{N_2}{N_1}$$

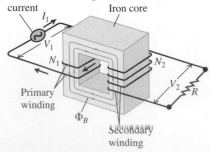

Here's how a transformer works. The ac source causes an alternating current in the primary, which sets up an alternating flux in the core; this induces an emf in each winding, in accordance with Faraday's law. The induced emf in the secondary gives rise to an alternating current in the secondary, and this delivers energy to the device to which the secondary is connected. All currents and emfs have the same frequency as the ac source.

Let's see how the voltage across the secondary can be made larger or smaller in amplitude than the voltage across the primary. We neglect the resistance of the windings and assume that all the magnetic field lines are confined to the iron core, so at any instant the magnetic flux Φ_B is the same in each turn of the primary and secondary windings. The primary winding has N_1 turns and the secondary winding has N_2 turns. When the magnetic flux changes because of changing currents in the two coils, the resulting induced emfs are

$$\mathcal{E}_1 = -N_1 \frac{d\Phi_B}{dt} \quad \text{and} \quad \mathcal{E}_2 = -N_2 \frac{d\Phi_B}{dt} \tag{31.33}$$

The flux *per turn* Φ_B is the same in both the primary and the secondary, so Eqs. (31.33) show that the induced emf *per turn* is the same in each. The ratio of the secondary emf $\mathcal{E}_2$ to the primary emf $\mathcal{E}_1$ is therefore equal at any instant to the ratio of secondary to primary turns:

$$\frac{\mathcal{E}_2}{\mathcal{E}_1} = \frac{N_2}{N_1} \tag{31.34}$$

Since $\mathcal{E}_1$ and $\mathcal{E}_2$ both oscillate with the same frequency as the ac source, Eq. (31.34) also gives the ratio of the amplitudes or of the rms values of the induced emfs. If the windings have zero resistance, the induced emfs $\mathcal{E}_1$ and $\mathcal{E}_2$ are equal to the terminal voltages across the primary and the secondary, respectively; hence

$$\frac{V_2}{V_1} = \frac{N_2}{N_1} \qquad \text{(terminal voltages of transformer primary and secondary)} \tag{31.35}$$

where V_1 and V_2 are either the amplitudes or the rms values of the terminal voltages. By choosing the appropriate turns ratio N_2/N_1, we may obtain any desired secondary voltage from a given primary voltage. If $N_2 > N_1$, as in Fig. 31.21, then $V_2 > V_1$ and we have a *step-up* transformer; if $N_2 < N_1$, then $V_2 < V_1$ and we have a *step-down* transformer. At a power generating station, step-up transformers are used; the primary is connected to the power source and the secondary is connected to the transmission lines, giving the desired high voltage for transmission. Near the consumer, step-down transformers lower the voltage to a value suitable for use in home or industry (Fig. 31.22).

Even the relatively low voltage provided by a household wall socket is too high for many electronic devices, so a further step-down transformer is necessary. This is the role of an "ac adapter" (also called a "power cube" or "power adapter"), such as those used to recharge a mobile phone or laptop computer from line voltage. Such adapters contain a step-down transformer that converts line voltage to a lower value, typically 3 to 12 volts, as well as diodes to convert alternating current to the direct current that small electronic devices require (Fig. 31.23).

Energy Considerations for Transformers

If the secondary circuit is completed by a resistance R, then the amplitude or rms value of the current in the secondary circuit is $I_2 = V_2/R$. From energy considerations, the power delivered to the primary equals that taken out of the secondary (since there is no resistance in the windings), so

$$V_1 I_1 = V_2 I_2 \qquad \text{(currents in transformer primary and secondary)} \tag{31.36}$$

31.22 The cylindrical can near the top of this power pole is a step-down transformer. It converts the high-voltage ac in the power lines to low-voltage (120 V) ac, which is then distributed to the surrounding homes and businesses.

31.23 An ac adapter like this one converts household ac into low-voltage dc for use in electronic devices. It contains a step-down transformer to lower the voltage and diodes to rectify the output current (see Fig. 31.3).

31.24 (a) Primary and secondary windings in a transformer. (b) Eddy currents in the iron core, shown in the cross section at *AA*. (c) Using a laminated core reduces the eddy currents.

(a) Schematic transformer

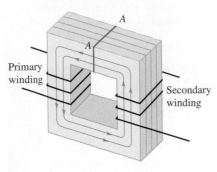

Primary winding

Secondary winding

(b) Large eddy currents in solid core

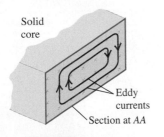

Solid core

Eddy currents

Section at *AA*

(c) Smaller eddy currents in laminated core

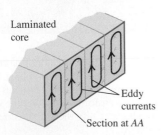

Laminated core

Eddy currents

Section at *AA*

We can combine Eqs. (31.35) and (31.36) and the relationship $I_2 = V_2/R$ to eliminate V_2 and I_2; we obtain

$$\frac{V_1}{I_1} = \frac{R}{(N_2/N_1)^2} \qquad (31.37)$$

This shows that when the secondary circuit is completed through a resistance R, the result is the same as if the *source* had been connected directly to a resistance equal to R divided by the square of the turns ratio, $(N_2/N_1)^2$. In other words, the transformer "transforms" not only voltages and currents, but resistances as well. More generally, we can regard a transformer as "transforming" the *impedance* of the network to which the secondary circuit is completed.

Equation (31.37) has many practical consequences. The power supplied by a source to a resistor depends on the resistances of both the resistor and the source. It can be shown that the power transfer is greatest when the two resistances are *equal*. The same principle applies in both dc and ac circuits. When a high-impedance ac source must be connected to a low-impedance circuit, such as an audio amplifier connected to a loudspeaker, the source impedance can be *matched* to that of the circuit by use of a transformer with an appropriate turns ratio N_2/N_1.

Real transformers always have some energy losses. (That's why an ac adapter like the one shown in Fig. 31.23 feels warm to the touch after it's been in use for a while; the transformer is heated by the dissipated energy.) The windings have some resistance, leading to i^2R losses. There are also energy losses through hysteresis in the core (see Section 28.8). Hysteresis losses are minimized by the use of soft iron with a narrow hysteresis loop.

Another important mechanism for energy loss in a transformer core involves eddy currents (see Section 29.6). Consider a section *AA* through an iron transformer core (Fig. 31.24a). Since iron is a conductor, any such section can be pictured as several conducting circuits, one within the other (Fig. 31.24b). The flux through each of these circuits is continually changing, so eddy currents circulate in the entire volume of the core, with lines of flow that form planes perpendicular to the flux. These eddy currents are very undesirable; they waste energy through i^2R heating and themselves set up an opposing flux.

The effects of eddy currents can be minimized by the use of a *laminated* core, that is, one built up of thin sheets or laminae. The large electrical surface resistance of each lamina, due either to a natural coating of oxide or to an insulating varnish, effectively confines the eddy currents to individual laminae (Fig. 31.24c). The possible eddy-current paths are narrower, the induced emf in each path is smaller, and the eddy currents are greatly reduced. The alternating magnetic field exerts forces on the current-carrying laminae that cause them to vibrate back and forth; this vibration causes the characteristic "hum" of an operating transformer. You can hear this same "hum" from the magnetic ballast of a fluorescent light fixture (see Section 30.2).

Thanks to the use of soft iron cores and lamination, transformer efficiencies are usually well over 90%; in large installations they may reach 99%.

Example 31.9   **"Wake up and smell the (transformer)!"**

A friend brings back from Europe a device that she claims to be the world's greatest coffeemaker. Unfortunately, it was designed to operate from a 240-V line to obtain the 960 W of power that it needs. (a) What can she do to operate it at 120 V? (b) What current will the coffeemaker draw from the 120-V line? (c) What is the resistance of the coffeemaker? (The voltages are rms values.)

SOLUTION

IDENTIFY: Our friend needs a step-up transformer to convert the 120-V ac available in the home to the 240-V ac that the cof-

feemaker requires. This problem is about the properties of this transformer.

SET UP: We use Eq. (31.35) to determine the transformer turns ratio N_2/N_1, the relationship $P_{av} = V_{rms}I_{rms}$ for a resistor to find the current draw, and Eq. (31.37) to calculate the resistance.

EXECUTE: (a) To get $V_2 = 240$ V from $V_1 = 120$ V, the required turns ratio is $N_2/N_1 = V_2/V_1 = (240\ \text{V})/(120\ \text{V}) = 2$. That is, the secondary coil (connected to the coffeemaker) should have twice as many turns as the primary coil (connected to the 120-V line).

(b) The rms current I_1 in the 120-V primary is found by using $P_{av} = V_1 I_1$, where P_{av} is the average power drawn by the coffeemaker and hence the power supplied by the 120-V line. (We're assuming that there are no energy losses in the transformer.) Hence $I_1 = P_{av}/V_1 = (960 \text{ W})/(120 \text{ V}) = 8.0 \text{ A}$. The secondary current is then $I_2 = P_{av}/V_2 = (960 \text{ W})/(240 \text{ V}) = 4.0 \text{ A}$.

(c) We have $V_1 = 120 \text{ V}$, $I_1 = 8.0 \text{ A}$, and $N_2/N_1 = 2$, so

$$\frac{V_1}{I_1} = \frac{120 \text{ V}}{8.0 \text{ A}} = 15 \, \Omega$$

From Eq. (31.37),

$$R = 2^2 (15 \, \Omega) = 60 \, \Omega$$

EVALUATE: As a check, $V_2/R = (240 \text{ V})/(60 \, \omega) = 4.0 \text{ A} = I_2$, the same value obtained previously. you can also check this result for r by using the expression $P_{av} = V_2^2/R$ for the power drawn by the coffeemaker.

Test Your Understanding of Section 31.6   Each of the following four transformers has 1000 turns in its primary coil. Rank the transformers from largest to smallest number of turns in the secondary coil. (i) converts 120-V ac into 6.0-V ac; (ii) converts 120-V ac into 240-V ac; (iii) converts 240-V ac into 6.0-V ac; (iv) converts 240-V ac into 120-V ac.

Phasors and alternating current: An alternator or ac source produces an emf that varies sinusoidally with time. A sinusoidal voltage or current can be represented by a phasor, a vector that rotates counterclockwise with constant angular velocity ω equal to the angular frequency of the sinusoidal quantity. Its projection on the horizontal axis at any instant represents the instantaneous value of the quantity.

For a sinusoidal current, the rectified average and rms (root-mean-square) currents are proportional to the current amplitude I. Similarly, the rms value of a sinusoidal voltage is proportional to the voltage amplitude V. (See Example 31.1.)

$$I_{\text{rav}} = \frac{2}{\pi}I = 0.637I \tag{31.3}$$

$$I_{\text{rms}} = \frac{I}{\sqrt{2}} \tag{31.4}$$

$$V_{\text{rms}} = \frac{V}{\sqrt{2}} \tag{31.5}$$

Voltage, current, and phase angle: In general, the instantaneous voltage between two points in an ac circuit is not in phase with the instantaneous current passing through those points. The quantity ϕ is called the phase angle of the voltage relative to the current.

$$i = I\cos\omega t$$
$$v = V\cos(\omega t + \phi) \tag{31.2}$$

Resistance and reactance: The voltage across a resistor R is in phase with the current. The voltage across an inductor L leads the current by 90° ($\phi = +90°$), while the voltage across a capacitor C lags the current by 90° ($\phi = -90°$). The voltage amplitude across each type of device is proportional to the current amplitude I. An inductor has inductive reactance $X_L = \omega L$, and a capacitor has capacitive reactance $X_C = 1/\omega C$. (See Examples 31.2 and 31.3.)

$$V_R = IR \tag{31.7}$$

$$V_L = IX_L \tag{31.13}$$

$$V_C = IX_C \tag{31.19}$$

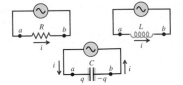

Impedance and the L-R-C series circuit: In a general ac circuit, the voltage and current amplitudes are related by the circuit impedance Z. In an L-R-C series circuit, the values of L, R, C, and the angular frequency ω determine the impedance and the phase angle ϕ of the voltage relative to the current. (See Examples 31.4 and 31.5.)

$$V = IZ \tag{31.22}$$

$$Z = \sqrt{R^2 + (X_L - X_C)^2}$$
$$= \sqrt{R^2 + [\omega L - (1/\omega C)]^2} \tag{31.23}$$

$$\tan\phi = \frac{\omega L - 1/\omega C}{R} \tag{31.24}$$

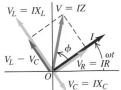

Power in ac circuits: The average power input P_{av} to an ac circuit depends on the voltage and current amplitudes (or, equivalently, their rms values) and the phase angle ϕ of the voltage relative to the current. The quantity $\cos\phi$ is called the power factor. (See Examples 31.6 and 31.7.)

$$P_{\text{av}} = \frac{1}{2}VI\cos\phi$$
$$= V_{\text{rms}}I_{\text{rms}}\cos\phi \tag{31.31}$$

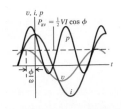

Resonance in ac circuits: In an L-R-C series circuit, the current becomes maximum and the impedance becomes minimum at an angular frequency called the resonance angular frequency. This phenomenon is called resonance. At resonance the voltage and current are in phase, and the impedance Z is equal to the resistance R. (See Example 31.8.)

$$\omega_0 = \frac{1}{\sqrt{LC}} \tag{31.32}$$

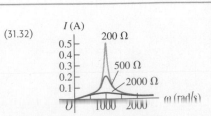

Transformers: A transformer is used to transform the voltage and current levels in an ac circuit. In an ideal transformer with no energy losses, if the primary winding has N_1 turns and the secondary winding has N_2 turns, the amplitudes (or rms values) of the two voltages are related by Eq. (31.35). The amplitudes (or rms values) of the primary and secondary voltages and currents are related by Eq. (31.36). (See Example 31.9.)

$$\frac{V_2}{V_1} = \frac{N_2}{N_1} \qquad (31.35)$$

$$V_1 I_1 = V_2 I_2 \qquad (31.36)$$

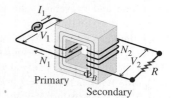

Key Terms

Answer to Chapter Opening Question ?

Yes. In fact, the radio simultaneously detects transmissions at *all* frequencies. However, a radio is an *L-R-C* series circuit, and at any given time it is tuned to have a resonance at just one frequency. Hence the response of the radio to that frequency is much greater than its response to any other frequency, which is why you hear only one broadcasting station through the radio's speaker. (You can sometimes hear a second station if its frequency is sufficiently close to the tuned frequency.)

Answers to Test Your Understanding Questions

31.1 Answers: (a) D; (b) A; (c) B; (d) C   For each phasor, the actual current is represented by the projection of that phasor onto the horizontal axis. The phasors all rotate counterclockwise around the origin with angular speed ω, so at the instant shown the projection of phasor A is positive but trending toward zero; the projection of phasor B is negative and becoming more negative; the projection of phasor C is negative but trending toward zero; and the projection of phasor D is positive and becoming more positive.

31.2 Answers: (a) (iii); (b) (ii); (c) (i)   For a resistor, $V_R = IR$, so $I = V_R/R$. The voltage amplitude V_R and resistance R do not change with frequency, so the current amplitude I remains constant. For an inductor, $V_L = IX_L = I\omega L$, so $I = V_L/\omega L$. The voltage amplitude V_L and inductance L are constant, so the current amplitude I decreases as the frequency increases. For a capacitor, $V_C = IX_C = I/\omega C$, so $I = V_C\omega C$. The voltage amplitude V_C and capacitance C are constant, so the current amplitude I increases as the frequency increases.

31.3 Answer: (iv), (ii), (i), (iii)   For the circuit in Example 31.4, $I = V/Z = (50 \text{ V})/(500 \ \Omega) = 0.10 \text{ A}$. If the capacitor and inductor are removed so that only the ac source and resistor remain, the circuit is like that shown in Fig. 31.7a; then $I = V/R = (50 \text{ V})/(300 \ \Omega) = 0.17 \text{ A}$. If the resistor and capacitor are removed so that only the ac source and inductor remain, the circuit is like that shown in Fig. 31.8a; then $I = V/X_L = (50 \text{ V})/(600 \ \Omega) = 0.083 \text{ A}$. Finally, if the resistor and inductor are removed so that only the ac source and capacitor remain, the circuit is like that shown in Fig. 31.9a; then $I = V/X_C = (50 \text{ V})/(200 \ \Omega) = 0.25 \text{ A}$.

31.4 Answers: (a) (v); (b) (iv)   The energy cannot be extracted from the resistor, since energy is dissipated in a resistor and cannot be recovered. Instead, the energy must be extracted from either the inductor (which stores magnetic-field energy) or the capacitor (which stores electric-field energy). Positive power means that energy is being transferred from the ac source to the circuit, so *negative* power implies that energy is being transferred back into the source.

31.5 Answer: (ii)   The capacitance C increases if the plate spacing is decreased (see Section 24.1). Hence the resonance frequency $f_0 = \omega_0/2\pi = 1/2\pi\sqrt{LC}$ decreases.

31.6 Answer: (ii), (iv), (i), (iii)   From Eq. (31.35) the turns ratio is $N_2/N_1 = V_2/V_1$, so the number of turns in the secondary is $N_2 = N_1V_2/V_1$. Hence for the four cases we have (i) $N_2 = (1000)(6.0 \text{ V})/(120 \text{ V}) = 50$ turns; (ii) $N_2 = (1000)(240 \text{ V})/(120 \text{ V}) = 2000$ turns; (iii) $N_2 = (1000)(6.0 \text{ V})/(240 \text{ V}) = 25$ turns; and (iv) $N_2 = (1000)(120 \text{ V})/(240 \text{ V}) = 500$ turns. Note that (i), (iii), and (iv) are step-down transformers with fewer turns in the secondary than in the primary, while (ii) is a step-up transformer with more turns in the secondary than in the primary.

PROBLEMS

For instructor-assigned homework, go to **www.masteringphysics.com**

Discussion Questions

Q31.1. Household electric power in most of western Europe is supplied at 240 V, rather than the 120 V that is standard in the United States and Canada. What are the advantages and disadvantages of each system?

Q31.2. The current in an ac power line changes direction 120 times per second, and its average value is zero. Explain how it is possible for power to be transmitted in such a system.

Q31.3. In an ac circuit, why is the average power for an inductor and a capacitor zero, but not for a resistor?

Q31.4. Equation (31.14) was derived by using the relationship $i = dq/dt$ between the current and the charge on the capacitor. In Fig. 31.9a the positive counterclockwise current increases the charge on the capacitor. When the charge on the left plate is positive but decreasing in time, is $i = dq/dt$ still correct or should it be $i = -dq/dt$? Is $i = dq/dt$ still correct when the right-hand plate has positive charge that is increasing or decreasing in magnitude? Explain.

Q31.5. Fluorescent lights often use an inductor, called a ballast, to limit the current through the tubes. Why is it better to use an inductor rather than a resistor for this purpose?

Q31.6. Equation (31.9) says that $v_{ab} = L\, di/dt$ (see Fig. 31.8a). Using Faraday's law, explain why point a is at higher potential than point b when i is in the direction shown in Fig. 31.8a and is increasing in magnitude. When i is counterclockwise and decreasing in magnitude, is $v_{ab} = L\, di/dt$ still correct, or should it be $v_{ab} = -L\, di/dt$? Is $v_{ab} = L\, di/dt$ still correct when i is clockwise and increasing or decreasing in magnitude? Explain.

Q31.7. Is it possible for the power factor of an L-R-C series ac circuit to be zero? Justify your answer on *physical* grounds.

Q31.8. In a series L-R-C circuit, can the instantaneous voltage across the capacitor exceed the source voltage at that same instant? Can this be true for the instantaneous voltage across the inductor? Across the resistor? Explain.

Q31.9. In a series L-R-C circuit, what are the phase angle ϕ and power factor $\cos\phi$ when the resistance is much smaller than the inductive or capacitive reactance and the circuit is operated far from resonance? Explain.

Q31.10. When a series L-R-C circuit is connected across a 120-V ac line, the voltage rating of the capacitor may be exceeded even if it is rated at 200 or 400 V. How can this be?

Q31.11. In Example 31.6 (Section 31.4), a hair dryer was treated as a pure resistor. But because there are coils in the heating element and in the motor that drives the blower fan, a hair dryer also has inductance. Qualitatively, does including an inductance increase or decrease the values of R, I_{rms}, and P?

Q31.12. A light bulb and a parallel-plate capacitor with air between the plates are connected in series to an ac source. What happens to the brightness of the bulb when a dielectric is inserted between the plates of the capacitor? Explain.

Q31.13. A coil of wire wrapped on a hollow tube and a light bulb are connected in series to an ac source. What happens to the brightness of the bulb when an iron rod is inserted in the tube?

Q31.14. A circuit consists of a light bulb, a capacitor, and an inductor connected in series to an ac source. What happens to the brightness of the bulb when the inductor is removed? When the inductor is left in the circuit but the capacitor is removed? Explain.

Q31.15. A circuit consists of a light bulb, a capacitor, and an inductor connected in series to an ac source. Is it possible for both the capacitor and the inductor to be removed and the brightness of the bulb to remain the same? Explain.

Q31.16. Can a transformer be used with dc? Explain. What happens if a transformer designed for 120-V ac is connected to a 120-V dc line?

Q31.17. An ideal transformer has N_1 windings in the primary and N_2 windings in its secondary. If you double only the number of secondary windings, by what factor does (a) the voltage amplitude

in the secondary change, and (b) the effective resistance of the secondary circuit change?

Q31.18. Some electrical appliances operate equally well on ac or dc, and others work only on ac or only on dc. Give examples of each, and explain the differences.

Exercises

Section 31.1 Phasors and Alternating Currents

31.1. The plate on the back of a certain computer scanner says that the unit draws 0.34 A of current from a 120-V, 60-Hz line. Find (a) the root-mean-square current, (b) the current amplitude, (c) the average current; (d) the average square of the current.

31.2. A sinusoidal current $i = I\cos\omega t$ has an rms value $I_{rms} = 2.10$ A. (a) What is the current amplitude? (b) The current is passed through a full-wave rectifier circuit. What is the rectified average current? (c) Which is larger: I_{rms} or I_{rav}? Explain, using graphs of i^2 and of the rectified current.

31.3. The voltage across the terminals of an ac power supply varies with time according to Eq. (31.1). The voltage amplitude is $V = 45.0$ V. What are (a) the root-mean-square potential difference V_{rms}? and (b) the average potential difference V_{av} between the two terminals of the power supply?

Section 31.2 Resistance and Reactance

31.4. A 2.20-μF capacitor is connected across an ac source whose voltage amplitude is kept constant at 60.0 V but whose frequency can be varied. Find the current amplitude when the angular frequency is (a) 100 rad/s; (b) 1000 rad/s; (c) 10,000 rad/s. (d) Show the results of parts (a) through (c) in a plot of log I versus log ω.

31.5. A 5.00-H inductor with negligible resistance is connected across the ac source of Exercise 31.4. Find the current amplitude when the angular frequency is (a) 100 rad/s; (b) 1000 rad/s; (c) 10,000 rad/s. (d) Show the results of parts (a) through (c) in a plot of log I versus log ω.

31.6. A capacitance C and an inductance L are operated at the same angular frequency. (a) At what angular frequency will they have the same reactance? (b) If $L = 5.00$ mH and $C = 3.50$ μF, what is the numerical value of the angular frequency in part (a), and what is the reactance of each element?

31.7. In each circuit described next, an ac voltage source producing a current $i = I\cos\omega t$ is connected to an additional circuit element. (a) The ac source is connected across a resistor R. Sketch graphs of the current in the circuit and the potential difference across the resistor as functions of time, covering two cycles of oscillation. Put both graphs on the *same* set of axes so you can compare them. (b) Do the same as in part (a), except suppose the resistor is replaced by an inductor L. Sketch the same graphs as in part (a), but this time across the inductor instead of the resistor. (c) Do the same as in part (a), except suppose the resistor is replaced by a capacitor C. Sketch the same graphs as in part (a), except now across the capacitor instead of the resistor. (d) Sketch phasor diagrams for each of the preceding cases.

31.8. (a) Compute the reactance of a 0.450-H inductor at frequencies of 60.0 Hz and 600 Hz. (b) Compute the reactance of a 2.50-μF capacitor at the same frequencies. (c) At what frequency is the reactance of a 0.450-H inductor equal to that of a 2.50-μF capacitor?

31.9. (a) What is the reactance of a 3.00-H inductor at a frequency of 80.0 Hz? (b) What is the inductance of an inductor whose reactance is 120 Ω at 80.0 Hz? (c) What is the reactance of a 4.00-μF capacitor at a frequency of 80.0 Hz? (d) What is the capacitance of a capacitor whose reactance is 120 Ω at 80.0 Hz?

31.10. A Radio Inductor. You want the current amplitude through a 0.450-mH inductor (part of the circuitry for a radio receiver) to be 2.60 mA when a sinusoidal voltage with amplitude 12.0 V is applied across the inductor. What frequency is required?

31.11. Kitchen Capacitance. The wiring for a refrigerator contains a starter capacitor. A voltage of amplitude 170 V and frequency 60.0 Hz applied across the capacitor is to produce a current amplitude of 0.850 A through the capacitor. What capacitance C is required?

31.12. A 250-Ω resistor is connected in series with a 4.80-μF capacitor. The voltage across the capacitor is $v_C = (7.60 \text{ V}) \sin[(120 \text{ rad/s})t]$. (a) Determine the capacitive reactance of the capacitor. (b) Derive an expression for the voltage v_R across the resistor.

31.13. A 150-Ω resistor is connected in series with a 0.250-H inductor. The voltage across the resistor is $v_R = (3.80 \text{ V}) \cos[(720 \text{ rad/s})t]$. (a) Derive an expression for the circuit current. (b) Determine the inductive reactance of the inductor. (c) Derive an expression for the voltage v_L across the inductor.

Section 31.3 The *L-R-C* Series Circuit

31.14. You have a 200-Ω resistor, a 0.400-H inductor, and a 6.00-μF capacitor. Suppose you take the resistor and inductor and make a series circuit with a voltage source that has voltage amplitude 30.0 V and an angular frequency of 250 rad/s. (a) What is the impedance of the circuit? (b) What is the current amplitude? (c) What are the voltage amplitudes across the resistor and across the inductor? (d) What is the phase angle ϕ of the source voltage with respect to the current? Does the source voltage lag or lead the current? (e) Construct the phasor diagram.

31.15. (a) For the *R-L* circuit of Exercise 31.14, graph v, v_R, and v_L versus t for $t = 0$ to $t = 50.0$ ms. The current is given by $i = I\cos\omega t$, so $v = V\cos(\omega t + \phi)$. (b) What are v, v_R, and v_L at $t = 20.0$ ms? Compare $v_R + v_L$ to v at this instant. (c) Repeat part (b) for $t = 40.0$ ms.

31.16. Repeat Exercise 31.14 with the circuit consisting of only the capacitor and the inductor in series. For part (c), calculate the voltage amplitudes across the capacitor and across the inductor.

31.17. Repeat Exercise 31.14 with the circuit consisting of only the resistor and the capacitor in series. For part (c), calculate the voltage amplitudes across the resistor and across the capacitor.

31.18. (a) For the *R-C* circuit of Exercise 31.17, graph v, v_R, and v_C versus t for $t = 0$ to $t = 50.0$ ms. The current is given by $i = I\cos\omega t$, so $v = V\cos(\omega t + \phi)$. (b) What are v, v_R, and v_C at $t = 20.0$ ms? Compare $v_R + v_C$ to v at this instant. (c) Repeat part (b) for $t = 40.0$ ms.

31.19. The resistor, inductor, capacitor, and voltage source described in Exercise 31.14 are connected to form an *L-R-C* series circuit. (a) What is the impedance of the circuit? (b) What is the current amplitude? (c) What is the phase angle of the source voltage with respect to the current? Does the source voltage lag or lead the current? (d) What are the voltage amplitudes across the resistor, inductor, and capacitor? (e) Explain how it is possible for the voltage amplitude across the capacitor to be greater than the voltage amplitude across the source.

31.20. (a) For the *L-R-C* circuit of Exercise 31.19, graph v, v_R, v_L, and v_C versus t for $t = 0$ to $t = 50.0$ ms. The current is given by $i = I\cos\omega t$, so $v = V\cos(\omega t + \phi)$. (b) What are v, v_R, v_L, and v_C at $t = 20.0$ ms? Compare $v_R + v_L + v_C$ to v at this instant. (c) Repeat part (b) for $t = 40.0$ ms.

31.21. Analyzing an *L-R-C* Circuit. You have a 200-Ω resistor, a 0.400-H inductor, a 5.00-μF capacitor, and a variable-frequency ac source with an amplitude of 3.00 V. You connect all four elements together to form a series circuit. (a) At what frequency will the current in the circuit be greatest? What will be the current amplitude at this frequency? (b) What will be the current amplitude at an angular frequency of 400 rad/s? At this frequency, will the source voltage lead or lag the current?

31.22. An *L-R-C* series circuit is constructed using a 175-Ω resistor, a 12.5-μF capacitor, and an 8.00-mH inductor, all connected across an ac source having a variable frequency and a voltage amplitude of 25.0 V. (a) At what angular frequency will the impedance be smallest, and what is the impedance at this frequency? (b) At the angular frequency in part (a), what is the maximum current through the inductor? (c) At the angular frequency in part (a), find the potential difference across the ac source, the resistor, the capacitor, and the inductor at the instant that the current is equal to one-half its greatest positive value. (d) In part (c), how are the potential differences across the resistor, inductor, and capacitor related to the potential difference across the ac source?

31.23. In an *L-R-C* series circuit, the rms voltage across the resistor is 30.0 V, across the capacitor it is 90.0 V, and across the inductor it is 50.0 V. What is the rms voltage of the source?

31.24. Define the reactance X of an *L-R-C* circuit to be $X = X_L - X_C$. (a) Show that $X = 0$ when the angular frequency ω of the current is equal to the resonance angular frequency ω_0. (b) What is the sign of X when $\omega > \omega_0$? (c) What is the sign of X when $\omega < \omega_0$? (d) Graph X versus ω.

Section 31.4 Power in Alternating-Current Circuits

31.25. The power of a certain CD player operating at 120 V rms is 20.0 W. Assuming that the CD player behaves like a pure resistance, find (a) the maximum instantaneous power; (b) the rms current; (c) the resistance of this player.

31.26. In a series *L-R-C* circuit, the components have the following values: $L = 20.0$ mH, $C = 140$ nF, and $R = 350$ Ω. The generator has an rms voltage of 120 V and a frequency of 1.25 kHz. Determine (a) the power supplied by the generator; and (b) the power dissipated in the resistor.

31.27. (a) Show that for an *L-R-C* series circuit the power factor is equal to R/Z. (*Hint:* Use the phasor diagram; see Fig. 31.13b.) (b) Show that for any ac circuit, not just one containing pure resistance only, the average power delivered by the voltage source is given by $P_{av} = I_{rms}^2 R$.

31.28. An *L-R-C* series circuit is connected to a 120-Hz ac source that has $V_{rms} = 80.0$ V. The circuit has a resistance of 75.0 Ω and an impedance at this frequency of 105 Ω. What average power is delivered to the circuit by the source?

31.29. An *L-R-C* series circuit with $L = 0.120$ H, $R = 240$ Ω, and $C = 7.30$ μF carries an rms current of 0.450 A with a frequency of 400 Hz. (a) What are the phase angle and power factor for this circuit? (b) What is the impedance of the circuit? (c) What is the rms voltage of the source? (d) What average power is delivered by the source? (e) What is the average rate at which electrical energy is converted to thermal energy in the resistor? (f) What is the average rate at which electrical energy is dissipated (converted to other forms) in the capacitor? (g) In the inductor?

31.30. A series ac circuit contains a 250-Ω resistor, a 15-mH inductor, a 3.5-μF capacitor, and an ac power source of voltage amplitude 45 V operating at an angular frequency of 360 rad/s, (a) What is the power factor of this circuit? (b) Find the average power delivered to the entire circuit. (c) What is the average power delivered to the resistor, to the capacitor, and to the inductor?

Section 31.5 Resonance in Alternating-Current Circuits

31.31. In an *L-R-C* series circuit, $R = 300\ \Omega$, $L = 0.400$ H, and $C = 6.00 \times 10^{-8}$ F. When the ac source operates at the resonance frequency of the circuit, the current amplitude is 0.500 A. (a) What is the voltage amplitude of the source? (b) What is the amplitude of the voltage across the resistor, across the inductor, and across the capacitor? (c) What is the average power supplied by the source?

31.32. An *L-R-C* series circuit consists of a source with voltage amplitude 120 V and angular frequency 50.0 rad/s, a resistor with $R = 400\ \Omega$ an inductor with $L = 9.00$ H, and a capacitor with capacitance *C*. (a) For what value of *C* will the current amplitude in the circuit be a maximum? (b) When *C* has the value calculated in part (a), what is the amplitude of the voltage across the inductor?

31.33. In an *L-R-C* series circuit, $R = 150\ \Omega$, $L = 0.750$ H, and $C = 0.0180\ \mu$F. The source has voltage amplitude $V = 150$ V and a frequency equal to the resonance frequency of the circuit. (a) What is the power factor? (b) What is the average power delivered by the source? (c) The capacitor is replaced by one with $C = 0.0360\ \mu$F and the source frequency is adjusted to the new resonance value. Then what is the average power delivered by the source?

31.34. In an *L-R-C* series circuit, $R = 400\ \Omega$, $L = 0.350$ H, and $C = 0.0120\ \mu$F. (a) What is the resonance angular frequency of the circuit? (b) The capacitor can withstand a peak voltage of 550 V. If the voltage source operates at the resonance frequency, what maximum voltage amplitude can it have if the maximum capacitor voltage is not exceeded?

31.35. A series circuit consists of an ac source of variable frequency, a 115-Ω resistor, a 1.25-μF capacitor, and a 4.50-mH inductor. Find the impedance of this circuit when the angular frequency of the ac source is adjusted to (a) the resonance angular frequency; (b) twice the resonance angular frequency; (c) half the resonance angular frequency.

31.36. In an *L-R-C* series circuit, $L = 0.280$ H and $C = 4.00\ \mu$F. The voltage amplitude of the source is 120 V. (a) What is the resonance angular frequency of the circuit? (b) When the source operates at the resonance angular frequency, the current amplitude in the circuit is 1.70 A. What is the resistance *R* of the resistor? (c) At the resonance angular frequency, what are the peak voltages across the inductor, the capacitor, and the resistor?

Section 31.6 Transformers

31.37. A Step-Down Transformer. A transformer connected to a 120-V (rms) ac line is to supply 12.0 V (rms) to a portable electronic device. The load resistance in the secondary is 5.00 Ω. (a) What should the ratio of primary to secondary turns of the transformer be? (b) What rms current must the secondary supply? (c) What average power is delivered to the load? (d) What resistance connected directly across the 120-V line would draw the same power as the transformer? Show that this is equal to 5.00 Ω times the square of the ratio of primary to secondary turns.

31.38. A Step-Up Transformer. A transformer connected to a 120-V (rms) ac line is to supply 13,000 V (rms) for a neon sign. To reduce shock hazard, a fuse is to be inserted in the primary circuit; the fuse is to blow when the rms current in the secondary circuit exceeds 8.50 mA. (a) What is the ratio of secondary to primary turns of the transformer? (b) What power must be supplied to the

transformer when the rms secondary current is 8.50 mA? (c) What current rating should the fuse in the primary circuit have?

31.39. Off to Europe! You plan to take your hair blower to Europe, where the electrical outlets put out 240 V instead of the 120 V seen in the United States. The blower puts out 1600 W at 120 V. (a) What could you do to operate your blower via the 240-V line in Europe? (b) What current will your blower draw from a European outlet? (c) What resistance will your blower appear to have when operated at 240 V?

Problems

31.40. Figure 31.12a shows the crossover network in a loudspeaker system. One branch consists of a capacitor *C* and a resistor *R* in series (the tweeter). This branch is in parallel with a second branch (the woofer) that consists of an inductor *L* and a resistor *R* in series. The same source voltage with angular frequency ω is applied across each parallel branch. (a) What is the impedance of the tweeter branch? (b) What is the impedance of the woofer branch? (c) Explain why the currents in the two branches are equal when the impedances of the branches are equal. (d) Derive an expression for the frequency *f* that corresponds to the crossover point in Fig. 31.12b.

31.41. A coil has a resistance of 48.0 Ω. At a frequency of 80.0 Hz the voltage across the coil leads the current in it by 52.3°. Determine the inductance of the coil.

31.42. Five infinite-impedance voltmeters, calibrated to read rms values, are connected as shown in Fig 31.25. Let $R = 200\ \Omega$, $L = 0.400$ H, $C = 6.00\ \mu$F, and $V = 30.0$ V. What is the reading of each voltmeter if (a) $\omega = 200$ rad/s; and (b) $\omega = 1000$ rad/s?

Figure **31.25** Problem 31.42.

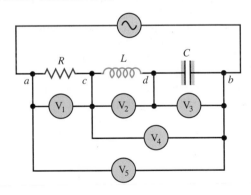

31.43. A sinusoidal current is given by $i = I\cos\omega t$. The full-wave rectified current is shown in Fig. 31.3b. (a) Let t_1 and t_2 be the two smallest positive times at which the rectified current is zero. Express t_1 and t_2 in terms of ω. (b) Find the area under the rectified *i* versus *t* curve between t_1 and t_2 by computing the integral $\int_{t_1}^{t_2} i\, dt$. Since $dq = i\, dt$, this area equals the charge that flows during the t_1 to t_2 time interval. (c) Set the result in part (b) equal to $I_{rav}(t_2 - t_1)$ and calculate I_{rav} in terms of the current amplitude *I*. Compare your answer to Eq. (31.3).

31.44. A large electromagnetic coil is connected to a 120-Hz ac source. The coil has resistance 400 Ω, and at this source frequency the coil has inductive reactance 250 Ω. (a) What is the inductance of the coil? (b) What must the rms voltage of the source be if the coil is to consume an average electrical power of 800 W?

31.45. A series circuit has an impedance of 60.0 Ω and a power factor of 0.720 at 50.0 Hz. The source voltage lags the current. (a) What circuit element, an inductor or a capacitor, should be placed in series with the circuit to raise its power factor? (b) What size element will raise the power factor to unity?

31.46. A circuit consists of a resistor and a capacitor in series with an ac source that supplies an rms voltage of 240 V. At the frequency of the source the reactance of the capacitor is 50.0 Ω. The rms current in the circuit is 3.00 A. What is the average power supplied by the source?

31.47. An *L-R-C* series circuit consists of a 50.0-Ω resistor, a 10.0-μF capacitor, a 3.50-mH inductor, and an ac voltage source of voltage amplitude 60.0 V operating at 1250 Hz. (a) Find the current amplitude and the voltage amplitudes across the inductor, the resistor, and the capacitor. Why can the voltage amplitudes add up to *more* than 60.0 V? (b) If the frequency is now doubled, but nothing else is changed, which of the quantities in part (a) will change? Find the new values for those that do change.

31.48. At a frequency ω_1 the reactance of a certain capacitor equals that of a certain inductor. (a) If the frequency is changed to $\omega_2 = 2\omega_1$, what is the ratio of the reactance of the inductor to that of the capacitor? Which reactance is larger? (b) If the frequency is changed to $\omega_3 = \omega_1/3$, what is the ratio of the reactance of the inductor to that of the capacitor? Which reactance is larger? (c) If the capacitor and inductor are placed in series with a resistor of resistance *R* to form a series *L-R-C* circuit, what will be the resonance angular frequency of the circuit?

31.49. A High-Pass Filter. One application of *L-R-C* series circuits is to high-pass or low-pass filters, which filter out either the low- or high-frequency components of a signal. A high-pass filter is shown in Fig. 31.26, where the output voltage is taken

Figure 31.26 Problem 31.49.

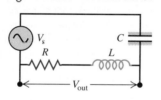

across the *L-R* combination. (The *L-R* combination represents an inductive coil that also has resistance due to the large length of wire in the coil.) Derive an expression for V_{out}/V_s, the ratio of the output and source voltage amplitudes, as a function of the angular frequency ω of the source. Show that when ω is small, this ratio is proportional to ω and thus is small, and show that the ratio approaches unity in the limit of large frequency.

31.50. A Low-Pass Filter. Figure 31.27 shows a low-pass filter (see Problem 31.49); the output voltage is taken across the capacitor in an *L-R-C* series circuit. Derive an expression for V_{out}/V_s, the ratio of the output and source voltage amplitudes, as a function of the angular frequency ω of the source. Show that when ω is large, this ratio is proportional to ω^{-2} and thus is very small, and show that the ratio approaches unity in the limit of small frequency.

Figure 31.27 Problem 31.50.

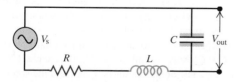

31.51. An *L-R-C* series circuit is connected to an ac source of constant voltage amplitude *V* and variable angular frequency ω. (a) Show that the current amplitude, as a function of ω, is

$$I = \frac{V}{\sqrt{R^2 + (\omega L - 1/\omega C)^2}}$$

(b) Show that the average power dissipated in the resistor is

$$P = \frac{V^2 R/2}{R^2 + (\omega L - 1/\omega C)^2}$$

(c) Show that *I* and *P* are *both* maximum when $\omega = 1/\sqrt{LC}$; that is, when the source frequency equals the resonance frequency of the circuit. (d) Graph *P* as a function of ω for $V = 100$ V, $R = 200$ Ω, $L = 2.0$ H, and $C = 0.50$ μF. Compare to the light purple curve in Fig. 31.19. Discuss the behavior of *I* and *P* in the limits $\omega = 0$ and $\omega \to \infty$.

31.52. An *L-R-C* series circuit is connected to an ac source of constant voltage amplitude *V* and variable angular frequency ω. Using the results of Problem 31.51, find an expression for (a) the amplitude V_L of the voltage across the inductor as a function of ω; and (b) the amplitude V_C of the voltage across the capacitor as a function of ω. (c) Graph V_L and V_C as functions of ω for $V = 100$ V, $R = 200$ Ω, $L = 2.0$ H, and $C = 0.50$ μF. (d) Discuss the behavior of V_L and V_C in the limits $\omega = 0$ and $\omega \to \infty$. For what value of ω is $V_L = V_C$? What is the significance of this value of ω?

31.53. An *L-R-C* series circuit is connected to an ac source of constant voltage amplitude *V* and variable angular frequency ω. (a) Show that the time-averaged energy stored in the inductor is $U_B = \frac{1}{4}LI^2$ and the time-averaged energy stored in the capacitor is $U_E = \frac{1}{4}CV^2$. (b) Use the results of Problems 31.51 and 31.52 to find expressions for U_B and U_E as functions of ω. (c) Graph U_B and U_E as functions of ω for $V = 100$ V, $R = 200$ Ω, $L = 2.0$ H, and $C = 0.50$ μF. (d) Discuss the behavior of U_B and U_E in the limits $\omega = 0$ and $\omega \to \infty$. For what value of ω is $U_B = U_E$? What is the significance of this value of ω?

31.54. The *L-R-C* Parallel Circuit. A resistor, inductor, and capacitor are connected in parallel to an ac source with voltage amplitude *V* and angular frequency ω. Let the source voltage be given by $v = V\cos\omega t$. (a) Show that the instantaneous voltages v_R, v_L, and v_C at any instant are each equal to *v* and that $i = i_R + i_L + i_C$, where *i* is the current through the source and i_R, i_L, and i_C are the currents through the resistor, the inductor, and the capacitor, respectively. (b) What are the phases of i_R, i_L, and i_C with respect to *v*? Use current phasors to represent i, i_R, i_L, and i_C. In a phasor diagram, show the phases of these four currents with respect to *v*. (c) Use the phasor diagram of part (b) to show that the current amplitude *I* for the current *i* through the source is given by $I = \sqrt{I_R^2 + (I_C - I_L)^2}$. (d) Show that the result of part (c) can be written as $I = V/Z$, with $1/Z = \sqrt{1/R^2 + (\omega C - 1/\omega L)^2}$.

31.55. Parallel Resonance. The impedance of an *L-R-C* parallel circuit was derived in Problem 31.54. (a) Show that at the resonance angular frequency $\omega_0 = 1/\sqrt{LC}$, $I_C = I_L$, and *I* is a *minimum*. (b) Since *I* is a minimum at resonance, is it correct to say that the power delivered to the resistor is also a minimum at $\omega = \omega_0$? Explain. (c) At resonance, what is the phase angle of the source current with respect to the source voltage? How does this compare to the phase angle for an *L-R-C series* circuit at resonance? (d) Draw the circuit diagram for an *L-R-C* parallel circuit. Arrange the circuit elements in your diagram so that the resistor is closest to the ac source. Justify the following statement: When the angular frequency of the source is $\omega = \omega_0$, there is *no* current flowing between (i) the part of the circuit that includes the source and the resistor and (ii) the part that includes the inductor and capacitor, so you could cut the wires connecting these two parts of the circuit without affecting the currents. (e) Is the statement in part (d) still valid if we consider that any real inductor or capacitor also has some resistance of its own? Explain.

31.56. A 400-Ω resistor and a 6.00-μF capacitor are connected in parallel to an ac generator that supplies an rms voltage of 220 V at an angular frequency of 360 rad/s. Use the results of Problem 31.54. Note that since there is no inductor in the circuit, the $1/\omega L$ term is not present in the expression for Z. Find (a) the current amplitude in the resistor; (b) the current amplitude in the capacitor; (c) the phase angle of the source current with respect to the source voltage; (d) the amplitude of the current through the generator. (e) Does the source current lag or lead the source voltage?

31.57. An L-R-C parallel circuit is connected to an ac source of constant voltage amplitude V and variable angular frequency ω. (a) Using the results of Problem 31.54, find expressions for the amplitudes I_R, I_L, and I_C of the currents through the resistor, inductor, and capacitor as functions of ω. (b) Graph I_R, I_L, and I_C as functions of ω for $V = 100$ V, $R = 200\ \Omega$, $L = 2.0$ H, and $C = 0.50\ \mu$F. (c) Discuss the behavior of I_L and I_C in the limits $\omega = 0$ and $\omega \to \infty$. Explain why I_L and I_C behave as they do in these limits. (d) Calculate the resonance frequency (in Hz) of the circuit, and sketch the phasor diagram at the resonance frequency. (e) At the resonance frequency, what is the current amplitude through the source? (f) At the resonance frequency, what is the current amplitude through the resistor, through the inductor, and through the capacitor?

31.58. An L-R-C series circuit consists of a 2.50-μF capacitor, a 5.00-mH inductor, and a 75.0-Ω resistor connected across an ac source of voltage amplitude 15.0 V having variable frequency. (a) Under what circumstances is the average power delivered to the circuit equal to $\frac{1}{2}V_{\text{rms}}I_{\text{rms}}$? (b) Under the conditions of part (a), what is the average power delivered to each circuit element and what is the maximum current through the capacitor?

31.59. In an L-R-C series circuit the magnitude of the phase angle is 54.0°, with the source voltage lagging the current. The reactance of the capacitor is 350 Ω, and the resistor resistance is 180 Ω. The average power delivered by the source is 140 W. Find (a) the reactance of the inductor; (b) the rms current; (c) the rms voltage of the source.

31.60. An L-R-C series circuit has $R = 500\ \Omega$, $L = 2.00$ H, $C = 0.500\ \mu$F, and $V = 100$ V. (a) For $\omega = 800$ rad/s, calculate V_R, V_L, V_C, and ϕ. Using a single set of axes, graph v, v_R, v_L, and v_C as functions of time. Include two cycles of v on your graph. (b) Repeat part (a) for $\omega = 1000$ rad/s. (c) Repeat part (a) for $\omega = 1250$ rad/s.

31.61. In an L-R-C series circuit, the source has a voltage amplitude of 120 V, $R = 80.0\ \Omega$, and the reactance of the capacitor is 480 Ω. The voltage amplitude across the capacitor is 360 V. (a) What is the current amplitude in the circuit? (b) What is the impedance? (c) What two values can the reactance of the inductor have? (d) For which of the two values found in part (c) is the angular frequency less than the resonance angular frequency? Explain.

31.62. A series circuit consists of a 1.50-mH inductor, a 125-Ω resistor, and a 25.0-nF capacitor connected across an ac source having an rms voltage of 35.0 V and variable frequency. (a) At what angular frequency will the current amplitude be equal to $\frac{1}{3}$ of its maximum possible value? (b) At the frequency in part (a) what are the current amplitude and the voltage amplitude across each of the circuit elements (including the ac source)?

31.63. The current in a certain circuit varies with time as shown in Fig. 31.28. Find the average current and the rms current in terms of I_0.

Figure **31.28** Problem 31.63.

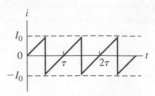

31.64. The Resonance Width. Consider an L-R-C series circuit with a 1.80-H inductor, a 0.900-μF capacitor, and a 300-Ω resistor. The source has terminal rms voltage $V_{\text{rms}} = 60.0$ V and variable angular frequency ω. (a) What is the resonance angular frequency ω_0 of the circuit? (b) What is the rms current through the circuit at resonance, $I_{\text{rms-0}}$? (c) For what two values of the angular frequency, ω_1 and ω_2, is the rms current half the resonance value? (d) The quantity $|\omega_1 - \omega_2|$ defines the *resonance width*. Calculate $I_{\text{rms-0}}$ and the resonance width for $R = 300\ \Omega$, $30.0\ \Omega$, and $3.00\ \Omega$. Describe how your results compare to the discussion in Section 31.5.

31.65. An inductor, a capacitor, and a resistor are all connected in series across an ac source. If the resistance, inductance, and capacitance are all doubled, by what factor does each of the following quantities change? Indicate whether they increase or decrease: (a) the resonance angular frequency; (b) the inductive reactance; (c) the capacitive reactance. (d) Does the impedance double?

31.66. A transformer consists of 275 primary windings and 834 secondary windings. If the potential difference across the primary coil is 25.0 V, (a) what is the voltage across the secondary coil, and (b) what is the effective load resistance of the secondary coil if it is connected across a 125-Ω resistor?

31.67. You want to double the resonance angular frequency of a series R-L-C circuit by changing only the *pertinent* circuit elements all by the same factor. (a) Which ones should you change? (b) By what factor should you change them?

31.68. A resistance R, capacitance C, and inductance L are connected in series to a voltage source with amplitude V and variable angular frequency ω. If $\omega = \omega_0$, the resonance angular frequency, find (a) the maximum current in the resistor; (b) the maximum voltage across the capacitor; (c) the maximum voltage across the inductor; (d) the maximum energy stored in the capacitor; (e) the maximum energy stored in the inductor. Give your answers in terms of R, C, L, and V.

31.69. Repeat Problem 31.68 for the case $\omega = \omega_0/2$.

31.70. Repeat Problem 31.68 for the case $\omega = 2\omega_0$.

31.71. Finding an Unknown Inductance. Your boss gives you an inductor and asks you to measure its inductance. You have available a resistor, an ac voltmeter of high impedance, a capacitor, and an ac source. Explain how you might use these to determine the inductance, and cite any other piece of equipment you may need. Be sure to explain clearly how to use the equipment and what you need to measure to find the unknown inductance.

31.72. An L-R-C series circuit draws 220 W from a 120-V (rms), 50.0-Hz ac line. The power factor is 0.560, and the source voltage leads the current. (a) What is the net resistance R of the circuit? (b) Find the capacitance of the series capacitor that will result in a power factor of unity when it is added to the original circuit. (c) What power will then be drawn from the supply line?

31.73. In an L-R-C series circuit the current is given by $i = I\cos\omega t$. The voltage amplitudes for the resistor, inductor, and capacitor are V_R, V_L, and V_C. (a) Show that the instantaneous power into the resistor is $p_R = V_R I \cos^2 \omega t = \frac{1}{2}V_R I(1 + \cos 2\omega t)$. What does this expression give for the average power into the resistor? (b) Show that the instantaneous power into the inductor is $p_L = -V_L I \sin \omega t \cos \omega t = -\frac{1}{2}V_L I \sin 2\omega t$. What does this expression give for the average power into the inductor? (c) Show that the instantaneous power into the capacitor is $p_C = V_C I \sin \omega t \cos \omega t = \frac{1}{2}V_C I \sin 2\omega t$. What does this expression give for the average power into the capacitor? (d) The instantaneous power delivered by the source is shown in Section 31.4 to be $p = VI\cos \omega t \,(\cos \phi \cos \omega t - \sin \phi \sin \omega t)$. Show that $p_R + p_L + p_C$ equals p at each instant of time.

Challenge Problems

31.74. (a) At what angular frequency is the voltage amplitude across the *resistor* in an L-R-C series circuit at maximum value? (b) At what angular frequency is the voltage amplitude across the *inductor* at maximum value? (c) At what angular frequency is the voltage amplitude across the *capacitor* at maximum value? (You may want to refer to the results of Problem 31.52.)

31.75. Complex Numbers in a Circuit. The voltage across a circuit element in an ac circuit is not necessarily in phase with the current through that circuit element. Therefore the voltage amplitudes across the circuit elements in a branch in an ac circuit do not add algebraically. A method that is commonly employed to simplify the analysis of an ac circuit driven by a sinusoidal source is to represent the impedance Z as a *complex* number. The resistance R is taken to be the real part of the impedance, and the reactance $X = X_L - X_C$ is taken to be the imaginary part. Thus, for a branch containing a resistor, inductor, and capacitor in series, the complex impedance is $Z_{cpx} = R + iX$, where $i^2 = -1$. If the voltage amplitude across the branch is V_{cpx}, we define a *complex* current amplitude by $I_{cpx} = V_{cpx}/Z_{cpx}$. The *actual* current amplitude is the absolute value of the complex current amplitude, that is, $I = (I_{cpx}{}^* I_{cpx})^{1/2}$. The phase angle ϕ of the current with respect to

the source voltage is given by $\tan \phi = \mathrm{Im}(I_{cpx})/\mathrm{Re}(I_{cpx})$. The voltage amplitudes $V_{R\text{-}cpx}$, $V_{L\text{-}cpx}$, and $V_{C\text{-}cpx}$ across the resistance, inductance, and capacitance, respectively, are found by multiplying I_{cpx} by R, iX_L, or $-iX_C$, respectively. From the complex representation for the voltage amplitudes, the voltage across a branch is just the algebraic sum of the voltages across each circuit element; $V_{cpx} = V_{R\text{-}cpx} + V_{L\text{-}cpx} + V_{C\text{-}cpx}$. The actual value of any current amplitude or voltage amplitude is the absolute value of the corresponding complex quantity. Consider the series L-R-C circuit shown in Fig. 31.29. The values of the circuit elements, the source voltage amplitude, and the source angular frequency are as shown. Use the phasor diagram techniques presented in Section 31.1 to solve for (a) the current amplitude; and (b) the phase angle ϕ of the current with respect to the source voltage. (Note that this angle is the negative of the phase angle defined in Fig. 31.13.) Now analyze the same circuit using the complex-number approach. (c) Determine the complex impedance of the circuit, Z_{cpx}. Take the absolute value to obtain Z, the actual impedance of the circuit. (d) Take the voltage amplitude of the source, V_{cpx}, to be real, and find the complex current amplitude I_{cpx}. Find the actual current amplitude by taking the absolute value of I_{cpx}. (e) Find the phase angle ϕ of the current with respect to the source voltage by using the real and imaginary parts of I_{cpx}, as explained above. (f) Find the complex representations of the voltages across the resistance, the inductance, and the capacitance. (g) Adding the answers found in part (f), verify that the sum of these complex numbers is real and equal to 200 V, the voltage of the source.

Figure 31.29 Challenge Problem 31.75.

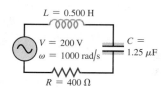

32 ELECTROMAGNETIC WAVES

LEARNING GOALS

By studying this chapter, you will learn:

- Why there are both electric and magnetic fields in a light wave.

- How the speed of light is related to the fundamental constants of electricity and magnetism.

- How to describe the propagation of a sinusoidal electromagnetic wave.

- What determines the amount of power carried by an electromagnetic wave.

- How to describe standing electromagnetic waves.

? Metal objects reflect not only visible light but also radio waves. What aspect of metals makes them so reflective?

What is light? This question has been asked by humans for centuries, but there was no answer until electricity and magnetism were unified into the single discipline of *electromagnetism,* as described by Maxwell's equations. These equations show that a time-varying magnetic field acts as a source of electric field and that a time-varying electric field acts as a source of magnetic field. These $\vec{E}$ and $\vec{B}$ fields can sustain each other, forming an *electromagnetic wave* that propagates through space. Visible light emitted by the glowing filament of a light bulb is one example of an electromagnetic wave; other kinds of electromagnetic waves are produced by sources such as TV and radio stations, microwave oscillators for ovens and radar, x-ray machines, and radioactive nuclei.

In this chapter we'll use Maxwell's equations as the theoretical basis for understanding electromagnetic waves. We'll find that these waves carry both energy and momentum. In sinusoidal electromagnetic waves, the $\vec{E}$ and $\vec{B}$ fields are sinusoidal functions of time and position, with a definite frequency and wavelength. The various types of electromagnetic waves—visible light, radio, x rays, and others—differ only in their frequency and wavelength. Our study of optics in the following chapters will be based in part on the electromagnetic nature of light.

Unlike waves on a string or sound waves in a fluid, electromagnetic waves do not require a material medium; the light that you see coming from the stars at night has traveled without difficulty across tens or hundreds of light-years of (nearly) empty space. Nonetheless, electromagnetic waves and mechanical waves have much in common and are described in much the same language. Before reading further in this chapter, you should review the properties of mechanical waves as discussed in Chapters 15 and 16.

32.1 Maxwell's Equations and Electromagnetic Waves

In the last several chapters we studied various aspects of electric and magnetic fields. We learned that when the fields don't vary with time, such as an electric field produced by charges at rest or the magnetic field of a steady current, we can analyze the electric and magnetic fields independently without considering interactions between them. But when the fields vary with time, they are no longer independent. Faraday's law (see Section 29.2) tells us that a time-varying magnetic field acts as a source of electric field, as shown by induced emfs in inductors and transformers. Ampere's law, including the displacement current discovered by Maxwell (see Section 29.7), shows that a time-varying electric field acts as a source of magnetic field. This mutual interaction between the two fields is summarized in Maxwell's equations, presented in Section 29.7.

Thus, when *either* an electric or a magnetic field is changing with time, a field of the other kind is induced in adjacent regions of space. We are led (as Maxwell was) to consider the possibility of an electromagnetic disturbance, consisting of time-varying electric and magnetic fields, that can propagate through space from one region to another, even when there is no matter in the intervening region. Such a disturbance, if it exists, will have the properties of a *wave,* and an appropriate term is **electromagnetic wave.**

Such waves do exist; radio and television transmission, light, x rays, and many other kinds of radiation are examples of electromagnetic waves. Our goal in this chapter is to see how such waves are explained by the principles of electromagnetism that we have studied thus far and to examine the properties of these waves.

Electricity, Magnetism, and Light

As often happens in the development of science, the theoretical understanding of electromagnetic waves evolved along a considerably more devious path than the one just outlined. In the early days of electromagnetic theory (the early 19th century), two different units of electric charge were used: one for electrostatics and the other for magnetic phenomena involving currents. In the system of units used at that time, these two units of charge had different physical dimensions. Their *ratio* had units of velocity, and measurements showed that the ratio had a numerical value that was precisely equal to the speed of light, 3.00×10^8 m/s. At the time, physicists regarded this as an extraordinary coincidence and had no idea how to explain it.

In searching to understand this result, Maxwell (Fig. 32.1) proved in 1865 that an electromagnetic disturbance should propagate in free space with a speed equal to that of light and hence that light waves were likely to be electromagnetic in nature. At the same time, he discovered that the basic principles of electromagnetism can be expressed in terms of the four equations that we now call **Maxwell's equations,** which we discussed in Section 29.7. These four equations are (1) Gauss's law for electric fields; (2) Gauss's law for magnetic fields, showing the absence of magnetic monopoles; (3) Ampere's law, including displacement current; and (4) Faraday's law:

32.1 James Clerk Maxwell (1831–1879) was the first person to truly understand the fundamental nature of light. He also made major contributions to thermodynamics, optics, astronomy, and color photography. Albert Einstein described Maxwell's accomplishments as "the most profound and the most fruitful that physics has experienced since the time of Newton."

$$\oint \vec{E} \cdot d\vec{A} = \frac{Q_{\text{encl}}}{\epsilon_0} \quad \text{(Gauss's law)} \tag{29.18}$$

$$\oint \vec{B} \cdot d\vec{A} = 0 \quad \text{(Gauss's law for magnetism)} \tag{29.19}$$

$$\oint \vec{B} \cdot d\vec{l} = \mu_0 \left(i_C + \epsilon_0 \frac{d\Phi_E}{dt} \right)_{\text{encl}} \quad \text{(Ampere's law)} \tag{29.20}$$

$$\oint \vec{E} \cdot d\vec{l} = -\frac{d\Phi_B}{dt} \quad \text{(Faraday's law)} \tag{29.21}$$

32.2 (a) Every mobile phone, wireless modem, or radio transmitter emits signals in the form of electromagnetic waves that are made by accelerating charges.
(b) Power lines carry a strong alternating current, which means that a substantial amount of charge is accelerating back and forth and generating electromagnetic waves. These waves can produce a buzzing sound from your car radio when you drive near the lines.

These equations apply to electric and magnetic fields *in vacuum*. If a material is present, the permittivity ϵ_0 and permeability μ_0 of free space are replaced by the permittivity ϵ and permeability μ of the material. If the values of ϵ and μ are different at different points in the regions of integration, then ϵ and μ have to be transferred to the left sides of Eqs. (29.18) and (29.20), respectively, and placed inside the integrals. The ϵ in Eq. (29.20) also has to be included in the integral that gives $d\Phi_E/dt$.

According to Maxwell's equations, a point charge at rest produces a static $\vec{E}$ field but no $\vec{B}$ field; a point charge moving with a constant velocity (see Section 28.1) produces both $\vec{E}$ and $\vec{B}$ fields. Maxwell's equations can also be used to show that in order for a point charge to produce electromagnetic waves, the charge must *accelerate*. In fact, it's a general result of Maxwell's equations that *every* accelerated charge radiates electromagnetic energy (Fig. 32.2).

Generating Electromagnetic Radiation

One way in which a point charge can be made to emit electromagnetic waves is by making it oscillate in simple harmonic motion, so that it has an acceleration at almost every instant (the exception is when the charge is passing through its equilibrium position). Figure 32.3 shows some of the electric field lines produced by such an oscillating point charge. Field lines are *not* material objects, but you may nonetheless find it helpful to think of them as behaving somewhat like strings that extend from the point charge off to infinity. Oscillating the charge up and down makes waves that propagate outward from the charge along these "strings." Note that the charge does not emit waves equally in all directions; the waves are strongest at 90° to the axis of motion of the charge, while there are *no* waves along this axis. This is just what the "string" picture would lead you to conclude. There is also a *magnetic* disturbance that spreads outward from the charge; this is not shown in Fig. 32.3. Because the electric and magnetic disturbances spread or radiate away from the source, the name **electromagnetic radiation** is used interchangeably with the phrase "electromagnetic waves."

Electromagnetic waves with macroscopic wavelengths were first produced in the laboratory in 1887 by the German physicist Heinrich Hertz. As a source of waves, he used charges oscillating in *L-C* circuits of the sort discussed in Section 30.5; he detected the resulting electromagnetic waves with other circuits tuned to the same frequency. Hertz also produced electromagnetic *standing waves* and measured the distance between adjacent nodes (one half-wavelength) to determine the wavelength. Knowing the resonant frequency of his circuits, he then found the speed of the waves from the wavelength–frequency relationship $v = \lambda f$. He established that their speed was the same as that of light; this verified Maxwell's theoretical prediction directly. The SI unit of frequency is named in honor of Hertz: One hertz (1 Hz) equals one cycle per second.

32.3 Electric field lines of a point charge oscillating in simple harmonic motion, seen at five instants during an oscillation period T. The charge's trajectory is in the plane of the drawings. At $t = 0$ the point charge is at its maximum upward displacement. The arrow shows one "kink" in the lines of $\vec{E}$ as it propagates outward from the point charge. The magnetic field (not shown) comprises circles that lie in planes perpendicular to these figures and concentric with the axis of oscillation.

(a) $t = 0$

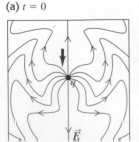

$\vec{E}$

(b) $t = T/4$

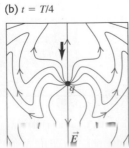

$\vec{E}$

(c) $t = T/2$

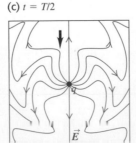

$\vec{E}$

(d) $t = 3T/4$

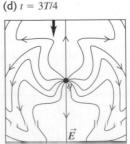

$\vec{E}$

(e) $t = T$

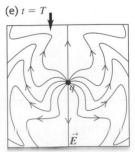

$\vec{E}$

The modern value of the speed of light, which we denote by the symbol c, is 299,792,458 m/s. (Recall from Section 1.3 that this value is the basis of our standard of length: one meter is defined to be the distance that light travels in 1/299,792,458 second.) For our purposes, $c = 3.00 \times 10^8$ m/s is sufficiently accurate.

The possible use of electromagnetic waves for long-distance communication does not seem to have occurred to Hertz. It remained to Marconi and others to make radio communication a familiar household experience. In a radio *transmitter,* electric charges are made to oscillate along the length of the conducting antenna, producing oscillating field disturbances like those shown in Fig. 32.3. Since many charges oscillate together in the antenna, the disturbances are much stronger than those of a single oscillating charge and can be detected at a much greater distance. In a radio *receiver* the antenna is also a conductor; the fields of the wave emanating from a distant transmitter exert forces on free charges within the receiver antenna, producing an oscillating current that is detected and amplified by the receiver circuitry.

For the remainder of this chapter our concern will be with electromagnetic waves themselves, not with the rather complex problem of how they are produced.

The Electromagnetic Spectrum

Electromagnetic waves cover an extremely broad spectrum of wavelength and frequency. This **electromagnetic spectrum** encompasses radio and TV transmission, visible light, infrared and ultraviolet radiation, x rays, and gamma rays. Electromagnetic waves have been detected with frequencies from at least 1 to 10^{24} Hz; the most commonly encountered portion of the spectrum is shown in Fig. 32.4, which gives approximate wavelength and frequency ranges for the various segments. Despite vast differences in their uses and means of production, these are all electromagnetic waves with the same propagation speed (in vacuum) $c = 299,792,458$ m/s. Electromagnetic waves may differ in frequency f and wavelength λ, but the relationship $c = \lambda f$ in vacuum holds for each.

We can detect only a very small segment of this spectrum directly through our sense of sight. We call this range **visible light.** Its wavelengths range from about 400 to 700 nm (400 to 700×10^{-9} m), with corresponding frequencies from about 750 to 430 THz (7.5 to 4.3×10^{14} Hz). Different parts of the visible spectrum evoke in humans the sensations of different colors. Wavelengths for colors in the visible spectrum are given (very approximately) in Table 32.1.

Ordinary white light includes all visible wavelengths. However, by using special sources or filters, we can select a narrow band of wavelengths within a range of a few nm. Such light is approximately *monochromatic* (single-color) light. Absolutely monochromatic light with only a single wavelength is an unattainable

Table 32.1 Wavelengths of Visible Light

400 to 440 nm	Violet
440 to 480 nm	Blue
480 to 560 nm	Green
560 to 590 nm	Yellow
590 to 630 nm	Orange
630 to 700 nm	Red

32.4 The electromagnetic spectrum. The frequencies and wavelengths found in nature extend over such a wide range that we have to use a logarithmic scale to show all important bands. The boundaries between bands are somewhat arbitrary.

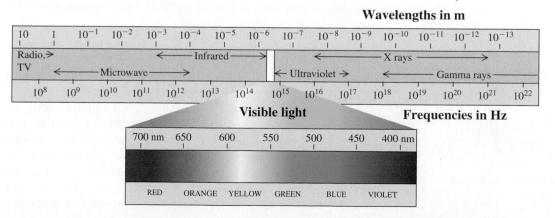

idealization. When we use the expression "monochromatic light with $\lambda = 550$ nm" with reference to a laboratory experiment, we really mean a small band of wavelengths *around* 550 nm. Light from a *laser* is much more nearly monochromatic than is light obtainable in any other way.

Invisible forms of electromagnetic radiation are no less important than visible light. Our system of global communication, for example, depends on radio waves: AM radio uses waves with frequencies from 5.4×10^5 Hz to 1.6×10^6 Hz, while FM radio broadcasts are at frequencies from 8.8×10^7 Hz to 1.08×10^8 Hz. (Television broadcasts use frequencies that bracket the FM band.) Microwaves are also used for communication (for example, by cellular phones and wireless networks) and for weather radar (at frequencies near 3×10^9 Hz). Many cameras have a device that emits a beam of infrared radiation; by analyzing the properties of the infrared radiation reflected from the subject, the camera determines the distance to the subject and automatically adjusts the focus. Ultraviolet radiation has shorter wavelengths than visible light; as we will learn in Chapter 36, this property allows it to be focused into very narrow beams for high-precision applications such as LASIK eye surgery. X rays are able to penetrate through flesh, which makes them invaluable in dentistry and medicine. The shortest-wavelength electromagnetic radiation, gamma rays, is produced in nature by radioactive materials (see Chapter 43). Gamma rays, which are very energetic, are used in medicine to destroy cancer cells.

Test Your Understanding of Section 32.1   (a) Is it possible to have a purely electric wave propagate through empty space—that is, a wave made up of an electric field but no magnetic field? (b) What about a purely magnetic wave, with a magnetic field but no electric field?

32.2 Plane Electromagnetic Waves and the Speed of Light

We are now ready to develop the basic ideas of electromagnetic waves and their relationship to the principles of electromagnetism. Our procedure will be to postulate a simple field configuration that has wavelike behavior. We'll assume an electric field $\vec{E}$ that has only a y-component and a magnetic field $\vec{B}$ with only a z-component, and we'll assume that both fields move together in the $+x$-direction with a speed c that is initially unknown. (As we go along, it will become clear why we choose $\vec{E}$ and $\vec{B}$ to be perpendicular to the direction of propagation as well as to each other.) Then we will test whether these fields are physically possible by asking whether they are consistent with Maxwell's equations, particularly Ampere's law and Faraday's law. We'll find that the answer is yes, provided that c has a particular value. We'll also show that the *wave equation,* which we encountered during our study of mechanical waves in Chapter 15, can be derived from Maxwell's equations.

A Simple Plane Electromagnetic Wave

Using an *xyz*-coordinate system (Fig. 32.5), we imagine that all space is divided into two regions by a plane perpendicular to the *x*-axis (parallel to the *yz*-plane). At every point to the left of this plane there are a uniform electric field $\vec{E}$ in the $+y$-direction and a uniform magnetic field $\vec{B}$ in the $+z$-direction, as shown. Furthermore, we suppose that the boundary plane, which we call the *wave front,* moves to the right in the $+x$-direction with a constant speed c, the value of which we'll leave undetermined for now. Thus the $\vec{E}$ and $\vec{B}$ fields travel to the right into previously field-free regions with a definite speed. The situation, in short, describes a rudimentary electromagnetic wave. A wave such as this, in which at

32.5 An electromagnetic wave front. The plane representing the wave front moves to the right (in the positive *x*-direction) with speed *c*.

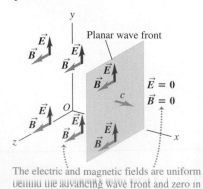

The electric and magnetic fields are uniform behind the advancing wave front and zero in front of it.

any instant the fields are uniform over any plane perpendicular to the direction of propagation, is called a **plane wave.** In the case shown in Fig. 32.5, the fields are zero for planes to the right of the wave front and have the same values on all planes to the left of the wave front; later we will consider more complex plane waves.

We won't concern ourselves with the problem of actually *producing* such a field configuration. Instead, we simply ask whether it is consistent with the laws of electromagnetism—that is, with Maxwell's equations. We'll consider each of these four equations in turn.

Let us first verify that our wave satisfies Maxwell's first and second equations—that is, Gauss's laws for electric and magnetic fields. To do this, we take as our Gaussian surface a rectangular box with sides parallel to the *xy*, *xz*, and *yz* coordinate planes (Fig. 32.6). The box encloses no electric charge. You can show that the total electric flux and magnetic flux through the box are both zero, even if part of the box is in the region where $E = B = 0$. This would *not* be the case if $\vec{E}$ or $\vec{B}$ had an *x*-component, parallel to the direction of propagation. We leave the proof as a problem (see Problem 32.42). Thus to satisfy Maxwell's first and second equations, the electric and magnetic fields must be perpendicular to the direction of propagation; that is, the wave must be **transverse.**

The next of Maxwell's equations to be considered is Faraday's law:

$$\oint \vec{E} \cdot d\vec{l} = -\frac{d\Phi_B}{dt} \tag{32.1}$$

To test whether our wave satisfies Faraday's law, we apply this law to a rectangle *efgh* that is parallel to the *xy*-plane (Fig. 32.7a). As shown in Fig. 32.7b, a cross section in the *xy*-plane, this rectangle has height a and width Δx. At the time shown, the wave front has progressed partway through the rectangle, and $\vec{E}$ is zero along the side *ef*. In applying Faraday's law we take the vector area $d\vec{A}$ of rectangle *efgh* to be in the $+z$-direction. With this choice the right-hand rule requires that we integrate $\vec{E} \cdot d\vec{l}$ *counterclockwise* around the rectangle. At every point on side *ef*, $\vec{E}$ is zero. At every point on sides *fg* and *he*, $\vec{E}$ is either zero or perpendicular to $d\vec{l}$. Only side *gh* contributes to the integral. On this side, $\vec{E}$ and $d\vec{l}$ are opposite, and we obtain

$$\oint \vec{E} \cdot d\vec{l} = -Ea \tag{32.2}$$

Hence, the left-hand side of Eq. (32.1) is nonzero.

To satisfy Faraday's law, Eq. (32.1), there must be a component of $\vec{B}$ in the *z*-direction (perpendicular to $\vec{E}$) so that there can be a nonzero magnetic flux Φ_B through the rectangle *efgh* and a nonzero derivative $d\Phi_B/dt$. Indeed, in our wave, $\vec{B}$ has *only* a *z*-component. We have assumed that this component is in the *positive z*-direction; let's see whether this assumption is consistent with Faraday's law. During a time interval dt the wave front moves a distance $c\,dt$ to the right in Fig. 32.7b, sweeping out an area $ac\,dt$ of the rectangle *efgh*. During this interval the magnetic flux Φ_B through the rectangle *efgh* increases by $d\Phi_B = B(ac\,dt)$, so the rate of change of magnetic flux is

$$\frac{d\Phi_B}{dt} = Bac \tag{32.3}$$

Now we substitute Eqs. (32.2) and (32.3) into Faraday's law, Eq. (32.1); we get

$$-Ea = -Bac$$

$$E = cB \quad \text{(electromagnetic wave in vacuum)} \tag{32.4}$$

This shows that our wave is consistent with Faraday's law only if the wave speed c and the magnitudes of the perpendicular vectors $\vec{E}$ and $\vec{B}$ are related as in

32.6 Gaussian surface for a plane electromagnetic wave.

The electric field is the same on the top and bottom sides of the Gaussian surface, so the total electric flux through the surface is zero.

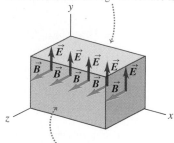

The magnetic field is the same on the left and right sides of the Gaussian surface, so the total magnetic flux through the surface is zero.

32.7 (a) Applying Faraday's law to a plane wave. (b) In a time dt, the magnetic flux through the rectangle in the *xy*-plane increases by an amount $d\Phi_B$. This increase equals the flux through the shaded rectangle with area $ac\,dt$; that is, $d\Phi_B = Bac\,dt$. Thus $d\Phi_B/dt = Bac$.

(a) In time dt, the wave front moves a distance $c\,dt$ in the $+x$-direction.

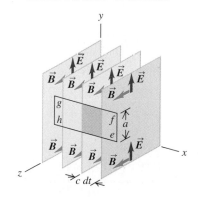

(b) Side view of situation in **(a)**

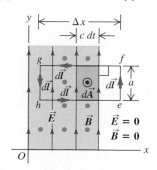

Eq. (32.4). Note that if we had assumed that $\vec{B}$ was in the *negative z*-direction, there would have been an additional minus sign in Eq. (32.4); since E, c, and B are all positive magnitudes, no solution would then have been possible. Furthermore, any component of $\vec{B}$ in the *y*-direction (parallel to $\vec{E}$) would not contribute to the changing magnetic flux Φ_B through the rectangle *efgh* (which is parallel to the *xy*-plane) and so would not be part of the wave.

Finally, we carry out a similar calculation using Ampere's law, the remaining member of Maxwell's equations. There is no conduction current $(i_C = 0)$, so Ampere's law is

$$\oint \vec{B} \cdot d\vec{l} = \mu_0 \epsilon_0 \frac{d\Phi_E}{dt} \qquad (32.5)$$

To check whether our wave is consistent with Ampere's law, we move our rectangle so that it lies in the *xz*-plane, as shown in Fig. 32.8, and we again look at the situation at a time when the wave front has traveled partway through the rectangle. We take the vector area $d\vec{A}$ in the $+y$-direction, and so the right-hand rule requires that we integrate $\vec{B} \cdot d\vec{l}$ counterclockwise around the rectangle. The $\vec{B}$ field is zero at every point along side *ef*, and at each point on sides *fg* and *he* it is either zero or perpendicular to $d\vec{l}$. Only side *gh*, where $\vec{B}$ and $d\vec{l}$ are parallel, contributes to the integral, and we find

$$\oint \vec{B} \cdot d\vec{l} = Ba \qquad (32.6)$$

Hence, the left-hand side of Ampere's law, Eq. (32.5), is nonzero; the right-hand side must be nonzero as well. Thus $\vec{E}$ must have a *y*-component (perpendicular to $\vec{B}$) so that the electric flux Φ_E through the rectangle and the time derivative $d\Phi_E/dt$ can be nonzero. We come to the same conclusion that we inferred from Faraday's law: In an electromagnetic wave, $\vec{E}$ and $\vec{B}$ must be mutually perpendicular.

In a time interval dt the electric flux Φ_E through the rectangle increases by $d\Phi_E = E(ac\, dt)$. Since we chose $d\vec{A}$ to be in the $+y$-direction, this flux change is positive; the rate of change of electric field is

$$\frac{d\Phi_E}{dt} = Eac \qquad (32.7)$$

Substituting Eqs. (32.6) and (32.7) into Ampere's law, Eq. (32.5), we find

$$Ba = \epsilon_0 \mu_0 Eac$$

$$B = \epsilon_0 \mu_0 cE \qquad \text{(electromagnetic wave in vacuum)} \qquad (32.8)$$

Thus our assumed wave obeys Ampere's law only if B, c, and E are related as in Eq. (32.8).

Our electromagnetic wave must obey *both* Ampere's law and Faraday's law, so Eqs. (32.4) and (32.8) must both be satisfied. This can happen only if $\epsilon_0 \mu_0 c = 1/c$, or

$$c = \frac{1}{\sqrt{\epsilon_0 \mu_0}} \qquad \text{(speed of electromagnetic waves in vacuum)} \qquad (32.9)$$

Inserting the numerical values of these quantities, we find

$$c = \frac{1}{\sqrt{(8.85 \times 10^{-12} \text{ C}^2/\text{N} \cdot \text{m}^2)(4\pi \times 10^{-7} \text{ N/A}^2)}}$$

$$3.00 \times 10^8 \text{ m/s}$$

32.8 (a) Applying Ampere's law to a plane wave. (Compare to Fig. 32.7a.) (b) In a time dt, the electric flux through the rectangle in the *xz*-plane increases by an amount $d\Phi_E$. This increase equals the flux through the shaded rectangle with area $ac\, dt$; that is, $d\Phi_E = Eac\, dt$. Thus $d\Phi_E/dt = Eac$.

(a) In time dt, the wave front moves a distance $c\, dt$ in the $+x$-direction.

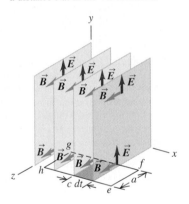

(b) Top view of situation in **(a)**

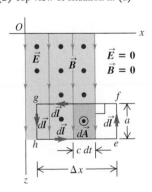

Our assumed wave is consistent with all of Maxwell's equations, provided that the wave front moves with the speed given above, which you should recognize as the speed of light! Note that the *exact* value of c is defined to be 299,792,458 m/s; the modern value of ϵ_0 is defined to agree with this when used in Eq. (32.9) (see Section 21.3).

Key Properties of Electromagnetic Waves

We chose a simple wave for our study in order to avoid mathematical complications, but this special case illustrates several important features of *all* electromagnetic waves:

1. The wave is *transverse;* both $\vec{E}$ and $\vec{B}$ are perpendicular to the direction of propagation of the wave. The electric and magnetic fields are also perpendicular to each other. The direction of propagation is the direction of the vector product $\vec{E} \times \vec{B}$ (Fig. 32.9).
2. There is a definite ratio between the magnitudes of $\vec{E}$ and $\vec{B}$: $E = cB$.
3. The wave travels in vacuum with a definite and unchanging speed.
4. Unlike mechanical waves, which need the oscillating particles of a medium such as water or air to transmit a wave, electromagnetic waves require no medium. What's "waving" in an electromagnetic wave are the electric and magnetic fields.

We can generalize this discussion to a more realistic situation. Suppose we have several wave fronts in the form of parallel planes perpendicular to the x-axis, all of which are moving to the right with speed c. Suppose that the $\vec{E}$ and $\vec{B}$ fields are the same at all points within a single region between two planes, but that the fields differ from region to region. The overall wave is a plane wave, but one in which the fields vary in steps along the x-axis. Such a wave could be constructed by superposing several of the simple step waves we have just discussed (shown in Fig. 32.5). This is possible because the $\vec{E}$ and $\vec{B}$ fields obey the superposition principle in waves just as in static situations: When two waves are superposed, the total $\vec{E}$ field at each point is the vector sum of the $\vec{E}$ fields of the individual waves, and similarly for the total $\vec{B}$ field.

We can extend the above development to show that a wave with fields that vary in steps is also consistent with Ampere's and Faraday's laws, provided that the wave fronts all move with the speed c given by Eq. (32.9). In the limit that we make the individual steps infinitesimally small, we have a wave in which the $\vec{E}$ and $\vec{B}$ fields at any instant vary *continuously* along the x-axis. The entire field pattern moves to the right with speed c. In Section 32.3 we will consider waves in which $\vec{E}$ and $\vec{B}$ are *sinusoidal* functions of x and t. Because at each point the magnitudes of $\vec{E}$ and $\vec{B}$ are related by $E = cB$, the periodic variations of the two fields in any periodic traveling wave must be *in phase*.

Electromagnetic waves have the property of **polarization.** In the above discussion the choice of the y-direction for $\vec{E}$ was arbitrary. We could just as well have specified the z-axis for $\vec{E}$; then $\vec{B}$ would have been in the $-y$-direction. A wave in which $\vec{E}$ is always parallel to a certain axis is said to be **linearly polarized** along that axis. More generally, *any* wave traveling in the x-direction can be represented as a superposition of waves linearly polarized in the y- and z-directions. We will study polarization in greater detail, with special emphasis on polarization of light, in Chapter 33.

*Derivation of the Electromagnetic Wave Equation

Here is an alternative derivation of Eq. (32.9) for the speed of electromagnetic waves. It is more mathematical than our other treatment, but it includes a derivation of the wave equation for electromagnetic waves. This part of the section can be omitted without loss of continuity in the chapter.

32.9 A right-hand rule for electromagnetic waves relates the directions of $\vec{E}$, $\vec{B}$, and the direction of propagation.

Right-hand rule for an electromagnetic wave:

(1) Point the thumb of your right hand in the wave's direction of propagation.

(2) Imagine rotating the $\vec{E}$ field vector 90° in the sense your fingers curl.

That is the direction of the $\vec{B}$ field.

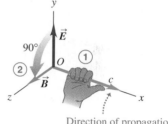

Direction of propagation
= direction of $\vec{E} \times \vec{B}$.

32.10 Faraday's law applied to a rectangle with height a and width Δx parallel to the xy-plane.

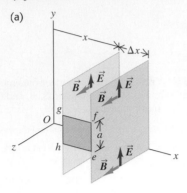

(a)

(b) Side view of the situation in (a)

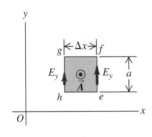

32.11 Ampere's law applied to a rectangle with height a and width Δx parallel to the xz-plane.

(a)

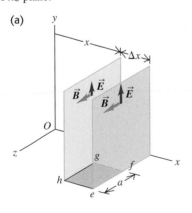

(b) Top view of the situation in (a)

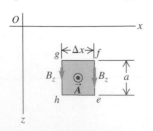

During our discussion of mechanical waves in Section 15.3, we showed that a function $y(x, t)$ that represents the displacement of any point in a mechanical wave traveling along the x-axis must satisfy a differential equation, Eq. (15.12):

$$\frac{\partial^2 y(x, t)}{\partial x^2} = \frac{1}{v^2}\frac{\partial^2 y(x, t)}{\partial t^2} \tag{32.10}$$

This equation is called the **wave equation,** and v is the speed of propagation of the wave.

To derive the corresponding equation for an electromagnetic wave, we again consider a plane wave. That is, we assume that at each instant, E_y and B_z are uniform over any plane perpendicular to the x-axis, the direction of propagation. But now we let E_y and B_z vary continuously as we go along the x-axis; then each is a function of x and t. We consider the values of E_y and B_z on two planes perpendicular to the x-axis, one at x and one at $x + \Delta x$.

Following the same procedure as previously, we apply Faraday's law to a rectangle lying parallel to the xy-plane, as in Fig. 32.10. This figure is similar to Fig. 32.7. Let the left end gh of the rectangle be at position x, and let the right end ef be at position $(x + \Delta x)$. At time t, the values of E_y on these two sides are E_y (x, t) and $E_y(x + \Delta x, t)$, respectively. When we apply Faraday's law to this rectangle, we find that instead of $\oint \vec{E} \cdot d\vec{l} = -Ea$ as before, we have

$$\oint \vec{E} \cdot d\vec{l} = -E_y(x, t)a + E_y(x + \Delta x, t)a$$
$$= a[E_y(x + \Delta x, t) - E_y(x, t)] \tag{32.11}$$

To find the magnetic flux Φ_B through this rectangle, we assume that Δx is small enough that B_z is nearly uniform over the rectangle. In that case, $\Phi_B = B_z(x, t)A = B_z(x, t)a\,\Delta x$, and

$$\frac{d\Phi_B}{dt} = \frac{\partial B_z(x, t)}{\partial t}a\,\Delta x$$

We use partial-derivative notation because B_z is a function of both x and t. When we substitute this expression and Eq. (32.11) into Faraday's law, Eq. (32.1), we get

$$a[E_y(x + \Delta x, t) - E_y(x, t)] = -\frac{\partial B_z}{\partial t}a\,\Delta x$$
$$\frac{E_y(x + \Delta x, t) - E_y(x, t)}{\Delta x} = -\frac{\partial B_z}{\partial t}$$

Finally, imagine shrinking the rectangle down to a sliver so that Δx approaches zero. When we take the limit of this equation as $\Delta x \to 0$, we get

$$\frac{\partial E_y(x, t)}{\partial x} = -\frac{\partial B_z(x, t)}{\partial t} \tag{32.12}$$

This equation shows that if there is a time-varying component B_z of magnetic field, there must also be a component E_y of electric field that varies with x, and conversely. We put this relationship on the shelf for now; we'll return to it soon.

Next we apply Ampere's law to the rectangle shown in Fig. 32.11. The line integral $\oint \vec{B} \cdot d\vec{l}$ becomes

$$\oint \vec{B} \cdot d\vec{l} = -B_z(x + \Delta x, t)a + B_z(x, t)a \tag{32.13}$$

Again assuming that the rectangle is narrow, we approximate the electric flux Φ_E through it as $\Phi_E = E_y(x, t)A = E_y(x, t)a\,\Delta x$. The rate of change of Φ_E, which we need for Ampere's law, is then

$$\frac{d\Phi_E}{dt} = \frac{\partial E_y(x, t)}{\partial t}a\,\Delta x$$

Now we substitute this expression and Eq. (32.13) into Ampere's law, Eq. (32.5):

$$-B_z(x + \Delta x, t)a + B_z(x, t)a = \epsilon_0\mu_0\frac{\partial E_y(x, t)}{\partial t}a\,\Delta x$$

Again we divide both sides by $a\,\Delta x$ and take the limit as $\Delta x \to 0$. We find

$$-\frac{\partial B_z(x, t)}{\partial x} = \epsilon_0\mu_0\frac{\partial E_y(x, t)}{\partial t} \tag{32.14}$$

Now comes the final step. We take the partial derivatives with respect to x of both sides of Eq. (32.12), and we take the partial derivatives with respect to t of both sides of Eq. (32.14). The results are

$$-\frac{\partial^2 E_y(x, t)}{\partial x^2} = \frac{\partial^2 B_z(x, t)}{\partial x \partial t}$$

$$-\frac{\partial^2 B_z(x, t)}{\partial x \partial t} = \epsilon_0\mu_0\frac{\partial^2 E_y(x, t)}{\partial t^2}$$

Combining these two equations to eliminate B_z, we finally find

$$\frac{\partial^2 E_y(x, t)}{\partial x^2} = \epsilon_0\mu_0\frac{\partial^2 E_y(x, t)}{\partial t^2} \qquad \begin{array}{l}\text{(electromagnetic wave}\\\text{equation in vacuum)}\end{array} \tag{32.15}$$

This expression has the same form as the general wave equation, Eq. (32.10). Because the electric field E_y must satisfy this equation, it behaves as a wave with a pattern that travels through space with a definite speed. Furthermore, comparison of Eqs. (32.15) and (32.10) shows that the wave speed v is given by

$$\frac{1}{v^2} = \epsilon_0\mu_0 \qquad \text{or} \qquad v = \frac{1}{\sqrt{\epsilon_0\mu_0}}$$

This agrees with Eq. (32.9) for the speed c of electromagnetic waves.

We can show that B_z also must satisfy the same wave equation as E_y, Eq. (32.15). To prove this, we take the partial derivative of Eq. (32.12) with respect to t and the partial derivative of Eq. (32.14) with respect to x and combine the results. We leave this derivation as a problem (see Problem 32.37).

Test Your Understanding of Section 32.2   For each of the following electromagnetic waves, state the direction of the magnetic field. (a) The wave is propagating in the positive z-direction, and $\vec{E}$ is in the positive x-direction; (b) the wave is propagating in the positive y-direction, and $\vec{E}$ is in the negative z-direction; (c) the wave is propagating in the negative x-direction, and $\vec{E}$ is in the positive z-direction.

32.3 Sinusoidal Electromagnetic Waves

Sinusoidal electromagnetic waves are directly analogous to sinusoidal transverse mechanical waves on a stretched string, which we studied in Section 15.3. In a sinusoidal electromagnetic wave, $\vec{E}$ and $\vec{B}$ at any point in space are sinusoidal functions of time, and at any instant of time the *spatial* variation of the fields is also sinusoidal.

Some sinusoidal electromagnetic waves are *plane waves;* they share with the waves described in Section 32.2 the property that at any instant the fields are uniform over any plane perpendicular to the direction of propagation. The entire pattern travels in the direction of propagation with speed c. The directions of $\vec{E}$ and $\vec{B}$ are perpendicular to the direction of propagation (and to each other), so the wave is *transverse*. Electromagnetic waves produced by an oscillating point charge, shown in Fig. 32.3, are an example of sinusoidal waves that are *not* plane

10.1   Properties of Mechanical Waves

32.12 Waves passing through a small area at a sufficiently great distance from a source can be treated as plane waves.

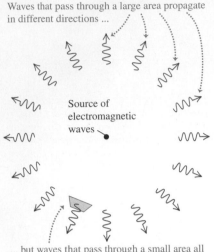

Waves that pass through a large area propagate in different directions ...

Source of electromagnetic waves

... but waves that pass through a small area all propagate in nearly the same direction, so we can treat them as plane waves.

32.13 Representation of the electric and magnetic fields as functions of x for a linearly polarized sinusoidal plane electromagnetic wave. One wavelength of the wave is shown at time $t = 0$. The fields are shown only for points along the x-axis.

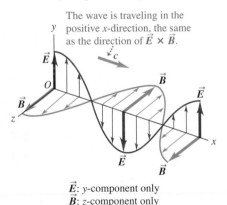

The wave is traveling in the positive x-direction, the same as the direction of $\vec{E} \times \vec{B}$.

$\vec{E}$: y-component only
$\vec{B}$: z-component only

waves. But if we restrict our observations to a relatively small region of space at a sufficiently great distance from the source, even these waves are well approximated by plane waves (Fig. 32.12). In the same way, the curved surface of the (nearly) spherical earth appears flat to us because of our small size relative to the earth's radius. In this section we'll restrict our discussion to plane waves.

The frequency f, the wavelength λ, and the speed of propagation c of any periodic wave are related by the usual wavelength–frequency relationship $c = \lambda f$. If the frequency f is the power-line frequency of 60 Hz, the wavelength is

$$\lambda = \frac{c}{f} = \frac{3 \times 10^8 \text{ m/s}}{60 \text{ Hz}} = 5 \times 10^6 \text{ m} = 5000 \text{ km}$$

which is of the order of the earth's radius! For a wave with this frequency, even a distance of many kilometers includes only a small fraction of a wavelength. But if the frequency is 10^8 Hz (100 MHz), typical of commercial FM radio broadcasts, the wavelength is

$$\lambda = \frac{3 \times 10^8 \text{ m/s}}{10^8 \text{ Hz}} = 3 \text{ m}$$

and a moderate distance can include many complete waves.

Fields of a Sinusoidal Wave

Figure 32.13 shows a linearly polarized sinusoidal electromagnetic wave traveling in the $+x$-direction. The $\vec{E}$ and $\vec{B}$ vectors are shown for only a few points on the positive x-axis. Note that the electric and magnetic fields oscillate in phase: $\vec{E}$ is maximum where $\vec{B}$ is maximum and $\vec{E}$ is zero where $\vec{B}$ is zero. Note also that where $\vec{E}$ is in the $+y$-direction, $\vec{B}$ is in the $+z$-direction; where $\vec{E}$ is in the $-y$-direction, $\vec{B}$ is in the $-z$-direction. At all points the vector product $\vec{E} \times \vec{B}$ is in the direction in which the wave is propagating (the $+x$-direction). We mentioned this in Section 32.2 in the list of characteristics of electromagnetic waves.

CAUTION **In a plane wave, $\vec{E}$ and $\vec{B}$ are everywhere** Figure 32.13 may give you the erroneous impression that the electric and magnetic fields exist only along the x-axis. In fact, in a sinusoidal plane wave there are electric and magnetic fields at *all* points in space. Imagine a plane perpendicular to the x-axis (that is, parallel to the yz-plane) at a particular point, at a particular time; the fields have the same values at all points in that plane. The values are different on different planes. ∎

We can describe electromagnetic waves by means of *wave functions*, just as we did in Section 15.3 for waves on a string. One form of the wave function for a transverse wave traveling in the $+x$-direction along a stretched string is Eq. (15.7):

$$y(x, t) = A \cos(kx - \omega t)$$

where $y(x, t)$ is the transverse displacement from its equilibrium position at time t of a point with coordinate x on the string. The quantity A is the maximum displacement, or *amplitude,* of the wave; ω is its *angular frequency,* equal to 2π times the frequency f; and k is the *wave number,* equal to $2\pi/\lambda$, where λ is the wavelength.

Let $E_y(x, t)$ and $B_z(x, t)$ represent the instantaneous values of the y-component of $\vec{E}$ and the z-component of $\vec{B}$, respectively, in Fig. 32.13, and let E_{max} and B_{max} represent the maximum values, or *amplitudes,* of these fields. The wave functions for the wave are then

$$E_y(x, t) = E_{\text{max}} \cos(kx - \omega t) \qquad B_z(x, t) = B_{\text{max}} \cos(kx - \omega t) \qquad (32.16)$$

(sinusoidal electromagnetic plane wave, propagating in $+x$-direction)

We can also write the wave functions in vector form:

$$\vec{E}(x, t) = \hat{j}E_{max}\cos(kx - \omega t)$$
$$\vec{B}(x, t) = \hat{k}B_{max}\cos(kx - \omega t)$$

(32.17)

CAUTION **The symbol k has two meanings** Note the two different k's: the unit vector $\hat{k}$ in the z-direction and the wave number k. Don't get these confused! ▮

The sine curves in Fig. 32.13 represent instantaneous values of the electric and magnetic fields as functions of x at time $t = 0$—that is, $\vec{E}(x, t = 0)$ and $\vec{B}(x, t = 0)$. As time goes by, the wave travels to the right with speed c. Equations (32.16) and (32.17) show that at any point the sinusoidal oscillations of $\vec{E}$ and $\vec{B}$ are *in phase*. From Eq. (32.4) the amplitudes must be related by

$$E_{max} = cB_{max} \qquad \text{(electromagnetic wave in vacuum)} \qquad \text{(32.18)}$$

These amplitude and phase relationships are also required for $E(x, t)$ and $B(x, t)$ to satisfy Eqs. (32.12) and (32.14), which came from Faraday's law and Ampere's law, respectively. Can you verify this statement? (See Problem 32.36.)

Figure 32.14 shows the electric and magnetic fields of a wave traveling in the *negative x-direction*. At points where $\vec{E}$ is in the positive y-direction, $\vec{B}$ is in the *negative z-direction*; where $\vec{E}$ is in the negative y-direction, $\vec{B}$ is in the *positive z*-direction. The wave functions for this wave are

$$E_y(x, t) = E_{max}\cos(kx + \omega t) \quad B_z(x, t) = -B_{max}\cos(kx + \omega t) \quad \text{(32.19)}$$

(sinusoidal electromagnetic plane wave, propagating in $-x$-direction)

As with the wave traveling in the $+x$-direction, at any point the sinusoidal oscillations of the $\vec{E}$ and $\vec{B}$ fields are *in phase,* and the vector product $\vec{E} \times \vec{B}$ points in the direction of propagation.

The sinusoidal waves shown in Figs. 32.13 and 32.14 are both linearly polarized in the y-direction; the $\vec{E}$ field is always parallel to the y-axis. Example 32.1 concerns a wave that is linearly polarized in the z-direction.

32.14 Representation of one wavelength of a linearly polarized sinusoidal plane electromagnetic wave traveling in the negative x-direction at $t = 0$. The fields are shown only for points along the x-axis. (Compare with Fig. 32.13.)

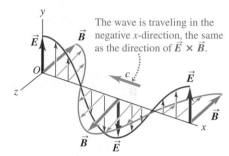

$\vec{E}$: y-component only
$\vec{B}$: z-component only

Problem-Solving Strategy 32.1 **Electromagnetic Waves**

IDENTIFY *the relevant concepts:* Many of the same ideas that apply to mechanical waves (discussed in Chapters 15 and 16) also apply to electromagnetic waves. The new feature is that the wave is described by two quantities, electric field $\vec{E}$ and magnetic field $\vec{B}$, instead of by a single quantity, such as the displacement of a string.

SET UP *the problem* using the following steps:
1. Draw a diagram showing the direction of wave propagation and the directions of $\vec{E}$ and $\vec{B}$.
2. Determine the target variables.

EXECUTE *the solution* as follows:
1. For problems involving electromagnetic waves, the best approach is to concentrate on basic relationships, such as the relationship of $\vec{E}$ to $\vec{B}$ (both magnitude and direction), how the wave speed is determined, the transverse nature of the waves, and so on. Keep these relationships in mind when working through the mathematical details.
2. For sinusoidal electromagnetic waves, you need to use the language developed for sinusoidal mechanical waves in Chap-

ters 15 and 16. Don't hesitate to go back and review that material, including the problem-solving strategies suggested in those chapters.
3. Keep in mind the basic relationships for periodic waves: $v = \lambda f$ and $\omega = vk$. For electromagnetic waves in vacuum, $v = c$. Be careful to distinguish between ordinary frequency f, usually expressed in hertz, and angular frequency $\omega = 2\pi f$, expressed in rad/s. Also remember that the wave number is $k = 2\pi/\lambda$.

EVALUATE *your answer:* Check that your result is reasonable. For electromagnetic waves in vacuum, the magnitude of the magnetic field in teslas is much smaller (by a factor of 3.00×10^8) than the magnitude of the electric field in volts per meter. If your answer suggests otherwise, you probably made an error using the relationship $E = cB$. (We'll see later in this section that the relationship between E and B is different for electromagnetic waves in a material medium.)

Example 32.1 **Fields of a laser beam**

A carbon dioxide laser emits a sinusoidal electromagnetic wave that travels in vacuum in the negative x-direction. The wavelength is 10.6 μm and the $\vec{E}$ field is parallel to the z-axis, with maximum magnitude of 1.5 MV/m. Write vector equations for $\vec{E}$ and $\vec{B}$ as functions of time and position.

SOLUTION

IDENTIFY: This problem concerns a sinusoidal electromagnetic wave of the sort we have described in this section.

SET UP: Equations (32.19) describe a wave traveling in the negative x-direction with $\vec{E}$ along the y-axis—that is, a wave that is linearly polarized along the y-axis. By contrast, the wave in this example is linearly polarized along the z-axis. At points where $\vec{E}$ is in the positive z-direction, $\vec{B}$ must be in the positive y-direction for the vector product $\vec{E} \times \vec{B}$ to be in the negative x-direction (the direction of propagation). Figure 32.15 shows a wave that satisfies these requirements.

EXECUTE: A possible pair of wave functions that describe the wave shown in Fig. 32.15 are

$$\vec{E}(x, t) = \hat{k}E_{max}\cos(kx + \omega t)$$
$$\vec{B}(x, t) = \hat{j}B_{max}\cos(kx + \omega t)$$

32.15 Our sketch for this problem.

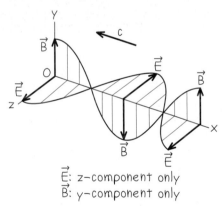

$\vec{E}$: z-component only
$\vec{B}$: y-component only

The plus sign in the arguments of the cosine functions indicates that the wave is propagating in the negative x-direction, as it should. Faraday's law requires that $E_{max} = cB_{max}$ [Eq. (32.18)], so

$$B_{max} = \frac{E_{max}}{c} = \frac{1.5 \times 10^6 \text{ V/m}}{3.0 \times 10^8 \text{ m/s}} = 5.0 \times 10^{-3} \text{ T}$$

To check unit consistency, note that $1 \text{ V} = 1 \text{ Wb/s}$ and $1 \text{ Wb/m}^2 = 1 \text{ T}$.

We have $\lambda = 10.6 \times 10^{-6}$ m, so the wave number and angular frequency are

$$k = \frac{2\pi}{\lambda} = \frac{2\pi \text{ rad}}{10.6 \times 10^{-6} \text{ m}} = 5.93 \times 10^5 \text{ rad/m}$$
$$\omega = ck = (3.00 \times 10^8 \text{ m/s})(5.93 \times 10^5 \text{ rad/m})$$
$$= 1.78 \times 10^{14} \text{ rad/s}$$

Substituting these values into the above wave functions, we get

$$\vec{E}(x, t) = \hat{k}(1.5 \times 10^6 \text{ V/m})\cos[(5.93 \times 10^5 \text{ rad/m})x$$
$$+ (1.78 \times 10^{14} \text{ rad/s})t]$$

$$\vec{B}(x, t) = \hat{j}(5.0 \times 10^{-3} \text{ T})\cos[(5.93 \times 10^5 \text{ rad/m})x$$
$$+ (1.78 \times 10^{14} \text{ rad/s})t]$$

With these equations we can find the fields in the laser beam at any particular position and time by substituting specific values of x and t.

EVALUATE: As we expect, the magnitude B_{max} in teslas is much smaller than the magnitude E_{max} in volts per meter. To check the directions of $\vec{E}$ and $\vec{B}$, note that $\vec{E} \times \vec{B}$ is in the direction of $\hat{k} \times \hat{j} = -\hat{i}$. This is as it should be for a wave that propagates in the negative x-direction.

Our expressions for $\vec{E}(x, t)$ and $\vec{B}(x, t)$ are not the only possible solutions. We could always add a phase ϕ to the arguments of the cosine function, so that $kx + \omega t$ would become $kx + \omega t + \phi$. To determine the value of ϕ we would need to know $\vec{E}$ and $\vec{B}$ either as functions of x at a given time t or as functions of t at a given coordinate x. However, the statement of the problem doesn't include this information.

Electromagnetic Waves in Matter

So far, our discussion of electromagnetic waves has been restricted to waves in *vacuum*. But electromagnetic waves can also travel in *matter;* think of light traveling through air, water, or glass. In this subsection we extend our analysis to electromagnetic waves in nonconducting materials—that is, *dielectrics.*

In a dielectric the wave speed is not the same as in vacuum, and we denote it by v instead of c. Faraday's law is unaltered, but in Eq. (32.4), derived from Faraday's law, the speed c is replaced by v. In Ampere's law the displacement current is given not by $\epsilon_0 \, d\Phi_E/dt$, where Φ_E is the flux of $\vec{E}$ through a surface, but by $\epsilon \, d\Phi_E/dt = K\epsilon_0 \, d\Phi_E/dt$, where K is the dielectric constant and ϵ is the permittivity of the dielectric. (We introduced these quantities in Section 24.4.) Also, the constant μ_0 in Ampere's law must be replaced by $\mu = K_m\mu_0$, where K_m is the relative permeability of the dielectric and μ is its permeability (see Section 28.8). Hence Eqs. (32.4) and (32.8) are replaced by

$$E = vB \quad \text{and} \quad B = \epsilon\mu vE \tag{32.20}$$

Following the same procedure as for waves in vacuum, we find that the wave speed v is

$$v = \frac{1}{\sqrt{\epsilon\mu}} = \frac{1}{\sqrt{KK_m}} \frac{1}{\sqrt{\epsilon_0\mu_0}} = \frac{c}{\sqrt{KK_m}} \quad \begin{array}{l}\text{(speed of electromagnetic}\\ \text{waves in a dielectric)}\end{array} \quad (32.21)$$

For most dielectrics the relative permeability K_m is very nearly equal to unity (except for insulating ferromagnetic materials). When $K_m \cong 1$,

$$v = \frac{1}{\sqrt{K}} \frac{1}{\sqrt{\epsilon_0\mu_0}} = \frac{c}{\sqrt{K}}$$

Because K is always greater than unity, the speed v of electromagnetic waves in a dielectric is always *less* than the speed c in vacuum by a factor of $1/\sqrt{K}$ (Fig. 32.16). The ratio of the speed c in vacuum to the speed v in a material is known in optics as the **index of refraction** n of the material. When $K_m \cong 1$,

$$\frac{c}{v} = n = \sqrt{KK_m} \cong \sqrt{K} \quad (32.22)$$

Usually, we can't use the values of K in Table 24.1 in this equation because those values are measured using *constant* electric fields. When the fields oscillate rapidly, there is usually not time for the re-orientating of electric dipoles that occurs with steady fields. Values of K with rapidly varying fields are usually much *smaller* than the values in the table. For example, K for water is 80.4 for steady fields but only about 1.8 in the frequency range of visible light. Thus the dielectric "constant" K is actually a function of frequency, called the *dielectric function* in more advanced treatments.

32.16 The dielectric constant K of water is about 1.8 for visible light, so the speed of visible light in water is slower than in vacuum by a factor of $1/\sqrt{K} = 1/\sqrt{1.8} = 0.75$.

Example 32.2   **Electromagnetic waves in different materials**

(a) While visiting a jewelry store one evening, you hold a diamond up to the light of a street lamp. The heated sodium vapor in the street lamp emits yellow light with a frequency of 5.09×10^{14} Hz. Find the wavelength in vacuum, the speed of wave propagation in diamond, and the wavelength in diamond. At this frequency, diamond has the properties $K = 5.84$ and $K_m = 1.00$. (b) A radio wave with a frequency of 90.0 MHz (in the FM radio broadcast band) passes from vacuum into an insulating ferrite (a ferromagnetic material used in computer cables to suppress radio interference). Find the wavelength in vacuum, the speed of wave propagation in the ferrite, and the wavelength in the ferrite. At this frequency, the ferrite has the properties $K = 10.0$ and $K_m = 1000$.

SOLUTION

IDENTIFY: We use the relationship among wave speed, wavelength, and frequency. We also use the relationship among the speed of electromagnetic waves in a medium and the values of dielectric constant K and relative permeability K_m for the medium.

SET UP: In each case we find the wavelength in vacuum using $c = \lambda f$. The wave speed v is given by Eq. (32.21). Once we know the value of v, we use $v = \lambda f$ to find the wavelength in the material in question.

EXECUTE: (a) The wavelength in vacuum of the sodium light is

$$\lambda_{\text{vacuum}} = \frac{c}{f} = \frac{3.00 \times 10^8 \text{ m/s}}{5.09 \times 10^{14} \text{ Hz}} = 5.89 \times 10^{-7} \text{ m} = 589 \text{ nm}$$

The wave speed in diamond is

$$v_{\text{diamond}} = \frac{c}{\sqrt{KK_m}} = \frac{3.00 \times 10^8 \text{ m/s}}{\sqrt{(5.84)(1.00)}} = 1.24 \times 10^8 \text{ m/s}$$

This is about two-fifths of the speed in vacuum. The wavelength is proportional to the wave speed and so is reduced by the same factor:

$$\lambda_{\text{diamond}} = \frac{v_{\text{diamond}}}{f} = \frac{1.24 \times 10^8 \text{ m/s}}{5.09 \times 10^{14} \text{ Hz}}$$
$$= 2.44 \times 10^{-7} \text{ m} = 244 \text{ nm}$$

(b) Following the same steps as in part (a), we find that the wavelength in vacuum of the radio wave is

$$\lambda_{\text{vacuum}} = \frac{c}{f} = \frac{3.00 \times 10^8 \text{ m/s}}{90.0 \times 10^6 \text{ Hz}} = 3.33 \text{ m}$$

The wave speed in the ferrite is

$$v_{\text{ferrite}} = \frac{c}{\sqrt{KK_m}} = \frac{3.00 \times 10^8 \text{ m/s}}{\sqrt{(10.0)(1000)}} = 3.00 \times 10^6 \text{ m/s}$$

Continued

This is only 1% of the speed of light in a vacuum, so the wavelength is likewise 1% as large as the wavelength in vacuum:

$$\lambda_{\text{ferrite}} = \frac{v_{\text{ferrite}}}{f} = \frac{3.00 \times 10^9 \text{ m/s}}{90.0 \times 10^6 \text{ Hz}} = 3.33 \times 10^{-2} \text{ m} = 3.33 \text{ cm}$$

EVALUATE: The speed of light in transparent materials like diamond is typically between c and $0.2c$. As our results in part (b) show, the speed of electromagnetic waves in dense materials like ferrite can be *far* slower than in vacuum.

Test Your Understanding of Section 32.3   The first of Eqs. (32.17) gives the electric field for a plane wave as measured at points along the x-axis. For this plane wave, how does the electric field at points *off* the x-axis differ from the expression in Eqs. (32.17)? (i) The amplitude is different; (ii) the phase is different; (iii) both the amplitude and phase are different; (iv) none of these.

32.4 Energy and Momentum in Electromagnetic Waves

It is a familiar fact that energy is associated with electromagnetic waves; think of the energy in the sun's radiation. Practical applications of electromagnetic waves, such as microwave ovens, radio transmitters, and lasers for eye surgery, all make use of the energy that these waves carry. To understand how to utilize this energy, it's helpful to derive detailed relationships for the energy in an electromagnetic wave.

We begin with the expressions derived in Sections 24.3 and 30.3 for the **energy densities** in electric and magnetic fields; we suggest you review those derivations now. Equations (24.11) and (30.10) show that in a region of empty space where $\vec{E}$ and $\vec{B}$ fields are present, the total energy density u is given by

$$u = \frac{1}{2}\epsilon_0 E^2 + \frac{1}{2\mu_0}B^2 \tag{32.23}$$

where ϵ_0 and μ_0 are, respectively, the permittivity and permeability of free space. For electromagnetic waves in vacuum, the magnitudes E and B are related by

$$B = \frac{E}{c} = \sqrt{\epsilon_0 \mu_0}\, E \tag{32.24}$$

Combining Eqs. (32.23) and (32.24), we can also express the energy density u in a simple electromagnetic wave in vacuum as

$$u = \frac{1}{2}\epsilon_0 E^2 + \frac{1}{2\mu_0}(\sqrt{\epsilon_0 \mu_0}\, E)^2 = \epsilon_0 E^2 \tag{32.25}$$

This shows that in vacuum, the energy density associated with the $\vec{E}$ field in our simple wave is equal to the energy density of the $\vec{B}$ field. In general, the electric-field magnitude E is a function of position and time, as for the sinusoidal wave described by Eqs. (32.16); thus the energy density u of an electromagnetic wave, given by Eq. (32.25), also depends in general on position and time.

Electromagnetic Energy Flow and the Poynting Vector

Electromagnetic waves such as those we have described are *traveling* waves that transport energy from one region to another. For instance, in the wave described in Section 32.2 the $\vec{E}$ and $\vec{B}$ fields advance with time into regions where originally no fields were present and carry the energy density u with them as they advance. We can describe this energy transfer in terms of energy transferred *per unit time per unit cross-sectional area,* or *power per unit area,* for an area perpendicular to the direction of wave travel.

To see how the energy flow is related to the fields, consider a stationary plane, perpendicular to the x-axis, that coincides with the wave front at a certain time. In a time dt after this, the wave front moves a distance $dx = c\,dt$ to the right of the plane. Considering an area A on this stationary plane (Fig. 32.17), we note that the energy in the space to the right of this area must have passed through the area to reach the new location. The volume dV of the relevant region is the base area A times the length $c\,dt$, and the energy dU in this region is the energy density u times this volume:

$$dU = u\,dV = (\epsilon_0 E^2)(Ac\,dt)$$

This energy passes through the area A in time dt. The energy flow per unit time per unit area, which we will call S, is

$$S = \frac{1}{A}\frac{dU}{dt} = \epsilon_0 c E^2 \qquad \text{(in vacuum)} \qquad (32.26)$$

Using Eqs. (32.15) and (32.25), we can derive the alternative forms

$$S = \frac{\epsilon_0}{\sqrt{\epsilon_0\mu_0}}E^2 = \sqrt{\frac{\epsilon_0}{\mu_0}}E^2 = \frac{EB}{\mu_0} \qquad \text{(in vacuum)} \qquad (32.27)$$

The derivation of Eq. (32.27) from Eq. (32.26) is left as a problem (see Exercise 32.29). The units of S are energy per unit time per unit area, or power per unit area. The SI unit of S is $1\ \text{J/s}\cdot\text{m}^2$ or $1\ \text{W/m}^2$.

We can define a *vector* quantity that describes both the magnitude and direction of the energy flow rate:

$$\vec{S} = \frac{1}{\mu_0}\vec{E}\times\vec{B} \qquad \text{(Poynting vector in vacuum)} \qquad (32.28)$$

The vector $\vec{S}$ is called the **Poynting vector;** it was introduced by the British physicist John Poynting (1852–1914). Its direction is in the direction of propagation of the wave (Fig. 32.18). Since $\vec{E}$ and $\vec{B}$ are perpendicular, the magnitude of $\vec{S}$ is $S = EB/\mu_0$; from Eqs. (32.26) and (32.27) this is the energy flow per unit area and per unit time through a cross-sectional area perpendicular to the propagation direction. The total energy flow per unit time (power, P) out of any closed surface is the integral of $\vec{S}$ over the surface:

$$P = \oint \vec{S}\cdot d\vec{A}$$

For the sinusoidal waves studied in Section 32.3, as well as for other more complex waves, the electric and magnetic fields at any point vary with time, so the Poynting vector at any point is also a function of time. Because the frequencies of typical electromagnetic waves are very high, the time variation of the Poynting vector is so rapid that it's most appropriate to look at its *average* value. The magnitude of the average value of $\vec{S}$ at a point is called the **intensity** of the radiation at that point. The SI unit of intensity is the same as for S, $1\ \text{W/m}^2$ (watt per square meter).

Let's work out the intensity of the sinusoidal wave described by Eqs. (32.17). We first substitute $\vec{E}$ and $\vec{B}$ into Eq. (32.28):

$$\vec{S}(x,t) = \frac{1}{\mu_0}\vec{E}(x,t)\times\vec{B}(x,t)$$

$$= \frac{1}{\mu_0}[\hat{\jmath}E_{max}\cos(kx-\omega t)]\times[\hat{k}B_{max}\cos(kx-\omega t)]$$

32.17 A wave front at a time dt after it passes through the stationary plane with area A.

At time dt, the volume between the stationary plane and the wave front contains an amount of electromagnetic energy $dU = uAc\,dt$.

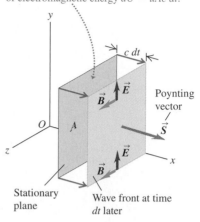

32.18 These rooftop solar panels are tilted to be face-on to the sun—that is, face-on to the Poynting vector of electromagnetic waves from the sun, so that the panels can absorb the maximum amount of wave energy.

The vector product of the unit vectors is $\hat{\jmath} \times \hat{k} = \hat{\imath}$ and $\cos^2(kx - \omega t)$ is never negative, so $\vec{S}(x, t)$ always points in the positive x-direction (the direction of wave propagation). The x-component of the Poynting vector is

$$S_x(x, t) = \frac{E_{max}B_{max}}{\mu_0}\cos^2(kx - \omega t) = \frac{E_{max}B_{max}}{2\mu_0}[1 + \cos 2(kx - \omega t)]$$

The time average value of $\cos 2(kx - \omega t)$ is zero because at any point, it is positive during one half-cycle and negative during the other half. So the average value of the Poynting vector over a full cycle is $\vec{S}_{av} = \hat{\imath}S_{av}$, where

$$S_{av} = \frac{E_{max}B_{max}}{2\mu_0}$$

That is, the magnitude of the average value of $\vec{S}$ for a sinusoidal wave (the intensity I of the wave) is $\frac{1}{2}$ the maximum value. By using the relationships $E_{max} = B_{max}c$ and $\epsilon_0\mu_0 = 1/c^2$, we can express the intensity in several equivalent forms:

$$I = S_{av} = \frac{E_{max}B_{max}}{2\mu_0} = \frac{E_{max}^2}{2\mu_0 c}$$
$$= \frac{1}{2}\sqrt{\frac{\epsilon_0}{\mu_0}}E_{max}^2 = \frac{1}{2}\epsilon_0 c E_{max}^2 \qquad \text{(intensity of a sinusoidal wave in vacuum)} \qquad (32.29)$$

We invite you to verify that these expressions are all equivalent.

For a wave traveling in the $-x$-direction, represented by Eqs. (32.19), the Poynting vector is in the $-x$-direction at every point, but its magnitude is the same as for a wave traveling in the $+x$-direction. Verifying these statements is left to you (see Exercise 32.24).

CAUTION **Poynting vector vs. intensity** At any point x, the magnitude of the Poynting vector varies with time. Hence, the *instantaneous* rate at which electromagnetic energy in a sinusoidal plane wave arrives at a surface is not constant. This may seem to contradict everyday experience; the light from the sun, a light bulb, or the laser in a grocery-store scanner appears steady and unvarying in strength. In fact the Poynting vector from these sources *does* vary in time, but the variation isn't noticeable because the oscillation frequency is so high (around 5×10^{14} Hz for visible light). All that you sense is the *average* rate at which energy reaches your eye, which is why we commonly use intensity (the average value of S) to describe the strength of electromagnetic radiation. ∎

Throughout this discussion we have considered only electromagnetic waves propagating in vacuum. If the waves are traveling in a dielectric medium, however, the expressions for energy density [Eq. (32.23)], the Poynting vector [Eq. (32.28)], and the intensity of a sinusoidal wave [Eq. (32.29)] must be modified. It turns out that the required modifications are quite simple: Just replace ϵ_0 with the permittivity ϵ of the dielectric, replace μ_0 with the permeability μ of the dielectric, and replace c with the speed v of electromagnetic waves in the dielectric. Remarkably, the energy densities in the $\vec{E}$ and $\vec{B}$ fields are equal even in a dielectric.

Example 32.3 **Energy in a nonsinusoidal wave**

For the nonsinusoidal wave described in Section 32.2, suppose that $E = 100$ V/m $= 100$ N/C. Find the value of B, the energy density, and the rate of energy flow per unit area S.

SOLUTION

IDENTIFY: In the wave described in Section 32.2, the electric and magnetic fields are uniform behind the wave front. Hence the target variables B, u, and S must also be uniform behind the wave front.

SET UP: Given the value of the magnitude E, we calculate the magnitude B using Eq. (32.4), the energy density u using Eq. 32.25), and the rate of energy flow per unit area S using Eq. (32.27). (Note that we cannot use Eq. (32.29), which applies to sinusoidal waves only.)

EXECUTE: From Eq. (32.4),

$$B = \frac{E}{c} = \frac{100 \text{ V/m}}{3.00 \times 10^8 \text{ m/s}} = 3.33 \times 10^{-7} \text{ T}$$

From Eq. (32.25),

$$u = \epsilon_0 E^2 = (8.85 \times 10^{-12} \, C^2/N \cdot m^2)(100 \, N/C)^2$$
$$= 8.85 \times 10^{-8} \, N/m^2 = 8.85 \times 10^{-8} \, J/m^3$$

The magnitude of the Poynting vector is

$$S = \frac{EB}{\mu_0} = \frac{(100 \, V/m)(3.33 \times 10^{-7} \, T)}{4\pi \times 10^{-7} \, T \cdot m/A}$$
$$= 26.5 \, V \cdot A/m^2 = 26.5 \, W/m^2$$

EVALUATE: We can check our result for S by using an alternative formula from Eq. (32.26):

$$S = \epsilon_0 c E^2$$
$$= (8.85 \times 10^{-12} \, C^2/N \cdot m^2)(3.00 \times 10^8 \, m/s)(100 \, N/C)^2$$
$$= 26.5 \, W/m^2$$

Since $\vec{E}$ and $\vec{B}$ have the same values at all points behind the wave front, the energy density u and Poynting vector magnitude S likewise have the same value everywhere behind the wave front. In front of the wave front, $\vec{E} = 0$ and $\vec{B} = 0$ and so $u = 0$ and $S = 0$; where there are no fields, there is no field energy.

Example 32.4 Energy in a sinusoidal wave

A radio station on the surface of the earth radiates a sinusoidal wave with an average total power of 50 kW (Fig. 32.19). Assuming that the transmitter radiates equally in all directions above the ground (which is unlikely in real situations), find the amplitudes E_{max} and B_{max} detected by a satellite at a distance of 100 km from the antenna.

SOLUTION

IDENTIFY: This is a sinusoidal wave, so we use the idea that the intensity is equal to the magnitude of the average value of the Poynting vector. We are not given the value of the intensity, but we *are* given the average total power of the transmitter. We use the idea that the intensity is the same as the average power per unit area.

SET UP: Figure 32.19 shows a hemisphere of radius 100 km centered on the transmitter. We divide the average power of the transmitter by the surface area of this hemisphere to find the intensity I at this distance from the transmitter. We then use Eq. (32.29) to find the electric-field magnitude and Eq. (32.4) to find the magnetic-field magnitude.

EXECUTE: The surface area of a hemisphere of radius $r = 100 \, km = 1.00 \times 10^5 \, m$ is

$$A = 2\pi R^2 = 2\pi (1.00 \times 10^5 \, m)^2 = 6.28 \times 10^{10} \, m^2$$

All the radiated power passes through this surface, so the average power per unit area (that is, the intensity) is

$$I = \frac{P}{A} = \frac{P}{2\pi R^2} = \frac{5.00 \times 10^4 \, W}{6.28 \times 10^{10} \, m^2} = 7.96 \times 10^{-7} \, W/m^2$$

From Eqs. (32.29), $I = S_{av} = E_{max}^2/2\mu_0 c$, so

$$E_{max} = \sqrt{2\mu_0 c S_{av}}$$
$$= \sqrt{2(4\pi \times 10^{-7} \, T \cdot m/A)(3.00 \times 10^8 \, m/s)(7.96 \times 10^{-7} \, W/m^2)}$$
$$= 2.45 \times 10^{-2} \, V/m$$

From Eq. (32.4),

$$B_{max} = \frac{E_{max}}{c} = 8.17 \times 10^{-11} \, T$$

EVALUATE: Note that the magnitude of E_{max} is comparable to fields commonly seen in the laboratory, but B_{max} is extremely small in comparison to $\vec{B}$ fields we saw in previous chapters. For this reason, most detectors of electromagnetic radiation respond to the effect of the electric field, not the magnetic field. Loop radio antennas are an exception.

32.19 A radio station radiates waves into the hemisphere shown.

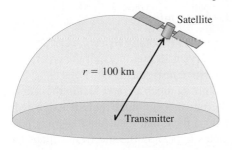

Electromagnetic Momentum Flow and Radiation Pressure

By using the observation that energy is required to establish electric and magnetic fields, we have shown that electromagnetic waves transport energy. It can also be shown that electromagnetic waves carry *momentum p*, with a corresponding momentum density (momentum dp per volume dV) of magnitude

$$\frac{dp}{dV} = \frac{EB}{\mu_0 c^2} = \frac{S}{c^2} \qquad (32.30)$$

This momentum is a property of the field; it is not associated with the mass of a moving particle in the usual sense.

There is also a corresponding momentum flow rate. The volume dV occupied by an electromagnetic wave (speed c) that passes through an area A in time dt is

$dV = Ac\,dt$. When we substitute this into Eq. (32.30) and rearrange, we find that the momentum flow rate per unit area is

$$\frac{1}{A}\frac{dp}{dt} = \frac{S}{c} = \frac{EB}{\mu_0 c} \qquad \text{(flow rate of electromagnetic momentum)} \quad (32.31)$$

This is the momentum transferred per unit surface area per unit time. We obtain the *average* rate of momentum transfer per unit area by replacing S in Eq. (32.31) by $S_{\text{av}} = I$.

This momentum is responsible for the phenomenon of **radiation pressure.** When an electromagnetic wave is completely absorbed by a surface, the wave's momentum is also transferred to the surface. For simplicity we'll consider a surface perpendicular to the propagation direction. Using the ideas developed in Section 8.1, we see that the rate dp/dt at which momentum is transferred to the absorbing surface equals the *force* on the surface. The average force per unit area due to the wave, or *radiation pressure* p_{rad}, is the average value of dp/dt divided by the absorbing area A. (We use the subscript "rad" to distinguish pressure from momentum, for which the symbol p is also used.) From Eq. (32.31) the radiation pressure is

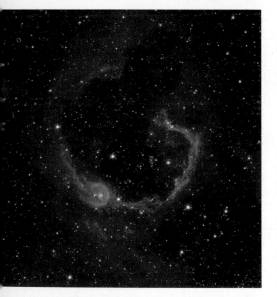

32.20 At the center of this interstellar gas cloud is a group of intensely luminous stars that exert tremendous radiation pressure on their surroundings. Aided by a "wind" of particles emanating from the stars, over the past million years the radiation pressure has carved out a bubble within the cloud 70 light-years across.

$$p_{\text{rad}} = \frac{S_{\text{av}}}{c} = \frac{I}{c} \qquad \text{(radiation pressure, wave totally absorbed)} \quad (32.32)$$

If the wave is totally reflected, the momentum change is twice as great, and the pressure is

$$p_{\text{rad}} = \frac{2S_{\text{av}}}{c} = \frac{2I}{c} \qquad \text{(radiation pressure, wave totally reflected)} \quad (32.33)$$

For example, the value of I (or S_{av}) for direct sunlight, before it passes through the earth's atmosphere, is approximately $1.4\ \text{kW/m}^2$. From Eq. (32.32) the corresponding average pressure on a completely absorbing surface is

$$p_{\text{rad}} = \frac{I}{c} = \frac{1.4 \times 10^3\ \text{W/m}^2}{3.0 \times 10^8\ \text{m/s}} = 4.7 \times 10^{-6}\ \text{Pa}$$

From Eq. (32.33) the average pressure on a totally *reflecting* surface is twice this: $2I/c$ or $9.4 \times 10^{-6}\ \text{Pa}$. These are very small pressures, of the order of 10^{-10} atm, but they can be measured with sensitive instruments.

The radiation pressure of sunlight is much greater *inside* the sun than at the earth (see Problem 32.43). Inside stars that are much more massive and luminous than the sun, radiation pressure is so great that it substantially augments the gas pressure within the star and so helps to prevent the star from collapsing under its own gravity. In some cases the radiation pressure of stars can have dramatic effects on the material surrounding the stars (Fig. 32.20).

Example 32.5   **Power and pressure from sunlight**

An earth-orbiting satellite has solar-energy–collecting panels with a total area of $4.0\ \text{m}^2$ (Fig. 32.21). If the sun's radiation is perpendicular to the panels and is completely absorbed, find the average solar power absorbed and the average force associated with radiation pressure.

SOLUTION

IDENTIFY: This problem uses the relationships among intensity, power, radiation pressure, and force.

SET UP: In the above discussion we calculated the intensity I (power per unit area) of sunlight as well as the radiation pressure p_{rad} (force per unit area) of sunlight on an absorbing surface. (We calculated these values for points above the atmosphere, which is where the satellite orbits.) Multiplying each value by the area of the solar panels gives the average power absorbed and the net radiation force on the panels.

EXECUTE: The intensity I (power per unit area) is 1.4×10^3 W/m^2. Although the light from the sun is not a simple sinusoidal wave, we can still use the relationship that the average power P is the intensity I times the area A:

$$P = IA = (1.4 \times 10^3 \text{ W/m}^2)(4.0 \text{ m}^2)$$
$$= 5.6 \times 10^3 \text{ W} = 5.6 \text{ kW}$$

The radiation pressure of sunlight on an absorbing surface is $p_{rad} = 4.7 \times 10^{-6}$ Pa $= 4.7 \times 10^{-6}$ N/m^2. The total force F is the pressure p_{rad} times the area A:

$$F = p_{rad}A = (4.7 \times 10^{-6} \text{ N/m}^2)(4.0 \text{ m}^2) = 1.9 \times 10^{-5} \text{ N}$$

EVALUATE: The absorbed power is quite substantial. Part of it can be used to power the equipment aboard the satellite; the rest goes into heating the panels, either directly or due to inefficiencies in the photocells contained in the panels.

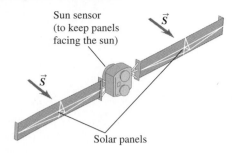

32.21 Solar panels on a satellite.

Sun sensor
(to keep panels
facing the sun)

$\vec{S}$

$\vec{S}$

Solar panels

The total radiation force is comparable to the weight (on earth) of a single grain of salt. Over time, however, this small force can have a noticeable effect on the orbit of a satellite like that in Fig. 32.21, and so radiation pressure must be taken into account.

Test Your Understanding of Section 32.4   Figure 32.13 shows one wavelength of a sinusoidal electromagnetic wave at time $t = 0$. For which of the following four values of x is (a) the energy density a maximum; (b) the energy density a minimum; (c) the magnitude of the instantaneous (not average) Poynting vector a maximum; (d) the magnitude of the instantaneous (not average) Poynting vector a minimum? (i) $x = 0$; (ii) $x = \lambda/4$; (iii) $x = \lambda/2$; (iv) $x = 3\lambda/4$.

32.5 Standing Electromagnetic Waves

Electromagnetic waves can be *reflected;* the surface of a conductor (like a polished sheet of metal) or of a dielectric (such as a sheet of glass) can serve as a reflector. The superposition principle holds for electromagnetic waves just as for electric and magnetic fields. The superposition of an incident wave and a reflected wave forms a **standing wave.** The situation is analogous to standing waves on a stretched string, discussed in Section 15.7; you should review that discussion.

Suppose a sheet of a perfect conductor (zero resistivity) is placed in the yz-plane of Fig. 32.22 and a linearly polarized electromagnetic wave, traveling in the negative x-direction, strikes it. As we discussed in Section 23.4, $\vec{E}$ cannot have a component parallel to the surface of a perfect conductor. Therefore in the present situation, $\vec{E}$ must be zero everywhere in the yz-plane. The electric field of the *incident* electromagnetic wave is *not* zero at all times in the yz-plane. But this incident wave induces oscillating currents on the surface of the conductor, and these currents give rise to an additional electric field. The *net* electric field, which is the vector sum of this field and the incident $\vec{E}$, is zero everywhere inside and on the surface of the conductor.

The currents induced on the surface of the conductor also produce a *reflected* wave that travels out from the plane in the $+x$-direction. Suppose the incident wave is described by the wave functions of Eqs. (32.19) (a sinusoidal wave traveling in the $-x$-direction) and the reflected wave by the negative of Eqs. (32.16) (a sinusoidal wave traveling in the $+x$-direction). We take the *negative* of the wave given by Eqs. (32.16) so that the incident and reflected electric fields cancel at $x = 0$ (the plane of the conductor, where the total electric field must be zero). The superposition principle states that the total $\vec{E}$ field at any point is the vector sum of the $\vec{E}$ fields of the incident and reflected waves, and similarly for the $\vec{B}$ field. Therefore the wave functions for the superposition of the two waves are

$$E_y(x, t) = E_{max}[\cos(kx + \omega t) - \cos(kx - \omega t)]$$
$$B_z(x, t) = B_{max}[-\cos(kx + \omega t) - \cos(kx - \omega t)]$$

32.22 Representation of the electric and magnetic fields of a linearly polarized electromagnetic standing wave when $\omega t = 3\pi/4$ rad. In any plane perpendicular to the x-axis, E is maximum (an antinode) where B is zero (a node), and vice versa. As time elapses, the pattern does *not* move along the x-axis; instead, at every point the $\vec{E}$ and $\vec{B}$ vectors simply oscillate.

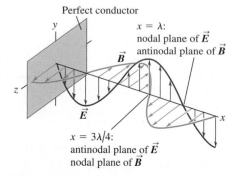

Perfect conductor

y

$\vec{B}$

z

$\vec{E}$

$x = \lambda$:
nodal plane of $\vec{E}$
antinodal plane of $\vec{B}$

x

$x = 3\lambda/4$:
antinodal plane of $\vec{E}$
nodal plane of $\vec{B}$

We can expand and simplify these expressions, using the identities

$$\cos(A \pm B) = \cos A \cos B \mp \sin A \sin B$$

The results are

$$E_y(x, t) = -2E_{max} \sin kx \sin \omega t \tag{32.34}$$

$$B_z(x, t) = -2B_{max} \cos kx \cos \omega t \tag{32.35}$$

Equation (32.34) is analogous to Eq. (15.28) for a stretched string. We see that at $x = 0$ the electric field $E_y(x = 0, t)$ is *always* zero; this is required by the nature of the ideal conductor, which plays the same role as a fixed point at the end of a string. Furthermore, $E_y(x, t)$ is zero at *all* times at points in those planes perpendicular to the x-axis for which $\sin kx = 0$; that is, $kx = 0, \pi, 2\pi, \ldots$. Since $k = 2\pi/\lambda$, the positions of these planes are

$$x = 0, \frac{\lambda}{2}, \lambda, \frac{3\lambda}{2}, \ldots \quad \text{(nodal planes of } \vec{E}) \tag{32.36}$$

These planes are called the **nodal planes** of the $\vec{E}$ field; they are the equivalent of the nodes, or nodal points, of a standing wave on a string. Midway between any two adjacent nodal planes is a plane on which $\sin kx = \pm 1$; on each such plane, the magnitude of $E(x, t)$ equals the maximum possible value of $2E_{max}$ twice per oscillation cycle. These are the **antinodal planes** of $\vec{E}$, corresponding to the antinodes of waves on a string.

The total magnetic field is zero at all times at points in planes on which $\cos kx = 0$. This occurs where

$$x = \frac{\lambda}{4}, \frac{3\lambda}{4}, \frac{5\lambda}{4}, \ldots \quad \text{(nodal planes of } \vec{B}) \tag{32.37}$$

These are the nodal planes of the $\vec{B}$ field; there is an antinodal plane of $\vec{B}$ midway between any two adjacent nodal planes.

Figure 32.22 shows a standing-wave pattern at one instant of time. The magnetic field is *not* zero at the conducting surface $(x = 0)$, and there is no reason it should be. The surface currents that must be present to make $\vec{E}$ exactly zero at the surface cause magnetic fields at the surface. The nodal planes of each field are separated by one half-wavelength. The nodal planes of one field are mid-way between those of the other; hence the nodes of $\vec{E}$ coincide with antinodes of $\vec{B}$, and conversely. Compare this situation to the distinction between pressure nodes and displacement nodes in Section 16.4.

The total electric field is a *sine* function of t, and the total magnetic field is a *cosine* function of t. The sinusoidal variations of the two fields are therefore 90° out of phase at each point. At times when $\sin \omega t = 0$, the electric field is zero *everywhere*, and the magnetic field is maximum. When $\cos \omega t = 0$, the magnetic field is zero everywhere, and the electric field is maximum. This is in contrast to a wave traveling in one direction, as described by Eqs. (32.16) or (32.19) separately, in which the sinusoidal variations of $\vec{E}$ and $\vec{B}$ at any particular point are in *phase*. It is interesting to check that Eqs. (32.34) and (32.35) satisfy the wave equation, Eq. (32.15). They also satisfy Eqs. (32.12) and (32.14) (the equivalents of Faraday's and Ampere's laws); we leave the proofs of these statements to you (see Exercise 32.34).

Standing Waves in a Cavity

Pursuing the stretched-string analogy, we may now insert a second conducting plane, parallel to the first and a distance L from it, along the $+x$-axis. The cavity between the two planes is analogous to a stretched string held at the points $x = 0$ and $x = L$. Both conducting planes must be nodal planes for $\vec{E}$; a standing wave can exist only when the second plane is placed at one of the positions where $E(x, t) = 0$. That is, for a standing wave to exist, L must be an integer multiple of $\lambda/2$. The wavelengths that satisfy this condition are

$$\lambda_n = \frac{2L}{n} \qquad (n = 1, 2, 3, \ldots) \tag{32.38}$$

The corresponding frequencies are

$$f_n = \frac{c}{\lambda_n} = n\frac{c}{2L} \qquad (n = 1, 2, 3, \ldots) \tag{32.39}$$

Thus there is a set of *normal modes,* each with a characteristic frequency, wave shape, and node pattern (Fig. 32.23). By measuring the node positions, we can measure the wavelength. If the frequency is known, the wave speed can be determined. This technique was first used by Hertz in the 1880s in his pioneering investigations of electromagnetic waves.

A laser has two mirrors; a standing wave is set up in the cavity between the mirrors. One of the mirrors has a small, partially transmitting aperture that allows waves to escape from this end of the laser.

Conducting surfaces are not the only reflectors of electromagnetic waves. Reflections also occur at an interface between two insulating materials with different dielectric or magnetic properties. The mechanical analog is a junction of two strings with equal tension but different linear mass density. In general, a wave incident on such a boundary surface is partly transmitted into the second material and partly reflected back into the first. For example, light is transmitted through a glass window, but its surfaces also reflect light.

32.23 A typical microwave oven sets up a standing electromagnetic wave with $\lambda = 12.2$ cm, a wavelength that is strongly absorbed by the water in food. Because the wave has nodes spaced $\lambda/2 = 6.1$ cm apart, the food must be rotated while cooking. Otherwise, the portion that lies at a node—where the electric-field amplitude is zero—will remain cold.

Example 32.6   Intensity in a standing wave

Calculate the intensity of the standing wave discussed in this section.

SOLUTION

IDENTIFY: The intensity I of the wave is the average value S_{av} of the magnitude of the Poynting vector.

SET UP: We first find the instantaneous value of the Poynting vector and then average it over a whole number of cycles of the wave to determine I.

EXECUTE: Using the wave functions of Eqs. (32.34) and (32.35) in the expression for the Poynting vector $\vec{S}$, Eq. (32.28), we find

$$\vec{S}(x, t) = \frac{1}{\mu_0}\vec{E}(x, t) \times \vec{B}(x, t)$$

$$= \frac{1}{\mu_0}[-2\hat{j}E_{max}\sin kx\cos\omega t] \times [-2\hat{k}B_{max}\cos kx\sin\omega t]$$

$$= \hat{i}\frac{E_{max}B_{max}}{\mu_0}(2\sin kx\cos kx)(2\sin\omega t\cos\omega t)$$

$$= \hat{i}S_x(x, t)$$

Using the identity $\sin 2A = 2\sin A\cos A$, we can rewrite $S_x(x, t)$ as

$$S_x(x, t) = \frac{E_{max}B_{max}\sin 2kx\sin 2\omega t}{\mu_0}$$

The average value of a sine function over any whole number of cycles is zero. Thus *the time average of $\vec{S}$ at any point is zero;* $I = S_{av} = 0$.

EVALUATE: This is just what we should expect. We formed our standing wave by superposing two waves with the same frequency and amplitude, traveling in opposite directions. All the energy transferred by one wave is completely cancelled by an equal amount transferred in the opposite direction by the other wave. When we use waves to transmit power, it is important to avoid reflections that give rise to standing waves.

CHAPTER 32 Electromagnetic Waves

Example 32.7   Standing waves in a cavity

Electromagnetic standing waves are set up in a cavity with two parallel, highly conducting walls separated by 1.50 cm. (a) Calculate the longest wavelength and lowest frequency of electromagnetic standing waves between the walls. (b) For this longest-wavelength standing wave, where in the cavity does $\vec{E}$ have maximum magnitude? Where is $\vec{E}$ zero? Where does $\vec{B}$ have maximum magnitude? Where is $\vec{B}$ zero?

SOLUTION

IDENTIFY: This problem uses the idea that only certain electromagnetic normal modes are possible for electromagnetic waves in a cavity, just as only certain normal modes are possible for standing waves on a string.

SET UP: The longest possible wavelength and lowest possible frequency correspond to the $n = 1$ mode in Eqs. (32.38) and (32.39). We use these equations to determine the values of λ and f. Equations (32.36) and (32.37) then tell us the locations of the nodal planes of $\vec{E}$ and $\vec{B}$; the antinodal planes of each field are midway between adjacent nodal planes.

EXECUTE: (a) From Eq. (32.38), the $n = 1$ wavelength is

$$\lambda_1 = 2L = 2(1.50 \text{ cm}) = 3.00 \text{ cm}$$

The corresponding frequency is given by Eq. (32.38) with $n = 1$:

$$f_1 = \frac{c}{2L} = \frac{3.00 \times 10^8 \text{ m/s}}{2(1.50 \times 10^{-2} \text{ m})} = 1.00 \times 10^{10} \text{ Hz} = 10 \text{ GHz}$$

(b) With $n = 1$ there is a single half-wavelength between the walls. The electric field has nodal planes $(\vec{E} = 0)$ at the walls and an antinodal plane (where the maximum magnitude of $\vec{E}$ occurs) midway between them. The magnetic field has *antinodal* planes at the walls and a nodal plane midway between them.

EVALUATE: One application of standing waves of this kind is to produce an oscillating $\vec{E}$ field of definite frequency, which in turn is used to probe the behavior of a small sample of material placed inside the cavity. To subject the sample to the strongest possible field, the sample should be placed near the center of the cavity, at the antinode of $\vec{E}$.

Test Your Understanding of Section 32.5   In the standing wave described in Example 32.7, is there any point in the cavity where the energy density is zero at all times? If so, where? If not, why not?

Maxwell's equations and electromagnetic waves: Maxwell's equations predict the existence of electromagnetic waves that propagate in vacuum at the speed of light c. The electromagnetic spectrum covers frequencies from at least 1 to 10^{24} Hz and a correspondingly broad range of wavelengths. Visible light, with wavelengths from 400 to 700 nm, is only a very small part of this spectrum. In a plane wave, $\vec{E}$ and $\vec{B}$ are uniform over any plane perpendicular to the propagation direction. Faraday's law and Ampere's law both give relationships between the magnitudes of $\vec{E}$ and $\vec{B}$; requiring both of these relationships to be satisfied gives an expression for c in terms of ϵ_0 and μ_0. Electromagnetic waves are transverse; the $\vec{E}$ and $\vec{B}$ fields are perpendicular to the direction of propagation and to each other. The direction of propagation is the direction of $\vec{E} \times \vec{B}$.

$$E = cB \qquad (32.4)$$

$$B = \epsilon_0 \mu_0 cE \qquad (32.8)$$

$$c = \frac{1}{\sqrt{\epsilon_0 \mu_0}} \qquad (32.9)$$

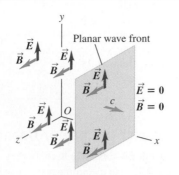

Sinusoidal electromagnetic waves: Equations (32.17) and (32.18) describe a sinusoidal plane electromagnetic wave traveling in vacuum in the $+x$-direction. (See Example 32.1.)

$$\vec{E}(x, t) = \hat{j} E_{max} \cos(kx - \omega t)$$
$$\vec{B}(x, t) = \hat{k} B_{max} \cos(kx - \omega t) \qquad (32.17)$$

$$E_{max} = cB_{max} \qquad (32.18)$$

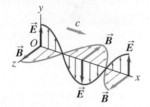

Electromagnetic waves in matter: When an electromagnetic wave travels through a dielectric, the wave speed v is less than the speed of light in vacuum c. (See Example 32.2.)

$$v = \frac{1}{\sqrt{\epsilon \mu}} = \frac{1}{\sqrt{KK_m}} \frac{1}{\sqrt{\epsilon_0 \mu_0}}$$
$$= \frac{c}{\sqrt{KK_m}} \qquad (32.21)$$

Energy and momentum in electromagnetic waves: The energy flow rate (power per unit area) in an electromagnetic wave in a vacuum is given by the Poynting vector $\vec{S}$. The magnitude of the time-averaged value of the Poynting vector is called the intensity I of the wave. Electromagnetic waves also carry momentum. When an electromagnetic wave strikes a surface, it exerts a radiation pressure p_{rad}. If the surface is perpendicular to the wave propagation direction and is totally absorbing, $p_{rad} = I/c$; if the surface is a perfect reflector, $p_{rad} = 2I/c$. (See Examples 32.3–32.5.)

$$\vec{S} = \frac{1}{\mu_0} \vec{E} \times \vec{B} \qquad (32.28)$$

$$I = S_{av} = \frac{E_{max} B_{max}}{2\mu_0} = \frac{E_{max}^2}{2\mu_0 c}$$
$$= \frac{1}{2} \sqrt{\frac{\epsilon_0}{\mu_0}} E_{max}^2$$
$$= \frac{1}{2} \epsilon_0 c E_{max}^2 \qquad (32.29)$$

$$\frac{1}{A} \frac{dp}{dt} = \frac{S}{c} = \frac{EB}{\mu_0 c} \qquad (32.31)$$
(flow rate of electromagnetic momentum)

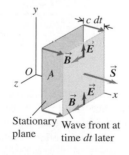

Standing electromagnetic waves: If a perfect reflecting surface is placed at $x = 0$, the incident and reflected waves form a standing wave. Nodal planes for $\vec{E}$ occur at $kx = 0, \pi, 2\pi, \ldots$, and nodal planes for $\vec{B}$ at $kx = \pi/2, 3\pi/2, 5\pi/2, \ldots$. At each point, the sinusoidal variations of $\vec{E}$ and $\vec{B}$ with time are 90° out of phase. (See Examples 32.6 and 32.7.)

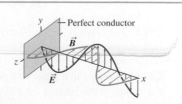

Key Terms

Answer to Chapter Opening Question ?

Metals are reflective because they are good conductors of electricity. When an electromagnetic wave strikes a conductor, the electric field of the wave sets up currents on the conductor surface that generate a reflected wave. For a perfect conductor, this reflected wave is just as intense as the incident wave. Tarnished metals are less shiny because their surface is oxidized and less conductive; polishing the metal removes the oxide and exposes the conducting metal.

Answers to Test Your Understanding Questions

32.1 Answers: (a) no, (b) no A purely electric wave would have a varying electric field. Such a field necessarily generates a magnetic field through Ampere's law, Eq. (29.20), so a purely electric wave is impossible. In the same way, a purely magnetic wave is impossible: The varying magnetic field in such a wave would automatically give rise to an electric field through Faraday's law, Eq. (29.21).

32.2 Answers: (a) positive y-direction, (b) negative x-direction, (c) positive y-direction You can verify these answers by using the right-hand rule to show that $\vec{E} \times \vec{B}$ in each case is in the direction of propagation, or by using the rule shown in Fig. 32.9.

32.3 Answer: (iv) In an ideal electromagnetic plane wave, at any instant the fields are the same anywhere in a plane perpendicular to the direction of propagation. The plane wave described by Eqs. (32.17) is propagating in the x-direction, so the fields depend on the coordinate x and time t but do *not* depend on the coordinates y and z.

32.4 Answers: (a) (i) and (iii), (b) (ii) and (iv), (c) (i) and (iii), (d) (ii) and (iv) Both the energy density u and the Poynting vector magnitude S are maximum where the $\vec{E}$ and $\vec{B}$ fields have their maximum magnitudes. (The direction of the fields doesn't matter.) From Fig. 32.13, this occurs at $x = 0$ and $x = \lambda/2$. Both u and S have a minimum value of zero; that occurs where $\vec{E}$ and $\vec{B}$ are both zero. From Fig. 32.13, this occurs at $x = \lambda/4$ and $x = 3\lambda/4$.

32.5 Answer: no There are places where $\vec{E} = 0$ at all times (at the walls) and the electric energy density $\frac{1}{2}\epsilon_0 E^2$ is always zero. There are also places where $\vec{B} = 0$ at all times (on the plane midway between the walls) and the magnetic energy density $B^2/2\mu_0$ is always zero. However, there are *no* locations where both $\vec{E}$ and $\vec{B}$ are always zero. Hence the energy density at any point in the standing wave is always nonzero.

PROBLEMS

For instructor-assigned homework, go to **www.masteringphysics.com**

Discussion Questions

Q32.1. By measuring the electric and magnetic fields at a point in space where there is an electromagnetic wave, can you determine the direction from which the wave came? Explain.

Q32.2. According to Ampere's law, is it possible to have both a conduction current and a displacement current at the same time? Is it possible for the effects of the two kinds of current to cancel each other exactly so that *no* magnetic field is produced? Explain.

Q32.3. Give several examples of electromagnetic waves that are encountered in everyday life. How are they all alike? How do they differ?

Q32.4. Sometimes neon signs located near a powerful radio station are seen to glow faintly at night, even though they are not turned on. What is happening?

Q32.5. Is polarization a property of all electromagnetic waves, or is it unique to visible light? Can sound waves be polarized? What fundamental distinction in wave properties is involved? Explain.

Q32.6. Suppose that a positive point charge q is initially at rest on the x-axis, in the path of the electromagnetic plane wave described in Section 32.2. Will the charge move after the wave front reaches it? If not, why not? If the charge does move, describe its motion qualitatively. (Remember that $\vec{E}$ and $\vec{B}$ have the same value at all points behind the wave front.)

Q32.7. The light beam from a searchlight may have an electric-field magnitude of 1000 V/m, corresponding to a potential difference of 1500 V between the head and feet of a 1.5-m-tall person on whom the light shines. Does this cause the person to feel a strong electric shock? Why or why not?

Q32.8. For a certain sinusoidal wave of intensity I, the amplitude of the magnetic field is B. What would be the amplitude (in terms of B) in a similar wave of twice the intensity?

Q32.9. The magnetic-field amplitude of the electromagnetic wave from the laser described in Example 32.1 (Section 32.3) is about 100 times greater than the earth's magnetic field. If you illuminate a compass with the light from this laser, would you expect the compass to deflect? Why or why not?

Q32.10. Most automobiles have vertical antennas for receiving radio broadcasts. Explain what this tells you about the direction of polarization of $\vec{E}$ in the radio waves used in broadcasting.

Q32.11. If a light beam carries momentum, should a person holding a flashlight feel a recoil analogous to the recoil of a rifle when it is fired? Why is this recoil not actually observed?

Q32.12. A light source radiates a sinusoidal electromagnetic wave uniformly in all directions. This wave exerts an average pressure p on a perfectly reflecting surface a distance R away from it. What average pressure (in terms of p) would this wave exert on a perfectly absorbing surface that was twice as far from the source?

Q32.13. Does an electromagnetic *standing* wave have energy? Does it have momentum? Are your answers to these questions the same as for a *traveling* wave? Why or why not?

Q32.14. When driving on the upper level of the Bay Bridge, westbound from Oakland to San Francisco, you can easily pick up a number of radio stations on your car radio. But when driving eastbound on the lower level of the bridge, which has steel girders on either side to support the upper level, the radio reception is much worse. Why is there a difference?

Exercises

Section 32.2 Plane Electromagnetic Waves and the Speed of Light

32.1. (a) How much time does it take light to travel from the moon to the earth, a distance of 384,000 km? (b) Light from the star Sirius takes 8.61 years to reach the earth. What is the distance from earth to Sirius in kilometers?

32.2. TV Ghosting. In a TV picture, ghost images are formed when the signal from the transmitter travels to the receiver both directly and indirectly after reflection from a building or other large metallic mass. In a 25-inch set, the ghost is about 1.0 cm to the right of the principal image if the reflected signal arrives 0.60 μs after the principal signal. In this case, what is the difference in path lengths for the two signals?

32.3. For an electromagnetic wave propagating in air, determine the frequency of a wave with a wavelength of (a) 5.0 km; (b) 5.0 m; (c) 5.0 μm; (d) 5.0 nm.

32.4. Ultraviolet Radiation. There are two categories of ultraviolet light. Ultraviolet A (UVA) has a wavelength ranging from 320 nm to 400 nm. It is not so harmful to the skin and is necessary for the production of vitamin D. UVB, with a wavelength between 280 nm and 320 nm, is much more dangerous because it causes skin cancer. (a) Find the frequency ranges of UVA and UVB. (b) What are the ranges of the wave numbers for UVA and UVB?

Section 32.3 Sinusoidal Electromagnetic Waves

32.5. A sinusoidal electromagnetic wave having a magnetic field of amplitude 1.25 μT and a wavelength of 432 nm is traveling in the $+x$-direction through empty space. (a) What is the frequency of this wave? (b) What is the amplitude of the associated electric field? (c) Write the equations for the electric and magnetic fields as functions of x and t in the form of Eqs. (32.17).

32.6. An electromagnetic wave of wavelength 435 nm is traveling in vacuum in the $-z$-direction The electric field has amplitude 2.70×10^{-3} V/m and is parallel to the x-axis. What are (a) the frequency and (b) the magnetic-field amplitude? (c) Write the vector equations for $\vec{E}(z, t)$ and $\vec{B}(z, t)$.

32.7. A sinusoidal electromagnetic wave of frequency 6.10×10^{14} Hz travels in vacuum in the $+z$-direction. The $\vec{B}$-field is parallel to the y-axis and has amplitude 5.80×10^{-4} T. Write the vector equations for $\vec{E}(z, t)$ and $\vec{B}(z, t)$.

32.8. The electric field of a sinusoidal electromagnetic wave obeys the equation $E = -(375 \text{ V/m}) \sin[(5.97 \times 10^{15} \text{ rad/s})t + (1.99 \times 10^7 \text{ rad/m})x]$. (a) What are the amplitudes of the electric and magnetic fields of this wave? (b) What are the frequency, wavelength, and period of the wave? Is this light visible to humans? (c) What is the speed of the wave?

32.9. An electromagnetic wave has an electric field given by $\vec{E}(y, t) = -(3.10 \times 10^5 \text{ V/m})\hat{k} \sin[ky - (12.65 \times 10^{12} \text{ rad/s})t]$. (a) In which direction is the wave traveling? (b) What is the wavelength of the wave? (c) Write the vector equation for $\vec{B}(y, t)$.

32.10. An electromagnetic wave has a magnetic field given by $\vec{B}(x, t) = (8.25 \times 10^{-9} \text{ T})\hat{j} \sin[(1.38 \times 10^4 \text{ rad/m})x + \omega t]$. (a) In which direction is the wave traveling? (b) What is the frequency f of the wave? (c) Write the vector equation for $\vec{E}(x, t)$.

32.11. Radio station WCCO in Minneapolis broadcasts at a frequency of 830 kHz. At a point some distance from the transmitter, the magnetic-field amplitude of the electromagnetic wave from WCCO is 4.82×10^{-11} T. Calculate (a) the wavelength; (b) the wave number; (c) the angular frequency; (d) the electric-field amplitude.

32.12. The electric-field amplitude near a certain radio transmitter is 3.85×10^{-3} V/m What is the amplitude of $\vec{B}$? How does this compare in magnitude with the earth's field?

32.13. An electromagnetic wave with frequency 5.70×10^{14} Hz propagates with a speed of 2.17×10^8 m/s in a certain piece of glass. Find (a) the wavelength of the wave in the glass; (b) the wavelength of a wave of the same frequency propagating in air; (c) the index of refraction n of the glass for an electromagnetic wave with this frequency; (d) the dielectric constant for glass at this frequency, assuming that the relative permeability is unity.

32.14. An electromagnetic wave with frequency 65.0 Hz travels in an insulating magnetic material that has dielectric constant 3.64 and relative permeability 5.18 at this frequency. The electric field has amplitude 7.20×10^{-3} V/m. (a) What is the speed of propagation of the wave? (b) What is the wavelength of the wave? (c) What is the amplitude of the magnetic field? (d) What is the intensity of the wave?

Section 32.4 Energy and Momentum in Electromagnetic Waves

32.15. Fields from a Light Bulb. We can reasonably model a 75-W incandescent light-bulb as a sphere 6.0 cm in diameter. Typically, only about 5% of the energy goes to visible light; the rest goes largely to nonvisible infrared radiation. (a) What is the visible-light intensity (in W/m^2) at the surface of the bulb? (b) What are the amplitudes of the electric and magnetic fields at this surface, for a sinusoidal wave with this intensity?

32.16. Consider each of the following electric and magnetic-field orientations. In each case, what is the direction of propagation of the wave? (a) $\vec{E} = E\hat{i}$, $\vec{B} = -B\hat{j}$; (b) $\vec{E} = E\hat{j}$, $\vec{B} = B\hat{i}$; (c) $\vec{E} = -E\hat{k}$, $\vec{B} = -B\hat{i}$; (d) $\vec{E} = E\hat{i}$, $\vec{B} = -B\hat{k}$.

32.17. A sinusoidal electromagnetic wave is propagating in a vacuum in the $+z$-direction. If at a particular instant and at a certain point in space the electric field is in the $+x$-direction and has magnitude 4.00 V/m, what are the magnitude and direction of the magnetic field of the wave at this same point in space and instant in time?

32.18. A sinusoidal electromagnetic wave from a radio station passes perpendicularly through an open window that has area 0.500 m^2. At the window, the electric field of the wave has rms value 0.0200 V/m. How much energy does this wave carry through the window during a 30.0-s commercial?

32.19. Testing a Space Radio Transmitter. You are a NASA mission specialist on your first flight aboard the space shuttle. Thanks to your extensive training in physics, you have been assigned to evaluate the performance of a new radio transmitter on board the International Space Station (ISS). Perched on the shuttle's movable arm, you aim a sensitive detector at the ISS, which is 2.5 km away. You find that the electric-field amplitude of the radio waves coming from the ISS transmitter is 0.090 V/m and that the frequency of the waves is 244 MHz. Find the following: (a) the intensity of the radio wave at your location; (b) the magnetic-field amplitude of the wave at your location; (c) the total power output of the ISS radio transmitter. (d) What assumptions, if any, did you make in your calculations?

32.20. The intensity of a cylindrical laser beam is 0.800 W/m^2. The cross-sectional area of the beam is $3.0 \times 10^{-4} \text{ m}^2$ and the intensity is uniform across the cross section of the beam. (a) What is the average power output of the laser? (b) What is the rms value of the electric field in the beam?

32.21. A space probe 2.0×10^{10} m from a star measures the total intensity of electromagnetic radiation from the star to be $5.0 \times 10^3 \text{ W/m}^2$. If the star radiates uniformly in all directions, what is its total average power output?

32.22. A sinusoidal electromagnetic wave emitted by a cellular phone has a wavelength of 35.4 cm and an electric-field amplitude of 5.40×10^{-2} V/m at a distance of 250 m from the antenna. Calculate (a) the frequency of the wave; (b) the magnetic-field amplitude; (c) the intensity of the wave.

32.23. A monochromatic light source with power output 60.0 W radiates light of wavelength 700 nm uniformly in all directions. Calculate E_{max} and B_{max} for the 700-nm light at a distance of 5.00 m from the source.

32.24. For the electromagnetic wave represented by Eq. (32.19), show that the Poynting vector (a) is in the same direction as the propagation of the wave and (b) has average magnitude given by Eqs. (32.29).

32.25. An intense light source radiates uniformly in all directions. At a distance of 5.0 m from the source, the radiation pressure on a perfectly absorbing surface is 9.0×10^{-6} Pa. What is the total average power output of the source?

32.26. Television Broadcasting. Public television station KQED in San Francisco broadcasts a sinusoidal radio signal at a power of 316 kW. Assume that the wave spreads out uniformly into a hemisphere above the ground. At a home 5.00 km away from the antenna, (a) what average pressure does this wave exert on a totally reflecting surface, (b) what are the amplitudes of the electric and magnetic fields of the wave, and (c) what is the average density of the energy this wave carries? (d) For the energy density in part (c), what percentage is due to the electric field and what percentage is due to the magnetic field?

32.27. If the intensity of direct sunlight at a point on the earth's surface is 0.78 kW/m^2, find (a) the average momentum density (momentum per unit volume) in the sunlight and (b) the average momentum flow rate in the sunlight.

32.28. In the 25-ft Space Simulator facility at NASA's Jet Propulsion Laboratory, a bank of overhead arc lamps can produce light of intensity 2500 W/m^2 at the floor of the facility. (This simulates the intensity of sunlight near the planet Venus.) Find the average radiation pressure (in pascals and in atmospheres) on (a) a totally absorbing section of the floor and (b) a totally reflecting section of the floor. (c) Find the average momentum density (momentum per unit volume) in the light at the floor.

32.29. Verify that all the expressions in Eqs. (32.27) are equivalent to Eq. (32.26).

Section 32.5 Standing Electromagnetic Waves

32.30. An electromagnetic standing wave in air of frequency 750 MHz is set up between two conducting planes 80.0 cm apart. At which positions between the planes could a point charge be placed at rest so that it would *remain* at rest? Explain.

32.31. A standing electromagnetic wave in a certain material has frequency 2.20×10^{10} Hz. The nodal planes of $\vec{B}$ are 3.55 mm apart. Find (a) the wavelength of the wave in this material; (b) the

distance between adjacent nodal planes of the $\vec{E}$ field; (c) the speed of propagation of the wave.

32.32. An electromagnetic standing wave in air has frequency 75.0 MHz. (a) What is the distance between nodal planes of the $\vec{E}$ field? (b) What is the distance between a nodal plane of $\vec{E}$ and the closest nodal plane of $\vec{B}$?

32.33. An electromagnetic standing wave in a certain material has frequency 1.20×10^{10} Hz and speed of propagation 2.10×10^8 m/s. (a) What is the distance between a nodal plane of $\vec{B}$ and the closest antinodal plane of $\vec{B}$? (b) What is the distance between an antinodal plane of $\vec{E}$ and the closest antinodal plane of $\vec{B}$? (c) What is the distance between a nodal plane of $\vec{E}$ and the closest nodal plane of $\vec{B}$?

32.34. Show that the electric and magnetic fields for standing waves given by Eqs. (32.34) and (32.35) (a) satisfy the wave equation, Eq. (32.15), and (b) satisfy Eqs. (32.12) and (32.14).

32.35. Microwave Oven. The microwaves in a certain microwave oven have a wavelength of 12.2 cm. (a) How wide must this oven be so that it will contain five antinodal planes of the electric field along its width in the standing wave pattern? (b) What is the frequency of these microwaves? (c) Suppose a manufacturing error occurred and the oven was made 5.0 cm longer than specified in part (a). In this case, what would have to be the frequency of the microwaves for there still to be five antinodal planes of the electric field along the width of the oven?

Problems

32.36. Consider a sinusoidal electromagnetic wave with fields $\vec{E} = E_{max}\hat{j}\sin(kx - \omega t)$ and $\vec{B} = B_{max}\hat{k}\sin(kx - \omega t + \phi)$, with $-\pi \le \phi \le \pi$. Show that if $\vec{E}$ and $\vec{B}$ are to satisfy Eqs. (32.12) and (32.14), then $E_{max} = cB_{max}$ and $\phi = 0$. (The result $\phi = 0$ means the $\vec{E}$ and $\vec{B}$ fields oscillate in phase.)

32.37. Show that the *magnetic* field $B_z(x, t)$ in a plane electromagnetic wave propagating in the $+x$-direction must satisfy Eq. (32.15). (*Hint:* Take the partial derivative of Eq. (32.12) with respect to t and the partial derivative of Eq. (32.14) with respect to x. Then combine the results.)

32.38. For a sinusoidal electromagnetic wave in vacuum, such as that described by Eq. (32.16), show that the *average* energy density in the electric field is the same as that in the magnetic field.

32.39. A satellite 575 km above the earth's surface transmits sinusoidal electromagnetic waves of frequency 92.4 MHz uniformly in all directions, with a power of 25.0 kW. (a) What is the intensity of these waves as they reach a receiver at the surface of the earth directly below the satellite? (b) What are the amplitudes of the electric and magnetic fields at the receiver? (c) If the receiver has a totally absorbing panel measuring 15.0 cm by 40.0 cm oriented with its plane perpendicular to the direction the waves travel, what average force do these waves exert on the panel? Is this force large enough to cause significant effects?

32.40. A plane sinusoidal electromagnetic wave in air has a wavelength of 3.84 cm and an $\vec{E}$-field amplitude of 1.35 V/m. (a) What is the frequency? (b) What is the $\vec{B}$-field amplitude? (c) What is the intensity? (d) What average force does this radiation exert on a totally absorbing surface with area 0.240 m^2 perpendicular to the direction of propagation?

32.41. A small helium-neon laser emits red visible light with a power of 3.20 mW in a beam that has a diameter of 2.50 mm. (a) What are the amplitudes of the electric and magnetic fields of the light? (b) What are the average energy densities associated with the electric field and with the magnetic field? (c) What is the total energy contained in a 1.00-m length of the beam?

32.42. Consider a plane electromagnetic wave such as that shown in Fig. 32.5, but in which $\vec{E}$ and $\vec{B}$ also have components in the x-direction (along the direction of wave propagation). Use Gauss's law for electric and magnetic fields to show that the components E_x and B_x must both be equal to zero so that the fields $\vec{E}$ and $\vec{B}$ are both transverse. (*Hint:* Use a Gaussian surface like that shown in Fig. 32.6. Of the two faces parallel to the yz-plane, choose one to be to the left of the wave front and the other to be to the right of the wave front.)

32.43. The sun emits energy in the form of electromagnetic waves at a rate of 3.9×10^{26} W. This energy is produced by nuclear reactions deep in the sun's interior. (a) Find the intensity of electromagnetic radiation and the radiation pressure on an absorbing object at the surface of the sun (radius $r = R = 6.96 \times 10^5$ km) and at $r = R/2$, in the sun's interior. Ignore any scattering of the waves as they move radially outward from the center of the sun. Compare to the values given in Section 32.4 for sunlight just before it enters the earth's atmosphere. (b) The gas pressure at the sun's surface is about 1.0×10^4 Pa; at $r = R/2$, the gas pressure is calculated from solar models to be about 4.7×10^{13} Pa Comparing with your results in part (a), would you expect that radiation pressure is an important factor in determining the structure of the sun? Why or why not?

32.44. It has been proposed to place solar-power collecting satellites in earth orbit. The power they collect would be beamed down to the earth as microwave radiation. For a microwave beam with a cross-sectional area of 36.0 m² and a total power of 2.80 kW at the earth's surface, what is the amplitude of the electric field of the beam at the earth's surface?

32.45. Two square reflectors, each 1.50 cm on a side and of mass 4.00 g, are located at opposite ends of a thin, extremely light, 1.00-m rod that can rotate without friction and in a vacuum

Figure 32.24 Problem 32.45.

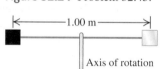

Axis of rotation

about an axle perpendicular to it through its center (Fig. 32.24). These reflectors are small enough to be treated as point masses in moment of-inertia calculations. Both reflectors are illuminated on one face by a sinusoidal light wave having an electric field of amplitude 1.25 N/C that falls uniformly on both surfaces and always strikes them perpendicular to the plane of their surfaces. One reflector is covered with a perfectly absorbing coating, and the other is covered with a perfectly reflecting coating. What is the angular acceleration of this device?

32.46. The plane of a flat surface is perpendicular to the propagation direction of an electromagnetic wave of intensity I. The surface absorbs a fraction w of the incident intensity, where $0 \le w \le 1$, and reflects the rest. (a) Show that the radiation pressure on the surface equals $(2 - w)I/c$. (b) Show that this expression gives the correct results for a surface that is (i) totally absorbing and (ii) totally reflective. (c) For an incident intensity of 1.40 kW/m², what is the radiation pressure for 90% absorption? For 90% reflection?

32.47. A cylindrical conductor with a circular cross section has a radius a and a resistivity ρ and carries a constant current I. (a) What are the magnitude and direction of the electric-field vector $\vec{E}$ at a point just inside the wire at a distance a from the axis? (b) What are the magnitude and direction of the magnetic-field vector $\vec{B}$ at the same point? (c) What are the magnitude and direction of the Poynting vector $\vec{S}$ at the same point? (The direction of $\vec{S}$ is the direction in which electromagnetic energy flows into or out of the conductor.) (d) Use the result in part (c) to find the rate of flow of energy into the volume occupied by a length l of the conductor.

(*Hint:* Integrate $\vec{S}$ over the surface of this volume.) Compare your result to the rate of generation of thermal energy in the same volume. Discuss why the energy dissipated in a current-carrying conductor, due to its resistance, can be thought of as entering through the cylindrical sides of the conductor.

32.48. A source of sinusoidal electromagnetic waves radiates uniformly in all directions. At 10.0 m from this source, the amplitude of the electric field is measured to be 1.50 N/C. What is the electric-field amplitude at a distance of 20.0 cm from the source?

32.49. A circular loop of wire can be used as a radio antenna. If a 18.0-cm-diameter antenna is located 2.50 km from a 95.0-MHz source with a total power of 55.0 kW, what is the maximum emf induced in the loop? (Assume that the plane of the antenna loop is perpendicular to the direction of the radiation's magnetic field and that the source radiates uniformly in all directions.)

32.50. In a certain experiment, a radio transmitter emits sinusoidal electromagnetic waves of frequency 110.0 MHz in opposite directions inside a narrow cavity with reflectors at both ends, causing a standing wave pattern to occur. (a) How far apart are the nodal planes of the magnetic field? (b) If the standing wave pattern is determined to be in its eighth harmonic, how long is the cavity?

32.51. Flashlight to the Rescue. You are the sole crew member of the interplanetary spaceship *T:1339 Vorga*, which makes regular cargo runs between the earth and the mining colonies in the asteroid belt. You are working outside the ship one day while at a distance of 2.0 AU from the sun. [1 AU (astronomical unit) is the average distance from the earth to the sun, 149,600,000 km.] Unfortunately, you lose contact with the ship's hull and begin to drift away into space. You use your spacesuit's rockets to try to push yourself back toward the ship, but they run out of fuel and stop working before you can return to the ship. You find yourself in an awkward position, floating 16.0 m from the spaceship with zero velocity relative to it. Fortunately, you are carrying a 200-W flashlight. You turn on the flashlight and use its beam as a "light rocket" to push yourself back toward the ship. (a) If you, your spacesuit, and the flashlight have a combined mass of 150 kg, how long will it take you to get back to the ship? (b) Is there another way you could use the flashlight to accomplish the same job of returning you to the ship?

32.52. The 19th-century inventor Nikola Tesla proposed to transmit electric power via sinusoidal electromagnetic waves. Suppose power is to be transmitted in a beam of cross-sectional area 100 m². What electric- and magnetic-field amplitudes are required to transmit an amount of power comparable to that handled by modern transmission lines (that carry voltages and currents of the order of 500 kV and 1000 A)?

32.53. Global Positioning System (GPS). The GPS network consists of 24 satellites, each of which makes two orbits around the earth per day. Each satellite transmits a 50.0-W (or even less) sinusoidal electromagnetic signal at two frequencies, one of which is 1575.42 MHz. Assume that a satellite transmits half of its power at each frequency and that the waves travel uniformly in a downward hemisphere. (a) What average intensity does a GPS receiver on the ground, directly below the satellite, receive? (*Hint:* First use Newton's laws to find the altitude of the satellite.) (b) What are the amplitudes of the electric and magnetic fields at the GPS receiver in part (a), and how long does it take the signal to reach the receiver? (c) If the receiver is a square panel 1.50 cm on a side that absorbs all of the beam, what average pressure does the signal exert on it? (d) What wavelength must the receiver be tuned to?

32.54. NASA is giving serious consideration to the concept of *solar sailing*. A solar sailcraft uses a large, low-mass sail and the energy and momentum of sunlight for propulsion. (a) Should the sail be absorbing or reflective? Why? (b) The total power output of the sun is 3.9×10^{26} W. How large a sail is necessary to propel a 10,000-kg spacecraft against the gravitational force of the sun? Express your result in square kilometers. (c) Explain why your answer to part (b) is independent of the distance from the sun.

32.55. Interplanetary space contains many small particles referred to as *interplanetary dust*. Radiation pressure from the sun sets a lower limit on the size of such dust particles. To see the origin of this limit, consider a spherical dust particle of radius R and mass density ρ. (a) Write an expression for the gravitational force exerted on this particle by the sun (mass M) when the particle is a distance r from the sun. (b) Let L represent the luminosity of the sun, equal to the rate at which it emits energy in electromagnetic radiation. Find the force exerted on the (totally absorbing) particle due to solar radiation pressure, remembering that the intensity of the sun's radiation also depends on the distance r. The relevant area is the cross-sectional area of the particle, *not* the total surface area of the particle. As part of your answer, explain why this is so. (c) The mass density of a typical interplanetary dust particle is about 3000 kg/m^3. Find the particle radius R such that the gravitational and radiation forces acting on the particle are equal in magnitude. The luminosity of the sun is 3.9×10^{26} W. Does your answer depend on the distance of the particle from the sun? Why or why not? (d) Explain why dust particles with a radius less than that found in part (c) are unlikely to be found in the solar system. [*Hint:* Construct the ratio of the two force expressions found in parts (a) and (b).]

Challenge Problems

32.56. The Classical Hydrogen Atom.   The electron in a hydrogen atom can be considered to be in a circular orbit with a radius of 0.0529 nm and a kinetic energy of 13.6 eV. If the electron behaved classically, how much energy would it radiate per second (see Challenge Problem 32.57)? What does this tell you about the use of classical physics in describing the atom?

32.57. Electromagnetic radiation is emitted by accelerating charges. The rate at which energy is emitted from an accelerating charge that has charge q and acceleration a is given by

$$\frac{dE}{dt} = \frac{q^2 a^2}{6\pi\epsilon_0 c^3}$$

where c is the speed of light. (a) Verify that this equation is dimensionally correct. (b) If a proton with a kinetic energy of 6.0 MeV is traveling in a particle accelerator in a circular orbit of radius 0.750 m, what fraction of its energy does it radiate per second? (c) Consider an electron orbiting with the same speed and radius. What fraction of its energy does it radiate per second?

32.58. Electromagnetic waves propagate much differently in *conductors* than they do in dielectrics or in vacuum. If the resistivity of the conductor is sufficiently low (that is, if it is a sufficiently good conductor), the oscillating electric field of the wave gives rise to an oscillating conduction current that is much larger than the displacement current. In this case, the wave equation for an electric field $\vec{E}(x, t) = E_y(x, t)\hat{j}$ propagating in the $+x$-direction within a conductor is

$$\frac{\partial^2 E_y(x, t)}{\partial x^2} = \frac{\mu}{\rho} \frac{\partial E_y(x, t)}{\partial t}$$

where μ is the permeability of the conductor and ρ is its resistivity. (a) A solution to this wave equation is

$$E_y(x, t) = E_{max} e^{-k_C x} \sin(k_C x - \omega t)$$

where $k_C = \sqrt{\omega\mu/2\rho}$. Verify this by substituting $E_y(x, t)$ into the above wave equation. (b) The exponential term shows that the electric field decreases in amplitude as it propagates. Explain why this happens. (*Hint:* The field does work to move charges within the conductor. The current of these moving charges causes $i^2 R$ heating within the conductor, raising its temperature. Where does the energy to do this come from?). (c) Show that the electric-field amplitude decreases by a factor of $1/e$ in a distance $1/k_C = \sqrt{2\rho/\omega\mu}$, and calculate this distance for a radio wave with frequency $f = 1.0$ MHz in copper (resistivity 1.72×10^{-8} $\Omega \cdot$ m; permeability $\mu = \mu_0$). Since this distance is so short, electromagnetic waves of this frequency can hardly propagate at all into copper. Instead, they are reflected at the surface of the metal. This is why radio waves cannot penetrate through copper or other metals, and why radio reception is poor inside a metal structure.

APPENDIX A

THE INTERNATIONAL SYSTEM OF UNITS

The Système International d'Unités, abbreviated SI, is the system developed by the General Conference on Weights and Measures and adopted by nearly all the industrial nations of the world. The following material is adapted from B. N. Taylor, ed., National Institute of Standards and Technology Spec. Pub. 811 (U.S. Govt. Printing Office, Washington, DC, 1995). See also **http://physics.nist.gov/cuu**

Quantity	Name of unit	Symbol	Equivalent units
SI base units			
length	meter	m	
mass	kilogram	kg	
time	second	s	
electric current	ampere	A	
thermodynamic temperature	kelvin	K	
amount of substance	mole	mol	
luminous intensity	candela	cd	
SI derived units			
area	square meter	m^2	
volume	cubic meter	m^3	
frequency	hertz	Hz	s^{-1}
mass density (density)	kilogram per cubic meter	kg/m^3	
speed, velocity	meter per second	m/s	
angular velocity	radian per second	rad/s	
acceleration	meter per second squared	m/s^2	
angular acceleration	radian per second squared	rad/s^2	
force	newton	N	$kg \cdot m/s^2$
pressure (mechanical stress)	pascal	Pa	N/m^2
kinematic viscosity	square meter per second	m^2/s	
dynamic viscosity	newton-second per square meter	$N \cdot s/m^2$	
work, energy, quantity of heat	joule	J	$N \cdot m$
power	watt	W	J/s
quantity of electricity	coulomb	C	$A \cdot s$
potential difference, electromotive force	volt	V	J/C, W/A
electric field strength	volt per meter	V/m	N/C
electric resistance	ohm	Ω	V/A
capacitance	farad	F	$A \cdot s/V$
magnetic flux	weber	Wb	$V \cdot s$
inductance	henry	H	$V \cdot s/A$
magnetic flux density	tesla	T	Wb/m^2
magnetic field strength	ampere per meter	A/m	
magnetomotive force	ampere	A	
luminous flux	lumen	lm	$cd \cdot sr$
luminance	candela per square meter	cd/m^2	
illuminance	lux	lx	lm/m^2
wave number	1 per meter	m^{-1}	
entropy	joule per kelvin	J/K	
specific heat capacity	joule per kilogram-kelvin	$J/kg \cdot K$	
thermal conductivity	watt per meter-kelvin	$W/m \cdot K$	

Quantity	Name of unit	Symbol	Equivalent units
radiant intensity	watt per steradian	W/sr	
activity (of a radioactive source)	becquerel	Bq	s^{-1}
radiation dose	gray	Gy	J/kg
radiation dose equivalent	sievert	Sv	J/kg
SI supplementary units			
plane angle	radian	rad	
solid angle	steradian	sr	

Definitions of SI Units

meter (m) The *meter* is the length equal to the distance traveled by light, in vacuum, in a time of 1/299,792,458 second.

kilogram (kg) The *kilogram* is the unit of mass; it is equal to the mass of the international prototype of the kilogram. (The international prototype of the kilogram is a particular cylinder of platinum-iridium alloy that is preserved in a vault at Sévres, France, by the International Bureau of Weights and Measures.)

second (s) The *second* is the duration of 9,192,631,770 periods of the radiation corresponding to the transition between the two hyperfine levels of the ground state of the cesium-133 atom.

ampere (A) The *ampere* is that constant current that, if maintained in two straight parallel conductors of infinite length, of negligible circular cross section, and placed 1 meter apart in vacuum, would produce between these conductors a force equal to 2×10^{-7} newton per meter of length.

kelvin (K) The *kelvin*, unit of thermodynamic temperature, is the fraction 1/273.16 of the thermodynamic temper-ature of the triple point of water.

ohm (Ω) The *ohm* is the electric resistance between two points of a conductor when a constant difference of potential of 1 volt, applied between these two points, produces in this conductor a current of 1 ampere, this conductor not being the source of any electromotive force.

coulomb (C) The *coulomb* is the quantity of electricity transported in 1 second by a current of 1 ampere.

candela (cd) The *candela* is the luminous intensity, in a given direction, of a source that emits monochromatic radiation of frequency 540×10^{12} hertz and that has a radiant intensity in that direction of 1/683 watt per steradian.

mole (mol) The *mole* is the amount of substance of a system that contains as many elementary entities as there are carbon atoms in 0.012 kg of carbon 12. The elementary entities must be specified and may be atoms, molecules, ions, electrons, other particles, or specified groups of such particles.

newton (N) The *newton* is that force that gives to a mass of 1 kilogram an acceleration of 1 meter per second per second.

joule (J) The *joule* is the work done when the point of application of a constant force of 1 newton is displaced a distance of 1 meter in the direction of the force.

watt (W) The *watt* is the power that gives rise to the production of energy at the rate of 1 joule per second.

volt (V) The *volt* is the difference of electric potential between two points of a conducting wire carrying a constant current of 1 ampere, when the power dissipated between these points is equal to 1 watt.

weber (Wb) The *weber* is the magnetic flux that, linking a circuit of one turn, produces in it an electromotive force of 1 volt as it is reduced to zero at a uniform rate in 1 second.

lumen (lm) The *lumen* is the luminous flux emitted in a solid angle of 1 steradian by a uniform point source having an intensity of 1 candela.

farad (F) The *farad* is the capacitance of a capacitor between the plates of which there appears a difference of potential of 1 volt when it is charged by a quantity of electricity equal to 1 coulomb.

henry (H) The *henry* is the inductance of a closed circuit in which an electromotive force of 1 volt is produced when the electric current in the circuit varies uniformly at a rate of 1 ampere per second.

radian (rad) The *radian* is the plane angle between two radii of a circle that cut off on the circumference an arc equal in length to the radius.

steradian (sr) The *steradian* is the solid angle that, having its vertex in the center of a sphere, cuts off an area of the surface of the sphere equal to that of a square with sides of length equal to the radius of the sphere.

SI Prefixes The names of multiples and submultiples of SI units may be formed by application of the prefixes listed in Appendix F.

APPENDIX B

USEFUL MATHEMATICAL RELATIONS

Algebra

$$a^{-x} = \frac{1}{a^x} \qquad a^{(x+y)} = a^x a^y \qquad a^{(x-y)} = \frac{a^x}{a^y}$$

Logarithms: If $\log a = x$, then $a = 10^x$. $\qquad \log a + \log b = \log(ab) \qquad \log a - \log b = \log(a/b) \qquad \log(a^n) = n\log a$

If $\ln a = x$, then $a = e^x$. $\qquad \ln a + \ln b = \ln(ab) \qquad \ln a - \ln b = \ln(a/b) \qquad \ln(a^n) = n\ln a$

Quadratic formula: If $ax^2 + bx + c = 0$, $\qquad x = \dfrac{-b \pm \sqrt{b^2 - 4ac}}{2a}$.

Binomial Theorem

$$(a + b)^n = a^n + na^{n-1}b + \frac{n(n-1)a^{n-2}b^2}{2!} + \frac{n(n-1)(n-2)a^{n-3}b^3}{3!} + \cdots$$

Trigonometry

In the right triangle ABC, $x^2 + y^2 = r^2$.

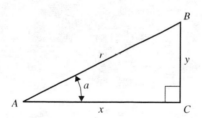

Definitions of the trigonometric functions: $\sin a = y/r \qquad \cos a = x/r \qquad \tan a = y/x$

Identities:

$$\sin^2 a + \cos^2 a = 1 \qquad\qquad \tan a = \frac{\sin a}{\cos a}$$

$$\sin 2a = 2\sin a \cos a \qquad\qquad \cos 2a = \cos^2 a - \sin^2 a = 2\cos^2 a - 1$$
$$= 1 - 2\sin^2 a$$

$$\sin\tfrac{1}{2}a = \sqrt{\frac{1 - \cos a}{2}} \qquad\qquad \cos\tfrac{1}{2}a = \sqrt{\frac{1 + \cos a}{2}}$$

$$\sin(-a) = -\sin a \qquad\qquad \sin(a \pm b) = \sin a \cos b \pm \cos a \sin b$$
$$\cos(-a) = \cos a \qquad\qquad \cos(a \pm b) = \cos a \cos b \mp \sin a \sin b$$
$$\sin(a \pm \pi/2) = \pm\cos a \qquad\qquad \sin a + \sin b = 2\sin\tfrac{1}{2}(a + b)\cos\tfrac{1}{2}(a - b)$$
$$\cos(a \pm \pi/2) = \mp\sin a \qquad\qquad \cos a + \cos b = 2\cos\tfrac{1}{2}(a + b)\cos\tfrac{1}{2}(a - b)$$

Geometry

Circumference of circle of radius r: $\qquad C = 2\pi r$

Area of circle of radius r: $\qquad A = \pi r^2$

Volume of sphere of radius r: $\qquad V = 4\pi r^3/3$

Surface area of sphere of radius r: $\qquad A = 4\pi r^2$

Volume of cylinder of radius r and height h: $\qquad V = \pi r^2 h$

Calculus

Derivatives:

$$\frac{d}{dx}x^n = nx^{n-1}$$

$$\frac{d}{dx}\sin ax = a\cos ax$$

$$\frac{d}{dx}\cos ax = -a\sin ax$$

$$\frac{d}{dx}e^{ax} = ae^{ax}$$

$$\frac{d}{dx}\ln ax = \frac{1}{x}$$

$$\int \frac{dx}{\sqrt{a^2 - x^2}} = \arcsin\frac{x}{a}$$

$$\int \frac{dx}{\sqrt{x^2 + a^2}} = \ln\left(x + \sqrt{x^2 + a^2}\right)$$

$$\int \frac{dx}{x^2 + a^2} = \frac{1}{a}\arctan\frac{x}{a}$$

$$\int \frac{dx}{(x^2 + a^2)^{3/2}} = \frac{1}{a^2}\frac{x}{\sqrt{x^2 + a^2}}$$

$$\int \frac{x\,dx}{(x^2 + a^2)^{3/2}} = -\frac{1}{\sqrt{x^2 + a^2}}$$

Integrals:

$$\int x^n dx = \frac{x^{n+1}}{n+1} \quad (n \neq -1)$$

$$\int \frac{dx}{x} = \ln x$$

$$\int \sin ax\,dx = -\frac{1}{a}\cos ax$$

$$\int \cos ax\,dx = \frac{1}{a}$$

$$\int e^{ax} dx = \frac{1}{a}e^{ax}$$

Power series (convergent for range of x shown):

$$(1 + x)^n = 1 + nx + \frac{n(n-1)x^2}{2!} + \frac{n(n-1)(n-2)}{3!}x^3 + \cdots \quad (|x| < 1)$$

$$\sin x = x - \frac{x^3}{3!} + \frac{x^5}{5!} - \frac{x^7}{7!} + \cdots \quad (\text{all } x)$$

$$\cos x = 1 - \frac{x^2}{2!} + \frac{x^4}{4!} - \frac{x^6}{6!} + \cdots \quad (\text{all } x)$$

$$\tan x = x + \frac{x^3}{3} + \frac{2x^2}{15} + \frac{17x^7}{315} + \cdots \quad (|x| < \pi/2)$$

$$e^x = 1 + x + \frac{x^2}{2!} + \frac{x^3}{3!} + \cdots \quad (\text{all } x)$$

$$\ln(1 + x) = x - \frac{x^2}{2} + \frac{x^3}{3} - \frac{x^4}{4} + \cdots \quad (|x| < 1)$$

APPENDIX C

THE GREEK ALPHABET

Name	Capital	Lowercase	Name	Capital	Lowercase
Alpha	A	α	Nu	N	ν
Beta	B	β	Xi	Ξ	ξ
Gamma	Γ	γ	Omicron	O	o
Delta	Δ	δ	Pi	Π	π
Epsilon	E	ϵ	Rho	P	ρ
Zeta	Z	ζ	Sigma	Σ	σ
Eta	H	η	Tau	T	τ
Theta	Θ	θ	Upsilon	Υ	υ
Iota	I	ι	Phi	Φ	ϕ
Kappa	K	κ	Chi	X	χ
Lambda	Λ	λ	Psi	Ψ	ψ
Mu	M	μ	Omega	Ω	ω

APPENDIX D

PERIODIC TABLE OF THE ELEMENTS

Group Period	1	2	3	4	5	6	7	8	9	10	11	12	13	14	15	16	17	18
1	1 **H** 1.008																	2 **He** 4.003
2	3 **Li** 6.941	4 **Be** 9.012											5 **B** 10.811	6 **C** 12.011	7 **N** 14.007	8 **O** 15.999	9 **F** 18.998	10 **Ne** 20.180
3	11 **Na** 22.990	12 **Mg** 24.305											13 **Al** 26.982	14 **Si** 28.086	15 **P** 30.974	16 **S** 32.065	17 **Cl** 35.453	18 **Ar** 39.948
4	19 **K** 39.098	20 **Ca** 40.078	21 **Sc** 44.956	22 **Ti** 47.867	23 **V** 50.942	24 **Cr** 51.996	25 **Mn** 54.938	26 **Fe** 55.845	27 **Co** 58.933	28 **Ni** 58.693	29 **Cu** 63.546	30 **Zn** 65.409	31 **Ga** 69.723	32 **Ge** 72.64	33 **As** 74.922	34 **Se** 78.96	35 **Br** 79.904	36 **Kr** 83.798
5	37 **Rb** 85.468	38 **Sr** 87.62	39 **Y** 88.906	40 **Zr** 91.224	41 **Nb** 92.906	42 **Mo** 95.94	43 **Tc** (98)	44 **Ru** 101.07	45 **Rh** 102.906	46 **Pd** 106.42	47 **Ag** 107.868	48 **Cd** 112.411	49 **In** 114.818	50 **Sn** 118.710	51 **Sb** 121.760	52 **Te** 127.60	53 **I** 126.904	54 **Xe** 131.293
6	55 **Cs** 132.905	56 **Ba** 137.327	71 **Lu** 174.967	72 **Hf** 178.49	73 **Ta** 180.948	74 **W** 183.84	75 **Re** 186.207	76 **Os** 190.23	77 **Ir** 192.217	78 **Pt** 195.078	79 **Au** 196.967	80 **Hg** 200.59	81 **Tl** 204.383	82 **Pb** 207.2	83 **Bi** 208.980	84 **Po** (209)	85 **At** (210)	86 **Rn** (222)
7	87 **Fr** (223)	88 **Ra** (226)	103 **Lr** (262)	104 **Rf** (261)	105 **Db** (262)	106 **Sg** (266)	107 **Bh** (264)	108 **Hs** (269)	109 **Mt** (268)	110 **Ds** (271)	111 **Rg** (272)	112 **Uub** (285)	113 **Uut** (284)	114 **Uuq** (289)	115 **Uup** (288)	116 **Uuh** (292)	117 **Uus**	118 **Uuo**

Lanthanoids	57 **La** 138.905	58 **Ce** 140.116	59 **Pr** 140.908	60 **Nd** 144.24	61 **Pm** (145)	62 **Sm** 150.36	63 **Eu** 151.964	64 **Gd** 157.25	65 **Tb** 158.925	66 **Dy** 162.500	67 **Ho** 164.930	68 **Er** 167.259	69 **Tm** 168.934	70 **Yb** 173.04
Actinoids	89 **Ac** (227)	90 **Th** (232)	91 **Pa** (231)	92 **U** (238)	93 **Np** (237)	94 **Pu** (244)	95 **Am** (243)	96 **Cm** (247)	97 **Bk** (247)	98 **Cf** (251)	99 **Es** (252)	100 **Fm** (257)	101 **Md** (258)	102 **No** (259)

For each element the average atomic mass of the mixture of isotopes occurring in nature is shown. For elements having no stable isotope, the approximate atomic mass of the longest-lived isotope is shown in parentheses. For elements that have been predicted but not yet detected, no atomic mass is given. All atomic masses are expressed in atomic mass units ($1\ u = 1.66053886(28) \times 10^{-27}$ kg), equivalent to grams per mole (g/mol).

APPENDIX E

UNIT CONVERSION FACTORS

Length
1 m = 100 cm = 1000 mm = 10^6 μm = 10^9 nm
1 km = 1000 m = 0.6214 mi
1 m = 3.281 ft = 39.37 in.
1 cm = 0.3937 in.
1 in. = 2.540 cm
1 ft = 30.48 cm
1 yd = 91.44 cm
1 mi = 5280 ft = 1.609 km
1 Å = 10^{-10} m = 10^{-8} cm = 10^{-1} nm
1 nautical mile = 6080 ft
1 light year = 9.461 × 10^{15} m

Area
1 cm^2 = 0.155 $in.^2$
1 m^2 = 10^4 cm^2 = 10.76 ft^2
1 $in.^2$ = 6.452 cm^2
1 ft = 144 $in.^2$ = 0.0929 m^2

Volume
1 liter = 1000 cm^3 = 10^{-3} m^3 = 0.03531 ft^3 = 61.02 $in.^3$
1 ft^3 = 0.02832 m^3 = 28.32 liters = 7.477 gallons
1 gallon = 3.788 liters

Time
1 min = 60 s
1 h = 3600 s
1 d = 86,400 s
1 y = 365.24 d = 3.156 × 10^7 s

Angle
1 rad = 57.30° = 180°/π
1° = 0.01745 rad = π/180 rad
1 revolution = 360° = 2π rad
1 rev/min (rpm) = 0.1047 rad/s

Speed
1 m/s = 3.281 ft/s
1 ft/s = 0.3048 m/s
1 mi/min = 60 mi/h = 88 ft/s
1 km/h = 0.2778 m/s = 0.6214 mi/h
1 mi/h = 1.466 ft/s = 0.4470 m/s = 1.609 km/h
1 furlong/fortnight = 1.662 × 10^{-4} m/s

Acceleration
1 m/s^2 = 100 cm/s^2 = 3.281 ft/s^2
1 cm/s^2 = 0.01 m/s^2 = 0.03281 ft/s^2
1 ft/s^2 = 0.3048 m/s^2 = 30.48 cm/s^2
1 mi/h · s = 1.467 ft/s^2

Mass
1 kg = 10^3 g = 0.0685 slug
1 g = 6.85 × 10^{-5} slug
1 slug = 14.59 kg
1 u = 1.661 × 10^{-27} kg
1 kg has a weight of 2.205 lb when g = 9.80 m/s^2

Force
1 N = 10^5 dyn = 0.2248 lb
1 lb = 4.448 N = 4.448 × 10^5 dyn

Pressure
1 Pa = 1 N/m^2 = 1.450 × 10^{-4} $lb/in.^2$ = 0.209 lb/ft^2
1 bar = 10^5 Pa
1 $lb/in.^2$ = 6895 Pa
1 lb/ft^2 = 47.88 Pa
1 atm = 1.013 × 10^5 Pa = 1.013 bar
       = 14.7 $lb/in.^2$ = 2117 lb/ft^2
1 mm Hg = 1 torr = 133.3 Pa

Energy
1 J = 10^7ergs = 0.239 cal
1 cal = 4.186 J (based on 15° calorie)
1 ft · lb = 1.356 J
1 Btu = 1055 J = 252 cal = 778 ft · lb
1 eV = 1.602 × 10^{-19} J
1 kWh = 3.600 × 10^6 J

Mass–Energy Equivalence
1 kg $\leftrightarrow$ 8.988 × 10^{16} J
1 u $\leftrightarrow$ 931.5 MeV
1 eV $\leftrightarrow$ 1.074 × 10^{-9} u

Power
1 W = 1 J/s
1 hp = 746 W = 550 ft · lb/s
1 Btu/h = 0.293 W

APPENDIX F

NUMERICAL CONSTANTS

Fundamental Physical Constants*

Name	Symbol	Value
Speed of light	c	2.99792458×10^8 m/s
Magnitude of charge of electron	e	$1.60217653(14) \times 10^{-19}$ C
Gravitational constant	G	$6.6742(10) \times 10^{-11}$ N $\cdot$ m^2/kg^2
Planck's constant	h	$6.6260693(11) \times 10^{-34}$ J $\cdot$ s
Boltzmann constant	k	$1.3806505(24) \times 10^{-23}$ J/K
Avogadro's number	N_A	$6.0221415(10) \times 10^{23}$ molecules/mol
Gas constant	R	$8.314472(15)$ J/mol $\cdot$ K
Mass of electron	m_e	$9.1093826(16) \times 10^{-31}$ kg
Mass of proton	m_p	$1.67262171(29) \times 10^{-27}$ kg
Mass of neutron	m_n	$1.67492728(29) \times 10^{-27}$ kg
Permeability of free space	μ_0	$4\pi \times 10^{-7}$ Wb/A $\cdot$ m
Permittivity of free space	$\epsilon_0 = 1/\mu_0 c^2$	$8.854187817 \ldots \times 10^{-12}$ C^2/N $\cdot$ m^2
	$1/4\pi\epsilon_0$	$8.987551787 \ldots \times 10^9$ N $\cdot$ m^2/C^2

Other Useful Constants*

Name	Symbol	Value
Mechanical equivalent of heat		4.186 J/cal (15° calorie)
Standard atmospheric pressure	1 atm	1.01325×10^5 Pa
Absolute zero	0 K	-273.15°C
Electron volt	1 eV	$1.60217653(14) \times 10^{-19}$ J
Atomic mass unit	1 u	$1.66053886(28) \times 10^{-27}$ kg
Electron rest energy	$m_e c^2$	$0.510998918(44)$ MeV
Volume of ideal gas (0°C and 1 atm)		$22.413996(39)$ liter/mol
Acceleration due to gravity (standard)	g	9.80665 m/s^2

*Source: National Institute of Standards and Technology (**http://physics.nist.gov/cuu**). Numbers in parentheses show the uncertainty in the final digits of the main number; for example, the number 1.6454(21) means 1.6454 ± 0.0021. Values shown without uncertainties are exact.

Astronomical Data[†]

Body	Mass (kg)	Radius (m)	Orbit radius (m)	Orbit period
Sun	1.99×10^{30}	6.96×10^8	—	—
Moon	7.35×10^{22}	1.74×10^6	3.84×10^8	27.3 d
Mercury	3.30×10^{23}	2.44×10^6	5.79×10^{10}	88.0 d
Venus	4.87×10^{24}	6.05×10^6	1.08×10^{11}	224.7 d
Earth	5.97×10^{24}	6.38×10^6	1.50×10^{11}	365.3 d
Mars	6.42×10^{23}	3.40×10^6	2.28×10^{11}	687.0 d
Jupiter	1.90×10^{27}	6.91×10^7	7.78×10^{11}	11.86 y
Saturn	5.68×10^{26}	6.03×10^7	1.43×10^{12}	29.45 y
Uranus	8.68×10^{25}	2.56×10^7	2.87×10^{12}	84.02 y
Neptune	1.02×10^{26}	2.48×10^7	4.50×10^{12}	164.8 y
Pluto[‡]	1.31×10^{22}	1.15×10^6	5.91×10^{12}	247.9 y

[†]Source: NASA Jet Propulsion Laboratory Solar System Dynamics Group (**http://ssd.jpl.nasa.gov**), and P. Kenneth Seidelmann, ed., ***Explanatory Supplement to the Astronomical Almanac*** (University Science Books, Mill Valley, CA, 1992), pp. 704–706. For each body, "radius" is its radius at its equator and "orbit radius" is its average distance from the sun (for the planets) or from the earth (for the moon).

[‡]In August 2006, the International Astronomical Union reclassified Pluto and other small objects that orbit the sun as "dwarf planets."

Prefixes for Powers of 10

Power of ten	Prefix	Abbreviation	Pronunciation
10^{-24}	yocto-	y	*yoc*-toe
10^{-21}	zepto-	z	*zep*-toe
10^{-18}	atto-	a	*at*-toe
10^{-15}	femto-	f	*fem*-toe
10^{-12}	pico-	p	*pee*-koe
10^{-9}	nano-	n	*nan*-oe
10^{-6}	micro-	μ	*my*-crow
10^{-3}	milli-	m	*mil*-i
10^{-2}	centi-	c	*cen*-ti
10^3	kilo-	k	*kil*-oe
10^6	mega-	M	*meg*-a
10^9	giga-	G	*jig*-a or *gig*-a
10^{12}	tera-	T	*ter*-a
10^{15}	peta-	P	*pet*-a
10^{18}	exa-	E	*ex*-a
10^{21}	zetta-	Z	*zet*-a
10^{24}	yotta-	Y	*yot*-a

Examples:

1 femtometer = 1 fm = 10^{-15} m

1 picosecond = 1 ps = 10^{-12} s

1 nanocoulomb = 1 nC = 10^{-9} C

1 microkelvin = 1 μK = 10^{-6} K

1 millivolt = 1 mV = 10^{-3} V

1 kilopascal = 1 kPa = 10^3 Pa

1 megawatt = 1 MW = 10^6 W

1 gigahertz = 1 GHz = 10^9 Hz

ANSWERS TO ODD-NUMBERED PROBLEMS

Chapter 1

1.1 a) 1.61 km b) 3.28×10^3 ft
1.3 1.02 ns
1.5 5.36 L
1.7 31.7 y
1.9 a) 23.4 km/L b) 1.42 tanks
1.11 9.0 cm
1.13 a) $1.1 \times 10^{-3}\%$ b) no
1.15 a) 0.1% b) 0.008% c) 0.03%
1.17 a) 28 ± 0.3 cm^3 b) 170 ± 20
1.19 a) no b) no c) no d) no e) no
1.21 10^6
1.23 10^9
1.25 $70 million
1.29 9×10^{14}; about 3×10^6
1.31 7.8 km, 38° north of east
1.33 144 m, 41° south of west
1.35 $A_x = 0$, $A_y = -8.00$ m; $B_x = 7.50$ m,
$B_y = 13.0$ m; $C_x = -10.9$ m, $C_y = -5.07$ m;
$D_x = -7.99$ m, $D_y = 6.02$ m
1.37 1190 N; 13.4° above forward direction
1.39 a) 9.01 m, 33.7° b) 9.01 m, 33.7°
c) 22.3 m, 250.3° d) 22.3 m, 70.3°
1.41 5.06 km, 20.2° north of west
1.43 a) 2.48 cm, 18.3° b) 4.10 cm, 83.7°
c) 4.10 cm, 263.7°
1.45 781 N, 166°
1.47 $\vec{A} = -(8.00 \text{ m})\hat{\jmath}$; $\vec{B} = (7.50 \text{ m})\hat{\imath} + (13.0 \text{ m})\hat{\jmath}$;
$\vec{C} = -(10.9 \text{ m})\hat{\imath} + (-5.07 \text{ m})\hat{\jmath}$;
$\vec{D} = (-7.99 \text{ m})\hat{\imath} + (6.02 \text{ m})\hat{\jmath}$
1.49 a) $\vec{A} = (1.23 \text{ m})\hat{\imath} + (3.38 \text{ m})\hat{\jmath}$;
$\vec{B} = (-2.08 \text{ m})\hat{\imath} + (-1.20 \text{ m})\hat{\jmath}$
b) $\vec{C} = (12.01 \text{ m})\hat{\imath} + (14.94 \text{ m})\hat{\jmath}$
c) 19.17 m; 51.2°
1.51 a) no; yes; ± 0.20
1.53 a) -104 m^2 b) -148 m^2 c) 40.6 m^2
1.55 a) 165° b) 28° c) 90°
1.57 a) 63.9 m; $-\hat{k}$ b) 63.9 m; $+\hat{k}$
1.59 a) 4.61 cm^2; $-z$ b) 4.61 cm^2; $+z$
1.61 a) 1.65×10^4 km b) 2.6 earth radii
1.63 10^{28}
1.65 a) 2.94 cm b) 1.82 cm
1.67 a) 10^{50} b) 10^{57} c) 10^{79}
1.69 149 N; 32.2° north of east
1.71 a) $A_x = 3.03$ cm, $A_y = 8.10$ cm c) 8.65 cm;
69.5° from the $+x$-axis toward the $+y$-axis
1.73 144 m, 41° south of west
1.75 a) 46 N, 139°
1.77 a) (87, 258) b) 136 pixels, 25° below
straight left
1.79 380 km, 28.8° south of east
1.81 160 N, 13° below horizontal
1.83 a) 911 m; 8.9° west of south
1.87 b) 90°
1.89 a) $A = 5.39$, $B = 4.36$
b) $-5.00\hat{\imath} + 2.00\hat{\jmath} + 7.00\hat{k}$ c) 8.83; yes
1.93 a) 54.7° b) 35.3°
1.95 $C_x = 8.0$, $C_y = 6.1$
1.97 b) 72.2
1.99 38.5 yd, 24.6° to right of downfield
1.101 a) 76 ly b) 129°

Chapter 2

2.1 a) 197 m/s b) 169 m/s
2.3 1 h 10 min
2.5 a) 17.1 s b) faster: 106 m; slower: 94 m
2.7 250 km
2.9 a) 12.0 m/s b) 0 m/s, 15.0 m/s, 12.0 m/s
c) 13.3 s
2.11 a) 2.3 m/s, 2.3 m/s b) 2.3 m/s, 0.33 m/s
2.13 a) no b) (i) 12.8 m/s^2 (ii) 3.5 m/s^2
(iii) 0.72 m/s^2; yes
2.15 a) 2.00 cm/s, 50.0 cm, -0.125 cm/s^2
b) 16.0 s c) 32.0 s d) 6.20 s, 1.22 cm/s;
25.8 s, -1.22 cm/s; 36.4 s, -2.55 cm/s

2.17 a) 3 m/s^2 b) 10 m/s^2 c) depends on
positive coordinate direction
2.21 a) 5.0 m/s b) 1.43 m/s^2
2.23 a) 675 m/s^2 b) 0.067 s
2.25 1.70
2.27 a) (i) 5.59 m/s^2 (ii) 7.74 m/s^2
b) 179 m (ii) 12,800 m
2.29 a) $+2.7$ cm/s, -1.3 cm/s b) -1.3 cm/s^2
c) 22.5 cm; 25.5 cm
2.31 a) 0, 6.3 m/s^2, -11.2 m/s^2
b) 100 m, 230 m, 320 m
2.33 a) 1.80×10^4 m/s b) 0.957
c) 6 h 11 min
2.35 b) 1 s, 3 s d) 2 s e) 3 s f) 1 s
2.37 a) A: 20.5 m/s^2; B: 3.8 m/s^2; C: 53 m/s^2
b) 721 km
2.39 a) 2.94 m/s b) 0.599 s
2.41 a) $t = \sqrt{2d/g}$ b) 0.190 s
2.43 a) 646 m b) 16.4 s, 112 m/s
2.45 a) 25.6 m/s b) 31.6 m c) 15.2 m/s
2.47 a) 249 m/s^2 b) 25.4 c) 101 m d) no
2.49 0.0868 m/s^2
2.51 a) $x(t) = (0.250 \text{ m/s}^3)t^3 - (0.0100 \text{ m/s}^4)t^4$;
$v_x(t) = (0.750 \text{ m/s}^3)t^2 - (0.0400 \text{ m/s}^4)t^3$
b) 39.1 m/s
2.53 a) 30.0 cm/s
2.55 b) 0.627 s, 1.60 s c) negative at 0.627 s,
positive at 1.60 s d) 1.11 s e) 2.45 m
f) 2.00 s, 0 s
2.57 a) 82 km/h b) 31 km/h
2.59 a) 3.5 m/s^2 b) 0 c) 1.5 m/s^2
2.61 a) 92.0 m b) 92.0 m
2.63 a) 464 m/s b) 2.99×10^4 m/s c) 7.48
2.65 50.0 m
2.67 4.6 m/s^2
2.69 a) 6.17 s b) 24.8 m
c) $v_{\text{truck}} = 13.0$ m/s, $v_{\text{auto}} = 21.0$ m/s
2.71 a) 7.85 cm/s b) 5.00 cm/s, horizontal from
the initial to final position
2.73 a) 15.9 s b) 393 m c) 29.5 m/s
2.75 a) -4.00 m/s b) 12.0 m/s
2.77 a) 2.64H b) 2.64T
2.79 a) no b) yes; 14.4 m/s; not physically
attainable
2.81 a) $6.79 \times 10^4 g$ b) 1.45 m/s c) $H/4$
2.83 a) 7.59 m/s b) 5.14 m c) 1.60 s
2.85 a) 7.7 m/s b) 0.78 s c) 0.59 s d) 1.3 m
2.87 270 m
2.89 a) 20.5 m/s b) yes
2.91 a) 947 m b) 393 m
2.93 a) A b) 2.27 s, 5.73 s c) 1.00 s, 4.33 s
d) 2.67 s
2.95 a) 9.55 s, 4.78 m b) 1.62 m/s d) 8.38 m/s
e) no f) 3.69 m/s, 21.7 s, 80.0 m
2.97 a) 8.18 m/s b) (i) 0.411 m (ii) 1.15 km
c) 9.80 m/s d) 4.90 m/s

Chapter 3

3.1 a) $v_{\text{av-}x} = 1.4$ m/s, $v_{\text{av-}y} = -1.3$ m/s
b) 1.9 m/s, $-43°$
3.3 a) 7.1 cm/s, 45° b) 5.0 cm/s, 90°; 7.1 cm/s;
45°; 11 cm/s, 27°
3.5 b) $a_{\text{av-}x} = -8.67$ m/s^2, $a_{\text{av-}y} = -2.33$ m/s^2
c) 8.98 m/s^2, 195°
3.7 b) $\vec{v} = \alpha\hat{\imath} + (-2\beta t)\hat{\jmath}$; $\vec{a} = -2\beta\hat{\jmath}$
c) $v = 5.4$ m/s, $-63°$; $a = 2.4$ m/s^2, $-90°$
d) speeding up and turning right
3.9 b) 0.600 m b) 0.385 m c) $v_x = 1.10$ m/s,
$v_y = -3.43$ m/s; $v = 3.60$ m/s, 72.2° below
the horizontal
3.11 3.32 m
3.13 a) 30.6 m/s b) 36.3 m/s
3.15 1.29 m/s^2
3.17 a) 40.0 m/s, 69.3 m/s b) 7.07 c) c) 245 m
d) 565 m e) $a_x = 0$, $a_y = -9.80$ m/s^2;
$v_x = 40.0$ m/s, $v_y = 0$

3.19 a) 0.682 s, 2.99 s b) 24.0 m/s, 11.3 m/s;
24.0 m/s, -11.3 m/s c) 30.0 m/s, $-36.9°$
3.21 a) 1.5 m/s b) -0.89 m/s
3.23 a) 13.6 m b) 34.6 m/s c) 103 m
3.25 a) 296 m b) 176 m c) 198 m
d) horizontal: 15 m/s; vertical: 58.8 m/s
e) horizontal: 15 m/s; vertical: 78.8 m/s
3.27 795 m
3.29 a) 0.034 m/s^2, 0.0034g b) 1.4h
3.31 a) 3.07 s b) 1.68 s
3.33 a) 3.50 m/s^2, upward b) 3.50 m/s^2,
downward c) 12.6 s
3.35 a) 32.9 m/s b) 27.7 m/s^2 c) 35.5 rpm
3.37 a) 14 s b) 70 s
3.39 0.36 m/s, 38° west of south
3.41 a) 4.7 m/s, 25° south of east b) 190 s
c) 380 m
3.43 b) -7.1 m/s, -42 m/s c) 43 m/s, 9.5° west
of south
3.45 a) $A = B = 2.00$ m/s^2, $C = 50.0$ m,
$D = 0.50$ m/s^3 b) $\vec{a} = (4.00 \text{ m/s}^2)\hat{\imath}$, $v = 0$
c) $v_x = 40.0$ m/s, $v_y = 150$ m/s, $v = 155$ m/s
c) $\vec{r} = (200 \text{ m})\hat{\imath} + (550 \text{ m})\hat{\jmath}$
3.47 a) 124 m b) 280 m
3.49 22 m/s
3.51 40 m/s
3.53 274 m
3.55 a) 42.8 m/s b) 42.0 m
3.57 a) $\sqrt{2gh}$ b) 30.0° c) 6.93h
3.59 c) less than 45°
3.61 b) 15°, 75°
3.63 a) 17.8 m/s b) in river, 28.4 m from the near
bank
3.65 a) 81.6 m b) in cart c) 245 m d) 53.1°
3.67 a) 49 m/s b) 50 m
3.69 a) 2000 m b) 2180 m
3.71 a) 38.5 m/s b) (i) 25.0 m/s, 0
(ii) 25.0 m/s, 38.5 m/s c) (i) 0°
(ii) 57.0° d) 499 m
3.73 $\pm 25.4°$
3.77 b) $v_x = R\omega(1 - \cos\omega t)$, $v_y = R\omega\sin\omega t$,
$a_x = R\omega^2\sin\omega t$, $a_y = R\omega^2\cos\omega t$ c) $t = 0$,
$2\pi/\omega$, $4\pi/\omega$, ...; $x = 0$, $2\pi R$, $4\pi R$, ...;
$y = 0$; $a = R\omega^2$ in the $+y$ direction d) no
3.79 a) 2.50g b) 0.614n
3.81 44.7 km/h, 26.6° west of south
b) 10.5° north of west
3.83 a) 0.659 s b) (i) 9.10 m/s (ii) 6.46 m/s
c) 3.00 m, 2.13 m
3.85 7.39 m/s, 12.4° north of east
3.87 a) 80 m b) 1.6×10^{-3} c) overall effect is
to reduce radius
3.89 a) $\left(\dfrac{2v_0^2}{g}\right)\left[\tan(\theta + \phi) - \tan\theta\right]\dfrac{\cos^2(\theta + \phi)}{\cos\theta}$
b) $\dfrac{\pi}{4} - \dfrac{\theta}{2}$
3.91 $\Delta t = 0.5$ s: 9.589 m/s^2, 118.6°; $\Delta t = 0.1$ s:
9.983 m/s^2, 95.73°; $\Delta t = 0.05$ s: 9.996 m/s^2,
92.86°
3.93 a) 1.5 km/h b) 3.5 km/h

Chapter 4

4.1 a) 0° b) 90° c) 180°
4.3 7.1 N to the right, 7.1 N downward
4.5 494 N, 31.7°
4.7 2.2 m/s^2
4.9 16.0 kg
4.11 a) 3.13 m, 3.13 m/s b) 21.9 m, 6.25 m/s
4.13 a) 45.0 N; $t = 2$ s to 4 s b) 2 s to 4 s
c) 0, 6 s
4.15 a) $A = 100$ N, $B = 12.5$ N/s^2 b) (i) 21.6 N,
2.70 m/s^2 (ii) 134 N, 16.8 m/s^2
c) 26.6 m/s^2
4.17 2.94×10^3 N
4.19 a) 4.49 kg b) 4.49 kg, 8.13 N
4.21 825 N, blocks

4.23 a) gravity exerted by earth on bottle; force of air on bottle   b) gravity exerted by bottle on earth; force of bottle on air
4.25 7.4×10^{-23} m/s²
4.27 b) yes
4.29 yes, in part (a)
4.31 b) 142 N
4.33 c) force exerted by the ground on the truck
4.35 1840 N, 135°
4.37 a) 17 N, 90° clockwise from +x-direction   b) 840 N
4.39 a) 4.8 m/s   b) 16 m/s²   c) 2360 N
4.41 b) 5.83 m/s²
4.43 a) 2.50 m/s²   b) 10.0 N   c) to the right; F d) 25.0 N
4.45 a) 2.93 m/s²   b) 11.1 m/s²
4.47 b) 79.6 N
4.49 a) mg b) mg c) $m(g + |\vec{a}|)$ d) $m(g - |\vec{a}|)$
4.51 a) 7.80 m/s   b) 50.6 m/s²   c) 4532 N, 6.16mg
4.53 a) w b) 0   c) $w/2$
4.55 b) 1390 N
4.57 b) (i) 3.5 m/s²   (ii) 8.0 N
4.59 $-6mBt$

Chapter 5

5.1 a) 25.0 N   b) 50.0 N
5.3 a) 990 N, 735 N   b) 926 N
5.5 48°
5.7 4.10×10^3 N
5.9 a) A: 0.732w; B: 0.897w; C: w b) A: 2.73w; B: 3.35w; C: w
5.11 a) 337 N   b) 343 N
5.13 a) 470 N   b) 163 N
5.15 b) 1.22mg c) 0.70mg
5.17 a) 4610 m/s², 470g b) 9.70×10^5 N, 471w c) 18.7 ms
5.19 b) 2.96 m/s²   c) 191 N; more than the bricks, less than the counterweight
5.21 b) 2.50 m/s²   c) 1.37 kg   d) $T = 0.745w$
5.23 a) 0.832 m/s²   b) 17.3 s
5.25 1.38°
5.29 a) 22 N   b) 3.1 m
5.31 a) 0.710, 0.472   b) 258 N   c) (i) 51.8 N   (ii) 4.97 m/s²
5.33 a) 57.1 N   b) 146 N, up the ramp
5.35 11 times farther
5.37 a) $\mu_k(m_A + m_B)g$ b) $\mu_k m_A g$
5.39 3.82 m/s²
5.41 a) 0.218 m/s   b) 11.7 N
5.43 a) $\mu_k mg/(\cos\theta - \mu_k \sin\theta)$ b) $1/\tan\theta = \mu_k$
5.45 a) 8.75 N   b) 30.8 N   c) 1.54 m/s²
5.47 a) 0.44 kg/m   b) 42 m/s
5.49 a) 3.61 m/s   b) bottom   c) 3.33 m/s
5.51 a) 21.0°; no   b) car: 1.18×10^4 N; truck: 2.36×10^4 N
5.53 upper cable: 1410 N; horizontal cable: 8360 N
5.55 a) 1.49 rev/min   b) 0.918 rev/min
5.57 a) 138 km/h   b) 3580 N
5.59 2.43 m/s
5.61 a) rope making 60° angle   b) 6400 N
5.63 a) $Mg/(2\sin\theta)$ b) $Mg/(2\tan\theta)$ c) $T \to \infty$
5.65 a) $m_1(\sin\alpha + \mu_k \cos\alpha)$
    b) $m_1(\sin\alpha - \mu_k \cos\alpha)$
    c) $m_1(\sin\alpha - \mu_s \cos\alpha) < m_2 < m_1(\sin\alpha + \mu_s \cos\alpha)$
5.67 a) 1.44 N   b) 1.80 N
5.69 a) 1.3×10^{-4} N; 62.5w b) 2.9×10^{-4} N at 1.2 ms   c) 1.2 m/s
5.71 1040 N
5.73 a) 11 m/s   b) 7.5 m/s
5.75 0.40
5.77 a) $g\left(\dfrac{m_B + m_{\text{rope}}d/L}{m_A + m_B + m_{\text{rope}}}\right)$; increases   b) 0.63 m   c) will not work for any value of d
5.79 a) 66 N, northward   b) 59 N, southward
5.81 a) 294 N, 152 N, 152 N   b) 40.0 N
5.83 2.52 N
5.85 a) 12.9 kg   b) 47.2 N in left-hand cord; 191 N in right-hand cord

5.87 $a_1 = 2m_2 g/(4m_1 + m_2)$; $a_2 = 2m_2 g/(4m_1 + m_2)$
5.89 1.46 m above the floor
5.91 g/μ_s
5.93 b) 0.450
5.95 0.34
5.97 a) 170 m   b) 18 m/s, 41 mi/h   c) 25 m/s, 56 mi/h
5.99 a) move up   b) remains constant   c) remains constant   d) stop
5.101 a) 6.00 m/s²   b) 0.380 m/s²   c) 7.36 m/s   d) 8.18 m/s   e) 7.78 m, 6.29 m/s, 1.38 m/s²   f) 3.14 s
5.103 1/3
5.105 a) $v_y(t) = v_t + (v_0 - v_t)e^{-kt/m}$ b) $v_y(t) = v_t(\sin\beta - 0.015\cos\beta)^{1/2}$
5.107 a) 0.015; 0.036 N·s²/m²   b) 29 m/s   c) ratio is $(\sin\beta - 0.015\cos\beta)^{1/2}$
5.109 a) 120 N   b) 3.79 m/s
5.111 a) 0.28   b) no
5.113 a) right   b) 120 m
5.115 a) 81.1°   b) no   c) bead rides at bottom of hoop ($\beta = 0$)
5.119 $T_{\text{max}} = 2\pi\sqrt{\left(\dfrac{h\tan\beta}{g}\right)\left(\dfrac{\sin\beta + \mu_s \cos\beta}{\cos\beta - \mu_s \sin\beta}\right)}$;

$T_{\text{min}} = 2\pi\sqrt{\left(\dfrac{h\tan\beta}{g}\right)\left(\dfrac{\sin\beta - \mu_s \cos\beta}{\cos\beta + \mu_s \sin\beta}\right)}$
5.121 $(M + m)g\tan\alpha$
5.123 a) $F = \dfrac{\mu_k w}{\cos\theta + \mu_k \sin\theta}$ b) $\theta = \tan^{-1}(\mu_k) = 14.0°$
5.125 a) $a_3 = g\left(\dfrac{-4m_1 m_2 + m_2 m_3 + m_3 m_1}{4m_1 m_2 + m_2 m_3 + m_3 m_1}\right)$
    b) $a_B = -a_3$
    c) $a_1 = g\left(\dfrac{4m_1 m_2 - 3m_2 m_3 + m_3 m_1}{4m_1 m_2 + m_2 m_3 + m_3 m_1}\right)$
    d) $a_2 = g\left(\dfrac{4m_1 m_2 + m_2 m_3 - 3m_3 m_1}{4m_1 m_2 + m_2 m_3 + m_3 m_1}\right)$
    e) $T_A = \frac{1}{2}T_C$
    f) $T_C = \dfrac{8gm_1 m_2 m_3}{4m_1 m_2 + m_2 m_3 + m_3 m_1}$
    g) $a_1 = a_2 = a_3 = a_B = 0$, $T_C = 2m_2 g$, $T_A = m_2 g$; yes
5.127 $\cos^2\beta$

Chapter 6

6.1 a) 3.60 J   b) −0.900 J   c) 2.70 J
6.3 a) 74 N   b) 330 J   c) −330 J   d) zero; zero   e) zero
6.5 a) −1750 J   b) no
6.7 a) (i) 9.00 J   (ii) −9.00 J   b) (i) 0   (ii) 9.00 J   (iii) −9.00 J   (iv) 0   c) zero for each block
6.9 a) (i) zero   (ii) zero   b) (i) zero   (ii) −25.1 J
6.11 a) 1.0×10^{16} J   b) about 2 times greater
6.13 a) 42.85V b) 1836K
6.15 a) 43.2 m/s   b) 101 m/s   c) 5.80 m   d) 3.53 m/s   e) 7.35 m
6.17 $(2gh[1 + \mu_k/\tan\alpha])^{1/2}$
6.19 a) 9D b) $D/3$
6.21 32.0 N
6.23 a) 4.48 m/s   b) 3.61 m/s
6.25 a) 4.96 m/s   b) $a = 1.43$ m/s²; $v = 4.96$ m/s; same
6.27 a) $v_0^2/2\mu_k g$ b) 1/2   c) 4   d) 2
6.29 a) 48.0 N, 64.0 N   b) 0.360 J, 0.640 J
6.31 a) 2.8 m/s   b) 3.5 m/s
6.33 8.5 cm
6.35 a) 1.76   b) 0.67 m/s
6.37 a) 4.0 J   b) zero   c) −1.0 J   d) 3.0 J   e) −1.0 J
6.39 a) 2.83 m/s   b) 2.40 m/s
6.41 a) 5.65 cm   b) no; 0.57 J
6.43 3.6×10^5 J; 100 m/s
6.45 $4.0 \times 10^{13}P$
6.47 743 W, 0.995 hp
6.49 a) 1.4   b) 0.38
6.51 a) 5.4×10^9 J   b) 0.72 MW

6.53 2.96×10^4 W
6.55 877 J
6.57 a) 532 J   b) −315 J   c) zero   d) −203 J   e) 14.7 J   f) 1.21 m/s
6.59 a) $1/\sin\alpha$ b) $W_{\text{in}} = W_{\text{out}}$
6.61 a) 2.59×10^{12} J   b) 4800 J
6.63 b) $k_{\text{eff}} = k_1 + k_2 + \cdots + k_N$
6.65 a) $k\left(\dfrac{1}{x_2} - \dfrac{1}{x_1}\right)$; negative   b) $k\left(\dfrac{1}{x_1} - \dfrac{1}{x_2}\right)$; positive   c) same magnitude and opposite sign, since net work is zero
6.67 a) 5.11 m   b) 0.304   c) 10.3 m
6.69 a) 0.15 N   b) 9.4 N   c) 0.44 J
6.71 a) 2.56 m/s   b) 5.28 N   c) 19.7 J
6.73 a) −910 J   b) 3.17×10^3 J
6.75 1.0×10^5 N/m
6.77 1.1 m from where spring is released
6.79 a) 1.02×10^4 N/m, 8.16 m
6.81 a) 0.600 m   b) 1.50 m/s
6.83 0.786
6.85 1.5 m
6.87 a) 1.10×10^5 J   b) 1.30×10^5 J   c) 3.99 kW
6.89 3.6 h
6.91 1.30×10^3 m³/s
6.93 a) 1.26×10^5 J   b) 1.46 W
6.95 a) 2.4 MW   b) 61 MW   c) 6.0 MW
6.97 a) 513 W   b) 355 W   c) 52.1 W
6.99 a) 358 N   b) 47.2 hp   c) 4.06 hp   d) 2.03%
6.101 a) $\frac{1}{2}MV^2$ b) 6.1 m/s   c) 3.9 m/s   d) $K_{\text{ball}} = 0.40$ J, $K_{\text{spring}} = 0.60$ J
6.103 a) 2.0×10^5 J   b) 2.8×10^5 J   c) 2.8×10^5 J   d) 5 km/h

Chapter 7

7.1 a) 6.6×10^5 J   b) -7.7×10^5 J
7.3 a) 820 N   b) (i) zero   (ii) 740 J
7.5 a) 24.0 m/s   b) 24.0 m/s   c) part (b)
7.7 2.5 m/s
7.9 a) (i) zero   (ii) 0.98 J   b) 2.8 m/s   c) constant: gravity; not constant: normal, friction   d) 5.0 N
7.11 −5400 J
7.13 a) 880 J   b) −157 J   c) 471 J   d) 253 J   e) $a = 3.16$ m/s²; $v = 7.11$ m/s; $\Delta K = 253$ J; same
7.15 a) 80.0 J   b) 5.00 J
7.17 a) (i) $4U_0$ (ii) $U_0/4$ b) (i) $x_0\sqrt{2}$ (ii) $x_0/\sqrt{2}$
7.19 a) 6.32 cm   b) 12 cm
7.21 ±0.092 m
7.23 a) 3.03 m/s; as mass leaves spring   b) 95.9 m/s²; just after mass is released
7.25 a) 4.46×10^5 N/m   b) 0.128 m
7.27 a) −308 J   b) −616 J   c) nonconservative
7.29 a) −3.6 J   b) −3.6 J   c) −7.2 J   d) nonconservative
7.31 a) $\frac{1}{2}k(x_1^2 - x_2^2)$ b) $-\frac{1}{2}k(x_1^2 - x_2^2)$; zero   c) $-\frac{1}{2}k(x_3^2 - x_1^2)$; $-\frac{1}{2}k(x_2^2 - x_3^2)$; $-\frac{1}{2}k(x_2^2 - x_1^2)$; same
7.33 2.46 N, +x-direction
7.35 c) attracts
7.37 a) $F(r) = (12a/r^{13}) - (6b/r^7)$ b) $(2a/b)^{1/6}$; stable   c) $b^2/4a$ d) $a = 6.68 \times 10^{-138}$ J·m¹², $b = 6.41 \times 10^{-78}$ J·m⁶
7.39 a) zero, 637 N   b) 2.99 m/s
7.41 a) no   b) yes, $150
7.43 0.41
7.45 a) 15.9 J   b) 4.0 J   c) 3.0 J
7.47 a) 20.0 m from left-hand edge of horizontal section   b) −78.4 J
7.49 a) 22.2 m/s   b) 16.4 m   c) no
7.51 0.602 m
7.53 15.5 m/s
7.55 4.4 m/s
7.57 a) $x_0\sqrt{k/m}$ b) kx_0/m c) $x = 0, x = -x_0$ d) x_0 e) system oscillates and never stops
7.59 a) 7.00 m/s   b) 2.94 N
7.61 b) $m_k(1 - A/d)$ c) 110 N

7.63   c) $\sqrt{2gh(1 - y/d)}$

7.63 $48.2°$

7.65   a) 0.392 b) -0.832 J

7.67   a) $U(x) = (30.0\ \text{N/m})x^2 + (6.00\ \text{N/m}^2)x^3$ b) 7.85 m/s

7.69 7.01 m/s

7.71   a) $m(g + a)^2/2gh$ b) $2gh/(g + a)$

7.73 119 J

7.75   a) 3.87 m/s   b) 0.10 m

7.77   a) $F_x = -m\omega_0^2 x,\ F_y = -m\omega_0^2 x$,   b) $\frac{1}{2}m\omega_0^2(x^2 + y^2)$ (i) $\frac{1}{2}m\omega_0^2(x_0^2 + y_0^2)$ (ii) $\frac{1}{2}m\omega_0^2(x_0^2 + y_0^2)$

7.79   a) 4.4×10^{12} J   b) 2.7×10^3 m³; 0.90 mm

7.81   c) attracts

7.83   a) -50.6 J   b) -67.5 J   c) nonconservative

7.85   a) no   b) $x_0 = F/k$ d) no   e) $3F/k,\ -F/k$ f) $v_{max} = 2F/\sqrt{mk}$ at $x = x_0 = F/k$

7.87   b) $v(x) = \left[\dfrac{2\alpha}{mx_0^2}\left(\dfrac{x_0}{x} - \left[\dfrac{x_0}{x}\right]^2\right)\right]^{1/2}$

     c) $x = 2x_0,\ v = \sqrt{\alpha/2mx_0^2}$ d) zero

     e) $v(x) = \left[\dfrac{2\alpha}{mx_0^2}\left(\dfrac{x_0}{x} - \left[\dfrac{x_0}{x}\right]^2 - \dfrac{2}{9}\right)\right]^{1/2}$

     f) first case: x_0, ∞; second case: $3x_0/2, 3x_0$

Chapter 8

8.1   a) 1.20×10^5 kg · m/s   b) i) 60.0 m/s   ii) 26.8 m/s

8.3   b) baseball, 0.525 c) woman, 0.643

8.5   a) 22.5 kg · m/s, to the left   b) 838 J

8.7 562 N, no

8.9   a) 10.8 m/s, to the right   b) 0.75 m/s, to the left

8.11   a) 500 N/s²   b) 5810 kg · m/s   c) 2.70 m/s

8.13   a) 2.50 N · s   b) i) $+6.25$ m/s, to the right   b) ii) 3.75 m/s, to the right

8.15   a) 6.79 m/s   b) 55.2 J

8.17   a) 0.790 m/s   b) -0.0023 J

8.19 0.866 kg · m/s

8.21   a) 0.0559 m/s   b) 0.0313 m/s

8.23 3.65×10^5 m/s

8.25   a) 7.20 m/s   b) -680 J

8.27 3.56 m/s

8.29   a) 0.846 m/s   b) 2.10 J

8.31   a) 1.4×10^{-6} km/h, which is not noticeable.   b) 6.7×10^{-8} km/h, which is not noticeable.

8.33 5.9 m/s at $32°$ east of north

8.35   a) Both cars have the same change in momentum, but the smaller car has a greater velocity change.   b) $2.5\ \Delta v$ c) Those in the smaller car

8.37 19.5 m/s (car), 21.9 m/s (truck)

8.39   a) 2.93 cm   b) 866 J   c) 1.73 J

8.41   a) 0.333 m/s, 3.33 J   b) -1.33 m/s (A), $+0.67$ m/s (B)

8.43   a) -0.100 m/s (A), 0.500 m/s (B) b) 0.009 kg · m/s for both   c) -4.5×10^{-4} J (A), 4.5×10^{-4} J (B), same magnitudes because the collision is elastic

8.45   a) $1/3$ b) $1/9$ c) 10

8.47 $x_{cm} = 0.044$ m, $y_{cm} = 0.056$ m

8.49 2520 km from the center of Pluto

8.51 0.700 m upward and 0.700 m to the right

8.53 0.47 m/s

8.55 $F_x = (-1.50\ \text{N/s})t,\ F_y = 0.25$ N, $F_z = 0$

8.57   a) 53 g   b) 5.22 N

8.59 2.4 km/s

8.61 45.1

8.63   a) 0.47 N · s   b) 237 N

8.65   a) $J_x = -1.14$ N · s, $J_y = 0.33$ N · s   b) $v_{2x} = 0.0500$ m/s; $v_{2y} = 1.78$ m/s

8.67 2.67 m/s (convertible), 3.46 m/s (SUV)

8.69   a) $v_{Cx} = 1.75$ m/s, $v_{Cy} = 0.26$ m/s   b) -0.092 J

8.71 15.0 m/s

8.73 36.4 N

8.75   a) 2.60 m/s   b) 325 m/s

8.77   a) 5.28 m/s   b) 5.7 m

8.79 $68.8°$

8.81 102 N

8.83   a) 0.222 b) -291 J   c) 0.784 J

8.85   b) $M = m$ c) zero

8.87   a) 9.35 m/s   b) 3.29 m/s

8.89   b) $\frac{1}{2}Mv_{cm}^2$

8.91   a) 3.56 m/s   b) 5.22 m/s   c) 4.67 m/s

8.93 0.00544%

8.95 1.61×10^{-22} kg · m/s, to the left

8.97 A: 13.6 m/s; B: 6.34 m/s, $65.0°$

8.99   a) $(L/2)\cos(\alpha/2)$, along axis from apex   b) $(L/3)$, along bisector from bottom   c) $L/\sqrt{8}$ along bisector   d) $L/\sqrt{12}$ from each side

8.101 0.400 m/s

8.103   a) 1.40 kg: 14.3 m/s; 0.28 kg: 71.6 m/s   b) 347 m

8.105 222 m/s, 1.01×10^3 m/s; $v_{Kr} = 1.5v_{Ba}$

8.107   a) zero   b) 1 d) 0.87 m   f) 0.089 m

8.109   a) yes   b) no; kinetic energy decreases by 4.8×10^3 J

8.111   a) $1.37v_{ex}$ b) $1.18v_{ex}$ c) $2.38v_{ex}$ d) 2.94 km/s

8.113   b) $2L/3$

8.115   a) $l^2\lambda g/32$ b) $l^2\lambda g/32$

Chapter 9

9.1   a) $34.4°$ b) 6.27 cm   c) 1.05 m

9.3   a) A: rad/s; B: rad/s³   b) (i) 0 (ii) 15.0 rad/s²   c) 9.50 rad

9.5   a) $\omega_z(t) = (0.400\ \text{rad/s}) + (0.0360\ \text{rad/s}^3)t^2$ b) 0.400 rad/s   c) $\omega_z = 1.30$ rad/s; $\omega_{av-z} = 0.700$ rad/s

9.7   a) $a = \pi/4$ rad, $b = 2.00$ rad/s, $c = -0.139$ rad/s³   b) zero   c) 19.5 rad; 9.35 rad/s

9.9   a) 2.25 rad/s   b) 4.69 rad

9.11   a) 24.0 s   b) 68.8 rev

9.13 10.5 rad/s

9.15   a) 300 rpm   b) 75.0 s; 312 rev

9.17 9.00 rev

9.19   a) 540 rad   b) 12.3 s   c) -8.17 rad/s²

9.21   a) 1.99×10^{-7} rad/s   b) 7.27×10^{-5} rad/s   c) 2.99×10^4 m/s   d) 464 m/s   e) 0.0337 m/s²; zero

9.23   a) 15.1 m/s²   b) 15.1 m/s²

9.25   a) 0.180 m/s²; 0; 0.180 m/s²   b) 0.180 m/s²; 0.377 m/s²; 0.418 m/s²   c) 0.180 m/s²; 0.754 m/s²; 0.775 m/s²

9.27 10.7 cm; no

9.29   a) 0.831 m/s   b) 109 m/s²

9.31   a) 2.29 b) 1.51 c) 15.7 m/s, $108g$

9.33 2.99 cm

9.35   a) (i) 0.469 kg · m²   (ii) 0.117 kg · m²   (iii) zero   b) (i) 0.0433 kg · m²   (ii) 0.0722 kg · m²   c) (i) 0.0288 kg · m²   (ii) 0.0144 kg · m²

9.37   a) 0.0640 kg · m²   b) 0.0320 kg · m²   c) 0.0320 kg · m²

9.39 0.193 kg · m²

9.41 8.52 kg · m²

9.43   a) 3.15×10^{23} J   b) 158 y; no

9.45 0.600 kg · m²

9.47 7.35×10^4 J

9.49   a) 67.3 cm   b) 45.5%

9.51   a) f^5 b) 6.37×10^8 J

9.53 -88.2 J

9.55   on an axis parallel to a diameter and $(2/\sqrt{15})R$ from the center of the sphere

9.57 $\frac{1}{3}M(a^2 + b^2)$

9.59   a) $ML^2/12$ b) $ML^2/12$

9.61 $MR^2/2$

9.63   a) $\gamma L^2/2$ b) $ML^2/2$; larger   c) $ML^2/6$; one-third result of (b)

9.65   in 128 d

9.67   a) 0.600 m/s³   b) $\alpha = (2.40\ \text{rad/s}^3)t$ c) 3.54 s   d) 17.7 rad

9.69   a) 0.050 rad/s²   b) 0.300 rad/s   c) 5.40 m/s²   e) 6.18 m/s²; 7.66×10^3 N   f) $60.9°$

9.71   a) 1.70 m/s   b) 84.8 rad/s

9.73   b) 2.00 m/s²   d) 0.208 kg · m²

9.77   a) 7.36 m   b) 327 m/s²

9.79   a) 2.14×10^{29} J   b) 2.66×10^{33} J

9.81   a) $Mb^2/6$ b) 182 J

9.83   a) -0.784 J   b) 5.42 rad/s   c) 5.42 rad/s   d) particle speed $= 4.43$ m/s

9.85 $\sqrt{(2gd)(m_B - \mu_k m_A)/(m_A + m_B + I/R^2)}$

9.87 $\sqrt{(g/R)(1 - \cos\beta)}$

9.89   a) 2.25×10^{-3} kg · m²   b) 3.40 m/s   c) 4.95 m/s

9.91 7.23 m

9.93   a) $(247/512)MR^2$ b) $(383/512)MR^2$

9.95   b) $\frac{1}{4}M(R_1^2 + R_2^2)$

9.97   a) $\frac{3}{5}MR^2$ b) larger

9.99   b) 5.97×10^{24} kg   c) $0.334MR^2$

9.101   a) $s = r_0\theta + \beta\theta^2/2$ b) $\theta = (1/\beta)[\sqrt{r_0^2 + 2\beta vt} - r_0]$ c) $\omega_z = \dfrac{v}{\sqrt{r_0^2 + 2\beta vt}},\ \alpha_z = \dfrac{\beta v^2}{(r_0^2 + 2\beta vt)^{3/2}}$; no   d) $r_0 = 2.50$ cm, $\beta = 0.247$ μm/rad; 2.13×10^4 rev

Chapter 10

10.1   a) 40.0 N · m, out of the page   b) 34.6 N, out of the page   c) 20.0 N · m, out of the page   d) 17.3 N · m, into the page   e) zero   f) zero

10.3 2.50 N · m, counterclockwise

10.5   b) into page   c) $(-1.05\ \text{N} \cdot \text{m})\hat{k}$

10.7 13.1 N · m

10.9   a) 14.8 rad/s²   b) 1.52 s

10.11 7.47 N

10.13 0.482

10.15   a) 7.5 N in horizontal part, 18.2 N in hanging part   b) 0.0160 kg · m²

10.17   a) 2.65 rad/s²   b) no   c) 3.31 m/s²; no

10.19   a) 1.80 m/s   b) 7.13 J   c) (i) 3.60 m/s, to the right   (ii) 0 (iii) 2.55 m/s, $45°$ below horizontal   d) (i) 1.80 m/s, to the right   (ii) 1.80 m/s, to the left   (iii) 1.80 m/s, downward

10.21   a) $1/3$ b) $2/7$ c) $2/5$ d) $5/13$

10.23   a) 0.613 b) no, requires $\mu_s = 0.858$ c) no slipping

10.25 11.7 m

10.27   a) 0.309 rad/s   b) 100 J   c) 6.67 W

10.29   a) 0.38 N · m   b) 160 rad   c) 59 J   d) 59 J

10.31   b) 65.6 N

10.33   a) 358 N · m   b) 1.79×10^3 N   c) 83.8 m/s

10.35   a) 115 kg · m²/s, into the page   b) 125 kg · m²/s², out of the page

10.37 4.71×10^{-6} kg · m²/s

10.39 4.6×10^3 rad/s

10.41 1.14 rev/s

10.43 0.60 rev

10.45   a) 0.120 rad/s   b) 3.20×10^{-4} J; work done by bug

10.47   a) 5.88 rad/s

10.49   a) 1.62 N   b) 1.80×10^3 rev/min

10.51   a) halved   b) doubled   c) halved   d) doubled   e) unchanged

10.53   a) 67.6 N   b) 62.9 N   c) 3.27 s

10.55   a) 840 rpm   b) 75 mph   c) 60 mph

10.57   a) 16.3 rad/s²   b) no; decreases   c) 5.70 rad/s

10.59   a) at $x = l$ b) at $x = l$ c) at $x = (l/2)(1 + [2h/l]^2)$ for $l > 2h$; at $x = l$ for $l < 2h$

10.61   a) FR b) FR; yes   c) $\sqrt{4F/MR}$ d) $2F/M$ e) $4F/M$

10.63   a) 266 N   b) 4.71 rad/s²

10.65   a) 2.88 m/s²   b) 6.13 m/s²; greater in case (b)

10.67 239 N

10.69 $a = \dfrac{2g}{2 + (R/b)^2}$; $\alpha = \dfrac{2g}{2b + R^2/b}$; $T = \dfrac{2mg}{2(b/R)^2 + 1}$

10.71   clockwise; clockwise; clockwise

10.73   a) 1.41 s; 70.5 m/s   b) t larger, v smaller

10.75 29.0 m/s

10.77   a) 26.0 m/s   b) unchanged

10.79   a) $\sqrt{20hy/7}$ b) no   c) rolling friction   d) $\sqrt{8hy/3}$

10.81 b) R = radius of wheel,
T = period of wheel's rotation

c) $v_x = \dfrac{2\pi R}{T}\left[1 - \cos\left(\dfrac{2\pi t}{T}\right)\right]$,

$v_y = \dfrac{2\pi R}{T}\sin\left(\dfrac{2\pi t}{T}\right)$; $a_x = \left(\dfrac{2\pi R}{T}\right)^2 R\sin\left(\dfrac{2\pi t}{T}\right)$,

$a_y = \left(\dfrac{2\pi R}{T}\right)^2 R\cos\left(\dfrac{2\pi t}{T}\right)$

d) $t = 0, T, 2T, \ldots$; $a_x = 0, a_y = \dfrac{4\pi^2 R}{T^2}$

e) $\dfrac{4\pi^2 R}{T^2}$, independent of time

10.83 $g/3$
10.85 1.87 m
10.87 a) $6v/19L$ b) $3/19$
10.89 a) 5.46 rad/s   b) 3.17 cm
   c) 1.01×10^3 m/s
10.91 a) 2.00 rad/s   b) 6.57 rad/s
10.93 0.30 rad/s, clockwise
10.97 -4.2×10^{-16} rad/s per year; decreasing
10.101 a) $a = +\mu_k g$, $\alpha = -2\mu_k g/R$
   b) $\omega_0^2 R^2/18\mu_k g$ c) $-M\omega_0^2 R^2/6$
10.103 a) $mv_1^2 r_1^2/r^3$ b) $(mv_1^2/2)[(r_1/r_2)^2 - 1]$
   c) same

Chapter 11

11.1 29.8 cm
11.3 20.0 kg
11.5 5450 N
11.7 a) 1000 N, 1.20 m from end where 400-N force
   is applied   b) 800 N, 1.25 m from end where
   400-N force is applied
11.9 a) 550 N   b) 0.614 m from A
11.11 a) 1920 N   b) 1140 N
11.13 a) $T = 2.60w$; $F_{\text{pivot}} = 3.28w$ at $37.6°$
   b) $T = 4.10w$; $F_{\text{pivot}} = 5.38w$ at $48.8°$
11.15 140 N by each hinge
11.17 246 N; 0.34 m behind front feet
11.19 $T_{\text{left}} = 270$ N, $T_{\text{right}} = 304$ N, $\theta = 40°$
11.21 a) 0.800 m   b) clockwise   c) 0.800 m,
   clockwise
11.23 1.4 mm
11.25 2.00×10^{11} Pa
11.27 a) upper: 3.1×10^{-3}; lower: 2.0×10^{-3}
   b) upper: 1.6 mm; lower: 0.98 mm
11.29 9.1×10^6 N
11.31 a) 3.33×10^6 Pa   b) 1.33×10^5 Pa
11.33 a) 4.8×10^9 Pa; 2.1×10^{-10} Pa^{-1}
11.35 b) 6.60×10^5 N   c) 1.8 mm
11.37 3.41×10^7 Pa
11.39 10.2 m/s^2
11.41 a) 525 N   b) 222 N, 328 N   c) 1.48
11.43 wing force: 7300 N upward; tail force: 600 N
   downward
11.45 a) 140 N   b) 6 cm to the right
11.47 a) 424 N   b) 170 N
11.49 120 N to the right, 160 N upward
11.53 b) $(Mg/2)\sin\theta$
11.55 a) $V = mg + w$, $H = T = (w + mg/4)\cot\theta$
   b) 950 N   c) $4.00°$
11.57 7600 N
11.59 a) 2700 N   b) 19
11.61 a) 4.90 m   b) 60 N
11.63 a) $\theta = \arctan(h/d)$; $T = (Wd/2)\sqrt{h^2 + d^2}$
   b) $\dfrac{Whd}{2(h^2 + d^2)}$; $W\dfrac{2h^2 + d^2}{2(h^2 + d^2)}$
11.65 a) 1150 N   b) 1940 N   c) 918 N   d) 0.473
11.67 person above: 590 N; person below: 1370 N;
   above
11.69 a) $w_{\text{max}} = T_{\text{max}}hD/(L\sqrt{h^2 + D^2})$
11.71 a) 7140 N; tall walls   b) 7900 N
11.73 a) 268 N   b) 232 N   c) 366 N
11.75 a) A: 0.424 N; B: 1.47 N; C 0.424 N
   b) 0.848 N
11.77 a) tips at $27°$, slips at $31°$; the bale tips before it
   slips   b) tips at $27°$ slips at $22°$ the bale slips
   before it tips
11.79 a) $F_A = 80$ N, $F_B = 870$ N   b) 1.92 m
11.81 a) 3.7 kN, 2.0 kN vertically upward
11.83 a) $0.012w$ b) less   c) $25.0°$; tips

11.85 a) 5.4 mm   b) 4.2 mm
11.87 a) 0.70 m from wire A b) 0.45 m from wire B
11.89 a) 1.63 m   b) brass: 2.00×10^8 Pa; nickel:
   4.00×10^8 Pa   c) brass: 2.2×10^{-3}; nickel:
   1.9×10^{-3}
11.91 a) 0.36 mm   b) 0.045 mm   c) 0.33 mm
11.93 a) $(F\cos^2\theta)/A$ b) $(F\sin 2\theta)/2A$ c) 0
   d) $45°$
11.95 a) 600 N   b) 13.5 kN
   c) slide: $\mu_s w/(\sin\theta - \mu_s\cos\theta)$; tip:
   $w/[(\tfrac{1}{9})\cos\theta + 2\sin\theta]$; $66°$
11.97 the lesser of $h^2/L + L/2$ and L
11.99 $[(A^2 x/F) - k_O V_O]/V_S$
11.101 a) 0.662 mm   b) 2.20×10^{-2} J
   c) 8.33×10^{-3} J   d) -3.04×10^{-2} J
   e) 3.04×10^{-2} J

Chapter 12

12.1 2.18
12.3 0.026 mm
12.5 a) 2.59×10^8 m   b) no
12.7 a) 2.40×10^{-3} N   b) 3.6×10^{-6}
12.9 a) 6.30×10^{20} N, toward sun
   b) 4.77×10^{20} N, $24.6°$ toward earth from sun
   c) 2.37×10^{20} N toward sun
12.11 a) 0.366 m from mass m b) (i) unstable
   (ii) stable
12.13 2.1×10^{-9} m/s^2, down
12.15 1.38×10^7 m
12.17 a) 0.37 m/s^2 b) 1700 kg/m^3
12.19 610 N; 83% of weight at surface
12.21 5.98×10^{24} kg
12.23 0.83 m/s; yes
12.25 a) 5.02×10^3 m/s   b) 6.06×10^4 m/s
12.27 a) 7.46×10^3 m/s   b) 1.68 h
12.29 2.01×10^{30} kg
12.31 a) 4.7 m/s; yes   b) 2.2 h
12.33 a) 8.3×10^4 m/s   b) 1.3×10^6 s
12.35 a) 4.45×10^{12} m, 4.55×10^{12} m   b) 248 y
12.39 a) (i) 5.31×10^{-9} N   (ii) 2.67×10^{-9} N
12.41 a) $-GMm/\sqrt{a^2 + x^2}$
   c) $GMmx/(a^2 + x^2)^{3/2}$ toward center of ring
   e) $-GMm/a$, zero
12.43 a) 53 N   b) 52 N
12.45 1.39×10^{-9}
12.47 a) 4.3×10^{37} kg, $2.1 \times 10^7 M_{\text{sun}}$ b) no
   c) 6.3×10^{10} m; yes
12.49 a) 9.67×10^{-12} N, midway between x and y
   axes   b) 3.02×10^{-5} m/s
12.51 b) 5.39×10^{-13} N · m, clockwise
12.53 a) (i) 1.63×10^{-5} m/s, 4.08×10^{-6} m/s
   (ii) 2.04×10^{-5} m/s   c) 31.9 m/s
12.55 a) 3.58×10^7 m
12.57 1.8×10^2 m/s
12.59 a) 1.39×10^7 m   b) 3.59×10^7 m
12.61 $0.01 R_E = 64$ km
12.63 0.28%
12.65 6.06×10^3 km/h
12.67 $\sqrt{2Gm_E h/(R_E^2 + hR_E)}$
12.69 a) 13.7 km/s   b) 13.3 km/s   c) 13.2 km/s
12.71 a) (i) 2.8 y   (ii) 6.1 y 4.90×10^8 km
   c) 4.22×10^8 km
12.73 a) $GM^2/4R^2$ b) $\sqrt{GM/4R}$, $4\pi\sqrt{R^3/GM}$
   c) $GM^2/4R$
12.75 6.8×10^4 m/s
12.77 a) 7.91×10^3 s   b) 1.53
   c) 8.43×10^3 m/s, 5.51×10^3 m/s
   d) 2.41×10^3 m/s, 3.26×10^3; perigee
12.79 3.22×10^9 J
12.81 9.36 m/s^2
12.83 $\dfrac{GmM}{x(x + L)}$
12.85 a) $U(r) = \dfrac{Gm_E m}{2R_E^3}r^2$ b) 7.90×10^3 m/s
12.87 a) against the direction of motion in all cases
   b) 2.24×10^7 s   c) $44.1°$
12.89 $F = \dfrac{2GMm}{l^2}\left[1 - \dfrac{x}{\sqrt{a^2 + x^2}}\right]$, toward the
   center of the disk

Chapter 13

13.1 a) 4.54×10^{-3} s, 1.38×10^3 rad/s
   b) 2.27×10^{-3} s, 2.76×10^3 rad/s
13.3 5.53×10^3 rad/s, 1.14×10^{-3} s
13.5 0.0500 s
13.7 a) 0.167 s   b) 37.7 rad/s   c) 8.44×10^{-2} kg
13.9 a) 0.375 s   b) 2.66 Hz   c) 16.7 rad/s
13.11 a) 0.98 m   b) $\pi/2$ rad
   c) $x(t) = (-0.98$ m$)\sin([12.2$ rad/s$]t)$
13.13 a) -2.71 m/s^2
   b) $x(t) = (1.46$ cm$)\cos([15.7$ rad/s$]t$
   $+ 0.715$ rad$)$,
   $v_x(t) = (-22.9$ cm/s$)\sin([15.7$ rad/s$]t$
   $+ 0.715$ rad$)$,
   $a_x(t) = (-359$ cm/s$^2)\cos([15.7$ rad/s$]t$
   $+ 0.715$ rad$)$
13.15 120 kg
13.17 a) 0.253 kg   b) 1.22 cm   c) 3.05 N
13.19 a) 1.51 s   b) 26.0 N/m   c) 0.308 m/s
   d) 1.92 N   e) -0.0125 m; 0.303 m/s;
   0.216 m/s^2
13.21 a) 1.48 m/s   b) 2.96×10^{-5} J
13.23 a) 1.20 m/s   b) 1.11 m/s   c) 36 m/s^2
   d) 13.5 m/s^2 e) 0.36 J
13.25 $m = 3M$; $\tfrac{3}{4}$
13.27 0.240 m
13.29 a) 0.0778 m   b) 1.28 Hz   c) 0.624 m/s
13.31 a) 4.06 cm   b) 1.21 m/s   c) 29.8 rad/s
13.33 b) 23.9 cm; 1.45 Hz
13.35 a) 2.7×10^{-8} kg · m^2
   b) 4.3×10^{-6} N · m/rad
13.37 5.12×10^{-2} kg · m^2
13.41 a) 0.25 s   b) 0.25 s
13.43 0.407 swings/s
13.45 2.00 m
13.47 10.7 m/s^2
13.49 0.129 kg · m^2
13.53 A: $2\pi\sqrt{L/g}$; B: $(4\pi\sqrt{2}/3)\sqrt{L/g} = 0.943T_A$;
   pendulum A
13.55 A: $2\pi\sqrt{L/g}$; B: $2\pi\sqrt{\dfrac{11L}{10g}} = 1.05T_A$;
   pendulum B
13.57 a) 0.393 Hz   b) 1.73 kg/s
13.59 a) A b) magnitude $= bA/2m$, in
   $-x$-direction; slope is negative
   c) $a_x(0) = A\left(\dfrac{b^2}{2m^2} - \dfrac{k}{m}\right)$; if $b < \sqrt{2mk}$,
   $a(0) < 0$; if $b = \sqrt{2mk}$, $a(0) = 0$; if
   $b > \sqrt{2mk}$, $a(0) > 0$
13.61 a) kg/s   b) (i) $5.0F_{\text{max}}/k$ (ii) $2.5F_{\text{max}}/k$
13.63 a) 6.72×10^3 m/s^2 b) 3.02 kN
   c) 18.3 m/s, 75.6 J   d) 17.6 kW   e) 12.1 kN,
   36.7 m/s, 302 J, 141 kW
13.65 a) all unchanged   b) 1/4 as large   c) halved
   d) $1/\sqrt{5}$ as great   e) U: unchanged; K: 1/5 as
   large
13.67 a) 24.4 cm   b) 0.220 s   c) 1.19 m/s
13.69 a) 0.318 Hz, 0.500 m, 3.14 m   b) 1.57 s
13.71 $\dfrac{1}{2\pi}\sqrt{\dfrac{3\sqrt{2}}{5}}\sqrt{\dfrac{g}{L}} = 0.921\left(\dfrac{1}{2\pi}\sqrt{\dfrac{g}{L}}\right)$
13.73 a) 1.49 s   b) -2.12×10^{-4} s per s; shorter
   c) 0.795 s
13.75 a) 0.150 m/s   b) 0.112 m/s^2, downward
   c) 0.700 s   d) 4.38 m
13.77 a) 2.6 m/s   b) 0.21 m   c) 0.49 s
13.79 9.08×10^{24} kg
13.81 1.17 s
13.83 a) yes   c) 2.40×10^3 s   d) no
13.87 c) -7.57×10^{-19} J   e) 8.39×10^{12} Hz
13.89 0.705 Hz; $14.5°$
13.91 $2\pi\sqrt{M/3k}$
13.93 $\dfrac{1}{4\pi}\sqrt{\dfrac{3g}{\sqrt{2}L}}$
13.95 c) 0.430 m
13.97 a) $k_{\text{eff}} = k_1 + k_2$ b) $k_{\text{eff}} = k_1 + k_2$
   c) $k_{\text{eff}} = \dfrac{k_1 k_2}{k_1 + k_2}$ d) $\sqrt{2}$

13.99 a) $Mv^2/6$ c) $\omega = \sqrt{3k/M}$; $M' = M/3$
13.101 579 N/m

Chapter 14

14.1 $w = 41.8$ N; no
14.3 7.02×10^3 kg/m³; yes
14.5 1.6
14.7 61.7 N
14.9 a) 1.86×10^6 Pa   b) 184 m
14.11 0.581
14.13 a) absolute:
46.7 lb/in.² $= 3.22 \times 10^5$ Pa $= 3.18$ atm;
gauge:
32.0 $lb/in.^2 = 2.21 \times 10^5$ Pa $= 2.18$ atm
b) no   c) 432 cm²
14.15 6.27×10^6 Pa $= 61.9$ atm
14.17 6.0×10^4 Pa
14.19 1.41×10^5 Pa; 4.03×10^4 Pa
14.21 2.3×10^5 N
14.23 a) 637 Pa   b) (i) 1170 Pa   (ii) 1170 Pa
14.25 1.66×10^5 Pa $= 1.64$ atm
14.27 6.43×10^{-4} m³, 2.78×10^3 kg/m³
14.29 a) $\rho < \rho_{\text{fluid}}$ c) submerged: ρ/ρ_{fluid}; above:
$(\rho_{\text{fluid}} - \rho)/\rho_{\text{fluid}}$ d) 32%
14.31 a) 116 Pa   b) 921 Pa   c) 0.822 kg,
822 kg/m³
14.33 1.91×10^3 kg/m³
14.35 9.6 m/s
14.37 a) 17.0 m/s   b) 0.317 m
14.39 28.4 m/s
14.41 1.47×10^5 Pa
14.43 12,600 N
14.45 2.03×10^4 Pa
14.47 a) $(p_0 - p)\pi D^2/4$ b) 776 N
14.49 a) 5.9×10^5 N   b) 1.76×10^5 N
14.51 c) independent of surface area
14.53 $(p - p_0)VR^2/Gmd$
14.55 a) 12,700 kg/m³, 3140 kg/m³
14.57 a) 1470 Pa   b) 13.9 cm
14.59 9.8×10^6 kg; yes
14.61 a) 30%   b) 70%
14.63 4.66×10^{-4} m³; 5.27 kg
14.65 a) 1.10×10^4 m³   b) 112 kN
14.67 a) 0.107 m   b) 2.42 s
14.69 a) $H/2$ b) H
14.71 0.0958 kg
14.73 33.5 N
14.75 b) 12.2 N   c) 11.8 N
14.77 b) 2.52×10^{-4} m³, 0.124
14.79 risen by 5.57×10^{-4} m
14.81 a) $1 - \rho_B/\rho_L$ b) $(\rho_L - \rho_B)L/(\rho_L - \rho_W)$
c) 4.60 cm
14.83 a) la/g b) $\omega^2 l^2/2g$
14.87 a) $2\sqrt{h(H - h)}$ b) h
14.89 a) 0.200 m³/s   b) 6.97×10^4 Pa
14.91 $3h_1$
14.93 a) $r = r_0(1 + 2gy/v_0^2)^{-1/4}$ b) 1.10 m
14.95 a) 80.4 N
14.97 a) $\sqrt{2gh}$ b) $(p_a/\rho g) - h$

Chapter 15

15.1 a) 0.439 m; 1.28 ms   b) 0.219 m
15.3 220 m/s $= 800$ km/h
15.5 a) 4.3×10^{14} Hz to 7.5×10^{14} Hz;
1.3×10^{-15} s to 2.3×10^{-15} s   b) no
15.7 a) $f = 25.0$ Hz, $T = 0.0400$ s, $k = 19.6$ rad/m
b) $y(x, t) = (0.0700 \text{ m})\cos 2\pi\left(\dfrac{x}{0.320 \text{ m}} + \dfrac{t}{0.0400 \text{ s}}\right)$ c) $+0.0495$ m   d) 0.0050 s
15.9 c) $-x$-direction for both
d) $v_y(x, t) = \omega A \cos(kx + \omega t)$,
$a_y(x, t) = -\omega^2 A \sin(kx + \omega t)$
15.11 a) 4.0 mm   b) 0.040 s   c) 0.14 m, 3.6 m/s
d) 0.24 m, 6.0 m/s   e) no
15.13 b) $+x$-direction
15.15 a) 16.3 m/s   b) 0.136 m   c) both increase by
factor of $\sqrt{2}$

15.17 0.390 s
15.19 a) 10.0 m/s   b) 0.250 m
c) $y(x, t) = (3.00 \text{ cm})\cos[(8.00\pi \text{ rad/s})x - (80.0\pi \text{ rad/s})t]$ d) 1890 m/s²   e) yes
15.21 a) 95 km   b) 2.5×10^{-7} W/m²
c) 1.1×10^5 W
15.23 a) 0.050 W/m²   b) 2.2×10^4 J
15.25 707 W
15.33 a) $(1.33 \text{ m})n$, $n = 0, 1, 2, 3, \ldots$
b) $(1.33 \text{ m})(n + \frac{1}{2})$, $n = 0, 1, 2, 3, \ldots$
15.39 a) 96.0 m/s   b) 461 N   c) 1.13 m/s,
426 m/s²
15.41 a) 2.80 cm   c) 277 cm   d) 185 cm, 0.126 s,
1470 cm/s   e) 280 cm/s
f) $y(x, t) = (5.60 \text{ cm})\sin[(0.0907 \text{ rad/cm})x]$
$\sin([133 \text{ rad/s}]t)$
15.43 a) $y(x,t) = (4.60 \text{ mm})\sin[(6.98 \text{ rad/m})x]$
$\sin([742 \text{ rad/s}]t)$ b) 3ʳᵈ   c) 39.4 Hz
15.45 a) 45.0 cm   b) no
15.47 a) 311 m/s   b) 246 Hz   c) 245 Hz, 1.40 m
15.49 a) 20.0 Hz, 126 rad/s, 3.49 rad/m
b) $y(x,t) = (2.50 \text{ mm})\cos[(3.49 \text{ rad/m})x - (126 \text{ rad/s})t]$
c) $y(t) = (2.50 \text{ mm})\cos[(126 \text{ rad/s})t]$
d) $y(t) = (2.50 \text{ mm})\cos[3\pi/2 - (126 \text{ rad/s})t]$ e) 0.314 m/s
f) -2.50 mm, 0
15.51 a) $(7L/2)\sqrt{\mu_1/F}$ b) no
15.53 a) $(2\pi A/\lambda)\sqrt{FL/M}$ b) increase by a factor
of 4
15.55 a) $4\pi^2 F \Delta x/\lambda^2$
15.57 a) 1, 0; 2, +; 3, -; 4, 0; 5, -; 6, +   b) 1, -;
2, +; 3, -; 4, +; 5, -; 6, 0   c) (a): answers
would reverse sign; (b): no change
15.61 c) C/B
15.63 b) k decreases by a factor of $2\sqrt{2}$; ω decreases
by a factor of $\sqrt{2}$
15.65 a) 7.07 cm   b) 400.0 W
15.67 $\alpha = (v_1^2 - v_2^2)\rho/Y\Delta T$
15.69 $n(0.800 \text{ Hz})$, $n = 1, 2, 3, \ldots$
15.71 c) yes
15.73 c) $2A$, $2A\omega$, $2A\omega^2$
15.75 230 N
15.77 a) 0, L b) 0, $L/2$, L d) no
15.79 a) 148 N   b) 26%
15.81 b) $\frac{1}{2}\mu\omega^2 A^2 \sin^2(kx - \omega t)$
e) $\frac{1}{2}Fk^2 A^2 \sin^2(kx - \omega t)$
15.83 $\pi/\omega\sqrt{2}$
15.85 a) 99.4 N   c) -4.25 Hz, falls

Chapter 16

16.1 a) 0.344 m   b) 1.2×10^{-5} m
c) 6.9 m, 50 Hz
16.3 a) 7.78 Pa   b) 77.8 Pa   c) 778 Pa
16.5 a) 1.33×10^{10} Pa   b) 9.47×10^{10} Pa
16.7 90.8 m
16.9 81.5°C
16.11 0.208 s
16.13 $Y/900$
16.15 a) 9.44×10^{-11} m; 0.434 m
b) 5.66×10^{-9} m; 0.101 m
c) air; $A_{\text{air}}/A_{\text{water}} = 60.0$
16.17 a) 1.94 Pa   b) 4.58×10^{-3} W/m²
c) 96.6 dB
16.19 a) 4.4×10^{-12} W/m²   b) 6.39 dB
c) 5.8×10^{-11} m
16.21 14.0 dB
16.23 a) 20.0
16.25 a) *fundamental:* displacement node at 0.60 m,
pressure nodes at 0 and 1.20 m; *first overtone:*
displacement nodes at 0.30 m and 0.90 m,
pressure nodes at 0, 0.60 m, and 1.20 m; *second
overtone:* displacement nodes at 0.20 m, 0.60 m,
and 1.00 m, pressure nodes at 0, 0.40 m, 0.80 m,
and 1.20 m   b) *fundamental:* displacement
node at 0, pressure node at 1.20 m; *first
overtone:* displacement nodes at 0 and 0.80 m,
pressure nodes at 0.40m and 1.20 m, and; *second
overtone:* displacement nodes at 0, 0.48 m, and
0.96 m, pressure nodes at 0.24 m, 0.72 m, 1.20 m

16.27 506 Hz, 1520 Hz, 2530 Hz
16.29 a) 267 Hz   b) no
16.31 a) 614 Hz   b) 1.23 kHz
16.33 a) 172 Hz   b) 86 Hz
16.35 0.125 m
16.37 a) 4 beats/s   b) 3.0×10^{-8} m, 0
16.39 1.3 Hz
16.41 780 m/s
16.43 a) 375 Hz   b) 371 Hz   c) 4 Hz
16.45 a) 0.25 m/s   b) 0.91 m
16.47 19.8 m/s
16.49 26.8 Hz
16.51 $0.095c$; toward us
16.53 a) 36.0°   b) 2.23 s
16.55 a) 1.00   b) 8.00   c) 47.3 nm
16.57 b) $3f_0$ c) $v = 4Lf_0$
16.59 flute harmonic $3N(N = 1, 3, \ldots)$ resonates
with string harmonic $4N$
16.61 a) stopped   b) $n = 7$, $n = 9$ c) 43.9 cm
16.63 a) $v/(2L)$, v/L, $3v/(2L)$
16.65 a) 375 m/s   b) 1.39   c) 0.8 cm
16.67 a) $n(77.3 \text{ Hz})$, $n = 1, 2, 3, \ldots$
16.69 1.27
16.71 a) 548 Hz   b) 652 Hz
16.73 a) $I = 2\pi^2\sqrt{\rho}Bf^2(\Delta R)^2$
b) $P = 8\pi^3\sqrt{\rho}Bf^2R^2(\Delta R)^2$
c) $A = (R/d)\Delta R$, $p_{\max} = 2\pi\sqrt{\rho}B(Rf/d)\Delta R$,
$I = 2\pi^2\sqrt{\rho}B(fR/d)^2(\Delta R)^2$
16.75 a) 6.74 cm   b) 147 Hz
16.77 b) 2.0 m/s
16.79 a) 1.2×10^6 m/s   b) 3.6×10^{16} m $= 3.8$ ly
c) 5.2×10^3 ly; 4100 BCE
16.81 a) $f_0\left(\dfrac{2v_W}{v - v_W}\right)$ b) $f_0\left(\dfrac{2v_W}{v + v_W}\right)$
16.83 d) 9.69 cm/s; 6.67×10^2 m/s²

Chapter 17

17.1 a) -81.0°F   b) 134.1°F   c) 88.0°F
17.3 38 F°
17.5 a) -18.0 F°   b) -10.0 C°
17.7 a) 104.4°F; yes   b) 54°F
17.9 a) 216.5 K   b) 325.9 K   c) 205.4 K
17.11 a) -210°C   b) 63 K
17.13 0.964 atm
17.15 a) -282°C   b) no, 4.76×10^4 Pa
17.17 0.39 m
17.19 a) 1.9014 cm   b) 1.8964 cm
17.21 2.3×10^{-5} (C°)⁻¹
17.23 11 L
17.25 1.7×10^{-5} (C°)⁻¹
17.27 a) 1.431 cm²   b) 1.437 cm²
17.29 0.261 mm
17.31 a) 3.2×10^{-5} (C°)⁻¹   b) 2.5×10^9 Pa
17.33 5.79×10^5 J
17.35 240 J/kg · K
17.37 1.4×10^3 s
17.39 1.21×10^{-2} C°
17.41 45.1 C°
17.43 a) 114 C°   b) 6.35 C°
17.45 a) 215 J/kg · K   b) water   c) too small
17.47 8 min
17.49 3.64×10^4 J $= 8.69 \times 10^3$ cal $= 34.5$ Btu
17.51 2.39×10^4 Btu/h $= 7.01 \times 10^3$ W
17.53 357 m/s
17.55 3.45 L
17.57 5.50×10^5 J
17.59 0.0940 kg
17.61 2.10 kg
17.63 190 g
17.65 a) 222 K/m   b) 10.7 W   c) 73.3°C
17.67 a) -5.8°C   b) 11 W/m²
17.69 7.1×10^2 Btu $= 7.5 \times 10^5$ J
17.71 105.5°C
17.73 a) 21.3 kW   b) 6.44 kW
17.75 167 W
17.77 2.1 cm²
17.79 a) 35.2°M   b) 39.6 C°
17.81 a) 5.0×10^{-3} cm³, -23 kg/m³
17.83 37.5°C
17.85 35.0°C
17.87 23.0 cm, 7.0 cm

17.89 b) 1.9×10^8 Pa
17.91 a) 87°C b) −80°C
17.93 20.2°C
17.95 a) 54.3
17.97 a) 83.6 J b) 1.86 J/mol · K
    c) 5.60 J/mol · K
17.99 a) 2.7×10^7 J b) 6.89 K c) 19.3 K
17.101 2.53 cm
17.103 a) 86.1°C b) no ice, 0.130 kg liquid water,
    no steam
17.105 a) 100°C b) 0.0214 kg steam, 0.219 kg
    liquid water
17.107 1.743 kg
17.109 a) 94 W b) 1.3
17.111 2.9
17.113 a) 6.0×10^5 s (about 170 h) d) 1.5×10^{10} s
    (about 500 y); no
17.115 0.106 W/m · K
17.117 5.82×10^{-3} kg
17.119 a) 69.6°C
17.121 1.76 C°
17.123 a) 103°C b) 27 W
17.125 a) the reverse b) 1.2×10^{-4} c) 5.2 s
    d) to within 1.93 C°
17.127 a) (i) 280 W (ii) 0.248 W
    (iii) 2.10×10^3 W (iv) 116 W; radiation
    from the sun b) 3.72 L/h c) 1.4 L/h

Chapter 18

18.1 a) 56.2 mol b) 6.81×10^6 Pa = 67.2 atm
18.3 0.959 atm
18.5 a) 3×10^{27} molecules
    b) 3×10^{19} molecules/cm³
18.7 503.0°C
18.9 3.36×10^5 Pa
18.11 0.159 L
18.13 1.05 atm
18.15 a) 70.2°C b) yes
18.17 850 m
18.19 density at sea level is 1.2% larger
18.21 2.28×10^4 Pa
18.23 a) \$8720 b) 3.88 cm
18.25 a) 8.2×10^{-17} atm b) no
18.27 55.6 mol, 3.35×10^{25} molecules
18.29 a) 9.00×10^{-5} m³ b) 3.10×10^{-10} m
    c) about the same
18.31 b) 1.004
18.33 a) could be true b) could be true
    c) not true d) must be true e) could be true
18.35 a) 1.9×10^6 m/s; no, 0.64% of c
    b) 7.3×10^{10} K
18.37 a) 6.21×10^{-21} J b) 2.34×10^5 m²/s²
    c) 484 m/s d) 2.57×10^{-13} kg · m/s
    e) 1.24×10^{-19} N f) 1.24×10^{-17} Pa
    g) 8.15×10^{21} molecules
    h) 2.45×10^{22} molecules
18.39 3800°C
18.41 a) 1560 J b) 935 J
18.43 a) 741 J/kg · K b) 5.65 kg; 4850 L
18.45 a) 924 J/kg · K b) Table 17.3 gives
    910 J/kg · K
18.49 a) 337 m/s b) 380 m/s c) 412 m/s
18.51 a) 610 Pa; solid → vapor b) 2.21×10^7 Pa;
    solid → liquid → vapor
18.53 no; no
18.55 0.213 kg
18.57 a) −178°C b) 1.17×10^{26} molecules/m³
    c) Titan's is 4.7 times Earth's
18.59 1.92 atm
18.61 a) 31 b) 8.41×10^3 N c) 7.8×10^3 N
18.63 a) 26.2 m/s b) 16.1 m/s, 5.44 m/s
    c) 1.74 m
18.65 5.0×10^{27}
18.67 a) same translational kinetic energy; A has
    greater rms speed b) B c) 4250°C d) B
18.69 b) 303 mol/m³ c) van der Waals
18.71 a) 4.65×10^{-26} kg b) 6.11×10^{-21} J
    c) 2.04×10^{24} molecules d) 1.24×10^4 J
18.73 b) r_2 c) $r_1 = R_0/2^{16}$, $r_2 = R_0$, $r_1/r_2 = 2^{-16}$
    d) U_0
18.75 a) 517 m/s b) 299 m/s
18.77 b) 1.40×10^5 K, 1.01×10^4 K
    c) 6.37×10^3 K, 4.59×10^2 K

18.79 a) 1.24×10^{-14} kg b) 4.16×10^{11}
    c) 2.95×10^{-6} m, no
18.81 a) $2R$ b) less
18.83 CO_2: 20.79 J/mol · K, 0.270; SO_2:
    24.94 J/mol · K, 0.205; H_2S: 24.94 J/mol · K,
    0.039
18.87 b) $0.0420N$ c) $(2.94 \times 10^{-21})N$
    d) $0.0297N$, $(2.08 \times 10^{-21})N$ e) $0.0595N$,
    $(4.15 \times 10^{-21})N$
18.89 42.6%
18.91 a) 4.5×10^{11} m b) 703 m/s, 6.4×10^8 s
    (about 20 y). no c) 1.4×10^{-14} Pa
    d) about 650 m/s; evaporate
    f) 2×10^5 K; no
18.93 d) $T_c = 8a/27Rb$, $(V/n)_c = 3b$
    e) $p_c = a/27b^2$ f) 8/3 g) 3.28, 3.44, 4.35

Chapter 19

19.1 b) 1330 J
19.3 b) −6540 J
19.5 a) 0.88 atm
19.7 a) $(p_1 - p_2)(V_2 - V_1)$ b) negative of work
    done in reverse direction
19.9 a) 3.78×10^4 J b) 7.72×10^4 J c) no
19.11 a) 410 J b) rises
19.13 a) 16.4 min b) 139 m/s = 501 km/h
19.15 a) internal energy b) ab c) none
19.17 a) positive b) I: positive; II: negative
    c) into d) I: into; II: out of
19.19 a) 1.67×10^5 J b) 2.03×10^6 J
19.21 b) 208 J c) on the piston d) 712 J
    e) 920 J f) 208 J
19.23 a) 948 K b) 900 K
19.25 2/5
19.27 a) 25.0 C° b) 17.9 C° c) a
19.29 a) −605 J b) 0 c) yes, 605 J, liberates
19.31 a) 747 J b) 1.30
19.33 a) 4.76×10^5 Pa b) -1.06×10^4 J
    c) 1.59; heated
19.35 5.1×10^3 J; increases; increases
19.37 b) 224 J c) $Q = 0$ d) −224 J
19.39 11.6°C
19.41 a) increases b) 4800 J
19.43 a) 45.0 J b) liberates 65.0 J
    c) $Q_{ad} = 23.0$ J, $Q_{ab} = 22.0$ J
19.45 a) same b) absorbs 4000 J
    c) absorbs 8000 J
19.47 b) −2460 J
19.49 a) 1173 K b) 1.22×10^4 J
    c) 4.26×10^4 J d) 4.57×10^4 J
19.51 −0.226 m³
19.53 a) 4.32×10^{-4} m³ b) 648 J
    c) 7.15×10^5 J d) 7.14×10^5 J
    e) no substantial difference
19.55 3.4×10^5 J/kg
19.57 b) 11.9 C°
19.59 a) 0.173 m b) 206°C c) 7.46×10^4 J
19.61 a) $Q = 300$ J, $\Delta U = 0$ b) $Q = 0$,
    $\Delta U = -300$ J c) $Q = 750$ J, $\Delta U = 450$ J
19.63 a) $W = 738$ J, $Q = 2588$ J, $\Delta U = 1850$ J
    b) $W = 0$, $Q = -1850$ J, $\Delta U = -1850$ J
    c) 0
19.65 a) $W = -187$ J, $Q = -654$ J, $\Delta U = -467$ J
    b) $W = 113$ J, $Q = 0$, $\Delta U = -113$ J
    c) $W = 0$, $Q = 580$ J, $\Delta U = 580$ J
19.67 a) 360 K, 2.67×10^5 Pa b) 1.14 L

Chapter 20

20.1 a) 6500 J b) 34%
20.3 a) 23% b) 12,400 J c) 0.350 g
    d) 222 kW = 298 hp
20.5 a) 25% b) 970 MW
20.7 13.8
20.9 a) 1.62×10^4 J b) 5.02×10^4 J
20.11 a) 767 W b) 7.27
20.13 a) 215 J b) 378 K c) 39.1%
20.15 a) 4.2×10^4 J b) 715 K
20.17 a) 492 J b) 212 W c) 5.4
20.19 a) 400 W b) 10.7 c) 36.9 kg
20.21 4300 J
20.23 37.1 hp
20.25 a) 428 J/K b) −392 J/K c) 36 J/K

20.27 a) irreversible b) $+1.25 \times 10^4$ J/K; it is
    consistent
20.29 6.31 J/K
20.31 a) 6.05×10^3 J/K b) five time greater for
    vaporization
20.33 gallium: +6.63 J/K; hand: −6.48 J/K; greater
    for gallium
20.35 a) no b) 18.3 J/K c) 18.3 J/K
20.37 a) 0.200 b) 8000 J
20.39 a) 27.8 K b) 15.3 K
20.41 a) absorbed: bc; rejected: ab, ca
    c) $T_a = T_b = 241$ K, $T_c = 481$ K
    d) $Q_{net} = W_{net} = 610$ J e) 8.7%
20.43 a) enters: 2.10×10^4 J; leaves: 1.66×10^4 J
    b) 4.4×10^3 J; 21% c) maximum is
    $e = 67\%$
20.45 a) 7.0% b) 3.0×10^6 J/s; 2.8×10^6 J/s
    c) 6×10^5 kg/h = 6×10^5 L/h
20.47 a) $p_1 = 2.00$ atm, $V_1 = 4.00$ L; $p_2 = 2.00$ atm,
    $V_2 = 6.00$ L; $p_3 = 1.11$ atm, $V_3 = 6.00$ L;
    $p_4 = 1.67$ atm, $V_4 = 4.00$ L
    b) (i) $Q = 1422$ J, $W = 405$ J
    (ii) $Q = -1355$ J, $W = 0$
    (iii) $Q = W = -274$ J (iv) $Q = 339$ J,
    $W = 0$ c) 131 J d) 7.5%; $e_{Carnot} = 44\%$
20.49 a) $a \rightarrow b$: $Q = 2.25 \times 10^5$ J,
    $W = 0.90 \times 10^5$ J, $\Delta U = 1.35 \times 10^5$ J; $b \rightarrow c$:
    $Q = -2.40 \times 10^5$ J, $W = 0$,
    $\Delta U = -2.40 \times 10^5$ J; $c \rightarrow a$:
    $Q = 0.45 \times 10^5$ J, $W = -0.60 \times 10^5$ J,
    $\Delta U = 1.05 \times 10^5$ J) b)
    $Q = W = 0.30 \times 10^5$ J, $\Delta U = 0$ c) 11.1%
20.51 $\left(\dfrac{T_H - T'}{T_H}\right)\left(\dfrac{T' - T_C}{T'}\right)$; less
20.53 a) 122 J, 78 J b) 5.10×10^{-4} m³
    c) $p_b = 2.32 \times 10^6$ Pa, $V_b = 4.81 \times 10^{-5}$ m³,
    $T_b = 771$ K; $p_c = 4.00 \times 10^6$ Pa,
    $V_c = 4.81 \times 10^{-5}$ m³, $T_c = 1333$ K;
    $p_d = 1.47 \times 10^5$ Pa, $V_d = 5.10 \times 10^{-4}$ m³,
    $T_d = 518$ K d) $e = 61.1\%$; $e_{Carnot} = 77.5\%$
20.55 a) 6.20×10^4 J c) 3.42×10^4 J
    d) before: 6.20×10^4J; after: 3.42×10^4 J
20.57 a) 88.5 J b) 17.7 J
20.59 a) $b \rightarrow c$: $nC_V \ln(T_c/T_b)$; $d \rightarrow a$: $nC_V \ln(T_a/T_d)$
    b) $nC_V \ln\left(\dfrac{T_c T_a}{T_b T_d}\right)$
20.61 a) −143 J/K b) +196 J/K c) zero
    d) +53 J/K

Chapter 21

21.1 a) 2.0×10^{10} b) 8.58×10^{-13}
21.3 2.10×10^{28} electrons, 3.35×10^9 C
21.5 3.71×10^3 m
21.7 a) 7.42×10^{-7} C on each sphere
    b) 3.71×10^{-7} C on one and 1.48×10^{-6} C on
    the other
21.9 1.43×10^{13}, away from each other
21.11 a) 2.20×10^4 m/s
21.13 +0.750 nC
21.15 1.8×10^{-4} N, +x-direction
21.17 $x = -0.144$ m
21.19 2.58×10^{-6} N, −y-direction
21.21 b) $F_x = 0$, $F_y = +2kqQa/(a^2 + x^2)^{3/2}$
    c) $2kqQ/a^2$, +y-direction
21.23 b) $kq^2(1 + 2\sqrt{2})/2L^2$
21.25 a) 4.40×10^{-16} N b) 2.63×10^{11} m/s²
    c) 2.63×10^5 m/s
21.27 a) 3.31×10^6 N/C, to the left
    b) 1.42×10^{-8} s c) 1.80×10^3 N/C, to the
    right
21.29 a) $-21.9\mu C$ b) 1.02×10^{-7} N/C
21.31 a) 8.75×10^3 N/C, to the right
    b) 6.54×10^3 N/C, to the right
    c) 1.40×10^{-15} N, to the right
21.33 a) 364 N/C b) no, 2.73 μm downward
21.35 1.79×10^6 m/s
21.37 a) $mg = 8.93 \times 10^{-30}$ N; $F_e = 1.60 \times 10^{-15}$ N;
    yes
    b) 1.63×10^{-16} kg = $1.79 \times 10^{14} m_H$ c) no
21.39 a) $-j$ b) $(i + j)/\sqrt{2}$ c) $-0.390i + 0.921j$
21.41 a) 6.33×10^5 m/s b) 1.59×10^4 m/s

21.43 a) 0 b) $E_x = -2kq(x^2 + a^2)/(x^2 - a^2)^2$, for $x < -a$; $E_x = +2kq(x^2 + a^2)/(x^2 - a^2)^2$, for $x > +a$

21.45 a) (i) 574 N/C, $+x$-direction
(ii) 268 N/C, $-x$-direction
(iii) 404 N/C, $-x$-direction
b) (i) 9.20×10^{-17} N, $-x$-direction
(ii) 4.30×10^{-17} N, $+x$-direction
(iii) 6.48×10^{-17} N, $+x$-direction

21.47 1.04×10^7 N/C, to the left

21.49 a) $E_x = E_y = E = 0$
b) $E_x = +2.66 \times 10^3$ N/C, $E_y = 0$;
$E = 2.66 \times 10^3$ N/C, $+x$-direction
c) $E_x = +129$ N/C, $E_y = -510$ N/C;
$E = 526$ N/C, $284°$ clockwise from $+x$-axis
d) $E_x = 0, E_y = E = +1.38 \times 10^3$ N/C, $+y$-direction

21.51 a) $E_x = -4.79 \times 10^3$ N/C, $E_y = 0$;
$E = 4.79 \times 10^3$ N/C, $-x$-direction
b) $E_x = +2.13 \times 10^3$ N/C, $E_y = 0$;
$E = 2.13 \times 10^3$ N/C, $+x$-direction

21.53 a) $\vec{E} = \dfrac{2k\lambda}{x\sqrt{x^2/a^2 + 1}}\hat{\imath}$ b) $\vec{E} = \dfrac{2k\lambda}{x}\hat{\imath}$

21.55 a) $(7.0\text{N/C})\hat{\imath}$ b) $(1.75 \times 10^{-5}\,\text{N})\hat{\imath}$

21.57 a) 0 b) 0 c) σ/ϵ_0 directed downward

21.59 a) yes b) no

21.61 An infinite line of charge has a radial field in the plane through the wire, and constant in the plane of the wire, mirror-imaged about the wire

21.63 a) 1.4×10^{-11} C · m from q_1 toward q_2
b) 860 N/C

21.65 b) This also gives the correct expression for E_y since y appears in the full expression's denominator squared, so the signs carry through correctly.

21.67 b) Opposite charges are closest so the dipoles attract.

21.69 a) The torque is zero when $\vec{p}$ is aligned either in the *same* direction as $\vec{E}$ or in the *opposite* directions
b) The stable orientation is when $\vec{p}$ is aligned in the *same* direction as $\vec{E}$

21.71 1680 N, from $+5.00\ \mu$C charge toward $-5.00\ \mu$C charge
b) 22.3 N · m, clockwise

21.73 a) $\sqrt{\dfrac{kqQ}{m\pi^2 a^3}}$ b) accelerating along the y-axis away from origin

21.75 b) 2.80×10^{-6}C c) $39.5°$

21.77 a) 2.09×10^{21} N b) 5.90×10^{23} m/s² c) no

21.79 a) $6kq^2/L^2$, away from vacant corner
b) $(3kq^2/2L^2)(1 + 2\sqrt{2})$, toward center of square

21.81 a) 6.0×10^{23}
b) $F_g = 4.1 \times 10^{-31}$ N, $F_e = 5.1 \times 10^5$ N
c) yes for F_e and no for F_g

21.83 a) $(2kq/x^2)[1 - (1 + a^2/x^2)^{-3/2}]$, $-x$-direction
b) $3kqa^2/x^4$

21.85 a) 3.5×10^{20} b) 1.6 C; 2.4×10^{10} N

21.87 a) $(mv_0^2\sin^2\alpha)/2eE$ b) $(mv_0^2\sin^2\alpha)/eE$
c) $h_{max} = 0.418$ m, $d = 2.89$ m

21.89 a) $E_x = \dfrac{kQ}{a}\left(\dfrac{1}{r} - \dfrac{1}{a+r}\right)$, $E_y = 0$
b) $\dfrac{kqQ}{a}\left(\dfrac{1}{x-a} - \dfrac{1}{x}\right)\hat{\imath}$

21.91 a) $-(7850\text{N/C})\hat{\imath}$ b) smaller c) 18 cm

21.93 a) $+(0.89\text{N/C})\hat{\imath}$ b) smaller c) (i) 1.2%
(ii) 4.5%

21.95 a) $F = \dfrac{2kqQ}{a}\left(\dfrac{1}{y} - \dfrac{1}{\sqrt{a^2 + y^2}}\right)$, $-x$-direction
b) $F = \dfrac{kqQ}{a}\left(\dfrac{1}{x-a} - \dfrac{1}{x+a} - \dfrac{2}{x}\right)$, $+x$-direction

21.97 $E_x = E_y = 2kQ/a^2$

21.99 a) 6.25×10^4 N/C, $225°$ measured counterclockwise from $+x$-axis
b) 1.00×10^{-14} N, $45°$ measured counterclockwise from $+x$-axis

21.101 a) 1.19×10^6 N/C, to the left

b) 1.19×10^5 N/C, to the left
c) 1.19×10^5 N/C, to the right

21.103 $\vec{E} = \dfrac{\sigma}{2\epsilon_0}\left[-\dfrac{x}{|x|}\hat{\imath} + \dfrac{z}{|z|}\hat{k}\right]$

21.105 b) $q_1 < 0, q_2 > 0$ c) $0.844\ \mu$C d) 56.2 N

21.107 a) $\dfrac{kQ}{L}\left[\dfrac{1}{x + a/2} - \dfrac{1}{x + L + a/2}\right]$

Chapter 22

22.1 a) 1.75 N·m²/C b) no c) i) 0 ii) 90°

22.3 a) 3.53×10^5 N·m²/C b) 3.13×10^{-6}C

22.5 $\Phi = E\pi r^2$

22.7 a) 2.71×10^5 N·m²/C
b) 2.71×10^5 N·m²/C
c) 5.42×10^5 N·m²/C

22.9 a) zero b) 3.75×10^7 N/C radially inward
c) 1.11×10^7 N/C radially inward

22.11 b) no

22.13 a) 1.81×10^5 N·m²/C b) no change

22.15 a) 4.50×10^4 N/C b) 9.18×10^2 N/C

22.17 a) 3.00×10^{-7}C b) 1.20×10^5 N/C

22.19 a) $q = 3.27 \times 10^{-9}$ C b) $n_e = 2.04 \times 10^{10}$

22.21 8.06×10^5 N/C, toward negatively charged sphere

22.23 a) 5.73×10^{-6} C/m² b) 6.48×10^5 N/C
c) -5.65×10^4 N·m²/C

22.25 a) 2.59×10^{-7} C/m³ b) 1.96×10^3 N/C

22.27 a) $\vec{E} = \sigma/\epsilon_0$ b) 0

22.29 a) $\lambda = 2\pi r\sigma$ b) $\sigma R/r\epsilon_0$

22.31 a) yes; $+Q$ b) no c) yes d) no; no
e) no; yes; no

22.33 a) 750 N·m²/C b) 0 c) 577 N/C

22.35 a) -5.98×10^{-10} C

22.37 a) $\lambda/2\pi\epsilon_0 r$, radially outward
b) $\lambda/2\pi\epsilon_0 r$, radially outward
d) inner: $-\lambda$; outer: $+\lambda$

22.39 a) i) $\alpha/2\pi\epsilon_0 r$, radially outward ii) 0 iii) 0
b) i) $-\alpha$ ii) 0

22.41 $\theta = 19.8°$

22.43 a) $0 < r < R$, $E = 0$
$R < r < 2R$, $E = Q/4\pi\epsilon_0 r^2$, radially outward;
$r > 2R$, $E = 2Q/4\pi\epsilon_0 r^2$, radially outward

22.45 a) i) 0 ii) 0 iii) $q/2\pi\epsilon_0 r^2$, radially outward
iv) 0 v) $3q/2\pi\epsilon_0 r^2$, radially outward b) i) 0
ii) $+2q$ iii) $-2q$ iv) $+6q$

22.47 a) i) 0 ii) 0 iii) $q/2\pi\epsilon_0 r^2$, radially outward
iv) 0 v) $q/2\pi\epsilon_0 r^2$, radially inward b) i) 0
ii) $+2q$ iii) $-2q$ iv) $-2q$

22.49 a) $Qq/4\pi\epsilon_0 r^2$, toward the center of the shell
b) 0

22.51 a) The given σ is on both sides, so E is twice as great b) $\Phi = (\sigma A)/\epsilon_0$, but $E_{out} = \sigma/\epsilon_0$, so $E_{in} = 0$

22.53 $d = R/2$

22.55 b) for $|x| \le d$: $\vec{E} = (\rho_0 x^3/3\epsilon_0 d^2)\hat{\imath}$;
for $|x| \ge d$: $\vec{E} = (\rho_0 d/3\epsilon_0)(x/|x|)\hat{\imath}$

22.57 c) $E(r) = \dfrac{Q}{\pi\epsilon_0 R}\left(\dfrac{r}{R} - \dfrac{3r^2}{4R^2}\right)$
e) $E_{max} = Q/3\pi\epsilon_0 R^2$ at $r = 2R/3$

22.59 a) $\Phi = 4\pi Gm$ b) $\Phi = -4\pi GM_{encl}$

22.61 $\rho\vec{b}/3\epsilon_0$

22.63 a) $-(Q/16\pi\epsilon_0 R^2)\hat{\imath}$ b) $(Q/72\pi\epsilon_0 R^2)\hat{\imath}$

22.65 a) $Q(r) = Qe^{-2r/a_0}[2(r/a_0)^2 + 2(r/a_0) + 1]$
b) $E = \dfrac{kQe^{-2r/a_0}}{r^2}[2(r/a_0)^2 + 2(r/a_0) + 1]$

22.67 c) 0.807

Chapter 23

23.3 3.46×10^{-13} J

23.5 a) 12.5 m/s b) 0.323 m

23.7 a) 0.198 J b) i) 26.6 m/s ii) 36.7 m/s
iii) 37.6 m/s

23.9 a) -3.60×10^{-7} J b) $x = 0.0743$ m

23.11 $-q/2$

23.13 B: larger C: smaller D: same

23.15 7.42 m/s; faster

23.17 a) 0 b) $+7.50 \times 10^{-4}$ J
c) -2.06×10^{-3} J

23.19 a) 2.50 mm b) 7.49 mm

23.21 a) -737 V b) -704 V c) $+8.2 \times 10^{-8}$ J

23.23 b) 0 d) 0

23.25 b) $V = \dfrac{q}{4\pi\epsilon_0}\left(\dfrac{1}{|x|} - \dfrac{2}{|x - a|}\right)$

23.27 1.02×10^7 m/s

23.29 a) b b) 800 V/m c) -4.8×10^{-5} J

23.31 a) increase of 156 V b) decrease of 182 V

23.33 a) oscillatory b) 1.67×10^7 m/s

23.35 a) $\lambda = 9.51$ C/m b) no. less.
V decreases in direction of $\vec{E}$.
$\lambda > 0$: V inversely proportional to r c) 0

23.37 a) 7.81×10^4 V b) 0

23.41 a) 8.00 kV/m b) 1.92×10^{-7} N
c) 8.64×10^{-7} J d) -8.64×10^{-7} J

23.43 b) -20 nC c) no

23.47 a) $E_x = -Ay + 2Bx$, $E_y = -Ax - C$, $E_z = 0$
b) $x = -C/A$, $y = -2BC/A^2$, any value of z

23.49 a) i) for $r < r_a$, $V = \dfrac{q}{4\pi\epsilon_0}\left(\dfrac{1}{r_a} - \dfrac{1}{r_b}\right)$
ii) for $r_a < r < r_b$, $V = \dfrac{q}{4\pi\epsilon_0}\left(\dfrac{1}{r} - \dfrac{1}{r_b}\right)$
iii) for $r > r_b$, $V = 0$
b) $V_{ab} = \dfrac{q}{4\pi\epsilon_0}\left(\dfrac{1}{r_a} - \dfrac{1}{r_b}\right)$
c) for $r_a < r < r_b$, $E = \dfrac{V_{ab}}{\left(\frac{1}{r_a} - \frac{1}{r_b}\right)}\dfrac{1}{r^2}$
d) $E = 0$

23.51 a) concentric cylinders
b) 10 V: 2.90×10^{-2} m; 20 V: 4.20×10^{-2} m

23.53 a) -2.15×10^{-5} J b) $W_E = +2829$ V
c) $E = 3.54 \times 10^4$ V/m

23.55 a) 7.85×10^4 V/m$^{4/3}$
b) $\vec{E} = (-1.0 \times 10^5$ V/m$^{4/3})x^{1/3}\hat{\imath}$
c) $\vec{F} = (3.13 \times 10^{-15}$ N$)\hat{\imath}$

23.57 a) $-1.46q^2/\pi\epsilon_0 d$

23.59 a) -8.62×10^{-18} J b) 2.87×10^{-11} m

23.61 a) i) $V = (\lambda/2\pi\epsilon_0)\ln(b/a)$
ii) $V = (\lambda/2\pi\epsilon_0)\ln(b/r)$ iii) $V = 0$
d) $(\lambda/2\pi\epsilon_0)\ln(b/a)$

23.63 a) 1.76×10^{-16} N, downward
b) 1.93×10^{14} m/s², downward c) 8.24 mm
d) $15.4°$ e) 4.12 cm

23.65 a) 9.71×10^4 V/m b) 3.03×10^{-11} C

23.67 a) $r \le R$: $V = \left(\dfrac{\lambda}{4\pi\epsilon_0}\right)[1 - (r/R)^2]$;
$r \ge R$: $V = -\left(\dfrac{\lambda}{2\pi\epsilon_0}\right)\ln(r/R)$

23.69 $Q/4\pi\epsilon_0\sqrt{x^2 + a^2}$

23.71 $Q^2/8\pi\epsilon_0 R$

23.73 a) $Q/8\pi\epsilon_0 R$ b) i) center c) ii) surface

23.75 b) yes c) no

23.77 $Q/8\pi\epsilon_0 R$

23.79 a) $(Q/4\pi\epsilon_0 a)\ln[1 + (a/x)]$
b) $(Q/4\pi\epsilon_0 a)\ln[(a/y) + \sqrt{1 + (a/y)^2}]$
c) in (a), $(Q/4\pi\epsilon_0 x)$ in (b), $(Q/4\pi\epsilon_0 y)$

23.81 a) 1/3 b) 3

23.83 a) $E = Q_1/4\pi\epsilon_0 R_1^2$; $V = Q_1/4\pi\epsilon_0 R_1$
b) sphere 1: $Q_1 R_1/(R_1 + R_2)$;
sphere 2: $Q_1 R_2/(R_1 + R_2)$
c) $V = Q_1/4\pi\epsilon_0(R_1 + R_2)$ for either sphere
d) sphere 1: $E = Q_1/4\pi\epsilon_0 R_1(R_1 + R_2)$;
sphere 2: $E = Q_1/4\pi\epsilon_0 R_2(R_1 + R_2)$

23.85 a) 7.6×10^6 m/s b) 7.3×10^6 m/s
c) 2.3×10^9 K: 6.9×10^9 K

23.87 a) 5.9×10^{-15} m b) 4.14×10^{-11} J
c) 2.55×10^{25} nuclei

23.89 a) 1.01×10^{-12} m, 1.11×10^{-13} m, 2.54×10^{-14} m

23.91 c) 3 electrons, $0.507\ \mu$m

Chapter 24

24.1 1.82×10^{-4} C

24.3 a) 604 V b) 9.1×10^{-3} m²
c) 1.84×10^6 V/m d) 1.63×10^{-5} C/m²

24.5 a) $120\ \mu$C b) $C = \epsilon_0 A/d$ c) $480\ \mu$C

24.7 2.8 mm

24.9 a) 4.35×10^{-12} F b) 2.30 V

24.11 a) 6.56×10^{-11} F/m   b) 6.43×10^{-11} C
24.13 a) 1.50×10^{-11} F   b) 3.08 cm
c) 3.13×10^{4} N/C
24.15 a) $C_{eq} = 2.40\ \mu$F; $Q_{total} = 6.72 \times 10^{-5}$ C;
$Q_{12} = 2.24 \times 10^{-5}$ C; $Q_3 = 4.48 \times 10^{-5}$ C;
$Q_1 = Q_2 = Q_{12} = 2.24 \times 10^{-5}$ C
24.17 a) $Q_1 = 1.56 \times 10^{-5}$ C; $Q_i = 2.6 \times 10^{-4}$ C
b) 52.0 V
24.19 $V_2 = 50$ V; $V_3 = 70$ V
24.21 $C_{eq} = \dfrac{\epsilon_0 A}{d_1 + d_2}$
24.23 57 μF
24.25 0.0283 J/m^3
24.27 19.6 J
24.29 a) $Q^2 x/2\epsilon_0 A$ b) $(Q^2/2\epsilon_0 A)dx$ c) $Q^2/2\epsilon_0 A$
24.31 b) yes   c) flat sheets parallel to the plates
24.33 a) 24.2 μC
b) $V = 220$ V: $Q_{35} = 7.7\ \mu$C, $Q_{75} = 16.5\ \mu$C
c) 2.66 mJ   d) 35 nF: 0.85 mJ; 75 nF: 1.81 mJ
e) 220V for each capacitor
24.35 a) 1.60 nC   b) 8.0
24.37 a) $U_{parallel} = 4U_{series}$ b) $Q_{parallel} = 2Q_{series}$
c) $E_{parallel} = 2E_{series}$
24.39 a) 6.20×10^{-7} C/m^2 b) 1.28
24.41 0.0135 m^2
24.43 a) 2.3×10^{-11} C^2/N·m^2 b) 40 kV
c) $\sigma = 4.6 \times 10^{-4}$ C/m^2, $\sigma_i = 2.8 \times 10^{-4}$ C/m^2
24.45 a) 10.1 V   b) 2.25
24.47 a) 3.6 mJ; 13.5 mJ   b) increased by 9.9 mJ
24.49 a) $Q/k\epsilon_0 A$ b) $Qd/k\epsilon_0 A$ c) $k\epsilon_0 A/d$
24.51 a) 2.4×10^{-11} F   b) 2.9×10^{-10} C
c) 1.3×10^{3} d) 1.7×10^{-9} J
24.53 a) 421 J   b) 5.39×10^{-9} F
24.55 for $d \ll r_a$: $C \approx \dfrac{\epsilon_0 A}{d}$
24.57 a) $U_{tot} = 158\ \mu$J   b) $U_{4.5} = 72.1\ \mu$J
24.59 a) 2.5 μF   b) $Q_1 = 5.5 \times 10^{-4}$ C, $V_1 = 66$ V ;
$Q_2 = 3.7 \times 10^{-4}$ C, $V_2 = 88$ V ;
$Q_3 = 1.8 \times 10^{-4}$ C, $V_3 = 44$ V ;
$Q_4 = 1.8 \times 10^{-4}$ C, $V_4 = 44$ V ;
$Q_5 = 5.5 \times 10^{-4}$ C, $V_5 = 66$ V
24.61 a) 76 μC   b) 1.4×10^{-3} J   c) 11 V
d) 1.2×10^{-3} J
24.63 a) 2.3 μF   b) $C_1 = 9.7 \times 10^{-4}$ C;
$C_2 = 6.4 \times 10^{-4}$ C   d) 47 V
24.65 a) 3.91   b) 22.8 V
24.67 c) 710 μF
24.69 a) 6.5×10^{-2} F   b) $Q = 2.3 \times 10^{4}$ C
c) 4.0×10^{9} J
24.71 $C_{eq} = \dfrac{2\epsilon_0 A}{d}\left(\dfrac{K_1 K_2}{K_1 + K_2}\right)$
24.73 a) 14 μF   c) 72.0 μF: 505 μC, 7.02 V;
28.0 μF: 259 μC, 9.24 V;
18.0 μF: 229 μC, 12.7 V;
27.0 μF: 276 μC, 10.2 V;
6.0 μF: 14.9 μC, 2.49 V
24.75 a) $(\epsilon_0 L/D)[L + (K - 1)x]$
24.77 b) 2.38×10^{-9} F

Chapter 25

25.1 3.89×10^{4} C
25.3 a) 3.13×10^{19} b) $J = 1.51 \times 10^{6}$ A/m^2
c) $v_d = 1.11 \times 10^{-4}$ m/s
d) J would decrease; v_d would decrease
25.5 a) 110 min   b) 442 min   c) $v_d \propto 1/d$
25.7 a) 329 C   b) 41.1 A   c) 1333 min
25.9 5.86×10^{28} e$^-$/m^3
25.11 a) $1.216\Omega \cdot$m @ 20 °C
25.13 a) tungsten $E = 5.16 \times 10^{-3}$ V/m
b) aluminum $E = 2.70 \times 10^{-3}$ V/m
25.15 a) $E_{max} = 1.21$ V/m   b) $R = 1.45 \times 10^{-2}$ Ω
c) $V_{max} = 1.82 \times 10^{-1}$ V = 0.182 V
25.17 0.125 Ω
25.19 15 g
25.21 1.53×10^{-8} Ω
25.23 a) 1.55×10^{-12} b) $R = 2.4\ \Omega$
25.25 a) 11.1 A   b) 3.13 V   c) 0.28 Ω
25.27 a) 99.54 Ω b) 0.0158 Ω
25.29 a) $4.67 \times 10^{-5}\ \Omega$ b) $6.74 \times 10^{-4}\ \Omega$
25.31 a) 0.219 Ω b) $P = 3422$ J/s, $E = 1.23 \times 10^{7}$ J

25.33 a) $\mathcal{E} = 9.0$ V   b) $r = 4.5\ \Omega$
25.35 a) $I = 0$ b) $\mathcal{E} = 5.0\ V$ c) 5.0 V
25.37 a) $\mathcal{E} = 3.08$ V   b) $r = 0.067\ \Omega$ c) 1.8 Ω
25.39 a) 1.41 A   b) -13.7 V   c) -1.0 V
25.41 b) yes; linear
25.43 a) 144 Ω b) $2.40 \times 10^{2}\ \Omega$
c) 100 W bulb, $I = 0.833$ A
d) 120 W bulb, $I = 0.500$ A
25.45 a) 29.8 W   b) 0.248 A
25.47 a) $P = JE$ b) $p = J^2\rho$ c) $p = E^2/\rho$
25.49 a) 2.59×10^{6} J   b) 0.062 L   c) 1.6 h
25.51 12.3%
25.53 a) 24 W   b) 4.0 W   c) 20 W
25.55 a) 26.7 Ω b) 4.5 A   c) 454 W
25.57 a) $3.65 \times 10^{-8}\ \Omega \cdot$m   b) 172 A
c) 2.58×10^{-3} m/s
25.59 0.060 Ω
25.61 a) 2.5 mA   b) 2.14×10^{-5} V/m
c) 8.55×10^{-5} V/m   d) 1.80×10^{-4} V
25.63 a) $R = \dfrac{\rho h}{\pi r_1 r_2}$ b) $R = \dfrac{\rho L}{A}$
25.65 $I = \dfrac{Q}{\kappa \epsilon_0 \rho}$
25.67 a) 0.057 Ω b) $3.34 \times 10^{-8}\Omega \cdot$m   c) 0.86 mm
d) $2.40 \times 10^{-3}\ \Omega$
e) 1.1×10^{-3} (°C)$^{-1}$
25.69 a) 0.2 Ω b) 8.7 V
25.71 a) 1000 Ω b) 100 V   c) 10 W
25.73 1.42 A
25.75 a) $I_A\left(1 + \dfrac{R_A}{r + R}\right)$ b) 0.0425 Ω
25.77 b) 8-gauge   c) 106 W
d) 66 W, 175 kWh, $19.25
25.79 a) 0.40 A   b) 1.6 W   c) 4.8 W   d) 3.2 W
25.81 a) $\dfrac{a}{E}$ b) 2.59×10^{6} J   c) 4.32×10^{5} J
d) 0.96 Ω e) 1.73×10^{6} J
25.83 a) $I = \dfrac{v_0 A}{\rho_0 L (1 - e^{-1})}$
b) $E(x) = \dfrac{v_0 e^{-x/L}}{L(1 - e^{-1})}$
c) $V(x) = V_0 \dfrac{(e^{-x/L} - e^{-1})}{(1 - e^{-1})}$

Chapter 26

26.1 $\dfrac{3R}{4}$
26.3 a) $R_q < R_1$ b) $R_{eq} < R_1$
26.5 a) $I = 3.50$ A   b) $I = 4.50$ A   c) $I = 3.15$ A
d) $I = 3.25$ A
26.7 0.769 A
26.9 a) 8.8 Ω b) 3.18 A   c) 3.18 A
d) $V_{2.4} = 7.64$ V; $V_{1.6} = 5.09$ V; $V_{4.8} = 15.3$ V
26.11 $R_{eq} = 5.00\ \Omega$; $I_{total} = 12.0$ A; $I_{12} = 3.00$ A;
$I_4 = 9.00$ A; $I_3 = 8.00$ A; $I_6 = 4.00$ A
26.13 a) $I_1 = 1.50$ A, $I_2 = I_3 = I_4 = 0.50$ A
b) $P_1 = 10.1$ W, $P_2 = P_3 = P_4 = 1.12$ W;
c) $I_1 = 1.33$ A, $I_2 = I_3 = 0.667$ A
d) $P_1 = 8.00$ W, $P_2 = P_3 = 2.00$ W
e) $R_2 + R_3$ is brighter; R_1 is dimmer
26.15 a) 18.0 V; 3.00 A
26.17 a) 0.100 A for each
b) 400-Ω bulb: 4.00 W; 800-Ω bulb: 8.00 W
c) 400-Ω bulb: 0.300 A; 800-Ω bulb: 0.150 A
d) 400-Ω bulb: 36.0 W; 800-Ω bulb: 18.0 W;
total: 54.0 W
e) in series, 800-Ω bulb is brighter; in parallel,
400-Ω bulb is brighter and total light output is
greater
26.19 1010 s
26.21 a) 2.00 A   b) 5.00 Ω c) 42.0 V   d) 3.50 A
26.23 a) 8.00 A   b) $\mathcal{E}_1 = 36.0$ V, $\mathcal{E}_2 = 54.0$ V
c) 9.00 Ω
26.25 a) 1.60 A, 1.40 A, 0.20 A   b) 10.4 V
26.27 a) $\mathcal{E} = 36.40$ V   b) 0.500 A
26.29 a) $I_{100} = 0.250$ A; $I_{75} = 0.200$ A; higher potential
$I_A = 0.500$ A downward; V = 0
26.31 a) 0.041 A   b) 9.5 A
26.33 a) 17.8 V   b) 22.7 V   c) 27.5%

26.35 c) 3.34 V
26.37 a) 543 Ω b) 1.88 mA   c) 203 Ω
26.39 a) $C = 8.49 \times 10^{-7}$ F   b) $\tau = 2.89$ s
26.41 a) $t = 4.21 \times 10^{-3}$ s   b) $I = 0.125$ A
26.43 190 μC
26.45 $I = 13.6$ A
26.47 a) 0.938 A   b) 0.606 A
26.49 a) 1.33×10^{-4} C
b) $v_R = 9.12$ V, $v_C = 8.88$ V
c) $v_R = v_C = 8.88$ V   d) 6.75×10^{-5} C
26.51 900 W
26.53 a) 6.0 A, 720 W   b) 3.5 A, 420 W
26.55 a) 13.6 $\mu\Omega = 1.36 \times 10^{-5}\ \Omega$
b) $2.14 \times 10^{-8}\ \Omega$
26.57 a) 9.9 W   b) 16.3 W, brighter
26.59 a) 18.7 Ω b) 7.5 Ω
26.61 $I_1 = 0.848$ A, $I_2 = 2.14$ A, $I_3 = 0.171$ A
26.63 2.00-Ω resistor: 5.21 A; 4-Ω resistor: 1.11 A;
5-Ω resistor: 6.32 A
26.65 a) 0.222 V   b) 0.464 A
26.67 12.7 V
26.69 a) 186 V, upper terminal +
b) 3.00 A from − to + terminal
c) 20.0 Ω
26.71 a) $P_1 + P_2$ $\dfrac{P_1 P_2}{(P_1 + P_2)}$
26.73 a) -12.0 V   b) 1.71 V   c) 4.20 V
26.75 $R_3 = 10.8\ \Omega$, $R_2 = 1.08\ \Omega$, $R_1 = 0.12\ \Omega$
26.77 a) 114.4 V   b) 263 V   c) 266 V
26.79 b) 1897 Ω
26.81 a) 224-Ω resistor: 24.8 V; 589-Ω: 65.2 V
b) 3.87 kΩ c) 62.6 V   d) no

Chapter 27

27.1 a) $(-6.68 \times 10^{-4}$ N$)\hat{k}$
b) $(+ 6.68 \times 10^{-4}$ N$)\hat{i} + (7.27 \times 10^{-4}$ N$)\hat{j}$
27.3 a) positive   b) 5.05×10^{-2}N
27.5 9.47×10^{6} m/s
27.7 a) $\vec{B}_x = -0.175$ T, $\vec{B}_z = -0.256$ T
b) yes, $\vec{B}_y$ d) zero, 90°
27.9 a) $\vec{B} = 1.46$ T at 40.0° from the $+x$-axis,
toward the z-axis in the xz plane
b) $\vec{F} = 7.48 \times 10^{-16}$ N, at 50° from the
$+x$-axis toward the $+z$-axis
27.11 a) 3.05×10^{-3} Wb   b) 1.83×10^{-3} Wb   c) 0
27.13 -7.79×10^{-4} Wb
27.15 a) 1.60×10^{-4} T, into the page
b) 1.11×10^{-7} s
27.17 7.93×10^{-10} N, south
27.19 a) 1.2×10^{7} m/s   b) 0.10 T
27.21 a) 8.35×10^{5} m/s   b) 2.62×10^{-8} s
c) 7.26 kV
27.23 a) 107 T   b) no
27.25 a) 8.38×10^{-4} T
27.27 a) no   b) 1.40 cm
27.29 $B = 4.45 \times 10^{-2}$ T
27.31 1.29×10^{-25} kg, 78
27.33 a) 1.34×10^{4} A   b) horizontal
27.35 $F = 0.724$ N, at 63.4° below the $+x$-axis
27.37 9.7 A
27.39 a) 817 V   b) 113 m/s^2
27.41 a) $-(ILB)\hat{j}$ b) yes
27.43 a) 1.5×10^{-16} s   b) 1.1 mA
c) 9.3×10^{-24} A·m^2
27.45 a) rotates about axis A_z b) $\alpha = 294$ rad/s^2
27.47 -2.42 J
27.49 a) 1.13 A   b) 3.69 A   c) 98.2 V   d) 362 W
27.51 a) 4.7 mm/s
b) 4.5×10^{-3} V/m in the $+z$-direction
c) 53 μV
27.53 a) F_2/qv in the $-y$-direction   b) $F_2/\sqrt{2}$
27.55 $\vec{B} = 3.68$ T at a right angle to v_i
27.57 a) 8.9×10^{-17} J = 5.5×10^{5} eV
b) 7.7×10^{-8} s   c) 1.2 T   d) same as in (a)
27.59 4.46 A
27.61 a) -1.98×10^{-6} C
b) $(9.69 \times 10^{10}$ m/s$)(4\hat{\imath} + 3\hat{\jmath})$
c) $R = 5.69$ cm
d) 1.17×10^{7} Hz   e) $(R, 0, 1.72$ m$)$
27.63 9τ

27.65 1.6 mm

27.67 $(Mg\tan\theta/LB)$, right to left

27.71 a) 8.46×10^{-3} T   b) 0.271 m
c) 2.14×10^{-2} m

27.73 1.80 N to the left

27.75 0.0242 T, in the $+y$-direction

27.77 a) 0.0442 N·m clockwise   b) stretched
c) 7.98×10^{-3} J

27.79 0.444 N, in the $-y$-direction

27.81 b) side $(0, 0)$ to $(0, L)$: $(B_0IL/2)\hat{\imath}$;
side $(0, L)$ to (L, L): $(-B_0IL)\hat{\jmath}$;
side (L, L) to $(L, 0)$: $(-B_0IL/2)\hat{\imath}$;
side $(L, 0)$ to $(0, 0)$: 0   c) $(-B_0IL)\hat{\jmath}$

27.83 2.52 m/s   b) 7.60 A   c) 0.197 Ω

27.85 a) $\vec{\mu} = -IA\hat{k}$ b) $B_x = 3D/IA$, $B_y = 4D/IA$,
$B_z = -12D/IA$

27.87 $-\beta r/2$

27.89 a) 5.14 m   b) 1.72×10^{-6} s   c) 6.09 mm
d) 3.04 cm

Chapter 28

28.1 a) $(-1.92 \times 10^{-5}$ T$)\hat{k}$ b) 0

28.3 a) $\vec{B} = 6.00 \times 10^{-10}$ T out of the paper
b) $\vec{B} = 1.20 \times 10^{-9}$ T out of the paper   c) 0

28.5 a) 0   b) $(-1.31 \times 10^{-6}$ T$)\hat{k}$ out of the paper
c) $(-4.62 \times 10^{-7}$ T$)\hat{k}$
d) $(1.31 \times 10^{-6}$ T$)\hat{\jmath}$

28.7 a) attractive   b) 1.00×10^{-6}

28.9 a) 4.00×10^{-7} T out of the paper
b) 1.52×10^{-8} T out of the paper   c) 0

28.11 a) $(5.00 \times 10^{-11}$ T$)\hat{\jmath}$ b) $(-5.00 \times 10^{-11}$ T$)\hat{\imath}$
c) $(-1.77 \times 10^{-11}$ T$)\hat{k}$ d) 0

28.13 1.76×10^{-5} T into the paper

28.15 a) 8.0×10^{-4} T
b) 4.00×10^{-5} T, 20 times larger

28.17 a) 10.0 A   b) above the wire
c) directly east of the wire.

28.19 a) $(-1.0 \times 10^{-7}$ T$)\hat{\imath}$
b) $(2.19 \times 10^{-6}$ T$)$, $\theta = 46.8°$ from x toward z
c) $(7.9 \times 10^{-6}$ T$)\hat{\imath}$

28.21 a) 0   b) 6.67×10^{-6} T
c) 7.53×10^{-6} T to the left

28.23 a) 0   b) 0   c) 4.0×10^{-4} T to the right

28.25 a) 6.00×10^{-6} N, repulsive
b) 2.40×10^{-5} N

28.27 4.6×10^{-5} N/m, repulsive but negligible

28.29 $\mu_0 I^2/2\pi\lambda g$

28.31 $m_0|I_1 - I_2|/4R,0$

28.33 a) 9.42×10^{-3} T   b) 1.34×10^{-4} T

28.35 a) 305 A   b) -3.83×10^{-4} T·m

28.37 a) $\dfrac{\mu_0 I}{2\pi r}$ b) 0

28.39 $B = \dfrac{\mu_0 I}{2\pi r}$; $r = R/2$; $r = 2R$

28.41 a) 1790 turns/m   b) 63.0 m

28.43 a) 3.72×10^6 A   b) 2.49×10^5 A   c) 237 A

28.45 1.11×10^{-3} T

28.47 a) 0.0725 A   b) 0.0195 A

28.49 a) i) 1.1×10^{-3} T   ii) 4.7×10^{-6} A/m
iii) 5.9 T

28.51 a) 1.00×10^{-6} T into the paper
b) $(7.49 \times 10^{-8}$ N$)\hat{\jmath}$

28.53 a) 1.1×10^{13} m/s^2, away from the wire
b) 62.5 N/C, away from the wire
c) $mg \approx 10^{-29}$ N, negligible

28.55 5.75×10^{-6} T; 2.21×10^{-21} N perpendicular
to line ab and to velocity

28.57 a) ± 607 m/s   b) 9.2×10^{-6} T

28.59 a) 2.00 A out of the paper
b) 2.13×10^{-6} T, to the right
c) 2.06×10^{-6} T

28.61 a) 1.11×10^{-5} N/m
b) out of page: 1.11×10^{-5} N/m upward

28.63 23.2 A

28.65 a) $\mu_0\pi NN'II'a^2a'^2(\sin\theta)/2x^3$
b) $-\mu_0\pi NN'II'a^2a'^2(\cos\theta)/2x^3$

28.67 a) $(\mu_0 NIa^2/2)[((x + a/2)^2 + a^2)^{-3/2} + ((x - a/2)^2 + a^2)^{-3/2}]$
c) $(\mu_0 NI/a)(4/5)^{3/2}$

d) 0.0202 T   e) 0, 0

28.69 $\mu_0 I/8R$, out of the paper

28.71 a) $3I/2\pi R^3$ b) i) $\mu_0 Ir^2/2\pi R^3$ ii) $\mu_0 I/2\pi r$

28.73 zero

28.75 $16a/3$

28.77 b) $\mu_0 I_0/2\pi r$
c) $(I_0 r^2/a^2)(2 - r^2/a^2)$
d) $(\mu_0 I_0 r/2\pi a^2)(2 - r^2/a^2)$

28.79 $\mu_0 I$

28.81 a) $\mu_0 nI/2$, in the $+x$-direction
b) $\mu_0 nI/2$, in the $-x$-direction

28.83 7.73×10^{-23} J/T = 0.0833 μ_B

28.85 c) 6.15 mm

28.87 $\mu_0 Qn/a$

Chapter 29

29.1 a) 4.50 Wb   b) 20.3 V

29.3 a) $Q = NBA/R$ b) no

29.5 a) $+34$ V   b) counterclockwise

29.7 a) $I = i$; $B = \dfrac{\mu_0 i}{2\pi r}$ into the page
b) $d\Phi_B = \dfrac{\mu_0 i}{2\pi r}L\,dr$ c) $\Phi_B = \dfrac{\mu_0 iL}{2\pi}\ln(b/a)$
d) $\mathcal{E} = \dfrac{\mu_0 L}{2\pi}\ln(b/a)\dfrac{di}{dt}$

29.9 a) 5.44 mV   b) clockwise

29.11 a) $\mathcal{E} = +Abv$ b) clockwise   c) $\mathcal{E} = -Abv$
d) counterclockwise

29.13 10.4 rad/s

29.15 a) counterclockwise   b) clockwise   c) $I = 0$

29.17 a) a to b b) b to a c) b to a

29.19 a) clockwise   b) 0   c) counterclockwise

29.21 a) $V_{ab} = 0.675$ V
b) b at higher potential than a
c) $E = 2.25$ V/m from b to a
d) b has excess of positive charge   e) i) 0
ii) 0

29.23 46.2 m/s; no

29.25 a) 3.00 V   b) clockwise
c) 0.800 N to the right
d) 6.00 W $= P_{mech} = P_{elec}$

29.27 a) 4.23 V   b) 4.23 V   c) 0
d) for width $w \ll L$, it does not matter.
$\mathcal{E} = 4.23$ V as long as the longitudinal axis of
the rod is in the x-y plane.

29.29 a) $\pi r_1^2\dfrac{dB}{dt}$ b) $\dfrac{r_1}{2}\dfrac{dB}{dt}$ c) $\dfrac{R^2}{2r_2}\dfrac{dB}{dt}$ e) $\dfrac{\pi R^2}{4}\dfrac{dB}{dt}$
f) $\pi R^2\dfrac{dB}{dt}$ g) $\pi R^2\dfrac{dB}{dt}$

29.31 9.21 A/s

29.33 9.50×10^{-4} V

29.35 $K = 2.34$

29.37 a) 5.99×10^{-10} C
b) 6.00×10^{-3} A
c) 6.00×10^{-3} A

29.39 a) 0.15 V/m   b) 38 V/m·s
c) 3.4×10^{-10} A/m^2
d) $B_D = 2.38 \times 10^{-21}$ T, negligible;
$B_C = 5.33 \times 10^{-5}$ T

29.41 For any continuous superconducting path,
$R_{\text{total}} = 0$

29.43 a) $-(4.38 \times 10^4$ A/m$)\hat{\imath}$ b) $(15.0$ T$)\hat{\imath}$

29.45 a) 3.7 A   b) 54 μA   c) counterclockwise

29.47 a) $\dfrac{\mu_0 i\pi a}{2C}$ c) $i = i_0\exp(-2Rt/\mu_0\pi a)$
d) 45 μs

29.49 a) $\mu_0 Iabv/2\pi r(a + r)$ b) clockwise

29.51 191 rpm

29.53 a) 0.126 V   b) a to b

29.55 b) FR/B^2L^2

29.57 1.2 V

29.59 $\dfrac{\mu_0 IW}{4\pi}$

29.61 a) $(\mu_0 IV/2\pi)\ln((L + d)/d)$ b) a c) 0

29.63 a) 0.165 V   b) 0.165 V   c) 0; 0.0142 V

29.65 a) B^2a^2V/R

29.67 a) $(qr/2)\dfrac{dB}{dt}$, to the left
b) $(qr/2)\dfrac{dB}{dt}$, upward   c) 0

29.73 a) 1.96×10^{-4} A/m^2
b) 3.00×10^{-9} A/m^2
c) 7.82×10^6 Hz

29.75 b) $\dfrac{a}{2}\dfrac{dB}{dt}$ c) 7.37×10^{-4} A
d) 1.75×10^{-4} V

29.77 a) a to b b) $v_t = \dfrac{Rmg\tan\theta}{L^2B^2\cos\theta}$ c) $\dfrac{mg\tan\theta}{LB}$
d) $\dfrac{Rm^2g^2(\tan\theta)^2}{L^2B^2}$ e) same as (d)

Chapter 30

30.1 a) 0.270 V, yes   b) 0.270 V

30.5 a) 1.96 H   b) 7.12×10^{-3} Wb

30.7 a) 0.250 H   b) 4.5×10^{-4} Wb

30.9 a) 4.68 mV   b) a

30.11 $\dfrac{\mu_0 N^2 A}{l}$

30.13 2850

30.15 a) 1.61×10^{-1} T   b) 1.03×10^4 J/m^3
c) 0.129 J   d) 4.03×10^{-5} H

30.19 a) 2.40 A/s   b) 0.800 A/s   c) 0.413 A
d) 0.750 A

30.21 a) 17.3μs   b) 30.7μs

30.25 a) 0.250 A   b) 0.137 A   c) 32.9 V, c
d) 4.62×10^{-4} s

30.27 a) $(4.50$ W$)[1 - \exp(-(3.20$ s$^{-1})t)]$
b) $(4.50$ W$)[1 - \exp(-(3.20$ s$^{-1})t)]^2$
c) $(4.50$ W$)[\exp(-(3.20$ s$^{-1})t)$
$- \exp(-(6.40$ s$^{-1})t)]$

30.29 a) 25.0 mH   b) 9.00×10^{-8} C
c) 5.40×10^{-7} J   d) 6.57 mA

30.31 a) 105 rad/s, 59.6 ms   b) 7.20×10^{-4} C
c) 4.32×10^{-3} J   d) -543 μC
e) 49.9 mA   f) 2.45×10^{-3} J, capacitor;
1.87×10^{-3} J, inductor

30.33 a) $f = 2.13 \times 10^3$ Hz   b) $V_E = 0.225$ J
c) $V_B = 0.223$ J

30.35 a) $U_C = (Q^2/2C)\cos^2(\omega t + \phi)$;
$U_L = (Q^2/2C)\sin^2(\omega t + \phi)$

30.37 $\sqrt{LC} = \sqrt{(V \cdot s/A)(A \cdot s/V)} = \sqrt{s^2} = $ s

30.41 a) 298 rad/s   b) 83.8 Ω

30.43 a) $m = 4.80 \times 10^{-6}$ H
b) $\mathcal{E} = \pm1.80 \times 10^{-4}$ V

30.49 a) $\dfrac{\mu_0 i}{2\pi r}$ b) $\left(\dfrac{\mu_0 i^2 l}{4\pi r}\right)dr$ c) $\left(\dfrac{\mu_0 i^2 l}{4\pi}\right)\ln(b/a)$

30.51 a) $L = 8.89$ H   b) $l = 56.3$ m; no

30.53 a) 0.281 J   b) 0.517 J   c) 0.236 J

30.57 222 μF; 9.31 μH

30.59 2×10^4 m/s

30.61 a) solenoid   c) 50 V   d) 3.5 A
e) 4.3 Ω;43 mH

30.63 a) $V_1 = 40.0$ V; $A_1 = A_4 = 0.80$ A, all others
are zero
b) $V_1 = 24.0$ V, $V_2 = 0$, $V_3 = V_4 = V_5 = 16.0$;
$A_1 = 0.48$ A, $A_2 = 0.16$ A, $A_3 = 0.32$ A,
$A_4 = 0$ c) 192 μC

30.65 a) $A_1 = A_4 = 0.45$ A, $A_2 = A_3 = 0$
b) $A_1 = 0.58$ A, $A_2 = 0.32$ A, $A_3 = 0.16$ A,
$A_4 = 0.11$ A

30.67 a) 60.0 V   b) a c) 60.0 V   d) c
e) -96.0 V   f) b g) -156 V   h) d

30.69 a) $i_0 = 0$, $V_{ac} = 0$, $V_{cb} = 36.0$ V
b) $i_0 = 0.180$ A, $V_{ac} = 9.00$ V, $V_{cb} = 27.0$ V
c) $i_0 = (0.180$ A$)[1 - \exp(-(50.0$s$^{-1})t)]$,
$V_{ac} = (9.00$ V$)[1 - \exp(-(50.0$s$^{-1})t)]$,
$V_{cb} = 27.0$ V $+ (9.00$ V$)\exp(-(50.0$ s$^{-1})t)$

30.71 a) 0; 20 V   b) 0.267 A; 0   c) 0.147 A; 9.0 V

30.75 a) $i_1 = \mathcal{E}/R_1$, $i_2 = (\mathcal{E}/R_2)[1 - \exp(-R_2t/L)]$
b) $i_1 = \mathcal{E}/R_1$, $i_2 = \mathcal{E}/R_2$
c) $i = (\mathcal{E}/R_2)\exp(-(R_1 + R_2)t/L)$

30.77 a) $d = [(L - L_0)/(L_F - L_0)]D$
b) 0.63024 H, 0.63048 H, 0.63072 H, 0.63096 H
c) 0.63000 H, 0.62999 H, 0.62999 H, 0.62998 H

30.79 a) $i_1 = (\mathcal{E}/R_1)[1 - \exp(R_1t/L)]$,
$i_2 = (\mathcal{E}/R_2)\exp(-t/R_2C)$,
$q_2 = C\mathcal{E}[1 - \exp(-t/R_2C)]$
b) 0, 9.6 mA   c) 1.9 A, 0   d) 1.6 ms
e) 9.4 mA   f) 0.22 s

Chapter 31

31.1   a) $I_{rms} = 0.34$ A   b) $I = 0.48$ A   c) 0
     d) $(i^2)_{av} = 0.12$ A^2

31.3   a) 31.8 V   b) 0

31.5   a) 0.0132 A   b) 0.132 A   c) 1.32 A

31.9   a) 1.51 kΩ   b) 0.239 H   c) 497 Ω   d)16.6 μF

31.11   13.3 μF

31.13   a) $i = (0.0253$ A$) \cos[(720$ rad/s$)t]$
     b) 180 Ω
     c) $v_L = (-4.56$ V$) \sin[(720$ rad/s$)t]$

31.15   b) $v = 20.5$ V, $v_c = 7.6$ V, $v_L = 12.9$ V
     c) $v = -15.2$ V, $v_R = -22.5$ V, $v_L = 7.3$ V

31.17   a) 696 Ω   b) 0.0431 A
     c) $v_R = 8.62$ V, $v_c = 28.7$ V   d) $-73.3°$

31.19   a) 601 Ω   b) 49.9 mA   c) $-70.6°$, lags
     d) $v_R = 9.98$ V, $v_L = 4.99$ V, $v_c = 33.3$ V

31.21   a) 113 Hz; 15 mA   b) 7.61 mA; lag

31.23   50.0 V

31.25   a) $P_{max} = 40.0$ W   b) $I_{rms} = 0.167$ A
     c) $R = 7.20 \times 10^2$ Ω

31.29   a) $+45.8°$,0.697   b) 344 Ω   c) 155 V
     d) 48.6 W   e) 48.6 W   f) 0   g) 0

31.31   a) 150 V   b) 150 V, 1290 V, 1290 V
     c) 37.5 W

31.33   a) 1.00   b) 75.0 W   c) 75.0 W

31.35   a) $Z = 115$ Ω   b) $Z = 146$ Ω   c) $Z = 146$ Ω

31.37   a) 10   b) 2.40 A   c) 28.8 A   d) 500 Ω

31.39   a) $N_2 = \frac{1}{2}N_1$ b) 13 A   c) 9.0 Ω

31.41   0.124 H

31.43   a) $t_1 = \pi/2\omega$, $t_2 = 3\pi/2\omega$ b) $2I/\omega$
     c) $I_{rav} = 2I/\omega$

31.45   a) inductor   b) 0.133 H

31.47   a) $I = 1.15$ A, $V_L = 31.6$ V, $V_R = 57.5$ V,
     $V_C = 14.7$ V
     b) $I = 0.860$ A, $V_L = 47.3$ V, $V_R = 43.0$ V,
     $V_C = 5.47$ V

31.49 $\sqrt{(R^2 + \omega^2 L^2)/[R^2 + (\omega L - 1/\omega C)^2]}$

31.53   b) $V_B = LV^2/4[R^2 + (\omega L - 1/\omega C)^2]$,
     $V_E = V^2/4\omega C[R^2 + (\omega L - 1/\omega C)^2]$
     d) $\omega = 0$; $U_B = 0$; $U_E = CV^2/4$; $\omega \to \infty$;
     both U_B and $U_E \to 0$;
     $U_B = U_E$ at $\omega = \omega_0 = 1/\sqrt{LC}$

31.57   a) $I_R = V/R$, $I_L = V/\omega L$, $I_C = \omega CV$
     c) $\omega \to 0$: $I_L \to \infty$, $I_C \to 0$; $\omega \to \infty$: $I_L = 0$,
     $I_C \to \infty$ d) 159 Hz   e) 0.50 A
     f) $I_R = 0.50$ A, $I_L = I_C = 0.050$ A

31.59   a) 102 Ω   b) 0.882 A   c) 270 V

31.61   a) 0.750 A   b) 160 Ω   c) 619 Ω, 341 Ω
     d) 341 Ω

31.63 $i_{av} = 0$, $i_{rms} = I_0/\sqrt{3}$

31.65   a) ω_0 decreases by $\frac{1}{2}$ b) X_C doubles

     c) X_C decreases by $\frac{1}{2}$ d) no

31.67   a) L and C b) factor of $\frac{1}{2}$

31.69   a) $V/\sqrt{R^2 + 9L/4C}$
     b) $[2V/\sqrt{R^2 + 9L/4C}]\sqrt{L/C}$
     c) $[V/2\sqrt{R^2 + 9L/4C}]\sqrt{L/C}$
     d) $2LV^2/(R^2 + 9L/4C)$
     e) $LV^2/2(R^2 + 9L/4C)$

31.73   a) $V_R I/2$ b) 0   c) 0

31.75   a) 0.400 A   b) 36.9°
     c) $Z_{cpx} = (400\,Ω) - i(300\,Ω)$, $Z = 500$ Ω
     d) $I_{cpx} = (0.320$ A$) - i(240$ A$)$

Chapter 32

32.1   a) 1.28 s   b) 8.15×10^{15} km

32.3   a) 6.0×10^4 Hz   b) 6.0×10^7 Hz
     c) 6.0×10^{13} Hz   d) 6.0×10^{16} Hz

32.5   a) $f = 6.94 \times 10^{14}$ Hz   b) $E_{max} = 375$ V/m

32.7 $\vec{E}(z,t) = (1.74 \times 10^5$ V/m$)\hat{\imath} \times$
     $\cos[(1.28 \times 10^7$ rad/m$)z -$
     $(3.83 \times 10^{15}$ rad/s$)t]$
     $\vec{B}(z,t) = (5.80 \times 10^{-4}$ T$)\hat{\jmath} \times$
     $\cos[(1.28 \times 10^7$ rad/m$)z -$
     $(3.83 \times 10^{15}$ rad/s$)t]$

32.9   a) +y-direction   b) 7.11 × 10⁻⁴ m

c) $\vec{B}(y,t) = (-1.03 \times 10^{-2}$ T$)\hat{\imath} \times$
     $\sin[(8.84 \times 10^3$ rad/m$)y -$
     $(2.65 \times 10^{12}$ rad/s$)t]$

32.11   a) 361 m   b) 0.0174 rad/m
     c) 5.22×10^6 rad/s   d) 0.0144 V/m

32.13   a) 381 nm   b) 526 nm   c) 1.38   d) 1.91

32.15   a) 330 W/m^2 b) 500 V/m; 1.7 μT

32.17 1.33×10^{-8} T, + y-direction

32.19   a) 1.1×10 W/m^2 b) 3.0×10^{-10} T
     c) 840 W; assuming isotropic transmission

32.21 2.5×10^{25} J

32.23 $E_{max} = 12.0$ V/m, $B_{max} = 4.00 \times 10^{-8}$ T

32.25 8.5×10^5 W

32.27   a) 8.68×10^{-15} kg/m$^2 \cdot$ s
     b) 2.60×10^{-6} kg/m$\cdot$s^2

32.29 $S = \epsilon_0 cE^2$

32.31   a) 7.10 mm   b) 3.55 mm   c) 1.56×10^8 m/s

32.33   a) 4.38 mm   b) 1.38 mm   c) 4.38 mm

32.35   a) $L = 30.5$ cm   b) $f = 2.46 \times 10^9$ Hz
     c) $L = 35.5$ cm: $f = 2.11 \times 10^9$ Hz

32.39   a) $I = 0.00602$ W/m^2
     b) 2.13 N/C, 7.10×10^{-9} T
     c) 1.20×10^{-12} N

32.41   a) $E_{max} = 701$ V/m, $B_{max} = 2.34 \times 10^{-6}$ T
     b) $\mu_E = \mu_B = 1.09 \times 10^{-6}$ J/m^3
     c) 1.07×10^{-11} J

32.43   a) $r = R$: $I = 6.4 \times 10^7$ W/m^2, $p_{rod} = 0.21$ Pa;
     $r = R/2$: $I = 2.6 \times 10^8$ W/m^2, $p_{rod} = 0.85$ Pa

32.45 7.78×10^{-13} rad/s

32.47   a) $I\rho/\pi a^2$ in direction of current
     b) current out of page: $\mu_0 I/2\pi a$, clockwise
     c) $I^2\rho/2\pi^2 a^3$, radially inward
     d) $I^2\rho l/\pi a^2 = I^2 R$

32.49   0.0368 V

32.51   a) 23.6 h   b) throw it

32.53   a) 2.66×10^7 m   b) 0.0673 s
     c) 6.50×10^{-23} Pa   d) 0.190 m

32.55   a) $4\pi R^3 \rho Gm^3/3r^2$ b) $LR^2/4r^2 c$
     c) 1.90^{-7} m, independent of r

32.57   b) 1.4×10^{-11} s^{-1} c) 2.6×10^{-8} s^{-1}

Chapter 33

33.1   39.4°

33.3   a) 1.55   b) 549 nm

33.5   a) 5.17×10^{-7} m   b) 3.40×10^{-7} m

33.7   a) 47.5°   b) 66.0°

33.9 2.51×10^8 m/s

33.13   a) frequency $= f$; wavelength $= n\lambda$;
     speed $= nf\lambda = nv$ b) frequency $= f$;
     wavelength $= \left(\dfrac{n}{n'}\right)\lambda$; speed $= \left(\dfrac{n}{n'}\right)f\lambda = \left(\dfrac{n}{n'}\right)v$

33.15   71.8°

33.17   a) 51.3°   b) 33.8°

33.19   a) 58.1°   b) 22.8°

33.21   1.77

33.23   24.4°

33.25   a) A: $I_0/2$ B: $I_0/8$ C: $3I_0/32$ b) 0

33.27   a) 1.40   b) 35.5°

33.29 $\alpha = \arccos\left(\dfrac{\cos\theta}{\sqrt{2}}\right) = \cos^{-1}\left(\dfrac{\cos\theta}{\sqrt{2}}\right)$

33.31   6.38 W/m^2

33.33   a) first: $I = I_0/2$, second: $I = 0.25 I_0$,
     third: $I = 0.125 I_0$ all linearly polarized along
     the axis of their respective filters.

33.35   a) $I_R = 0.374I$ b) $I_V = 2.35I$

33.39   a) $\sin\theta_3 = (n_1 \sin\theta_1)/n_3$ c) yes

33.41   72.0°

33.45   1.53

33.47   1.8

33.49   a) 48.6°   b) 48.6°

33.51   39.1°

33.53   a) $n = 1.11$ b) i) 9.75 ns
     ii) 4.07 ns; total = 8.95 ns

33.55   b) 0.22°

33.61   b) 38.9°   c) 5.0°

33.63   a) 35°   b) 10.1 W/m^2, 19.9 W/m^2

33.67   a) $\Delta = 2\theta_A - \theta\sin^{-1}\left(\dfrac{1}{n}\sin\theta_A\right) + 2\pi$
     b) $\cos^2\theta_2 = (n^2 - 1)/8$

c) red: $\theta_2 = 71.9°$; $\Delta = 230.1°$;
     violet: $\theta_2 = 71.6°$, $\Delta = 233.2°$; violet

Chapter 34

34.1   39.2 cm to right of mirror; 4.85 cm

34.3   image at (x_0, y_0)

34.5   b) 33.0 cm to left of vertex, 1.20 cm tall,
     inverted, real

34.7   0.213 mm

34.9   18.0 m from convex side of glass shell, 0.50 cm
     tall, erect, virtual

34.11   a) $m = \dfrac{f}{(f - s)}$ c) $s > f$ d) $s < f$ e) $-\infty$
     f) $s = f$ g) $s' = 0$ i) $s < f$ j) $s > f$
     k) $s > 2f$ l) it becomes infinite

34.13   a) concave   b) $f = 2.50$ cm, $R = 5.00$ cm

34.15   2.67 cm

34.17   a) at the center of the ball, $m = +1.33$ b) no

34.19 $s = 0.395$ m

34.21   8.35 cm to left of vertex, 0.326 mm, erect

34.23   a) 1.06 m to right of lens, 17.7 mm tall, real,
     inverted   b) all same as (a)

34.25   71.2 cm to right of lens, $m = -2.97$

34.27 $f = 3.69$ cm, object is 2.82 cm to left of lens

34.29 $n = 1.67$

34.33   Object is 26.3 cm from lens with height
     1.24 cm; image is erect; same side

34.35   10.2 m

34.37   a) 1.4×10^{-4} b) 5.25×10^{-4} c) 1.50×10^{-3}

34.39   a) 85 mm   b) 135 mm

34.41   a) 11   b) 2.160×10^{-3} s

34.43   a) convex   b) 50 mm to 56 mm

34.45   a) 80.0 cm   b) 76.9 cm

34.47   a) +2.33 diopters   b) -1.67 diopters

34.49   a) 6.06 cm   b) 4.12 mm

34.51   4.17 cm from lens; image is located on same
     side as ant

34.53   a) 8.37 mm   b) 21.4   c) 297

34.55   19.4 m

34.57   a) -6.33 b) 1.90 cm   c) 0.126 rad = 7.22°

34.59   a) 66.1 cm   b) -59.1

34.61   4.80 m/s

34.63 $n/2$

34.65   a) 13.3 cm   b) 26.2 cm

34.67   a) 46.2 cm from mirror, on opposite side of
     mirror; virtual   b) 2.88 cm, erect   c) no

34.69   a) -12.0 cm $< s < 0$ b) erect

34.71 $f = \pm 4.4$ cm, ± 13.3 cm

34.73 $v = 31$ m/s

34.75   b) i) 120.00 cm from mirror, 119.96 cm from
     mirror   ii) $m = -0.600$, $m' = -0.360$
     c) faces perpendicular to axis: squares with side
     0.600 mm: faces parallel to axis: rectangles
     with sides of length 0.360 mm (parallel to axis)
     and 0.600 mm (perpendicular to axis)

34.77   b) image = 2.4 cm high; $m = -0.13$

34.79   a) -3.3 cm   b) virtual   c) 1.9 cm to right of
     vertex at right end of rod   d) real, inverted
     e) 105 mm

34.81   a) $f = 58.7$ cm, converging
     b) $h = 4.47$ mm, virtual

34.83   a) 2.53 mm

34.85   a) $R = 8.8$ mm   b) no. behind the retina
     c) $s' = 14$ mm from the cornea. In front of the
     retina. Yes. The lens needs to complete the
     focusing.

34.87   2.00

34.89   a) 3.75 cm to left of first lens   b) 332 cm
     c) real   d) $h = 60.0$ mm. inverted.

34.91   10.6 cm

34.93   a) 0.24 m   b) 0.24 m

34.95   Inside the glass, 72.1 cm from the spherical
     surface

34.97   0.80 cm

34.99 -26.7 cm

34.101   1.24 cm above page

34.103   a) 46.7 cm   b) 35.0 m

34.105   134 cm to left of object

Chapter 35

35.1   a) 2.50 m   b) 1.00 m, 4.00 m

35.3   0.75 m, 2.00 m, 3.25 m, 4.50 m 5.75 m,
     7.00 m, 8.25 m

35.5 a) 2.0 m b) constructively
  c) 1.0 m; destructively
35.9 0.83 mm
35.11 590 nm
35.13 12.6 cm
35.15 1200 nm
35.17 a) $m = 19$, 39 bright fringes
  b) $m = \pm 19$, $\theta = \pm 73.3°$
35.19 a) $0.750 I_0$ b) 80 nm
35.21 1670 rad
35.23 a) 0.888 mm b) 0.444 mm
35.25 71.4 m
35.27 114 nm
35.29 0.0235°
35.31 a) $\Delta T = 56$ nm b) i) 2180 nm
  ii) 198.5 nm; 11.0 wavelengths
35.33 a) 514 nm; green b) 603 nm; orange
35.35 0.11 μm
35.37 0.570 mm
35.39 1.82 mm
35.41 $n = 1.730$
35.43 27.3°, 66.5°
35.45 $n = 1.57$
35.47 b) constructive: $r_2 - r_1 = (m + \phi/2\pi)\lambda$,
  $m = 0, \pm 1, \pm 2, \pm 3, \ldots$;
  destructive: $r_2 - r_1 = \left(m + \dfrac{1}{2} + \phi/2\pi\right)\lambda$,
  $m = 0, \pm 1, \pm 2, \pm 3, \ldots$
35.49 a) $\sqrt{x^2 + (y+d)^2} - \sqrt{x^2 + (y-d)^2} = m\lambda$
  c) $\sqrt{x^2 + (y+d)^2} - \sqrt{x^2 + (y-d)^2} =$
  $\left(m + \dfrac{1}{2}\right)\lambda$
35.51 6.8×10^{-5} $(C°)^{-1}$
35.53 $\lambda/2d$, independent of m
35.55 b) 72 cm
35.57 $n = 1.42$
35.59 a) pattern moves down the screen
  b) $I = I_0 \cos^2[(\pi/\lambda)(d\sin\theta + (n-1)L)]$
  c) $d\sin\theta = m\lambda - (n-1)L$
35.61 14.0

Chapter 36

36.1 506 nm
36.3 $m_{max} = 113$; 226 dark fringes
36.5 ± 45.4 cm
36.9 $\pm 16.0°$, $\pm 33.4°$, $\pm 55.6°$
36.11 0.920 μm
36.13 a) 10.8 mm b) 5.4 mW
36.15 a) 6.75 mm b) 2.43×10^{-6} W/m^2
36.17 a) 668 nm b) $9.36 \times 10^{-5} I_0$
36.19 a) $\pm 13.0°$, $\pm 26.7°$, $\pm 42.4°$, $\pm 64.1°$
  b) $I = 2.08$ W/m^2
36.21 a) 3 b) 2
36.23 a) $\pm 0.0627°$ b) $0.249 I_0$ c) $0.0256 I_0$
36.25 cases (i), (iii): slits 1 and 3 and slits 2 and 4;
  case (ii): slits 1 and 2 and slits 3 and 4
36.27 $a = 1.50 \times 10^4$ nm in width;
  $d = 4.50 \times 10^4$ nm in separation
36.29 a) 4790 b) 19.0°, 40.7° c) no
36.31 a) yes b) 13.3 nm
36.33 23.3°, 52.3°
36.35 10.5°, 21.3°, 33.1°
36.37 a) $R = 17{,}500$ b) yes
  c) i) 587.8170 nm ii) 587.7834 nm
  iii) 587.7834 nm $<$ λ $<$ 587.8170 nm
36.39 0.232 nm
36.41 a) 0.461 m
36.43 1.9 m
36.45 92 cm
36.47 1.45 m
36.49 a) Hubble: 77 m; Arecibo: 1.1×10^6 m
  b) 1500 km
36.51 no
36.53 a) i) 25.6° ii) 10.2° iii) 5.1° b) i) 60.0°
  ii) 23.1° iii) 11.5°
36.55 2.07
36.57 a) 1.80 mm b) 0.798 mm
36.59 $\Delta\theta_\perp = \dfrac{2\lambda}{dN}$
36.61 b) for $3\pi/2$: any two slits separated by one
  other slit; for the other cases: any two slits
  separated by three other slits

36.65 513 nm
36.67 second order
36.69 c) ± 2.6 rad
36.71 492 km

Chapter 37

37.1 Flash at AA'
37.3 2.60×10^8 m/s
37.5 a) $0.998c$ b) 126 m
37.7 1.12 h, clock on spacecraft
37.9 92.5 m
37.11 a) 6.6×10^2 m
  b) 4.92×10^{-5} s, 1.48×10^4 m; yes c) 447 m
37.13 a) 3.57 km b) 9.00×10^{-5} s
  c) 8.92×10^{-5} s
37.15 a) $0.806c$ b) $0.974c$ c) $0.997c$
37.17 $0.385c$
37.19 $0.784c$
37.21 $v = 0.611c$
37.23 $0.837c$, away
37.25 a) $0.159c$ b) $\$1.72 \times 10^8$
37.27 b) $a = (F/m)(1 - v^2/c^2)^{1/2}$
37.29 a) $a = (\sqrt{3}/2)c = 0.866c$
  b) $c\sqrt{1 - \left(\dfrac{1}{2}\right)^{2/3}} = 0.608c$
37.31 a) $(\sqrt{3}/2)c = 0.866c$ b) $\sqrt{35/36}\,c = 0.986c$
37.33 a) 4.50×10^{-10} J b) 1.94×10^{-18} kg·m/s
  c) $0.968c$
37.35 a) 3.3×10^{-14} %; no
  b) 4.0×10^{-16} kg; increases; no
37.37 a) 1.1×10^2 kg b) 0.24 m
37.39 a) 8.68×10^{-10} J b) 2.71×10^{-10} J c) 0.453
37.41 a) nonrelativistic: 5.34×10^{-12} J;
  relativistic: 5.65×10^{-12} J; 1.06
  b) nonrelativistic: 6.78×10^{-11} J;
  relativistic: 3.31×10^{-10} J; 4.88
37.43 a) 2.06×10^6 V b) 3.30×10^{-13} J
  c) 2.06 MeV
37.45 $v = 0.652c$
37.47 a) 4.2×10^9 kg/s; 4.6×10^6 tons
  b) 1.5×10^{13} y
37.49 a) $\Delta = 2.11 \times 10^{-5}$ b) 2.15×10^4 MeV
37.51 $0.700c$
37.53 a) $0.995c$ b) 1.0%
37.55 a) $v = (1 - 9 \times 10^{-9})c$ b) $m_{rel} = 7 \times 10^3 m$
37.57 1.68×10^5 eV
37.59 a) $0.800c$ b) $1.00c$ c) i) 2.33×10^{-11} J
  ii) 1.00×10^{-10} J
  d) i) 1.88×10^{-11} J ii) 4.81×10^{-11} J
37.65 b) $\Delta x' - \sqrt{(\Delta x)^2 - (c\Delta t)^2}$
  c) 1.44×10^{-8} s
37.67 $0.357c$, receding
37.69 a) 140% b) 5500% c) 63000%
37.75 a) 13.1 km/s, toward
  b) 5.96×10^9 m = 0.040 Earth-sun distance
  (AU); 5.55×10^{29} kg = $0.279 m_{sun}$
37.77 a) $0.7554c$ b) 2.526
  c) center of momentum: less energy

Chapter 38

38.1 a) about 8.3×10^{-19} J = 5.2 eV
  b) about 6.1×10^{-34} J·s = 3.8×10^{-15} eV·s
38.3 a) 5.77×10^{14} Hz, 1.27×10^{-27} kg·m/s,
  3.82×10^{-19} J b) 2.38 eV
38.5 a) 5.92×10^{20} Hz b) 5.06×10^{-13} m
38.7 2.5×10^5 m/s
38.9 a) 5.0×10^{14} Hz b) 2.3×10^{20} photons/s
  c) no
38.11 a) $K_2 = 4K_1$ b) $E_2 = 2E_1$
38.13 a) 264 nm b) 4.70 eV
38.15 a) 434.1 nm b) 6.906×10^{14} Hz
  c) 4.576×10^{-19} J = 2.856 eV
38.17 a) -5.08 eV b) -5.63 eV
38.19 a) $E_1 = -17.50$ eV, $E_1 = -4.38$ eV,
  $E_1 = -1.95$ eV, $E_1 = -1.10$ eV
  $E_1 = -0.71$ eV
38.21 a) 5.82×10^{-13} J = 3.63 MeV
  b) 5.82×10^{-13} J = 3.63 MeV
  c) 1.32×10^7 m/s
38.23 $3h = 3.16 \times 10^{-34}$ kg·m^2/s

38.25 a) -218 eV, 16 times greater
  b) 218 eV, 16 times greater c) 7.63 nm
  d) 1/4 as large
38.27 a) $v_1 = 2.19 \times 10^6$ m/s, $v_2 = 1.09 \times 10^6$ m/s,
  $v_3 = 7.29 \times 10^5$ m/s
  b) $T_1 = 1.52 \times 10^{-16}$ s, $T_2 = 1.22 \times 10^{-15}$ s,
  $T_3 = 4.10 \times 10^{-15}$ s c) 8.22×10^6
38.29 4.00×10^{17}
38.31 a) 1.2×10^{-33} b) 3.4×10^{-17}
  c) 5.9×10^{-9}
38.33 0.310 nm, the same
38.35 a) $f_{min} = 6.04 \times 10^{18}$ Hz
  b) $\lambda_{min} = 0.0497$ nm
38.37 0.0714 nm, 180°
38.39 a) 4.39×10^{-4} nm b) 0.04294 nm
  c) $\Delta E_r = -300$ eV d) $\Delta E_e = +300$ eV
38.43 a) 2.06×10^4 K b) 141 nm
38.45 1.06 mm, microwave
38.47 a) $\lambda = \dfrac{hc}{4.965kT}$ b) $\lambda_m T = 2.90 \times 10^{-3}$ m·K
38.51 a) 1.04 eV b) 1.20 μm c) 2.51×10^{14} Hz
  d) 4.14×10^{-7} eV
38.53 a) 4.59×10^{14} Hz b) 653 nm c) 1.89 eV
  d) 6.59×10^{-34} J·s
38.55 a) $hc(\lambda_1 - \lambda_2)/e\lambda_1\lambda_2$ b) 0.476 V
38.57 a) 5.1×10^{-3} J b) 11 W c) $N = 1.5 \times 10^{16}$
38.59 a) 1.69×10^{-28} kg b) -2.53 keV
  c) 0.653 nm
38.61 a) 6.99×10^{-24} kg·m/s b) 705 eV
38.63 a) 12.09 eV b) 3 possibilities:
  $3 \to 2$ (656 nm), $3 \to 1$ (103 nm),
  $2 \to 1$ (122 nm)
38.65 a) 0.90 eV
38.67 a) 5×10^{49} photons/s b) 3×10^4
38.69 2.98×10^4 K
38.71 a) $\Delta\lambda = \dfrac{h}{2mc}$ b) 6.61×10^{-16} m for any n
38.73 a) 5×10^{-33} m b) $(4 \times 10^{-9})°$ c) 0.1 mm
38.75 a) 5.10×10^{-17} J = 319 eV, 1.06×10^7 m/s
  b) 3.89 nm
38.77 5.67×10^{-8} W/(m^2·K^4)
38.79 $f \approx \dfrac{me^4}{4\epsilon_0^2 n^3 h^3}$
38.81 b) 7.08×10^{-15} m c) gamma rays

Chapter 39

39.1 a) 1.55×10^{-10} m b) 8.44×10^{-14} m
39.3 a) 2.37×10^{-24} kg·m/s
  b) 3.67×10^{-18} J = 19.2 eV
39.5 a) 3.32×10^{-10} m b) 1.33×10^{-9} m
39.7 a) $m = 75$ kg, $v = 1.0$ m/s: $\lambda = 8.8 \times 10^{-36}$ m
39.9 a) photon: 620 nm; electron: 0.274 nm
  b) photon: 4.96 eV; electron: 2.41×10^{-5} eV
  c) 250 nm; electron
39.11 3.90×10^{-34} m; no
39.13 a) 7.3×10^6 m/s b) 150 eV c) 12 keV
  d) electrons
39.15 0.431 eV
39.17 a) $m = 1$: 2.07°; $m = 2$: 4.14°
  b) 1.81 cm, 3.61 cm, 1.81 cm
39.19 a) 8.79×10^{-32} m/s; no
39.21 the claim is not valid
39.23 2.03×10^{-32} J = 1.27×10^{-13} eV
39.25 0.087 MeV = $2.8 \times 10^{-5} E$
39.27 a) 8.25×10^3 b) electrons
39.29 a) $x = (2n + 1)(\lambda/4)$, n an integer
  b) $x = n\lambda/2$, n an integer
39.31 a) $\displaystyle\int_{-\infty}^{\infty} |\Psi|^2 dV = 1$
  integrating the probability density function
  between infinite limits must equal unity
  b) no. no. not a valid wave function.
  c) $A = \sqrt{2b}$ m$^{-1/2}$
39.33 1
39.35 a) 1.414 m$^{-1/2}$ c) i) $P = 0.865$ ii) $P = \dfrac{1}{2}$
  iii) $P = 0.0585$
39.37 ψ cannot be a solution
39.39 a) 12 eV b) 1.5×10^{-4} V, 7.3×10^3 m/s,
  c) 8.2×10^{-8} V; 4.0 m/s

39.41 a) 9.42×10^5 m/s; nonrelativistic
b) $V_{acc} = 2.53$ V
39.43 a) $E = c\sqrt{2mK} = 4.05 \times 10^{-7}\sqrt{K}$
b) $E_{photon} > E_{electron}$
39.45 1.66×10^{-17} m; no
39.47 a) 1.10×10^{-10} m b) 9.09×10^{-13} m
39.49 a) $(1/\sqrt{15})(h/mc)$
b) i) 1.53 MeV, 6.26×10^{-13} m
ii) 2.81×10^3 MeV, 3.41×10^{-16} m
39.51 a) 2.1×10^{-20} kg·m/s b) 39 MeV
c) 0.29 MeV; no
39.53 1.4×10^{-35} kg $= (5.8 \times 10^{-8}\,m_{pion})$
39.55 a) 1.1×10^{-35} m/s b) 2.3×10^{27} y, no
39.57 a) 7.27×10^5 m/s, nonrelativistic
b) $V = 1.50$ V
39.59 a) $2d\sin\theta = m\lambda$, $m = 1, 2, 3\ldots$ b) 53.1°
c) less
39.61 a) $A|x|/x, x \neq 0$ b) $(3/2)(h^2A^2/m)^{1/3}$
39.63 $\omega = E/\hbar$
39.65 a) 0.21 kg·m/s b) 1.7 m
39.67 $P = 4\pi|A|^2 r^2 e^{-2\alpha r} dr$, r $= 1/\sqrt{2\alpha}$; no
39.69 a) $\psi(x) = (\sin k_0 x)/k_0 x$ b) L c) $2L$
d) h, h
39.71 2.2×10^{-16} m

Chapter 40

40.1 a) 1.2×10^{-67} J b) 1.1×10^{-33} m/s
c) 1.4×10^{33} s d) 3.7×10^{-67} J
40.3 $L = 1.66 \times 10^{-10}$ m
40.5 0.61 nm
40.7 a) $0, L/2, L$ b) $L/4, 3L/4$ c) yes
40.11 a) 6.0×10^{-10} m, 1.1×10^{-24} kg·m/s
b) 3.0×10^{-10} m, 2.2×10^{-24} kg·m/s
c) 2.0×10^{-10} m, 3.3×10^{-24} kg·m/s
40.15 3.43×10^{-10} m
40.19 2.2×10^{-14} m
40.21 a) 4.3×10^{-8} b) 4.2×10^{-4}
40.23 $1/\sqrt{2}$
40.25 a) 1.3×10^{-3} b) 10^{-143}
40.27 a) 1.11×10^{-33} J $= 6.90 \times 10^{-15}$ eV;
2.21×10^{-33} J $= 1.38 \times 10^{-14}$ eV
40.29 a) 0.21 eV b) 5900 N/m
40.31 $\Delta x\Delta p = (2n + 1)\hbar$
40.33 a) 5.9×10^{-3} eV b) 106 μm
c) 0.0118 eV $= 1.18 \times 10^{-2}$ eV
40.35 $B = \dfrac{K_1 - K_2}{K_1 + K_2}A$; $C = \dfrac{2K_1}{K_1 + K_2}A$
40.37 a) 19.2 μm b) 11.5 μm
40.39 a) $\left(\dfrac{1}{2} + 1/\pi\right)$ b) $\dfrac{1}{2}$ c) yes
40.41 a) $2dx/L$ b) 0 c) $2dx/L$
40.45 a) $B = C, A\sin\dfrac{\sqrt{2mE}}{\hbar}L + B\cos\dfrac{\sqrt{2mE}}{\hbar}L = De^{-\kappa L}$
b) $\dfrac{\sqrt{2mE}}{\hbar}A = \kappa C$, $\dfrac{\sqrt{2mE}}{\hbar}\left(A\cos\dfrac{\sqrt{2mE}}{\hbar}L - B\sin\dfrac{\sqrt{2mE}}{\hbar}L\right) = -\kappa De^{-\kappa L}$
40.49 6.63×10^{-34} J $= 4.14 \times 10^{-15}$ eV,
1.33×10^{-33} J $= 8.27 \times 10^{-15}$ eV, no
40.51 b) $A_0 = \left(\dfrac{m\omega}{\hbar\pi}\right)^{1/4}$
c) classical turning points $A = \pm\sqrt{\dfrac{\hbar}{\omega m}}$
40.53 a) $(n_x + n_y + n_z + (3/2))\hbar\omega$
b) $(3/2)\hbar\omega, (5/2)\hbar\omega$
40.55 a) $E_n = n^2h^2/8mL^2$, $n = 2, 4, 6\ldots$
b) $E_n = n^2h^2/8mL^2$, $n = 1, 3, 5\ldots$ c) same
d) odd in part (a), even in part (b)
40.57 b) increases c) infinite
40.59 a) $-E/A, +E/A$ c) decrease

Chapter 41

41.1 a) Possible values of l and l: $l = \hbar$ and
$L_z = 0$; $L = \sqrt{2}\hbar$ and $L_z = -\hbar, 0$, or $+\hbar$
$L = \sqrt{6}\hbar$ and $L_z = -2\hbar, -\hbar, 0, +\hbar$ or $+2\hbar$

b) For $L = \hbar$: $\theta_L = 90.0°$;
For $L = \sqrt{2}\hbar$: $\theta_L = 135°, 90.0°$, or $45°$;
For $L = \sqrt{6}\hbar$: $\theta_L = 144.7°, 114°, 90.0°, 65.9°$,
or $35.3°$
41.3 $l = 4$
41.5 $1.414\hbar, 19.49\hbar, 199.5\hbar$
41.7 -14.4 eV
41.9 b) $1/\sqrt{2\pi}$
41.11 a) 5.29×10^{-11} m b) 1.06×10^{-10} m
c) 2.85×10^{-13} m
41.15 a) 9 b) 3.47×10^{-5} eV c) 2.78×10^{-4} eV
41.17 a) 0.468 T b) 3
41.19 1.68×10^{-4} eV; $m_s = 1/2$
41.21 g
41.23 a) 2.5×10^{30} rad/s
b) 2.5×10^{13} m/s, not valid
41.25

e^-	n	l	m_l	m_s
1	1	0	0	$\frac{1}{2}$
2	1	0	0	$-\frac{1}{2}$
3	2	0	0	$\frac{1}{2}$
4	2	0	0	$-\frac{1}{2}$
5	2	1	-1	$\frac{1}{2}$
6	2	1	0	$\frac{1}{2}$
7	2	1	$+1$	$\frac{1}{2}$
8	2	1	-1	$-\frac{1}{2}$
9	2	1	0	$-\frac{1}{2}$
10	2	1	$+1$	$-\frac{1}{2}$

41.27 4.18 eV
41.29 a) $1s^2 2s^2 2p^1$ b) -30.6 eV
c) $1s^2 2s^2 2p^6 3s^2 3p^1$ d) -13.6 eV
41.31 a) -13.6 eV b) -3.4 eV
41.33 a) 8.95×10^{17} Hz, 3.70 keV, 0.335 nm
b) 1.68×10^{18} Hz, 6.93 keV, 0.179 nm
c) 5.48×10^{18} Hz, 22.7 keV, 0.0547 nm
41.35 a) $0, \sqrt{2}\hbar, \sqrt{6}\hbar\sqrt{12}\hbar, \sqrt{20}\hbar$
b) 7470 nm, infrared, not visible
41.37 a) $1.51e$ ii) $-2.75e$
41.39 a) $2a$ b) 0.238
41.41 b) 0.176
41.43 $\cos^{-1}(-\sqrt{1 - (1/m)})$
41.45 $4a$
41.47 $2 \to 1, 1 \to 0, 0 \to -1, e\hbar B/2m$;
$1 \to 1, 0 \to 0, -1 \to -1, 0$;
$0 \to 1, -1 \to 0, -2 \to -1, e\hbar B/2m$
41.49 3.00 T
41.51 a) $1 - 2 \times 10^{-7}$ b) 0.9978 c) 0.978
41.53 a) 4, 20 b) $1s^4 2s^4 2p^3$
41.55 a) 122 nm b) 1.52×10^{-3} nm; increases
41.57 a) 0.188 nm, 0.250 nm;
b) 0.0471 nm, 0.0624 nm
41.59 b) O shell

Chapter 42

42.1 a) 6.1 K b) 3.47×10^4 K
42.3 5.65×10^{-13} m
42.5 a) carbon: 0.0644 nm; oxygen: 0.0484 nm
b) 1.45×10^{-46} kg·m²; yes
42.7 a) 1.03×10^{12} rad/s
b) carbon; 66.3 m/s oxygen: 49.8 m/s
c) 6.11×10^{-12} s
42.9 a) 1.20×10^{-21} J $= 7.52 \times 10^{-3}$ eV
b) 0.165 mm
42.11 b) $\hbar l/2\pi I$
42.13 a) 963 m/s b) 8.22×10^{-20} J $= 0.513$ eV
c) 2.42 μm, infrared
42.15 2.16×10^3 kg/m³
42.17 a) 1.12 eV
42.19 1.19×10^6
42.21 1.5×10^{22} states/eV
42.23 b) ground: $E = 3\pi^2\hbar^2/2mL^2$, 2;
first: $E = 6\pi^2\hbar^2/2mL^2$, 6;
second: $E = 9\pi^2\hbar^2/2mL^2$, 6
42.25 a) $0.0233 R$ b) 7.65×10^{-3} c) no; the ions
42.27 $f(E) = 0.31 = 31\%$
42.29 0.20 eV below the band
42.31 a) 5.56 mA b) -5.18 mA; -3.77 mA
42.33 a) 977 N/m b) 1.26×10^{14} Hz
42.35 a) 3.8×10^{-29} C·m b) 1.3×10^{-19} C

c) 0.78 d) 0.059
42.37 a) 0.96 nm b) 1.8 nm
42.39 a) 0.129 nm b) 8, 7, 6, 5, 4 c) 484 μm
d) 118 μm, 135 μm, 157 μm, 189 μm, 236 μm
42.41 a) i) 2.94 ii) 4.73 iii) 7.58 iv) 0.837
v) 5.5×10^{-9}
42.43 a) 1.147 cm, 2.239 cm
b) 1.172 cm, 2.344 cm; 0.025 cm, 0.050 cm
42.45 4.38×10^{-20} J $= 0.273$ eV
42.47 a) 4.24×10^{-47} kg·m² b) i) 4.30 μm
ii) 4.28 μm iii) 4.40 μm
42.49 2.03 eV
42.51 a) 4.66×10^{28} atom/m³ b) 4.7 eV
42.53 b) 3.80×10^{10} Pa $= 3.75 \times 10^5$ atm
42.55 a) 1.66×10^{33} m⁻³ b) yes c) 7×10^{35} m⁻³
d) no
42.57 a) $-p^2/2\pi\epsilon_0 r^3$ b) $+p^2/2\pi\epsilon_0 r^3$

Chapter 43

43.1 a) $Z = 14, N = 14$ b) $Z = 37, N = 48$
c) $Z = 81, N = 124$
43.3 0.533 T
43.5 a) parallel, 70.3 MHz, 4.27 m, radio
b) antiparallel, 46.2 MHz, 6.48 mm, microwave
43.7 5.575×10^{-13} m
43.9 1.13×10^7 m/s
43.11 a) 76.21 MeV b) 76.67 MeV
c) 0.6%
43.13 a) $^{235}_{92}$U b) $^{24}_{12}$Mg c) $^{15}_{7}$N
43.15 0.0500 MeV
43.17 156 keV
43.19 a) 0.836 MeV b) 0.700 MeV
43.21 1.58×10^{12} s
43.23 a) 159 decays/min b) 0.43 decay/min
43.25 a) $^3_2$He b) 40.9 y
43.27 2.80 days
43.29 5730 y
43.31 a) 2.02×10^{15} b) $1.01 \times 10^{15}, 3.78 \times 10^{11}$ Bq
c) $2.52 \times 10^{14}, 9.45 \times 10^{10}$ Bq
43.33 a) 0.421 Bq b) 1.14×10^{-11} Ci
43.35 500 rad, 2000 rem, 5.0 J/kg
43.37 a) 1.75×10^3 Gy $= 1.75 \times 10^3$ Sv
$= 1.75 \times 10^5$ rem, 263 J
b) 1.75×10^3 Gy $= 2.63 \times 10^3$ Sv
$= 2.63 \times 10^5$ rem, 263 J
43.39 a) 12.5 rad, 12.5 rem b) the antineutrinos are
not absorbed
43.41 a) $= 3, A = 6$ b) -10.14 MeV
c) 11.60 MeV
43.43 a) $Z = 3, A = 7$ b) 7.151 MeV
c) 1.4 MeV
43.45 a) 173.3 MeV b) 4.42×10^{23} MeV/g
43.47 1.586 MeV
43.53 23.9858 u, 0.021%, 0.9%
43.55 a) $^{25}_{13}$Al $\to$ $^{25}_{12}$Mg
b) β^+ decay or electron capture
c) 3.255 eV or 4.277 MeV
43.57 a) $^{14}_6$C $\to$ $^{14}_7$N $+ \beta^- + \bar{\nu}_e$
b) 0.1565 MeV/decay
c) 1.35×10^4 g, 3.44×10^3 decays/s
d) 539 MeV/s $= 8.63 \times 10^{-11}$ J/s
e) 3.63×10^{-5} Gy $= 3.63 \times 10^{-3}$ rad,
RBE = 1.0: 36 μSv $= 3.6$ mrem
43.59 0.960 MeV
43.61 1.287×10^{-3} u
43.65 a) 5.0×10^4 b) $10^{-15000} \approx 0$
43.67 29.2%
43.69 a) 9.6×10^{-7} J b) 1.9×10^{-4} rad
c) 1.3×10^{-4} rem d) 1.5×10^6 s $= 17$ d
43.71 1.3×10^4 y
43.73 a) 0.48 MeV
b) 3.270 MeV $= 5.239 \times 10^{-11}$ J
c) 3.155×10^{11} J/mol
43.77 185 MeV
43.79 b) 4.1×10^4 Bq, 3.6×10^5 Bq, 7.5×10^5 Bq,
1.1×10^6 Bq, 1.3×10^6 Bq, 1.5×10^6 Bq
c) 3.2×10^9 d) 1.5×10^6 Bq

Chapter 44

44.1 a) 1.27×10^{-14} J b) 9.46×10^{-14} J
c) 2.10 pm; smaller

44.3 69 MeV, 1.7×10^{22} Hz,
1.8×10^{-14} m, gamma ray

44.5 a) 32 MeV

44.7 1.68×10^{-11} J $= 105$ MeV

44.9 7.2×10^{19} J

44.11 a) 1.18 T   b) 3.41 MeV, 1.81×10^7 m/s

44.13 a) 30.6 GeV   b) 8.0 GeV

44.15 a) 3.2 TeV   b) 38.7 GeV

44.17 1.63×10^{-25} kg; 97.2

44.19 116 MeV

44.21 a) no   b) yes   c) no   d) yes

44.23 a) no   b) no   c) yes   d) yes

44.27 a) $0, 1, -1, 0$ b) $0, 0, 0, 1$ c) $-e, 1, 0, 0$
d) $-e, 0, 0, -1$

44.29 a) $\bar{\mathbf{u}}\mathbf{dd}$ b) no   c) yes

44.31 $u \rightarrow d; p \rightarrow n + \beta^+ + \nu_e$

44.33 a) 3.28×10^7 m/s   b) 1640 Mly

44.35 a) 1.04×10^8 m/s   b) 1.44

44.37 a) 5.494 MeV   b) 1.0×10^5 TeV

44.39 -783 keV, endoergic

44.41 $0.966 \ \mu$m

44.43 a) 14.0 TeV   b) 1.05×10^5 TeV

44.45 a) $F_e = 200$ N, $F_g = 2 \times 10^{39}$ N
b) $F_{str} = 3 \times 10^4$ N, $F_{weak} = 3 \times 10^{-5}$ N
c) $F_{str} > F_e > F_{weak} > F_g$ d) $F_e \approx 1 \times 10^{36} F_g$;
$F_{str} \approx 100 F_e \approx 1 \times 10^{28} F_g$
$F_{weak} \approx 1 \times 10^{-9} F_{str} \approx 1 \times 10^{29} F_g$

44.47 2496 MeV

44.49 $\lambda = 2.43$ pm; gamma rays

44.51 87 keV, 2.8×10^{-5}

44.53 a) 16.0 MeV

PHOTO CREDITS

About the Author Hugh D. Young; John P. Surey

Chapter 1 Opener: NASA; 1.1a: G. Ross/Photo Researchers, Inc.; 1.1b: NASA; 1.4: National Institute of Standards and Technology (NIST); 1.5a: R. Williams (STScI), the HDF-S Team, and NASA; 1.5b: SOHO (ESA & NASA); 1.5c: Courtesy of NASA/JPL/Caltech; 1.5d: Photodisc Green/Getty Images; 1.5e: Chad Baker/PhotoDisc/Getty Images; 1.5f: Purdue University. Veeco Instruments, Inc.; 1.5g: SPL/Photo Researchers; 1.6: Pearson Addison Wesley, San Francisco, California; 1.7: ND-Viollet/Roger Viollet/Liaison Agency, Inc.

Chapter 2 Opener: Mike Hewitt/Getty Images; 2.4: Pete Saloutos/Corbis; 2.5: DiMaggio/Kalish/Corbis; 2.22: Richard Megna/Fundamental Photographs; 2.26: Corbis

Chapter 3 Opener: Schlegelmilch/Corbis; 3.8: PhotoAlto/Getty Images; 3.16: Richard Megna/Fundamental Photographs; 3.19a: Richar d Megna/Fundamental Photographs; 3.19b: Stuart Westmorland/Getty Images; 3.31: AFP/Getty Images

Chapter 4 Opener: Balfour Studios/Alamy; 4.12: Wayne Eastep/Getty Images; 4.17: AFP/Getty Images; 4.20: James H. Robinson/Animals Animals; 4.29: E. Klaswitter/Corbis

Chapter 5 Opener: Kevin Schafer/Peter Arnold; 5.11: NASA/Photo Researchers; 5.16: AFP/Getty Images; 5.26b: Jump Run Productions/Getty Images; 5.38b: Helen Hansma, University of California, Santa Barbara; 5.38:d David Malin, Anglo-Australian Observatory

Chapter 6 Opener: Stephen Dalton/Photo Researchers; 6.1: Christina Hoehn/Getty Images; 6.13: Corbis; 6.26: Hulton Archive/Getty Images; 6.27a: Jeffrey H. Whitesell, Airliners of America; 6.27b: Jeffrey H. Whitesell, Airliners of America

Chapter 7 Opener: Mark A. Johnson/Corbis; 7.1: Purestock/Alamy; 7.3a: Dennis O'Clair/Getty Images; 7.5: Joe McBride/Corbis; 7.12: Phil Mislinski/Omni-Photo Communications; 7.15: Arco Images/Alamy; 7.21: The Picture House/Alamy

Chapter 8 Opener: Getty Images; 8.2: David Woods/Corbis; 8.4: Jim Cummins/Getty Images; 8.6a: Andrew Davidhazy; 8.16: Getty Images; 8.21: David Leah/Getty Images; 8.29: Richard Megna/Fundamental Photographs; 8.33: NASA

Chapter 9 Opener: George Hall/Corbis; 9.19: Jose Azel/Aurora Photos; 9.38: NASA

Chapter 10 Opener: Reuters/Corbis; 10.7: Corbis; 10.14: picturesbyrob/Alamy; 10.17: Pete Saloutos/Corbis; 10.22: Lester Lefkowitz/Getty Images; 10.28: Gerard Lacz/Natural History Photographic Agency

Chapter 11 Opener: Ruth Tomlinson/Getty Images; 11.3: Jeremy Woodhouse/Getty Images; 11.12a: Walter Bibikow/Getty Images; 11.12b: Jonathan Blair/Corbis; 11.12c: Photodisc Green/Getty Images

Chapter 12 Opener: NASA/JPL/Space Science Institute; 12.3: NASA/JPL/Caltech; 12.6: NASA; 12.7: George Hall/Corbis; 12.13: NASA; 12.16: NASA; 12.17a: NASA; 12.17b: NASA; 12.18: NASA; 12.21: Smithsonian Astrophysical Observatory; 12.27: NASA/Johnson Space Center; 12.28: NASA; 12.29: NASA; 12.30: Keck/UCLA Galactic Center Group

Chapter 13 Opener: Mark Antman/The Image Works; 13.7: American Diagnostic Corporation; 13.21a: Frank Herholdt/Getty Images; 13.25: Christopher Griffin/Alamy; 13.29a: AP/Wide World Photos; 13.29b: AP/Wide World Photos

Chapter 14 Opener: Digital Vision/AGE Fotostock; 14.2: Nicholas Pinturas/Getty Images; 14.7: Cenco Physics; 14.10b: Photodisc Green/Getty Images; 14.15: Robert B. Suter, Vassar College; 14.20: Pearson Addison Wesley; 14.21: Cordelia Molloy/Photo Researchers; 14.28: Digital Vision/AGE Fotostock; 14.30a: Photodisc Green/Getty Images; 14.30b: Colin Barker/ Getty Images; 14.31f: The Harold E. Edgerton 1992 Trust, Palm Press, Inc.

Chapter 15 Opener: David Hume Kennerly/Getty Images; 15.2: Tony Arruza/Corbis; 15.12: R. Dolan/Camerique/H. Armstrong Roberts; 15.18: Reproduced from *PSSC Physics*, 2nd ed. (1965), D.C. Heath & Company with Educational Development Center, Inc., Newton Massachusets; 15.25: Photodisc Green/Getty Images; 15.27: National Optical Astronomy Observatories

Chapter 16 Opener: John Powell/The Image Works; 16.5a: Lisa Pines/Getty Images; 16.5c: David Young-Wolff/PhotoEdit Inc.; 16.6: Dorling Kindersley; 16.9: Bernard Benoit/Photo Researchers; 16.10: Eastcott-Momatiuk/The Image Works; 16.20: Martin Bough/Fundamental Photographs; 16.25: David Young-Wolff/PhotoEdit Inc.;16.28: Mark Reinstein/The Image Works; 16.36: NASA/Robert A. Hoover, Dryden Flight Research Center

Chapter 17 Opener: Cameramann/The Image Works; 17.4: Exergen Corporation; 17.11: NASA/Jim Ross, Dryden Flight Research Center; 17.13: Marshall Henrichs; 17.18: Paul Seheult/Corbis; 17.19: Adam Hart-Davis/Photo Researchers; 17.20: Richard Megna/Fundamental Photographs; 17.22: John Giustina/Getty Images; 17.24: Russ Underwood, Lockheed Martin Missiles & Space Company, Inc.; 17.28: Nancy Rogers; 17.29: Dr. Arthur Tucker/Photo Researchers

Chapter 18 Opener: James Marshall/The Image Works; 18.2: John Powell/The Image Works; 18.10: Park Scientific Instruments; 18.13: Stone/Getty Images; 18.14: Tatsuyuki Tayama/The Image Works; 18.16: David Grossman/The Image Works; 18.25: PhotoDisc/Getty Images; 18.28: Royal Observatory, Edinburgh/Anglo-AustralianObsevatory; 18.30: David Malin, Anglo-Australian Observatory

Chapter 19 Opener: Richard A. Cooke III/Getty Images; 19.1: John P. Surey; 19.2a: PhotoDisc/StockTrek/Getty Images; 19.2b: Lawrence Migdale/Photo Researchers; 19.10: John Kelly/Getty Images; 19.14: Tom Branch/Photo Researchers; 19.15: Patrick Watson/The Image Works; 19.32: Thomas Eisner and Daniel Aneshansley

Chapter 20 Opener: Stock Food/Getty Images; 20.2: Bruno Perousse/AGE Fotostock; 20.12: Bill Bachman/Photo Researchers; 20.16: Mark Wagner/Getty Images; 20.17: Erich Schrempp/Photo Researchers; 20.21: Paul Silverman/Fundamental Photographs; Summary: Paul Silverman/Fundamental Photographs

Chapter 21 Opener: Ilja C. Hendel/The Image Works; 21.5: Journal-Courier/The Image Works; 21.8a: Richard Megna/Fundamental Photographs; 21.30a: Reproduced from *PSSC Physics*, 2nd ed. (1965), D.C. Heath & Company with Education Development Center, Inc., Newton, Massachusetts; 21.31b: Tony Craddock/Photo Researchers

Chapter 22 Opener: Department of Energy/Photo Researchers; 22.10: AKG London Ltd.; 22.28b: Russ Kinne/Comstock

Chapter 23 Opener: Ted Kurihara/Getty Images; 23.9: NASA/JPL/Caltech; 23.11: © Lester V. Berman/Corbis; 23/13: Fermilab Visual Media Services; 23.18: Hulton Archive/Keystone/Getty Images; 23.23: U.S. Geological Survey, Denver

Chapter 24 Opener: Digital Vision/Agefotostock; 24.3: Design Pics/Indexstock; 24.4: Andrew Lambert/Photo Researchers; 24.7: Paul Silverman/Fundamental Photographs; 24.11: Sandia National Laboratories; 24.17: Stanford Linear Accelerator/Science Photo Library/Photo Researchers

Chapter 25 Opener: David Sacks/Getty Images; 25.4: Fundamental Photographs; 25.5: PhotoDisc/Getty Images; 25.8: Mitch Wojnarowicz/The Image Works; 25.13: Doug Scott/Agefotostock

INDEX